McGraw Hill Education | **connect**®

McGraw-Hill Connect ™ is a web-based assignment and assessment platform that gives students the means to better connect with their coursework, with their instructors and with the important concepts they will need to know for success now and in the future. With Connect, instructors can deliver assignments, quizzes and tests easily online. Students can practise important skills at their own pace and on their own schedule. With Connect, students also get 24/7 online access to an eBook—an online edition of the text—to aid them in successfully completing their work, wherever and whenever they choose. Now students can access LearnSmart and SmartBook for many McGraw-Hill Products through Connect.

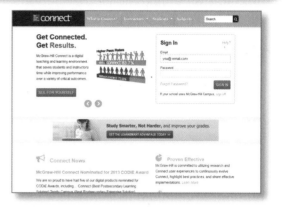

McGraw Hill Education | **LEARNSMART**®

No two students are alike. Why should their learning paths be? LearnSmart uses revolutionary adaptive technology to build a learning experience unique to each student's individual needs. It starts by identifying the topics a student knows and does not know. As the student progresses, LearnSmart adapts and adjusts the content based on his or her individual strengths, weaknesses and confidence, ensuring that every minute spent studying with LearnSmart is the most efficient and productive study time possible.

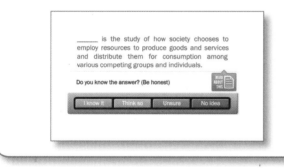

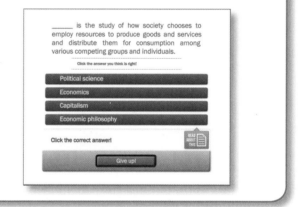

McGraw Hill Education | **SMARTBOOK**™

As the first and only adaptive reading experience, SmartBook is changing the way students read and learn. SmartBook creates a personalized reading experience by highlighting the most important concepts a student needs to learn at that moment in time. As a student engages with SmartBook, the reading experience continuously adapts by highlighting content based on what each student knows and doesn't know. This ensures that he or she is focused on the content needed to close specific knowledge gaps, while it simultaneously promotes long-term learning.

Cumulative Areas under the Standard Normal Curve

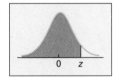

z	.00	.01	.02	.03	.04	.05	.06	.07	.08	.09
0.0	.5000	.5040	.5080	.5120	.5160	.5199	.5239	.5279	.5319	.5359
0.1	.5398	.5438	.5478	.5517	.5557	.5596	.5636	.5675	.5714	.5753
0.2	.5793	.5832	.5871	.5910	.5948	.5987	.6026	.6064	.6103	.6141
0.3	.6179	.6217	.6255	.6293	.6331	.6368	.6406	.6443	.6480	.6517
0.4	.6554	.6591	.6628	.6664	.6700	.6736	.6772	.6808	.6844	.6879
0.5	.6915	.6950	.6985	.7019	.7054	.7088	.7123	.7157	.7190	.7224
0.6	.7257	.7291	.7324	.7357	.7389	.7422	.7454	.7486	.7517	.7549
0.7	.7580	.7611	.7642	.7673	.7704	.7734	.7764	.7794	.7823	.7852
0.8	.7881	.7910	.7939	.7967	.7995	.8023	.8051	.8078	.8106	.8133
0.9	.8159	.8186	.8212	.8238	.8264	.8289	.8315	.8340	.8365	.8389
1.0	.8413	.8438	.8461	.8485	.8508	.8531	.8554	.8577	.8599	.8621
1.1	.8643	.8665	.8686	.8708	.8729	.8749	.8770	.8790	.8810	.8830
1.2	.8849	.8869	.8888	.8907	.8925	.8944	.8962	.8980	.8997	.9015
1.3	.9032	.9049	.9066	.9082	.9099	.9115	.9131	.9147	.9162	.9177
1.4	.9192	.9207	.9222	.9236	.9251	.9265	.9279	.9292	.9306	.9319
1.5	.9332	.9345	.9357	.9370	.9382	.9394	.9406	.9418	.9429	.9441
1.6	.9452	.9463	.9474	.9484	.9495	.9505	.9515	.9525	.9535	.9545
1.7	.9554	.9564	.9573	.9582	.9591	.9599	.9608	.9616	.9625	.9633
1.8	.9641	.9649	.9656	.9664	.9671	.9678	.9686	.9693	.9699	.9706
1.9	.9713	.9719	.9726	.9732	.9738	.9744	.9750	.9756	.9761	.9767
2.0	.9772	.9778	.9783	.9788	.9793	.9798	.9803	.9808	.9812	.9817
2.1	.9821	.9826	.9830	.9834	.9838	.9842	.9846	.9850	.9854	.9857
2.2	.9861	.9864	.9868	.9871	.9875	.9878	.9881	.9884	.9887	.9890
2.3	.9893	.9896	.9898	.9901	.9904	.9906	.9909	.9911	.9913	.9916
2.4	.9918	.9920	.9922	.9925	.9927	.9929	.9931	.9932	.9934	.9936
2.5	.9938	.9940	.9941	.9943	.9945	.9946	.9948	.9949	.9951	.9952
2.6	.9953	.9955	.9956	.9957	.9959	.9960	.9961	.9962	.9963	.9964
2.7	.9965	.9966	.9967	.9968	.9969	.9970	.9971	.9972	.9973	.9974
2.8	.9974	.9975	.9976	.9977	.9977	.9978	.9979	.9979	.9980	.9981
2.9	.9981	.9982	.9982	.9983	.9984	.9984	.9985	.9985	.9986	.9986
3.0	.9987	.9987	.9987	.9988	.9988	.9989	.9989	.9989	.9990	.9990
3.1	.9990	.9991	.9991	.9991	.9992	.9992	.9992	.9992	.9993	.9993
3.2	.9993	.9993	.9994	.9994	.9994	.9994	.9994	.9995	.9995	.9995
3.3	.9995	.9995	.9995	.9996	.9996	.9996	.9996	.9996	.9996	.9997
3.4	.9997	.9997	.9997	.9997	.9997	.9997	.9997	.9997	.9997	.9998

Third Canadian Edition

BUSINESS
STATISTICS
in Practice

Bruce L. Bowerman
Miami University

Richard T. O'Connell
Miami University

Julie Aitken Schermer
The University of Western Ontario

Emily S. Murphree
Miami University

Andrew M. Johnson
The University of Western Ontario

Business Statistics in Practice
Third Canadian Edition

ISBN-13: 978-0-07-133960-5
ISBN-10: 0-07-133960-4

1 2 3 4 5 6 7 8 9 TCP 1 9 8 7 6 5 4

Printed and bound in Canada.

Director of Product Management: *Rhondda McNabb*
Senior Product Manager: *Kimberley Veevers*
Marketing Manager: *Cathie Lefebvre*
Product Developer: *Sarah Fulton*
Senior Product Team Associate: *Christine Lomas*
Supervising Editor: *Stephanie Gay*
Copy Editor: *June Trusty*
Proofreader: *Laurel Sparrow*
Plant Production Coordinator: *Scott Morrison*
Manufacturing Production Coordinator: *Lena Keating*
Cover Design: *Katherine Strain*
Cover Image: *Forest Woodward/GettyImages (RM)*
Interior Design: *Katherine Strain*
Page Layout: *Aptara®, Inc.*
Printer: *Transcontinental Printing Group*

Library and Archives Canada Cataloguing in Publication

Bowerman, Bruce L., author Business statistics in practice / Bruce L. Bowerman, Miami University, Richard T. O'Connell, Miami University, Julie Aitken Schermer, The University of Western Ontario, Emily S. Murphree, Miami University, Andrew M. Johnson, The University of Western Ontario. — Third Canadian edition.

Revision of: Business statistics in practice / Bruce L. Bowerman ... [et al.] ; with MegaStat software and other contributions by J. Burdene Orris. — 2nd Canadian ed. — [Whitby, ON] : McGraw-Hill Ryerson, c2011. Includes bibliographical references and indexes. ISBN 978-0-07-133960-5 (bound)

Bruce L. Bowerman

To my wife, children, sister, and other family members:
Drena, Michael, Jinda, Benjamin, and Lex,
Asa and Nicole, Susan, Fiona, Radeesa,
and Barney, Daphne, Chloe, and Edgar,
Gwyneth and Tony, Bobby and Callie,
Marmalade, Randy, and Penney,
Clarence, Quincy, Teddy, Julius,
Charlie, and Sally

Julie Aitken Schermer

To my husband, Clark

Andrew M. Johnson

None of my work on this edition of the textbook
would have been possible without the love and
support of my wife Barbara and my daughter
Rachel. I dedicate my work on this to you.

Richard T. O'Connell

To my children and grandchild: Christopher,
Bradley, and Sam

Emily S. Murphree

To Kevin and the Math Ladies

ABOUT THE AUTHORS

Bruce L. Bowerman is emeritus professor of decision sciences at Miami University in Oxford, Ohio. He received his PhD degree in statistics from Iowa State University in 1974, and he has over 40 years of experience teaching basic statistics, regression analysis, time series forecasting, survey sampling, and design of experiments to both undergraduate and graduate students. In 1987 Professor Bowerman received an Outstanding Teaching award from the Miami University senior class, and in 1992 he received an Effective Educator award from the Richard T. Farmer School of Business Administration. Together with Richard T. O'Connell, Professor Bowerman has written 19 textbooks. These include *Forecasting and Time Series: An Applied Approach*; *Forecasting, Time Series, and Regression: An Applied Approach* (also coauthored with Anne B. Koehler); and *Linear Statistical Models: An Applied Approach*. The first edition of *Forecasting and Time Series* earned an Outstanding Academic Book award from *Choice* magazine. Professor Bowerman has also published a number of articles in applied stochastic processes, time series forecasting, and statistical education. In his spare time, Professor Bowerman enjoys watching movies and sports, playing tennis, and designing houses.

Julie Aitken Schermer (formerly Harris) is an associate professor in the Management and Organizational Studies Program at The University of Western Ontario, London, Canada, where she teaches courses in the areas of business statistics and occupational health and safety. She received her PhD in personality psychology from The University of Western Ontario in 1999. She has published more than 70 articles in peer-reviewed journals in areas of individual differences such as intelligence, personality, vocational interests, and behaviour genetics. She has also been involved in more than 90 conference presentations. When not working, she spends time with her husband Clark and their dogs Misty and Moose.

Andrew M. Johnson is the chair of the Health and Rehabilitation Sciences Program at The University of Western Ontario. He has taught statistics and methodology at Western for more than 15 years, and has supervised numerous students at the masters and PhD levels. Primarily interested in the study of human individual differences, he published some of the earliest research on the genetic basis of leadership. He has consulted on statistical and measurement issues in both the private and the public sector, and has presented at numerous professional and scientific conferences on topics related to evidence-based decision making.

Richard T. O'Connell is emeritus professor of decision sciences at Miami University in Oxford, Ohio. He has more than 35 years of experience teaching basic statistics, statistical quality control and process improvement, regression analysis, time series forecasting, and design of experiments to both undergraduate and graduate business students. He also has extensive consulting experience and has taught workshops dealing with statistical process control and process improvement for a variety of companies in the Midwest. In 2000 Professor O'Connell received an Effective Educator award from the Richard T. Farmer School of Business Administration. Together with Bruce L. Bowerman, he has written 19 textbooks. These include *Forecasting and Time Series: An Applied Approach*; *Forecasting, Time Series, and Regression: An Applied Approach* (also coauthored with Anne B. Koehler); and *Linear Statistical Models: An Applied Approach.* Professor O'Connell has published a number of articles in the area of innovative statistical education. He is one of the first college instructors in the United States to integrate statistical process control and process improvement methodology into his basic business statistics course. He (with Professor Bowerman) has written several articles advocating this approach. He has also given presentations on this subject at meetings such as the Joint Statistical Meetings of the American Statistical Association and the Workshop on Total Quality Management: Developing Curricula and Research Agendas (sponsored by the Production and Operations Management Society). Professor O'Connell received an MS degree in decision sciences from Northwestern University in 1973, and he is currently a member of both the Decision Sciences Institute and the American Statistical Association. In his spare time, Professor O'Connell enjoys fishing, collecting 1950s and 1960s rock music, and following the Green Bay Packers and Purdue University sports.

Emily S. Murphree is associate professor of statistics in the Department of Mathematics and Statistics at Miami University in Oxford, Ohio. She received her PhD degree in statistics from the University of North Carolina and does research in applied probability. Professor Murphree received Miami's College of Arts and Science Distinguished Educator Award in 1998. In 1996, she was named one of Oxford's Citizens of the Year for her work with Habitat for Humanity and for organizing annual Sonia Kovalevsky Mathematical Sciences Days for area high school girls. In 2012 she was recognized as "A Teacher Who Made a Difference" by the University of Kentucky.

BRIEF TABLE OF CONTENTS

Appendices Available on Mc Graw Hill Education **connect**

TABLE OF CONTENTS

Appendices all available on McGraw Hill Education **connect**

PREFACE

In *Business Statistics in Practice, Third Canadian Edition*, we provide a modern, practical, and unique framework for teaching the first course in business statistics. As in previous editions, we employ real or realistic examples and data, while we incorporate a business improvement theme. In addition, we have endeavoured to make this book the most clearly written, motivating, and easy-to-use business statistics resource available.

What's New in *Business Statistics in Practice, Third Canadian Edition*?

- "Theory to Practice" boxed features: This new pedagogical feature shows students how statistics are used in a practical way by different business units, such as marketing, sales, and finance.

- "Roadblock" boxed features: This new pedagogical feature provides tips and tricks for students becoming accustomed to new material.

- New continuing examples have been added and, as with the previous editions, each time a continuing example is revisited, there is no need to flip back to previous pages or computer outputs, as all of the necessary data and information are included in the current discussion.

- In addition to a thorough update and refreshing of the examples, data sets, and end-of-chapter material, more exercises and problems have been added throughout this new edition.

CHAPTER-BY-CHAPTER CHANGES

Chapter 1

- Enhanced introduction
- Examples added in Section 1.4: Levels of Measurement: Nominal, Ordinal, Interval, and Ratio
- The terms *parameter* and *statistic* are introduced in Section 1.1: Populations and Samples

Chapter 2

- Clarified percentiles in Section 2.4: Percentiles, Quartiles, and Box-and-Whiskers Displays
- Levels of measurement brought to the major examples

Chapter 3

- New lottery example (Example 3.6)

Chapter 4

- Two new lottery expected value questions
- Index fund example added in Section 4.5: The Hypergeometric Distribution

Chapter 6

- New "Roadblock" feature provides direct linkage and contrast between the sample distribution and the sampling distribution
- Introduction of the idea of effect size estimation and the importance of establishing substantive significance

Chapter 7

- Chapters 7 and 8 completely reorganized—z tests are in Chapter 7 and t tests are in Chapter 8

- Added emphasis throughout Chapter 7 on the importance of effect size estimates and practical significance

- New Section 7.7: Standardized Effect Size Estimation for Mean Differences

- Addresses possible confusion over "null" versus "nil" hypotheses, through the use of "Roadblock" feature

- Substantial information added throughout the chapter, reminding the reader that p-values are not a substitute for effect size estimates

- The issue of confusing p with alpha (a frequent problem for students and researchers) addressed in a "Roadblock" feature

- Foreshadows the importance of confidence intervals in the interpretation of effects, preparing the student for the context in which Chapter 9 will be presented

Chapter 8

- As mentioned above, Chapters 7 and 8 completely reorganized—z tests are in Chapter 7 and t tests are in Chapter 8

- Augmented information presented on the difference between the equal variances t test and the unequal variances t test

Chapter 9

- Content rearranged throughout Chapters 7 and 8 so that all confidence intervals (CIs) are presented in Chapter 9

- Chapter rearranged so that the general form of CIs is presented at the outset

- Increased emphasis on confidence intervals as methods for interpreting statistically significant effects

- Information from the Canadian census provided in the "Internet Exercise"

- Decreased emphasis on z-based intervals; rationale for this decision presented

- Updated statistical analysis section

Chapter 10

- Concept of quasi-experimental designs introduced

- Increasing of sample size discussed as one method of reducing within-group variance

Chapter 11

- Used example data to further demonstrate residuals

- Use of the chi-square statistic to test the assumption of normality of error terms demonstrated

Chapter 12

- Content on multicollinearity now in a separate section, immediately following the section on assumptions

- Further information provided on stepwise regression and backward elimination, with instructions to turn to Appendix K for further detailed information

- Information added regarding the link between ANOVA and regression

Chapter 13

* Emphasis on how sample size shapes influence hypothesis testing

Chapter 14

* Multiple changes made to Section 14.1 to clarify how expected frequencies are calculated

Chapter 15

* Highlights the fact that expected payoffs may not be the same as real payoffs
* Concept of "perfect information" discussed

Chapter 16

* Updated Canadian Consumer Price Index (CPI) information
* Further information on error calculations

ACKNOWLEDGEMENTS

The authors are grateful to Bruce Bowerman, Richard O'Connell, and Emily Murphree, authors of the U.S. edition, for providing the foundation on which this third Canadian adaptation has been built. We would also like to thank the following people at McGraw-Hill Ryerson for their support: Senior Product Manager Kimberley Veevers, Product Developer Sarah Fulton May, Copy Editor June Trusty, and Supervising Editor Stephanie Gay.

Reviewers for the Third Canadian Edition

Edward Acquah, Athabasca University

Les Barnhouse, Grant MacEwan University

Imad Hasan, Algonquin College

Ali Hassanlou, Kwantlen Polytechnic Institute

Kalinga Jagoda, Mount Royal University

Peggy Ng, York University

Mahmut Parlar, McMaster University

Steven Schecter, University of British Columbia

Samie Li Shang Ly, Concordia University

Jill Simmons, University of Victoria

Don St. Jean, George Brown College

John W. Walker, Brock University

Marty Yalovsky, McGill University

Cleusa Yamamoto, Douglas College

Victor Yu, University of Toronto at Scarborough

Kate Zhang, University of Guelph

GUIDED TOUR

Business Statistics in Practice, Third Canadian Edition, was written with students' needs in mind. Its clear and understandable explanations and use of real-world examples present content in a way that business students can relate to.

Chapter Introductions

Each chapter opens with chapter learning objectives and a list of the section topics that are covered in each chapter, along with a brief introduction discussing how the statistical topics to be discussed apply to real business problems.

Continuous Examples and Business Improvement Conclusions

The text provides a unique use of examples that span individual chapters and groups of chapters. Examples are used to introduce the concepts, to demonstrate the methods, and to provide students with motivating exercises. These continuous examples help students see how statistics is used in business and can be instrumental in improving processes.

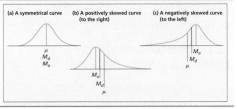

Example 2.7 DVD Recorder Satisfaction

The manufacturer of a DVD recorder randomly selects a sample of 20 purchasers who have owned the recorder for one year. Each purchaser in the sample is asked to rank his or her satisfaction with the recorder on the following ten-point interval scale:

1	2	3	4	5	6	7	8	9	10
Not satisfied				Fairly satisfied					Extremely satisfied

Suppose that the following rankings, arranged in increasing order, are obtained:

1   3   5   5   7   8   8   8   8   (8)(8)   9   9   9   9   9   10   10   10   10

Because the number of satisfaction ratings is even, the median of this sample is the average of the two middle ratings. Both of these ratings are 8—they are circled. Therefore, the median of this sample is 8, and we estimate that the median satisfaction rating of all the DVD recorder owners is 8. This estimated median satisfaction rating seems relatively high. Note, however, that there are four rather low individual satisfaction ratings: 1, 3, 5, and 5. This suggests that some DVD recorders may be of low quality. If the manufacturer wishes to satisfy all of its customers, it must investigate the situation.

Comparing the mean, median, and mode To compare the mean, median, and mode, look at Figure 2.16. Part (a) of this figure depicts a population described by a symmetrical relative frequency curve. For such a population, the mean (μ), median (M_d), and mode (M_o) are all equal. Note that in this case, all three of these quantities are located under the highest point of the curve. It follows that when the frequency distribution of a sample of measurements is approximately symmetrical (normal or mound-shaped), then the sample mean, median, and mode will be nearly the same. For instance, consider a sample of 49 DVD price points, and note that the stem-and-leaf display of these prices is given in the margin of this page. Because the number of prices is odd, the median is the middle price, the 25th price. Counting 25 prices from the top of the stem-and-leaf display, we find that the median is 31.6. Furthermore, since the stem-and-leaf display is fairly symmetrical, this sample median is approximately equal to the sample mean, which is 31.55.

DVD Prices

29	8
30	1344
30	5666889
31	001233444
③①	555⑥6777889
32	0001122344
32	556788
33	3

FIGURE **2.16** Relationships among the Mean (μ), the Median (M_d), and the Mode (M_o)

(a) A symmetrical curve	(b) A positively skewed curve (to the right)	(c) A negatively skewed curve (to the left)
μ M_d M_o	M_o M_d μ	M_o M_d μ

CHAPTER **1**
An Introduction to Business Statistics

LEARNING OBJECTIVES

After reading this chapter, you should be able to

LO1 Explain the function of research samples

LO2 Define the term *random sample*

LO3 Explain how a random sample can be generated

LO4 Describe how a process is sampled

LO5 Identify the four levels of measurement

LO6 List some of the potential problems associated with surveys

CHAPTER OUTLINE

1.1 Populations and Samples

1.2 Sampling a Population of Existing Units

1.3 Sampling a Process

1.4 Levels of Measurement: Nominal, Ordinal, Interval, and Ratio

1.5 A Brief Introduction to Surveys

1.6 An Introduction to Survey Sampling

The subject of statistics involves the study of how to collect, summarize, and interpret data. Data are numerical facts and figures from which conclusions can be drawn. Data are typically collected from a sample in order to make an inference about a population. This process is important for making decisions in many professions and organizations. For example, government officials use conclusions drawn from the latest data on unemployment and inflation to make policy decisions. Financial planners use recent trends in stock market prices to make investment decisions. Businesses decide which products to develop and market by using data that reveal consumer preferences. Production supervisors use manufacturing data to evaluate, control, and improve product quality. All aspects of businesses rely on collecting and interpreting data.

To emphasize the text's theme of business improvement, icons are placed in the page margins to identify when statistical analysis has led to an important business improvement conclusion.

Student-Friendly Presentation

The authors make learning easier for students. The following examples highlight some of these improvements.

Figures and Tables

Throughout the text, charts, graphs, tables, and Excel and MegaStat outputs are used to illustrate statistical concepts. For example:

Greater Accessibility of Continuing Examples

Each time a continuing example is revisited, any needed computer output and, whenever possible, relevant background information is included with the current example discussion. Consequently, students seldom need to refer back to previously covered material in order to grasp the content included in a given example segment.

- In Chapter 2 (Descriptive Statistics), in the "DVD Price Points" example, a consumer uses the empirical rule to find estimates of the "typical," "lowest," and "highest" price points on individual DVD purchases. The following are used to help explain the empirical rule.

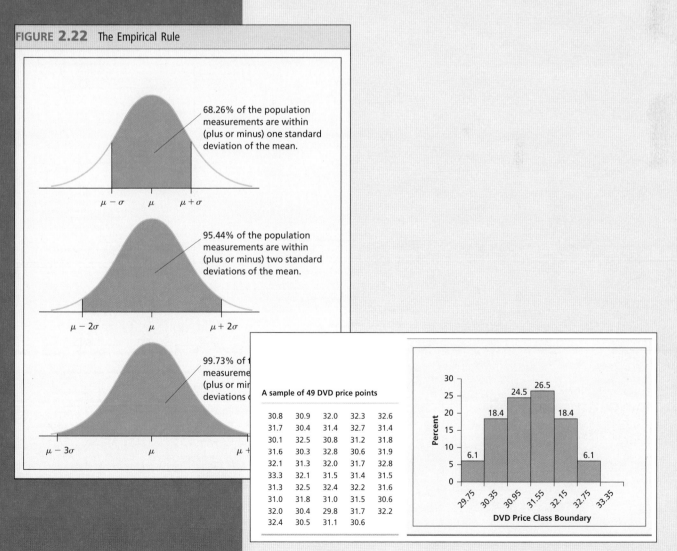

FIGURE **2.22** The Empirical Rule

68.26% of the population measurements are within (plus or minus) one standard deviation of the mean.

$\mu - \sigma$ μ $\mu + \sigma$

95.44% of the population measurements are within (plus or minus) two standard deviations of the mean.

$\mu - 2\sigma$ μ $\mu + 2\sigma$

99.73% of the measureme (plus or mi deviations

$\mu - 3\sigma$ μ $\mu +$

A sample of 49 DVD price points

30.8	30.9	32.0	32.3	32.6
31.7	30.4	31.4	32.7	31.4
30.1	32.5	30.8	31.2	31.8
31.6	30.3	32.8	30.6	31.9
32.1	31.3	32.0	31.7	32.8
33.3	32.1	31.5	31.4	31.5
31.3	32.5	32.4	32.2	31.6
31.0	31.8	31.0	31.5	30.6
32.0	30.4	29.8	31.7	32.2
32.4	30.5	31.1	30.6	

- In Chapter 6 (Sampling Distributions), the figures shown below (and others) are used to help explain the sampling distribution of the sample mean and central limit theorem. In addition, the figures describe different applications of random sampling in the "Fuel Efficiency" example, so this example is used as an integrative tool to help students understand sampling distributions.

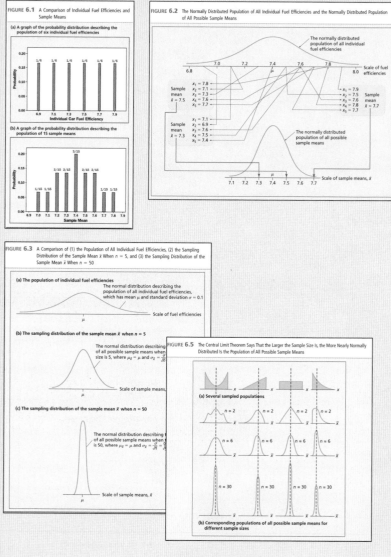

- In Chapter 7 (Hypothesis Testing), a five-step hypothesis testing procedure, hypothesis testing summary boxes, and many graphics are used to show how to carry out hypothesis tests.

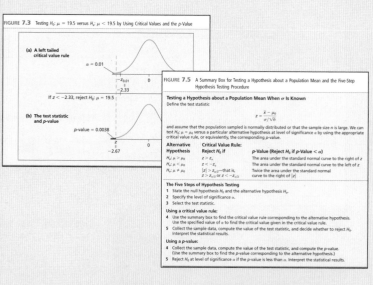

- In Chapter 9 (Confidence Intervals), the figure shown below is one of the illustrations used to help explain the meaning of a 95 percent confidence interval for the population mean. Furthermore, in the "Estimating Demand for a Seasonal Box of Chocolates" example, a confectioner uses a confidence interval procedure to determine the fiscal responsibility of increasing production by predicting surpluses and shortfalls at a variety of retail locations.

- In Chapter 11 (Correlation Coefficient and Simple Linear Regression Analysis) and Chapter 12 (Multiple Regression), a substantial number of data plots and Excel and MegaStat output and other graphics are used to teach simple and multiple regression analysis.

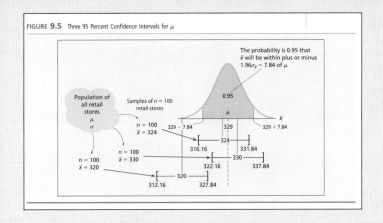

FIGURE **9.5** Three 95 Percent Confidence Intervals for μ

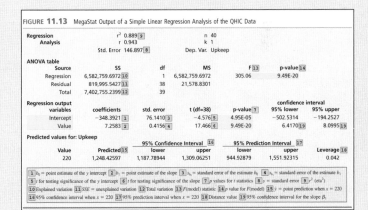

FIGURE **11.13** MegaStat Output of a Simple Linear Regression Analysis of the QHIC Data

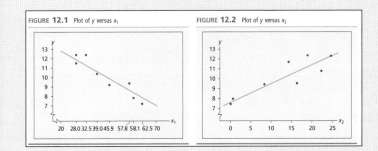

FIGURE **12.1** Plot of y versus x_1

FIGURE **12.2** Plot of y versus x_2

FIGURE **12.5** A Correlation Matrix for the Sales Territory Performance Data

Exercises

Many of the exercises in the text require the analysis of real data. Data sets are identified by an icon in the text and are included on *Connect*. Exercises in each section are broken into two parts—"Concepts" and "Methods and Applications"—and there are supplementary exercises and an Internet exercise at the end of each chapter. The methods and applications exercises vary in rigour from routine calculations to fairly sophisticated analysis.

Excel and MegaStat Tutorials

The end-of-chapter appendices (available on *Connect*) contain helpful tutorials that teach students how to carry out statistical analysis using Excel and MegaStat. These tutorials include step-by-step instructions for performing almost every type of statistical method presented in the book.

Exercises for Section **2.1**

CONCEPTS

2.1 What does each population shape look like? Describe each shape and then draw a picture to illustrate.
a. Symmetrical and bell-shaped.
b. Double-peaked.
c. Negatively skewed (with a tail to the left).
d. Positively skewed (with a tail to the right).

2.2 Explain each of the following:
a. How to construct a stem-and-leaf display, a histogram, and a dot plot.
b. How class limits, class boundaries, and class midpoints differ.
c. What outliers are and how they are handled.

METHODS AND APPLICATIONS

2.3 Given in Table 2.6 are the median total incomes by metropolitan areas for Canada for 2006 through 2010 as reported by Statistics Canada. Construct stem-and-leaf plots for 2006 and 2010 (using a stem unit of $10,000). Comparing the two plots, what can you say about the median income values?

2.4 THE VIDEO GAME SATISFACTION RATING EXAMPLE

Table 2.7 presents the satisfaction ratings for the XYZ-Box video game system that have been given by 65 randomly selected purchasers. Figure 2.11 gives the MegaStat output of a stem-and-leaf display, and Figure 2.12 gives the Excel output of a frequency histogram of the 65 satisfaction ratings.
a. Verify that the classes and class frequencies given in Figure 2.12 are those obtained by using the histogram construction method discussed in this section.
b. Using Figures 2.11 and 2.12, infer the shape of the relative frequency distribution describing the population of all possible customer satisfaction ratings for the XYZ-Box video game system.
c. Construct a relative frequency histogram of the 65 satisfaction ratings.

2.5 THE BANK CUSTOMER WAITING TIME EXAMPLE

Table 2.8 presents the waiting times for teller service during peak business hours of 100 randomly selected bank customers. Figure 2.13 gives the Excel output of a frequency histogram of the 100 waiting times.
a. Verify that the class boundaries and the class frequencies (see Figure 2.13) are those obtained by using the histogram construction method discussed in this section.
b. Using Figure 2.13, infer the shape of the relative frequency distribution describing the population of all possible customer waiting times during peak business hours.

2.6 THE TRASH BAG EXAMPLE

Table 2.9 presents the breaking strengths of 40 trash bags selected during a 40-hour pilot production run. Figure 2.14 gives the MegaStat output of a relative frequency histogram and Figure 2.15 gives the MegaStat output of a stem-and-leaf display of the 40 breaking strengths.
a. Verify that the classes and class relative frequencies given in Figure 2.14 are those obtained by using the histogram construction method discussed in this section.
b. Using Figures 2.14 and 2.15, infer the shape of the relative frequency distribution describing the population of all possible trash bag breaking strengths.

2.7 Babe Ruth's record of 60 home runs in a single year was broken by Roger Maris, who hit 61 home runs in 1961. The yearly home run totals for Ruth in his career as a New York Yankee are (arranged in increasing order) 22, 25, 34, 35, 41, 41, 46, 46, 47, 49, 54, 54, 59, and 60. The yearly home run totals for Maris over his career in the American League are (arranged in increasing order) 8, 13, 14, 16, 23, 26, 28, 33, 39, and 61. Compare Ruth's and Maris's home run totals by constructing a back-to-back stem-and-leaf display. What would you conclude about Maris's record-breaking year?

Appendix 1.1 ■ Getting Started with Excel

Because Excel 2007 may be new to some readers, and because the Excel 2007 window looks quite different from previous versions of Excel, we will begin by describing some characteristics of the Excel 2007 window. Previous versions of Excel employed many drop-down menus. This meant that many features were "hidden" from the user, which resulted in a steep learning curve for beginners. In Excel 2007, Microsoft tried to reduce the number of features that are hidden in drop-down menus. Therefore, Excel 2007 displays all of the applicable commands needed for a particular type of task at the top of the Excel window. These commands are represented by a tab-and-group arrangement called the **ribbon**—see the right side of the illustration of an Excel 2007 window below. The commands displayed in the ribbon are regulated by a series of **tabs** located near the top of the ribbon. For example, in the illustration below, the **Home tab** is selected. If we selected a different tab, say, for example, the **Page Layout tab**, the commands displayed by the ribbon would be different.

We now briefly describe some basic features of the Excel 2007 window:

1 **Office button:** By clicking on this button, the user obtains a menu of often used commands—for example, Open, Save, Print, and so forth. This is very similar to the "File menu" in older versions of Excel. However, some menu items are unique to Excel 2007. This menu also provides access to a large number of Excel options settings.

2 **Tabs:** Clicking on a tab results in a ribbon display of features, commands, and options related to a particular type of task. For example, when the *Home tab* is selected (as in the figure below), the features, commands, and options displayed by the ribbon are all related to making entries into the Excel worksheet. As another example, if the *Formula tab* is selected, all of the features, commands, and options displayed in the ribbon relate to using formulas in the Excel worksheet.

3 **Quick access toolbar:** This toolbar displays buttons that provide shortcuts to often used commands. Initially, this toolbar displays Save, Undo, and Redo buttons. The user can customize this toolbar by adding shortcut buttons for other commands (such as, New, Open, Quick Print, and so forth). This can be done by clicking on the arrow button directly to the right of the Quick access toolbar and by making selections from the "Customize" drop-down menu that appears.

SUPPLEMENTS

CONNECT

McGraw-Hill *Connect*™ is a Web-based assignment and assessment platform that gives students the means to better connect with their coursework, with their instructors, and with the important concepts that they will need to know for success now and in the future.

With *Connect*, instructors can deliver assignments, quizzes, and tests online. Select in-text questions are presented in an autogradable format and tied to the text's learning objectives. Instructors can edit existing questions and author entirely new problems—track individual student performance (by question, by assignment, or in relation to the class overall) with detailed grade reports—integrate grade reports easily with Learning Management Systems (LMS) such as WebCT and Blackboard—and much more.

By choosing *Connect*, instructors are providing their students with a powerful tool for improving academic performance and truly mastering course material. *Connect* allows students to practise important skills at their own pace and on their own schedule. Importantly, students' assessment results and instructors' feedback are all saved online—so students can continually review their progress and plot their course to success.

Connect also provides 24/7 online access to an eBook—an online edition of the text—to aid students in successfully completing their work, wherever and whenever they choose.

LEARN SMART

No two students are alike. Why should their learning paths be? LearnSmart uses revolutionary adaptive technology to build a learning experience unique to each student's individual needs. It starts by identifying the topics a student knows and does not know. As the student progresses, LearnSmart adapts and adjusts the content based on his or her individual strengths, weaknesses, and confidence, ensuring that every minute spent studying with LearnSmart is the most efficient and productive study time possible.

SMARTBOOK

As the first and only adaptive reading experience, SmartBook is changing the way students read and learn. SmartBook creates a personalized reading experience by highlighting the most important concepts a student needs to learn at that moment in time. As a student engages with SmartBook, the reading experience continuously adapts by highlighting content based on what each student knows and doesn't know. This ensures that he or she is focused on the content needed to close specific knowledge gaps, while it simultaneously promotes long-term learning.

INSTRUCTOR'S SUPPLEMENTS

Instructor's Solutions Manual Prepared by the authors and adapted to reflect this latest Canadian edition, this manual includes worked-out solutions to all of the exercises in the text. Technical checkers for the ISM and textbook were David Roberts of Southern Alberta Institute of Technology and Les Barnhouse of MacEwan University.

Computerized Test Bank Prepared by Wayne Horn of Carleton University, the computerized test bank has been extensively revised and technically checked for accuracy. The computerized test bank contains a variety of questions, including true/false, multiple-choice, and short-answer questions requiring analysis and written answers. The computerized test bank is available through EZ Test Online—a flexible and easy-to-use electronic testing program that allows instructors to create tests from book-specific items. EZ Test accommodates a wide range of question types and allows instructors to add their own questions. Test items are also available in Word format (rich text format). For secure online testing, exams created in EZ Test can be exported to WebCT and Blackboard. EZ Test Online is supported at mhhe.com/eztest, where users can download a *Quick Start Guide*, access FAQs, or log a ticket for help with specific issues.

Microsoft®PowerPoint® Lecture Slides   Prepared by Kalinga Jagoda of Mount Royal University, the PowerPoint slides draw on the highlights of each chapter and provide an opportunity for the instructor to emphasize the most relevant visuals in class discussions.

ONLINE TECHNOLOGY

Excel and MegaStat   *Business Statistics in Practice, Third Canadian Edition*, features a modern use of the statistical capabilities of the software package Excel and its add-in MegaStat. Throughout the book, we provide abundant outputs from both applications in both examples and exercises that allow students to concentrate on statistical interpretations. This use of outputs is particularly prominent in statistical areas where manual calculations are impractical and where having students run their own programs (while theoretically optimal) would, because of time constraints, not allow them to see a wide variety of applications. These areas include descriptive statistics, analysis of variance, regression, and time series forecasting. In addition, appendixes for each chapter (available on *Connect*) show in detail how to use Excel and Mega-Stat to implement the statistical techniques discussed in the chapter. MegaStat is a comprehensive, accurate, and easy-to-use Excel add-in application. In addition to remedying most of the computational problems associated with Excel data analysis tools, MegaStat is specifically designed to enhance the use of *Business Statistics in Practice, Third Canadian Edition*.

In addition, MegaStat is fully capable of performing analyses related to discrete and continuous probability distributions, time series forecasting, nonparametric statistics, and chi-square tests—virtually all topics covered by *Business Statistics in Practice, Third Canadian Edition*.

SUPERIOR LEARNING SOLUTIONS AND SUPPORT

The McGraw-Hill Ryerson team is ready to help you assess and integrate any of our products, technology, and services into your course for optimal teaching and learning performance. Whether it's helping your students improve their grades or putting your entire course online, the McGraw-Hill Ryerson team is here to help you do it. Contact your Learning Solutions Consultant today to learn how to maximize all of McGraw-Hill Ryerson's resources!

For more information on the latest technology and learning solutions offered by McGraw-Hill Ryerson and its partners, please visit us online: **mcgrawhill.ca/he/solutions**

CHAPTER **1**
An Introduction to Business Statistics

The subject of statistics involves the study of how to collect, summarize, and interpret data. Data are numerical facts and figures from which conclusions can be drawn. Data are typically collected from a sample in order to make an inference about a population. This process is important for making decisions in many professions and organizations. For example, government officials use conclusions drawn from the latest data on unemployment and inflation to make policy decisions. Financial planners use recent trends in stock market prices to make investment decisions. Businesses decide which products to develop and market by using data that reveal consumer preferences. Production supervisors use manufacturing data to evaluate, control, and improve product quality. All aspects of businesses rely on collecting and interpreting data.

1.1 POPULATIONS AND SAMPLES

Statistical methods are very useful for learning about populations. Population can be defined in various ways, including the following:

A **population** is a set of units (usually people, objects, or events).

Examples of populations are (1) all of last year's graduates of the Sauder School of Business at the University of British Columbia, (2) all consumers who bought a vacuum cleaner last year, (3) all potential consumers who might purchase a house next year, (4) all accounts receivable invoices accumulated last year by Procter & Gamble, (5) all Toyota Corollas produced last year, and (6) all fires reported last month to the Ottawa fire department.

We usually focus on studying one or more characteristics of the population units.

Any characteristic of a population unit is called a **variable**.

For instance, if we study the starting salaries of last year's graduates of an MBA program, the variable of interest is starting salary. If we study the fuel efficiency obtained in city driving by last year's Toyota Corolla, the variable of interest is litres per 100 km of city driving.

We carry out a **measurement** to assign a value of a variable to each population unit. For example, we might measure the starting salary of an MBA graduate to the nearest dollar. Or we might measure the fuel efficiency obtained by a car in city driving to the nearest litre per 100 km by conducting a test on a driving course prescribed by the Ministry of Transportation. If the possible measurements are numbers that represent quantities (that is, "how much" or "how many"), then the variable is said to be a **quantitative variable**. For example, starting salary and fuel efficiency are both quantitative. However, if we simply record into which of several categories a population unit falls, then the variable is said to be a **qualitative** or **categorical variable**. Examples of categorical variables are (1) a person's sex, (2) the make of an automobile, (3) the aisle number where soup is located in a grocery store, and (3) whether a person who purchases a product is satisfied with the product.[1]

If we measure each and every population unit, we have a population of measurements (sometimes called *observations*). If the population is small, it is reasonable to do this. For instance, if 150 students graduated last year from an MBA program, it might be feasible to survey the graduates and to record all of their starting salaries. In general, we have the following:

If we examine all of the population measurements, we say that we are conducting a **census** of the population, and we can therefore generate population parameters (statistics based on the entire population).

LO1

The population that we want to study is often very large, and it is too time-consuming or costly to conduct a census. In such a situation, we select and analyze a sample (or portion) of the population.

A **sample** is a subset of the units in a population.

For example, suppose that 8,742 students graduated last year from a large university. It would probably be too time-consuming to take a census of the population of all of their starting salaries. Therefore, we would select a sample of graduates, and we would obtain and record their starting salaries. When we measure the units in a sample, we say that we have a sample of measurements. These measurements can then be used to calculate sample statistics.

---

[1] In Section 1.4, we discuss two types of quantitative variables (ratio and interval) and two types of qualitative variables (ordinal and nominative). To remember the difference between quantitative and qualitative, remember that quantitative has the letter "*n*" and "*n* is for number." Qualitative has an "*l*" and "*l* is for letter," so you have to use words to describe the data.

We often want to describe a population or sample. The science of describing the important aspects of a set of measurements is called *descriptive statistics*. As an example, if we are studying a set of starting salaries, we might want to describe (1) how large or small they tend to be, (2) what a typical salary might be, and (3) how much the salaries differ from each other (how to calculate these descriptive statistics is introduced in Chapter 2).

When the population of interest is small and we can conduct a census of the population, we can directly describe the important aspects of the population measurements. However, if the population is large and we need to select a sample from it, then we use what is called *statistical inference*.

Statistical inference is the science of using a sample of measurements to make generalizations about the important aspects of a population of measurements.

For instance, we might use a sample of starting salaries to estimate the important aspects of a population of starting salaries. In the next section, we begin to look at how statistical inference is carried out.

1.2 SAMPLING A POPULATION OF EXISTING UNITS

LO2
LO3

Random samples If the information contained in a sample is to accurately reflect the population under study, the sample should be randomly selected from the population. To intuitively illustrate random sampling, suppose that a small company employs 15 people and wants to randomly select two of them to attend a convention. To make the random selections, we number the employees from 1 to 15, and we place in a hat 15 identical slips of paper numbered from 1 to 15. We thoroughly mix the slips of paper in the hat and, blindfolded, choose one. The number on the chosen slip of paper identifies the first randomly selected employee. Then, still blindfolded, we choose another slip of paper from the hat. The number on the second slip identifies the second randomly selected employee.

Of course, it is impractical to carry out such a procedure when the population is very large. It is easier to use a **random number table** or a computerized random number generator. To show how to use such a table, we must more formally define *random sample.*[2]

A **random sample** is selected so that, on each selection from the population, every unit remaining in the population on that selection has the same chance of being chosen.

To understand this definition, first note that we can randomly select a sample with or without replacement. When **sampling with replacement**, we place the unit chosen on any particular selection back into the population, giving this unit a chance to be chosen again on any succeeding selection. In such a case, all of the units in the population remain as candidates to be chosen for every selection. Randomly choosing two employees with replacement to attend a convention would make no sense because we want to send two different employees to the convention. When **sampling without replacement**, we do not place the unit chosen on a particular selection back into the population, so we do not give this unit a chance to be selected on any succeeding selection. In this case, the units remaining as candidates for a particular selection are all of the units in the population except those that have previously been selected.

It is best to sample without replacement. Intuitively, because we will use the sample to learn about the population, sampling without replacement will give us the fullest possible look at the population. This is true because choosing the sample without replacement guarantees that all of the units in the sample will be different (and that we are looking at as many different units from the population as possible).

In Example 1.1, we illustrate how to use a random number table, or computer-generated random numbers, to select a random sample.

---

[2]There are several different kinds of random samples. The type we will define is sometimes called a *simple random sample*. For brevity's sake, however, we will use the term *random sample*.

Example 1.1   Estimating Cellphone Costs

Businesses and students have at least two things in common—both find cellphones to be nearly indispensable because of their convenience and mobility, and both often rack up unpleasantly high cellphone bills. Students' high bills are usually the result of overage—students use more minutes than their plans allow. For example, the television program *Marketplace* on CBC broadcasts a segment entitled, "Canada's Worst Cellphone Bill." According to the presenters, many Canadians claim that their bill warrants the title of the "worst" bill. Businesses also lose money due to overage and, in addition, lose money due to underage, when some employees do not use all of the (already-paid-for) minutes allowed by their plans. Because cellular carriers offer a very large number of rate plans, it is nearly impossible for a business to intelligently choose calling plans that will meet its needs at a reasonable cost. Rising cellphone costs have forced companies with large numbers of cellular users to hire services to manage their cellular and other wireless resources. These cellular management services use sophisticated software and mathematical models to choose cost-efficient cellphone plans for their clients.

In this example, we will demonstrate how a bank can use a random sample of cellphone users to study its cellphone costs. Based on this cost information, the bank will decide whether to hire a cellular management service to choose calling plans for the bank's employees. While the bank has over 10,000 employees on a variety of calling plans, a study of the calling patterns of cellular users on 500-minute plans may help the bank accurately assess whether its cellphone costs can be substantially reduced.

The bank has 2,136 employees on a 500-minute-per-month plan, with a monthly cost of $50. The overage charge is 40 cents per minute, and there are additional charges for long distance and roaming. The bank will estimate its cellular cost per minute for this plan by examining the number of minutes used last month by each of 100 randomly selected employees on this 500-minute plan. According to the cellular management service, if the cellular cost per minute for the random sample of 100 employees is over 18 cents per minute, the bank should benefit from automated cellular management of its calling plans.

In order to randomly select the sample of 100 cellphone users, the bank will make a numbered list of the 2,136 users on the 500-minute plan. This list is called a **frame**. The bank can then use a random number table, such as Table 1.1(a), to select the needed sample. To see how this is done, note that any one-digit number in the table is assumed to have been randomly selected from the digits 0 to 9. Any two-digit number in the table is assumed to have been

TABLE **1.1**   Random Numbers

(a) A portion of a random number table							(b) Excel output of 100 different four-digit random numbers between 1 and 2,136					
33276	85590	79936	56865	05859	90106	78188						
03427	90511	69445	18663	72695	52180	90322	1968	1766	1350	1340	1585	1943
92737	27156	33488	36320	17617	30015	74952	1717	545	974	1492	1843	647
85689	20285	52267	67689	93394	01511	89868	845	1842	1575	462	1868	319
08178	74461	13916	47564	81056	97735	90707	259	180	398	792	454	1147
51259	63990	16308	60756	92144	49442	40719	64	321	974	2074	2026	1941
60268	44919	19885	55322	44819	01188	55157	431	531	312	36	1971	1496
94904	01915	04146	18594	29852	71585	64951	1863	1275	380	229	2068	1778
58586	17752	14513	83149	98736	23495	35749	2024	1914	587	1772	341	77
09998	19509	06691	76988	13602	51851	58104	171	1259	801	1533	380	252
14346	61666	30168	90229	04734	59193	32812	517	2079	1181	1064	1648	1863
74103	15227	25306	76468	26384	58151	44592	170	69	1790	1644	97	1678
24200	64161	38005	94342	28728	35806	22851	207	2005	662	73	102	1129
87308	07684	00256	45834	15398	46557	18510	1350	1690	99	1858	1017	56
07351	86679	92420	60952	61280	50001	94953	1523	255	384	1714	2126	1220
							1942	1335	503	1536	484	2041
							73	1067	1344	666	2119	
							785	2095	1703	1510	1940	

randomly selected from the numbers 00 to 99. Any three-digit number is assumed to have been randomly selected from the numbers 000 to 999, and so forth. Note that the table entries are segmented into groups of five to make the table easier to read. Because the total number of cellphone users on the 500-minute plan (2,136) is a four-digit number, we arbitrarily select any set of four digits in the table (these digits are circled). This number, which is 0511, identifies the first randomly selected user. Then, moving in any direction from the 0511 (up, down, right, or left—it does not matter which), we select additional sets of four digits. These succeeding sets of digits identify additional randomly selected users. Here we arbitrarily move down from 0511 in the table. The first seven sets of four digits we obtain are

$$0511 \quad 7156 \quad 0285 \quad 4461 \quad 3990 \quad 4919 \quad 1915$$

(See Table 1.1(a)—these numbers are enclosed in a rectangle.) Since there are no users numbered 7,156, 4,461, 3,990, or 4,919 (remember only 2,136 users are on the 500-minute plan), we ignore these numbers. This implies that the first three randomly selected users are those numbered 0511, 0285, and 1915. Continuing this procedure, we can obtain the entire random sample of 100 users. Notice that, because we are sampling without replacement, we should ignore any set of four digits previously selected from the random number table.

While using a random number table is one way to select a random sample, this approach has a disadvantage that is illustrated by the current situation. Specifically, because most four-digit random numbers are not between 0001 and 2136, obtaining 100 different four-digit random numbers between 0001 and 2136 will require ignoring a large number of random numbers in the random number table, and we will in fact need to use a random number table that is larger than Table 1.1(a). Although larger random number tables are readily available in books of mathematical and statistical tables, a good alternative is to use a computer software program that can generate random numbers that are between whatever values we specify. For example, Table 1.1(b) gives the Excel output of 100 different four-digit random numbers that are between 0001 and 2136 (note that the leading zeros are not included in these four-digit numbers). To obtain these values, the function RANDBETWEEN(1,2136) is used in the Excel program. If used, the random numbers in Table 1.1(b) identify the 100 employees who should form the random sample.

After the random sample of 100 employees is selected, the number of cellular minutes used by each employee during the month (the employee's cellular usage) is found and recorded. The 100 cellular usage figures are given in Table 1.2. Looking at this table, we can see that there is substantial overage and underage—many employees used far more than 500 minutes, while many others failed to use all of the 500 minutes allowed by their plan.

TABLE **1.2** A Sample of Cellular Usage (in Minutes) for 100 Randomly Selected Employees

75	485	37	547	753	93	897	694	797	477
654	578	504	670	490	225	509	247	597	173
496	553	0	198	507	157	672	296	774	479
0	822	705	814	20	513	546	801	721	273
879	433	420	521	648	41	528	359	367	948
511	704	535	585	341	530	216	512	491	0
542	562	49	505	461	496	241	624	885	259
571	338	503	529	737	444	372	555	290	830
719	120	468	730	853	18	479	144	24	513
482	683	212	418	399	376	323	173	669	611

Approximately random samples In general, to take a random sample we must have a list, or frame, of all of the population units because we must be able to number the population units in order to make random selections from them (by, for example, using a random number table). In Example 1.1, where we wanted to study a population of 2,136 cellphone users who were on the bank's 500-minute cellular plan, we were able to produce a frame (list) of the population units. Therefore, we were able to select a random sample. Sometimes, however, it is not possible to list and thus number all of the units in a population. In such a situation, we often select a systematic sample, which approximates a random sample, as illustrated in Example 1.2.

Example 1.2   The Marketing Research Example: Rating a New Bottle Design[3]

The design of a package or bottle can have an important effect on a company's bottom line. For example, an article in the September 16, 2004, issue of *USA Today* reported that the introduction of a contoured 1.5-L bottle for Coke drinks played a major role in Coca-Cola's failure to meet third-quarter earnings forecasts in 2004. According to the article, Coke's biggest bottler, Coca-Cola Enterprises, "said it would miss expectations because of the 1.5-liter bottle and the absence of common 2-liter and 12-pack sizes . . . in supermarkets."[4]

In this case, a brand group is studying whether changes should be made in the bottle design for a popular soft drink. To research consumer reaction to a new design, the brand group will use the "mall intercept method," in which shoppers at a large metropolitan shopping mall are intercepted and asked to participate in a consumer survey. Each shopper will be shown the new bottle design and asked to rate the bottle image. Bottle image will be measured by combining consumers' responses to five items, with each response measured using a seven-point Likert scale.[5] The five items and the scale of possible responses are shown in Figure 1.1. Because we describe the least favourable response and the most favourable response (and we do not describe the responses between them), we say that the scale is anchored at its ends. Responses to the five items will be summed to obtain a composite score for each respondent. It follows that the minimum composite score possible is 5 and the maximum composite score possible is 35. Experience has shown that the smallest acceptable composite score for a successful bottle design is 25.

In this situation, it is not possible to list and number every shopper at the mall while the study is being conducted. Consequently, we cannot use random numbers (as we did in the cellphone case) to obtain a random sample of shoppers. Instead, we can select a **systematic sample**. To do this, every 100th shopper passing a specified location in the mall will be invited to participate in the survey. Here, selecting every 100th shopper is arbitrary—we could select every 200th, every 300th, and so forth. If we select every 100th shopper, it is probably reasonable to believe that the responses of the survey participants are not related. Therefore, it is reasonable to assume that the sampled shoppers obtained by the systematic sampling process make up an approximate random sample.

FIGURE **1.1**   The Bottle Design Survey Instrument

Please circle the response that most accurately describes whether you agree or disagree with each statement about the bottle you have examined.

Statement	Strongly Disagree						Strongly Agree
The size of this bottle is convenient.	1	2	3	4	5	6	7
The contoured shape of this bottle is easy to handle.	1	2	3	4	5	6	7
The label on this bottle is easy to read.	1	2	3	4	5	6	7
This bottle is easy to open.	1	2	3	4	5	6	7
Based on its overall appeal, I like this bottle design.	1	2	3	4	5	6	7

[3]This example was motivated by an example in the book *Essentials of Marketing Research,* by W. R. Dillon, T. J. Madden, and N. H. Firtle (Burr Ridge, IL: Richard D. Irwin, 1993). The authors also want to thank Professor L. Unger of the Department of Marketing at Miami University for helpful discussions concerning how this type of marketing study would be carried out.

[4]Source: "Coke says earnings will come up short," by Theresa Howard, *USA Today,* September 16, 2004, p. 801.

[5]The Likert scale is named after Rensis Likert (1903–1981), who originally developed this numerical scale for measuring attitudes in his PhD dissertation in 1932. [Source: *Psychology in America: A Historical Survey,* by E. R. Hilgard (San Diego, CA: Harcourt Brace Jovanovich, 1987).]

TABLE **1.3**   A Sample of Bottle Design Ratings (Composite Scores for a Systematic Sample of 60 Shoppers) 🖋

34	33	33	29	26	33	28	25	32	33
32	25	27	33	22	27	32	33	32	29
24	30	20	34	31	32	30	35	33	31
32	28	30	31	31	33	29	27	34	31
31	28	33	31	32	28	26	29	32	34
32	30	34	32	30	30	32	31	29	33

During a Saturday afternoon and evening, a sample of 60 shoppers is selected by using the systematic sampling process. Each shopper is asked to rate the bottle design by responding to the five items in Figure 1.1, and a composite score is calculated for each shopper. The 60 composite scores obtained are given in Table 1.3. Because these scores range from 20 to 35, we might infer that *most* of the shoppers at the mall on the afternoon and evening of the study would rate the new bottle design between 20 and 35. Furthermore, because 57 of the 60 composite scores are at least 25, we might estimate that the proportion of all shoppers at the mall on the study date who would give the bottle design a composite score of at least 25 is 57/60 = 0.95. That is, we estimate that 95 percent of the shoppers would give the bottle design a composite score of at least 25. In Chapter 2, we will see how to estimate a typical composite score, and we will further analyze the composite scores in Table 1.3.

In some situations, we need to decide whether a sample taken from one population can be employed to make statistical inferences about another, related population. Logical reasoning is often used to do this. For instance, we might reason that the bottle design ratings given by shoppers at the mall on the afternoon and evening of the research study would be representative of the ratings given by (1) shoppers at the same mall at other times, (2) shoppers at other malls, and (3) consumers in general. However, if we have no data or other information to back up this reasoning, making such generalizations is dangerous. In practice, marketing research firms choose locations and sampling times that data and experience indicate will produce a representative cross-section of consumers. To simplify our presentation, we will assume that this has been done in the bottle design case. Therefore, we will suppose that it is reasonable to use the 60 bottle design ratings in Table 1.3 to make statistical inferences about *all consumers*.

To conclude this section, we emphasize the importance of taking a random (or approximately random) sample. Statistical theory tells us that when we select a random (or approximately random) sample, we can use the sample to make valid statistical inferences about the sampled population. However, if the sample is not random, we cannot do this. For example, television and radio stations, as well as newspaper columnists, websites, and restaurant comment cards, use voluntary response samples. In such samples, participants self-select—that is, whoever wants to participate does so (usually expressing some opinion). These samples over-represent people with strong (usually negative) opinions. We further discuss random sampling in Sections 1.5 and 1.6.

Exercises for Sections **1.1** and **1.2**

CONCEPTS

1.1   Define a population. Give an example of a population that you might study when you start your career after graduating from university or college.

1.2   Define what we mean by a variable, and explain the difference between a quantitative variable and a qualitative (categorical) variable.

1.3   Below we list several variables. Which of these variables are quantitative and which are qualitative? Explain.
   a.   The dollar amount on an accounts receivable invoice.
   b.   The net profit for a company in 2014.
   c.   The ranking of a company's stock.
   d.   The national debt of Canada in 2014.
   e.   The advertising medium (radio, television, Internet, or print) used to promote a product.

1.4 Explain the difference between a census and a sample.

1.5 Explain each of the following terms:
   a. Descriptive statistics.
   b. Statistical inference.
   c. Random sample.
   d. Systematic sample.

1.6 Explain why sampling without replacement is preferred to sampling with replacement.

METHODS AND APPLICATIONS

1.7 Below is the store directory for the shops of Confederation Court Mall in Charlottetown, Prince Edward Island. A researcher wants to select a random sample of stores for a mall service satisfaction survey.
   a. What is the first step required to treat the list so that a random sample can be selected?
   b. Using a random number table or a random number generator, select ten stores to be included in the survey.

Mall Directory: The Shops of Confederation Court Mall 🖋

Footwear
Uptown Shoes

Women's Fashions
Bizou Accessories
Chameleon's Hanger
Cotton Ginny/Cotton Ginny Plus
Dow's Fashions for Ladies
Eclipse
Lady Slipper Lingerie & Accessories
Marianna's
TABI

Jewellery
Norton's Jewellers
Taylor's Jewellers

Pharmacy
Shoppers Drug Mart

Beauty and Health
Allison's Hair Design
Merle Norman Cosmetics Studio
Senses
Zoja's Hair Salon

Sight and Sound
CD Plus

Furniture & Home Accessories
Frameworld

The Kitchen Store
Wicker Emporium

Men's Fashions
Dow's Men's Wear

Books
The Bookmark

Home & Office
Denis Office Products
The Source

Specialty & Variety
Colleen's Elite Tailoring
Critters Pet Shop
Dollaroo
Luna Eclectic Emporium
MacAulay's Bakery & Deli
The Loto Booth/Cigar Corner
The Root Cellar
True Value General Store

Gifts & Handcrafts
Holder's Card & Gift Shop
The P.E.I. Co. Store

Sporting Goods
API Hockey & Sports

Women's & Men's Fashion
Island Beach Co.
KC Clothing Company
Roots
Vogue Optical

1.8 THE VIDEO GAME SATISFACTION RATING EXAMPLE 🖋

A company that produces and markets video game systems wants to assess its customers' level of satisfaction with a relatively new model, the XYZ-Box. In the six months since the introduction of the model, the company has received 73,219 warranty registrations from purchasers. The company will randomly select 65 of these registrations and conduct telephone interviews with the purchasers. Specifically, each purchaser will be asked to state his or her level of agreement with each of the seven statements listed on the survey instrument given in Figure 1.2. Here the level of agreement for each statement is measured on a seven-point Likert scale. Purchaser satisfaction will be measured by adding the purchaser's responses to the seven statements. It follows that for each consumer the minimum composite score possible is 7 and the maximum is 49. Experience has shown that a purchaser of a video game system is "very satisfied" if that purchaser's composite score is at least 42.

   a. Assume that the warranty registrations are numbered from 1 to 73,219 on a computer. Starting in the upper left corner of Table 1.1(a) and moving down, the first three five-digit numbers obtained that are between 1 and 73,219 are

   33276   03427   08178

   Starting with these three random numbers and moving down in Table 1.1(a) to find more five-digit random numbers between 1 and 73,219, randomly select the numbers of the first 10 warranty registrations to be included in the sample of 65 registrations.

   b. Suppose that when the 65 customers are interviewed, their composite scores are obtained and are as given in Table 1.4. Using the data, estimate limits between which most of the 73,219 composite scores would fall. Also estimate the proportion of the 73,219 composite scores that would be at least 42.

1.9 THE BANK CUSTOMER WAITING TIME EXAMPLE 🖋

A bank manager has developed a new system to reduce the time customers spend waiting to be served by tellers during peak business hours. Typical waiting times during peak business hours under the current system are roughly nine to ten minutes. The bank manager hopes that the new system will lower typical waiting times to less than six minutes.

FIGURE 1.2 The Video Game Satisfaction Survey Instrument 🖋

Statement	Strongly Disagree						Strongly Agree
The game console of the XYZ-Box is well designed.	1	2	3	4	5	6	7
The game controller of the XYZ-Box is easy to handle.	1	2	3	4	5	6	7
The XYZ-Box has high-quality graphics capabilities.	1	2	3	4	5	6	7
The XYZ-Box has high-quality audio capabilities.	1	2	3	4	5	6	7
The XYZ-Box serves as a complete entertainment centre.	1	2	3	4	5	6	7
There is a large selection of XYZ-Box games to choose from.	1	2	3	4	5	6	7
I am totally satisfied with my XYZ-Box game system.	1	2	3	4	5	6	7

TABLE 1.4 Composite Scores for the Video Game Satisfaction Rating Example

39	44	46	44	44
45	42	45	44	42
38	46	45	45	47
42	40	46	44	43
42	47	43	46	45
41	44	47	48	
38	43	43	44	
42	45	41	41	
46	45	40	45	
44	40	43	44	
40	46	44	44	
39	41	41	44	
40	43	38	46	
42	39	43	39	
45	43	36	41	

TABLE 1.5 Waiting Times (in Minutes) for the Bank Customer Waiting Time Example

1.6	6.2	3.2	5.6	7.9	6.1	7.2
6.6	5.4	6.5	4.4	1.1	3.8	7.3
5.6	4.9	2.3	4.5	7.2	10.7	4.1
5.1	5.4	8.7	6.7	2.9	7.5	6.7
3.9	0.8	4.7	8.1	9.1	7.0	3.5
4.6	2.5	3.6	4.3	7.7	5.3	6.3
6.5	8.3	2.7	2.2	4.0	4.5	4.3
6.4	6.1	3.7	5.8	1.4	4.5	3.8
8.6	6.3	0.4	8.6	7.8	1.8	5.1
4.2	6.8	10.2	2.0	5.2	3.7	5.5
5.8	9.8	2.8	8.0	8.4	4.0	
3.4	2.9	11.6	9.5	6.3	5.7	
9.3	10.9	4.3	1.3	4.4	2.4	
7.4	4.7	3.1	4.8	5.2	9.2	
1.8	3.9	5.8	9.9	7.4	5.0	

A 30-day trial of the new system is conducted. During the trial run, every 150th customer who arrives during peak business hours is selected until a systematic sample of 100 customers is obtained. Each of the sampled customers is observed, and the time spent waiting for teller service is recorded. The 100 waiting times obtained are given in Table 1.5. The bank manager feels that this systematic sample is as representative as a random sample of waiting times would be. Using the data, estimate limits between which the waiting times of most of the customers arriving during peak business hours would be.

Also estimate the proportion of waiting times of customers arriving during peak business hours that are less than six minutes.

1.10 A researcher in a large company would like to use employee identification (ID) numbers to take a random sample of 20 people from a population of 1,000 employees. In this company, ID numbers have six digits and start at 000001. In Excel, generate a potential list of numbers for the researcher (using the RANDBETWEEN function). How would you expect your list to compare to another student's list?

1.3 SAMPLING A PROCESS

A population is not always a set of *existing* units. We are often interested in studying the population of all of the units that will be or could potentially be produced by a process.

LO4

A **process** is a sequence of operations that takes inputs (labour, materials, methods, machines, and so on) and turns them into outputs (e.g., products and services).

Processes produce output *over time*. For example, this year's Toyota Corolla manufacturing process produces Toyota Corollas over time. Early in the model year, Toyota Canada might want to study the population of the city-driving fuel efficiency of all Toyota Corollas that will be produced during the year. Or, even more hypothetically, Toyota Canada might want to study the population of the city-driving fuel efficiency of all Toyota Corollas that could *potentially* be produced by this year's manufacturing process. The first population is called a **finite population** because only a finite number of cars will be produced during the year. Any population of existing units is also finite. The second population is called an **infinite population** because the manufacturing process that produces this year's model could in theory always be used to build one more car. That is, theoretically there is no limit to the number of cars that could be produced by this year's process.

There are many other examples of finite and infinite hypothetical populations. For instance, we might study the population of all waiting times that will or could potentially be experienced by patients of a hospital emergency room. Or we might study the population of all the amounts of raspberry jam that will be or could potentially be dispensed into 500-mL jars by an automated filling machine. To study a population of potential process outputs, we sample the process—usually at equally spaced time points—over time. This is illustrated in Example 1.3.

Example 1.3 The Coffee Temperature Example: Monitoring Coffee Temperatures

On June 22, 2012, Nansy Saad filed a claim with the BC Supreme Court stating that on Nov. 1, 2011 she was burnt by the hot coffee she received at a McDonald's drive-through (http://bc.ctvnews.ca/b-c-woman-suing-mcdonald-s-over-hot-coffee-spill-1.850016). In another case, Stella Liebeck of Albuquerque, New Mexico, was awarded $US160,000 in compensatory damages and $US480,000 in punitive damages for a similar law suit (http://www.apnewsarchive.com/1994/URGENT-Judge-Reduces-Award-in-Coffee-Scalding-Case/id-1e17e94bbdc278d7f3166ef6256e52a4). A postverdict investigation in the United States revealed that the coffee temperature at the Albuquerque McDonald's had dropped from about 85°C before the trial to about 70°C after the trial.

Because of the possibility of future litigation and possibly to improve the coffee's taste, a restaurant wants to study and monitor the temperature of the coffee it serves. To do this, the restaurant personnel measure the temperature of the coffee being dispensed (in degrees Celsius) at half-hour intervals from 10 A.M. to 9:30 P.M. on a given day. Table 1.6 gives the 24 temperature measurements obtained in the time order in which they were observed. Here time equals 1 at 10 A.M. and 24 at 9:30 P.M.

TABLE 1.6 24 Coffee Temperatures Observed in Time Order

Time		Coffee Temperature	Time		Coffee Temperature	Time		Coffee Temperature
(10:00 A.M.)	1	73°C	(2:00 P.M.)	9	71°C	(6:00 P.M.)	17	70°C
	2	76		10	68		18	77
	3	69		11	75		19	68
	4	67		12	72		20	72
(12:00 noon)	5	74	(4:00 P.M.)	13	67	(8:00 P.M.)	21	69
	6	70		14	74		22	75
	7	69		15	72		23	68
	8	72		16	68		24	73

Examining Table 1.6, we see that the coffee temperatures range from 67°C to 77°C. Based on this, is it reasonable to conclude that the temperature of most of the coffee that will or could potentially be served by the restaurant will be between 67°C and 77°C? The answer is yes if the restaurant's coffee-making process operates consistently over time. That is, this process must be in a state of statistical control.

A process is in **statistical control** if it does not exhibit any unusual process variations. This often means that the process displays a constant amount of variation around a constant, or horizontal, level.

To assess whether a process is in statistical control, we sample the process often enough to detect unusual variations or instabilities. The restaurant has sampled the coffee-making process every half hour. In other situations, we sample processes with other frequencies—for example, every minute, every hour, or every day. Using the observed process measurements, we can then construct a runs plot.

A **runs plot** (sometimes called a time series plot) is a graph of individual process measurements versus time.

Figure 1.3 shows the Excel output of a runs plot of the temperature data. (Some people call such plot a *line chart* when the plot points are connected by line segments as in the Excel output.) Here we plot each coffee temperature on the vertical scale (*y*-axis) versus its corresponding time index on the horizontal scale (*x*-axis). For instance, the first temperature (73°C) is plotted for time equals 1, the second temperature (76°C) is plotted when time equals 2, and

FIGURE **1.3**   Excel Runs Plot of Coffee Temperatures: The Process Is in Statistical Control

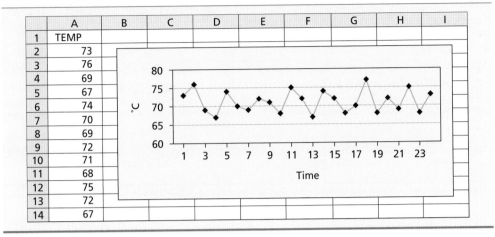

so forth. The runs plot suggests that the temperatures exhibit a relatively constant amount of variation around a relatively constant level. That is, the centre of the temperatures can pretty much be represented by a horizontal line (constant level), and the spread of the points around the line stays about the same (constant variation). Note that the plot points tend to form a horizontal band. Therefore, the temperatures are in statistical control.

In general, assume that we have sampled a process at different (usually equally spaced) time points and made a runs plot of the resulting sample measurements. If the plot indicates that the process is in statistical control, and if it is reasonable to believe that the process will remain in control, then it is probably reasonable to regard the sample measurements as an approximately random sample from the population of all possible process measurements. Furthermore, since the process remains in statistical control, the process performance is *predictable*. This allows us to make statistical inferences about the population of all possible process measurements that will or potentially could result from using the process. For example, assuming that the coffee-making process will remain in statistical control, it is reasonable to conclude that the temperature of most of the coffee that will be or could potentially be served will be between 67°C and 77°C.

To emphasize the importance of statistical control, suppose that another fast-food restaurant observes the 24 coffee temperatures that are plotted versus time in Figure 1.4. These temperatures range between 67°C and 80°C. However, we cannot infer from this that the temperature of most of the coffee that will be or could potentially be served by this other restaurant will be between 67°C and 80°C. This is because the downward trend in the runs plot of Figure 1.4 indicates that the coffee-making process is out of control and will soon produce temperatures below 67°C.

Another example of an out-of-control process is illustrated in Figure 1.5. Here the coffee temperatures seem to fluctuate around a constant level but with increasing variation (notice that the plotted temperatures fan out as time advances). In general, the specific pattern of out-of-control behaviour can suggest the reason for this behaviour. For example, the downward trend in the runs plot of Figure 1.4 might suggest that the restaurant's coffee maker has a defective heating element.

Visually inspecting a runs plot to check for statistical control can be tricky. One reason is that the scale of measurements on the vertical axis can influence whether the data appear to form a horizontal band. For now, we will simply emphasize that a process must be in statistical control in order to make valid statistical inferences about the population of all possible process observations. Also, note that being in statistical control does not necessarily imply that a process is *capable* of producing output that meets our requirements. For example, suppose that marketing research suggests that the restaurant's customers think that coffee tastes best if its temperature is between 67°C and 75°C. Table 1.6 indicates that the temperature of some of the coffee it serves is not in this range (note that two of the temperatures are 67°C, one is 76°C, and another is 77°C), so the restaurant might take action to reduce the variation of the coffee temperatures.

FIGURE 1.4 A Runs Plot of Coffee Temperatures: The Process Level Is Decreasing

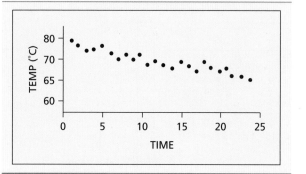

FIGURE 1.5 A Runs Plot of Coffee Temperatures: The Process Variation Is Increasing

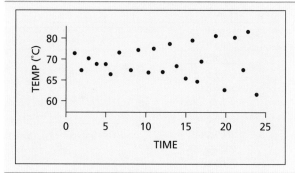

In summary, the marketing research and coffee temperature examples are both examples of using the statistical process to make a statistical inference. In Chapter 2, we will study more precise ways to both define and estimate a typical population value. In Chapters 3 through 7, we will study tools for assessing the reliability of estimation procedures and for estimating with confidence.

Exercises for Section **1.3**

CONCEPTS

1.11 Define a process. Give an example of a process you might study when you start your career after graduating from university or college.

1.12 Explain what it means to say that a process is in statistical control.

1.13 What is a runs plot? What does a runs plot look like when we sample and plot a process that is in statistical control?

METHODS AND APPLICATIONS

1.14 The data in the table below give 18 measurements of a critical dimension for an automobile part (measurements in centimetres). One part has been randomly selected each hour from the previous hour's production, and the measurements are given in time order.

Construct a runs plot and determine if the process appears to be in statistical control.

Hour	Measurement	Hour	Measurement
1	3.005	10	3.005
2	3.020	11	3.015
3	2.980	12	2.995
4	3.015	13	3.020
5	2.995	14	3.000
6	3.010	15	2.990
7	3.000	16	2.985
8	2.985	17	3.020
9	3.025	18	2.985

1.15 Table 1.7 presents the time (in days) needed to settle the 67 homeowners' insurance claims handled by an insurance agent over a year. The claims are given in time order by loss date.

a. Figure 1.6 shows an Excel runs plot of the claims data in Table 1.7. Does the claims-handling process seem to be in statistical control? Why or why not?

b. In March 2010, the region covered by the insurance company was hit by a widespread ice storm that caused heavy damage to homes in the area. Did this ice storm have a significant impact on the time needed to settle homeowners' claims? Should the agent consider improving procedures for handling claims in emergency situations? Why or why not?

1.16 In a *Quality Progress* article, the authors described a restaurant that catered to business travellers and had a self-service breakfast buffet. Interested in customer satisfaction, the manager conducted a survey over a three-week period and found that the main customer complaint was having to wait too long to be seated. On each day from September 11, 1989, to October 1, 1989, a problem-solving team recorded the percentage of patrons who had to wait more than one minute to be seated. A runs plot of the daily percentages is shown in Figure 1.7.[6] What does the runs plot suggest?

[6]The source of Figure 1.7 is "Accelerating improvement," by M. Gaudard, R. Coates, and L. Freeman, *Quality Progress,* October 1991, pp. 81–88. Copyright © 1991 American Society for Quality Control. Used with permission.

TABLE **1.7** Number of Days Required to Settle Homeowners' Insurance Claims (Claims Made from July 2, 2009, to June 25, 2010)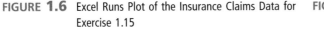

Claim	Loss Date	Days to Settle	Claim	Loss Date	Days to Settle	Claim	Loss Date	Days to Settle
1	2009-07-02	111	24	2009-11-05	34	47	2010-03-05	70
2	2009-07-06	35	25	2009-11-13	25	48	2010-03-05	67
3	2009-07-11	23	26	2009-11-21	22	49	2010-03-06	81
4	2009-07-12	42	27	2009-11-23	14	50	2010-03-06	92
5	2009-07-16	54	28	2009-11-25	20	51	2010-03-06	96
6	2009-07-27	50	29	2009-12-01	32	52	2010-03-06	85
7	2009-08-01	41	30	2009-12-08	27	53	2010-03-07	83
8	2009-08-13	12	31	2009-12-10	23	54	2010-03-07	102
9	2009-08-20	8	32	2009-12-20	35	55	2010-03-19	23
10	2009-08-20	11	33	2009-12-23	29	56	2010-03-27	11
11	2009-08-28	11	34	2009-12-31	25	57	2010-04-01	8
12	2009-09-03	31	35	2009-12-31	18	58	2010-04-11	11
13	2009-09-10	35	36	2009-12-31	16	59	2010-04-15	35
14	2009-09-17	14	37	2010-01-05	23	60	2010-04-19	29
15	2009-09-18	14	38	2010-01-08	26	61	2010-05-02	80
16	2009-09-29	27	39	2010-01-16	30	62	2010-05-15	18
17	2009-10-04	14	40	2010-01-18	36	63	2010-05-25	58
18	2009-10-06	23	41	2010-01-22	42	64	2010-06-06	4
19	2009-10-15	47	42	2010-01-25	45	65	2010-06-12	5
20	2009-10-23	17	43	2010-01-27	43	66	2010-06-24	15
21	2009-10-25	21	44	2010-02-05	39	67	2010-06-25	19
22	2009-10-30	18	45	2010-02-09	53			
23	2009-11-02	31	46	2010-02-23	64			

1.17 THE TRASH BAG EXAMPLE[7]

A company that produces and markets trash bags has developed an improved 130-L bag. The new bag is produced using a specially formulated plastic that is both stronger and more biodegradable than previously used plastics, and the company wants to evaluate the strength of this bag. The breaking strength of a trash bag is considered to be the mass (in kilograms) of a representative trash mix that, when loaded into a bag suspended in the air, will cause the bag to sustain significant damage (such as ripping or tearing). The company has decided to carry out a 40-hour pilot production run of the new bags. Each hour, at a randomly selected time during the hour, a bag is taken off the production line. The bag is then subjected to a breaking strength test. The 40 breaking strengths

FIGURE **1.6** Excel Runs Plot of the Insurance Claims Data for Exercise 1.15

FIGURE **1.7** Runs Plot of Daily Percentages of Customers Waiting More Than One Minute to Be Seated (for Exercise 1.16)

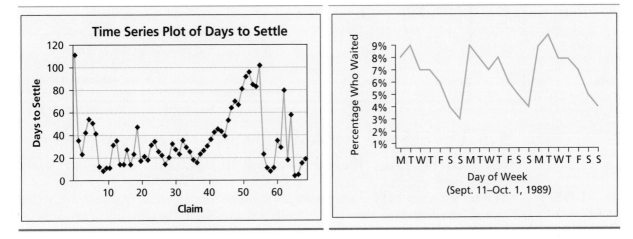

[7]This example is based on conversations that the authors had with several employees working for a leading producer of trash bags. For purposes of confidentiality, we have withheld the company's name.

TABLE 1.8 Breaking Strengths

22.0	23.9	23.0	22.5
23.8	21.6	21.9	23.6
24.3	23.1	23.4	23.6
23.0	22.6	22.3	22.2
22.9	22.7	23.5	21.3
22.5	23.1	24.2	23.3
23.2	24.1	23.2	22.4
22.0	23.1	23.9	24.5
23.0	22.7	23.3	22.4
22.8	22.8	22.5	23.4

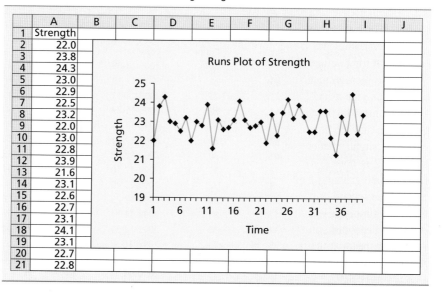

FIGURE 1.8 Excel Runs Plot of Breaking Strengths for Exercise 1.17

obtained during the pilot production run are given in Table 1.8, and an Excel runs plot of these breaking strengths is given in Figure 1.8.

a. Do the 40 breaking strengths appear to be in statistical control? Explain.

b. Estimate limits between which most of the breaking strengths of all trash bags would fall.

1.18 THE BANK CUSTOMER WAITING TIME EXAMPLE

In Exercise 1.9, recall that every 150th customer arriving during peak business hours was sampled until a systematic sample of 100 customers was obtained. This systematic sampling procedure is equivalent to sampling from a process. Figure 1.9 shows a MegaStat runs plot of the 100 waiting times from Table 1.5. Does the process appear to be in statistical control? Explain.

FIGURE 1.9 MegaStat Runs Plot of Waiting Times for Exercise 1.18

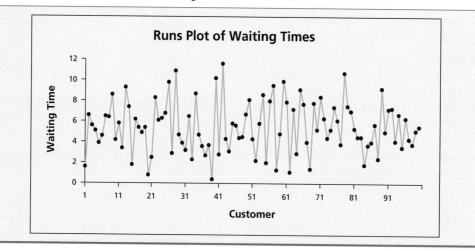

1.4 LEVELS OF MEASUREMENT: NOMINAL, ORDINAL, INTERVAL, AND RATIO

LO5

As stated in Section 1.1, a measure might be qualitative (or categorical) or quantitative. Within each of these distinctions, there are two levels of measurement. The qualitative **nominative (or nominal) measurement level** is the "lowest" level (most basic) of measurement. A nominative (or nominal) variable is used for categorizing only and has no meaningful order. For example, an individual's sex may be coded as 1 for males and 2 for females. These codes are simply labels and do not represent any other characteristic of the variable than designating group membership. Another example could be the colour of a car (with 1 = red, 2 = blue, 3 = grey, etc.). If you coded your sock drawer as 1 and your T-shirt drawer as 2, you would be engaging in a nominative (or nominal) level of measurement.

When variables are ranked in order, the numbers assigned have more meaning than at the nominative (or nominal) level. This ranking refers to the qualitative **ordinal level of measurement**. The measurements at the ordinal level may be nonnumerical or numerical. For example, a person may be asked to rank his or her four favourite colours. The person may say that yellow (1) is the most favourite colour, then green (2), red (3), and blue (4). If asked to expand further, the person may say that yellow and green are outstanding favourites and red and blue are "so-so," but red is slightly better than blue. This ranking does not have equal distances between points in that 1 to 2 is not the same as 2 to 3. Only the order is meaningful. Another example could be the top three grossing movies in an opening weekend. The dollar amount difference between the top and the second movie is not the same as the difference between the second and the third; the three are simply listed in order. Analyzing ordinal data may require the use of nonparametric statistics, depending on the same size and the type of analysis to be performed.

Within the quantitative level of measurement, the **interval level of measurement** is first. At the interval level, the distances between points are fixed and meaningful. For example, the 1 to 7 Likert scale

$$1 \quad 2 \quad 3 \quad 4 \quad 5 \quad 6 \quad 7$$

is an example of an interval scale. The distance from 2 to 3 is the same as the distance from 5 to 6. The scale could also have been written as

$$-3 \quad -2 \quad -1 \quad 0 \quad 1 \quad 2 \quad 3$$

Here the zero is the midpoint and represents the same concept as the number 4 in the 1 to 7 scale. Of note is the fact that the zero is arbitrary in that it does not represent a complete absence of the variable and is not a fixed point. For example, if you have ever asked someone to "rate" something on, say, a scale from 1 to 10, then you have used the interval level of measurement. The interval level is one of the most common levels of measurement in business statistics. For example, opinions, such as job satisfaction, are assessed using interval level Likert scales. Psychological properties, such as personality, intelligence, and vocational interests, are also measured on an interval level. The difference between an intelligence score of 95 to 100 (5 points) is the same as the difference between a score of 120 to 125 (5 points). Again, as in these examples, there is no meaningful zero point (you may have a neutral opinion about a business practice, but you do not have a "zero opinion").

When a variable has a meaningful zero and equal distances between points, then the variable is at the **ratio level of measurement.** An example of a ratio variable is money. Having $0 is meaningful and having $10 is twice as much as having $5. Grades are also ratio variables. A grade of zero on an exam is meaningful, and the difference between 65 percent and 70 percent is the same as the difference between 80 percent and 85 percent.[8]

A summary of the four levels is given in the following table:

Level	Sublevel	Example
Qualitative	• Nominative or nominal • Ordinal	• Grocery aisle 3 for soup and aisle 4 for condiments • Top ten realtors in a district
Quantitative	• Interval • Ratio	• Temperature • Money

In addition to these four levels of variables, data may also take the form of continuous or discrete values. Continuous variables are typically interval or ratio scale numbers and fall along a continuum so that decimals make sense (such as salary, age, mass, and height). In contrast, discrete variables are count data in which decimals do not make sense (such as number of employees in a company).

[8]To remember the levels of measurement, simply remember the French word for "black" (NOIR). This acronym is useful since it also puts the levels in order from the simplest level of measurement (nominal or nominative) to the most complex (ratio).

Exercises for Section **1.4**

CONCEPTS

1.19 Discuss the difference between a ratio level variable and an interval level variable.

1.20 Discuss the difference between an ordinal level variable and a nominative (or nominal) level variable.

METHODS AND APPLICATIONS

1.21 Classify each of the qualitative variables in the following table as ordinal or nominative (nominal). Explain your answers.

Qualitative Variable	Categories					
Statistics course letter mark	A	B	C	D	F	
Heads or tails when tossing a coin	Heads	Tails				
Television show classifications	C	C8	G	PG	14+	18+
Personal computer ownership	Yes	No				
Restaurant rating	*****	****	***	**	*	
Income tax filing status	Married	Living common-law	Widowed			
	Divorced	Separated	Single			

1.22 Classify each of the quantitative variables in the table to the right as interval or ratio. Explain your answer.

Quantitative Variable
Number of students in your class
An answer of 7 on a 9-point Likert scale
Salaries of five randomly selected people
Temperature in degrees Celsius
Years of education reported by a job candidate
Statistics exam grade

1.5 A BRIEF INTRODUCTION TO SURVEYS

The Likert scale, introduced in Section 1.2, has proven to be a valuable method of measuring topics such as attitudes (for example, job satisfaction), values (organizational commitment), personality traits, and market research feedback. This section is a brief introduction to survey types and some issues that arise with surveys.

Surveys are also known as questionnaires. The purpose of surveys is to elicit responses from the participants. Four steps are typically involved in creating a survey. The first involves deciding on the content (what is being studied and how the questions will be asked). Question types can vary. For example, the surveyor may want to know factual information (such as demographics of age, sex, and income). The variable of interest might be behavioural (such as what the person does on their holidays). The questions may also be opinion-based (such as what fragrance a person prefers in their laundry detergent). Basically, the questions can be about anything of interest to the surveyor.

THEORY TO PRACTICE

Surveys are particularly useful tools in business practices. Marketing research relies heavily on people's responses to surveys assessing services or products. Financial areas may use surveys to assess customer satisfaction in business practices such as billing. Human resources may use surveys to explore self-report stress levels experienced by employees.

After the content has been decided on, the questionnaire creator generates the questions. It is ideal if these questions are as short as possible and are easy to read and understand. Following the question creation, the response key has to be decided on. Here, there are two options: open and closed. Open-ended questions are ones in which the respondent can answer the question in any manner that person chooses. These types of responses provide rich information but are difficult to score or code. Closed-ended questions represent those that give the respondent a choice of answers. These responses are typically much easier to code and quantify.

Once the questions and the response system are determined, the questionnaire is compiled. The order of the questions is important, as questions themselves may influence people's responses to following questions. To address the quality of the survey created, the surveyor must complete the fourth step, which is to pilot-test the questionnaire and address issues such as stability (reliability) and validity (whether the questions actually measure what they were intended to measure). Following the creation of the survey, the delivery of the questionnaire must be determined.

LO6

In general, surveys are delivered using one of three methods: mailed (direct or mass/bulk), telephone, or in-person. Mailed surveys are relatively inexpensive and unobtrusive, but tend to have low response rates (the number of people who complete the survey compared to the number of surveys sent out). Another concern with mailed surveys is that you are never certain that the person who completed the survey is the person you wanted to complete the survey. Also, as a researcher, you are never certain that the person completing the survey fully understood your questions. In general, if you plan to use mailed surveys, pretest the survey with members of your target audience. A recent trend and variation on the mailed survey is online surveys, but the same concerns with mailed surveys hold true for these as well.

Telephone surveys are also popular. Telephone interviews are less expensive than in-person interviews and tend to be faster. For example, telephone surveys are conducted by organizations such as Environics Research Group and Ipsos Canada, both of which have offices across the country and in other countries. Results from telephone surveys can be conveyed to the public almost immediately. Surveyors can cover a wide geographical region without having to travel. Historically, surveyors used telephone directories to contact people. Most surveyors now use random digit dialling (RDD), which uses the same logic underlying the random number table presented near the start of this chapter. When a surveyor uses RDD, there is an equal probability of any telephone number appearing (including unlisted numbers). The drawbacks are that RDD will also produce telephone numbers that are not in use, fax machine numbers, and nonresidential numbers. The other concerns that telephone surveyors have are the growing public wariness of telemarketers and reluctance to participate in telephone surveys.

Another common type of survey is the in-person interview. The face-to-face method is the richest form of communication. The participant in the survey can ask for clarification of the questions. But the in-person method is costly and may be perceived as more intrusive.

In general, there are three types of in-person interviews. The first is the structured interview, in which each respondent is given the same questions in the same order. Many businesses now use this method when interviewing job candidates. The interviewer is trained to act in the same manner for each interviewee. Answers given by respondents are then scored. The second in-person interview type is the intensive interview. Here the style is unstructured and informal. Interviewees are not given the same questions in the same order as in the structured method. This method is typically used in career counselling, performance appraisal feedback, and clinical settings. The third method is the focus group. The logic behind the focus group is that a group of people will provide more information than will individuals. The groups typically range in size from 4 to 15 people, and they will discuss approximately ten issues. This method is common for market research. In it, responses are coded by a moderator and by observers of the group.

Exercises for Section **1.5**

CONCEPTS

1.23 Describe the steps involved in creating a questionnaire.

1.24 Give an example of how the content of a question might influence responses to subsequent questions.

1.25 What are the benefits and drawbacks of using each of the three methods of surveying?
  a. In-person.   **b.** Mailed.   **c.** Telephone.

1.26 Explain what we mean by a focus group. When would a researcher use a focus group?

1.27 Explain how you would go about requesting that people complete an online survey. How would you contact the people? How would you deal with the question of whether or not the person you contacted was the person who completed the survey?

1.6 AN INTRODUCTION TO SURVEY SAMPLING

Random sampling is not the only type of sampling. Methods for obtaining a sample are called *sampling designs,* and the sample we take is sometimes called a *sample survey.* In this section, we explain three sampling designs that are alternatives to random sampling—stratified random sampling, cluster sampling, and systematic sampling.

One common sampling design involves separately sampling important groups within a population. The samples are combined to form the entire sample. This approach is the idea behind **stratified random sampling**.

In order to select a stratified random sample, we divide the population into nonoverlapping groups of similar units (people, objects, etc.). These groups are called **strata**. A random sample is selected from each stratum, and these samples are combined to form the full sample.

It is wise to stratify when the population consists of two or more groups that differ with respect to the variable of interest. For instance, consumers could be divided into strata based on sex, age, language spoken, or income.

As an example, suppose that a department store chain proposes to open a new store in a location that would serve customers who live in a geographical region that consists of (1) an industrial city, (2) a suburban community, and (3) a rural area. In order to assess the potential profitability of the proposed store, the chain wants to study the incomes of all households in the region. In addition, the chain wants to estimate the proportion and the total number of households whose members would be likely to shop at the store. The department store chain feels that the industrial city, the suburban community, and the rural area differ with respect to income and the store's potential desirability. Therefore, it uses these subpopulations as strata and takes a stratified random sample.

A stratified sample takes advantage of the fact that units in the same stratum are similar to each other. It follows that a stratified sample can provide more accurate information than can a random sample of the same size. As a simple example, if all of the units in each stratum were exactly the same, then examining only one unit in each stratum would allow us to describe the entire population. Furthermore, stratification can make a sample easier (or possible) to select. Recall that in order to take a random sample, we must have a frame, or list, of all of the population units. Although a frame might not exist for the overall population, a frame might exist for each stratum. For example, suppose nearly all of the households in the department store's geographical region have land-line telephones. Although there might not be a telephone directory for the overall geographical region, there might be separate telephone directories for the industrial city, the suburb, and the rural area from which samples could be drawn (although recall some of the drawbacks of telephone surveying listed in the previous section).

Sometimes it is advantageous to select a sample in stages. This is a common practice when selecting a sample from a very large geographical region. In such a case, a frame often does not exist. For instance, there may not be a single list of all households in Canada. In this situation, we can use multistage **cluster sampling**. To illustrate this procedure, suppose we want to take a sample of households from all households in Canada. We might proceed as follows:

Stage 1: Randomly select a sample of electoral districts from across Canada (such as the information provided by Elections Canada).

Stage 2: Randomly select a sample of townships[9] in each county.

Stage 3: Randomly select a sample of households from each township.

We use the term *cluster sampling* to describe this type of sampling because at each stage we cluster the households into subpopulations. For instance, in Stage 1 we cluster the households into counties, and in Stage 2 we cluster the households in each county into townships.

---

[9]Not all parts of Canada use the term *township*. Other common terms are *canton* (Quebec) and *parish* (New Brunswick). We will continue to use *township* here for simplicity.

Also, notice that the random sampling at each stage can be carried out because there are lists of (1) all counties in Canada, (2) all townships in Canada, and (3) all households in each township.

Consider another way of sampling the households in Canada. We might use Stages 1 and 2 above to select areas of interest. Then, if there is a telephone directory of the households in each area, we can randomly sample households from each selected township by using its telephone directory. Because most households today have telephones, and telephone directories are readily available, most national polls are now conducted by telephone.

It is sometimes a good idea to combine stratification with multistage cluster sampling. For example, suppose a national polling organization wants to estimate the proportion of all registered voters who favour a particular federal party. Because the federal party preferences of voters might tend to vary by geographical region, the polling organization might divide Canada into regions (say, Atlantic Canada, Quebec, Ontario, and Western Canada). The polling organization might then use these regions as strata and take a multistage cluster sample from each stratum (region).[10]

	ROADBLOCK
Ensuring sample sizes are large enough As with many surveys, the surveyor may want to plan on surveying more people than actually required, because, in practice, some participants might not respond.	

To select a random sample, we must number the units in a frame of all of the population units. Then we use a random number table (or a random number generator on a computer) to make the selections. However, numbering all of the population units can be quite time-consuming. Moreover, random sampling is used in the various stages of many complex sampling designs (requiring the numbering of numerous populations). Therefore, it is useful to have an alternative to random sampling. One such alternative is systematic sampling, which we discussed in Example 1.2 in Section 1.2. In order to systematically select a sample of n units without replacement from a frame of N units, we divide N by n and round the result down to the nearest whole number. Calling the rounded result ℓ, we then randomly select one unit from the first ℓ units in the frame—this is the first unit in the systematic sample. The remaining units in the sample are obtained by selecting every ℓth unit following the first (randomly selected) unit.

For example, suppose we want to sample a population of $N = 14{,}327$ members of an international allergists' association to investigate how often they have prescribed a particular drug during the last year. The association has a directory listing the 14,327 allergists, and we want to draw a systematic sample of 500 allergists from this frame. Here we compute $14{,}327/500 = 28.654$, which is 28 when rounded down. Therefore, we number the first 28 allergists in the directory from 1 to 28, and we use a random number table to randomly select one of the first 28 allergists. Suppose we select allergist number 19. We interview allergist 19 and every 28th allergist in the frame thereafter, so we choose allergists 19, 47, 75, and so forth until we obtain our sample of 500 allergists. In this scheme, we must number the first 28 allergists, but we do not have to number the rest because we can count off every 28th allergist in the directory. Alternatively, we can measure the approximate amount of space in the directory that it takes to list 28 allergists. This measurement can then be used to select approximately every 28th allergist.

In this book, we concentrate on showing how to analyze data produced by random sampling. However, if the order of the population units in a frame is random with respect to the characteristic under study, then a systematic sample should be (approximately) a random sample and we can analyze the data produced by the systematic sample by using the same methods

[10]The analysis of data produced by multistage cluster sampling can be quite complicated. We explain how to analyze data produced by one- and two-stage cluster sampling in Appendix E (Part 2), available on *Connect*. This appendix also includes a discussion of an additional survey sampling technique called *ratio estimation*. For a more detailed discussion of cluster sampling and ratio estimation, see Scheaffer, Mendenhall, and Ott (1986).

employed to analyze random samples. For instance, it would seem reasonable to assume that the alphabetically ordered allergists in a medical directory would be random (that is, have nothing to do with the number of times the allergists prescribed a particular drug). Similarly, the alphabetically ordered people in a telephone directory would probably be random with respect to many of the people's characteristics that we might want to study.

When we employ random sampling, we eliminate bias in the choice of the sample from a frame. However, a proper sampling design does not guarantee that the sample will produce accurate information. One potential problem is *undercoverage.*

Undercoverage occurs when some population units are excluded from the process of selecting the sample.

This problem occurs when we do not have a complete, accurate list of all of the population units. For example, although telephone polls today are common, some people in Canada do not have land-line telephones. In general, undercoverage usually causes some people to be under-represented. If under-represented groups differ from the rest of the population with respect to the characteristic being studied, the survey results will be biased. A second potentially serious problem is nonresponse.

Nonresponse occurs when a population unit selected as part of the sample cannot be contacted or refuses to participate.

In some surveys, 35 percent or more of the selected individuals cannot be contacted, even when several callbacks are made. In such a case, other participants are often substituted for the people who cannot be contacted. If the substitute participants differ from the originally selected participants in relation to the characteristic under study, the survey will again be biased. Third, when people are asked potentially embarrassing questions, their responses might not be truthful, which is a situation called **response bias**. Fourth, the wording of the questions can influence the answers received. Slanted questions often evoke biased responses. For example, consider the following question:

Which of the following best describes your views on gun control?

1   The government should take away our guns, leaving us defenceless against heavily armed criminals.

2   We have the right to keep guns.

Exercises for Section **1.6**

CONCEPTS

1.28   When is it appropriate to use stratified random sampling? What are strata, and how should strata be selected?

1.29   When is cluster sampling used? Why do we describe this type of sampling by using the term *cluster?*

1.30   Explain each of the following terms:
   a. Undercoverage.
   b. Nonresponse.
   c. Response bias.

1.31   Explain how to take a systematic sample of 100 companies from the 1,853 companies that are members of an industry trade association.

1.32   Explain how a stratified random sample is selected. Discuss how you might define the strata to survey student opinion on a proposal to charge all students a $100 fee for a new university-run bus system that will provide transportation between off-campus apartments and campus locations.

1.33   Marketing researchers often use city blocks as clusters in cluster sampling. Using this fact, explain how a market researcher might use multistage cluster sampling to select a sample of consumers from all cities with a population of more than 10,000 in a region that has many such cities.

CHAPTER SUMMARY

In this chapter, we introduced the idea of using sample data to make statistical inferences—that is, drawing conclusions about populations and processes by using sample data. We began by learning that a population is a set of units that we want to study. We saw that because many populations are too large to examine in their entirety, we often study a population by selecting a sample, which is a subset of the population units. Next we learned that if the information contained in a sample is to accurately represent the population, then the sample should be randomly selected from the population, and we saw how random numbers (obtained from a random number table) can be used to select a random sample. We also learned that selecting a random sample requires a frame (that is, a list of all of the population units) and that, since a frame does not always exist, we sometimes select a systematic sample.

We then learned that to make statistical inferences about the population of all possible values of a variable that could be observed when using a process, the process must be in statistical control. We learned that a process is in statistical control if it does not exhibit any unusual process variations, and we demonstrated how we might sample a process and how to use a runs plot to try to judge whether a process is in control.

Next, in Section 1.4, we studied different types of quantitative and qualitative variables. We saw that there are two levels of qualitative (categorical) variables—the nominative (nominal) measurement level, for which there is no meaningful ordering of the categories of variables, and the ordinal measurement level, for which there is a meaningful ordering of the categories of variables. We also learned that there are two levels of quantitative variables—the interval measurement level, for which variable ratios are not meaningful and there is no inherently defined zero value, and the ratio level of measurement, in which variables are measured on a scale such that ratios of its values are meaningful and there is an inherently defined zero value.

We concluded this chapter with Sections 1.5 and 1.6, which discuss survey construction, types of survey methods, and survey sampling. We introduced stratified random sampling, in which we divide a population into groups (strata) and then select a random sample from each group. We also introduced multistage cluster sampling, which involves selecting a sample in stages, and we explained how to select a systematic sample. Finally, we discussed some potential problems encountered when conducting a sample survey—undercoverage, nonresponse, response bias, and slanted questions.

KEY TERMS

census
cluster sampling (multistage cluster sampling)
finite population
frame
infinite population
interval level of measurement
measurement
nominative (nominal) measurement level
nonresponse
ordinal level of measurement
population
process
qualitative or categorical variable
quantitative variable
random number table

random sample
ratio level of measurement
response bias
runs plot
sample
sampling with replacement
sampling without replacement
statistical control
statistical inference
strata
stratified random sampling
systematic sample
undercoverage
variable

SUPPLEMENTARY EXERCISES

connect Practise and learn online with *Connect*. Items that have online data sets are marked with.

1.34 Some television stations attempt to gauge public opinion by posing a question on the air and asking viewers to call in to give their opinions. Suppose that a particular television station asks viewers whether they support or oppose the federal gun registry. Viewers are to call one of two toll-free numbers to register support or opposition. When the results were tabulated, the station reported that 78 percent of those who called were opposed to the registry. What do you think of the sampling method used by the station? Do you think that the percentage of the entire population that opposes the registry is as high as the 78 percent of the sample that was opposed?

1.35 Classify each of the qualitative variables in the following table as ordinal or nominative (nominal). Explain your answers.

Qualitative Variable	Categories		
Personal computer operating system	Windows XP Unix	Mac OS-X Linux	Windows Vista Other
Movie classifications	G PG 14A 18A R		
Level of education	Elementary Middle school High school University or college Graduate school		
Rankings of top ten university hockey teams	1 2 3 4 5 6 7 8 9 10		
First three characters of postal code	B3J M1J T2K V7E		
Five Canadian telephone area codes	905 867 709 780 604		

1.36 Table 1.9 lists the top ten best Canadian employers as determined by the *Financial Post* (February 1, 2012). Use random numbers to select a sample of four of these companies. Based on your knowledge of surveys, what types of questions would you ask employees at these companies to determine whether or not you would agree that they are the best Canadian employers?

TABLE 1.9 Ten Best Companies to Work For 🖋

Employer	Industry	City	Full-Time Employees in Canada
Agrium Inc.	Fertilizer	Calgary	2,419
BMO Financial Group	Financial	Toronto	29,605
Bombardier Aerospace	Aircraft Manufacturing	Dorval, Que.	17,222
Cameco Corporation	Mining	Saskatoon	2,859
Cementation Canada Inc.	Mining	North Bay, Ont.	980
Desjardins Group	Credit Unions	Levis, Que.	34,713
Golder Associates Ltd.	Engineering Services	Calgary	2,586
Great Little Box Company Ltd.	Box Manufacturing	Richmond, BC	200
Ledcor Group of Companies	Industrial Building Construction	Vancouver	5,100
OpenText Corporation	Computer Programming Services	Waterloo, Ont.	1,276

Source: *Financial Post*, February 1, 2012.

1.37 A bank wants to study the amount of time it takes to complete a withdrawal transaction from one of its automated banking machines (ABMs). On a particular day, 63 withdrawal transactions are observed between 10 A.M. and noon. The time required to complete each transaction is given in Table 1.10. Figure 1.10 shows an Excel runs plot of the 63 transaction times. Do the transaction times seem to be in statistical control? Why or why not?

TABLE 1.10 ABM Transaction Times (in Seconds) for 63 Withdrawals 🖋

Transaction	Time	Transaction	Time	Transaction	Time
1	32	22	34	43	37
2	32	23	32	44	32
3	41	24	34	45	33
4	51	25	35	46	33
5	42	26	33	47	40
6	39	27	42	48	35
7	33	28	46	49	33
8	43	29	52	50	39
9	35	30	36	51	34
10	33	31	37	52	34
11	33	32	32	53	33
12	32	33	39	54	38
13	42	34	36	55	41
14	34	35	41	56	34
15	37	36	32	57	35
16	37	37	33	58	35
17	33	38	34	59	37
18	35	39	38	60	39
19	40	40	32	61	44
20	36	41	35	62	40
21	32	42	33	63	39

FIGURE **1.10** Excel Runs Plot of ABM Transaction Times for Exercise 1.37

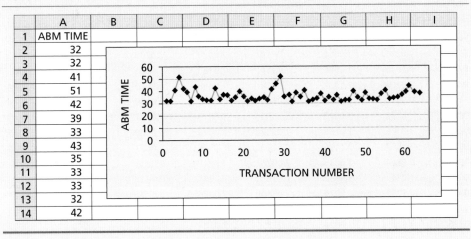

	A	B	C	D	E	F	G	H	I
1	ABM TIME								
2	32								
3	32								
4	41								
5	51								
6	42								
7	39								
8	33								
9	43								
10	35								
11	33								
12	33								
13	32								
14	42								

FIGURE **1.11** Runs Plot of Airline Hours Flown (for Exercise 1.38)

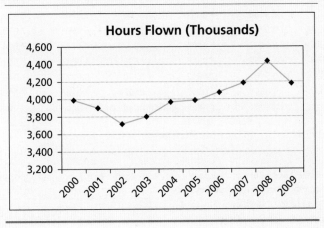

1.38 Figure 1.11 gives a runs plot of the total number of hours (in thousands) that Canadian airlines flew for each year from 2000 through 2009 according to the Transportation Safety Board of Canada (on the Internet, go to "Transportation Safety Board of Canada Aviation Statistics 2009"). Describe the pattern of the plot. Why was there a drop in hours in 2001?

1.39 THE TRASH BAG EXAMPLE

Recall that the company in Exercise 1.17 will carry out a 40-hour pilot production run of a new type of trash bag and will randomly select one bag each hour to be subjected to a breaking strength test.

a. Explain how the company can use random numbers to randomly select the times during the 40 hours of the pilot production run at which bags will be tested. *Hint:* Suppose that a randomly selected time will be determined to the nearest minute.

b. Use the following random numbers (obtained from Table 1.1 to select the times during the first five hours at which the first five bags to be tested will be taken from the production line: 61, 15, 64, 07, 86, 87, 57, 64, 66, 42, 59, 51.

1.40 In 1989, Steve Kopp, a lecturer in the Department of Statistical and Actuarial Sciences at the University of Western Ontario, decided to weigh 200 one-dollar coins (loonies) that were  minted in that year. From a production standpoint, the loonie would have to be minted within strict specifications. The loonie does in fact have specific minting requirements:

Composition: 91.5% nickel with 8.5% bronze plating
Mass: 7 g
Diameter: 26.5 mm
Thickness: 1.75 mm

A person at the Royal Canadian Mint might be interested in knowing whether the minted coins fall within an acceptable tolerance. Coins cannot be too light or too heavy or too large or too small, as vending machines are set to accept coins according to mass and size. A sample of 200 coins was obtained from a local bank in London, Ontario. The coins are packaged in rolls of 25, so eight

TABLE **1.11** Loonie Mass Data

7.0688	7.0196	7.008	7.0252	7.0912	6.9753	6.9720	7.0963
6.9651	6.9911	6.9156	7.0466	7.0948	7.0127	7.0470	7.0215
6.9605	7.0294	7.0050	7.0119	7.0929	7.0706	7.0459	6.9549
6.9797	7.0045	7.0898	7.0354	7.0186	6.9861	7.0339	6.9178
6.9861	6.9605	7.1322	6.9528	7.0648	6.9920	6.9334	7.0584
7.1227	6.9812	6.9873	7.0686	6.8479	7.0106	7.0340	7.0884
6.9861	7.0136	7.0572	6.8959	7.0079	7.0195	6.9888	7.0641
6.9692	7.0185	7.0158	7.0552	7.0478	7.0500	7.0919	7.0107
6.9018	7.1567	7.1135	6.9117	7.0346	7.0627	7.0561	6.8990
7.0574	6.9814	7.0016	7.0026	7.0212	7.0833	7.0343	7.0111
7.0467	7.0413	6.9892	7.0563	7.0374	7.0027	7.0012	7.2046
7.0386	6.9793	6.9074	7.0810	7.0076	7.0797	7.0132	6.9867
6.9799	7.0245	7.0461	6.9430	7.0934	7.0207	6.9364	6.9705
7.0326	7.0295	7.0024	6.9955	7.0184	7.0681	7.0046	7.0092
7.1380	7.0099	6.9936	6.9784	6.9475	7.0708	6.8821	7.0009
7.0908	6.9563	7.0364	6.9575	7.0118	7.0490	7.0426	7.0746
7.0335	6.9785	6.9005	7.1735	6.9034	6.9690	7.0137	6.9876
6.8788	7.0260	7.0216	7.0847	6.9481	6.9891	7.0943	6.9898
7.0654	6.9428	6.9986	6.8801	7.0640	7.0203	6.9521	7.0489
7.0610	7.0784	6.9741	6.9491	6.9541	6.9091	7.0732	6.9874
7.0057	6.9516	6.9477	7.0401	7.0017	7.0222	7.0941	6.8818
7.0277	7.0264	6.9862	7.0396	6.9685	7.0874	7.0024	7.0253
7.0438	7.0291	6.9582	7.0812	7.0780	6.9771	7.0463	7.0304
6.9977	6.9909	6.8358	7.0607	7.0652	7.0148	7.0909	6.9469
6.9531	6.9623	6.9785	6.8395	6.9618	7.0401	6.9994	7.0438

rolls were obtained at random. These coins may or may not have come from the same production run, but they were minted in the same year (1989). Each coin was carefully weighed, and the masses are given in Table 1.11.

Based on the plot of the masses in Figure 1.12, would you state that the minting process of the loonie is in statistical control? Based on the masses reported in Table 1.11, would you say the loonie is meeting the required standard of 7 g, as outlined by the Canadian Mint (mint.ca)?

1.41   INTERNET EXERCISE

The World Bank (worldbank.org) provides data on the countries of the world in terms of their gross national income per capita. As of 2013, there were 188 member countries. Discover where Canada fits within this system. Explain what type of measurement is used to determine the relative positioning of Canada compared to the other countries.

FIGURE **1.12** Loonie Mass Plot

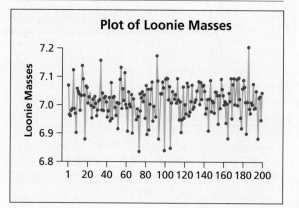

CHAPTER **2**
Descriptive Statistics

LEARNING OBJECTIVES

After reading this chapter, you should be able to

LO1 Explain what is demonstrated by a stem-and-leaf display that you have constructed

LO2 Describe how a histogram is constructed

LO3 Identify when a histogram should be used

LO4 Differentiate between a symmetrical distribution and a positively or negatively skewed distribution

LO5 Define the term *outlier*

LO6 Distinguish between a mean, a median, and a mode

LO7 Compute the variance and standard deviation from raw data

CHAPTER OUTLINE

2.1 Describing the Shape of a Distribution

2.2 Describing Central Tendency

2.3 Measures of Variation

2.4 Percentiles, Quartiles, and Box-and Whiskers Displays

2.5 Describing Qualitative Data

2.6 Using Scatter Plots to Study Relationships between Variables

2.7 Misleading Graphs and Charts

2.8 Weighted Means and Grouped Data

2.9 The Geometric Mean (Optional; see *Connect*)

In Chapter 1, we saw that although we can sometimes take a census of an entire population, typically we take a random selection or sample from a population. When we have taken a sample, we want to describe the observed data set in order to make inferences about the sampled population.

In this chapter, we learn about **descriptive statistics**, which is the science of describing the important characteristics of a population or sample. Generally, we look at several important aspects of a set of measurements. One such aspect is the **central tendency**, or middle, of the data set. For instance, we might estimate a typical bottle design rating in a marketing research case. Another important aspect of a data set is the *variability*, or spread, of the data. For example, we might measure the spread of the bottle design ratings. If the ratings are clustered closely together, consumers' ratings are

much the same (or are consistent). If the ratings are spread far apart, then consumers have widely varying opinions of the new bottle design. A third important aspect of a data set is the *shape* of the population or sample. Looking at a data set's shape tells us how the population or sample is distributed over various values. Still another important aspect is whether **outliers** exist. For instance, if there are extreme or outlying bottle design ratings, then some consumers have opinions about the design that are very different from the opinions of most of the sampled consumers (or an error has occurred in the collection or recording of the data). Descriptive statistics also involves using graphical methods to depict data sets and to study relationships between different variables. Typically these graphs assist in the interpretation of the data, as the information can be visualized.

2.1 DESCRIBING THE SHAPE OF A DISTRIBUTION

Diekhoff (1992) states, "one graph is worth a thousand statistics." As mentioned in Chapter 1, we typically sample from a population and use the sample to make inferences about the population. Visually displaying the data provides a means of better understanding the sample and, by extension, the population of interest. This section begins with several graphical methods—the stem-and-leaf display, the histogram, and the dot plot—all of which are used to portray shapes of distributions.

LO1

Stem-and-leaf displays Construction of a **stem-and-leaf display** is illustrated and use of the display is explained in Example 2.1.

Example 2.1 Cellphone Usage

Recall the 100 randomly selected bank employees' usage of their cellphones (in minutes in one month) introduced in Chapter 1. From this ratio level of data (repeated below), we construct the stem-and-leaf display presented in Figure 2.1. The first digit constitutes the stem (using a unit of 100 minutes) and the second digit is the leaf (using ten-minute units). The first column in Figure 2.1 presents the frequency of observations that make up that line. The first row (11 cases) represents all of the cellphone times that are less than 100 minutes. The second row (6 cases) represents the times that fall between 100 and 199 minutes. The last row represents the single case where the number of minutes is greater than 900. As we can see in Figure 2.1, the greatest number of cases are in the 500-minute to 599-minute range, with the second-greatest number of cases between 400 and 499 minutes.

FIGURE 2.1 Data and MegaStat Output of a Stem-and-Leaf Display of 100 Cellphone Usage Cases

Data Table

75	485	37	547	753	93	897	694	797	477
654	578	504	670	490	225	509	247	597	173
496	553	0	198	507	157	672	296	774	479
0	822	705	814	20	513	546	801	721	273
879	433	420	521	648	41	528	359	367	948
511	704	535	585	341	530	216	512	491	0
542	562	49	505	461	496	241	624	885	259
571	338	503	529	737	444	372	555	290	830
719	120	468	730	853	18	479	144	24	513
482	683	212	418	399	376	323	173	669	611

```
Stem-and-Leaf Plot for Usage (Minutes)
   Stem unit =  100
   Leaf unit =  10
      Frequency        Stem     Leaf
            11            0      0 0 0 1 2 2 3 4 4 7 9
             6            1      2 4 5 7 7 9
             9            2      1 1 2 4 4 5 7 9 9
             8            3      2 3 4 5 6 7 7 9
            15            4      1 2 3 4 6 6 7 7 7 8 8 9 9 9 9
            24            5      0 0 0 0 0 1 1 1 1 2 2 2 3 3 4 4 4 5 5 6 7 7 8 9
             9            6      1 2 4 5 6 7 7 8 9
             9            7      0 0 1 2 3 3 5 7 9
             8            8      0 1 2 3 5 7 8 9
             1            9      4
           100
```

We summarize how to set up a stem-and-leaf display in the following boxed feature.

Constructing a Stem-and-Leaf Display

1   Decide which units will be used for the stems and the leaves. As a general rule, choose units for the stems so that there will be somewhere between 5 and 20 stems.

2   Place the stems in a column with the smallest stem at the top of the column and the largest stem at the bottom.

3   Enter the leaf for each measurement into the row corresponding to the proper stem. The leaves should be single-digit numbers (these can be rounded values that were originally more than one digit).

4   If desired, rearrange the leaves so that they are in increasing order from left to right.

Frequency distributions and histograms   The count of the number of measurements in a class defined by a stem is called the **frequency** of the class. One advantage of a stem-and-leaf display is that it gives the frequencies of the different classes and also lists the specific measurements in each class. However, such listings for the different classes can be unwieldy if we are portraying a large number of measurements. For example, while it is convenient to display the ratings by 60 shoppers using the stem-and-leaf display, summarizing 500 ratings with the same type of format would be difficult.

When we have many measurements, it is best to group them into the classes of a **frequency distribution** and to display the data by using a **histogram**. We illustrate this in Example 2.2.

Example 2.2   The Payment Time Example: Reducing Payment Times

Major consulting firms employ statistical analysis to assess the effectiveness of the systems they design for their customers. In this case, a consulting firm has developed a computerized billing system for a trucking company. The system sends invoices electronically to each customer's computer and allows customers to easily check and correct errors. It is expected that the new billing system will substantially reduce the amount of time it takes customers to make payments. Typical payment times (*time* being a ratio level of measurement, measured from the date on an invoice to the date payment is received) using the trucking company's old billing system had been 39 days or more. This exceeded the industry standard payment time of 30 days.

In order to assess the system's effectiveness, the consulting firm selects a random sample of 65 invoices from the 7,823 invoices processed during the first three months of the new system's operation. The payment times for the 65 sample invoices are manually determined and are given in Table 2.1. If this sample can be used to establish that the new billing system substantially reduces payment times, the consulting firm plans to market the system to other trucking firms.

Looking at the payment times in Table 2.1, we can see that the shortest payment time is 10 days and the longest payment time is 29 days. Beyond that, it is pretty difficult to interpret the data in any meaningful way. To better understand the sample of 65 payment times, the consulting firm will form a frequency distribution of the data by first dividing the payment times into classes and then graphing the distribution by constructing a histogram.

TABLE 2.1   A Sample of Payment Times (in Days) for 65 Randomly Selected Invoices

22	29	16	15	18	17	12	13	17	16	15
19	17	10	21	15	14	17	18	12	20	14
16	15	16	20	22	14	25	19	23	15	19
18	23	22	16	16	19	13	18	24	24	26
13	18	17	15	24	15	17	14	18	17	21
16	21	25	19	20	27	16	17	16	21	

TABLE **2.2**　Recommended Number of Classes for Data Sets of n Measurements*

Number of Classes	Size, n, of the Data Set
2	$1 \leq n < 4$
3	$4 \leq n < 8$
4	$8 \leq n < 16$
5	$16 \leq n < 32$
6	$32 \leq n < 64$
7	$64 \leq n < 128$
8	$128 \leq n < 256$
9	$256 \leq n < 528$
10	$528 \leq n < 1056$

*For the sake of completeness we have included small values of n in this table. However, we do not recommend constructing a histogram with fewer than 16 measurements.

TABLE **2.3**　Seven Nonoverlapping Classes for a Frequency Distribution of the 65 Payment Times

Class 1	10 days to less than 13 days
Class 2	13 days to less than 16 days
Class 3	16 days to less than 19 days
Class 4	19 days to less than 22 days
Class 5	22 days to less than 25 days
Class 6	25 days to less than 28 days
Class 7	28 days to less than 31 days

Step 1: Find the number of classes One rule for finding an appropriate number of classes says that the number of classes should be the smallest whole number K that makes the quantity 2^K greater than the number of measurements in the data set. For the payment time data, we have 65 measurements. Because $2^6 = 64$ is less than 65 and $2^7 = 128$ is greater than 65, we should use $K = 7$ classes. Table 2.2 gives the appropriate number of classes (determined by the 2^K rule) to use for data sets of various sizes.

Step 2: Find the class length We find the length of each class by computing

$$\text{Class length} = \frac{\text{Largest measurement} - \text{Smallest measurement}}{\text{Number of classes}}$$

Because the largest and smallest payment times in Table 2.1 are 29 days and 10 days, the class length is $(29 - 10)/7 = 2.7143$ days. This says that in order to include the smallest and largest payment times in the 7 classes, each class must have a length of at least 2.7143 days. To obtain a more convenient class length, we round this value. Often the class length is rounded to the precision of the measurements, although this is a matter of preference. For instance, because the payment times are measured in days, we will round the class length from 2.7143 to 3 days.

Step 3: Form nonoverlapping classes of equal width We can form the classes of the frequency distribution by defining the boundaries of the classes. To find the first class boundary, we find the smallest payment time in Table 2.1, which is 10 days. This value is the lower boundary of the first class. Adding the class length of 3 to this lower boundary, we obtain $10 + 3 = 13$, which is the upper boundary of the first class and the lower boundary of the second class. Similarly, the upper boundary of the second class and the lower boundary of the third class are $13 + 3 = 16$. Continuing in this fashion, the lower boundaries of the remaining classes are 19, 22, 25, and 28. Adding the class length 3 to the lower boundary of the last class gives us the upper boundary of the last class, 31. These boundaries define seven nonoverlapping classes for the frequency distribution.

We summarize these classes in Table 2.3. For instance, the first class—10 days to less than 13 days—includes the payment times 10, 11, and 12 days; the second class—13 days to less than 16 days—includes the payment times 13, 14, and 15 days; and so forth. Notice that the largest *observed* payment time—29 days—is contained in the last class. Generally speaking, the guidelines we have given for forming classes are not inflexible rules. Rather, they are intended to help us find reasonable classes. Finally, the method we have used for forming classes results in classes of equal length. (Example 2.3 demonstrates a histogram with classes of unequal length.)

Step 4: Tally and count the number of measurements in each class Having formed the classes, we now count the number of measurements that fall into each class.

After examining all 65 payment times, we find the frequency for each class by counting the number recorded for the class. For instance, counting the number for the class "13 to <16," we obtain the frequency 14 for this class. The frequencies for all seven classes are summarized in Table 2.4. This summary is the frequency distribution for the 65 payment times. Table 2.4 also gives the **relative frequency** and the percent frequency for each of the seven classes. The relative frequency of a class is the proportion (fraction) of the total number of measurements that are in the class. For example, there are 14 payment times in the second class, so its relative frequency is $14/65 = 0.2154$. This says that the proportion of the 65 payment times that are in the second class is 0.2154, or, equivalently, that $100(0.2154)\% = 21.54\%$ of the payment times are in the second class. A list of all of the classes—along with each class's relative frequency—is called a *relative frequency distribution*. A list of all of the classes—along with each class percent frequency—is called a *percent frequency distribution*.

Step 5: Graph the histogram We can graphically portray the distribution of payment times by drawing a histogram. The histogram can be constructed using the frequency, relative frequency, or percent frequency distribution. To set up the histogram, we draw rectangles that correspond to the classes. The base of the rectangle corresponding to a class represents the payment times in the class. The height of the rectangle can represent the class frequency, relative frequency, or percent frequency.

LO2

We have drawn a frequency histogram of the 65 payment times in Figure 2.2. The first (leftmost) rectangle, or "bar," of the histogram represents the payment times 10, 11, and 12. Looking at Figure 2.2, we see that the base of this rectangle is drawn from the lower boundary (10) of the first class in the frequency distribution of payment times to the lower boundary (13) of the second class. The height of this rectangle tells us that the frequency of the first class is 3. The second histogram rectangle represents payment times 13, 14, and 15. Its base is drawn from the lower boundary (13) of the second class to the lower boundary (16) of the third class, and its height tells us that the frequency of the second class is 14. The other histogram bars are constructed similarly. Notice that there are no gaps between the adjacent rectangles in the histogram. Here, although the payment times are in days, the fact that the histogram bars touch each other emphasizes that a payment time could (in theory) be any number on the horizontal axis. In general, histograms are drawn so that adjacent bars touch each other.

Looking at the frequency distribution in Table 2.4 and the frequency histogram in Figure 2.2, we can describe the payment times:

1 None of the payment times exceed the industry standard of 30 days. (Actually, all of the payment times are less than 30—remember that the largest payment time is 29 days.)

2 The payment times are concentrated between 13 and 24 days (57 of the 65, or $(57/65) \times 100\% = 87.69\%$, of the payment times are in this range).

3 More payment times are in the class "16 to < 19" than are in any other class (23 payment times are in this class).

FIGURE 2.2 A Frequency Histogram of the 65 Payment Times

TABLE 2.4 Frequency Distributions of the 65 Payment Times

Class	Frequency	Relative Frequency	Percent Frequency
10 to < 13	3	$3/65 = 0.0462$	4.62%
13 to < 16	14	$14/65 = 0.2154$	21.54
16 to < 19	23	0.3538	35.38
19 to < 22	12	0.1846	18.46
22 to < 25	8	0.1231	12.31
25 to < 28	4	0.0615	6.15
28 to < 31	1	0.0154	1.54

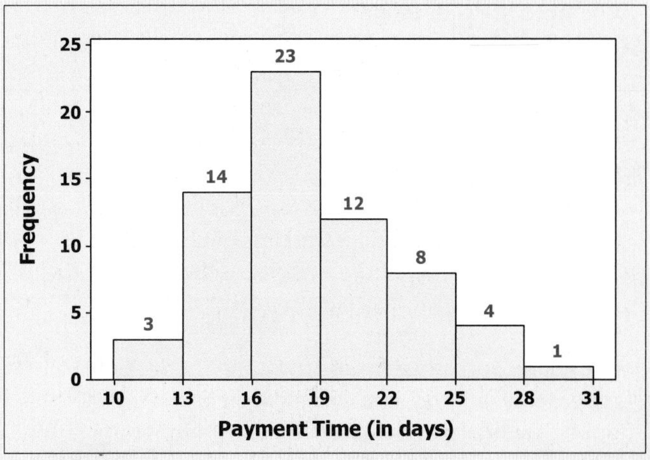

FIGURE 2.3   A Percent Frequency Histogram of the 65 Payment Times

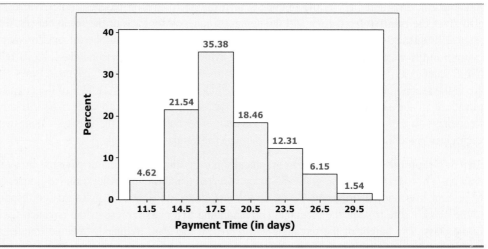

Notice that the frequency distribution and histogram allow us to make some helpful conclusions about the payment times, whereas looking at the raw data (the payment times in Table 2.1) did not.

LO3

A **relative frequency histogram** and a percent frequency histogram of the payment times would both be drawn like Figure 2.2 except that the heights of the rectangles represent, respectively, the relative frequencies and the percent frequencies in Table 2.4. For example, Figure 2.3 gives a percent frequency histogram of the payment times. This histogram also illustrates that we sometimes label the classes on the horizontal axis using the class midpoints. Each class midpoint is exactly halfway between the boundaries of its class. For instance, the midpoint of the first class, 11.5, is halfway between the class boundaries 10 and 13. The midpoint of the second class, 14.5, is halfway between the class boundaries 13 and 16. The other class midpoints are found similarly. The percent frequency distribution of Figure 2.3 tells us that 21.54 percent of the payment times are in the second class (which has midpoint 14.5 and represents the payment times 13, 14, and 15).

In the following box, we summarize the steps needed to set up a frequency distribution and histogram.

Constructing Frequency Distributions and Histograms

1   Find the number of classes. Generally, the number of classes K should equal the smallest whole number that makes the quantity 2^K greater than the total number of measurements n.

2   Compute the class length:

$$\frac{\text{Largest measurement} - \text{Smallest measurement}}{K}.$$

If desired, round this value to obtain a more convenient class length.

3   Form nonoverlapping classes of equal length. Form the classes by finding the class boundaries. The lower boundary of the first class is the smallest measurement in the data set. Add the class length to this boundary to obtain the next boundary. Successive boundaries are found by repeatedly adding the class length until the upper boundary of the last (Kth) class is found.

4   Tally and count the number of measurements in each class. The frequency for each class is the count of the number of measurements in the class. The relative frequency for each class is the fraction of measurements in the class. The percent frequency for each class is its relative frequency multiplied by 100 percent.

5   Graph the histogram. To draw a frequency histogram, plot each frequency as the height of a rectangle positioned over its corresponding class. Use the class boundaries to separate adjacent rectangles. A relative frequency histogram and a percent histogram are graphed in the same way except that the heights of the rectangles are, respectively, the relative frequencies and the percent frequencies.

Although we have given a procedure for determining the number of classes, it is often desirable to let the nature of the problem determine the classes. For example, to construct a histogram describing the ages of the residents of a certain city, it might be reasonable to use classes with ten-year lengths (that is, under 10 years, 10–19 years, 20–29 years, 30–39 years, and so on) or to have narrower class lengths with an open-ended class, as is given in Example 2.3.

Example 2.3 Age Groupings by Statistics Canada

Statistics Canada provides demographic information for communities based on the most recent population census. Figure 2.4 reports the frequency of age, grouped into classes. The group labelled "85+" is considered to be an open class in which no upper limit is given. Figure 2.4 provides the age groupings and frequency values for London, Ontario. Also in Figure 2.4 is the corresponding histogram.

FIGURE **2.4** Age Frequencies in London, Ontario

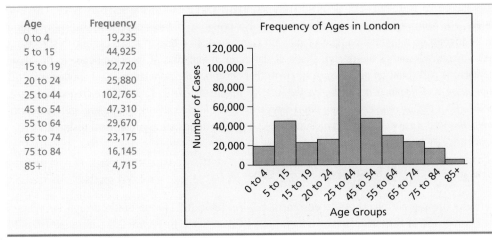

Age	Frequency
0 to 4	19,235
5 to 15	44,925
15 to 19	22,720
20 to 24	25,880
25 to 44	102,765
45 to 54	47,310
55 to 64	29,670
65 to 74	23,175
75 to 84	16,145
85+	4,715

Another example of a histogram with unequal class lengths would be grade distributions in a course. For example, if a professor records the distribution of grades by letters, then an F (0 percent to 49 percent) is not the same length as a D (50 percent to 59 percent.)

ROADBLOCK

Quantifying demographic information such as age
Note that age is typically viewed as being at the ratio level of measurement, such as when people are asked how many years or months old they are. If, as is common in many marketing surveys, people are asked which age bracket they fall into (such as 18 to 22 years), then age becomes nominal or categorical.

Some common population shapes We often construct a stem-and-leaf display or histogram for a sample to make inferences about the shape of the sampled population. It is sometimes useful to describe the shape of a population by using a smooth curve. If the stem-and-leaf display and/or the histogram look quite symmetrical and bell-shaped, then it is reasonable to infer that the population can be described by a symmetrical, bell-shaped curve. Such a curve is shown in Figure 2.5. Several different kinds of symmetrical, bell-shaped curves are used to describe populations. One such curve that is particularly useful is called the **normal curve.**

To intuitively understand the normal curve, recall from our discussion of histograms that if we use classes of equal lengths, then the height of the rectangle over a given class represents the relative

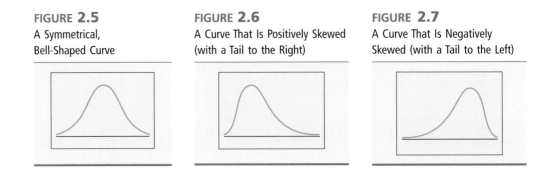

FIGURE **2.5**
A Symmetrical,
Bell-Shaped Curve

FIGURE **2.6**
A Curve That Is Positively Skewed
(with a Tail to the Right)

FIGURE **2.7**
A Curve That Is Negatively
Skewed (with a Tail to the Left)

proportion of measurements in the class. Similarly, *the height of the normal curve over a given point represents the relative proportion of population measurements that are near the given point.*

LO4
Many real populations are distributed according to the symmetrical, bell-shaped normal curve. We say that such populations are *normally distributed*. However, instead of being symmetrical and bell-shaped, the overall shape of a population may be **positively skewed** (with a tail to the right), as is the curve in Figure 2.6, or **negatively skewed** (with a tail to the left), as is the curve in Figure 2.7. Many other population shapes are also possible. If the stem-and-leaf display and/or the histogram of a random sample of measurements look like one of these curves, this suggests that the curve describes the overall shape of the entire population of measurements. In this case, the curve is called the *relative frequency curve* that describes the population. Said another way, *the population is distributed according to the relative frequency curve.* In a relative frequency curve, *the height of the curve over a given point represents the relative proportion of population measurements that are near the given point.* Example 2.4 demonstrates an asymmetrical distribution.

Example 2.4 The Marketing Research Example

Consider the sample of 60 bottle design ratings in Table 2.5. These bottle design ratings are the composites of responses to the interval level Likert scale in Figure 2.8 and range from 20 to 35. A percent frequency histogram of the ratings is shown in Figure 2.9. Looking at this display, we see that the distribution of bottle design ratings seems to be skewed toward the smaller ratings. Thus, the distribution is *skewed with a tail to the left* (or *negatively skewed*). This says that a few of the ratings are somewhat lower than the rest of the ratings.

TABLE **2.5**   A Sample of Bottle Design Ratings (Composite Scores for a Systematic Sample
of 60 Shoppers) 🖋

34	33	33	29	26	33	28	25	32	33
32	25	27	33	22	27	32	33	32	29
24	30	20	34	31	32	30	35	33	31
32	28	30	31	31	33	29	27	34	31
31	28	33	31	32	28	26	29	32	34
32	30	34	32	30	30	32	31	29	33

FIGURE **2.8**   The Bottle Design Survey Instrument

Please circle the response that most accurately describes whether you agree or disagree with each statement about the bottle you have examined.

Statement	Strongly Disagree						Strongly Agree
The size of this bottle is convenient.	1	2	3	4	5	6	7
The contoured shape of this bottle is easy to handle.	1	2	3	4	5	6	7
The label on this bottle is easy to read.	1	2	3	4	5	6	7
This bottle is easy to open.	1	2	3	4	5	6	7
Based on its overall appeal, I like this bottle design.	1	2	3	4	5	6	7

FIGURE **2.9**   MegaStat Output of 60 Bottle Design Ratings

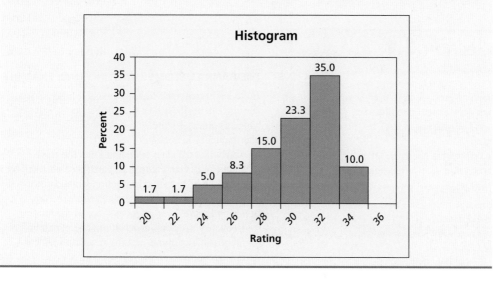

Frequency Distribution—Quantitative Rating

Lower		Upper	Midpoint	Width	Frequency	Percent	CUMULATIVE Frequency	CUMULATIVE Percent
20	<	22	21	2	1	1.7	1	1.7
22	<	24	23	2	1	1.7	2	3.3
24	<	26	25	2	3	5.0	5	8.3
26	<	28	27	2	5	8.3	10	16.7
28	<	30	29	2	9	15.0	19	31.7
30	<	32	31	2	14	23.3	33	55.0
32	<	34	33	2	21	35.0	54	90.0
34	<	36	35	2	6	10.0	60	100.0
					60	100.0		

Further graphical techniques, and detecting outliers   A professor recently taught a course in business statistics to a class of 40 students. A comparison of the scores received by these students on the first two 100-point exams is given by the two dot plots in Figure 2.10. Note that to make each dot plot, we draw a number line on which we measure the exam scores. We then place dots above the number line to represent the exam scores. The number of dots located above a particular exam score indicates how many students received that exam grade (recall that grades, in terms of raw scores or percentages, have meaningful zero points and are at the ratio level of measurement).

After noticing the two-peaked appearance of the dot plot for Exam 1, the professor investigated and found that most of the students who scored less than 70 on the exam had not been attending class regularly. Because of this, the professor reminded the students about the importance of attending class. The dot plot for Exam 2 is single-peaked and indicates a considerable improvement in student performance. Of course, this does not prove that attending class

FIGURE **2.10**   Dot Plots of the Scores on Exams 1 and 2

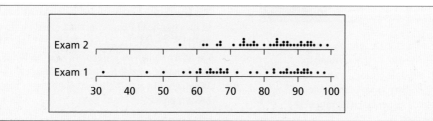

was solely responsible for the improved performance. However, many students told the professor that attending class improved their test scores.

LO5   Stem-and-leaf displays and dot plots are useful for detecting outliers, which are unusually large or small observations that are well separated from the remaining observations. For example, the dot plot for Exam 1 indicates that the score 32 seems unusually low. How we handle an outlier depends on its cause. If the outlier results from a measurement error or an error in recording or processing the data, it should be corrected. If the error cannot be corrected, it should be discarded. If an outlier is not the result of an error in measuring or recording the data, its cause may reveal important information. For example, the outlying exam score of 32 may have convinced the student that she or he needed a tutor. After working with a tutor, the student showed considerable improvement on Exam 2. A more precise way to detect outliers is presented in Section 2.4.

Exercises for Section **2.1**

CONCEPTS

2.1   What does each population shape look like? Describe each shape and then draw a picture to illustrate.
  a. Symmetrical and bell-shaped.
  b. Double-peaked.
  c. Negatively skewed (with a tail to the left).
  d. Positively skewed (with a tail to the right).

2.2   Explain each of the following:
  a. How to construct a stem-and-leaf display, a histogram, and a dot plot.
  b. How class limits, class boundaries, and class midpoints differ.
  c. What outliers are and how they are handled.

METHODS AND APPLICATIONS

2.3   Given in Table 2.6 are the median total incomes by metropolitan areas for Canada for 2006 through 2010 as reported by Statistics Canada. Construct stem-and-leaf plots for 2006 and 2010 (using a stem unit of $10,000). Comparing the two plots, what can you say about the median income values?

2.4   **THE VIDEO GAME SATISFACTION RATING EXAMPLE**

Table 2.7 presents the satisfaction ratings for the XYZ-Box video game system that have been given by 65 randomly selected purchasers. Figure 2.11 gives the MegaStat output of a stem-and-leaf display, and Figure 2.12 gives the Excel output of a frequency histogram of the 65 satisfaction ratings.

  a. Verify that the classes and class frequencies given in Figure 2.12 are those obtained by using the histogram construction method discussed in this section.
  b. Using Figures 2.11 and 2.12, infer the shape of the relative frequency distribution describing the population of all possible customer satisfaction ratings for the XYZ-Box video game system.
  c. Construct a relative frequency histogram of the 65 satisfaction ratings.

2.5   **THE BANK CUSTOMER WAITING TIME EXAMPLE**

Table 2.8 presents the waiting times for teller service during peak business hours of 100 randomly selected bank customers. Figure 2.13 gives the Excel output of a frequency histogram of the 100 waiting times.
  a. Verify that the class boundaries and the class frequencies (see Figure 2.13) are those obtained by using the histogram construction method discussed in this section.
  b. Using Figure 2.13, infer the shape of the relative frequency distribution describing the population of all possible customer waiting times during peak business hours.

2.6   **THE TRASH BAG EXAMPLE**

Table 2.9 presents the breaking strengths of 40 trash bags selected during a 40-hour pilot production run. Figure 2.14 gives the MegaStat output of a relative frequency histogram and Figure 2.15 gives the MegaStat output of a stem-and-leaf display of the 40 breaking strengths.
  a. Verify that the classes and class relative frequencies given in Figure 2.14 are those obtained by using the histogram construction method discussed in this section.
  b. Using Figures 2.14 and 2.15, infer the shape of the relative frequency distribution describing the population of all possible trash bag breaking strengths.

2.7   Babe Ruth's record of 60 home runs in a single year was broken by Roger Maris, who hit 61 home runs in 1961. The yearly home run totals for Ruth in his career as a New York Yankee are (arranged in increasing order) 22, 25, 34, 35, 41, 41, 46, 46, 46, 47, 49, 54, 54, 59, and 60. The yearly home run totals for Maris over his career in the American League are (arranged in increasing order) 8, 13, 14, 16, 23, 26, 28, 33, 39, and 61. Compare Ruth's and Maris's home run totals by constructing a back-to-back stem-and-leaf display. What would you conclude about Maris's record-breaking year?

TABLE **2.6** Median Total Income, by Family Type, by Census Metropolitan Area (All Census Families*)

	2006	2007	2008	2009	2010
Median Total Income			$		
Canada	63,600	66,550	68,860	68,410	69,860
St. John's (NL)	63,100	67,760	72,120	75,930	78,210
Halifax (NS)	67,600	70,610	74,040	75,050	76,500
Saint John (NB)	59,600	62,860	66,440	68,520	69,100
Saguenay (QC)	60,900	64,010	65,940	67,470	69,340
Québec (QC)	67,100	70,920	73,780	75,160	76,450
Sherbrooke (QC)	57,000	59,490	61,140	61,600	63,360
Trois-Rivières (QC)	56,900	59,640	61,610	62,160	63,510
Montréal (QC)	60,800	63,790	65,660	65,960	67,010
Ottawa–Gatineau (QC part, ON–QC)	70,900	74,670	77,440	80,110	81,040
Ottawa–Gatineau (ON part, ON–QC)	84,000	87,930	90,990	93,070	94,700
Kingston (ON)	69,100	71,980	74,830	75,210	77,140
Oshawa (ON)	78,900	81,570	83,220	81,560	82,270
Toronto (ON)	63,800	66,560	68,120	66,790	68,110
Hamilton (ON)	71,600	74,480	76,220	74,660	76,730
St. Catharines–Niagara (ON)	62,500	64,300	65,660	64,500	65,900
Kitchener–Cambridge–Waterloo (ON)	72,800	74,750	76,600	74,490	77,040
London (ON)	68,400	70,720	71,770	70,160	71,840
Windsor (ON)	70,000	70,810	70,510	67,220	69,480
Greater Sudbury/Grand Sudbury (ON)	69,700	74,840	79,570	75,240	76,710
Thunder Bay (ON)	69,400	71,480	73,460	72,960	75,640
Winnipeg (MB)	64,700	67,900	70,510	71,470	72,050
Regina (SK)	72,200	77,170	81,480	83,550	84,890
Saskatoon (SK)	68,300	72,970	77,740	79,100	80,570
Calgary (AB)	83,500	87,970	91,570	88,410	89,490
Edmonton (AB)	79,300	83,460	88,190	86,250	87,930
Abbotsford (BC)	58,900	61,970	63,680	62,370	62,320
Vancouver (BC)	62,900	66,330	68,670	67,550	67,090
Victoria (BC)	71,500	74,730	77,810	77,840	77,820

*Census families include couple families, with or without children, and lone-parent families.

Source: Statistics Canada, CANSIM, Table 111-0009.

TABLE **2.7** Composite Scores for the Video Game Satisfaction Rating Example

39	44	46	44	44
45	42	45	44	42
38	46	45	45	47
42	40	46	44	43
42	47	43	46	45
41	44	47	48	
38	43	43	44	
42	45	41	41	
46	45	40	45	
44	40	43	44	
40	46	44	44	
39	41	41	44	
40	43	38	46	
42	39	43	39	
45	43	36	41	

FIGURE **2.11** MegaStat Stem-and-Leaf Display of the 65 Satisfaction Ratings for Exercise 2.4

Stem-and-Leaf Plot for Rating

Stem unit = 1   leaf unit = 0.1

Frequency	Stem	Leaf
1	36	0
0	37	
3	38	000
4	39	0000
5	40	00000
6	41	000000
6	42	000000
8	43	00000000
12	44	000000000000
9	45	000000000
7	46	0000000
3	47	000
1	48	0
65		

FIGURE 2.12   Excel Frequency Histogram of the 65 Satisfaction Ratings for Exercise 2.4

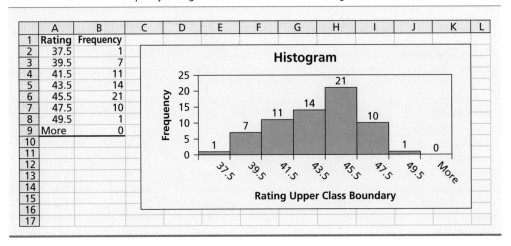

TABLE 2.8   Waiting Times (in Minutes) for the Bank Customer Waiting Time Example

1.6	6.2	3.2	5.6	7.9	6.1	7.2
6.6	5.4	6.5	4.4	1.1	3.8	7.3
5.6	4.9	2.3	4.5	7.2	10.7	4.1
5.1	5.4	8.7	6.7	2.9	7.5	6.7
3.9	0.8	4.7	8.1	9.1	7.0	3.5
4.6	2.5	3.6	4.3	7.7	5.3	6.3
6.5	8.3	2.7	2.2	4.0	4.5	4.3
6.4	6.1	3.7	5.8	1.4	4.5	3.8
8.6	6.3	0.4	8.6	7.8	1.8	5.1
4.2	6.8	10.2	2.0	5.2	3.7	5.5
5.8	9.8	2.8	8.0	8.4	4.0	
3.4	2.9	11.6	9.5	6.3	5.7	
9.3	10.9	4.3	1.3	4.4	2.4	
7.4	4.7	3.1	4.8	5.2	9.2	
1.8	3.9	5.8	9.9	7.4	5.0	

FIGURE 2.13   Excel Frequency Histogram of the 100 Waiting Times for Exercise 2.5

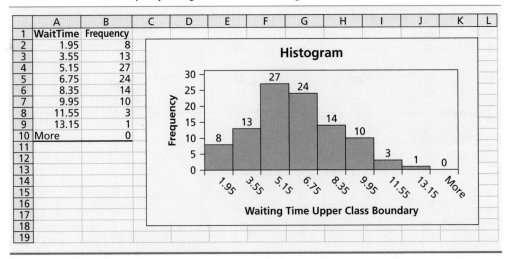

FIGURE **2.14** MegaStat Relative Frequency Histogram of the 40 Breaking Strengths for Exercise 2.6

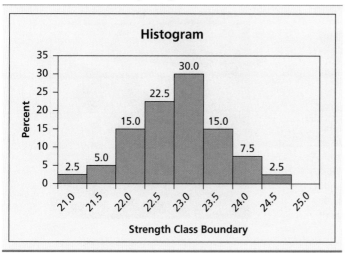

FIGURE **2.15** MegaStat Stem-and-Leaf Display of the Breaking Strengths for Exercise 2.6

Stem-and-Leaf Plot for Strength

Stem unit = 1   leaf unit = 0.1

Frequency	Stem	Leaf
1	21	3
2	21	6 9
6	22	0 0 2 3 4 4
9	22	5 5 5 6 7 7 8 8 9
12	23	0 0 0 1 1 1 2 2 3 3 4 4
6	23	5 6 6 8 9 9
3	24	1 2 3
1	24	5
40		

TABLE **2.9** Trash Bag Breaking Strengths

22.0	23.9	23.0	22.5
23.8	21.6	21.9	23.6
24.3	23.1	23.4	23.6
23.0	22.6	22.3	22.2
22.9	22.7	23.5	21.3
22.5	23.1	24.2	23.3
23.2	24.1	23.2	22.4
22.0	23.1	23.9	24.5
23.0	22.7	23.3	22.4
22.8	22.8	22.5	23.4

2.8 In this exercise, you will consider how to deal with class lengths that are unequal (and with open-ended classes) when setting up histograms. Data are often published in this form, and you will want to construct a histogram. An example is provided by data concerning the benefits of ISO 9000 registration published by CEEM Information Services. According to CEEM:[1]

> ISO 9000 is a series of international standards for quality assurance management systems. It establishes the organizational structure and processes for assuring that the production of goods or services meet a consistent and agreed-upon level of quality for a company's customers.

CEEM presents the results of a Quality Systems Update/Deloitte & Touche survey of ISO 9000-registered companies. Included in the results is a summary of the total annual savings associated with ISO 9000 implementation for surveyed companies. The findings (in the form of a frequency distribution of ISO 9000 savings) are given in the next column. Notice that the classes in this distribution have unequal lengths and that there is an open-ended class (> $500K). Note: K = 1,000.

To construct a histogram for these data, we select one of the classes as a base. It is often convenient to choose the shortest class as the base (although it is not necessary to do so). Using this choice, the 0 to $10K class is the base. This means that we will draw a rectangle over the 0 to $10K class with a height equal to 162 (the frequency given for this class in the published data). Because the other classes are longer than the base, the heights of the rectangles above these classes will be adjusted. Remembering that the area of a rectangle positioned over a particular class should represent the relative proportion of measurements in the class, we proceed as follows. The length of the $10K to $25K class differs from the base class by a factor of $(25 - 10)/(10 - 0) = 3/2$, and, therefore, we make the height of the rectangle over the $10K to $25K class equal to $(2/3)(62) = 41.333$. Similarly, the length of the $25K to $50K class differs from the length of the base class by a factor of $(50 - 25)/(10 - 0) = 5/2$, and, therefore, we make the height of the rectangle over the $25K to $50K class equal to $(2/5)(53) = 21.2$.

Annual Savings	Number of Companies
0 to $10K	162
$10K to $25K	62
$25K to $50K	53
$50K to $100K	60
$100K to $150K	24
$150K to $200K	19
$200K to $250K	22
$250K to $500K	21
(>$500K)	37

a. Use the procedure just outlined to find the heights of the rectangles drawn over all the other classes (with the exception of the open-ended class, > $500K).

[1]Source: *Is ISO 9000 for You?* (Fairfax, VA: CEEM Information Services).

b. Draw the appropriate rectangles over the classes (except for > $500K). Note that the $250K to $500K class is a lot longer than the others. This is fine as long as we adjust its rectangle's height.

c. We complete the histogram by placing a star (*) to the right of $500K on the scale of measurements and by noting "37" next to the * to indicate 37 companies saved more than $500K. Complete the histogram by doing this.

2.9 A basketball player practises free throws by taking 25 shots each day. He records the number of shots missed each day in order to track his progress. The numbers of shots missed on days 1 through 30 are 17, 15, 16, 18, 14, 15, 13, 12, 10, 11, 11, 10, 9, 10, 9, 9, 9, 10, 8, 10, 6, 8, 9, 8, 7, 9, 8, 7, 5, 8. Construct a stem-and-leaf display and a runs plot of the numbers of missed shots. Do you think that the stem-and-leaf display is representative of the numbers of shots that the player will miss on future days? Why or why not?

2.2 DESCRIBING CENTRAL TENDENCY

The mean, median, and mode In addition to describing the shape of the distribution of a sample or population of measurements, we also describe the data set's central tendency. A measure of central tendency represents the centre or middle of the data.

One important measure of central tendency for a population of measurements is the population mean.

The **population mean**, which is denoted by the Greek letter μ (*mu*, pronounced *mew*), is the average of the population measurements.

More precisely, the population mean is calculated by adding all of the population measurements and then dividing the resulting sum by the number of population measurements (N). For instance, consider the population of revenues for the five biggest companies in Canada in 2008 as reported by *Report on Business* magazine. The companies and revenues (to the nearest billion dollars) are as follows:

Company	Revenue (Billions)
Royal Bank of Canada	$38
Power Corp. of Canada	37
Power Financial	36
Manulife Financial	34
Great-West Life Co.	34

The mean, μ, of this population of revenues is

$$\mu = \frac{38 + 37 + 36 + 34 + 34}{5} = \frac{179}{5} = \$35.8 \text{ billion.}$$

This population of five revenues is small, so it is possible to compute the population mean. Often, however, a population is very large and we cannot obtain a measurement for each population unit. Therefore, we cannot compute the population mean. In such a case, we must estimate the population mean by using a sample of measurements.

In order to understand how to estimate a population mean, we must realize that the population mean is a population parameter.

A **population parameter** is a number calculated using the population measurements that describes some aspect of the population. That is, a population parameter is a descriptive measure of the population.

There are many population parameters, and we discuss several of them in this chapter. The simplest way to estimate a population parameter is to make what is called a *point estimate*.

A **point estimate** is a one-number estimate of the value of a population parameter.

Although a point estimate is a guess of a population parameter's value, it is not a blind guess. Rather, it is an educated guess based on sample data. One way to find a point estimate of a population parameter is to use a sample statistic.

A **sample statistic** is a number calculated using the sample measurements that describes some aspect of the sample. That is, a sample statistic is a descriptive measure of the sample.

The sample statistic that we use to estimate the population mean is the **sample mean**, which is denoted as $\bar{x}$ (*x bar*) or M (M = Mean, commonly used in the social sciences) and is the average of the sample measurements.

In order to write a formula for the sample mean, we employ the letter n to represent the number of sample measurements, and we refer to n as the **sample size** (N is used for the size of the population). Furthermore, we denote the sample measurements as $x_1, x_2, \ldots, x_n$. Here x_1 is the first sample measurement, x_2 is the second sample measurement, and so forth. We denote the last sample measurement as x_n. Moreover, when we write formulas we often use summation notation for convenience. For instance, we write the sum of the sample measurements

$$x_1 + x_2 + \cdots + x_n$$

as $\sum_{i=1}^{n} x_i$. Here the Greek letter Σ (*sigma*) says that we are writing out a sum of *like terms*. The general term x_i says that all the terms we are adding up look like x_i. The index $i = 1$ to n says that we let the subscript i in the general term x_i range from 1 to n, and we add up all these terms. Thus,

$$\sum_{i=1}^{n} x_i = x_1 + x_2 + \cdots + x_n.$$

LO6

Sample Mean

The *sample mean* $\bar{x}$ is defined to be

$$\bar{x} = \frac{\sum_{i=1}^{n} x_i}{n} = \frac{x_1 + x_2 + \cdots + x_n}{n}$$

and is the *point estimate of the population mean* μ. An example of this calculation is given in Example 2.5.

Example 2.5 Hourly Wages for Some Job Types in Ontario

Statistics Canada provides lists of average hourly wages for various types of jobs in different provinces and territories in Canada. The September 2009 statistics for Ontario suggested that the average hourly wage for certain vocational areas varied. For example, for management positions, the average hourly wage was \$35.58, for business and finance it was \$21.16, for natural and applied sciences it was \$31.43, for health occupations it was \$26.58, and for sales it was \$14.54. To calculate the average of these values, calculate the sum of the five hourly rates and divide the total by 5:

$$\sum_{i=1}^{5} x_i = x_1 + x_2 + x_3 + x_4 + x_5$$

$$= 35.58 + 21.16 + 31.43 + 26.58 + 14.54$$

$$= 129.29,$$

$$\bar{x} = \frac{129.29}{5} = 25.86$$

The results suggest that the average hourly rate of the five vocational types in Ontario was $25.86 and represented a point estimate of the average hourly wages. Due to concerns such as rounding, under-reporting, and failing to include all possible vocational types, the point estimate may be somewhat unreliable.

In later chapters, we discuss how to assess the reliability of the sample mean and how to use a measure of reliability to decide whether sample information provides definitive evidence. Also, available on *Connect* is an explanation of the geometric mean, which provides a measure of the rate of change exhibited by a variable over time.

Another descriptive measure of the central tendency of a population or a sample of measurements is the **median** (M_d). Intuitively, the median divides a population or sample into two roughly equal parts.[2]

The Median

Consider a population or a sample of measurements, and arrange the measurements in increasing order. The median, M_d, is found as follows:

1 If the number of measurements is odd, the median is the middle measurement in the ordering.

2 If the number of measurements is even, the median is the average of the two middle measurements in the ordering.

An example of the median is given in Example 2.6.

Example 2.6 Personal Expenditures

Statistics Canada compiles data on personal expenditures. Listed below are the average annual amounts people in Canada spent on rent (recall that money is at the ratio level of measurement) for the years 1997 through 2005 (covering nine years):

6,606   6,806   7,043   7,265   ⟨7,523⟩   7,873   8,207   8,533   8,856

Because the number of annual rent payment values is odd, the median of this sample is the middle value in the list (note that average annual rent has increased from 1997 to 2005, so the data are already in ascending order). The median is therefore $7,523 (it is circled).

A third measure of the central tendency of a population or sample is the mode, which is denoted M_o.

The **mode**, M_o, of a population or sample of measurements is the measurement that occurs most frequently.

For example, the mode of the satisfaction ratings given in Example 2.7 is 8, because more purchasers (six) gave the DVD recorder a rating of 8 than any other rating. Sometimes the highest frequency occurs at two or more different measurements. When this happens, two or more modes exist. When exactly two modes exist, we say the data are *bimodal*. When more than two modes exist, we say the data are *multimodal*. Finally, when data are presented in classes (such as in a frequency histogram), the class with the highest frequency is called the *modal class*.

---

[2]To remember the median, recall that it is the same name given to the boundary separating highway lanes, typically with an equal number of lanes on either side of the median.

Example 2.7 DVD Recorder Satisfaction

The manufacturer of a DVD recorder randomly selects a sample of 20 purchasers who have owned the recorder for one year. Each purchaser in the sample is asked to rank his or her satisfaction with the recorder on the following ten-point interval scale:

```
  1   2   3   4   5   6   7   8   9   10
 Not           Fairly          Extremely
satisfied     satisfied        satisfied
```

Suppose that the following rankings, arranged in increasing order, are obtained:

1   3   5   5   7   8   8   8   8 ⑧ ⑧ 9   9   9   9   9   10 10 10 10

Because the number of satisfaction ratings is even, the median of this sample is the average of the two middle ratings. Both of these ratings are 8—they are circled. Therefore, the median of this sample is 8, and we estimate that the median satisfaction rating of all the DVD recorder owners is 8. This estimated median satisfaction rating seems relatively high. Note, however, that there are four rather low individual satisfaction ratings: 1, 3, 5, and 5. This suggests that some DVD recorders may be of low quality. If the manufacturer wishes to satisfy all of its customers, it must investigate the situation.

Comparing the mean, median, and mode To compare the mean, median, and mode, look at Figure 2.16. Part (a) of this figure depicts a population described by a symmetrical relative frequency curve. For such a population, the mean (μ), median (M_d), and mode (M_o) are all equal. Note that in this case, all three of these quantities are located under the highest point of the curve. It follows that when the frequency distribution of a sample of measurements is approximately symmetrical (normal or mound-shaped), then the sample mean, median, and mode will be nearly the same. For instance, consider a sample of 49 DVD price points, and note that the stem-and-leaf display of these prices is given in the margin of this page. Because the number of prices is odd, the median is the middle price, the 25th price. Counting 25 prices from the top of the stem-and-leaf display, we find that the median is 31.6. Furthermore, since the stem-and-leaf display is fairly symmetrical, this sample median is approximately equal to the sample mean, which is 31.55.

DVD Prices

29	8
30	1344
30	5666889
31	001233444
㉛	555⑥6777889
32	0001122344
32	556788
33	3

FIGURE 2.16 Relationships among the Mean (μ), the Median (M_d), and the Mode (M_o)

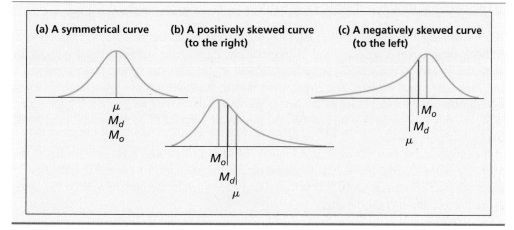

(a) A symmetrical curve

(b) A positively skewed curve (to the right)

(c) A negatively skewed curve (to the left)

Salaries

12	7
13	2 8
14	1 4 6
⑮	②4
16	2
17	1 7
18	
19	2
20	
21	
22	
23	
24	1

Ratings

1	0
2	
3	0
4	
5	0 0
6	
7	0
⑧	0 0 0 0 ⓪⓪
9	0 0 0 0 0
10	0 0 0 0

Figure 2.16(b) depicts a population that is positively skewed (to the right). Here the population mean is larger than the population median, and the population median is larger than the population mode (the mode is located under the highest point of the relative frequency curve). In this case, the population mean *averages in* the large values in the upper tail of the distribution, so the population mean is more affected by these large values than is the population median. To understand this, note the "Salaries" stem-and-leaf display in the margin of this page. This sample of 13 internists' salaries is skewed to the right. Here the mean of the 13 salaries, which is 159.769 (or $159,769), is affected by averaging in the large salaries (192 and 241) in the right-hand tail of the distribution. Thus, this mean is larger than the sample median, $152,000. The median is said to be *resistant* to the large salaries 192 and 241 because the value of the median is affected only by the fact that these salaries are the two largest salaries in the sample. The value of the median is not affected by the exact sizes of the salaries 192 and 241. For example, if the largest salary was smaller—say, 200—the median would remain the same but the mean would decrease. If the largest salary was larger—say, 300—the median would also remain the same but the mean would increase. Therefore, *the median is resistant to extreme values but the mean is not.*

Figure 2.16(c) depicts a population that is negatively skewed (to the left). Here the population mean is smaller than the population median, and the population median is smaller than the population mode. In this case, the population mean averages in the small values in the lower tail of the distribution, and the mean is more affected by these small values than is the median. For instance, the stem-and-leaf display of a sample of purchaser satisfaction ratings (in the page margin) is skewed to the left. In this case, the mean of these ratings, which equals 7.7, is affected by averaging in the smaller ratings (1, 3, 5, and 5) in the left-hand tail of the distribution, so the mean is smaller than the sample median, 8.

When a population is positively or negatively skewed (to the right or left) with a very long tail, the population mean can be substantially affected by the extreme values in the tail of the distribution. In such a case, the median might be better than the mean as a measure of central tendency. The following example illustrates that the choice of the mean or the median as a measure of central tendency can depend on the purpose of the study being conducted.

When a population is symmetrical or not highly skewed, then the population mean and the population median are either equal or roughly equal, and both provide a good measure of the population central tendency. In this situation, we usually make inferences about the population mean because much of statistical theory is based on the mean rather than the median. We illustrate these ideas in Example 2.8, which also shows that we can obtain the mean and the median by using Excel and MegaStat outputs.

Example 2.8   The Marketing Research Example

The Excel output in Figure 2.17(a) tells us that the mean and the median of the sample of 60 bottle design ratings are 30.35 and 31, respectively. Because the stem-and-leaf display of the bottle design ratings is not highly negatively skewed (to the left), the sample mean is not much less than the sample median. Therefore, using the mean as our measure of central tendency, we estimate that the mean rating of the new bottle design that would be given by all consumers is 30.35. This is considerably higher than the minimum standard of 25 for a successful bottle design.

To conclude this example, note that Figures 2.17(b), 2.17(c), and 2.18 give the Excel and MegaStat outputs of the previously discussed means and medians for internists' salaries, customer satisfaction ratings, and DVD prices. Other quantities in the outputs will be discussed as we proceed through this chapter.

FIGURE 2.17 Excel Outputs of Statistics Describing Three Data Sets

(a) Statistics describing the 60 bottle design ratings		(b) Statistics describing 13 internists' salaries		(c) Statistics describing 20 customer satisfaction ratings	
Mean	30.35	Mean	159.7692	Mean	7.7
Standard Error	0.401146	Standard Error	8.498985	Standard Error	0.543381
Median	31	Median	152	Median	8
Mode	32	Mode	#N/A	Mode	8
Standard Deviation	3.107263	Standard Deviation	30.64353	Standard Deviation	2.430075
Sample Variance	9.655085	Sample Variance	939.0256	Sample Variance	5.905263
Kurtosis	1.423397	Kurtosis	3.409669	Kurtosis	2.128288
Skewness	−1.17688	Skewness	1.695197	Skewness	−1.56682
Range	15	Range	114	Range	9
Minimum	20	Minimum	127	Minimum	1
Maximum	35	Maximum	241	Maximum	10
Sum	1821	Sum	2077	Sum	154
Count	60	Count	13	Count	20

FIGURE 2.18 MegaStat Output of Statistics Describing the 49 DVD Price Points

Descriptive statistics

	Prices	empirical rule	
count	49	mean − 1s	30.754
mean	31.553	mean + 1s	32.352
sample variance	0.639	percent in interval (68.26%)	63.3%
sample standard deviation	0.799	mean − 2s	29.955
minimum	29.8	mean + 2s	33.152
maximum	33.3	percent in interval (95.44%)	95.9%
range	3.5	mean − 3s	29.155
sum	1,546.100	mean + 3s	33.951
sum of squares	48,814.850	percent in interval (99.73%)	100.0%
deviation sum of squares (SS)	30.662		
1st quartile	31.000	low extremes	0
median	31.600	low outliers	0
3rd quartile	32.100	high outliers	0
interquartile range	1.100	high extremes	0
mode	31.700		

To conclude this section, note that the mean and the median convey useful information about a population having a relative frequency curve with a sufficiently regular shape. For instance, the mean and median would be useful in describing the mound-shaped, or single-peaked, distributions in Figure 2.16. However, these measures of central tendency do not adequately describe a double-peaked distribution. For example, the mean and the median of the exam scores in the double-peaked dot plot display in Figure 2.10 are 75.225 and 77. Looking at the display, neither the mean nor the median represents a typical exam score, because the exam scores really have no central value. In this case, the most important message conveyed by the double-peaked dot plot display is that the exam scores fall into two distinct groups.

Exercises for Section **2.2**

CONCEPTS

2.10 Explain the difference between the terms for each of the following:
   a. A population parameter and its point estimate.
   b. A population mean and a corresponding sample mean.

2.11 Explain how the population mean, median, and mode compare when the population's relative frequency curve is
   a. Symmetrical.
   b. Negatively skewed (with a tail to the left).
   c. Positively skewed (with a tail to the right).
   d. Normally distributed.

FIGURE 2.19 MegaStat Outputs of Statistics Describing Three Data Sets

(a) Satisfaction rating statistics

Descriptive statistics

	Rating
count	65
mean	42.95
median	43.00
sample variance	6.98
sample standard deviation	2.64
minimum	36
maximum	48
range	12
empirical rule	
mean − 1s	40.31
mean + 1s	45.60
percent in interval (68.26%)	63.1%
mean − 2s	37.67
mean + 2s	48.24
percent in interval (95.44%)	98.5%
mean − 3s	35.03
mean + 3s	50.88
percent in interval (99.73%)	100.0%

(b) Waiting time statistics

Descriptive statistics

	WaitTime
count	100
mean	5.460
median	5.250
sample variance	6.128
sample standard deviation	2.475
minimum	0.4
maximum	11.6
range	11.2
empirical rule	
mean − 1s	2.985
mean + 1s	7.935
percent in interval (68.26%)	66.0%
mean − 2s	0.509
mean + 2s	10.411
percent in interval (95.44%)	96.0%
mean − 3s	−1.966
mean + 3s	12.886
percent in interval (99.73%)	100.0%

(c) Breaking strength statistics

Descriptive statistics

	Strength
count	40
mean	22.990
median	23.000
sample variance	0.552
sample standard deviation	0.743
minimum	21.3
maximum	24.5
range	3.2
empirical rule	
mean − 1s	22.247
mean + 1s	23.733
percent in interval (68.26%)	67.5%
mean − 2s	21.504
mean + 2s	24.476
percent in interval (95.44%)	95.0%
mean − 3s	20.762
mean + 3s	25.218
percent in interval (99.73%)	100.0%

METHODS AND APPLICATIONS

2.12 Calculate the mean, median, and mode of each population of numbers:
   a. 9, 8, 10, 10, 12, 6, 11, 10, 12, 8
   b. 110, 120, 70, 90, 90, 100, 80, 130, 140

2.13 Calculate the mean, median, and mode of each population of numbers:
   a. 17, 23, 19, 20, 25, 18, 22, 15, 21, 20
   b. 505, 497, 501, 500, 507, 510, 501

2.14 THE VIDEO GAME SATISFACTION RATING EXAMPLE

Recall that Table 2.7 presents the satisfaction ratings for the XYZ-Box game system that have been given by 65 randomly selected purchasers. Figure 2.19(a) gives the MegaStat output of statistics describing the 65 satisfaction ratings.
   a. Does the sample mean $\bar{x} = 42.95$ provide evidence that the mean of the population of all possible customer satisfaction ratings for the XYZ-Box is at least 42? (Recall that a "very satisfied" customer gives a rating that is at least 42.) Explain your answer.
   b. Use the stem-and-leaf display in Figure 2.11 to verify that the median of the satisfaction ratings is 43. How do the mean and median compare? What does the stem-and-leaf display tell you about why they compare in this way?

2.15 THE BANK CUSTOMER WAITING TIME EXAMPLE

Recall that Table 2.8 presents the waiting times for teller service during peak business hours of 100 randomly selected bank customers. Figure 2.19(b) gives the MegaStat output of statistics describing the 100 waiting times.

a. Does the sample mean $\bar{x} = 5.460$ provide evidence that the mean of the population of all possible customer waiting times during peak business hours is less than six minutes (as is desired by the bank manager)? Explain your answer.
   b. The median of the waiting times is 5.250. How do the mean and median compare? What does the histogram in Figure 2.13 tell you about why they compare in this way?

2.16 THE TRASH BAG EXAMPLE

Consider the trash bag problem. Suppose that an independent laboratory has tested 130-L trash bags and has found that none of the bags currently on the market have a mean breaking strength of 23 kg or more. On the basis of these results, the producer of the new, improved trash bag feels sure that its bag will be the strongest such bag on the market if the new trash bag's mean breaking strength can be shown to be at least 23 kg. Recall that Table 2.9 presents the breaking strengths of 40 trash bags of the new type that were selected during a 40-hour pilot production run. Figure 2.19(c) gives the MegaStat output of statistics describing the 40 breaking strengths.
   a. Does the sample mean $\bar{x} = 22.990$ provide evidence that the mean of the population of all possible trash bag breaking strengths is at least 23 kg? Explain your answer.
   b. Use the stem-and-leaf display in Figure 2.15 to verify that the median of the breaking strengths is 23.00. How do the mean and median compare? What does the stem-and-leaf display tell you about why they compare in this way?

Exercises 2.17 through 2.21 refer to the information in Table 2.10, which gives data concerning the number of fatalities by different modes of transportation in 2003 for Canada, the United States, and Mexico. In each exercise:

a. Compute the mean and median.

b. Compare the mean and median and explain if there is a case to be made for skewness.

c. Plot the values for the separate countries.

2.17 Analyze the data concerning air fatalities in Table 2.10 as described above.

2.18 Analyze the data concerning passenger cars and light trucks in Table 2.10 as described above.

2.19 Analyze the data concerning pedestrians in Table 2.10 as described above.

2.20 Analyze the data concerning motorcycles in Table 2.10 as described above.

2.21 Analyze the data concerning total rail fatalities in Table 2.10 as described above.

2.22 Thirty adults were recently surveyed and were asked to report how much they would be willing to pay for a luxury car. The responses are given in Table 2.11. A frequency histogram of the data is given in Figure 2.20. Using these data, answer the following questions:

a. Calculate the mean and median values and comment on the shape of the distribution.

b. What percentage of people's estimates exceeds the mean car value estimate? Exceeds the median car value estimate?

TABLE **2.10**   Data Comparing 2003 Transportation Fatalities by Mode for North America

	Canada	United States	Mexico
Air	68	700	49
Air carriers	15	69	0
General aviation	53	631	49
Road	2,766	42,643	10,052
Passenger cars and light trucks	1,990	31,904	3,706
Passenger cars	U	19,460	3,586
Motorcycles	177	3,661	6
Buses	3	40	43
Large trucks	93	723	150
Pedestrians	376	4,749	1,478
Other	127	1,566	19
Pipeline	0	12	U
Rail	79	856	U
Grade crossing	27	329	59
Railroad	52	531	U
Transit, total	N	188	U
Transit rail	N	97	U
Water transport	U	816	28
Passenger vessels	U	U	N
Recreational boats	U	703	N
Commercial passenger vessels	4	U	N
Commercial freight vessels	2	N	U

Source: North American Transportation Statistics Database, Table 3-1, "Transportation Fatalities by Mode": nats.sct.gob. mx/3-1_en.html

U = Unavailable

N = Data are nonexistent

TABLE **2.11**   Car Value Data

77856.11	62458.14	48931.66	39249.75	34065.38	28547.5
76488.72	61675	46569	38857	34000	27200.5
68578.89	53833.8	42074.5	36402.58	33375	26127.5
68175.25	53296.75	40865.5	35908.74	32954.25	23400
63382.46	50895.75	39590	34455	30867.5	21932.5

FIGURE 2.20   Frequency Histogram of Car Value Responses

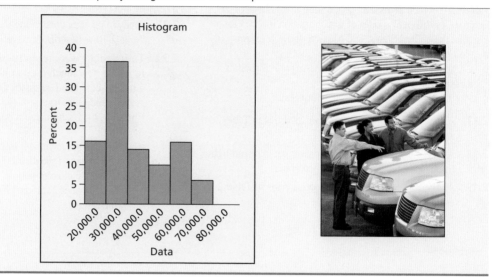

2.3 MEASURES OF VARIATION

Range, variance, and standard deviation   In addition to estimating a population's central tendency, it is important to estimate the variation of the population's individual values. For example, Figure 2.21 shows two histograms. Each portrays the distribution of 20 repair times (in days) for personal computers at a major service centre. Because the mean (and median and mode) of each distribution equals four days, the measures of central tendency do not indicate any difference between the Local Service Centre and the National Service Centre. However, the repair times for the Local Service Centre are clustered quite closely together, whereas the repair times for the National Service Centre are spread farther apart (the repair time might be as little as one day, but could also be as long as seven days). Therefore, we need measures of variation to express how the two distributions differ.

One way to measure the variation of a set of measurements is to calculate the range.

The **range** of the measurements is the largest measurement minus the smallest measurement.

In Figure 2.21, the smallest and largest repair times for the Local Service Centre are three days and five days; therefore, the range is 5 days − 3 days = 2 days. On the other hand, the range for the National Service Centre is 7 days − 1 day = 6 days. The National Service Centre's larger range indicates that this service centre's repair times exhibit more variation.

FIGURE 2.21   Repair Times for Personal Computers at Two Service Centres

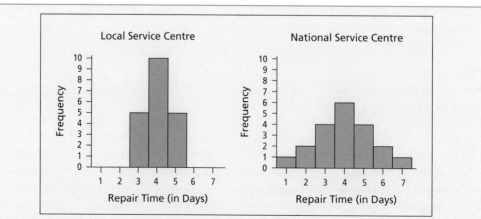

In general, the range is not the best measure of a data set's variation. One reason is that it is based only on the smallest and largest measurements in the data set and therefore may reflect an extreme measurement that is not entirely representative of the data set's variation. For example, in the marketing research case, the smallest and largest ratings in the sample of 60 bottle design ratings are 20 and 35. However, to simply estimate that most bottle design ratings are between 20 and 35 misses the fact that 57, or 95 percent, of the 60 ratings are at least as large as the minimum rating of 25 for a successful bottle design. In general, to fully describe a population's variation, it is useful to estimate intervals that contain *different percentages* (for example, 70 percent, 95 percent, or almost 100 percent) of the individual population values. To estimate such intervals, we use the population variance and the population standard deviation.

LO7

The Population Variance and Standard Deviation

The **population variance** σ^2 (*sigma squared*) is the average of the squared deviations of the individual population measurements from the population mean μ.

The **population standard deviation** σ (*sigma*) is the square root of the population variance.

For example, consider the population of revenues for five of the biggest companies in Canada as reported by *The Globe and Mail* for 2008. These revenues (in billions of dollars) are 38, 37, 36, 34, and 34. To calculate the variance and standard deviation of these revenues, we first calculate the population mean, which is 35.8. Next we calculate the deviations of the individual population measurements from the population mean $\mu = 35.8$ as follows:

$$38 - 35.8 = 2.2, \quad 37 - 35.8 = 1.2, \quad 36 - 35.8 = 0.2, \quad 34 - 35.8 = -1.8,$$
$$34 - 35.8 = -1.8$$

Then we compute the sum of the squares of these deviations:

$$2.2^2 + 1.2^2 + 0.2^2 + (-1.8)^2 + (-1.8)^2 = 4.84 + 1.44 + 0.04 + 3.24 + 3.24 = 12.8$$

Finally, we calculate the population variance σ^2, the average of the squared deviations, by dividing the sum of the squared deviations, 12.8, by the number of squared deviations, 5. That is, σ^2 equals $12.8/5 = 2.56$. Furthermore, this implies that the population standard deviation σ, the square root of σ^2, is $\sqrt{2.56} = 1.60$.

To see that the variance and standard deviation measure the variation, or spread, of the individual population measurements, suppose that the measurements are spread far apart. Then many measurements will be far from the mean μ, many of the squared deviations from the mean will be large, and the sum of squared deviations will be large. It follows that the average of the squared deviations—the population variance—will be relatively large. On the other hand, if the population measurements are clustered closely together, many measurements will be close to μ, many of the squared deviations from the mean will be small, and the average of the squared deviations—the population variance—will be small. Therefore, the more spread out the population measurements, the larger is the population variance, and the larger is the population standard deviation.

ROADBLOCK

Importance of variance
The concepts of variance and standard deviations are essential to master as they are used in almost all parametric statistics.

To further understand the population variance and standard deviation, note that one reason we square the deviations of the individual population measurements from the population mean is that the sum of the raw deviations themselves is zero. This is because the negative deviations cancel the positive deviations. For example, in the revenue situation, the raw deviations are 2.2, 1.2, 0.2, -1.8, and -1.8, which sum to zero. Of course, we could make the deviations

positive by finding their absolute values. We square the deviations instead because the resulting population variance and standard deviation have many important interpretations that we study throughout this book. Because the population variance is an average of squared deviations of the original population values, the variance is expressed in squared units of the original population values. On the other hand, the population standard deviation—the square root of the population variance—is expressed in the same units as the original population values. Because the population standard deviation is expressed in the same units as the population values, it is more often used to make practical interpretations about the variation of these values.

When a population is too large to measure all of the population units, we estimate the population variance and the population standard deviation by the sample variance and the sample standard deviation. We calculate the sample variance by dividing the sum of the squared deviations of the sample measurements from the sample mean by $n - 1$, the sample size minus one.[3] Although we might intuitively think that we should divide by n rather than by $n - 1$, it can be shown that dividing by n tends to produce an estimate of the population variance that is too small. On the other hand, dividing by $n - 1$ tends to produce a larger estimate that is more appropriate. Therefore, we obtain the following:

The Sample Variance and the Sample Standard Deviation

The **sample variance** s^2 (s squared) is defined to be

$$s^2 = \frac{\sum_{i=1}^{n} (x_i - \bar{x})^2}{n - 1} = \frac{(x_1 - \bar{x})^2 + (x_2 - \bar{x})^2 + \cdots + (x_n - \bar{x})^2}{n - 1}$$

and is the point estimate of the population variance σ^2.

The **sample standard deviation** $s = \sqrt{s^2}$ is the square root of the sample variance and is the point estimate of the population standard deviation σ. An example of the calculation of variance and standard deviation is given in Example 2.9.

Example 2.9 Canadian Manufacturing Statistics

2008/05	3.88
2008/06	5.23
2008/07	3.64
2008/08	3.91
2008/09	4.37
2008/10	4.52
2008/11	2.01
2008/12	2.45
2009/01	4.18
2009/02	5.24
2009/03	5.86
2009/04	4.50
2009/05	4.00

Statistics Canada compiles data on manufacturing statistics for Canada. Listed in the margin are the monthly numbers of asphalt shingle production (in millions of metric bundles) in Canada from May 2008 to May 2009.

The first step in calculating the sample variance and standard deviation is to compute the mean. For the asphalt production data, the mean is

$$\frac{3.88 + 5.23 + \cdots + 4.50 + 4.00}{13} = 4.14$$

It then follows that

$$\sum_{i=1}^{13} (x_i - \bar{x})^2 = (x_i - \bar{x})^2 + (x_2 - \bar{x})^2 + (x_3 - \bar{x})^2 + \cdots + (x_{13} - \bar{x})^2$$

$$= (3.88 - 4.14)^2 + (5.23 - 4.14)^2 + (3.64 - 4.14)^2 + \cdots + (4.00 - 4.14)^2 = 13.47$$

Therefore, the variance and the standard deviation of the sample are

$$s^2 = \frac{13.47}{12} = 1.12 \text{ and } s = \sqrt{1.12} = 1.06$$

[3]Note that this value of one represents a "lost degree of freedom." When dealing with a sample, one data point must remain fixed so that there is a reference point to examine the other data points. As an exercise, find a few friends and try to put yourselves in a line in terms of height from tallest to shortest. To do this, you will need one person to stand still to be a reference point to compare yourself and others to (you will not be able to form a line if everyone keeps moving around). This fixed point (person) is then no longer free to move and is said to be a lost degree (point) of freedom.

Here $s^2 = 1.12$ and $s = 1.06$ are the point estimates of the variance and standard deviation, σ^2 and σ, respectively, of the entire population. The sample standard deviation, s, is expressed in the same units as the sample values. Therefore, we say that $s = 1.06$ million metric bundles.

Before explaining how we can use s^2 and s in a practical way, we present a formula that makes it easier to compute s^2. This formula is useful when we are using a handheld calculator that is not equipped with a statistics mode to compute s^2.

Calculating the Sample Variance

The **sample variance** can be calculated using the computational formula

$$s^2 = \frac{1}{n-1}\left[\sum_{i=1}^{n}x_i^2 - \frac{\left(\sum_{i=1}^{n}x_i\right)^2}{n}\right]$$

A practical interpretation: The empirical rule A practical interpretation of the population standard deviation—the **empirical rule**—is presented in the boxed feature entitled "The Empirical Rule for a Normally Distributed Population."

The Empirical Rule for a Normally Distributed Population

If a population has mean μ and standard deviation σ and is described by a normal curve, then, as illustrated in Figure 2.22,

1   68.26 percent of the population measurements are within (plus or minus) one standard deviation of the mean and thus lie in the interval $[\mu - \sigma, \mu + \sigma] = [\mu \pm \sigma]$.

2   95.44 percent of the population measurements are within (plus or minus) two standard deviations of the mean and thus lie in the interval $[\mu - 2\sigma, \mu + 2\sigma] = [\mu \pm 2\sigma]$.

3   99.73 percent of the population measurements are within (plus or minus) three standard deviations of the mean and thus lie in the interval $[\mu - 3\sigma, \mu + 3\sigma] = [\mu \pm 3\sigma]$.

FIGURE 2.22 The Empirical Rule

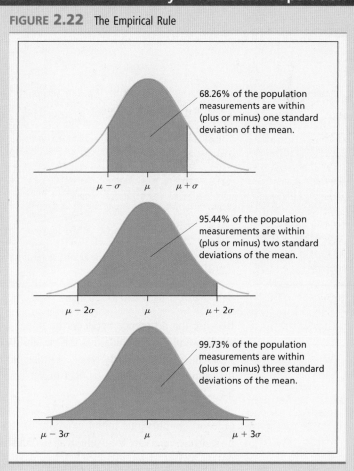

68.26% of the population measurements are within (plus or minus) one standard deviation of the mean.

95.44% of the population measurements are within (plus or minus) two standard deviations of the mean.

99.73% of the population measurements are within (plus or minus) three standard deviations of the mean.

In general, an interval that contains a specified percentage of the individual measurements in a population is called a **tolerance interval**. It follows that the one, two, and three standard deviation intervals around μ are tolerance intervals containing, respectively, 68.26 percent, 95.44 percent, and 99.73 percent of the measurements in a normally distributed population. Often we interpret the three-sigma interval $[\mu \pm 3\sigma]$ to be a tolerance interval that contains *almost all* of the measurements in a normally distributed population. Of course, we usually do not know the true values of μ and σ. Therefore, we must estimate the tolerance intervals by replacing μ and σ in these intervals with the mean $\bar{x}$ and standard deviation s of a sample that has been randomly selected from the normally distributed population (see Example 2.10).

Example 2.10 DVD Price Points

Consider the sample of 49 DVD prices given below. For these data, $\bar{x} = 31.5531$ and $s = 0.7992$ are the point estimates of the mean μ and the standard deviation σ, respectively, of the population of all DVD prices. Furthermore, the histogram of the 49 DVD prices suggests that the population of all DVD prices is normally distributed. To more simply illustrate the empirical rule, we will round $\bar{x}$ to 31.6 and s to 0.8. Using these values, we have the following:

1   Using the interval $[\bar{x} + s] = [31.6 \pm 0.8] = [31.6 - 0.8, 31.6 + 0.8] = [30.8, 32.4]$, we estimate that 68.26 percent of all individual DVDs will cost between \$30.80 and \$32.40.

2   Using the interval $[\bar{x} \pm 2s] = [31.6 \pm 2(0.8)] = [31.6 \pm 1.6] = [30.0, 33.2]$, we estimate that 95.44 percent of all individual DVDs will cost between \$30.00 and \$33.20.

3   Using the interval $[\bar{x} \pm 3s] = [31.6 \pm 3(0.8)] = [31.6 \pm 2.4] = [29.2, 34.0]$, we estimate that 99.73 percent of all individual DVDs will cost between \$29.20 and \$34.00.

A sample of 49 DVD price points

30.8	30.9	32.0	32.3	32.6
31.7	30.4	31.4	32.7	31.4
30.1	32.5	30.8	31.2	31.8
31.6	30.3	32.8	30.6	31.9
32.1	31.3	32.0	31.7	32.8
33.3	32.1	31.5	31.4	31.5
31.3	32.5	32.4	32.2	31.6
31.0	31.8	31.0	31.5	30.6
32.0	30.4	29.8	31.7	32.2
32.4	30.5	31.1	30.6	

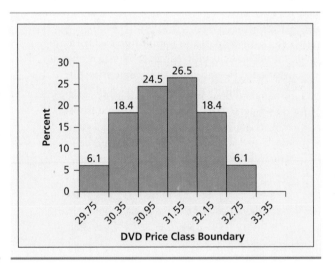

Because the difference between the upper and lower limits of each tolerance interval is fairly small, we might conclude that the variability of the individual DVD prices around the estimated mean of \$31.60 is fairly small. Furthermore, the interval $[\bar{x} \pm 3s] = [29.2, 34.0]$ implies that almost any individual DVD that a customer might purchase this year will cost between \$29.20 and \$34.00.

Before continuing, recall that we have rounded $\bar{x}$ and s to one decimal point accuracy in order to simplify our initial example of the empirical rule. If, instead, we calculate the empirical rule intervals by using $\bar{x} = 31.5531$ and $s = 0.7992$ and then round the interval endpoints to one decimal place accuracy at the end of the calculations, we obtain the same intervals as obtained above. In general, however, rounding intermediate calculated results can lead to inaccurate final results. Because of this, throughout this book we will avoid greatly rounding intermediate results.

We next note that if we actually count the number of the 49 DVD prices that are contained in each of the intervals $[\bar{x} \pm s] = [30.8, 32.4]$, $[\bar{x} \pm 2s] = [30.0, 33.2]$, and $[\bar{x} \pm 3s] = [29.2, 34.0]$, we find that these intervals contain, respectively, 33, 47, and 49 of the 49 DVD prices. The corresponding sample percentages—67.35 percent, 95.92 percent, and 100 percent—are close to the theoretical percentages—68.26 percent, 95.44 percent, and 99.73 percent—that apply to a normally distributed population. This is further evidence that the population of all DVD prices is (approximately) normally distributed and thus that the empirical rule holds for this population.

A quality improvement application: Meeting customer requirements Tolerance intervals are often used to determine whether customer requirements are being met. Customer requirements often specify that a quality characteristic must be inside an acceptable range of values called *specifications*. Specifications are written for individual measurements. For example, suppose that marketing research done by the restaurant in Chapter 1 (Example 1.3) suggests that coffee tastes best if its temperature is between 67°C and 75°C. Therefore, the customer requirements (specifications) would say that the temperature of each individual cup of coffee must be between 67°C and 75°C (this specification would typically be written as 71°C ± 4°C).

If a process is able to consistently produce output that meets customer requirements (specifications), we say that it is a **capable process** (capable of meeting the requirements). From a practical standpoint, this means that almost all of the individual measurements must be within the specification limits. Furthermore, if the population of all process measurements is approximately normally distributed, it is common practice to conclude that a process that is in statistical control is capable of meeting customer requirements if the three-sigma tolerance interval estimate $[\bar{x} \pm 3s]$ is within the specification limits. We say this because if this interval is within the specification limits, then we estimate that almost all (99.73 percent) of the process measurements are within the specification limits.

For example, recall that the runs plot of the 24 coffee temperatures in Figure 1.3 (reproduced below) indicates that the restaurant's coffee-making process is in statistical control. The mean and the standard deviation of these temperatures are $\bar{x} = 71.2083$ and s = 2.9779, respectively. It follows that we estimate that the interval

$$[\bar{x} \pm 3s] = [71.2083 \pm 3(2.9779)]$$
$$= [62.27, 80.14]$$

FIGURE 1.3 From Chapter 1   Excel Runs Plot of Coffee Temperatures: The Process Is in Statistical Control

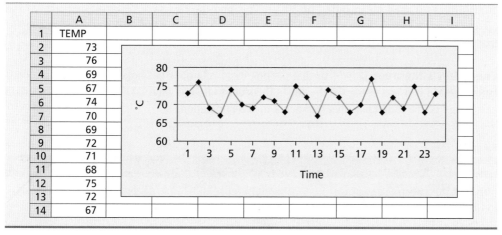

contains 99.73 percent of all coffee temperatures. Because this interval tells us that some coffee temperatures are outside the customer specifications of 67°C to 75°C, the coffee-making process is not capable of meeting customer requirements. Here, although the process is exhibiting a constant amount of variation around a constant level (or mean), the constant amount of variation—as indicated by the standard deviation of $s = 2.9779$—is too large.

Suppose that to reduce the standard deviation of the coffee temperatures, the restaurant tests a new coffee maker. A sample of 24 coffee temperatures is in control and approximately normally distributed with a mean of $\bar{x} = 71.1208$ and a reduced standard deviation of $s = 0.9597$. It follows that we estimate that the interval

$$[\bar{x} \pm 3s] = [71.1208 \pm 3(0.9597)]$$
$$= [68.24, 74.00]$$

contains 99.73 percent of all coffee temperatures. We infer that almost all coffee temperatures produced by the new coffee-making process are within the customer specifications of 65°C to 75°C. Therefore, the improved process is capable of meeting customer requirements.

Skewness and the empirical rule   The empirical rule holds for normally distributed populations. In addition, this rule also approximately holds for populations having **mound-shaped** (single-peaked) distributions that are not very positively or negatively skewed (to the right or left).

In some situations, the skewness of a mound-shaped distribution of population measurements can make it tricky to know whether and how to use the empirical rule. For example, we concluded in Example 2.8 that the distribution of 60 bottle design ratings is somewhat but not highly negatively skewed (to the left). The mean and the standard deviation of the 60 bottle design ratings are $\bar{x} = 30.35$ and $s = 3.1073$, respectively. If we actually count the number of ratings contained in each of the intervals $[\bar{x} \pm s] = [27.2, 33.5]$, $[\bar{x} \pm 2s] = [24.1, 36.6]$ and $[\bar{x} \pm 3s] = [21, 39.7]$, we find that these intervals contain, respectively, 44, 57, and 59 of the 60 ratings.

The corresponding sample percentages—73.33 percent, 95 percent, and 98.33 percent—are, respectively, greater than, approximately equal to, and less than the theoretical percentages—68.26 percent, 95.44 percent, and 99.73 percent—given by the empirical rule. Therefore, if we consider the population of all consumer ratings of the bottle design, we might estimate that (1) at least 68.26 percent of all ratings will be between 27 and 34, (2) approximately 95.44 percent of the ratings will be between 24 and 35 (a rating cannot exceed 35), and (3) less than 99.73 percent of the ratings will be between 21 and 35.

Result (3), and the low ratings of 20 and 22 found, suggest that the bottle design ratings distribution is too negatively skewed (to the left) to use the empirical rule to make conclusions about almost all ratings. However, we are not necessarily concerned about almost all ratings, because the bottle design will be successful if it appeals to a large percentage of consumers. Results (1) and (2), which describe 68.26 percent and 95.44 percent of all consumer ratings, imply that large percentages of consumer ratings will exhibit reasonably small variability around the estimated mean rating of 30.35. This and the fact that 57, or 95 percent, of the 60 ratings are at least as large as the minimum rating of 25 for a successful bottle design suggest that the bottle design will be successful.

Chebyshev's theorem   If we fear that the empirical rule does not hold for a particular population, we can consider using **Chebyshev's theorem** to find an interval that contains a specified percentage of the individual measurements in the population.

Chebyshev's Theorem

Consider any population that has mean μ and standard deviation σ. Then for any value of k greater than 1, at least $100(1 - 1/k^2)$ percent of the population measurements lie in the interval $[\mu \pm k\sigma]$.

For example, if we choose k equal to 2, then at least $100(1 - 1/2^2)\% = 100(3/4)\% = 75\%$ of the population measurements lie in the interval $[\mu \pm 2\sigma]$. As another example, if we choose k equal to 3, then at least $100(1 - 1/3^2)\% = 100(8/9)\% = 88.89\%$ of the population measurements lie in the interval $[\mu \pm 3\sigma]$. As yet a third example, suppose that we want to find an interval containing at least 99.73 percent of all population measurements. Here we would set $100(1 - 1/k^2)$ percent equal to 99.73 percent, which implies that $1 - 1/k^2 = 0.9973$. If we solve for k, we find that $k = 19.25$. This says that at least 99.73 percent of all population measurements lie in the interval $[\mu \pm 19.25\sigma]$. Unless σ is extremely small, this interval will be so long that it will tell us very little about where the population measurements lie. We conclude that Chebyshev's theorem can help us find an interval that contains a reasonably high percentage (such as 75 percent or 88.89 percent) of all population measurements. However, unless σ is extremely small, Chebyshev's theorem will not provide a useful interval that contains almost all (say, 99.73 percent) of the population measurements.

Although Chebyshev's theorem technically applies to any population, it is only of practical use when analyzing a *non-mound-shaped* (for example, a double-peaked) *population that is not extremely positively or negatively skewed (to the right or left)*. Why is this? First, *we would not use Chebyshev's theorem to describe a mound-shaped population that is not very skewed because we can use the empirical rule to do this*. In fact, the empirical rule is better for such a population because it gives us a shorter interval that will contain a given percentage of measurements. For example, if the empirical rule can be used to describe a population, the interval $[\mu \pm 3\sigma]$ will contain 99.73 percent of all measurements. On the other hand, if we use Chebyshev's theorem, the interval $[\mu \pm 19.25\sigma]$ is needed. As another example, the empirical rule tells us that 95.44 percent of all measurements lie in the interval $[\mu \pm 2\sigma]$, whereas Chebyshev's theorem tells us only that at least 75 percent of all measurements lie in this interval.

It is not appropriate to use Chebyshev's theorem—or any other result making use of the population standard deviation σ—to describe a population that is extremely skewed. This is because if a population is extremely skewed, the measurements in the long tail to the left or right will greatly inflate σ. This implies that tolerance intervals calculated using σ will be so long that they are of little use. In this case, it is best to measure variation by using percentiles, which are discussed in Section 2.4.

z scores We can determine the relative location of any value in a population or sample by using the mean and standard deviation to compute the value's z score. For any value x in a population or sample, the z score corresponding to x is defined as follows:

z Score

$$z = \frac{x - \text{Mean}}{\text{Standard deviation}}$$

The **z score**, which is also called the *standardized value*, is the number of standard deviations that x is from the mean. A positive z score says that x is above (greater than) the mean, while a negative z score says that x is below (less than) the mean. For instance, a z score equal to 2.3 says that x is 2.3 standard deviations above the mean. Similarly, a z score equal to 1.68 says that x is 1.68 standard deviations below the mean. A z score equal to zero says that x equals the mean.

A z score indicates the relative location of a value within a population or sample. For example, below we calculate the z scores for each of the revenues for the five biggest companies in Canada in 2008 as reported by *The Globe and Mail*. Recall that for these companies, the mean revenue is \$35.8 billion and the standard deviation is \$1.60 billion.

Company	Revenue	x − Mean	z score
Royal Bank of Canada	38	(38 − 35.8) = 2.2	2.2/1.60 = 1.375
Power Corp. of Canada	37	(37 − 35.8) = 1.2	1.2/1.60 = 0.75
Power Financial	36	(36 − 35.8) = 0.2	0.2/1.60 = 0.125
Manulife Financial	34	(34 − 35.8) = −1.8	−1.8/1.60 = −1.125
Great-West Life Company	34	(34 − 35.8) = −1.8	−1.8/1.60 = −1.125

These z scores tell us that the Royal Bank of Canada is the farthest above the mean, with revenues 1.375 standard deviations above the mean. If a company was found to have a z score of zero, then the company's revenues would be the same as the mean for the five companies.

Values in two different populations or samples with the same z score are the same number of standard deviations from their respective means and, therefore, have the same relative locations. For example, suppose that the mean score on the midterm exam for students in Section A of a statistics course is 65 and the standard deviation of the scores is 10. Meanwhile, the mean score on the same exam for students in Section B is 80 and the standard deviation is 5. A student in Section A who scores an 85 and a student in Section B who scores a 90 have the same relative locations within their respective sections because their z scores, $(85 − 65)/10 = 2$ and $(90 − 80)/5 = 2$, are equal.

The coefficient of variation Sometimes we need to measure the size of the standard deviation of a population or sample relative to the size of the population or sample mean. The coefficient of variation, which makes this comparison, is defined for a population or sample as follows:

Coefficient of Variation

$$\text{Coefficient of variation} = \frac{\text{Standard deviation}}{\text{Mean}} \times 100$$

The **coefficient of variation** compares populations or samples with different means and different standard deviations. For example, many financial websites give the mean and standard deviation for share fund returns. Suppose Fund X is found to have a mean return of 10.39 percent with a standard deviation of 16.18 percent, while the mean return for Fund Y is 17.7 percent with a standard deviation of 15.81 percent. Then the coefficient of variation for Fund X is $(16.18/10.39) \times 100 = 155.73$, and the coefficient of variation for Fund Y is $(15.81/17.7) \times 100 = 89.32$. This tells us that for Fund X, the standard deviation is 155.73 percent of the value of its mean return. For Fund Y, the standard deviation is 89.32 percent of the value of its mean return.

In the context of situations like the share fund comparison, the coefficient of variation is often used as a measure of risk because it measures the variation of the returns (the standard deviation) relative to the size of the mean return. For instance, although Funds X and Y have comparable standard deviations (16.18 percent versus 15.81 percent), Fund X has a higher coefficient of variation than does Fund Y (155.73 versus 89.32). This says that *relative to the mean return*, the variation in returns for Fund X is higher. That is, we would conclude that investing in Fund X is riskier than investing in Fund Y.

Exercises for Section **2.3**

CONCEPTS

2.23 Define the range, variance, and standard deviation for a population.

2.24 Discuss how the variance and the standard deviation measure variation.

2.25 Why are the variance and standard deviation usually considered more effective measures of variation than the range?

2.26 The empirical rule for a normally distributed population and Chebyshev's theorem have the same basic purpose. In your own words, explain what this purpose is.

2.27   When is a process capable, and what are process specification limits? Give an example of a situation in which process capability is important.

METHODS AND APPLICATIONS

2.28   Consider the following population of five numbers: 5, 8, 10, 12, 15. Calculate the range, variance, and standard deviation of this population.

2.29   Table 2.12 lists the number of university degrees, diplomas, and certificates granted in each province in Canada in 2003. These data are available from Statistics Canada. Calculate the range, variance, and standard deviation for these educational attainment numbers.

TABLE 2.12   University Degrees, Diplomas, and Certificates Granted by Provinces in 2003

Province	
Newfoundland and Labrador	2,975
Prince Edward Island	625
Nova Scotia	8,785
New Brunswick	4,555
Quebec	57,785
Ontario	79,000
Manitoba	5,870
Saskatchewan	5,865
Alberta	17,200
British Columbia	19,015

Source: Adapted from Statistics Canada, CANSIM, Table 477-0014.

2.30   Table 2.13 lists the aircraft movement statistics from Transport Canada for January 2006 compared to January 2005 at tower-controlled airports.
   a. Calculate the population range, variance, and standard deviation of the five percentage change values (note that negative values indicate that there was greater movement in 2005 than in 2006).
   b. Using the population of change values, compute and interpret the z score for each type of air transportation movement.

TABLE 2.13   Percentage Change of Movement of Aircraft in Tower-Controlled Airports in Canada

Air carriers	1.2
Other commercial	3.2
Private	11.0
Government	
• Civil	5.9
• Military	−1.5

Source: Based on Statistics Canada, International Trade Division, Catalogue No. 51-007, Vol. 1, No. 1, January 2006; and *Aircraft Movement Statistics: NAV CANADA Towers and Flights Service Stations*, Catalogue No. 51-007, Vol. 1, No. 1, January 2008.

2.31   In order to control costs, a company wants to study the amount of money its sales force spends entertaining clients. The following is a random sample of six entertainment expenses (lunch costs for four people)

from expense reports submitted by members of the sales force.

$157	$132	$109	$145	$125	$139

   a. Calculate $\bar{x}$, s^2, and s for the expense data. In addition, show that the two different formulas for calculating s^2 give the same result.
   b. Assuming that the distribution of entertainment expenses is approximately normally distributed, calculate estimates of tolerance intervals containing 68.26 percent, 95.44 percent, and 99.73 percent of all entertainment expenses by the sales force.
   c. If a member of the sales force submits an entertainment expense (lunch cost for four) of $190, should this expense be considered unusually high (and possibly worthy of investigation by the company)? Explain your answer.
   d. Compute and interpret the z score for each of the six entertainment expenses.

2.32   THE TRASH BAG EXAMPLE

The mean and the standard deviation of the sample of 40 trash bag breaking strengths are $\bar{x} = 22.990$ and $s = 0.7428$, respectively.
   a. What do the stem-and-leaf display and histogram in Figures 2.14 and 2.15 say about whether the empirical rule should be used to describe the trash bag breaking strengths?
   b. Use the empirical rule to calculate estimates of tolerance intervals containing 68.26 percent, 95.44 percent, and 99.73 percent of all possible trash bag breaking strengths.
   c. Does the estimate of a tolerance interval containing 99.73 percent of all breaking strengths provide evidence that almost any bag a customer might purchase will have a breaking strength that exceeds 20 kg? Explain your answer.
   d. How do the percentages of the 40 breaking strengths in Table 2.9 that actually fall into the intervals $[\bar{x} \pm s]$, $[\bar{x} \pm 2s]$, and $[\bar{x} \pm 3s]$ compare to those given by the empirical rule? Do these comparisons indicate that the statistical inferences you made in parts (b) and (c) are reasonably valid?

2.33   THE BANK CUSTOMER WAITING TIME EXAMPLE

The mean and the standard deviation of the sample of 100 bank customer waiting times are $\bar{x} = 5.46$ and $s = 2.475$, respectively.
   a. What does the histogram in Figure 2.13 say about whether the empirical rule should be used to describe the bank customer waiting times?
   b. Use the empirical rule to calculate estimates of tolerance intervals containing 68.26 percent, 95.44 percent, and 99.73 percent of all possible bank customer waiting times.
   c. Does the estimate of a tolerance interval containing 68.26 percent of all waiting times provide evidence that at least two-thirds of all customers will have to wait less than eight minutes for service? Explain your answer.
   d. How do the percentages of the 100 waiting times in Table 2.8 that actually fall into the intervals

$[\bar{x} \pm s], [\bar{x} \pm 2s],$ and $[\bar{x} \pm 3s]$ compare to those given by the empirical rule? Do these comparisons indicate that the statistical inferences you made in parts (b) and (c) are reasonably valid?

2.34   THE VIDEO GAME SATISFACTION RATING EXAMPLE

The mean and the standard deviation of the sample of 65 customer satisfaction ratings are $\bar{x} = 42.95$ and $s = 2.6424$, respectively.

a. What do the stem-and-leaf display and histogram in Figures 2.11 and 2.12 say about whether the empirical rule should be used to describe the satisfaction ratings?

b. Use the empirical rule to calculate estimates of tolerance intervals containing 68.26 percent, 95.44 percent, and 99.73 percent of all possible satisfaction ratings.

c. Does the estimate of a tolerance interval containing 99.73 percent of all satisfaction ratings provide evidence that 99.73 percent of all customers will give a satisfaction rating for the XYZ-Box game system that is at least 35 (the minimal rating of a "satisfied" customer)? Explain your answer.

d. How do the percentages of the 65 customer satisfaction ratings in Table 2.7 that actually fall into the intervals $[\bar{x} \pm s], [\bar{x} \pm 2s],$ and $[\bar{x} \pm 3s]$ compare to those given by the empirical rule? Do these comparisons indicate that the statistical inferences you made in parts (b) and (c) are reasonably valid?

2.35   Consider the 63 automated banking machine (ABM) transaction times in Table 2.14.

a. Construct a stem-and-leaf display for the 63 ABM transaction times. Describe the shape of the distribution of transaction times.

b. When we compute the sample mean and sample standard deviation for the transaction times, we find that $\bar{x} = 36.56$ and $s = 4.475$. Compute each of the intervals $[\bar{x} \pm s], [\bar{x} \pm 2s],$ and $[\bar{x} \pm 3s]$. Then count the number and find the percentage of transaction times that actually fall into each interval.

c. How do the percentages of transaction times that fall into the intervals $[\bar{x} \pm s], [\bar{x} \pm 2s],$ and $[\bar{x} \pm 3s]$ compare to those given by the empirical rule? How do the percentages of transaction times that fall into the intervals $[\bar{x} \pm 2s]$ and $[\bar{x} \pm 3s]$ compare to those given by Chebyshev's theorem?

d. Explain why the empirical rule does not describe the transaction times extremely well.

2.36   Three telecommunications companies reported their mean monthly profit and standard deviations for a year. The results are presented below.

	Company A	Company B	Company C
Mean	$10,930	$13,000	$34,450
Standard deviation	$4,196	$9,360	$4,116

a. For each company, find an interval within which you would expect 95.44 percent of all monthly profit values to fall (assuming that profits are normally distributed).

b. Using the intervals you computed in part (a), compare the three companies with respect to mean monthly profits and variability of profits.

c. Calculate the coefficient of variation for each company, and use the results to compare profits. Which company is more variable?

TABLE 2.14   ABM Transaction Times (in Seconds) for 63 Withdrawals

Transaction	Time	Transaction	Time	Transaction	Time
1	32	22	34	43	37
2	32	23	32	44	32
3	41	24	34	45	33
4	51	25	35	46	33
5	42	26	33	47	40
6	39	27	42	48	35
7	33	28	46	49	33
8	43	29	52	50	39
9	35	30	36	51	34
10	33	31	37	52	34
11	33	32	32	53	33
12	32	33	39	54	38
13	42	34	36	55	41
14	34	35	41	56	34
15	37	36	32	57	35
16	37	37	33	58	35
17	33	38	34	59	37
18	35	39	38	60	39
19	40	40	32	61	44
20	36	41	35	62	40
21	32	42	33	63	39

2.37 The following table gives 18 measurements of a critical dimension for an automobile part. Here one part has been randomly selected each hour from the previous hour's production, and the measurements are given in time order. Assume that the process producing this part is in statistical control.

Hour	Measurement (cm)	Hour	Measurement (cm)
1	3.005	10	3.005
2	3.020	11	3.015
3	2.980	12	2.995
4	3.015	13	3.020
5	2.995	14	3.000
6	3.010	15	2.990
7	3.000	16	2.985
8	2.985	17	3.020
9	3.025	18	2.985

a. When we compute the sample mean and sample standard deviation of the 18 dimensions, we obtain $\bar{x} = 3.0028$ and $s = 0.01437$, respectively. Assuming the dimensions are mound-shaped, use these values to compute an estimated tolerance interval that you would expect to contain almost all (99.73 percent) of the auto part's dimensions. Based on this interval, can you conclude that the process is capable of meeting specifications of 3.00 ± 0.03—that is, 2.97 to 3.03? Explain your answer.

b. After a research and development program is carried out to improve the manufacturing process that produces the auto part, the following 18 measurements of the dimension are obtained (they are given in time order). Does the process appear to be in statistical control? Justify your answer.

Hour	Measurement (cm)	Hour	Measurement (cm)
1	3.010	10	3.005
2	3.005	11	2.995
3	2.990	12	2.995
4	3.010	13	3.010
5	2.995	14	3.000
6	2.990	15	2.990
7	3.000	16	2.995
8	2.990	17	3.010
9	3.010	18	3.000

c. When we compute the sample mean and sample standard deviation of the 18 observed dimensions from the improved process, we obtain $\bar{x} = 3$ and $s = 0.00786$, respectively. Assuming the measurements are normally distributed, use these results to compute an estimated tolerance interval that you would expect to contain almost all (99.73 percent) of the dimensions produced by the improved process. Based on this interval, can you conclude that the improved process is capable of meeting specifications of 3.00 ± 0.03—that is, 2.97 to 3.03? Explain your answer.

2.4 PERCENTILES, QUARTILES, AND BOX-AND-WHISKERS DISPLAYS

Percentiles, quartiles, and five-number displays Here we consider percentiles and their applications. We begin by defining the pth percentile.

For a set of measurements arranged in increasing order, the **pth percentile** is a value such that p percent of the measurements fall at or below the value, and $(100 - p)$ percent of the measurements fall at or above the value.

Percentiles are used in a variety of settings. For example, many standardized tests used in selection settings (such as entry to graduate programs, employment screening, etc.) present the test scores for individuals as percentiles. There are various procedures for calculating percentiles. One procedure is as follows: To calculate the pth percentile for a set of n measurements, we first arrange the measurements in increasing order (by, for example, constructing a stem-and-leaf display). Then we calculate the index $i = (p/100)n$. If i is not an integer, the next integer greater than i denotes the position of the pth percentile in the ordered arrangement. If i is an integer, then the pth percentile is the average of the measurements in positions i and $i + 1$ in the ordered arrangement. For example, Figure 2.23(a) presents the stem-and-leaf display of 65 test scores. In order to calculate the 75th percentile of these 65 scores, we calculate the index $i = (75/100)65 = 48.75$. Because $i = 48.75$ is not an integer, the 75th percentile is the 49th score in the stem-and-leaf display. Counting up to the 49th score in this display, we find that the 75th percentile is 21 (see Figure 2.23(a)). This implies that we estimate that approximately 75 percent of all scores are less than or equal to 21.

FIGURE 2.23   Using Stem-and-Leaf Displays to Find Percentiles and Five-Number Summaries

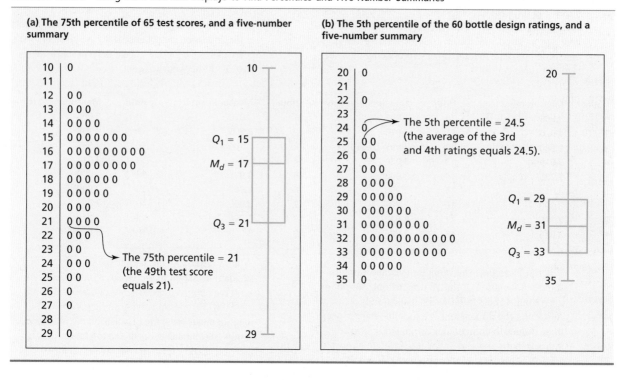

(a) The 75th percentile of 65 test scores, and a five-number summary

(b) The 5th percentile of the 60 bottle design ratings, and a five-number summary

As another example, Figure 2.23(b) presents the stem-and-leaf display of the 60 bottle design ratings. In order to calculate the fifth percentile of these 60 ratings, we calculate the index $i = (5/100)60 = 3$. Because $i = 3$ is an integer, the fifth percentile is the average of the third and fourth ratings in the stem-and-leaf display. Counting up to these ratings in this display, we find that the fifth percentile is $(24 + 25)/2 = 24.5$ (see Figure 2.23[b]). Since any rating is a whole number, we estimate that approximately 5 percent of all ratings are 24 or less and approximately 95 percent of all ratings are 25 or more.

In general, unless percentiles correspond to very high or very low percentages, they are resistant (like the median) to extreme values. For example, the 75th percentile of the test scores would remain 21 even if the three largest scores—26, 27, and 29—were, instead, 35, 56, and 84. On the other hand, the standard deviation in this situation would increase from 3.9612 to 10.2119. In general, if a population is highly positively or negatively skewed (to the right or left, respectively), it can be best to describe the variation of the population by using various percentiles. For example, we might describe the variation of the yearly incomes of all people in Canada by using the 10th, 25th, 50th, 75th, and 90th percentiles of these incomes.

One appealing way to describe the variation of a set of measurements is to divide the data into four parts, each containing approximately 25 percent of the measurements. This can be done by defining the first, second, and third quartiles as follows:

First, Second, and Third Quartiles

The **first quartile**, denoted Q_1, is the 25th percentile.
The **second quartile (or median)**, denoted M_d, is the 50th percentile.
The **third quartile**, denoted Q_3, is the 75th percentile.

Note that the second quartile is simply another name for the median. Furthermore, the procedure we have described here that would be used to find the 50th percentile (second quartile) will always give the same result as the previously described procedure for finding the median. For example, to find the second quartile of the 65 test scores, we find the 50th percentile by calculating $i = (50/100)65 = 32.5$, which says that the second quartile is the 33rd score in the stem-and-leaf display of Figure 2.23(a). Counting up to the 33rd score in the display, we find that the second quartile equals 17, which is the median of the scores.

Because $i = (25/100)65 = 16.25$, the first quartile (25th percentile) of the 65 test scores is the 17th score in the stem-and-leaf display of Figure 2.23(a). Therefore, $Q_1 = 15$. Remembering that the median of the scores is 17, and that the 75th percentile of the scores is 21, the quartiles are $Q_1 = 15$, $M_d = 17$, and $Q_3 = 21$.

We often describe a set of measurements by using a five-number summary. The summary consists of (1) the smallest measurement; (2) the first quartile, Q_1; (3) the median, M_d; (4) the third quartile, Q_3; and (5) the largest measurement. It is easy to graphically depict a five-number summary; we have done this for the 65 test scores beside the stem-and-leaf display of Figure 2.23(a). Notice that we have drawn a vertical line extending from the smallest score to the largest score. In addition, a rectangle is drawn that extends from Q_1 to Q_3, and a horizontal line is drawn to indicate the location of the median. The summary divides the scores into four parts, with the middle 50 percent of the scores depicted by the rectangle. The summary indicates that the largest 25 percent of the scores is more spread out than the smallest 25 percent, and that the second-largest 25 percent of the scores is more spread out than the second-smallest 25 percent. Overall, the summary indicates that the test scores are somewhat positively skewed (to the right).

As another example, for the 60 bottle design ratings, $Q_1 = 29$, $M_d = 31$, and $Q_3 = 33$. The graphical five-number summary of the ratings is shown alongside the stem-and-leaf display of the ratings in Figure 2.23(b). The summary shows that the smallest 25 percent of the ratings is more spread out than any of the other quarters of the ratings, and that the other three quarters are equally spread out. Overall, the summary shows that the bottle design ratings are negatively skewed (to the left).

Using the first and third quartiles, we define the **interquartile range** to be $IQR = Q_3 - Q_1$. This quantity can be interpreted as the length of the interval that contains the *middle 50 percent* of the measurements. For instance, Figure 2.23(a) tells us that the interquartile range of the sample of 65 test scores is $Q_3 - Q_1 = 21 - 15 = 6$. This says that we estimate that the middle 50 percent of all scores fall within a range of six points.

The procedure we have presented for calculating the first and third quartiles is not the only procedure for computing these quantities. In fact, several procedures exist, and, for example, different statistical computer packages use several somewhat different methods for computing the quartiles. One procedure calculates what are called *lower* and *upper hinges* and then defines the first quartile to be the lower hinge and the third quartile to be the upper hinge. In general, the different methods for computing the first and third quartiles sometimes produce somewhat different results. However, no matter what procedure is used to compute the quartiles, the objective is to divide the data into four parts, each containing approximately 25 percent of the measurements.

Box-and-whiskers displays (box plots) A more sophisticated modification of the graphical five-number summary is called a *box-and-whiskers display* (sometimes called a *box plot*). Such a display is constructed by using Q_1, M_d, Q_3, and the interquartile range. As an example, consider the following 20 customer satisfaction ratings on an interval scale from 1 (unsatisfied) to 10 (completely satisfied):

1   3   5   5   7   8   8   8   8   8   8   9   9   9   9   9   10   10   10   10

It can be shown that $Q_1 = 7.5$, $M_d = 8$, $Q_3 = 9$, and $IQR = Q_3 - Q_1 = 9 - 7.5 = 1.5$ for these ratings. To construct a box-and-whiskers display, we first draw a box that extends from Q_1 to Q_3. As shown in Figure 2.24(a), for the satisfaction ratings data, this box extends from $Q_1 = 7.5$ to $Q_3 = 9$. The box contains the middle 50 percent of the data set. Next, a vertical line is drawn through the box at the value of the median M_d (sometimes a plus sign [+] is plotted at the median instead of a vertical line). This line divides the data set into two roughly

FIGURE **2.24**   A Box-and-Whiskers Display of the Satisfaction Ratings

(a) Constructing the display

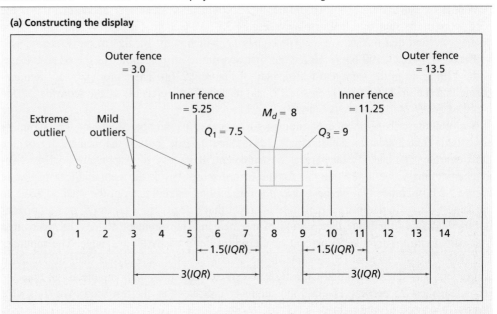

(b) MegaStat output

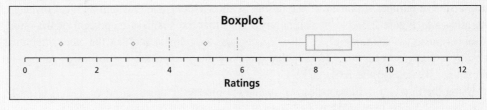

equal parts. We next define what we call **inner fences** and **outer fences**. The inner fences are located $1.5 \times IQR$ below Q_1 and $1.5 \times IQR$ above Q_3. For the satisfaction ratings data, the inner fences are

$$Q_1 - 1.5(IQR) = 7.5 - 1.5(1.5) = 5.25 \quad \text{and} \quad Q_3 + 1.5(IQR) = 9 + 1.5(1.5) = 11.25$$

The outer fences are located $3 \times IQR$ below Q_1 and $3 \times IQR$ above Q_3. For the satisfaction ratings data, the outer fences are

$$Q_1 - 3(IQR) = 7.5 - 3(1.5) = 3.0 \quad \text{and} \quad Q_3 + 3(IQR) = 9 + 3(1.5) = 13.5$$

The inner and outer fences help us to draw the plot's whiskers—dashed lines extending below Q_1 and above Q_3 (as in Figure 2.24(a)). One whisker is drawn from Q_1 to the smallest measurement between the inner fences. For the satisfaction ratings data, this whisker extends from $Q_1 = 7.5$ down to 7, because 7 is the smallest rating between the inner fences 5.25 and 11.25. The other whisker is drawn from Q_3 to the largest measurement between the inner fences. For the satisfaction ratings data, this whisker extends from $Q_3 = 9$ up to 10, because 10 is the largest rating between the inner fences 5.25 and 11.25.

The inner and outer fences are also used to identify outliers. An outlier is a measurement that is separated from (that is, different from) most of the other measurements in the data set. Measurements that are located between the inner and outer fences are considered to be **mild outliers**, whereas measurements that are located outside the outer fences are considered to be **extreme outliers**. In Figure 2.24, we indicate the locations of mild outliers by plotting these measurements with the symbol *, and we indicate the locations of extreme outliers by plotting these measurements with the symbol o. For the satisfaction ratings data, the ratings 3 and 5 are mild outliers (*) because these ratings are between the inner fence of 5.25 and the outer fence of 3.0. The rating 1 is an extreme outlier (o) because this rating is outside the outer fence 3.0. These outliers are plotted in Figure 2.24(a).

Part (b) of Figure 2.24 gives the MegaStat output of the box-and-whiskers plot. Notice that MegaStat identifies the median by using a vertical line. In addition, MegaStat plots all outliers using the same symbol and marks the inner and outer fences using vertical dashed lines. Note here that MegaStat computes the quartiles Q_1 and Q_3 and the inner and outer fences using methods that differ slightly from the methods we have described. The MegaStat Help menus describe how the calculations are done. Following is a summary of how to construct a box-and-whiskers display.

Constructing a Box-and-Whiskers Display (Box Plot)

1. Draw a box that extends from the first quartile Q_1 to the third quartile Q_3. Also draw a vertical line through the box located at the median M_d.

2. Determine the values of the inner fences and outer fences. The inner fences are located $1.5 \times IQR$ below Q_1 and $1.5 \times IQR$ above Q_3. That is, the inner fences are

$$Q_1 - 1.5(IQR) \quad \text{and} \quad Q_3 + 1.5(IQR)$$

The outer fences are located $3 \times IQR$ below Q_1 and $3 \times IQR$ above Q_3. That is, the outer fences are

$$Q_1 - 3(IQR) \quad \text{and} \quad Q_3 + 3(IQR)$$

3. Draw whiskers as dashed lines that extend below Q_1 and above Q_3. Draw one whisker from Q_1 to the *smallest* measurement that is between the inner fences. Draw the other whisker from Q_3 to the *largest* measurement that is between the inner fences.

4. Measurements that are located between the inner and outer fences are called *mild outliers*. Plot these measurements using the symbol*.

5. Measurements that are located outside the outer fences are called *extreme outliers*. Plot these measurements using the symbol o.

When interpreting a box-and-whiskers display, keep several points in mind. First, the box (between Q_1 and Q_3) contains the middle 50 percent of the data. Second, the median (which is inside the box) divides the data into two roughly equal parts. Third, if one of the whiskers is longer than the other, the data set is probably skewed in the direction of the longer whisker. Last, observations designated as outliers should be investigated. Understanding the causes behind the outlying observations will often provide useful information. For instance, understanding why several of the satisfaction ratings in the box plot of Figure 2.24 are substantially lower than the great majority of the ratings may suggest actions that can improve the DVD recorder manufacturer's product and/or service. Outliers can also be caused by inaccurate measuring, reporting, or plotting of the data. Such possibilities should be investigated, and incorrect data should be adjusted or eliminated.

Generally, a box plot clearly depicts the central tendency, variability, and overall range of a set of measurements. A box plot also portrays whether the measurements are symmetrically distributed. However, the exact shape of the distribution is better portrayed by a stem-and-leaf display and/or a histogram. For instance, Figure 2.25 shows the MegaStat output of the stem-and-leaf display and box plot of scores on a 100-point statistics exam. We see that although the box plot in Figure 2.25 tells us that the exam scores are somewhat negatively skewed with a tail to the left, it does not reveal the double-peaked nature of the exam score distribution. On the other hand, the stem-and-leaf display clearly shows that this distribution is double-peaked. In summary, graphical five-number summaries and box-and-whiskers displays are perhaps best used to compare different sets of measurements, for example, 3-month returns for investment funds of all types versus 12-month returns.

FIGURE **2.25**   MegaStat Output of a Stem-and-Leaf Display and Box Plot of Exam Scores

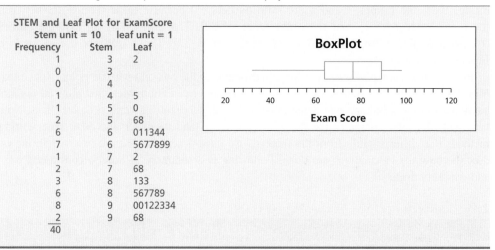

Exercises for Section **2.4**

CONCEPTS

2.38 **a.** Explain each of the following in your own words: a percentile; the first quartile, Q_1; the third quartile, Q_3; and the interquartile range, IQR.

b. What percentage of the data is found between the first quartile, Q_1, and the third quartile, Q_3?

2.39 Suppose that you are using a box-and-whiskers display to depict a population or sample of measurements. How would you interpret each of the following?

a. The whisker to the right is much longer than the whisker to the left.

b. The interquartile range is much longer than either of the whiskers and there are no outliers.

c. The distance between Q_1 and the median is far less than the distance between the median and Q_3.

d. The interquartile range is very short.

METHODS AND APPLICATIONS

2.40 Consider the 65 game system satisfaction ratings, the 40 trash bag breaking strengths, and the 100 bank customer waiting times.

a. Using the three following stem-and-leaf displays of these data sets, find for each data set

(1) The 90th percentile.

(2) The median.

(3) The first quartile.

(4) The third quartile.

(5) The 10th percentile.

(6) The interquartile range.

b. Construct a five-number summary and a box-and-whisker display for each data set.

MegaStat Stem-and-Leaf Display of the 65 Satisfaction Ratings

Stem-and-Leaf Plot for Satisfaction Ratings

Stem unit = 1   leaf unit = 0.1

Frequency	Stem	Leaf
1	36	0
0	37	
3	38	000
4	39	0000
5	40	00000
6	41	000000
6	42	000000
8	43	00000000
12	44	000000000000
9	45	000000000
7	46	0000000
3	47	000
1	48	0
65		

MegaStat Stem-and-Leaf Display of the Waiting Times

Stem-and-Leaf Plot for Waiting Times

Stem unit = 1   leaf unit = 0.1

Frequency	Stem	Leaf
2	0	4 8
6	1	1 3 4 6 8 8
9	2	0 2 3 4 5 7 8 9 9
11	3	1 2 4 5 6 7 7 8 8 9 9
17	4	0 0 1 2 3 3 3 4 4 5 5 5 6 7 7 8 9
15	5	0 1 1 2 2 3 4 4 5 6 6 7 8 8 8
13	6	1 1 2 3 3 3 4 5 5 6 7 7 8
10	7	0 2 2 3 4 4 5 7 8 9
7	8	0 1 3 4 6 6 7
6	9	1 2 3 5 8 9
3	10	2 7 9
1	11	6
100		

MegaStat Stem-and-Leaf Display of the Breaking Strengths

Stem-and-Leaf Plot for Strength
Stem unit = 1   leaf unit = 0.1

Frequency	Stem	Leaf
1	21	3
2	21	6 9
6	22	0 0 2 3 4 4
9	22	5 5 5 6 7 7 8 8 9
12	23	0 0 0 1 1 1 2 2 3 3 4 4
6	23	5 6 6 8 9 9
3	24	1 2 3
1	24	5
40		

2.41 Statistics Canada provides data about the average number of days lost per worker by cause for each province. Listed in the table below are the values of days lost for each province because of "Personal or Family Responsibility" (PorF) and "Illness or Disability" (IorD) for 2004.

   a. For the Personal or Family Responsibility values, compute the mean, median, mode, standard deviation, variance, and range.

   b. Based on the values computed in part (a), describe the shape of the distribution (this exercise might be easier to complete if you create a stem-and-leaf display).

   c. For the Illness or Disability values, compute the mean, median, mode, standard deviation, variance, and range.

   d. Based on the values computed in part (c), describe the shape of the distribution (this exercise might be easier to complete if you create a stem-and-leaf display).

Average Number of Days Lost per Worker by Cause

Province	PorF	IorD
Newfoundland and Labrador	1.5	8.8
Prince Edward Island	1.6	6.0
Nova Scotia	1.9	9.1
New Brunswick	1.7	8.0
Quebec	1.4	9.4
Ontario	1.9	6.7
Manitoba	1.8	8.0
Saskatchewan	2.2	8.0
Alberta	1.9	5.6
British Columbia	1.5	7.3

Source: Adapted from Statistics Canada, CANSIM, Table 279-0029, 2004.

2.42 In Section 2.4, we presented a commonly accepted way to compute the first, second, and third quartiles. Some statisticians, however, advocate an alternative method for computing Q_1 and Q_3. This method defines the first quartile, Q_1, as the *lower hinge* and the third quartile, Q_3, as the *upper hinge*. In order to calculate these quantities for a set of n measurements, we first arrange the measurements in increasing order. Then, if n is even, the lower hinge is the median of the smallest $n/2$ measurements, and the upper hinge is the median of the largest $n/2$ measurements. If n is odd, we insert M_d into the data set to obtain a set of $n + 1$ measurements. Then the lower hinge is the median of the smallest $(n + 1)/2$ measurements and the upper hinge is the median of the largest $(n + 1)/2$ measurements.

   a. Consider a sample of $n = 20$ customer satisfaction ratings:

1 3 5 5 7 8 8 8 8 8   8 9 9 9 9 9 10 10 10 10

The smallest 10 ratings   The largest 10 ratings

   Using the method presented in Section 2.4, find Q_1 and Q_3. Then find the lower hinge and the upper hinge for the satisfaction ratings. How do your results compare?

   b. Consider the following sample of $n = 11$ doctors' salaries (in thousands of dollars):

127 132 138 141 146 152 154 171 177 192 241

   Using the method presented in Section 2.4, find Q_1 and Q_3. The median of the 11 salaries is $M_d = 152$. If we insert this median into the data set, we obtain the following set of $n + 1 = 12$ salaries:

127 132 138 141 146 152   152 154 171 177 192 241

The smallest 6 salaries   The largest 6 salaries

   Find the lower hinge and the upper hinge for the salaries. Compare your values of Q_1 and Q_3 with the lower and upper hinges.

   c. For the 11 doctors' salaries, which quantities —Q_1, M_d, and Q_3 as defined in Section 2.4 or the lower hinge, M_d, and the upper hinge—in your opinion best divide the salaries into four parts?

2.5 DESCRIBING QUALITATIVE DATA

Bar charts and pie charts Recall that when we employ a qualitative or categorical variable, we simply record into which of several categories a population element falls. For example, for each automobile produced in Canada, we might record the manufacturer—Chrysler, Ford, General Motors, or some other manufacturer. We often display such data graphically. For instance, Table 2.15 gives the number of military personnel for each province in Canada in 2011 according to Statistics Canada. Figure 2.26 provides the same information in both a **bar chart** (a) and a pie chart (b) format.

TABLE **2.15**   Military Personnel

	2011 Annual average number of employees*
Canada and outside Canada	**93,914**
Newfoundland and Labrador	1,323
Prince Edward Island	247
Nova Scotia	10,740
New Brunswick	6,298
Quebec	18,534
Ontario	31,817
Manitoba	4,116
Saskatchewan	1,180
Alberta	9,823
British Columbia	7,886
Yukon	x
Northwest Territories	215
Nunavut	x
Outside Canada	1,725

*Civilian employees are excluded. Reservists are included as of January 1974.
x: Suppressed to meet the confidentiality requirements of the *Statistics Act*.

Notes:
—Employment data are not in full-time equivalent and do not distinguish between full-time and part-time employees.
—As at December 31.

Source: Statistics Canada, CANSIM, Table 183-0004 and Catalogue No. 68-213-XIB.

In general, bar charts and pie charts are convenient ways to summarize the percentages of population units that are contained in several different categories.

Estimating proportions   Suppose that a population unit can fall into one of several categories. We are often interested in a specific category, and, in such cases, we often want to estimate

p = Proportion of all population elements that are contained in the category of interest

In order to estimate this proportion, we can randomly select a sample from the population. Then the **sample proportion**

$\hat{p}$ = Proportion of the sample elements that are contained in the category of interest

is a reasonable point estimate of the **population proportion p**.

FIGURE **2.26**   Number of Military Personnel by Province and Territory

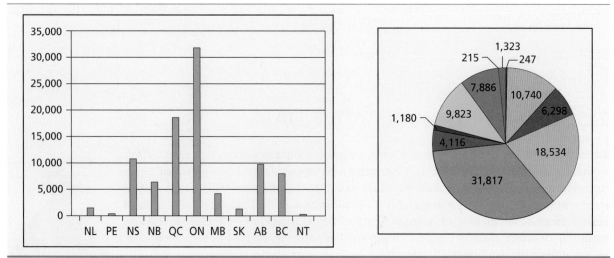

In Examples 2.11 and 2.12, we introduce two new situational examples that illustrate estimating a population proportion p.

Example 2.11 The Marketing Ethics Example: Estimating Marketing Researchers' Disapproval Rates

In the book *Essentials of Marketing Research*, Dillon, Madden, and Firtle discuss a survey of marketing professionals, the results of which were originally published by Ishmael P. Akaah and Edward A. Riordan in the *Journal of Marketing Research*. In the study, marketing researchers (participants) were presented with various scenarios involving ethical issues such as confidentiality, conflict of interest, and social acceptability. The participants were asked to indicate whether they approved or disapproved of the actions described in each scenario. For instance, one scenario that involved the issue of confidentiality was described as follows:

Use of ultraviolet ink A project director went to the marketing research director's office and requested permission to use an ultraviolet ink to precode a questionnaire for a mail survey. The project director pointed out that although the cover letter promised confidentiality, respondent identification was needed to permit adequate cross-tabulations of the data. The marketing research director gave approval.

Of the 205 marketing researchers who participated in the survey, 117 said they disapproved of the action taken in the scenario.

In this situation, we would like to make an inference about the population of all marketing researchers. Specifically, we want to estimate the population proportion:

p = Proportion of all marketing researchers who disapprove of
the actions taken in the ultraviolet ink scenario

Because 117 of the 205 surveyed marketing researchers said they disapproved, the sample proportion

$$\hat{p} = \frac{117}{205} = 0.57$$

is the point estimate of p. This point estimate says we estimate that p, the proportion of all marketing researchers who disapprove, is 0.57. That is, we estimate that 57 percent of all marketing researchers disapprove of the action taken in the ultraviolet ink scenario.

Example 2.12 The Electronic Article Surveillance Example: Estimating Consumer Reaction to False Alarms

In an article entitled "Consumer responses to electronic article surveillance alarms" in the *Journal of Retailing*, Scott Dawson studied the unintended effects of false electronic article surveillance (EAS) alarms. EAS, an important weapon used by retailers to combat shoplifting, places a small sensor on an item of merchandise. If a shoplifter attempts to exit the store with the item, an electronic alarm is set off by the sensor. When an item is legitimately purchased, the sales clerk removes the sensor to prevent the alarm from sounding when the customer exits the store. Sometimes, however, the clerk forgets to remove the sensor during the purchase. This results in a false alarm when the customer exits—an embarrassing situation for the customer. Such false alarms occur quite frequently. In fact, according to Dawson's article, "nearly half of all consumers have experienced an accidental EAS alarm."

Dawson conducted a survey to study consumer reaction to such false alarms. Based on a systematic random sample of 250 consumers, 40 of these consumers said that if they were to set off an EAS alarm because store personnel did not deactivate the merchandise, "they would never shop at the store again."

Suppose we want to estimate p, the population proportion of all consumers who would say they would never shop at the store again if subjected to an EAS false alarm. Since 40 of the 250 sampled consumers said they would never shop at the store again, the sample proportion $\hat{p} = 40/250 = 0.16$ is the point estimate of p. This point estimate says we estimate that 16 percent of all consumers would say they would never shop at the store again if subjected to an EAS false alarm.

Finally, suppose a retailer is considering installing an EAS system. In an attempt to convince the retailer to purchase the system, a company that markets EAS systems claims that no more than 5 percent of consumers would say that they would never shop at a store again if they were subjected to an EAS false alarm. Based on Dawson's survey results, the retailer would have a hard time believing the company's claim. That is, the sample proportion $\hat{p} = 0.16$ suggests that more than 5 percent of all consumers would say that they would never shop at the store again. But is the evidence here conclusive? We will address this question in later chapters.

The Pareto chart A **Pareto chart** is used to help identify important quality problems and opportunities for process improvement. By using these charts we can prioritize problem-solving activities. The Pareto chart is named for Vilfredo Pareto (1848–1923), an Italian economist. Pareto suggested that in many economies, most of the wealth is held by a small minority of the population. It has been found that the Pareto principle often applies to defects. That is, only a few defect types account for most of a product's quality problems.

Here defects can be divided into two categories—the vital few and the trivial many. The vital few are the small number of defects that account for a large percentage of the total, while the trivial many are the large number of defects that account for the small remaining percentage of the total. If the vital few defects are very costly to an organization, it may want to work on eliminating their causes before working to solve other problems.

To illustrate the use of a Pareto chart, suppose that a jam producer wants to evaluate the labels being placed on 500-mL jars of raspberry jam. Every day for two weeks, all defective labels found on inspection are classified by type of defect. If a label has more than one defect, the type of defect that is most noticeable will be recorded. The Excel output in Figure 2.27 presents the frequencies and percentages of the types of defects observed over the two-week period.

In general, the first step in setting up a Pareto chart summarizing data concerning types of defects (or categories) is to construct a frequency table like the one in Figure 2.27. Defects or categories should be listed at the left of the table in *decreasing order by frequencies*—the defect with the highest frequency will be at the top of the table, the defect with the second-highest frequency below the first, and so forth. If an "other" category is employed, it should be placed at the bottom of the table. The "other" category should make up less than 50 percent of the total of the frequencies, and the frequency for the "other" category should not exceed the frequency for the defect at the top of the table. If the frequency for the "other" category is too high, data should be collected so that the "other" category can be broken down into new categories. Once the frequency and the percentage for each category are determined, a cumulative percentage for each category is computed. As illustrated in Figure 2.27, the cumulative percentage for a particular category is the sum

FIGURE 2.27 Excel Frequency Table and Pareto Chart of Labelling Defects

Frequency Table

Type of Defect	Freq.	Percent	Cum. Percent
Crooked Label	78	36.97%	37.0%
Missing Label	45	21.33%	58.3%
Printing Error	33	15.64%	73.9%
Loose Label	23	10.90%	84.8%
Wrinkled Label	14	6.64%	91.5%
Smudged Label	6	2.84%	94.3%
Other	12	5.69%	100.0%
Total	211	100%	

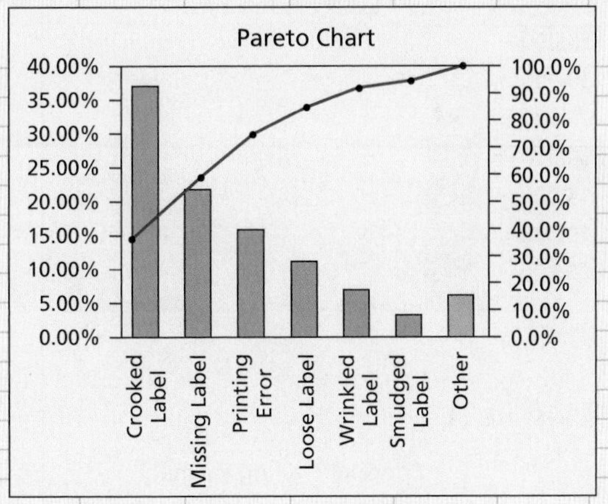

of the percentages corresponding to the particular category and the categories that are above that category in the table.

The Pareto chart is a bar chart. Different kinds of defects or problems are listed on the horizontal scale. The heights of the bars on the vertical scale typically represent the frequency of occurrence (or the percentage of occurrence) for each defect or problem. The bars are arranged in decreasing height from left to right, so the most frequent defect will be at the far left, the next most frequent defect to its right, and so forth. If an "other" category is employed, its bar is placed at the far right. In the Pareto chart for the labelling defects data given in Figure 2.27, the heights of the bars represent the percentages of occurrences for the different labelling defects, and the vertical scale on the far left corresponds to these percentages. The chart graphically illustrates that crooked labels, missing labels, and printing errors are the most frequent labelling defects.

As is also illustrated in Figure 2.27, a Pareto chart is sometimes augmented by plotting a cumulative percentage point for each bar in the Pareto chart. The vertical coordinate of this cumulative percentage point equals the cumulative percentage in the frequency table corresponding to the bar. The cumulative percentage points corresponding to the different bars are connected by line segments, and a vertical scale corresponding to the cumulative percentages is placed on the far right. Examining the cumulative percentage points in Figure 2.27, we see that crooked and missing labels make up 58.3 percent of the labelling defects, and crooked labels, missing labels, and printing errors make up 73.9 percent of the labelling defects.

Exercises for Section 2.5

CONCEPTS

2.43 Find an example of a pie chart or a bar chart in a newspaper or magazine. What information is conveyed by the chart?

2.44 What is a population proportion? Give an example of a population proportion that might interest you in the profession you intend to enter.

METHODS AND APPLICATIONS

2.45 Statistics Canada reports on exports to other countries on a monthly basis. In Figure 2.28(a), the export values to our principal trading partners for March 2006 are presented in table form and in Excel bar and pie charts. Write an analysis of which of these visual presentations is the most informative and why.

FIGURE 2.28 Export and Import Values for Canada's Principal Trading Partners, 2006

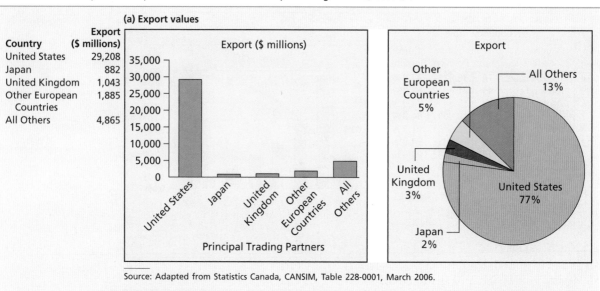

(a) Export values

Country	Export ($ millions)
United States	29,208
Japan	882
United Kingdom	1,043
Other European Countries	1,885
All Others	4,865

Source: Adapted from Statistics Canada, CANSIM, Table 228-0001, March 2006.

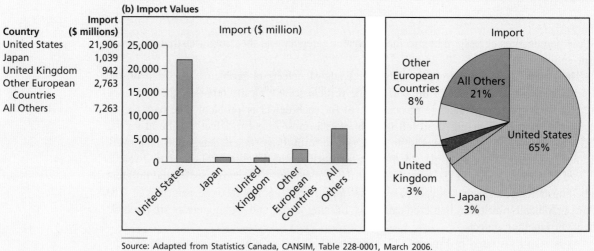

(b) Import Values

Country	Import ($ millions)
United States	21,906
Japan	1,039
United Kingdom	942
Other European Countries	2,763
All Others	7,263

Source: Adapted from Statistics Canada, CANSIM, Table 228-0001, March 2006.

2.46 Figure 2.28(b) presents the import values for Canada's principal trading partners for March 2006 in table form and in Excel bar and pie charts. Write an analysis of which of these visual presentation is the most informative and why.

2.47 Which chart (bar or pie chart) would you use to compare exports versus imports in Exercises 2.45 and 2.46?

2.48 THE MARKETING ETHICS EXAMPLE: CONFLICT OF INTEREST

Consider the marketing ethics study described in Example 2.11. One of the scenarios presented to the 205 marketing researchers is as follows:

A marketing testing firm to which X company gives most of its business recently went public. The marketing research director of X company had been looking for a good investment and proceeded to buy $20,000 of the marketing testing firm's shares. The firm continues as X company's leading supplier for testing.

Of the 205 marketing researchers who participated in the ethics survey, 111 said that they disapproved of the action taken in the scenario. Use this sample result to compute a point estimate of the proportion of all marketing researchers who disapprove of the action taken in this conflict of interest scenario.

2.49 The following data provide the percentage of funds in each of six categories in a mutual fund. Construct a pie chart of these data.

Category	% of Fund
Cash	0.1
Fixed Income	0.2
Canadian Equity	89.6
U.S. Equity	5.1
International Equity	0.7
Other	4.3

2.6 USING SCATTER PLOTS TO STUDY RELATIONSHIPS BETWEEN VARIABLES

Statistical methods are often used to study and quantify relationships between variables. The purpose of studying such relationships is often to describe, predict, or control a variable of interest called the **dependent variable** (which is denoted y). We accomplish this by relating y to one or more other variables that are called **independent variables**. One way to relate variables is to perform regression analysis. This technique allows us to find an equation that relates y to the independent variable(s). Then, for instance, we might use the regression equation to predict y on the basis of the independent variable(s). We explain regression analysis in detail in Chapters 11 and 12. A simpler way to relate variables is to graphically study relationships between the variables. We discuss the graphical approach in this section.

One way to explore the relationship between a dependent variable y and an independent variable (denoted x) is to make a **scatter plot**, or **scatter diagram**, of y versus x. First, data concerning the two variables are observed in pairs. To construct the scatter plot, each value of y is plotted against its corresponding value of x. If y and x are related, the plot shows us the direction of the relationship. That is, y could be positively related to x (y increases as x increases, as is seen in Example 2.13) or y could be negatively related to x (y decreases as x increases).

Example 2.13 Requirements of a Bulk Chemical Product

A manufacturer produces a bulk chemical product. Customer requirements state that this product must have a specified viscosity when melted at a temperature of 150°C (viscosity measures how thick and gooey the product is when melted). Chemical XB-135 is used in the production of this chemical product, and the company's chemists feel that the amount of chemical XB-135 may be related to viscosity. In order to verify and quantify this relationship, 24 batches of the product are produced. The amount (x) of chemical XB-135 (in kilograms) is varied from batch to batch and the viscosity (y) obtained for each batch is measured. Table 2.16 gives (in time order) the values of x and the corresponding values of y obtained for the 24 batches. The Excel output of a scatter plot of y versus x is given in Figure 2.29. The scatter plot indicates a strong positive relationship between y and x—that is, as the amount of chemical XB-135 used is increased, the viscosity of the product increases.

We must now be careful. It would be tempting to conclude that increases in the amount of chemical XB-135 *cause* increases in viscosity. However, this is not necessarily the case. Perhaps some other factor could be causing the apparent relationship. For instance, the 24 batches were produced in time order. If some other variable that affects viscosity (such as temperature or pressure in the reaction chamber, or the composition of a raw material) is

TABLE 2.16   Viscosity Data for 24 Batches of a Chemical Product Produced on August 1, 2013

Batch	Kilograms of Chemical XB-135 (x)	Viscosity (y)	Batch	Kilograms of Chemical XB-135 (x)	Viscosity (y)
1	10.0	31.76	13	11.2	32.93
2	10.0	31.91	14	11.2	33.19
3	10.2	32.02	15	11.4	33.35
4	10.2	31.85	16	11.4	32.76
5	10.4	32.17	17	11.6	33.33
6	10.4	32.30	18	11.6	33.19
7	10.6	32.60	19	11.8	33.28
8	10.6	32.15	20	11.8	33.57
9	10.8	32.52	21	12.0	33.60
10	10.8	32.46	22	12.0	33.43
11	11.0	32.41	23	12.2	33.91
12	11.0	32.77	24	12.2	33.76

FIGURE 2.29   Excel Output of a Scatter Plot of Viscosity versus Amount of Chemical XB-135

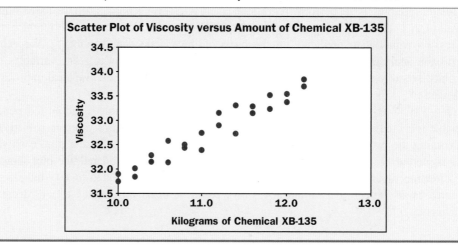

changing over time, this change could be responsible for the observed increases in viscosity. Assuming that we have held constant other variables that might affect viscosity, the evidence supporting a cause-and-effect relationship might be quite strong, because the manufacturer has purposely varied the amount of chemical XB-135 used. However, it is really up to the scientific community to establish and understand any cause-and-effect relationship that might exist.

If we are convinced that we can control viscosity by changing the amount of chemical XB-135, we may want to quantify the relationship between *y* and *x*. One way to do this is to calculate the covariance and the correlation coefficient between *y* and *x*, which is discussed in Chapter 11. We would also like to develop an equation relating *y* to *x*. This can be done by using regression analysis (see Chapter 11). With such an equation, we can predict *y* on the basis of *x*, and we can determine the amount of chemical XB-135 to use in order to achieve a specified viscosity.

Because the plot points in Figure 2.29 seem to fluctuate around a straight line, we say that there is a straight-line (or linear) relationship between *y* and *x*. However, not all relationships are linear. For example, demand for a product, *y*, might increase at an increasing or decreasing rate as advertising expenditure to promote the product, *x*, increases. In this case, we say that there is a curved relationship between *y* and *x*. We discuss curved relationships in Chapter 12.

Exercises for Section **2.6**

CONCEPTS

2.50 Draw a scatter plot of *y* versus *x* in which *y* increases in a linear (straight-line) fashion as *x* increases.

2.51 Draw a scatter plot of *y* versus *x* in which *y* decreases linearly as *x* increases.

2.52 What is the difference between a scatter plot and a runs plot?

METHODS AND APPLICATIONS

2.53 In the book *Essentials of Marketing Research*, Dillon, Madden, and Firtle present a scatter plot of the number of units sold of 20 varieties of a canned soup versus the amount of shelf space allocated to each variety. The scatter plot is shown in Figure 2.30.

    a. Does there appear to be a relationship between *y* (units sold) and *x* (shelf space)? Does the relationship appear to be straight-line (linear) or curved? How does *y* (units sold) change as *x* (shelf space) increases?

    b. If you were told that a variety of soup is allocated a small amount of shelf space, what would you guess about sales?

    c. Do you think that the amount of shelf space allocated to a variety causes sales to be higher or lower? Give an alternative explanation for the appearance of the scatter plot.

2.54 THE FAST-FOOD RESTAURANT RATING EXAMPLE

Researchers at Ohio State University studied U.S. consumer ratings of fast-food restaurants. Each of 406 randomly selected individuals rated the six fast-food restaurants shown in the Excel output of Figure 2.31. Each individual gave each restaurant a rating of 1, 2, 3, 4, 5, or 6 on the basis of taste, convenience, familiarity, and price and then ranked the restaurants from 1 through 6 on the basis of overall preference. In each case, 1 is the best rating and 6 the worst. The mean ratings given by the 406 individuals are given in Figure 2.31, along with a scatter plot of mean preference versus mean taste. Construct scatter plots of mean preference versus each of mean convenience, mean familiarity, and mean price. Then interpret all of the scatter plots.

FIGURE 2.30 A Scatter Plot of Units Sold versus Shelf Space

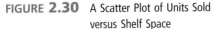

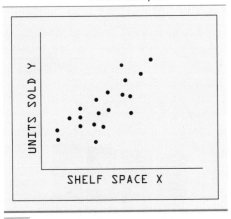

Source: *Essentials of Marketing Research,* by W. R. Dillon, T. J. Madden, and N. H. Firtle (Burr Ridge, IL: Richard D. Irwin, 1993), p. 452. Copyright © 1993. Reprinted by permission of McGraw-Hill Companies, Inc.

FIGURE 2.31 Excel Output of the Mean Restaurant Ratings and a Scatter Plot of Mean Preference versus Mean Taste

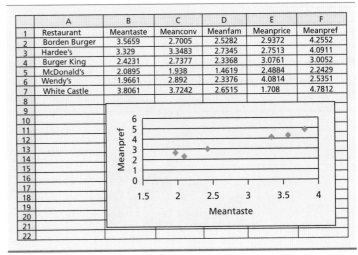

	A	B	C	D	E	F
1	Restaurant	Meantaste	Meanconv	Meanfam	Meanprice	Meanpref
2	Borden Burger	3.5659	2.7005	2.5282	2.9372	4.2552
3	Hardee's	3.329	3.3483	2.7345	2.7513	4.0911
4	Burger King	2.4231	2.7377	2.3368	3.0761	3.0052
5	McDonald's	2.0895	1.938	1.4619	2.4884	2.2429
6	Wendy's	1.9661	2.892	2.3376	4.0814	2.5351
7	White Castle	3.8061	3.7242	2.6515	1.708	4.7812

Source: Ohio State University.

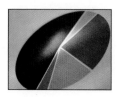

2.7 MISLEADING GRAPHS AND CHARTS

The statistical analyst's goal should be to present the most accurate and truthful portrayal of a data set that is possible. Such a presentation allows managers using the analysis to make informed decisions. However, it is possible to construct statistical summaries that are misleading. Although we do not advocate using misleading statistics, you should be aware of some of the ways statistical graphs and charts can be manipulated in order to distort the truth. By knowing what to look for, you can avoid being misled by unscrupulous practitioners.

As an example, suppose that the faculty at a major university will soon vote on a proposal to join a union. Both the union organizers and the university administration plan to distribute recent salary statistics to the entire faculty. Suppose that the mean faculty salary at the university and the mean salary increase at the university (expressed as a percentage) for each of the years 2007 through 2010 are as follows:

Year	Mean Salary (All Ranks)	Mean Salary Increase
2007	$60,000	3.0%
2008	61,600	4.0
2009	63,500	4.5
2010	66,100	6.0

The university administration does not want the faculty to unionize and, therefore, hopes to convince the faculty that substantial progress has been made to increase salaries without a union. On the other hand, the union organizers want to portray the salary increases as minimal so that the faculty will feel the need to unionize.

Figure 2.32 gives two bar charts of the mean salaries at the university for each year from 2007 through 2010. Notice that in Figure 2.32(a) the administration has started the vertical scale of the bar chart at a salary of $58,000 by using a scale break. Alternatively, the chart could be set up without the scale break by simply starting the vertical scale at $58,000. Starting the vertical scale at a value far above zero makes the salary increases look more dramatic. Notice that when the union organizers present the bar chart in Figure 2.32(b), which has a vertical scale starting at zero, the salary increases look far less impressive.

FIGURE 2.32 Two Bar Charts of the Mean Salaries at a Major University from 2007 through 2010

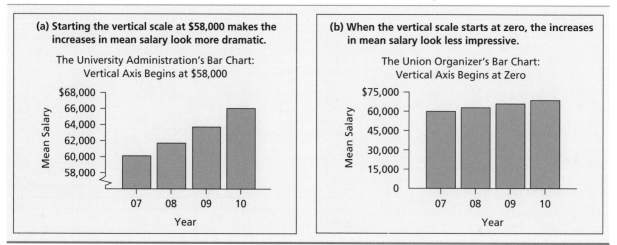

Figure 2.33 presents two bar charts of the mean salary increases (in percentages) at the university for each year from 2007 through 2010. In Figure 2.33(a), the administration has made the widths of the bars representing the percentage increases proportional to their heights. This makes the upward movement in the mean salary increases look more dramatic because the observer's eye tends to compare the areas of the bars, while the improvements in the mean salary increases are really only proportional to the heights of the bars. When the union organizers present the bar chart of Figure 2.33(b), the improvements in the mean salary increases look less impressive because each bar has the same width.

Figure 2.34 gives two runs plots (also called *time series plots*) of the mean salary increases at the university from 2007 through 2010. In Figure 2.34(a), the administration has stretched the vertical axis of the graph. That is, the vertical axis is set up so that the distances between the percentages are large. This makes the upward trend of the mean salary increases appear to be steep. In Figure 2.34(b), the union organizers have compressed the vertical axis (that is, the distances between the percentages are small). This makes the upward trend of the mean salary increases appear to be gradual. As we will see in the exercises, stretching and compressing the horizontal axis in a runs plot can also greatly affect the impression given by the plot.

FIGURE 2.33 Two Bar Charts of the Mean Salary Increases at a Major University from 2007 through 2010

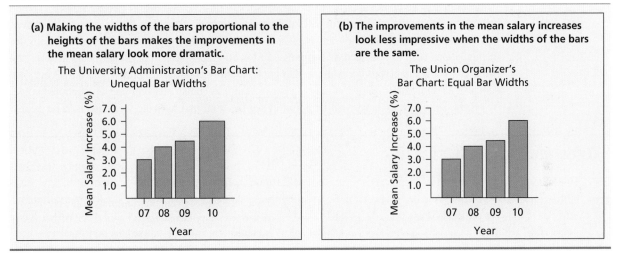

FIGURE 2.34 Two Runs Plots of the Mean Salary Increases at a Major University from 2007 through 2010

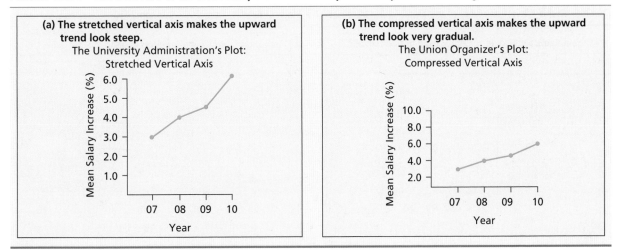

THEORY TO PRACTICE

Having a better understanding of statistics is essential to avoid being "taken in" by misleading graphs and figures. For example, if a marketing researcher reported satisfaction with a product or service using graphs similar to those in Figure 2.32, then 2.32(a) suggests more people like the product (if year 10 designated as "favourable" and year 07 as "unfavourable"), whereas a graph such as the one in 2.32(b) would suggest most people felt the same about the product or service. A similar analogy could be given for financial areas. If an individual wants to demonstrate growth in a stock's value, then that person would want to show results similar to the pattern in Figure 2.32(a) and not 2.32(b). The university example given in this section is a good example of an issue people in human resources face with respect to salaries. Remember to always look at and consider the *y*-axis.

It is also possible to create totally different interpretations of the same statistical summary by simply using different labelling or captions. For example, consider the bar chart of mean salary increases in Figure 2.33(b). To create a favourable interpretation, the university administration might use the caption "Salary Increase Is Higher for the Fourth Year in a Row." On the other hand, the union organizers might create a negative impression by using the caption "Salary Increase Fails to Reach 10% for Fourth Straight Year."

In summary, we do not approve of using statistics to mislead and distort reality. Statistics should be used to present the most truthful and informative summary of the data that is possible. However, it is important to carefully study any statistical summary so that you will not be misled. Look for manipulations such as stretched or compressed axes on graphs, axes that do not begin at zero, and bar charts with bars of varying widths. Also think carefully about assumptions, and draw your own conclusions about the meaning of any statistical summary, rather than relying on captions written by others. Doing these things will help you to see the truth and to make well-informed decisions.

Exercises for Section **2.7**

CONCEPTS

2.55 When you construct a bar chart or graph, what is the effect of starting the vertical axis at a value that is far above zero? Explain.

2.56 Find an example of a misleading use of statistics in a newspaper, magazine, corporate annual report, or other source. Then explain why your example is misleading.

METHODS AND APPLICATIONS

2.57 Figure 2.35 gives two more runs plots of the previously discussed salary increases. In Figure 2.35(a), the administration has compressed the horizontal axis. In Figure 2.33(b), the union organizers have stretched the horizontal axis. Discuss the different impressions given by the two runs plots.

FIGURE **2.35** Two Runs Plots of the Mean Salary Increases at a Major University from 2007 through 2010

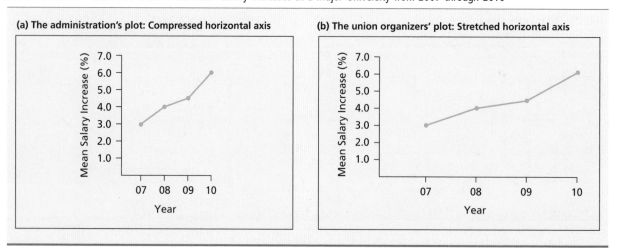

2.58 In the article "How to display data badly" in the May 1984 issue of *The American Statistician*, Howard Wainer presents a stacked bar chart of the number of public and private elementary schools (1929–1970). This bar chart is given in Figure 2.36. Wainer also provides a line graph of the number of private elementary schools (1930–1970). This graph is shown in Figure 2.37.

    a. Looking at the bar chart of Figure 2.36, does there appear to be an increasing trend in the number of private elementary schools from 1930 to 1970?

    b. Looking at the line graph of Figure 2.37, does there appear to be an increasing trend in the number of private elementary schools from 1930 to 1970?

    c. Which portrayal of the data do you think is more appropriate? Explain.

    d. Is either portrayal of the data entirely appropriate? Explain.

FIGURE **2.36** Wainer's Stacked Bar Chart

FIGURE **2.37** Wainer's Line Graph

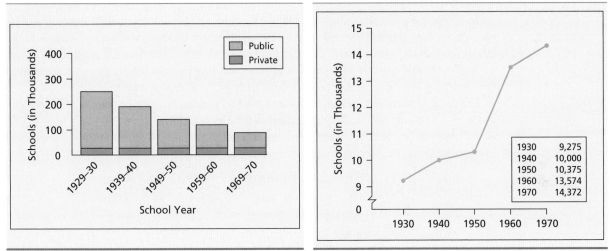

Source: "How to display data badly," by Howard Wainer, *The American Statistician*, May 1984, pp. 137–147.
Copyright © 1984 American Statistical Association. Used with permission.

2.8 WEIGHTED MEANS AND GROUPED DATA

Weighted means In Section 2.2, we studied the mean, which is an important measure of central tendency. In order to calculate a mean, we sum the population (or sample) measurements and then divide this sum by the number of measurements in the population (or sample). When we do this, each measurement counts equally. That is, each measurement is given the same importance or weight.

Sometimes it makes sense to give different measurements unequal weights. In such a case, a measurement's weight reflects its importance, and the mean calculated using the unequal weights is called a **weighted mean.** We calculate a weighted mean by multiplying each measurement by its weight, summing the resulting products, and dividing the resulting sum by the sum of the weights, as follows:

> **Weighted Mean**
>
> The weighted mean equals[4]
>
> $$\frac{\sum w_i x_i}{\sum w_i}$$
>
> where
> x_i = Value of the *i*th measurement
> w_i = Weight applied to the *i*th measurement

Such a quantity can be computed for a population of measurements or for a sample of measurements.

---
[4]We often drop the indices when using sigma (Σ) notation when it is clear what we are summing.

The following September 2009 unemployment rates for various regions in Canada illustrate the need for a weighted mean and the required calculations:

Census Region	Civilian Labour Force (Thousands)	Unemployment Rate
Atlantic	1,235	11.2%
Quebec	4,197	8.8
Ontario	7,182	9.2
West	5,774	6.1

Source: Adapted from Statistics Canada, CANSIM, Table 282-0087, October 2009.

To compute a mean unemployment rate for Canada, we should use a weighted mean because each of the four regional unemployment rates applies to a different number of workers in the labour force. For example, the 11.2 percent unemployed for Atlantic Canada applies to a labour force of 1,235,000 workers and thus should count less heavily than the 9.2 percent unemployed for Ontario, which applies to a larger labour force of 7,182,000 workers.

The unemployment rate measurements are $x_1 = 11.2$ percent, $x_2 = 8.8$ percent, $x_3 = 9.2$ percent, and $x_4 = 6.1$ percent, and the weights applied to these measurements are $w_1 = 1,235$, $w_2 = 4,197$, $w_3 = 7,182$, and $w_4 = 5,774$. That is, we are weighting the unemployment rates by the regional labour force sizes. The weighted mean is computed as follows:

$$\mu = \frac{1,235(11.2) + 4,197(8.8) + 7,182(9.2) + 5,774(6.1)}{1,235 + 4,197 + 7,182 + 5,774}$$

$$= \frac{152,061.4}{18,388}$$

$$= 8.27\%$$

In this case, the unweighted mean of the four regional unemployment rates is 8.825 percent. Therefore, the unweighted mean overestimates the Canadian unemployment rate by 0.56 percentage points (or overestimates Canadian unemployment by $0.0056(18,387,800) = 102,972$ workers).

ROADBLOCK

Applying the weighted mean
The weights chosen for calculating a weighted mean will vary depending on the situation. For example, in order to compute the mean percentage return for a portfolio of investments, the percentage returns for various investments might be weighted by the dollar amounts invested in each. Or, in order to compute a mean profit margin for a company consisting of several divisions, the profit margins for the different divisions might be weighted by the sales volumes of the divisions. Again, the idea is to choose weights that represent the relative importance of the measurements in the population or sample.

Students should be familiar with weighted means because course grades are typically based on a weighted mean. For example, if a course has three exams, the exams could all be given a one-third weight, or the exams could have different weights. If the final exam is viewed as the major exam in the course, then the final exam might be given a larger weight, say, 25 percent each for the first two exams and 50 percent for the final exam. To compute the student's course grade, the weighted grades would be summed: 0.25(first exam grade) + 0.25(second exam grade) + 0.50(final exam grade).

Descriptive statistics for grouped data We usually calculate measures of central tendency and variability using the individual measurements in a population or sample. However, sometimes the only data available are in the form of a frequency distribution or a histogram. For example, newspapers and magazines often summarize data using frequency distributions and histograms without giving the individual measurements in a data set. Data summarized in frequency distribution or histogram form are often called **grouped data**. In this section, we show how to compute descriptive statistics for such data.

Suppose we are given a frequency distribution summarizing a sample of 65 customer satisfaction ratings for a consumer product, as shown in the following table.

Satisfaction Rating	Frequency
36–38	4
39–41	15
42–44	25
45–47	19
48–50	2

Because we do not know each of the 65 individual satisfaction ratings, we cannot compute an exact value for the mean satisfaction rating. However, we can calculate an approximation of this mean. In order to do this, we use the midpoint of each class to represent the measurements in the class. When we do this, we are really assuming that the average of the measurements in each class equals the class midpoint. Letting M_i denote the midpoint of class i, and letting f_i denote the frequency of class i, we compute the mean by calculating a weighted mean of the class midpoints using the class frequencies as the weights. The logic here is that if f_i measurements are included in class i, then the midpoint of class i should count f_i times in the weighted mean. In this case, the sum of the weights equals the sum of the class frequencies, which equals the sample size. Therefore, we obtain the following equation for the sample mean of grouped data:

Sample Mean for Grouped Data

$$\bar{x} = \frac{\sum f_i M_i}{\sum f_i} = \frac{\sum f_i M_i}{n}$$

where
  f_i = Frequency for class i
  M_i = Midpoint for class i
  $n = \sum f_i$ = Sample size

Table 2.17 summarizes the calculation of the mean satisfaction rating for the previously given frequency distribution of satisfaction ratings. Note that in this table, each midpoint is halfway between its corresponding class limits. For example, for the first class $M_1 = (36 + 38)/2 = 37$. We find that the sample mean satisfaction rating is 43.

We can also compute an approximation of the sample variance for grouped data. Recall that when we compute the sample variance using individual measurements, we compute the squared deviation from the sample mean $(x_i - \bar{x})^2$ for each individual measurement x_i and then sum the squared deviations. For grouped data, we do not know each of the x_i values. Because of this, we again let the class midpoint M_i represent each measurement in class i. It follows that we compute the squared deviation $(M_i - \bar{x})^2$ for each class and then sum these squares, weighting each

TABLE 2.17   Calculating the Sample Mean of the Satisfaction Rating

Satisfaction Rating	Frequency (f_i)	Class Midpoint (M_i)	$f_i M_i$
36–38	4	37	4(37) = 148
39–41	15	40	15(40) = 600
42–44	25	43	25(43) = 1,075
45–47	19	46	19(46) = 874
48–50	2	49	2(49) = 98
	$n = 65$		2,795

$$\bar{x} = \frac{\sum f_i M_i}{n} = \frac{2,795}{65} = 43$$

squared deviation by its corresponding class frequency f_i. That is, we approximate $\sum (x_i - \bar{x})^2$ by using $\sum f_i(M_i - \bar{x})^2$. Finally, we obtain the sample variance for the grouped data by dividing this quantity by the sample size minus 1. We summarize this calculation in the following box:

Sample Variance for Grouped Data

$$s^2 = \frac{\sum f_i(M_i - \bar{x})^2}{n - 1}$$

where $\bar{x}$ is the sample mean for the grouped data.

Table 2.18 illustrates calculating the sample variance of the previously given frequency distribution of satisfaction ratings. We find that the sample variance is $s^2 = 8.15625$ and, therefore, that the sample standard deviation is $s = \sqrt{8.15625} = 2.8559$.

Finally, although we have illustrated calculating the mean and variance for grouped data in the context of a sample, similar calculations can be done for a population of measurements. If we let N be the size of the population, the grouped data formulas for the population mean and variance are given in the following box:

Population Mean for Grouped Data

$$\mu = \frac{\sum f_i M_i}{N}$$

Population Variance for Grouped Data

$$\sigma^2 = \frac{\sum f_i(M_i - \mu)^2}{N}$$

TABLE 2.18   Calculating the Sample Variance of the Satisfaction Ratings

Satisfaction Rating	Frequency f_i	Class Midpoint M_i	Deviation $(M_i - \bar{x})$	Squared Deviation $(M_i - \bar{x})^2$	$f_i(M_i - \bar{x})^2$
36–38	4	37	$37 - 43 = -6$	36	$4(36) = 144$
39–41	15	40	$40 - 43 = -3$	9	$15(9) = 135$
42–44	25	43	$43 - 43 = 0$	0	$25(0) = 0$
45–47	19	46	$46 - 43 = 3$	9	$19(9) = 171$
48–50	2	49	$49 - 43 = 6$	36	$2(36) = 72$
	65				$\sum f_i(M_i - \bar{x})^2 = 522$

$$s^2 = \text{Sample variance} = \frac{\sum f_i(M_i - \bar{x})^2}{n - 1} = \frac{522}{65 - 1} = 8.15625$$

Exercises for Section 2.8

CONCEPTS

2.59 Consider calculating a student's grade point average using a scale where 4.0 represents an A and 0.0 represents an F. Explain why the grade point average is a weighted mean. What are the x_i values? What are the weights?

2.60 When you perform grouped data calculations, you represent the measurements in a class by using the midpoint of the class. Describe the assumption that is being made when you do this.

2.61 When we compute the mean, variance, and standard deviation using grouped data, the results obtained are approximations of the population (or sample) mean, variance, and standard deviation. Explain why this is true.

METHODS AND APPLICATIONS

2.62 The 2013 total return percentages for several popular funds were as follows:

Fund	2013 Total Return %
Fund A	10.7
Fund B	21.7
Fund C	9.9
Fund D	5.8
Fund E	5.5

Suppose that an investor had $100,000 invested in Fund *A*, $500,000 invested in Fund *B*, $500,000 invested in Fund *C*, $200,000 invested in Fund *D*, and $50,000 invested in Fund *E*.

a. Compute a weighted mean that measures the 2013 average total return for the investor's portfolio.

b. Compare your weighted mean with the unweighted mean of the five total return percentages. Explain why they differ.

2.63 The following are the 2009 unemployment rates and civilian labour force sizes for five provinces in Canada:

Province	Size of Civilian Labour Force (Thousands)	Unemployment Rate (%)
NL	255.9	15.3
PE	78.9	11.8
NS	499.6	9.5
NB	400.1	8.1
QC	4,196.7	8.8

Source: Adapted from the Statistics Canada, CANSIM, Table 282-0087, October 2009.

Using a weighted mean, compute an average unemployment rate for the five provinces.

2.64 The following frequency distribution summarizes the masses of 195 fish caught by anglers participating in a professional fishing tournament.

Mass (kg)	Frequency
1–3	53
4–6	118
7–9	21
10–12	3

a. Calculate the (approximate) sample mean for these data.

b. Calculate the (approximate) sample variance for these data.

2.65 The following is a frequency distribution summarizing earnings per share (EPS) growth data for 30 firms.

EPS Growth (Percentage)	Frequency
0–49	1
50–99	17
100–149	5
150–199	4
200–249	1
250–299	2

Calculate the (approximate) population mean, variance, and standard deviation for these data.

2.66 The Data and Story Library website, which is devoted to applications of statistics, gives a histogram of the ages of a sample of 60 CEOs taken in 1993. We present the data below in the form of a frequency distribution to the right. Calculate the (approximate) sample mean, variance, and standard deviation of these data.

Age (Years)	Frequency
28–32	1
33–37	3
38–42	3
43–47	13
48–52	14
53–57	12
58–62	9
63–67	1
68–72	3
73–77	1

Source: The Data and Story Library: lib.stat.cmu.edu/DASL/Stories/ceo.html

CHAPTER SUMMARY

We began this chapter by studying how to depict the shape of the distribution of a data set. We learned that stem-and-leaf displays and histograms are useful graphics for portraying a data set's distribution. We also learned about some common population shapes. We saw that data sets often have shapes that are symmetrical, positively skewed (with a tail to the right), or negatively skewed (with a tail to the left).

Next we presented and compared several measures of central tendency. We defined the population mean and we saw how to estimate it by using a sample mean. We also defined the median and mode, and we compared the mean, median, and mode for symmetrical distributions and for distributions that are positively or negatively skewed (to the right or left). We then studied measures of variation (or spread). We defined the range, variance, and standard deviation, and we saw how to estimate a population variance and standard deviation by using a sample. We learned that a good way to interpret the standard deviation when a population is (approximately) normally

distributed is to use the empirical rule, and we applied this rule to assess whether it was a capable process. We next studied Chebyshev's theorem, which gives us intervals containing reasonably large fractions of the population units no matter what the population's shape might be. We also saw that when a data set is highly skewed, it is best to use percentiles and quartiles to measure variation.

After learning how to measure and depict central tendency and variability, we presented several methods for portraying qualitative data. In particular, we used bar charts for this purpose. We also discussed using a sample to estimate the proportion of population units that fall into a category of interest.

We studied using scatter plots to examine relationships between variables. Next we discussed misleading graphs and statistics, and we explained some of the tactics that are commonly used to try to distort the truth. We concluded with the concept of a weighted mean and then explained how to compute descriptive statistics for grouped data.

KEY TERMS

bar chart
capable process
central tendency
Chebyshev's theorem
coefficient of variation
dependent variable (denoted y)
descriptive statistics
empirical rule
extreme outlier (in a box-and-whiskers display)
first quartile (denoted Q_1)
frequency
frequency distribution
grouped data
histogram
independent variable (denoted x)
inner fences (in a box-and-whiskers display)
interquartile range (denoted IQR)
median (denoted M_d)
mild outliers (in a box-and-whiskers display)
mode (denoted M_o)
mound-shaped
negatively skewed (to the left)
normal curve
outer fences
outliers
pth percentile

Pareto chart
percentile
point estimate
population mean (denoted μ)
population parameter
population proportion (denoted p)
population standard deviation (denoted σ)
population variance (denoted σ^2)
positively skewed (to the right)
range
relative frequency
relative frequency histogram
sample mean (denoted $\bar{x}$)
sample proportion (denoted $\hat{p}$)
sample size (denoted n)
sample standard deviation (denoted s)
sample statistic
sample variance (denoted s^2)
scatter plot or scatter diagram
second quartile (or median)
stem-and-leaf display
third quartile (denoted Q_3)
tolerance interval
weighted mean
z score (of a measurement)

IMPORTANT FORMULAS

Sample mean, $\bar{x}$

Sample variance, s^2

Sample standard deviation, s

Computational formula for s^2

Empirical rule

Chebyshev's theorem

z score

Coefficient of variation

pth percentile

Weighted mean

Sample mean for grouped data

Sample variance for grouped data

Population mean for grouped data

Population variance for grouped data

SUPPLEMENTARY EXERCISES

connect Practise and learn online with Connect. Items for which there are online data sets are marked with 📎.

2.67 In the book *Modern Statistical Quality Control and Improvement*, Nicolas R. Farnum presents data concerning the elapsed times from the completion of medical lab tests until the results are recorded on patients' charts. Table 2.19 gives the times it took (in hours) to deliver and chart the results of 84 lab tests over one week.

a. Construct a frequency histogram and a relative frequency histogram for the lab test waiting time data.

b. Looking at the histogram, are most of the test results delivered and charted within several hours?

c. Are there some deliveries with excessively long waiting times? Which deliveries might be investigated in order to discover reasons behind unusually long delays?

2.68 Figure 2.38 depicts data for a study of 80 software projects at NASA's Goddard Space Flight Center. The figure shows the number of bugs per 1,000 lines of code from 1976 to 1990. Write a short paragraph describing how the reliability of the software has improved. Explain how the data indicate improvement.

2.69 Long-term investors know that portfolio diversification is important. The motto "Don't put all your eggs in one basket" rings very true in this case. That is, investors should invest in a variety of investments with differing levels of historical return and risk. This risk is often measured in terms of the volatility of an investment over time. When volatility, sometimes referred to as *standard deviation*,

increases, so too does the level of return. The opposite is also true.

The answer seems to lie in asset allocation. Investment experts know the importance of asset allocation. In a nutshell, asset allocation is a method of creating a diversified portfolio of investments that minimize historical risk and maximize potential returns to help you meet your retirement goals and needs.

The mean return and standard deviation combinations for the various investment classes are shown in Table 2.20.

Suppose that future returns of each investment class will continue to behave in the future as they have over the past ten years. That is, for each investment class, regard the mean return and standard deviation in Table 2.20 as the population mean and the population standard deviation of all possible future returns. Then do the following:

a. Assuming that future returns for the various investment classes are mound-shaped, for each investment class compute intervals that will contain approximately 68.26 percent and 99.73 percent of all future returns.

b. Making no assumptions about the population shapes of future returns, for each investment class, compute the intervals that will contain at least 75 percent and 88.89 percent of all future returns.

c. Assuming that future returns are mound-shaped, find
   (1) An estimate of the maximum return that might be realized for each investment class.
   (2) An estimate of the minimum return (or maximum loss) that might be realized for each investment class.

TABLE 2.19 Elapsed Time (in Hours) for Completing and Delivering Medical Lab Tests 📎

6.1	8.7	1.1	4.0
2.1	3.9	2.2	5.0
2.1	7.1	4.3	8.8
3.5	1.2	3.2	1.3
1.3	9.3	4.2	7.3
5.7	6.5	4.4	16.2
1.3	1.3	3.0	2.7
15.7	4.9	2.0	5.2
3.9	13.9	1.8	2.2
8.4	5.2	11.9	3.0
24.0	24.5	24.8	24.0
1.7	4.4	2.5	16.2
17.8	2.9	4.0	6.7
5.3	8.3	2.8	5.2
17.5	1.1	3.0	8.3
1.2	1.1	4.5	4.4
5.0	2.6	12.7	5.7
4.7	5.1	2.6	1.6
3.4	8.1	2.4	16.7
4.8	1.7	1.9	12.1
9.1	5.6	13.0	6.4

Source: *Modern Statistical Quality Control and Improvement*, by N. R. Farnum (Belmont, CA: Duxbury Press, 1994), p. 55. Reprinted by permission of Brooks/Cole, an imprint of the Wadsworth Group, a division of Thompson Learning. Fax 1-800-730-2215.

FIGURE 2.38 Software Performance at NASA's Goddard Space Center, 1976–1990

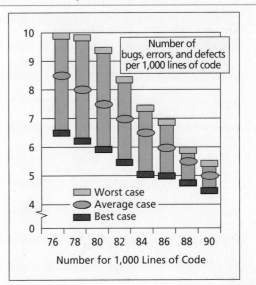

Source: Reprinted from the January 15, 1992, issue of *BusinessWeek* by special permission. Copyright © 1992 by The McGraw-Hill Companies.

TABLE **2.20**   Mean Return and Standard Deviation for Seven Investment Classes over a Ten-Year Period

Investment Class	Mean Return	Std. Deviation
Money Market	2.75%	0.08%
Fixed Income	0.8	1.0
Balanced	6.4	1.48
Canadian Equity	19.6	2.75
U.S. Equity	12.4	3.1
Global Equity	22.3	5.1
Sector Funds	33.1	5.9

TABLE **2.21**   Personal Expenditure on Food and Nonalcoholic Beverages, Alcoholic Beverages, and Tobacco in Canada (Figures are given in millions of dollars)

Year	1997	1998	1999	2000	2001	2002	2003	2004	2005
Food and nonalcoholic beverages	12,580	13,039	13,493	14,137	14,946	15,581	16,173	16,851	17,732
Alcoholic beverages bought in stores	2,476	2,620	2,781	2,915	3,105	3,329	3,509	3,645	3,831
Tobacco products	2,185	2,326	2,311	2,338	2,543	3,041	3,388	3,621	3,547

Source: Adapted from Statistics Canada, *National Income and Expenditure Accounts, Quarterly Estimates,* Catalogue No. 13-001-XIB, reference period 1997–2005.

2.70   Table 2.21 presents data on the average annual amount Canadians spent on food and nonalcoholic beverages, alcoholic beverages (bought in stores), and tobacco products for the years 1997 through 2005. Depict the data graphically and summarize what the data suggest in terms of changes in expenditures over time.

2.71   INTERNATIONAL BUSINESS TRAVEL EXPENSE

Suppose that a large international corporation wants to obtain its own benchmark for one-day travel expenses in Moscow. To do this, it records the one-day travel expenses for a random sample of 35 executives visiting Moscow. The mean and the standard deviation of these expenses are calculated to be $\bar{x} = \$538$ and $s = \$41$, respectively. Furthermore, a histogram shows that the expenses are approximately normally distributed.

a. Find an interval that you estimate contains 99.73 percent of all one-day travel expenses in Moscow.

b. If an executive submits an expense of $720 for a one-day stay in Moscow, should this expense be considered unusually high? Why or why not?

2.72   INSURANCE

Figure 2.39 summarizes information concerning insurance expenditures of households in a given country.

a. Approximately what percentage of households spent on life insurance?

b. What is the approximate average expenditure per household on life insurance? Note: The averages given in Figure 2.39 are for households that spend in the class.

FIGURE **2.39**   Insurance Expenditures of Households in a Given Country

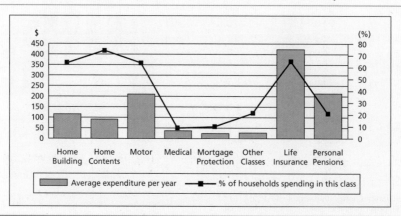

Source: CSO family expenditure survey.

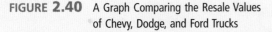
FIGURE **2.40** A Graph Comparing the Resale Values of Chevy, Dodge, and Ford Trucks

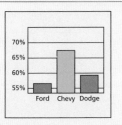

Source: Reprinted courtesy of General Motors Corporation.

69	47	52	68	59
52	79	77	69	78
57	78	85	85	67
46	90	86	88	78
41	94	65	80	55
98	78	87	75	64
51	82	97	53	82
87	98	98	94	66
55	58	44	87	86
95	53	57	84	72

2.73 Figure 2.40 was used in various Chevrolet magazine advertisements in 1997 to compare the overall resale values of Chevrolet, Dodge, and Ford trucks in the years from 1990 to 1997. What is somewhat misleading about this graph?

2.74 The final course grades for 50 students in a statistics course are presented in the table that follows.
  a. Convert each grade into a letter grade and construct a histogram of the grades.
  b. Compute the mean grade for the class.
  c. Compute the standard deviation for the class.
  d. If Samantha obtains a grade of 75 percent and Donald obtains a grade of 55 percent, who is farther away from the class mean?

2.75 INTERNET EXERCISE

Statistics Canada reports on its main page the latest indicators for Canada (typically, statistics current up to the previous month). Explore the "Unemployment rate" link and determine whether the unemployment graphs provided are histograms.

CHAPTER **3**
Probability

In Chapter 2 we explained how to use sample statistics as point estimates of population parameters. Starting in Chapter 7, we will focus on using sample statistics to make more sophisticated statistical inferences about population parameters. We will see that these statistical inferences are generalizations—based on calculating probabilities—about population parameters. In this chapter and in Chapters 4 and 5, we present the fundamental concepts about probability that are needed to understand how we make such statistical inferences. We begin our discussion in this chapter by considering rules for calculating probabilities.

To illustrate some of the concepts in this chapter, we will use data from BBM Canada (bbm.ca), a not-for-profit organization that provides consumer behaviour data to broadcasters, advertisers, and agencies. We will demonstrate how probabilities can be used in the interpretation of this data to analyze patterns of radio listenership in the Calgary market.

3.1 THE CONCEPT OF PROBABILITY

We use the concept of **probability** to deal with uncertainty. The probability of an event is the chance, or likelihood, that the event will occur. For instance, the probability that your favourite football team will win its next game measures the likelihood of a victory. The probability of an event is always a number between 0 and 1. The closer an event's probability is to 1, the higher is the likelihood that the event will occur; the closer the event's probability is to 0, the smaller is the likelihood that the event will occur. For example, if you believe that the probability that your favourite football team will win its next game is .95, then you are almost sure that your team will win. If, however, you believe that the probability of victory is only .10, then you have very little confidence that your team will win.

When performing statistical studies, we sometimes collect data by *performing a controlled experiment.* For instance, we might purposely vary the operating conditions of a manufacturing process in order to study the effects of these changes on the process output. Alternatively, we sometimes obtain data by *observing uncontrolled events.* For example, we might observe the closing price of a share of BlackBerry stock every day for 30 trading days. In order to simplify our terminology, we will use the word *experiment* to refer to either method of data collection.

LO1

An **experiment** is any process of observation that has an uncertain outcome. The process must be defined so that on any single repetition of the experiment, one and only one of the possible outcomes will occur. The possible outcomes for an experiment are called *experimental outcomes.*

For example, if the experiment consists of tossing a coin, the experimental outcomes are "head" and "tail." If the experiment consists of rolling a die, the experimental outcomes are 1, 2, 3, 4, 5, and 6. If the experiment consists of subjecting an automobile to a tailpipe emissions test, the experimental outcomes are "pass" and "fail."

We often want to assign probabilities to experimental outcomes. This can be done by several methods. Regardless of the method used, *probabilities must be assigned to the experimental outcomes so that two conditions are met:*

1   The probability assigned to each experimental outcome must be between 0 and 1. That is, if E represents an experimental outcome and if $P(E)$ represents the probability of this outcome, then $0 \le P(E) \le 1$.

2   The probabilities of all of the experimental outcomes must sum to 1.

Sometimes, when all of the experimental outcomes are equally likely, we can use logic to assign probabilities. This method, which is called the *classical method,* will be more fully discussed in the next section. As a simple example, consider the experiment of tossing a fair coin. Here, there are *two* equally likely experimental outcomes—head (H) and tail (T). Therefore, logic suggests that the probability of observing a head, denoted $P(H)$, is $1/2 = .5$, and that the probability of observing a tail, denoted $P(T)$, is also $1/2 = .5$. Notice that each probability is between 0 and 1. Furthermore, because H and T are all of the experimental outcomes, $P(H) + P(T) = 1$.

Probability is often interpreted to be a *long-run relative frequency.* As an example, consider repeatedly tossing a coin. If we get 6 heads in the first 10 tosses, then the relative frequency, or fraction, of heads is $6/10 = .6$. If we get 47 heads in the first 100 tosses, the relative frequency of heads is $47/100 = .47$. If we get 5,067 heads in the first 10,000 tosses, the relative frequency of heads is $5,067/10,000 = .5067$.[1] Since the relative frequency of heads is approaching (that is, getting closer to) .5, we might estimate that the probability of obtaining a head when tossing the coin is .5. When we say this, we mean that, if we tossed the coin an indefinitely large number of times (that is, a number of times

---

[1]The English mathematician John Kerrich actually obtained this result when he tossed a coin 10,000 times while imprisoned by the Nazis during World War II.

approaching infinity), the relative frequency of heads obtained would approach .5. Of course, in actuality, it is impossible to toss a coin (or perform any experiment) an indefinitely large number of times. Therefore, a relative frequency interpretation of probability is a mathematical idealization.

To summarize, suppose that *E* is an experimental outcome that might occur when a particular experiment is performed. Then the probability that *E* will occur, *P(E)*, can be interpreted to be the number that would be approached by the relative frequency of *E* if we performed the experiment an indefinitely large number of times. It follows that we often think of a probability in terms of the percentage of the time the experimental outcome would occur in many repetitions of the experiment. For instance, when we say that the probability of obtaining a head when we toss a coin is .5, we are saying that, when we repeatedly toss the coin an indefinitely large number of times, we will obtain a head on 50 percent of the repetitions.

Sometimes it is either difficult or impossible to use the classical method to assign probabilities. Since we can often make a relative frequency interpretation of probability, we can estimate a probability by performing the experiment in which an outcome might occur many times. Then, we estimate the probability of the experimental outcome to be the proportion of the time that the outcome occurs during the many repetitions of the experiment. For example, to estimate the probability that a randomly selected consumer prefers Coca-Cola to all other soft drinks, we perform an experiment in which we ask a randomly selected consumer for his or her preference. There are two possible experimental outcomes: "prefers Coca-Cola" and "does not prefer Coca-Cola." However, we have no reason to believe that these experimental outcomes are equally likely, so we cannot use the classical method. We might perform the experiment, say, 1,000 times by surveying 1,000 randomly selected consumers. Then, if 140 of those surveyed said that they prefer Coca-Cola, we would estimate the probability that a randomly selected consumer prefers Coca-Cola to all other soft drinks to be 140/1,000 = .14. This is called the *relative frequency method* for assigning probability.

If we cannot perform the experiment many times, we might estimate the probability by using our previous experience with similar situations, or intuition, or special expertise that we may possess. For example, a company president might estimate the probability of success for a one-time business venture to be .7. Here, on the basis of knowledge of the success of previous similar ventures, the opinions of company personnel, and other pertinent information, the president believes that there is a 70 percent chance the venture will be successful.

When we use experience, intuitive judgement, or expertise to assess a probability, we call this a **subjective probability**. Such a probability may or may not have a relative frequency interpretation. For instance, when the company president estimates that the probability of a successful business venture is .7, this may mean that, if business conditions similar to those that are about to be encountered could be repeated many times, then the business venture would be successful in 70 percent of the repetitions. Or, the president may not be thinking in relative frequency terms but rather may consider the venture a "one-shot" proposition. We will discuss some other subjective probabilities later. However, the interpretations of statistical inferences we will explain in later chapters are based on the relative frequency interpretation of probability. For this reason, we will concentrate on this interpretation.

3.2 SAMPLE SPACES AND EVENTS

LO2

In order to calculate probabilities by using the classical method, it is important to understand and use the idea of a *sample space*.

The **sample space** of an experiment is the set of all possible experimental outcomes. The experimental outcome in a sample space is often called a **sample space outcome**.

Example 3.1 Selecting a CEO

A company is choosing a new chief executive officer (CEO). It has narrowed the list of candidates to four finalists (identified by last name only)—Adams, Chung, Hill, and Rankin. If we consider our experiment to be making a final choice of the company's CEO, then the experiment's sample space consists of the four possible experimental outcomes:

A ≡ Adams is chosen as CEO.

C ≡ Chung is chosen as CEO.

H ≡ Hill is chosen as CEO.

R ≡ Rankin is chosen as CEO.

Each of these outcomes is a sample space outcome, and the set of these sample space outcomes is the sample space.

Next, suppose that industry analysts feel (subjectively) that the probabilities that Adams, Chung, Hill, and Rankin will be chosen as CEO are .1, .2, .5, and .2, respectively. That is, in probability notation

$$P(A) = .1 \quad P(C) = .2 \quad P(H) = .5 \quad \text{and} \quad P(R) = .2$$

Notice that each probability assigned to a sample space outcome is between 0 and 1 and that the sum of the probabilities equals 1.

Example 3.2 Predicting the Gender of a Child

A newly married couple plans to have two children. Naturally, they are curious about the odds of having boys, girls, or one of each. Therefore, we consider the experiment to be having two children. In order to find the sample space of this experiment, we let B denote that a child is a boy and G denote that a child is a girl. Then, it is useful to construct the tree diagram shown in Figure 3.1. This diagram pictures the experiment as a two-step process—having the first child, who could be either a boy or a girl (B or G), and then having the second child, who could also be either a boy or a girl (B or G). Each branch of the tree leads to a sample space outcome. These outcomes are

FIGURE **3.1** A Tree Diagram of the Genders of Two Children

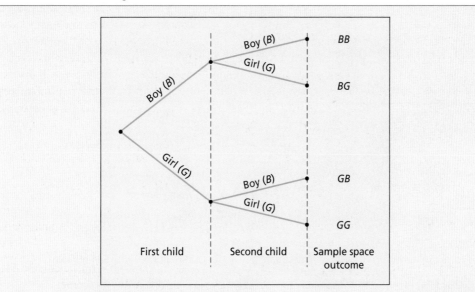

listed at the right ends of the branches. We see that there are four sample space outcomes. Therefore, the sample space (that is, the set of all the sample space outcomes) is

$$BB \quad BG \quad GB \quad GG$$

In order to consider the probabilities of these outcomes, suppose that boys and girls are equally likely each time a child is born. Intuitively, this says that each of the sample space outcomes is equally likely. That is, this implies that

$$P(BB) = P(BG) = P(GB) = P(GG) = \frac{1}{4}$$

This says that there is a 25 percent chance that each of these outcomes will occur. Again, notice that these probabilities sum to 1.

Example 3.3   Predicting Outcomes on a Quiz

A student takes a pop quiz that consists of three true–false questions. If we consider our experiment to be answering the three questions, each question can be answered correctly or incorrectly. We will let C denote answering a question correctly and I denote answering a question incorrectly. Then, Figure 3.2 depicts a tree diagram of the sample space outcomes for the experiment. The diagram portrays the experiment as a three-step process—answering the first question (correctly or incorrectly, that is, C or I), answering the second question, and answering the third question. The tree diagram has eight different branches, and the eight sample space outcomes are listed at the ends of the branches. We see that the sample space is

$$CCC \quad CCI \quad CIC \quad CII$$
$$ICC \quad ICI \quad IIC \quad III$$

Next, suppose that the student was totally unprepared for the quiz and had to blindly guess the answer to each question. That is, the student had a 50–50 chance (or .5 probability) of

FIGURE **3.2**   A Tree Diagram of Answering Three True–False Questions

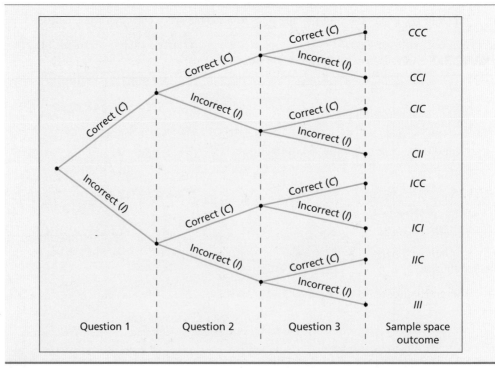

correctly answering each question. Intuitively, each of the eight sample space outcomes is equally likely to occur. That is,

$$P(CCC) = P(CCI) = \cdots = P(III) = \frac{1}{8}$$

Here, as in Examples 3.1 and 3.2, the sum of the probabilities of the sample space outcomes is equal to 1.

Events and finding probabilities by using sample spaces   At the beginning of this chapter, we informally talked about events. The formal definition of *event* is as follows.

An **event** is a set (or collection) of sample space outcomes.

For instance, if we consider the couple planning to have two children, the event "the couple will have at least one girl" consists of the sample space outcomes *BG*, *GB*, and *GG*. That is, the event "the couple will have at least one girl" will occur if and only if one of the sample space outcomes *BG*, *GB*, or *GG* occurs. As another example, in the pop quiz situation, the event "the student will answer at least two out of three questions correctly" consists of the sample space outcomes *CCC*, *CCI*, *CIC*, and *ICC*, while the event "the student will answer all three questions correctly" consists of the sample space outcome *CCC*. In general, we see that the word description of an event determines the sample space outcomes that correspond to the event.

Suppose that we want to find the probability that an event will occur. The probability of an event is the sum of the probabilities of the sample space outcomes that correspond to the event. As an example, in the CEO situation, suppose only Adams and Hill are internal candidates (they already work for the company). Letting *INT* denote the event that "an internal candidate is selected for the CEO position," then *INT* consists of the sample space outcomes *A* and *H* (that is, *INT* will occur if and only if either of the sample space outcomes *A* or *H* occurs). It follows that $P(INT) = P(A) + P(H) = .1 + .5 = .6$. This says that the probability that an internal candidate will be chosen to be CEO is .6.

The **probability of an event** is the *sum of the probabilities of the sample space outcomes* that correspond to the event.

In general, we have seen that the probability of any sample space outcome (experimental outcome) is a number between 0 and 1, and we have also seen that the probabilities of all the sample space outcomes sum to 1. It follows that the probability of an event (that is, the probability of a set of sample space outcomes) is a number between 0 and 1. That is,

If *A* is an event, then $0 \leq P(A) \leq 1$.

Moreover:

1   If an event never occurs, then the probability of this event equals 0.
2   If an event is certain to occur, then the probability of this event equals 1.

Example 3.4   Predicting the Gender of a Child

Consider the couple that is planning to have two children, and suppose that each child is equally likely to be a boy or girl. Recalling that in this case each sample space outcome has a probability equal to 1/4, we see that:

1   The probability that the couple will have two boys is

$$P(BB) = \frac{1}{4}$$

since two boys will be born if and only if the sample space outcome *BB* occurs.

2   The probability that the couple will have one boy and one girl is

$$P(BG) + P(GB) = \frac{1}{4} + \frac{1}{4} = \frac{1}{2}$$

since one boy and one girl will be born if and only if one of the sample space outcomes *BG* or *GB* occurs.

3   The probability that the couple will have two girls is

$$P(GG) = \frac{1}{4}$$

since two girls will be born if and only if the sample space outcome *GG* occurs.

4   The probability that the couple will have at least one girl is

$$P(BG) + P(GB) + P(GG) = \frac{1}{4} + \frac{1}{4} + \frac{1}{4} = \frac{3}{4}$$

since at least one girl will be born if and only if one of the sample space outcomes *BG*, *GB*, or *GG* occurs.

Example 3.5   Predicting Outcomes on a Quiz

Again consider the pop quiz consisting of three true–false questions, and suppose that the student blindly guesses the answers. Remembering that in this case each sample space outcome has a probability equal to 1/8, then

1   The probability that the student will get all three questions correct is

$$P(CCC) = \frac{1}{8}$$

2   The probability that the student will get exactly two questions correct is

$$P(CCI) + P(CIC) + P(ICC) = \frac{1}{8} + \frac{1}{8} + \frac{1}{8} = \frac{3}{8}$$

since two questions will be answered correctly if and only if one of the sample space outcomes *CCI*, *CIC*, or *ICC* occurs.

3   The probability that the student will get exactly one question correct is

$$P(CII) + P(ICI) + P(IIC) = \frac{1}{8} + \frac{1}{8} + \frac{1}{8} = \frac{3}{8}$$

since one question will be answered correctly if and only if one of the sample space outcomes *CII*, *ICI*, or *IIC* occurs.

4   The probability that the student will get all three questions incorrect is

$$P(III) = \frac{1}{8}$$

5   The probability that the student will get at least two questions correct is

$$P(CCC) + P(CCI) + P(CIC) + P(ICC) = \frac{1}{8} + \frac{1}{8} + \frac{1}{8} + \frac{1}{8} = \frac{1}{2}$$

since the student will get at least two questions correct if and only if one of the sample space outcomes *CCC*, *CCI*, *CIC*, or *ICC* occurs.

Notice that in the true–false question situation we find that, for instance, the probability that the student will get exactly two questions correct equals the ratio

$$\frac{\text{Number of sample space outcomes resulting in two correct answers}}{\text{Total number of sample space outcomes}} = \frac{3}{8}$$

In general, when a sample space is finite we can use the following method for computing the probability of an event.

> **Computing the Probability of an Event**
>
> *If all of the sample space outcomes are equally likely,* then the probability that an event will occur is equal to the ratio
>
> $$\frac{\text{Number of sample space outcomes that correspond to the event}}{\text{Total number of sample space outcomes}}$$

When we use this rule, we are using the *classical method* for computing probabilities. Furthermore, it is important to emphasize that we can use this rule only when all of the sample space outcomes are equally likely (as they are in the true–false question situation). For example, if we were to use this rule in the CEO situation, we would find that the probability of choosing an internal candidate as CEO is

$$P(INT) = \frac{\text{Number of internal candidates}}{\text{Total number of candidates}} = \frac{2}{4} = .5$$

This result is not equal to the correct value of $P(INT)$, which we previously found to be equal to .6. Here, this rule does not give us the correct answer because the sample space outcomes A, C, H, and R are not equally likely—recall that $P(A) = .1$, $P(C) = .2$, $P(H) = .5$, and $P(R) = .2$.

Example 3.6 Lotto 6/49

Lotto 6/49 is one of Canada's national lotteries, and is immensely popular across the country—particularly when the jackpot is large. To play, you choose 6 different numbers between 1 and 49. The more numbers that you match (in any order), the greater your prize:

Number of Matches	Win	Odds of Winning
6/6	80.5% of pool	1 in 13,983,816
5/6 + Bonus	5.75% of pool	1 in 2,330,636
5/6	4.75% of pool	1 in 55,492
4/6	9% of pool	1 in 1,033
3/6	$10	1 in 56.7
2/6 + Bonus	$5	1 in 81.2

Seven numbers are selected when the lottery occurs—6 winning numbers and a bonus number. Note that you don't select a separate number on your ticket for the bonus number—the bonus number is matched to one of your 6 chosen numbers in order to win either of the two prize categories that include the bonus.

Let's look at how the odds for the first three categories are determined. We'll do this with fractions, but it is possible to do this quite elegantly using counting rules. We describe these counting rules in online Appendix B. For now, consider that there are 49 possible numbers in each position on the ticket, and that numbers are never repeated in the draw. The first position on the ticket could have any one of the 6 winning numbers, and there are 49 possible numbers that could be selected. Likewise, the second position on the ticket could have any of the

5 remaining winning numbers, drawn from the 48 remaining numbers. Carrying this process through to the other positions on the ticket:

$$\frac{6}{49} * \frac{5}{48} * \frac{4}{47} * \frac{3}{46} * \frac{2}{45} * \frac{1}{44} = \frac{720}{10,068,347,520} = \frac{1}{13,983,816}$$

In other words, there are 13,983,816 ways in which you could select 6 numbers between 1 and 49, when the order of selection doesn't matter, and the numbers are drawn without replacement. Within this set of possible tickets, only 1 ticket will match the winning numbers.

Let's consider the odds for winning second or third prize. The number of possible 6 number combinations (13,983,816) remains unchanged, but there are more winning ticket combinations for each of these prize categories. To calculate these odds, you need to consider the number of winning numbers present (5 out of 6), and you also need to consider whether the bonus number was selected.

Let's look at the third prize first. This prize category requires that you select 5 out of 6 winning numbers and not have the bonus number. The simpler (albeit more pessimistic) calculation would be to consider that you have selected 1 non-winning number, and this non-winning number must have been selected from among the non-winning/non-bonus numbers. Since there are 49 numbers in total and 7 numbers are chosen during the draw, there are 42 non-winning/non-bonus numbers. As the order of the numbers does not factor into the prize category, the non-winning/non-bonus number could fall into any one of the six positions on your ticket. So there are 252 tickets (6 * 42) that would win third prize. The odds of winning third prize are, therefore,

$$\frac{6 * 42}{13,983,816} = \frac{252}{13,983,816} \approx \frac{1}{55,491}$$

Second prize requires that you select 5 out of 6 winning numbers and also have the bonus number. In other words, you must have selected 1 non-winning number, and that non-winning number must be the bonus number. As with our third prize calculation the non-winning number may fall in any of the six positions on your ticket. In this case, however, there is only one possibility for this non-winning number. There are, therefore, only 6 tickets that would win second prize. So the odds of winning second prize are

$$\frac{6 * 1}{13,983,816} = \frac{1}{2,330,636}$$

Given that the numbers are drawn at random, does drawing any particular number (or set of numbers) increase your chances of winning? Does it make a difference if you select your own numbers, or have the "quick pick" facility at your lottery retailer do it for you? As it happens, under certain circumstances, it does make a difference if you choose your own numbers rather than have the numbers randomly generated by a computer: You may actually reduce the expected value of your winnings if you select your own numbers! Certain sequences of numbers are selected more often by individuals, and this reduces the prize pool available to be won. As we will see in Chapter 4, this reduction in the prize pool has a direct impact on the expected value of your ticket—given that the odds of drawing any set of 6 numbers (regardless of how those 6 numbers are chosen) may be determined mathematically, due to the fact that it is entirely random.

ROADBLOCK

It is important to consider the order of events (if only to determine whether order is important) Note that in the Lotto 6/49 example, the order in which the numbers appears is not important. If the order of the selected numbers were important, it would significantly reduce your odds of winning, because there are more possible combinations of numbers that could be drawn. When order is important within a question, the number of possible combinations will always be larger than when order is not important.

Example 3.7 Probability of Subscribing to *The London Free Press*

Suppose that approximately 65,000 of the 100,000 households in London, Ontario, subscribe to *The London Free Press,* and consider randomly selecting one of the households in this city. That is, consider selecting one household by giving each and every household in the city (irrespective of newspaper subscription) the same chance of being selected. Let A be the event that the randomly selected household subscribes to *The London Free Press.* Then, because the sample space of this experiment consists of 100,000 equally likely sample space outcomes (households), it follows that

$$P(A) = \frac{\text{Number of households that subscribe to } \textit{The London Free Press}}{\text{Total number of households in London}}$$

$$= \frac{65,000}{100,000}$$

$$= .65$$

This says that the probability that the randomly selected household subscribes to *The London Free Press* is .65.

Example 3.8 Calculating the Time Spent Listening to Particular Radio Stations

BBM Canada is a not-for-profit company that provides consumer behaviour intelligence to radio and television broadcasters and advertisers. Table 3.1 gives portions of a BBM report on radio ratings in the Calgary market. This report gives estimates of the number and the percentage of Calgary residents who would name each of these radio stations as the station they listen to most.

TABLE 3.1 Market Share and Number of Individuals Exposed to Each Station Per Day, among the Top Ten Radio Stations in Calgary, Alberta (Feb. 27, 2012, to May 27, 2012)

Station	Market Share (%)	Average Number of Individuals Exposed to Station Each Day
CBR	10.4	119,800
CHQR	10.3	98,500
CKRY FM	8.4	104,500
CHFM FM	7.3	146,400
CIBK FM	7.1	183,500
CFXL FM	7.0	125,600
CKMP FM	6.0	137,700
CJAY FM	5.8	111,200
CJAQ FM	5.3	119,200
CFGQ FM	4.8	85,000

Source: *PPM Top-Line Radio Data*, BBM Canada.

To better understand the estimates in Table 3.1, we will consider how they were obtained. Although BBM Canada still utilizes user diaries to track listening and viewing habits, in certain large broadcasting markets in Canada (Montreal, Toronto, Calgary, Edmonton, and Vancouver), BBM Canada uses electronic meters called "portable people meters" (PPM). A PPM is an electronic device that is about the size of a pager that is carried around by an individual in the sample throughout the day. The PPM is able to pick up the radio or television station being listened to and transmit this information to BBM Canada at the end of each day. This example uses radio data drawn from a randomly selected group of approximately 450 households in the Calgary area, between February 27 and May 27, 2012, to estimate the proportion of time spent listening to each of the top ten radio stations in the area. It does this by using the time spent by individuals in the PPM sample listening to particular radio stations (the "market share" of each radio station) to estimate the market share of each station across radio listeners throughout the Calgary area.

Note that these data are measured as a percentage of time spent listening to the radio, so this data cannot be used to estimate the number of individuals listening to the radio. For example, if the time spent listening to CHQR was 116 out of 1,125 total hours spent listening to the radio, then $116/1,125 = .1031$ is an estimate of $P(\text{CHQR})$, the probability that a randomly selected Calgary radio listener would be listening to CHQR at any given time (note that the market share for CHQR is 10.3 percent in Table 3.1). Furthermore, if Calgary residents spend 1,125,000 hours listening to the radio during this time period, an estimate of the total number of hours spent listening to CHQR, between February 27 and May 27, 2012, would be

$$(1{,}125{,}000) \times (.1031) = 115{,}987.5$$

or 115,987 hours and 30 minutes.

Note that this table also includes the average number of individuals per day that were exposed to the station for at least one minute. If, on average, 98,500 individuals were exposed to CHQR each day, and Calgary has an approximate population of 1,249,000, this suggests that the proportion of the population that will listen to CHQR at some point during the day is $98{,}500/1{,}249{,}000 = .07886$, or approximately 7.9 percent.

Exercises for Sections **3.1** and **3.2**

CONCEPTS

3.1   Define the following terms: *experiment, event, probability, sample space.*

3.2   Explain the properties that must be satisfied by a probability.

METHODS AND APPLICATIONS

3.3   Two randomly selected grocery store patrons are each asked to take a blind taste test and to then state which of three diet colas (marked as A, B, or C) he or she prefers.
   a. Draw a tree diagram depicting the sample space outcomes for the test results.
   b. List the sample space outcomes that correspond to each of the following events:
      (1) Both patrons prefer diet cola A.
      (2) The two patrons prefer the same diet cola.
      (3) The two patrons prefer different diet colas.
      (4) Diet cola A is preferred by at least one of the two patrons.
      (5) Neither of the patrons prefers diet cola C.
   c. Assuming that all sample space outcomes are equally likely, find the probability of each of the events given in part (b).

3.4   Suppose that a couple will have three children. Letting B denote a boy and G denote a girl:
   a. Draw a tree diagram depicting the sample space outcomes for this experiment.
   b. List the sample space outcomes that correspond to each of the following events:
      (1) All three children will have the same gender.
      (2) Exactly two of the three children will be girls.

   (3) Exactly one of the three children will be a girl.
   (4) None of the three children will be a girl.
   c. Assuming that all sample space outcomes are equally likely, find the probability of each of the events given in part (b).

3.5   Four people enter an automobile showroom and each will either purchase a car (P) or not purchase a car (N).
   a. Draw a tree diagram depicting the sample space of all possible purchase decisions that could potentially be made by the four people.
   b. List the sample space outcomes that correspond to each of the following events:
      (1) Exactly three people will purchase a car.
      (2) Two or fewer people will purchase a car.
      (3) One or more people will purchase a car.
      (4) All four people will make the same purchase decision.
   c. Assuming that all sample space outcomes are equally likely, find the probability of each of the events given in part (b).

3.6   Consider the four customers in Exercise 3.5, but now consider that the probability of purchasing a car (P) is .10, and the probability of not purchasing a car (N) is .90. What is the probability that
   a. Exactly three people will purchase a car
   b. Two or fewer people will purchase a car
   c. One or more people will purchase a car
   d. All four people will make the same purchase decision

3.7   Using the information given in the BBM Canada figures presented in Table 3.1, find estimates of each of the following:

a. The probability that a randomly selected Calgary resident would be exposed to radio station CJAQ-FM on an average day.

b. The probability that a randomly selected Calgary resident would *not* be exposed to radio station CKMP on an average day.

c. The probability that a randomly encountered radio in Calgary will be tuned to CHQR, CFXL-FM, or CHFM-FM.

d. The number of hours spent listening to CKRY-FM within the assessment period, if the total number of radio listening hours in the assessment period was 1,125,000.

3.8 Let *A*, *B*, *C*, *D*, and *E* be sample space outcomes forming a sample space. Suppose that $P(A) = .2$, $P(B) = .15$, $P(C) = .3$, and $P(D) = .2$. What is $P(E)$? Explain how you got your answer.

3.9 If the probability of defaulting on a loan is 5 percent within a particular risk category, how many loans will go into default if a bank gives 1,748 such loans in a given month?

3.10 Consider Exercise 3.9 again. A bank is concerned that a branch is not accurately screening loan candidates. In a randomly selected batch of five loans within this risk category, four were found to be in default. What is the probability that this could occur simply due to chance?

3.11 You are gambling with a friend in a "winner takes all" game of dice. In the game, the person who rolls the highest number wins. If you assume fair dice and that no forms of mechanical cheating are present, the probability of winning is .50. You are lucky and win four games in a row. What is the probability that you will win a fifth time?

3.12 Consider Exercise 3.11, and imagine that you did, in fact, win the fifth game. What is the probability of winning five games in a row with these odds?

3.13 The game of craps is considerably more complex than simply rolling two dice and declaring the person with the higher score to be the winner. In craps, you are playing against "the house" (the gambling establishment)—not the other players. Accordingly, the payoff on various outcomes is determined by the odds of winning. Although there are a number of ways to win the game, the fastest way to win is with a "natural" (a 7 or 11) on the very first roll. Likewise, the fastest way to lose the game is to "crap out" with a roll of 2, 3, or 12. Calculate the probability of rolling a "natural" on your first roll of the dice, and compare this with the probability of rolling "craps" on the first roll. (Hint: Don't forget that there are a number of ways in which you can roll some of these numbers.)

3.3 SOME ELEMENTARY PROBABILITY RULES

We can often calculate probabilities by using formulas called *probability rules*. We will begin by presenting the simplest probability rule: the *rule of complements*. To start, we define the *complement of an event*:

The **complement of an event** is the opposite of an event—it is the set of all outcomes of an experiment that are not included in an event. For example, when the event is "male," the complement is "female." Or when the event is "heads," the complement is "tails." The complement of *A* is denoted $\overline{A}$. Furthermore, $P(\overline{A})$ denotes the probability that *A* will not occur.

LO3

Figure 3.3 is a Venn diagram depicting the complement $\overline{A}$ of an event *A*. In any probability situation, either an event *A* or its complement $\overline{A}$ must occur. Therefore, we have

$$P(A) + P(\overline{A}) = 1$$

which implies the following result:

The Rule of Complements

Consider an event *A*. Then, the probability that *A* will not occur is

$$P(\overline{A}) = 1 - P(A)$$

FIGURE **3.3** The Complement of an Event (the Shaded Region Is $\overline{A}$, the Complement of *A*)

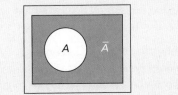

Example 3.9   Complementary Probability

Recall from Example 3.7 that the probability that a randomly selected household in London, Ontario, subscribes to *The London Free Press* is .65. It follows that the probability of the complement of this event (that is, the probability that a randomly selected household in London does *not* subscribe to *The London Free Press*) is $1 - .65 = .35$.

Example 3.10   Unions and Intersections

As in Example 3.7, suppose that 65,000 of the 100,000 households in London, Ontario, subscribe to *The London Free Press* and also, suppose that 50,000 households in the city receive another local newspaper, *The Londoner*). Further suppose that 25,000 households receive both *The London Free Press* and *The Londoner*. As in Example 3.7, we consider randomly selecting one household in the city, and we define the following events:

> $A \equiv$ Randomly selected household receives *The London Free Press.*
> $\overline{A} \equiv$ Randomly selected household does not receive *The London Free Press.*
> $B \equiv$ Randomly selected household receives *The Londoner.*
> $\overline{B} \equiv$ Randomly selected household does not receive *The Londoner.*

Using the notation $A \cap B$ to denote *both A and B*, we also define

> $A \cap B \equiv$ Randomly selected household receives both *The London Free Press* and *The Londoner.*

If 65,000 of the 100,000 households receive *The London Free Press* (that is, correspond to event A occurring), then 35,000 households do not receive *The London Free Press* (that is, correspond to event $\overline{A}$ occurring). Similarly, if 50,000 households receive *The Londoner* (B), 50,000 households do not receive *The Londoner* ($\overline{B}$). We summarize this information, as well as the 25,000 households that correspond to the event $A \cap B$ occurring, in Table 3.2.

TABLE **3.2**   A Summary of the Number of Households Corresponding to the Events A, $\overline{A}$, B, $\overline{B}$, and $A \cap B$

Events	Receives *The Londoner* B	Does Not Receive *The Londoner* B	Total
Receives *The London Free Press*, A	25,000		65,000
Does Not Receive *The London Free Press*, $\overline{A}$			35,000
Total	50,000	50,000	100,000

Next, consider the following events:

> $A \cap \overline{B} \equiv$ Randomly selected household receives *The London Free Press* and does not receive *The Londoner.*
> $\overline{A} \cap B \equiv$ Randomly selected household does not receive *The London Free Press* and does receive *The Londoner.*
> $\overline{A} \cap \overline{B} \equiv$ Randomly selected household does not receive *The London Free Press* and does not receive *The Londoner.*

Since 65,000 households subscribe to *The London Free Press* (A) and 25,000 households subscribe to both *The London Free Press* and *The Londoner* ($A \cap B$), it follows that $65,000 - 25,000 = 40,000$ households subscribe to *The London Free Press* but do not subscribe to *The Londoner* ($A \cap \bar{B}$). This subtraction is illustrated in Table 3.3(a). By similar logic, it also follows that

1   As illustrated in Table 3.3(b), $50,000 - 25,000 = 25,000$ households do not subscribe to *The London Free Press* but do subscribe to *The Londoner* ($\bar{A} \cap B$).

2   As illustrated in Table 3.3(c), $35,000 - 25,000 = 10,000$ households do not subscribe to *The London Free Press* and do not subscribe to *The Londoner* ($\bar{A} \cap \bar{B}$).

TABLE **3.3**   Subtracting to Find the Number of Households Corresponding to the Events $A \cap \bar{B}$, $\bar{A} \cap B$, and $\bar{A} \cap \bar{B}$

(a) The Number of Households Corresponding to (A and $\bar{B}$)

Events	Receives *The Londoner* B	Does Not Receive *The Londoner* $\bar{B}$	Total
Receives *The London Free Press*, A	25,000	65,000 − 25,000 = 40,000	65,000
Does Not Receive *The London Free Press*, $\bar{A}$			35,000
Total	50,000	50,000	100,000

(b) The Number of Households Corresponding to ($\bar{A}$ and B)

Events	Receives *The Londoner* B	Does Not Receive *The Londoner* $\bar{B}$	Total
Receives *The London Free Press*, A	25,000	65,000 − 25,000 = 40,000	65,000
Does Not Receive *The London Free Press*, $\bar{A}$	50,000 − 25,000 = 25,000		35,000
Total	50,000	50,000	100,000

(c) The Number of Households Corresponding to ($\bar{A}$ and $\bar{B}$)

Events	Receives *The Londoner* B	Does Not Receive *The Londoner* $\bar{B}$	Total
Receives *The London Free Press*, A	25,000	65,000 − 25,000 = 40,000	65,000
Does Not Receive *The London Free Press*, $\bar{A}$	50,000 − 25,000 = 25,000	50,000 − 40,000 = 10,000	35,000
Total	50,000	50,000	100,000

We summarize all of these results in Table 3.4, which is called a *contingency table*. Because we will randomly select one household (making all of the households equally likely to be chosen), the probability of any of the previously defined events is the ratio of the number of households corresponding to the event's occurrence to the total number of households in the city. Therefore, for example,

$$P(A) = \frac{65,000}{100,000} = .65 \qquad P(B) = \frac{50,000}{100,000} = .50$$

$$P(A \cap B) = \frac{25,000}{100,000} = .25$$

This last probability says that the probability that the randomly selected household receives both *The London Free Press* and *The Londoner* is .25.

Next, letting $A \cup B$ denote A or B (or both), we consider finding the probability of the event

$A \cup B \equiv$ Randomly selected household receives *The London Free Press* or *The Londoner* (or both)

—that is, receives at least one of the two newspapers.

TABLE 3.4   A Contingency Table Summarizing Circulation Data for *The London Free Press* and *The Londoner*

Events	Receives *The Londoner* B	Does Not Receive *The Londoner* $\bar{B}$	Total
Receives *The London Free Press*, A	25,000	40,000	65,000
Does Not Receive *The London Free Press*, $\bar{A}$	25,000	10,000	35,000
Total	50,000	50,000	100,000

Looking at Table 3.4, we see that the households receiving *The London Free Press* or *The Londoner* are (1) the 40,000 households that receive only *The London Free Press*, $(A \cap \bar{B})$, (2) the 25,000 households that receive only *The Londoner*, $(\bar{A} \cap B)$, and (3) the 25,000 households that receive both *The London Free Press* and *The Londoner*, $(A \cap B)$. Therefore, since a total of 90,000 households receive either *The London Free Press* or *The Londoner*, it follows that

$$P(A \cup B) = \frac{90,000}{100,000} = .90$$

This suggests that the probability of a randomly selected household receiving *The London Free Press* or *The Londoner* is .90. That is, 90 percent of the households in the city receive *The London Free Press* or *The Londoner*.

Notice that $P(A \cup B) = 0.90$ does not equal

$$P(A) + P(B) = .65 + .5 = 1.15$$

Logically, the reason for this is that both $P(A) = .65$ and $P(B) = .5$ count the 25 percent of the households that receive both newspapers. Therefore, the sum of $P(A)$ and $P(B)$ counts this 25 percent of the households once too often. It follows, then, that if we subtract $P(A \cap B) = 0.25$ from the sum of $P(A)$ and $P(B)$, then we will obtain $P(A \cup B)$. That is,

$$P(A \cup B) = P(A) + P(B) - P(A \cap B)$$
$$= .65 + .5 - .25 = .90$$

ROADBLOCK

Check your marginal totals
The row and column marginal totals are important aspects of your calculations—not only in this chapter, but for other topics in this textbook. A quick check to ensure that you have not made any arithmetic errors is to compare the sum of the row marginal totals to the sum of the column marginal totals. These sums should always be equivalent and should be equal to the total number of observations in your contingency table.

The Intersection and Union of Two Events

Given two events A and B,

1   The *intersection of A and B* is the event consisting of the sample space outcomes belonging to both A and B. The intersection is denoted by A ∩ B. Furthermore, P(A ∩ B) denotes *the probability that both A and B will simultaneously occur.*

2   The *union of A and B* is the event consisting of the sample space outcomes belonging to A or B (or both). The union is denoted A ∪ B. Furthermore, P(A ∪ B) denotes *the probability that A or B (or both) will occur.*

FIGURE **3.4** Venn Diagrams Depicting the Events *A, B, A ∩ B*, and *A ∪ B*

FIGURE **3.5** Two Mutually Exclusive Events

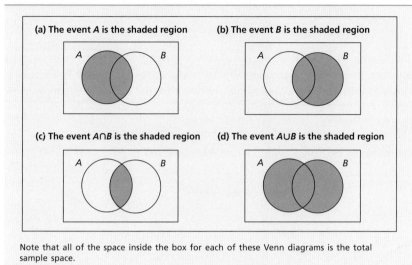

(a) The event *A* is the shaded region

(b) The event *B* is the shaded region

(c) The event *A∩B* is the shaded region

(d) The event *A∪B* is the shaded region

Note that all of the space inside the box for each of these Venn diagrams is the total sample space.

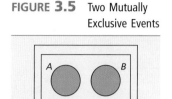

Noting that Figure 3.4 shows Venn diagrams depicting the events *A, B, A ∩ B*, and *A ∪ B*, we have the following general result:

The Addition Rule

Let *A* and *B* be events. Then, *the probability that A or B (or both) will occur* is

$$P(A \cup B) = P(A) + P(B) - P(A \cap B)$$

The reasoning behind this result was illustrated at the end of Example 3.10. Similarly, the Venn diagrams in Figure 3.4 show that when we compute $P(A) + P(B)$, we are counting each of the sample space outcomes in $A \cap B$ twice. We correct for this by subtracting $P(A \cap B)$.

Mutually Exclusive Events

Events *A* and *B* are **mutually exclusive events** if they have no sample space outcomes in common. In this case, the events *A* and *B* cannot occur simultaneously, so

$$P(A \cap B) = 0$$

Noting that Figure 3.5 is a Venn diagram depicting two mutually exclusive events, we consider Example 3.11.

Example 3.11 Mutually Exclusive Events

Consider randomly selecting a card from a standard deck of 52 playing cards. We define the following events:

$J \equiv$ Randomly selected card is a jack.

$Q \equiv$ Randomly selected card is a queen.

$R \equiv$ Randomly selected card is a red card (that is, a diamond or a heart).

Because there is no card that is both a jack and a queen, the events *J* and *Q* are mutually exclusive. On the other hand, there are two cards that are both jacks and red cards—the jack of diamonds and the jack of hearts—so the events *J* and *R* are not mutually exclusive.

We have seen that for any two events A and B, the probability that A or B (or both) will occur is

$$P(A \cup B) = P(A) + P(B) - P(A \cap B)$$

Therefore, when calculating $P(A \cup B)$, we should always subtract $P(A \cap B)$ from the sum of $P(A)$ and $P(B)$. However, when A and B are mutually exclusive, $P(A \cap B)$ equals 0. Therefore, in this case—and only in this case, the addition rule for two mutually exclusive events applies.

The Addition Rule for Two Mutually Exclusive Events

Let A and B be mutually exclusive events. Then, *the probability that A or B will occur* is

$$P(A \cup B) = P(A) + P(B)$$

Example 3.12 More on Mutually Exclusive Events

Again consider randomly selecting a card from a standard deck of 52 playing cards, and define the events

$J \equiv$ Randomly selected card is a jack.

$Q \equiv$ Randomly selected card is a queen.

$R \equiv$ Randomly selected card is a red card (a diamond or a heart).

Since there are four jacks, four queens, and 26 red cards, we have $P(J) = \frac{4}{52}$, $P(Q) = \frac{4}{52}$, and $P(R) = \frac{26}{52}$. Furthermore, since there is no card that is both a jack and a queen, the events J and Q are mutually exclusive, so $P(J \cap Q) = 0$. It follows that the probability that the randomly selected card is a jack or a queen is

$$P(J \cup Q) = P(J) + P(Q)$$
$$= \frac{4}{52} + \frac{4}{52} = \frac{8}{52} = \frac{2}{13}$$

Since there are two cards that are both jacks and red cards—the jack of diamonds and the jack of hearts—the events J and R are not mutually exclusive. Therefore, the probability that the randomly selected card is a jack or a red card is

$$P(J \cup R) = P(J) + P(R) - P(J \cap R)$$
$$= \frac{4}{52} + \frac{26}{52} - \frac{2}{52} = \frac{28}{52} = \frac{7}{13}$$

We now consider an arbitrary group of events—$A_1, A_2, \ldots, A_N$. We will denote the probability that A_1 or A_2 or ... or A_N occurs (that is, the probability that at least one of the events occurs) as $P(A_1 \cup A_2 \cup \ldots \cup A_N)$. Although there is a formula for this probability, it is quite complicated and we will not present it in this book. However, sometimes sample spaces can be used to reason out such a probability. For instance, in the playing card situation in Example 3.12, there are four jacks, four queens, and 22 red cards that are not jacks or queens (the 26 red cards minus the two red jacks and the two red queens). Therefore, because there are a total of 30 cards corresponding to the event, $J \cup Q \cup R$ it follows that

$$P(J \cup Q \cup R) = \frac{30}{52} = \frac{15}{26}$$

Because some cards are both jacks and red cards, and because some cards are both queens and red cards, we say that the events *J*, *Q*, and *R* are not mutually exclusive. When, however, a group of events is mutually exclusive, there is a simple formula for the probability that at least one of the events will occur, as shown in the boxed feature "The Addition Rule for *N* Mutually Exclusive Events."

The Addition Rule for *N* Mutually Exclusive Events

The events $A_1, A_2, \ldots, A_N$ are mutually exclusive if no two of the events have any sample space outcomes in common. In this case, no two of the events can occur simultaneously, and

$$P(A_1 \cup A_2 \cup \cdots \cup A_N) = P(A_1) + P(A_2) + \cdots + P(A_N)$$

As an example of using this formula, again consider the playing card situation and the events *J* and *Q*. If we define the event

$$K \equiv \text{Randomly selected card is a king}$$

then the events *J*, *Q*, and *K* are mutually exclusive. Therefore,

$$P(J \cup Q \cup K) = P(J) + P(Q) + P(K)$$
$$= \frac{4}{52} + \frac{4}{52} + \frac{4}{52} = \frac{12}{52} = \frac{3}{13}$$

Example 3.13 Probability of Listening to a Top Ten Radio Station

Recall that Table 3.1 gives the BBM Canada estimates of the number of individuals exposed to each of the top ten radio stations in the Calgary area, as well as the percentage of radio listening time that is spent listening to each of these Calgary radio stations. We will let the call letters of each station denote the event that a randomly selected radio is tuned to a particular station. Since each radio can be playing only a single station, and since the sample space includes only the time when the radio is turned on, the ten events

| CBR | CHQR | CKRY-FM | CHFM-FM | CIBK-FM |
| CFXL-FM | CKMP-FM | CJAY-FM | CJAQ-FM | CFGQ-FM |

are mutually exclusive. Therefore, for example, the probability that a randomly selected Calgary radio would be tuned to a station that is ranked among the top ten (according to market share)

$$P(\text{CBR} \cup \text{CHQR} \cup \cdots \cup \text{CFGQ-FM})$$

is the sum of the ten individual station market shares

$$P(\text{CBR}) + P(\text{CHQR}) + \cdots + P(\text{CFGQ-FM})$$

so we can estimate that the probability that a randomly selected Calgary radio would be tuned to a station that is ranked among the top ten is

$$.104 + .103 + .084 + .073 + .071 + .070 + .060 + .058 + .053 + .048 = .724$$

Note that these probabilities sum to less than 1 because there are more than ten stations in Calgary.

THEORY TO PRACTICE

Throughout this chapter, it should have become clear that we employ probability theory on a daily basis in both our personal and professional lives. Every time you say that something is "probably true" or is "a good bet," you are implicitly assigning a probability to its occurrence. Whether it's deciding whether a particular individual is a good candidate for a loan or is likely to be a good employee, a number of business decisions are made on the basis of probability. The insurance industry, in particular, is designed around the evaluation of probabilities—from determining an individual's likely lifespan to determining an individual's probability of being in a car accident.

In evaluating business transactions, we can (and should) examine the probability of success and weigh the value of this success against the penalty associated with failure. In making decisions of this sort, however, it is important to evaluate the source of your probability estimates. Are they empirically based (i.e., based on the results of experimentation and/or systematic observation)? Or are they entirely subjective? Although intuition and personal judgment can be valuable tools in making business decisions, subjective probabilities can lead to a superficial examination of the risks associated with decisions.

Exercises for Section **3.3**

CONCEPTS

3.14 Explain what it means for two events to be mutually exclusive for N events.

3.15 If A and B are events, define $\overline{A}$, $A \cup B$, $A \cap B$, and $\overline{A} \cap \overline{B}$.

METHODS AND APPLICATIONS

3.16 Consider a standard deck of 52 playing cards, a randomly selected card from the deck, and the following events:

R = Red B = Black A = Ace N = Nine
D = Diamond C = Club

   a. Describe the sample space outcomes that correspond to each of these events.
   b. For each of the following pairs of events, indicate whether the events are mutually exclusive. In each case, if you think the events are mutually exclusive, explain why the events have no common sample space outcomes. If you think the events are not mutually exclusive, list the sample space outcomes that are common to both events.
   (1) R and A **(3)** A and N **(5)** D and C
   (2) R and C **(4)** N and C

3.17 Of 10,000 students at a college, 2,500 have a MasterCard (M), 4,000 have a Visa (V), and 1,000 have both.
   a. Find the probability that a randomly selected student
   (1) Has a MasterCard.
   (2) Has a Visa.
   (3) Has both credit cards.
   b. Construct and fill in a contingency table summarizing the credit card data. Employ the following pairs of events: M and $\overline{M}$, V and $\overline{V}$.
   c. Use the contingency table to find the probability that a randomly selected student
   (1) Has a MasterCard or a Visa.
   (2) Has neither credit card.
   (3) Has exactly one of the two credit cards.

3.18 The card game of Euchre employs a deck that consists of all four of each of the aces, kings, queens, jacks, tens, and nines (one of each suit—clubs, diamonds, spades, and hearts). Find the probability that a randomly selected card from a Euchre deck is
   a. A jack (J).
   b. A spade (S).
   c. A jack or an ace (A).
   d. A jack or a spade.
   e. Are the events J and A mutually exclusive? J and S? Why or why not?

3.19 Each month a brokerage house studies various companies and rates each company's stock as being either "low risk" or "moderate to high risk." In a recent report, the brokerage house summarized its findings about 15 aerospace companies and 25 food retailers in the following table:

Company Type	Low Risk	Moderate to High Risk
Aerospace company	6	9
Food retailer	15	10

If we randomly select one of the total of 40 companies, find
   a. The probability that the company is a food retailer.
   b. The probability that the company's stock is "low risk."
   c. The probability that the company's stock is "moderate to high risk."
   d. The probability that the company is a food retailer and has a stock that is "low risk."
   e. The probability that the company is a food retailer or has a stock that is "low risk."

TABLE **3.5** Results of a Concept Study for a New Vodka-Based Drink 🔊

Rating	Total	Gender		Age Group		
		Male	Female	21–24	25–34	35–49
Extremely appealing (5)	151	68	83	48	66	37
(4)	91	51	40	36	36	19
(3)	36	21	15	9	12	15
(2)	13	7	6	4	6	3
Not at all appealing (1)	9	3	6	4	3	2

3.20 Three hundred consumers between 21 and 49 years old were randomly selected to evaluate a new vodka-based drink. After sampling the new beverage, each was asked to rate the appeal of the description

Not sweet like wine coolers, not filling like beer, and more refreshing than wine or mixed drinks

as it related to the new beverage. The rating was made on a scale from 1 to 5, with 5 representing "extremely appealing" and with 1 representing "not at all appealing." The results obtained are given in Table 3.5.

Based on these results, estimate the probability that a randomly selected 21- to 49-year-old consumer
a. Would give the phrase a rating of 5.
b. Would give the phrase a rating of 3 or higher.
c. Is in the 21–24 age group; the 25–34 age group; the 35–49 age group.
d. Is a male who gives the phrase a rating of 4.
e. Is a 35- to 49-year-old who gives the phrase a rating of 1.

3.21 Using the information in Table 3.1, find an estimate of the probability that a randomly selected Calgary radio would
a. Be tuned to one of the top three-ranked stations (CBR, CHQR, CKRY-FM).
b. Not be tuned to any one of the top five-ranked stations.
c. Be tuned to a station that is not ranked among the top seven stations.
d. Be tuned to a station that is neither ranked among the top three stations nor ranked lower than tenth in the list of the top ten-ranked radio stations in Calgary.

3.22 Retail clothing stores frequently carry accessory items, such as socks and belts, that are infrequently purchased individually but that can markedly improve the overall profitability of the store (owing in part to their smaller inventory footprint). To this end, sales clerks are usually coached to "upsell" these accessories at the point of purchase. You collect data on 100 purchases within your store, and note that, overall, accessory items are purchased in 40 percent of purchases. If 87.5 percent of accessories are purchased as a result of upselling, and your sales clerks attempt to upsell purchases 85 percent of the time, what is the probability that you will sell accessories without upselling?

3.23 You want to identify some of the important factors associated with auto insurance purchasing decisions, so you conduct a survey of 250 individuals with auto insurance, and find the following data (expressed as a percentage):

		Where Purchased			
		Agent	Web	Employer	Financial Advisor
	Price	4	20	1	0
Primary Factor Driving Purchase Decision	Quality of coverage	40	1	0	1
	Convenience	7	8	6	1
	Brand reputation	9	1	0	1

Based on this data, calculate the probability that
a. A randomly selected individual will purchase auto insurance on the web.
b. A randomly selected individual will consider quality of coverage to be the most important consideration.
c. An individual purchasing auto insurance on the web will have done so primarily because of the convenience.
d. An individual primarily concerned about price will have purchased insurance from an agent.

3.4 CONDITIONAL PROBABILITY AND INDEPENDENCE

Conditional probability In Table 3.6, we repeat the contingency table summarizing the circulation data for *The London Free Press* and *The Londoner*. Suppose that we randomly select a household and that the chosen household reports that it receives *The Londoner*. Given this new information, we want to find the probability that the household also receives *The London Free Press*. This new probability is called a *conditional probability*.

TABLE **3.6** Contingency Table Summarizing Circulation Data for
The London Free Press and *The Londoner*

Events	Receives *The Londoner* B	Does Not Receive *The Londoner* $\bar{B}$	Total
Receives *The London Free Press, A*	25,000	40,000	65,000
Does Not Receive *The London Free Press, $\bar{A}$*	25,000	10,000	35,000
Total	50,000	50,000	100,000

LO4

The probability of the event A, given the condition that the event B has occurred, is written as $P(A|B)$, which stands for "the probability of A, given B." We often refer to such a probability as the **conditional probability** of A, given B.

In order to find the conditional probability that a household receives *The London Free Press*, given that it receives *The Londoner,* notice that if we know that the randomly selected household receives *The Londoner,* we know that we are considering one of 50,000 households (see Table 3.6). That is, we are now considering what we might call a *reduced sample space* of 50,000 households. Since 25,000 of these 50,000 *Londoner* recipients also subscribe to *The London Free Press,* we have

$$P(A|B) = \frac{25,000}{50,000} = .5$$

This says that the probability that the randomly selected household receives *The London Free Press*, given that the household receives *The Londoner*, is .5. That is, 50 percent of households that receive *The Londoner* also receive *The London Free Press.*

Next, suppose that we randomly select another household from the community of 100,000 households in London, and suppose that this newly chosen household reports that it receives *The London Free Press.* We now want to find the probability that this household receives *The Londoner.* We write this new probability as $P(B|A)$, or "the probability of B, given A." If we know that this randomly selected household receives *The London Free Press,* we know that we are considering a reduced sample space of 65,000 households (see Table 3.6). Since 25,000 of these 65,000 *London Free Press* recipients also receive *The Londoner,* we have

$$P(B|A) = \frac{25,000}{65,000} = .3846$$

This says that the probability of a randomly selected household receiving *The Londoner*, given that the household receives *The London Free Press*, is .3846. That is, 38.46 percent of *London Free Press* recipients also receive *The Londoner.*

If we divide both the numerator and denominator of each of the conditional probabilities $P(A|B)$ and $P(B|A)$ by 100,000, we obtain

$$P(A|B) = \frac{25,000}{50,000} = \frac{25,000/100,000}{50,000/100,000} = \frac{P(A \cap B)}{P(B)}$$

$$P(B|A) = \frac{25,000}{65,000} = \frac{25,000/100,000}{65,000/100,000} = \frac{P(A \cap B)}{P(A)}$$

We express these conditional probabilities in terms of $P(A)$, $P(B)$, and $P(A \cap B)$ in order to obtain a more general formula for a conditional probability. We need a more general formula because, although we can use the reduced sample space approach we have demonstrated to find conditional probabilities when all of the sample space outcomes are equally likely, this approach may not give correct results when the sample space outcomes are *not* equally likely. See the boxed feature "Conditional Probability" for expressions for conditional probability that are valid for any sample space.

Conditional Probability

1 The conditional probability that *A* will occur, given that *B* will occur, is written $P(A|B)$ and is defined to be

$$P(A|B) = \frac{P(A \cap B)}{P(B)}$$

Here we assume that $P(B)$ is greater than 0.

2 The conditional probability that *B* will occur, given that *A* will occur, is written $P(B|A)$ and is defined to be

$$P(B|A) = \frac{P(A \cap B)}{P(A)}$$

Here we assume that $P(A)$ is greater than 0.

If we multiply both sides of the equation

$$P(A|B) = \frac{P(A \cap B)}{P(B)}$$

by $P(B)$, we obtain the equation

$$P(A \cap B) = P(B)P(A|B)$$

Similarly, if we multiply both sides of the equation

$$P(B|A) = \frac{P(A \cap B)}{P(A)}$$

by $P(A)$, we obtain the equation

$$P(A \cap B) = P(A)P(B|A)$$

In summary, we now have two equations that can be used to calculate $P(A \cap B)$. These equations are often referred to as the *general multiplication rule* for probabilities.

The General Multiplication Rule—Two Ways to Calculate $P(A \cap B)$

Given any two events *A* and *B*,

$$P(A \cap B) = P(A)P(B|A)$$
$$= P(B)P(A|B)$$

Example 3.14 Environmental Regulation Vs. Economic Growth

The trade-off between environmental regulation and economic growth is a controversial topic—and public opinion on the appropriate balance between these concerns differs by country. A 2011 Angus Reid poll asked participants from Canada, the United States, and Britain if they would favour protecting the environment, even at the risk of hampering economic growth, or if they would favour fostering economic growth, even at the risk of damaging the environment. Table 3.7 is based on the results of this poll.

TABLE 3.7   Contingency Table Summarizing Attitudes toward Environmental Protection and Fostering Economic Growth, across Canada, the United States, and Britain

	Canada	United States	Britain	Totals
Protect the environment	582	458	870	1,910
Foster economic growth	201	275	607	1,083
Totals	783	733	1,477	2,993

Source: These frequencies were based on the reported sample sizes and tabular percentages in the Angus Reid Public Opinion poll report, "Global Warming Skepticism Higher in U.S. and Britain Than Canada," June 27, 2011, New York.

From the data in Table 3.7, assuming representative samples, the probability that a randomly selected survey respondent is a Canadian who favours environmental protection, is

$$P(E \cap C) = \frac{582}{2,993} = .19$$

More interesting, however, are the conditional probabilities that can be calculated within this data, as they allow for cross-country comparisons.

The probability that a randomly selected individual from each country will favour protecting the environment over fostering economic growth is

$$P(E|C) = \frac{582}{783} = .74 \qquad P(E|US) = \frac{458}{733} = .62 \qquad P(E|GB) = \frac{870}{1,477} = .59$$

Finally, we can use the general multiplication rule, in combination with the conditional probabilities listed above, to derive each of the probabilities within the cells. For example, the probability of being a Canadian who favours environmental protection is .19, as previously noted. This could have been derived as follows:

$$P(E \cap C) = P(C){*}P(E|C) = \left(\frac{783}{2,993}\right)\left(\frac{582}{783}\right) = \frac{582}{2,993} = .19$$

or equivalently

$$P(E \cap C) = P(E){*}P(C|E) = \left(\frac{1,910}{2,993}\right)\left(\frac{582}{1,910}\right) = \frac{582}{2,993} = .19$$

Example 3.15 Soft Drink Taste Test

In a soft drink taste test, each of 1,000 consumers chose between two colas—Cola 1 and Cola 2— and stated whether she or he preferred a *sweet* or a *very sweet* cola drink. Unfortunately, some of the survey information was lost. The following information remains:

1   68.3 percent of the consumers (that is, 683 consumers) preferred Cola 1 to Cola 2.

2   62 percent of the consumers (that is, 620 consumers) preferred a *sweet* cola (rather than a *very sweet* one).

3   85 percent of the consumers who said that they liked a *sweet* cola preferred Cola 1 to Cola 2.

To recover all of the lost survey information, consider randomly selecting one of the 1,000 survey participants, and define the following events:

$C_1 \equiv$ Randomly selected consumer prefers Cola 1.

$C_2 \equiv$ Randomly selected consumer prefers Cola 2.

$S \equiv$ Randomly selected consumer prefers *sweet* cola drinks.

$V \equiv$ Randomly selected consumer prefers *very sweet* cola drinks.

From the survey information that remains, (1) says that $P(C_1) = .683$, (2) says that $P(S) = .62$, and (3) says that $P(C_1|S) = .85$.

We will see that we can recover all of the lost survey information if we can find $P(C_1 \cap S)$. The general multiplication rule says that

$$P(C_1 \cap S) = P(C_1)P(S|C_1) = P(S)P(C_1|S)$$

Although we know that $P(C_1) = .683$, we do not know $P(S|C_1)$. Therefore, we cannot calculate $P(C_1 \cap S)$ as $P(C_1)P(S|C_1)$. However, because we know that $P(S) = .62$ and that $P(C_1|S) = .85$, we can calculate

$$P(C_1 \cap S) = P(S)P(C_1|S) = (.62)(.85) = (.527)$$

This implies that 527 consumers preferred Cola 1 and preferred their cola *sweet*. Since 683 consumers preferred Cola 1 and 620 consumers preferred *sweet* cola drinks, we can summarize the numbers of consumers corresponding to the events C_1, C_2, S, V, and $(C_1 \cap S)$ as shown in Table 3.8. Furthermore, by performing subtractions as shown in Table 3.9, the numbers of consumers corresponding to the events $(C_1 \cap V)$, $(C_2 \cap S)$, and $(C_2 \cap V)$ can be obtained. We summarize all of our results in Table 3.10. We will use these results in the next subsection to investigate the relationship between cola preference and sweetness preference.

TABLE **3.8** A Summary of the Number of Consumers Corresponding to the Events C_1, C_2, S, V, and $C_1 \cap S$

Events	S (Sweet)	V (Very Sweet)	Total
C_1 (Cola 1)	527		683
C_2 (Cola 2)			317
Total	620	380	1,000

TABLE **3.9** Subtractions to Obtain the Number of Consumers Corresponding to the Events $C_1 \cap V$, $C_2 \cap S$, and $C_2 \cap V$

Events	S (Sweet)	V (Very Sweet)	Total
C_1 (Cola 1)	527	$683 - 527 = 156$	683
C_2 (Cola 2)	$620 - 527 = 93$	$380 - 156 = 224$	317
Total	620	380	1,000

TABLE **3.10** A Contingency Table Summarizing the Cola Brand and Sweetness Preferences

Events	S (Sweet)	V (Very Sweet)	Total
C_1 (Cola 1)	527	156	683
C_2 (Cola 2)	93	224	317
Total	620	380	1,000

Independence We saw in Example 3.15 that $P(C_1) = .683$, while $P(C_1|S) = .85$. Because $P(C_1|S)$ is greater than $P(C_1)$, the probability that a randomly selected consumer will prefer Cola 1 is higher if we know that the person prefers *sweet* cola than it is if we have no knowledge of the person's sweetness preference. Another way to see this is to use Table 3.10 to calculate

$$P(C_1|V) = \frac{P(C_1 \cap V)}{P(V)} = \frac{156/1,000}{380/1,000} = .4105$$

Since $P(C_1|S) = .85$ is greater than $P(C_1|V) = 0.4105$, the probability that a randomly selected consumer will prefer Cola 1 is higher if the consumer prefers *sweet* colas than it is if the consumer prefers *very sweet* colas. Since the probability of the event C_1 is influenced by whether the event S occurs, we say that the events C_1 and S are *dependent.* If $P(C_1|S)$ was equal to $P(C_1)$, then the probability of the event C_1 would not be influenced by whether S occurs. In this case we would say that the events C_1 and S are *independent.*

Independent Events

Two events A and B are **independent events** if and only if

1    $P(A|B) = P(A)$ or, equivalently,

2    $P(B|A) = P(B)$

Here we assume that $P(A)$ and $P(B)$ are greater than 0.

When we say that conditions (1) and (2) are equivalent, we mean that condition (1) holds if and only if condition (2) holds. Although we will not prove this, we will demonstrate it in Example 3.16.

Example 3.16 More on the Soft Drink Taste Test

In the soft drink taste test in Example 3.15, we saw that $P(C_1|S) = .85$ does not equal $P(C_1) = .683$. This implies that $P(S|C_1)$ does not equal $P(S)$. To demonstrate this, note from Table 3.10 that

$$P(S|C_1) = \frac{P(C_1 \cap S)}{P(C_1)} = \frac{527/1,000}{683/1,000} = .7716$$

This probability is larger than

$$P(S) = 620/1,000 = .62$$

In summary:

1   A comparison of $P(C_1|S) = .85$ and $P(C_1) = .683$ shows that a consumer is more likely to prefer Cola 1 if the consumer prefers *sweet* colas.

2   A comparison of $P(S|C_1) = .7716$ and $P(S) = .62$ shows that a consumer is more likely to prefer *sweet* colas if the consumer prefers Cola 1.

This suggests, but does not prove, that one reason Cola 1 is preferred to Cola 2 is that Cola 1 is *sweet* (as opposed to *very sweet*).

If the occurrences of the events A and B have nothing to do with each other, then we know that A and B are independent events. This implies that $P(A|B)$ equals $P(A)$ and that $P(B|A)$ equals $P(B)$. Recall that the general multiplication rule tells us that, for any two events A and B, we can say that

$$P(A \cap B) = P(A)P(B|A)$$

Therefore, if $P(B|A)$ equals $P(B)$, it follows that

$$P(A \cap B) = P(A)P(B)$$

which is called the *multiplication rule for independent events*.

The Multiplication Rule for Two Independent Events

If A and B are *independent events*, then

$$P(A \cap B) = P(A)P(B)$$

As a simple example of the *multiplication rule for independent events*, define the events C and P as follows:

$C \equiv$ Your favourite college football team wins its first game next season

$P \equiv$ Your favourite professional football team wins its first game next season

Suppose you believe that for next season $P(C) = .6$ and $P(P) = .6$. Then, because the outcomes of a college football game and a professional football game would probably have nothing to do with each other, it is reasonable to assume that C and P are independent events. It follows that

$$P(C \cap P) = P(C)P(P) = (.6)(.6) = .36$$

This probability might be surprisingly low. That is, since you believe that each of your teams has a 60 percent chance of winning, you might feel reasonably confident that both your college and professional teams will win their first game. Yet, the chance of this happening is really only .36!

Next, consider a group of events $A_1, A_2, \ldots, A_N$. Intuitively, the events $A_1, A_2, \ldots, A_N$ are independent if the occurrences of these events have nothing to do with each other. Denoting the probability that A_1 and A_2 and . . . and A_N will simultaneously occur as $P(A_1 \cap A_2 \cap \cdots \cap A_N)$, we have the following:

The Multiplication Rule for N Independent Events

If $A_1, A_2, \ldots, A_N$ are independent events, then

$$P(A_1 \cap A_2 \cap \cdots \cap A_N) = P(A_1)P(A_2) \cdots P(A_N)$$

This says that the multiplication rule for two independent events can be extended to any number of independent events.

ROADBLOCK

The independence of two events is usually determined on the basis of your understanding of the events

Consider the example of the two football teams—you are making the determination that the outcomes of these two events are likely to be independent. Accordingly, it is important that you carefully consider the nature of your events, and any relationships that are likely to exist between them before you undertake a calculation of the probability of their intersection.

Also, at this point, you may be confused about the distinction between events that are *independent* and events that are *mutually exclusive*. Events that are mutually exclusive cannot occur at the same time. For example, a football team cannot simultaneously win and lose a game (not counting tie games and philosophical discussions about sportsmanship). On the other hand, events that are independent can co-occur—but the occurrence of one event is not dependent on the occurrence of the other event.

Example 3.17 The Customer Satisfaction Example

This example is based on a real situation encountered by a major producer and marketer of consumer products. The company assessed the service it provides by surveying the attitudes of its customers regarding ten different aspects of customer service—order filled correctly, billing amount on invoice correct, delivery made on time, and so forth. When the survey results were analyzed, the company was dismayed to learn that only 59 percent of the survey participants indicated that they were satisfied with all ten aspects of the company's service. On investigation, each of the ten departments responsible for the aspects of service considered in the study insisted that it satisfied its customers 95 percent of the time. That is, each department claimed that its error rate was only 5 percent.

Company executives were confused and felt that there was a substantial discrepancy between the survey results and the claims of the departments providing the services. However, a company statistician pointed out that there was no discrepancy. To understand this, consider randomly selecting a customer from among the survey participants, and define ten events (corresponding to the ten aspects of service studied):

$A_1 \equiv$ Customer is satisfied that the order is filled correctly (aspect 1)

$A_2 \equiv$ Customer is satisfied that the billing amount on the invoice is correct (aspect 2)

$\vdots$

$A_{10} \equiv$ Customer is satisfied that the delivery is made on time (aspect 10)

Also, define the event

$S \equiv$ Customer is satisfied with all 10 aspects of customer service

Since ten different departments are responsible for the ten aspects of service being studied, it is reasonable to assume that all ten aspects of service are independent of each other. For instance, billing amounts would be independent of delivery times. Therefore, $A_1, A_2, \ldots, A_{10}$ are independent events, and

$$P(S) = P(A_1 \cap A_2 \cap \cdots \cap A_{10})$$
$$= P(A_1)P(A_2)\cdots P(A_{10})$$

If, as the departments claim, each department satisfies its customers 95 percent of the time, then the probability that the customer is satisfied with all ten aspects is

$$P(S) = (.95)(.95) \cdots (.95) = (.95)^{10} = .5987$$

This result is almost identical to the 59 percent satisfaction rate reported by the survey participants.

If the company wants to increase the percentage of its customers who are satisfied with all ten aspects of service, it must improve the quality of service provided by the ten departments. For example, to satisfy 95 percent of its customers with all ten aspects of service, the company must require each department to raise the fraction of the time it satisfies its customers to x, where

$$(x)^{10} = .95$$

It follows that

$$x = (.95)^{\frac{1}{10}} = .9949$$

and that each department must satisfy its customers 99.49 percent of the time (rather than the current 95 percent of the time).

Exercises for Section **3.4**

CONCEPTS

3.24 Explain the concept of a conditional probability. Give an example of a conditional probability that would be of interest to a college or university student. Give an example that would be of interest to a businessperson.

3.25 Explain what it means for two events to be independent.

METHODS AND APPLICATIONS

3.26 Recall from Exercise 3.17 that of 10,000 students at a college, 2,500 have a MasterCard (M) credit card, 4,000 have a Visa (V), and 1,000 have both. Find
   a. The proportion of MasterCard holders who also have Visa cards. Interpret and write this proportion as a conditional probability.

b. The proportion of Visa cardholders who have MasterCard. Interpret and write this proportion as a conditional probability.

c. Are the events *having a MasterCard* and *having a Visa* independent? Justify your answer.

3.27 Recall from Exercise 3.19 that each month a brokerage house studies various companies and rates each company's stock as being either "low risk" or "moderate to high risk." In a recent report, the brokerage house summarized its findings about 15 aerospace companies and 25 food retailers in the following table:

Company Type	Low Risk	Moderate to High Risk
Aerospace company	6	9
Food retailer	15	10

If we randomly select one of the total of 40 companies, find

a. The probability that the company's stock is moderate to high risk given that the firm is an aerospace company.

b. The probability that the company's stock is moderate to high risk given that the firm is a food retailer.

c. Determine if the *company type* is independent of the *level of risk* of the firm's stock.

3.28 John and Jane are married. The probability that John watches a certain television show is .4. The probability that Jane watches the show is .5. The probability that John watches the show, given that Jane does, is .7.

a. Find the probability that both John and Jane watch the show.

b. Find the probability that Jane watches the show, given that John does.

c. Do John and Jane watch the show independently of each other? Justify your answer.

3.29 In Exercise 3.28, find the probability that either John or Jane watches the show.

3.30 It is possible to use iTunes content ratings to block movies and TV shows with ratings above a particular threshold (e.g., PG-13, R, etc.). If 40 percent of Canadian families have access to an iTunes-enabled device (whether a computer or an Apple TV), and only 17 percent of parents use this functionality to control the content viewed by their children, consider the following:

a. What is the probability that a randomly selected Canadian family has used content ratings to control content viewed by their children?

b. If 50 percent of parents use other methods for controlling content viewing habits (e.g., timed access to the Internet), how does this compare to the percentage using integrated iTunes content screening functionality?

3.31 If you determine that 47 percent of parents who have purchased an Apple TV are aware of the content screening capabilities built into the device, and further determine that 36 percent of the individuals who are aware of this functionality have enabled content screening, use these results to find an estimate of the probability that a randomly selected parent who has purchased an Apple TV has enabled content screening.

3.32 Fifteen percent of the employees in a company have managerial positions and 25 percent of the employees in the company have MBA degrees. Also, 60 percent of the managers have MBA degrees. Using the probability formulas,

a. Find the proportion of employees who are managers and have MBA degrees.

b. Find the proportion of MBAs who are managers.

c. Are the events *being a manager* and *having an MBA* independent? Justify your answer.

3.33 In Exercise 3.32, find the proportion of employees who either have MBAs or are managers.

3.34 Consider Exercise 3.20. Using the results in Table 3.5, estimate the probability that a randomly selected 21- to 49-year-old consumer would

a. Give the phrase a rating of 4 or 5, given that the consumer is male, and give the phrase a rating of 4 or 5, given that the consumer is female. Based on these results, is the appeal of the phrase among males much different from the appeal of the phrase among females? Explain.

b. Give the phrase a rating of 4 or 5, given that the consumer is in the 21–24 age group; given that the consumer is in the 25–34 age group; and given that the consumer is in the 35–49 age group. Based on your results, which age group finds the phrase most appealing? Least appealing?

3.35 In a survey of 100 insurance claims, 40 are fire claims (*FIRE*), 16 of which are fraudulent (*FRAUD*). Also, there are a total of 40 fraudulent claims.

a. Construct a contingency table summarizing the claims data. Use the pairs of events *FIRE* and $\overline{FIRE}$, *FRAUD* and $\overline{FRAUD}$.

b. What proportion of the fire claims are fraudulent?

c. Are the events *a claim is fraudulent* and *a claim is a fire claim* independent? Use your probability of part (b) to prove your answer.

3.36 Recall from Exercise 3.3 that two randomly selected customers are each asked to take a blind taste test and then to state which of three diet colas (marked as *A*, *B*, or *C*) he or she prefers. Suppose that cola *A*'s distributor claims that 80 percent of all people prefer cola *A* and that only 10 percent prefer each of colas *B* and *C*.

a. Assuming that the distributor's claim is true and that the two taste test participants make independent cola preference decisions, find the probability of each sample space outcome.

b. Find the probability that neither taste test participant will prefer cola *A*.

c. If, when the taste test is carried out, neither participant prefers cola *A*, use the probability you computed in part (b) to decide whether the distributor's claim seems valid. Explain.

3.37 A sprinkler system inside an office building has two types of activation devices, D_1 and D_2, which operate independently. When there is a fire, if either device operates correctly, the sprinkler system is turned on.

In case of fire, the probability that D_1 operates correctly is .95, and the probability that D_2 operates correctly is .92. Find the probability that

a. Both D_1 and D_2 will operate correctly.

b. The sprinkler system will come on.

c. The sprinkler system will fail.

3.38 A product is assembled using ten different components, each of which must meet specifications for five different quality characteristics. Suppose that there is a .9973 probability that each individual specification will be met.

a. Assuming that all 50 specifications are met independently, find the probability that the product meets all 50 specifications.

b. Suppose that we want to have a 99.73 percent chance that all 50 specifications will be met. If each specification will have the same chance of being met, how large must we make the probability of meeting each individual specification?

3.39 In a murder trial in Toronto, the prosecution claims that the defendant was cut on the left middle finger at the murder scene, but the defendant claims the cut occurred in Vancouver the day after the murders had been committed. Because the defendant is a sports celebrity, many people noticed him before he reached Vancouver. Twenty-two people saw him casually, one person on the plane to Vancouver carefully studied his hands looking

for a championship ring, and another person stood with him as he signed autographs and drove him from the airport to the hotel. None of these 24 people saw a cut on the defendant's finger. If, in fact, he was not cut at all, it would be extremely unlikely that he left blood at the murder scene.

a. Since a person casually meeting the defendant would not be looking for a cut, assume that the probability is .9 that such a person would not have seen the cut, even if it was there. Furthermore, assume that the person who carefully looked at the defendant's hands had a .5 probability of not seeing the cut even if it was there, and that the person who drove the defendant from the airport to the hotel had a .6 probability of not seeing the cut even if it was there. Given these assumptions, and also assuming that all 24 people looked at the defendant independently of each other, what is the probability that all 24 people would not have seen the cut, even if it was there?

b. What is the probability that at least one of the 24 people would have seen the cut if it was there?

c. Given the result of part (b) and given the fact that none of the 24 people saw a cut, do you think the defendant had a cut on his hand before he reached Vancouver?

d. How might we estimate what the assumed probabilities in part (a) would actually be? (Note: This would not be easy.)

3.5 BAYES' THEOREM (OPTIONAL)

LO5

Sometimes we have an initial or **prior probability** that an event will occur. Then, based on new information, we revise the prior probability to what is called a **posterior probability**. This revision can be done by using a theorem called **Bayes' theorem**.

Example 3.18 The HIV Testing Example

HIV (human immunodeficiency virus) is the virus that causes AIDS. Although many have proposed mandatory testing for HIV, statisticians have frequently spoken against such proposals. In this example, we use Bayes' theorem to see why.

Let *HIV* represent the event that a randomly selected Canadian has the HIV virus, and let $\overline{HIV}$ represent the event that a randomly selected Canadian does not have this virus. In 2008, it was estimated that .2 percent of the Canadian population had the HIV virus:

$$P(HIV) = .002 \quad \text{and} \quad P(\overline{HIV}) = .998$$

A diagnostic test is used to attempt to detect whether a person has HIV. According to historical data, 99.9 percent of people with HIV receive a positive (*POS*) result when this test is administered, while 1 percent of people who do not have HIV receive a positive result. In other words, there is a 1 percent chance of receiving a *false positive*. In terms of conditional probabilities, this yields the following statements:

$$P(POS|HIV) = .999 \quad \text{and} \quad P(POS|\overline{HIV}) = .01$$

If we administer the test to a randomly selected Canadian (who may or may not have HIV) and the person receives a positive test result, what is the probability that the person actually has HIV? This probability is

$$P(HIV|POS) = \frac{P(HIV \cap POS)}{P(POS)}$$

The idea behind Bayes' theorem is that we can find $P(HIV \mid POS)$ by thinking as follows. A person will receive a positive result (POS) if the person receives a positive result and actually has HIV—that is, ($HIV \cap POS$)—or if the person receives a positive result and actually does not have HIV—that is, ($\overline{HIV} \cap POS$). Therefore,

$$P(POS) = P(HIV \cap POS) + P(\overline{HIV} \cap POS)$$

This implies that

$$
\begin{aligned}
P(HIV|POS) &= \frac{P(HIV \cap POS)}{P(POS)} \\[2mm]
&= \frac{P(HIV \cap POS)}{P(HIV \cap POS) + P(\overline{HIV} \cap POS)} \\[2mm]
&= \frac{P(HIV)P(POS|HIV)}{P(HIV)P(POS|HIV) + P(\overline{HIV})P(POS|\overline{HIV})} \\[2mm]
&= \frac{.002(.999)}{.002(.999) + (.998)(.01)} = .17
\end{aligned}
$$

This probability says that, if all Canadians were given an HIV test, only 17 percent of the people who get a positive result would actually have HIV. That is, 83 percent of Canadians identified as having HIV would actually be free of the virus! The reason for this rather surprising result is that, because so few people actually have HIV, the majority of people who test positive are people who are free of HIV and, therefore, erroneously test positive. This is why statisticians have spoken against proposals for mandatory HIV testing.

In the preceding example, there were two *states of nature*—HIV and $\overline{HIV}$—and two outcomes of the diagnostic test—POS and $\overline{POS}$. In general, there might be any number of states of nature and any number of experimental outcomes. This leads to a general statement of Bayes' theorem.

Bayes' Theorem

Let $S_1, S_2, \ldots, S_k$ be k mutually exclusive states of nature, one of which must be true, and suppose that $P(S_1), P(S_2), \ldots, P(S_k)$ are the prior probabilities of these states of nature. Also, let E be a particular outcome of an experiment designed to help determine which state of nature is really true. Then, the posterior probability of a particular state of nature, say S_i, given the experimental outcome E, is

$$P(S_i|E) = \frac{P(S_i \cap E)}{P(E)} = \frac{P(S_i)P(E|S_i)}{P(E)}$$

where

$$
\begin{aligned}
P(E) &= P(S_i \cap E) + P(S_2 \cap E) + \cdots + P(S_k \cap E) \\
&= P(S_1)P(E|S_1) + P(S_2)P(E|S_2) + \cdots + P(S_k)P(E|S_k)
\end{aligned}
$$

Specifically, if there are two mutually exclusive states of nature, S_1 and S_2, one of which must be true, then

$$P(S_i|E) = \frac{P(S_i)P(E|S_i)}{P(S_1)P(E|S_1) + P(S_2)P(E|S_2)}$$

We have illustrated Bayes' theorem when there are two states of nature in Example 3.18. In the next two examples, we consider three states of nature.

Example 3.19   The Oil Drilling Example

An oil company in Alberta is attempting to decide whether to drill for oil on a particular site. There are three possible states of nature:

1   No oil (state of nature S_1, which we will denote as *none*)

2   Some oil (state of nature S_2, which we will denote as *some*)

3   Much oil (state of nature S_3, which we will denote as *much*)

Based on experience and knowledge concerning the site's geological characteristics, the oil company feels that the prior probabilities of these states of nature are as follows:

$$P(S_1 \equiv \text{None}) = .7 \qquad P(S_2 \equiv \text{Some}) = .2 \qquad P(S_3 \equiv \text{Much}) = .1$$

To obtain more information about the potential drilling site, the oil company can perform a seismic experiment, which has three readings—low, medium, and high. Moreover, information exists concerning the accuracy of the seismic experiment. The company's historical records tell us that

1   Of 100 past sites that were drilled and produced no oil, 4 sites gave a high reading. Therefore,

$$P(\text{High}|\text{None}) = \frac{4}{100} = .04$$

2   Of 400 past sites that were drilled and produced some oil, 8 sites gave a high reading. Therefore,

$$P(\text{High}|\text{Some}) = \frac{8}{400} = .02$$

3   Of 300 past sites that were drilled and produced much oil, 288 sites gave a high reading. Therefore,

$$P(\text{High}|\text{Much}) = \frac{288}{300} = .96$$

Intuitively, these conditional probabilities tell us that sites that produce no oil or some oil seldom give a high reading, while sites that produce much oil often give a high reading.

Now, suppose that when the company performs the seismic experiment on the site in question, it obtains a high reading. The previously given conditional probabilities suggest that, given this new information, the company might feel that the likelihood of much oil is higher than its prior probability $P(\text{Much}) = .1$, and that the likelihoods of some oil and no oil are lower than the prior probabilities $P(\text{Some}) = .2$ and $P(\text{None}) = .7$. To be more specific, we want to *revise the prior probabilities* of *no*, *some*, and *much* oil to what we call *posterior probabilities*. We can do this by using Bayes' theorem as follows.

If we want to compute $P(\text{Much}|\text{High})$, we first calculate

$$P(\text{High}) = P(\text{None} \cap \text{High}) + P(\text{Some} \cap \text{High}) + P(\text{Much} \cap \text{High})$$

$$= P(\text{None})P(\text{High}|\text{None}) + P(\text{Some})P(\text{High}|\text{Some}) + P(\text{Much})P(\text{High}|\text{Much})$$

$$= (.7)(.04) + (.2)(.02) + (.1)(.96) = .128$$

Then Bayes' theorem says that

$$P(\text{Much}|\text{High}) = \frac{P(\text{Much} \cap \text{High})}{P(\text{High})} = \frac{P(\text{Much})P(\text{High}|\text{Much})}{P(\text{High})} = \frac{.1(0.96)}{.128} = .75$$

This revised probability tells us that, given that the seismic experiment gives a high reading, the revised probability of "much oil" is .75. Since this posterior probability is .75, we might conclude that we should drill on the oil site. However, this decision should also be based on economic considerations. The science of decision theory provides various criteria for making such a decision. An introduction to decision theory can be found in Chapter 15.

Example 3.20 The Student Loan Default Example

Human Resources and Skills Development Canada (hrsdc.gc.ca) tracks student loan information in the Canada Student Loan program. These loans are available to students in all Canadian provinces and territories, except Quebec, Nunavut, and the Northwest Territories, which have their own programs., Canada Student Loans provide financial support in the form of loans or grants to post-secondary students who demonstrate financial need to attend designated universities, colleges, and trade schools.

In the five-year period between 2003 and 2008, the overall default rate on student loans ranged from 14.7 percent to 28.0 percent. There is some evidence, however, that the default rate on these loans is dependent on the institution attended by the student. Students attending trade schools have a higher rate of default than colleges, and colleges have a higher default rate than universities. In a 2009–10 statistical review of the program, the following probabilities were reported:

The overall probability of default was 14.7 percent.

The probability of default among students attending university was 9.5 percent.

The probability of default among students attending college was 17.1 percent.

The probability of default among students attending trade schools and other private institutions was 29.4 percent.

A survey of 750,000 Ontario students suggested that, of those pursuing post-secondary education, approximately 56.7 percent were in a university program, 33.3 percent were in a college program, and 10.0 percent were in a trade school program.

Given this information, what is the probability that a randomly selected defaulted loan was held by a university student?

We are given the following probabilities:

$$P(D) = .147$$
$$P(U) = .567; P(C) = .333; P(T) = .100$$
$$P(D|U) = .095; P(D|C) = .171; P(D|T) = .294$$

The probability of interest is $P(U|D)$. We can use Bayes' theorem to calculate this probability as follows:

$$P(U|D) = \frac{P(U \cap D)}{P(D)} = \frac{P(U)P(D|U)}{P(D)} = \frac{.567*.095}{.147} = .366$$

Therefore, the probability that a randomly selected defaulted loan belonged to a university student is 36.6 percent.

In this section we have only introduced Bayes' theorem. There is an entire subject called **Bayesian statistics**, which uses Bayes' theorem to update prior belief about a probability or population parameter to posterior belief. The use of Bayesian statistics is controversial in the case where the prior belief is largely based on subjective considerations, because many statisticians do not believe that we should base decisions on subjective considerations. Realistically, however, we all do this in our daily lives. For example, how each of us viewed the evidence in the O. J. Simpson murder trial had a great deal to do with our prior beliefs about both O. J. Simpson and the police.

Exercises for Section **3.5**

CONCEPTS

3.40 What is a prior probability? What is a posterior probability?

3.41 Explain the purpose behind using Bayes' theorem.

METHODS AND APPLICATIONS

3.42 Suppose that A_1, A_2, and B are events where A_1 and A_2 are mutually exclusive and

$$P(A_1) = .8 \quad P(B|A_1) = .1$$
$$P(A_2) = .2 \quad P(B|A_2) = .3$$

Use this information to find $P(A_1|B)$ and $P(A_2|B)$.

3.43 Suppose that A_1, A_2, A_3, and B are events where A_1, A_2, and A_3 are mutually exclusive and

$$P(A_1) = .2 \qquad P(A_2) = .5 \qquad P(A_3) = .3$$
$$P(B|A_1) = .02 \quad P(B|A_2) = .05 \quad P(B|A_3) = .04$$

Use this information to find $P(A_1|B)$, $P(A_2|B)$ and $P(A_3|B)$.

3.44 Again consider the diagnostic test for HIV discussed in Example 3.18 and recall that $P(POS|HIV) = .999$ and $P(POS|\overline{HIV}) = .01$, where POS denotes a positive test result. Assuming that the percentage of people who have HIV is 1 percent, recalculate the probability that a randomly selected person has HIV, given that his or her test result is positive.

3.45 A department store is considering a new credit policy to try to reduce the number of customers defaulting on payments. A suggestion is made to discontinue credit to any customer who has been one week or more late with his or her payment at least twice. Past records show 95 percent of defaults were late at least twice. Also, 3 percent of all customers default, and 30 percent of those who have not defaulted have had at least two late payments.
 a. Find the probability that a customer with at least two late payments will default.
 b. Based on part (a), should the policy be adopted? Explain.

3.46 A company administers an "aptitude test for managers" to aid in selecting new management trainees. Prior experience suggests that 60 percent of all applicants for management trainee positions would be successful if they were hired. Furthermore, past experience with the aptitude test indicates that 85 percent of applicants who turn out to be successful managers pass the test and 90 percent of applicants who turn out not to be successful managers fail the test.
 a. If an applicant passes the "aptitude test for managers," what is the probability that the applicant will succeed in a management position?

 b. Based on your answer to part (a), do you think that the "aptitude test for managers" is a valuable way to screen applicants for management trainee positions? Explain.

3.47 Three data entry specialists enter requisitions into a computer. Specialist 1 processes 30 percent of the requisitions, specialist 2 processes 45 percent, and specialist 3 processes 25 percent. The proportions of incorrectly entered requisitions by data entry specialists 1, 2, and 3 are .03, .05, and .02, respectively. Suppose that a random requisition is found to have been incorrectly entered. What is the probability that it was processed by specialist 1? By specialist 2? By specialist 3?

3.48 A truth serum given to a suspect is known to be 90 percent reliable when the person is guilty and 99 percent reliable when the person is innocent. In other words, 10 percent of the guilty are judged innocent by the serum and 1 percent of the innocent are judged guilty. If the suspect was selected from a group of suspects of which only 5 percent are guilty of having committed a crime, and the serum indicates that the suspect is guilty of having committed a crime, what is the probability that the suspect is innocent?

3.49 A financial blogger has been very positive about a particular stock over the past year and his success at predicting the movement of the stock has been quite good—he boasts a 75 percent accuracy rate. Consider the following data on his last 100 predictions:

	Stock Increased	Stock Decreased
Predicted Stock Increase	72	14
Predicted Stock Decrease	11	3

 a. Consider the blogger's claim of 75 percent accuracy. Is this supported by the above data?
 b. Calculate the probability that the stock will increase when he predicts an increase.
 c. Calculate the probability that the stock will decrease when he predicts a decrease.

3.50 Using the information presented in Example 3.19, calculate the posterior probability of finding "some oil" and "no oil," given a seismic test indicator of "high."

3.51 Using the information presented in Example 3.20, calculate the posterior probability of a randomly selected defaulted loan belonging to a student in college or a student in a trade school.

CHAPTER SUMMARY

In this chapter, we studied probability of an event. We began by defining an event to be an experimental outcome that may or may not occur and by defining the *probability of an event* to be a number that measures the likelihood that the event will occur. We learned that a probability is often interpreted as a *long-run relative frequency*, and we saw that probabilities can be found by examining a sample space and by using probability rules. We learned several important probability rules—addition rules, multiplication rules, and the rule of complements. We also studied a special kind of probability called a *conditional probability*, which is the probability that one event will occur given that another event occurs, and we used probabilities to define independent events. We concluded this chapter by studying an optional topic, Bayes' theorem, which can be used to update a prior probability to a posterior probability based on receiving new information.

KEY TERMS

Bayes' theorem
Bayesian statistics
complement (of an event)
conditional probability
dependent events
event
experiment
independent events

mutually exclusive events
posterior probability
prior probability
probability of an event
sample space
sample space outcome
subjective probability

IMPORTANT FORMULAS

Probabilities when all sample space outcomes are equally likely

Rule of complements

Addition rule for two events

Addition rule for two mutually exclusive events

Addition rule for N mutually exclusive events

Conditional probability

General multiplication rule

Independence

Multiplication rule for two independent events

Multiplication rule for N independent events

Bayes' theorem

SUPPLEMENTARY EXERCISES

connect · Practise and learn online with *Connect*. Items with online data sets are marked with.

Exercises 3.52 through 3.55 are based on the following situation: An investor holds two stocks, each of which can rise (R), remain unchanged (U), or decline (D) on any particular day.

3.52 Construct a tree diagram showing all possible combined movements for both stocks on a particular day (for instance, *RR*, *RD*, and so on, where the first letter denotes the movement of the first stock, and the second letter denotes the movement of the second stock).

3.53 If all outcomes are equally likely, find the probability that both stocks rise; that both stocks decline; that exactly one stock declines.

3.54 Find the probabilities you found in Exercise 3.53 by assuming that for each stock $P(R) = .6$, $P(U) = .1$, and $P(D) = .3$, and assuming that the two stocks move independently.

3.55 Assume that for the first stock (on a particular day)

$$P(R) = .4, P(U) = .2, P(D) = .4$$

and that for the second stock (on a particular day)

$$P(R) = .8, P(U) = .1, P(D) = .1$$

Assuming that these stocks move independently, find the probability that both stocks decline; the probability that exactly one stock rises; the probability that exactly one stock is unchanged; the probability that both stocks rise.

Statistics Canada tracks a variety of employment statistics. In addition to tracking whether individuals are employed, it also collects interesting business statistics, such as union membership. In its report on union membership in 2010,[2] unionization rates were reported for men and women, separated by work sector (public versus private), and were also reported for different levels of education. Using the information contained in this table, do Exercises 3.56 through 3.60.

---

[2]Sharanjit Uppal,"Unionization 2011," *Perspectives on Labour and Income.* October 2011, Statistics Canada Catalogue No. 75-001-XIE.

Union Membership in 2010 🖈

Sex	Unionized Employees	Non-Unionized Employees	Total Employees
Male	2,023	5,152	7,175
Female	2,217	4,979	7,196
Sector			
Public	2,507	1,004	3,511
Private	1,733	9,127	10,860
Education			
Less than Grade 9	69	203	272
Some high school	263	1,032	1,295
High school graduation	721	2,130	2,851
Some post-secondary	268	951	1,219
Post-secondary certificate or diploma	1,704	3,423	5,127
University degree	1,216	2,391	3,607

3.56 Find the probability that a randomly selected individual within the public sector is in a union. 🖈

3.57 Compare the probability that a randomly selected female will be in a union, with the probability of a randomly selected male being in a union. 🖈

3.58 Find the probability that a randomly selected individual will be in a union if that person has less than a Grade 9 education. 🖈

3.59 Find the probability that a randomly selected individual will be in a union if he or she has at least some post-secondary education. 🖈

3.60 In general, do these data suggest that union membership depends on educational attainment? Explain your answer.

Suppose that in a survey of 1,000 BC residents, 721 residents believed that the amount of violent television programming had increased over the past ten years, 454 residents believed that the overall quality of television programming had decreased over the past ten years, and 362 residents believed both. Use this information to do Exercises 3.61 through 3.67.

3.61 What proportion of the 1,000 BC residents believed that the amount of violent programming had increased over the past ten years?

3.62 What proportion of the 1,000 BC residents believed that the overall quality of programming had decreased over the past ten years?

3.63 What proportion of the 1,000 BC residents believed that both the amount of violent programming had increased and the overall quality of programming had decreased over the past ten years?

3.64 What proportion of the 1,000 BC residents believed that either the amount of violent programming had increased or the overall quality of programming had decreased over the past ten years?

3.65 What proportion of the BC residents who believed that the amount of violent programming had increased believed that the overall quality of programming had decreased?

3.66 What proportion of the BC residents who believed that the overall quality of programming had decreased believed that the amount of violent programming had increased?

3.67 What sort of dependence seems to exist between whether BC residents believed that the amount of violent programming had increased and whether BC residents believed that the overall quality of programming had decreased? Explain your answer.

3.68 Sunbeam Products Canada has been running a television advertisement for Sunshine liquid laundry detergent. When a survey was conducted, .21 of the individuals surveyed had purchased Sunshine, .41 of the individuals surveyed had recalled seeing the advertisement, and .13 of the individuals surveyed had purchased Sunshine and recalled seeing the advertisement.
  a. What proportion of the individuals surveyed who recalled seeing the advertisement had purchased Sunshine?
  b. Based on your answer to part (a), does the advertisement seem to have been effective? Explain.

3.69 A company employs 400 salespeople. Of these, 83 received a bonus last year, 100 attended a special sales training program at the beginning of last year, and 42 both attended the special sales training program and received a bonus. (Note: The bonus was based totally on sales performance.)
  a. What proportion of the 400 salespeople received a bonus last year?
  b. What proportion of the 400 salespeople attended the special sales training program at the beginning of last year?
  c. What proportion of the 400 salespeople both attended the special sales training program and received a bonus?
  d. What proportion of the salespeople who attended the special sales training program received a bonus?
  e. Based on your answers to parts (a) and (d), does the special sales training program seem to have been effective? Explain your answer.

3.70 Suppose that A and B are events and that $P(A)$ and $P(B)$ are both positive.
  a. If A and B are mutually exclusive, what is $P(A \cap B)$?
  b. If A and B are independent events, explain why $P(A \cap B)$ is positive.
  c. Can two mutually exclusive events, each having a positive probability of occurrence, also be independent? Prove your answer using your answers to parts (a) and (b).

3.71 In Ontario, beaches are closed when *E. coli* levels exceed 100 organisms/100 mL. On any given summer day, the probability that Lake Ontario exceeds this recommended level is .10. Each day, a test is conducted to determine whether the *E. coli* counts exceed this recommended level. This test has proven correct 80 percent of the time. Suppose that on a particular day, the test indicates dangerous *E. coli* levels. What is the probability that the bacteria counts are actually above 100 organisms/100 mL?

3.72 A marketing major will interview for an internship with a major consumer products manufacturer/distributor. Before the interview, the marketing major feels that the chances of being offered an internship are 40 percent. Suppose that of the students who have been offered internships with this company, 90 percent had good interviews, and that of the students who have not been offered internships, 50 percent had good interviews. If the marketing major has a good interview, what is the probability that she or he will be offered an internship?

3.73 In the book *Making Hard Decisions: An Introduction to Decision Analysis,* Robert T. Clemen presents an example in which he discusses the 1982 John Hinckley trial. In describing the case, Clemen says:

> In 1982 John Hinckley was on trial, accused of having attempted to kill President Reagan. During Hinckley's trial, Dr. Daniel R. Weinberger told the court that when individuals diagnosed as schizophrenics were given computerized axial tomography (CAT) scans, the scans showed brain atrophy in 30 percent of the cases compared with only 2 percent of the scans done on normal people. Hinckley's defence attorney wanted to introduce as evidence Hinckley's CAT scan, which showed brain atrophy. The defence argued that the presence of atrophy strengthened the case that Hinckley suffered from mental illness.

a. Approximately 1.5 percent of the people in the United States suffer from schizophrenia. If we consider the prior probability of schizophrenia to be .015, use the information given to find the probability that a person has schizophrenia given that a person's CAT scan shows brain atrophy.

b. John Hinckley's CAT scan showed brain atrophy. Discuss whether your answer to part (a) helps or hurts the case that Hinckley suffered from mental illness.

c. It can be argued that .015 is not a reasonable prior probability of schizophrenia because .015 is the probability that a randomly selected U.S. citizen has schizophrenia. However, John Hinckley was not a randomly selected U.S. citizen. Rather, he was accused of attempting to assassinate the president, so it might be reasonable to assess a higher prior probability of schizophrenia. Suppose you are a juror who believes there is only a 10 percent chance that Hinckley suffers from schizophrenia. Using .10 as the prior probability of schizophrenia, find the probability that a person has schizophrenia given that a person's CAT scan shows brain atrophy.

d. If you are a juror with a prior probability of .10 that John Hinckley suffers from schizophrenia and, given your answer to part (c), does the fact that Hinckley's CAT scan showed brain atrophy help the case that Hinckley suffered from mental illness?

e. If you are a juror with a prior probability of .25 that Hinckley suffers from schizophrenia, find the probability of schizophrenia given that Hinckley's CAT scan showed brain atrophy. In this situation, how strong is the case that Hinckley suffered from mental illness?

3.74 INTERNET EXERCISE

Statistics Canada (statcan.gc.ca) is an excellent source of interesting statistical information that can be useful for a variety of purposes. Let's take a look at some of the freely available information that is posted in the "retail and wholesale" category on its website. If you "Browse by subject" and click on "Retail and wholesale," you will see a variety of subtopics, within which you can narrow your focus to concentrate on, for example, a particular type of store or type of product.

Let's imagine that we are providing advice to an auto manufacturer in relation to the busiest (and slowest) times of the year for auto purchases across Canada. If you click on "Retail sales by type of product" and then click on "Detailed tables from CANSIM," you'll see that Statistics Canada has collected consumer purchasing information on a wide variety of products. Let's set up a data table that tracks monthly purchases of new motor vehicles (CANSIM Table 079-0003). If you then click on the "Add/Remove data" tab, you should be able to customize your data. Let's generate a table that tracks the information available for each month of 2011 for Canada-wide purchases of passenger cars. You should be able to retrieve the following information:

Sales	Units
2011 January	32,183
2011 February	39,579
2011 March	69,255
2011 April	75,684
2011 May	69,403
2011 June	76,273
2011 July	62,868
2011 August	60,386
2011 September	56,675
2011 October	52,364
2011 November	50,763
2011 December	45,646

Given this information, which month seems to be the weakest for auto sales (i.e., which month has the lowest probability for purchasing a vehicle)? What is the probability that a randomly selected vehicle is purchased in May? In January?

CHAPTER **4**
Discrete Random Variables

We often use what we call *random variables* to describe the important aspects of the outcomes of experiments. In this chapter, we introduce two important types of random variables—*discrete random variables* and *continuous random* *variables*—and learn how to find probabilities concerning discrete random variables. As one application, we will calculate the expected value of a lottery ticket, using the odds of winning each of the prizes in Lotto 6/49.

4.1 TWO TYPES OF RANDOM VARIABLES

We begin with the definition of a random variable:

LO1

A **random variable** is a variable that assumes numerical values that are determined by the outcome of an experiment, where one and only one numerical value is assigned to each experimental outcome.

Before an experiment is carried out, its outcome is uncertain. It follows that, since a random variable assigns a number to each experimental outcome, a random variable can be thought of as *representing an uncertain numerical outcome.*

To illustrate the idea of a random variable, consider the purchase of iPods through Best Buy. Consider (the experiment of) selling an iPod Touch at a particular Best Buy location during a particular week. If we let x denote the number of iPods sold during the week, then x is a random variable. That is, looked at before the week, the number of iPods (x) that will be sold is uncertain and, therefore, x is a random variable.

Notice that x, the number of iPods sold in a week, might be 0 or 1 or 2 or 3, and so forth. In general, when the possible values of a random variable can be counted or listed, we say that the random variable is a **discrete random variable**. That is, either a discrete random variable might assume a finite number of possible values or the possible values may take the form of a *countable* sequence or list such as 0, 1, 2, 3, 4, . . . (a *countably infinite* list).

Some other examples of discrete random variables are

1   The number, x, of the next three customers entering a store who will make a purchase. Here x could be 0, 1, 2, or 3.

2   The number, x, of four patients taking a new antibiotic who experience gastrointestinal distress as a side effect. Here x could be 0, 1, 2, 3, or 4.

3   The number, x, of notebook computers in a sample of 8 five-year-old notebooks that have not needed a single repair. Here x could be any of the values 0, 1, 2, 3, 4, 5, 6, 7, or 8.

4   The number of stars, x, on a 1 through 5 scale given to a movie by a Netflix subscriber. Here x could be 1, 2, 3, 4, or 5.

5   The number, x, of major fires in a large city during the last two months. Here x could be 0, 1, 2, 3, and so forth (there is no definite maximum number of fires).

6   The number, x, of dirt specks in 1 square metre of plastic wrap. Here x could be 0, 1, 2, 3, and so forth (there is no definite maximum number of dirt specks).

The values of the random variables described in examples 1, 2, 3, and 4 above are countable and finite. In contrast, the values of the random variables described in 5 and 6 are countable and infinite (or countably infinite lists). For example, in theory there is no limit to the number of major fires that could occur in a city in two months.

Not all random variables have values that are countable. When a random variable might assume any numerical value in one or more intervals on the real number line, then we say that the random variable is a **continuous random variable**.

Example 4.1   Discrete versus Continuous Random Variables

The combined city and highway fuel efficiency, x, of a randomly selected midsized car is a continuous random variable. This is because, although we have measured fuel efficiency to the nearest one-tenth of a litre per 100 km, technically speaking, the potential values that might be obtained correspond (starting at, perhaps, 8 litres per 100 km) to an interval of numbers on the real line. We cannot count or list the numbers in such an interval because they are infinitesimally close together. That is, given any two numbers in an interval on the real line, there is always another number between them. To understand this, try listing the fuel efficiency values, starting with 8 litres per 100 kilometres. Would the next value be 8.1 L/100 km? No, because we could obtain a value of 8.05 L/100 km. Would 8.05 L/100 km be the next highest value? No, because we could obtain a value of 8.025 L/100 km. We could continue this line of reasoning indefinitely. That is, whatever value we would try to list as the *next highest value*, there would always be another value between this *next value* and 8 L/100 km.

Some other examples of continuous random variables are

1   The temperature (in degrees Celsius) of a cup of coffee served at Tim Hortons.
2   The weight (in grams) of strawberry preserves dispensed by an automatic filling machine into a 500-gram jar.
3   The time (in minutes) that a customer in a store must wait to receive a credit card authorization.
4   The interest rate (percentage) charged for a mortgage loan at a bank.

Exercises for Section 4.1

CONCEPTS

4.1   Explain the concept of a random variable.

4.2   Explain how the values of a discrete random variable differ from the values of a continuous random variable.

4.3   Classify each of the following random variables as discrete or continuous:
  a. x = Number of girls born to a couple who will have three children.
  b. x = Number of defects found on an automobile at final inspection.
  c. x = Weight (in grams) of the sandwich meat placed on a submarine sandwich.
  d. x = Number of incorrect lab procedures conducted at a hospital during a particular week.
  e. x = Number of customers served during a given day at a drive-through window.
  f. x = Time needed by a clerk to complete a task.
  g. x = Temperature of a pizza oven at a particular time.

4.2 DISCRETE PROBABILITY DISTRIBUTIONS

The value assumed by a discrete random variable depends on the outcome of an experiment. Because the outcome of the experiment will be uncertain, the value assumed by the random variable will also be uncertain. However, it is often useful to know the probabilities that are associated with the different values that the random variable can take on. That is, we often want to know the random variable's *probability distribution*.

LO2

The **probability distribution** of a discrete random variable is a table, graph, or formula that gives the probability associated with each possible value that the random variable can assume.

We denote the probability distribution of the discrete random variable x as $P(x)$. As will be demonstrated in Example 4.2, we can sometimes use the sample space of an experiment and probability rules to find the probability distribution of a random variable.

Example 4.2   Predicting Outcomes on a Quiz

Consider the pop quiz consisting of three true–false questions. Remember that the sample space when a student takes such a quiz consists of the outcomes

CCC CCI CIC ICC
CII   ICI   IIC   III

We now define the random variable x to be the number of questions that the student answers correctly. Here x can assume the values 0, 1, 2, or 3. That is, the student could answer between

TABLE 4.1 Finding the Probability Distribution of x = Number of Questions Answered Correctly When the Student Studies and Has a 90 Percent Chance of Answering Each Question Correctly

x (Number of Correct Answers)	Sample Space Outcomes Corresponding to x	Probability of Sample Space Outcome	$P(x)$ = Probability of x
0 (No correct answers)	III	$(.1)(.1)(.1) = .001$	$P(0) = .001$
1 (One correct answer)	CII	$(.9)(.1)(.1) = .009$	$P(1) = .009 + .009 + .009$
	ICI	$(.1)(.9)(.1) = .009$	$P(1) = .027$
	IIC	$(.1)(.1)(.9) = .009$	
2 (Two correct answers)	CCI	$(.9)(.9)(.1) = .081$	$P(2) = .081 + .081 + .081$
	CIC	$(.9)(.1)(.9) = .081$	$P(2) = .243$
	ICC	$(.1)(.9)(.9) = .081$	
3 (Three correct answers)	CCC	$(.9)(.9)(.9) = .729$	$P(3) = .729$

0 and 3 questions correctly. In Examples 3.3 and 3.5 we assumed that the student was totally unprepared for the quiz and so had only a .5 probability of answering each question correctly. We now assume that the student studies and has a .9 probability of answering each question correctly. Table 4.1 summarizes finding the probabilities associated with each of the values of x (0, 1, 2, and 3). As an example of the calculations, consider finding the probability that x equals 2. Two questions will be answered correctly if and only if we obtain one of the sample space outcomes.

$$CCI \quad CIC \quad ICC$$

Assuming that the three questions will be answered independently, these sample space outcomes have probabilities

$$P(CCI) = (.9)(.9)(.1) = .081$$
$$P(CIC) = (.9)(.1)(.9) = .081$$
$$P(ICC) = (.1)(.9)(.9) = .081$$

Therefore,

$$P(x = 2) = P(CCI) + P(CIC) + P(ICC)$$
$$= .081 + .081 + .081$$
$$= .243$$

Similarly, we can obtain probabilities associated with $x = 0$, $x = 1$, and $x = 3$. The probability distribution of x is summarized as follows:

x (Number of Questions Answered Correctly)	$P(x)$
0	$P(0) = P(x = 0) = .001$
1	$P(1) = P(x = 1) = .027$
2	$P(2) = P(x = 2) = .243$
3	$P(3) = P(x = 3) = .729$

Notice that the probabilities in this probability distribution sum to $.001 + .027 + .243 + .729 = 1$.

To show the advantage of studying, note that the above probability distribution says that if the student has a .9 probability of answering each question correctly, then the probability that the student will answer all three questions correctly is .729. Furthermore, the probability that the student will answer *at least* two out of three questions correctly is (since the events $x = 2$ and $x = 3$ are mutually exclusive)

$$P(x \geq 2) = P(x = 2 \text{ or } x = 3)$$
$$= P(x = 2) + P(x = 3)$$
$$= .243 + .729$$
$$= .972$$

By contrast, we saw in Example 3.5 that if the student is totally unprepared and has only a .5 probability of answering each question correctly, then the probabilities that the student will answer zero, one, two, and three questions correctly are, respectively, 1/8, 3/8, 3/8, and 1/8. Therefore, the probability that the unprepared student will answer all three questions correctly is only 1/8, and the probability that this student will answer at least two out of three questions correctly is only (3/8 + 1/8) = .5.

ROADBLOCK

Beware of the difference between specific probabilities and the probability of a range of events

A common mistake made in probability questions is to confuse $P(x \geq k)$ with $P(x = k)$. For example, if you were asked to determine the probability of answering 4 out of 5 questions correctly, $P(x \geq 4) = P(x = 4) + P(x = 5) \ldots$, which is, by definition, larger than $P(x = 4)$.

In general, a discrete probability distribution $P(x)$ must satisfy two conditions, as shown in the boxed feature "Properties of a Discrete Probability Distribution $P(x)$."

Properties of a Discrete Probability Distribution $P(x)$

A discrete probability distribution $P(x)$ must be such that

1 $P(x) \geq 0$ for each value of x

2 $\displaystyle\sum_{\text{All } x} P(x) = 1$

The first property of a discrete probability distribution notes that each probability in a probability distribution must be zero or positive. The second property requires that the probabilities in a probability distribution must sum to 1. Looking at the probability distribution illustrated in Example 4.2, we can see that these properties were satisfied.

Often it is not possible to examine the entire sample space of an experiment. In such a case, we sometimes collect data that will allow us to estimate the probabilities in a probability distribution.

Example 4.3   Estimating Sales Probabilities for iPods

Let's define the random variable x to be the number of iPods sold in a particular week at a particular Best Buy location. In order to know the true probabilities of the various values of x, we would have to observe sales during all of the (potentially infinite number of) weeks in which iPods could be sold. That is, if we consider an experiment in which we randomly select a week and observe sales of the iPod, the sample space would consist of a potentially infinite number of equally likely weeks. Obviously, it is not possible to examine this entire sample space.

Suppose, however, that Best Buy has kept historical records of iPod sales during the last 100 weeks. These records tell us that

1   No iPods have been sold in 3 (that is, 3/100 = .03) of the weeks.

2   One iPod has been sold in 20 (that is, .20) of the weeks.

3   Two iPods have been sold in 50 (that is, .50) of the weeks.

4   Three iPods have been sold in 20 (that is, .20) of the weeks.

5   Four iPods have been sold in 5 (that is, .05) of the weeks.

6   Five iPods have been sold in 2 (that is, .02) of the weeks.

7   No more than five iPods were sold in any of the past 100 weeks.

It follows that we might *estimate* that the probability distribution of x, the number of iPods sold during a particular week at this Best Buy location, is as shown in Table 4.2. A graph of this distribution is shown in Figure 4.1.

TABLE **4.2**   An Estimate (Based on 100 Weeks of Historical Data) of the Probability Distribution of x, the Number of iPods Sold at a Best Buy Location in a Week

x, Number of iPods Sold	$P(x)$
0	$P(0) = P(x = 0) = 3/100 = .03$
1	$P(1) = P(x = 1) = 20/100 = .20$
2	$P(2) = P(x = 2) = 50/100 = .50$
3	$P(3) = P(x = 3) = 20/100 = .20$
4	$P(4) = P(x = 4) = 5/100 = .05$
5	$P(5) = P(x = 5) = 2/100 = .02$

FIGURE **4.1**   A Graph of the Probability Distribution of x, the Number of iPods Sold at a Best Buy Location in a Week

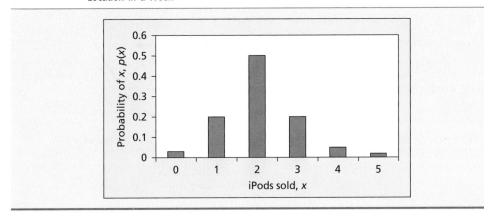

Finally, it is reasonable to use the historical sales data from the past 100 weeks to estimate the true probabilities associated with the various numbers of iPods sold if the sales process remains stable over time and is not seasonal (that is, if iPod sales are not higher at one time of the year than at others).

Suppose that the experiment described by a random variable x is repeated an indefinitely large number of times. If the values of the random variable x observed on the repetitions are recorded, we would obtain the population of all possible observed values of the random variable x. This population has a mean, which we denote as μ_x and which we sometimes call the *expected value of x*. In order to calculate μ_x, we multiply each value of x by its probability $P(x)$ and then sum the resulting products over all possible values of x.

The Mean, or Expected Value, of a Discrete Random Variable

The **mean, or expected value, of a discrete random variable** x is

$$\mu_x = \sum_{\text{All } x} x \cdot P(x)$$

In Example 4.4, we illustrate how to calculate μ_x and we reason that the calculation really does give the mean of all possible observed values of the random variable x.

Example 4.4   Using Probabilities to Predict the Number of iPods Sold

Remember that Table 4.2 gives the probability distribution of x, the number of iPods sold in a week at Best Buy. Using this distribution, it follows that

$$\mu_x = \sum_{\text{All } x} x \cdot P(x)$$

$$= 0P(0) + 1P(1) + 2P(2) + 3P(3) + 4P(4) + 5P(5)$$

$$= 0(.03) + 1(.20) + 2(.50) + 3(.20) + 4(.05) + 5(.02)$$

$$= 2.1$$

To see that such a calculation gives the mean of all possible observed values of x, recall from Example 4.3 that the probability distribution in Table 4.2 was estimated from historical records of iPod sales during the last 100 weeks. Also recall that these historical records tell us that during the last 100 weeks Best Buy sold

1   Zero iPods in 3 of the 100 weeks, for a total of $0(3) = 0$ iPods

2   One iPod in 20 of the 100 weeks, for a total of $1(20) = 20$ iPods

3   Two iPods in 50 of the 100 weeks, for a total of $2(50) = 100$ iPods

4   Three iPods in 20 of the 100 weeks, for a total of $3(20) = 60$ iPods

5   Four iPods in 5 of the 100 weeks, for a total of $4(5) = 20$ iPods

6   Five iPods in 2 of the 100 weeks, for a total of $5(2) = 10$ iPods

In other words, Best Buy sold a total of

$$0 + 20 + 100 + 60 + 20 + 10 = 210 \text{ iPods}$$

in 100 weeks, or an average of $210/100 = 2.1$ iPods per week. Now, the average

$$\frac{210}{100} = \frac{0 + 20 + 100 + 60 + 20 + 10}{100}$$

can be written as

$$\frac{0(3) + 1(20) + 2(50) + 3(20) + 4(5) + 5(2)}{100}$$

which can be rewritten as

$$0\left(\frac{3}{100}\right) + 1\left(\frac{20}{100}\right) + 2\left(\frac{50}{100}\right) + 3\left(\frac{20}{100}\right) + 4\left(\frac{5}{100}\right) + 5\left(\frac{2}{100}\right)$$

$$= 0(.03) + 1(.20) + 2(.50) + 3(.20) + 4(.05) + 5(.02)$$

which equals $\mu_x = 2.1$. That is, if observed sales values occur with relative frequencies equal to those specified by the probability distribution in Table 4.2, then the average number of iPods sold per week is equal to the expected value of x.

Of course, if we observe iPod sales for another 100 weeks, the relative frequencies of the observed sales values are unlikely to be exactly as specified by the estimated probabilities in Table 4.2. Rather, the observed relative frequencies would differ somewhat from the estimated probabilities in Table 4.2, and the average number of iPods sold per week would not exactly equal $\mu_x = 2.1$ (although the average would likely be close). However, the point is this: If the probability distribution in Table 4.2 was the true probability distribution of weekly iPod sales, and if we were to observe iPod sales for an indefinitely large number of weeks, then we would observe sales values with relative frequencies that are exactly equal to those specified by the probabilities in Table 4.2. In this case, when we calculate the expected value of x to be $\mu_x = 2.1$, we are saying that *in the long run* (that is, over an indefinitely large number of weeks) our selected Best Buy location would average sales of 2.1 iPods per week.

As another example, again consider Example 4.2, and let the random variable x denote the number of the three true–false questions that the student who studies answers correctly. Using the probability distribution shown in Table 4.1, the expected value of x is

$$\mu_x = 0(.001) + 1(.027) + 2(.243) + 3(.729)$$
$$= 2.7$$

This expected value says that if a student takes a large number of three-question true–false quizzes and has a .9 probability of answering any single question correctly, then the student will average approximately 2.7 correct answers per quiz.

Example 4.5 Profitability of Life Insurance

An insurance company sells a $20,000 life insurance policy for an annual premium of $300. Actuarial tables show that a person who would be sold such a policy with this premium has a .001 probability of death during a year. Let x be a random variable representing the insurance company's profit made on one of these policies during a year. The probability distribution of x is

x, Profit	P(x)
$300 (if the policyholder lives)	.999
$300 − $20,000 = −$19,700 (A $19,700 loss if the policyholder dies)	.001

The expected value of x (expected profit per year) is

$$\mu_x = \$300(.999) + (-\$19{,}700)(.001)$$
$$= \$280$$

This says that if the insurance company sells a very large number of these policies, it will average a profit of $280 per policy per year. Since insurance companies actually do sell large numbers of policies, it is reasonable for these companies to make profitability decisions based on expected values.

Next, suppose that we want to find the premium that the insurance company must charge for a $20,000 policy if the company wants the average profit per policy per year to be greater than $0. If we let *Prem* denote the premium the company will charge, then the probability distribution of the company's yearly profit x is

x, Profit	P(x)
Prem (if policyholder lives)	.999
Prem − $20,000 (if policyholder dies)	.001

The expected value of x (expected profit per year) is

$$\mu_x = Prem(.999) + (Prem - 20{,}000)(.001)$$
$$= Prem - 20$$

In order for this expected profit to be greater than zero, the premium must be greater than $20. If, as previously stated, the company charges $300 for such a policy, the $280 charged in excess of the needed $20 compensates the company for commissions paid to salespeople, administrative costs, dividends paid to investors, and other expenses.

In general, it is reasonable to base decisions on an expected value if we perform the experiment related to the decision (for example, if we sell the life insurance policy) many times.

If we do not (for instance, if we perform the experiment only once), then it may not be a good idea to base decisions on the expected value. For example, it might not be wise for you—as an individual—to sell one person a $20,000 life insurance policy for a premium of $300. To see this, again consider the probability distribution of yearly profit:

x, Profit	P(x)
$300 (if policyholder lives)	.999
$300 − $20,000 = −$19,700 (If policyholder dies)	.001

Then recall that the expected profit per year is $280. However, since you are selling only one policy, you will not receive the $280. You will either gain $300 (with probability .999) or you will lose $19,700 (with probability .001). Although the decision is personal, and although the chance of losing $19,700 is very small, many people would not risk such a loss when the potential gain is only $300.

Just as the population of all possible observed values of a discrete random variable x has a mean μ_x, this population also has a variance σ_x^2 and a standard deviation σ_x. Recall that the variance of a population is the average of the squared deviations of the different population values from the population mean. To find σ_x^2, we calculate $(x - \mu_x)^2$ for each value of x, multiply $(x - \mu_x)^2$ by the probability $P(x)$, and sum the resulting products over all possible values of x.

> **The Variance and Standard Deviation of a Discrete Random Variable**
>
> The **variance** of a discrete random variable x is
>
> $$\sigma_x^2 = \sum_{\text{All } x} (x - \mu_x)^2 P(x)$$
>
> The **standard deviation** of x is the positive square root of the variance of x. That is,
>
> $$\sigma_x = \sqrt{\sigma_x^2}$$

Example 4.6 Variability for Discrete Random Variables

Table 4.2 gives the probability distribution of x, the number of iPods sold in a week at our selected Best Buy location. Remembering that we have calculated μ_x (in Example 4.4) to be 2.1, it follows that

$$\sigma_x^2 = \sum_{\text{All } x} (x - \mu_x)^2 P(x)$$

$$= (0 - 2.1)^2 P(0) + (1 - 2.1)^2 P(1) + (2 - 2.1)^2 P(2) + (3 - 2.1)^2 P(3)$$
$$+ (4 - 2.1)^2 P(4) + (5 - 2.1)^2 P(5)$$

$$= (4.41)(.03) + (1.21)(.20) + (.01)(.50) + (.81)(.20) + (3.61)(.05) + (8.41)(.02)$$

$$= .89$$

and that the standard deviation of x is $\sigma_x = \sqrt{.89} = .9434$.

The variance σ_x^2 and the standard deviation σ_x measure the spread of the population of all possible observed values of the random variable. To see how to use σ_x, remember that Chebyshev's theorem tells us that, for any value of k that is greater than 1, at least $100(1 - 1/k^2)$ percent

FIGURE 4.2   The Interval $[\mu_x \pm 2\sigma_x]$ for the Probability Distribution Describing iPod Sales (see Table 4.2)

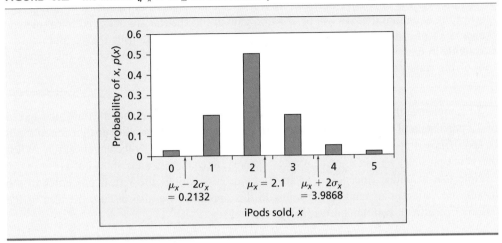

of all possible observed values of the random variable x lie in the interval $[\mu_x \pm k\sigma_x]$. Stated in terms of a probability, we have

$$P(x \text{ falls in the interval } [\mu_x \pm k\sigma_x]) \geq 1 - 1/k^2$$

For example, consider the probability distribution (in Table 4.2) of x, the number of iPods sold in a week at Best Buy. If we set k equal to 2, and if we use $\mu_x = 2.1$ and $\sigma_x = .9434$ to calculate the interval

$$[\mu_x \pm 2\sigma_x] = [2.1 \pm 2(.9434)]$$
$$= [.2132, 3.9868]$$

then Chebyshev's theorem tells us that

$$P(x \text{ falls in the interval } [.2132, 3.9868]) \geq 1 - 1/2^2 = 3/4$$

This says that in at least 75 percent of all weeks, Best Buy will sell between .2132 and 3.9868 iPods. As illustrated in Figure 4.2, there are three values of x between .2132 and 3.9868—namely, $x = 1$, $x = 2$, and $x = 3$. Therefore, the exact probability that x will be in the interval $[\mu_x \pm 2\sigma_x]$ is

$$P(1) + P(2) + P(3) = .20 + .50 + .20 = .90$$

This illustrates that, although Chebyshev's theorem guarantees us that at least $100(1 - 1/k^2)$ percent of all possible observed values of a random variable x fall in the interval $[\mu_x \pm k\sigma_x]$, often the percentage is considerably higher.

In some cases, the graph of the probability distribution of a discrete random variable has the symmetrical, bell-shaped appearance of a normal curve. For example, the graph in Figure 4.2 is roughly bell-shaped and symmetrical. In such a situation—and *under certain additional assumptions*—the probability distribution can sometimes be *approximated* by a normal curve. We will discuss these additional assumptions in Chapter 5. As an example of such assumptions, note that although the graph in Figure 4.2 is roughly bell-shaped and symmetrical, it can be shown that there are not enough values of x, and thus not enough probabilities $P(x)$, for us to approximate the probability distribution by using a normal curve. If, however, the probability distribution of a discrete random variable x can be approximated by a normal curve, then the **empirical rule** for normally distributed populations describes the population of all possible values of x. Specifically, we can say that approximately 68.26 percent, 95.44 percent, and 99.73 percent of all possible observed values of x fall in the intervals $[\mu_x \pm \sigma_x]$, $[\mu_x \pm 2\sigma_x]$, and $[\mu_x \pm 3\sigma_x]$.

ROADBLOCK

Be careful with the difference between the variance and standard deviation
Most of the equations that we will be working with in this chapter are designed to calculate the variance of a distribution—but the standard deviation is the statistic that is used most frequently in describing distributions. Remember that the standard deviation is the square root of the variance.

To summarize, the standard deviation σ_x of a discrete random variable measures the spread of the population of all possible observed values of x. When the probability distribution of x can be approximated by a normal curve, this spread can be characterized by the empirical rule. When this is not possible, we can use Chebyshev's theorem to characterize the spread of x.

Note that in online Appendix C, Part 2, we discuss various theoretical properties of the means and variances of random variables. In this appendix, we also discuss the idea of the covariance between two random variables.

Example 4.7   Expected Value of a Lotto 6/49 Ticket

In Chapter 3, we demonstrated the probability of winning each of the prize levels in Lotto 6/49. These probabilities are presented again as Table 4.3. It is possible to use this information to calculate the average value of a lottery ticket in a particular draw by calculating the value of each prize level and then summing the product of the probability and the prize value across all levels. Because the prize values are presented as a percentage of the prize pool, and lottery draws are usually advertised with particular jackpots that are not the same as the prize pool, this calculation requires an intermediate step. Because the jackpot represents 80.5 percent of the prize pool, we can calculate the prize pool for a given jackpot by dividing the jackpot by .805. For example, if the jackpot was advertised to be $7 million, the prize pool could be estimated to be

$$\frac{\$7,000,000}{.805} = \$8,695,652.17$$

The expected value of any given ticket increases, therefore, as the lottery pool grows. It is difficult, however, to calculate the expected value of a ticket before a draw, owing to the fact that more than one winner is likely in some of the categories that are expressed as a percentage of the prize pool. Consider the values presented in Table 4.4, as these are the actual prize values associated with the lottery draw held on Wednesday, October 17, 2012.

TABLE **4.3**   Winning Combinations, with Associated Odds and Prize Values

Number of Matches	Win	Odds of Winning
6/6	80.5% of pool	1 in 13,983,816
5/6 + Bonus	5.75% of pool	1 in 2,330,636
5/6	4.75% of pool	1 in 55,492
4/6	9% of pool	1 in 1,033
3/6	$10	1 in 56.7
2/6 + Bonus	$5	1 in 81.2

TABLE **4.4**   Lotto 6/49 Prize Values Won on October 17, 2012 6/49 prizes (and odds of winning) from October 17th, 2012

Number of Matches	Win	Number of Winners	Odds of Winning
6/6	$3,175,141.60	0	1 in 13,983,816
5/6 + Bonus	$226,795.80	0	1 in 2,330,636
5/6	$2,129.00	88	1 in 55,492
4/6	$75.00	4,731	1 in 1,033
3/6	$10	91,693	1 in 56.7
2/6 + Bonus	$5	54,840	1 in 81.2

It may be surprising to see how small the third and fourth prizes are—after all, they represent 4.75 percent and 9.00 percent of the prize pool, respectively. As the odds of winning in a category increase, however, there are (not surprisingly) more winners for that category. To illustrate how these prize values were computed:

$$\text{The prize pool was equal to } \frac{\$3,175,141.60}{.805} = \$3,944,275.28$$

2nd prize was equal to 5.75% of the pool, so it was worth $3,944,275.28(.0575) = $226,795.83

3rd prize was equal to 4.75% of the pool, so it was worth $3,944,275.28 (.0475) = $187,353.08

88 people split this prize, so each win was worth $187,353.08/88 = $2,129.01

4th prize was equal to 9.00% of the pool, so it was worth $3,944,275.28 (.09) = $354,984.78

4,731 people split this prize, so each win was worth $354,984.78/4,731 = $75.03

Since the odds of winning still hold as originally listed in Table 4.3, regardless of how many individuals won in a particular prize category, we can calculate the expected value of each ticket to be

$$E(x) = \frac{\$3,175,141.60}{13,983,816} + \frac{\$226,795.80}{2,330,636} + \frac{\$2,129.00}{55,492} + \frac{\$75}{1,033} + \frac{\$10}{56.70} + \frac{\$5}{81.20} = \$0.67$$

In other words, you would have expected to win 67 cents (on average) per ticket, if you bought a large number of tickets on that draw. Since Lotto 6/49 tickets cost $2 each at the time of the October 17, 2012, draw, you would expect to lose $1.33 per ticket—again assuming that you purchased a large number of tickets. Realistically, of course, you can expect to lose $2 per ticket, as your odds of winning anything are quite small!

A better question might be to ask how large the advertised jackpot would need to be before you could "expect" to break even, when tickets cost $2 each. To answer this question, we need to make some assumptions about the prize pool. As it is impossible to calculate with precision the number of individuals that will win in each prize category, we will assume that only one person will win the first and second prizes. We will similarly assume that the number of winners of the third and fourth prizes will increase in step with the size of the prize pool (as more individuals purchase tickets on the draw, owing to the size of the jackpot), so we will assign a value of $2,000 to the third prize and a value of $75 to the fourth prize. With these assumptions in place, the prize pool necessary to generate an expected value equal to $2 per ticket is $20,100,000. This would mean that the advertised jackpot would need to be $16,180,500, as illustrated below:

Number of Matches	Win	Odds of Winning
6/6	$16,180,500.00	1 in 13,983,816
5/6 + Bonus	$1,155,750.00	1 in 2,330,636
5/6	$2,000.00	1 in 55,492
4/6	$75.00	1 in 1,033
3/6	$10	1 in 56.7
2/6 + Bonus	$5	1 in 81.2

$$E(x) = \frac{\$16,180,500.00}{13,983,816} + \frac{\$1,155,750}{2,330,636} + \frac{\$2,000.00}{55,492} + \frac{\$75.00}{1,033} + \frac{\$10.00}{56.70} + \frac{\$5.00}{81.20} = \$2.00$$

Does this make a lottery ticket a good investment when the jackpot is greater than $16 million? Probably not. Remember that you must satisfy the requirement that you are purchasing a large number of tickets (with random numbers on each) in the same draw. And this requirement to purchase large numbers of tickets increases dramatically the overall cost of losing on the draw.

Exercises for Section **4.2**

CONCEPTS

4.4 What is a discrete probability distribution? Explain in your own words.

4.5 What conditions must be satisfied by the probabilities in a discrete probability distribution? Explain what these conditions mean.

4.6 Describe how to compute the mean (or expected value) of a discrete random variable, and explain what this quantity tells us about the observed values of the random variable.

4.7 Describe how to compute the standard deviation of a discrete random variable, and explain what this quantity tells us about the observed values of the random variable.

METHODS AND APPLICATIONS

4.8 Explain whether each of the following is a valid probability distribution. If the probability distribution is valid, show why. Otherwise, show which condition(s) of a probability distribution are not satisfied.

a.	x	P(x)	b.	x	P(x)	c.	x	P(x)	d.	x	P(x)
	−1	.2		1/2	−1		2	.25		.1	2/7
	0	.6		3/4	0		4	.35		.7	4/7
	1	.2		1	2		6	.3		.9	1/7

4.9 Consider each of the following probability distributions.

a.	x	P(x)	b.	x	P(x)	c.	x	P(x)
	0	.2		0	.25		−2	.1
	1	.8		1	.45		0	.3
				2	.2		2	.4
				3	.1		5	.2

Calculate μ_x and σ_x for each distribution. Then explain, using the probabilities, why μ_x is the mean of all possible observed values of x.

4.10 For each of the following Chapter 3 exercises, list all the possible values of x and also list the corresponding probabilities. Then graph the probability distribution of x.
  a. Referring to Exercise 3.3, let x equal the number of patrons who prefer diet cola A.
  b. Referring to Exercise 3.4, let x equal the number of girls born to the couple.
  c. Referring to Exercise 3.5, let x equal the number of people who will purchase a car.

4.11 For each of the following, find μ_x, σ_x^2, and σ_x. Then interpret in words the meaning of μ_x and employ Chebyshev's theorem to find intervals that contain at least 3/4 and 8/9 of the observed values of x.
  a. x = Number of patrons who prefer diet cola A as defined in Exercise 4.10(a).
  b. x = Number of girls born to the couple as defined in Exercise 4.10(b).
  c. x = Number of people who will purchase a car as defined in Exercise 4.10(c).

4.12 Suppose that the probability distribution of a random variable x can be described by the formula

$$P(x) = \frac{x}{15}$$

for each of the values x = 1, 2, 3, 4, and 5. For example, then, $P(x = 2) = P(2) = 2/15$.
  a. Write out the probability distribution of x.
  b. Show that the probability distribution of x satisfies the properties of a discrete probability distribution.
  c. Calculate the mean of x.
  d. Calculate the variance, σ_x^2, and the standard deviation, σ_x.

4.13 THE OIL DRILLING EXAMPLE

The following table summarizes investment outcomes and corresponding probabilities for a particular oil well:

x (the outcome in $)	P(x)
−$40,000 (no oil)	.25
10,000 (some oil)	.7
70,000 (much oil)	.05

  a. Graph P(x); that is, graph the probability distribution of x.
  b. Find the expected monetary outcome. Mark this value on your graph of part (a). Then interpret this value.

4.14 In the book *Foundations of Financial Management* (8th Canadian ed.), Block, Hirt, and Short discuss risk measurement for investments. They present an investment with the possible outcomes and associated probabilities given in Table 4.5. These probabilities are based on a variety of factors, but are summarized as representing a cluster of events that are pessimistic, optimistic, or somewhere in between.
  a. Use the probability distribution in Table 4.5 to calculate the expected value (mean) and the standard deviation of the investment outcomes. Interpret the expected value.

TABLE 4.5 Probability Distribution of Outcomes for an Investment

Outcome	Probability of Outcome	Assumptions
$300	.2	Pessimistic
600	.6	Moderately successful
900	.2	Optimistic

Source: S. B. Block, G. A. Hirt, and D. Short. *Foundations of Financial Management*, 8th Canadian ed., p. 432. Copyright © 2010. Reprinted by permission of McGraw-Hill Companies, Inc.

b. Block, Hirt, and Short interpret the standard deviation as being directly related to risk—to be specific, as the standard deviation increases, so too does the risk. Explain why this makes sense. Use Chebyshev's theorem to illustrate your point.

c. Block, Hirt, and Short also compare three investments having the following means and standard deviations of the investment outcomes:

Investment 1	Investment 2	Investment 3
$\mu = \$600$	$\mu = \$600$	$\mu = \$600$
$\sigma = \$20$	$\sigma = \$190$	$\sigma = \$300$

Which of these investments involves the most risk? The least risk? Explain why by using Chebyshev's theorem to compute an interval for each investment that will contain at least 8/9 of the investment outcomes.

d. Block, Hirt, and Short continue by comparing two more investments:

Investment A	Investment B
$\mu = \$6,000$	$\mu = \$600$
$\sigma = \$600$	$\sigma = \$190$

The authors explain that investment A appears to have a high standard deviation, but not when related to the expected value of the distribution. A standard deviation of $600 on an investment with an expected value of $6,000 may indicate less risk than a standard deviation of $190 on an investment with an expected value of only $600.

We can eliminate the size difficulty by developing a third measure, the coefficient of variation (V). This term calls for nothing more difficult than dividing the standard deviation of an investment by the expected value. Generally, the larger the coefficient of variation, the greater is the risk.

$$\text{Coefficient of variation}(V) = \frac{\sigma}{\mu}$$

Calculate the coefficient of variation for investments A and B. Which investment carries the greater risk?

e. Calculate the coefficient of variation for investments 1, 2, and 3 in part (c). Based on the coefficient of variation, which investment involves the most risk? The least risk? Do we obtain the same results as we did by comparing standard deviations (in part [c])? Why?

4.15 An insurance company will insure a $50,000 diamond for its full value against theft at a premium of $400 per year. Suppose that the probability that the diamond will be stolen is .005 and let x denote the insurance company's profit.

a. Set up the probability distribution of the random variable x.

b. Calculate the insurance company's expected profit.

c. Find the premium that the insurance company should charge if it wants its expected profit to be $1,000.

4.16 In the book *Foundations of Financial Management* (8th Canadian ed.), Block, Hirt, and Short discuss a semiconductor firm that is considering two choices: (1) expanding the production of semiconductors for sale to end users or (2) entering the highly competitive home computer market. The cost of both projects is $60 million, but the net present value of the cash flows from sales and the risks are different.

Figure 4.3 gives a tree diagram of the project choices. The tree diagram gives a probability distribution of expected sales for each project. It also gives the present value of cash flows from sales and the net present value

FIGURE 4.3 A Tree Diagram of Two Project Choices

		(1) Sales	(2) Probability	(3) Present Value of Cash Flow from Sales ($ millions)	(4) Initial Cost ($ millions)	(5) Net Present Value, NPV = (3) − (4) ($ millions)
Expand semiconductor capacity		High	0.50	$100	$60	$40
		Moderate	0.25	75	60	15
		Low	0.25	40	60	(20)
A Start B						
Enter home computer market		High	0.20	$200	$60	$140
		Moderate	0.50	75	60	15
		Low	0.30	25	60	(35)

(NPV = Present value of cash flow from sales minus initial cost) corresponding to each sales alternative. Note that figures in parentheses denote losses.

a. For each project choice, calculate the expected net present value.

b. For each project choice, calculate the variance and standard deviation of the net present value.

c. Calculate the coefficient of variation for each project choice. See Exercise 4.14(d) for a discussion of the coefficient of variation.

d. Which project has the higher expected net present value?

e. Which project carries the least risk? Explain.

f. In your opinion, which project should be undertaken? Justify your answer.

4.17 Five thousand raffle tickets are to be sold at $10 each to benefit a local community group. The prizes, the number of each prize to be given away, and the dollar value of winnings for each prize are as follows:

Prize	Number to Be Given Away	Dollar Value
Automobile	1	$20,000
Home theatre system	2	$3,000 each
iPod	5	$400 each
Gift certificate	50	$20 each

If you buy one ticket, calculate your expected winnings. (Form the probability distribution of x = your dollar winnings, and remember to subtract the cost of your ticket.)

4.18 Company A is considering the acquisition of two separate but large companies, Company B and Company C, which have sales and assets equal to its own. Table 4.6 gives the probabilities of returns for each of the three companies under various economic conditions. The table also gives the probabilities of returns for each possible combination: Company A plus Company B, and Company A plus Company C.

a. For each of Companies A, B, and C find the mean return and the standard deviation of returns.

b. Find the mean return and the standard deviation of returns for the combination of Company A plus Company B.

c. Find the mean return and the standard deviation of returns for the combination of Company A plus Company C.

d. Compare the mean returns for each of the two possible combinations—Company A plus Company B and Company A plus Company C. Is either mean higher? How do they compare to Company A's mean return?

e. Compare the standard deviations of the returns for each of the two possible combinations—Company A plus Company B and Company A plus Company C. Which standard deviation is smaller? Which possible combination involves less risk? How does the risk carried by this combination compare to the risk carried by Company A alone?

f. Which acquisition would you recommend—Company A plus Company B or Company A plus Company C?

TABLE 4.6　Return Distributions for Companies A, B, and C and for Two Possible Acquisitions

Economic Condition	Probability	Company A	Company B Returns	Company C Returns	Company A + B Returns	Company A + C Returns
1	.2	17%	19%	13%	18%	15%
2	.2	15%	17%	11%	16%	13%
3	.2	13%	15%	15%	14%	14%
4	.2	11%	13%	17%	12%	14%
5	.2	9%	11%	19%	10%	14%

4.3 THE BINOMIAL DISTRIBUTION

LO3

In this section, we discuss what is perhaps the most important discrete probability distribution—the binomial distribution. We begin with an example.

Example 4.8　Sales Predictions in a Department Store

Suppose that historical sales records indicate that 40 percent of all customers who enter a discount department store make a purchase. What is the probability that two of the next three customers will make a purchase?

To find this probability, we first note that the experiment of observing three customers making a purchase decision has several distinguishing characteristics:

1　The experiment consists of three identical *trials;* each trial consists of a customer making a purchase decision.

2 Two outcomes are possible on each trial: The customer makes a purchase (which we call a *success* and denote as *S*), or the customer does not make a purchase (which we call a *failure* and denote as *F*).

3 Since 40 percent of all customers make a purchase, it is reasonable to assume that *P(S)*, the probability that a customer makes a purchase, is .4 and is constant for all customers. This implies that *P(F)*, the probability that a customer does not make a purchase, is .6 and is constant for all customers.

4 We assume that customers make independent purchase decisions. That is, we assume that the outcomes of the three trials are independent of each other.

It follows that the sample space of the experiment consists of the following eight sample space outcomes:

$$
\begin{array}{ll}
SSS & FFS \\
SSF & FSF \\
SFS & SFF \\
FSS & FFF
\end{array}
$$

Here the sample space outcome *SSS* represents all three customers making purchases. On the other hand, the sample space outcome *SFS* represents the first customer making a purchase, the second customer not making a purchase, and the third customer making a purchase.

Two out of three customers make a purchase if one of the sample space outcomes *SSF*, *SFS*, or *FSS* occurs. Furthermore, since the trials (purchase decisions) are independent, we can simply multiply the probabilities associated with the different trial outcomes (each of which is *S* or *F*) to find the probability of a sequence of outcomes:

$$P(SSF) = P(S)P(S)P(F) = (.4)(.4)(.6) = (.4)^2(.6)$$
$$P(SFS) = P(S)P(F)P(S) = (.4)(.6)(.4) = (.4)^2(.6)$$
$$P(FSS) = P(F)P(S)P(S) = (.6)(.4)(.4) = (.4)^2(.6)$$

It follows that the probability that two out of the next three customers make a purchase is

$$
\begin{aligned}
P(SSF) &+ P(SFS) + P(FSS) \\
&= (.4)^2(.6) + (.4)^2(.6) + (.4)^2(.6) \\
&= 3(.4)^2(.6) = .288
\end{aligned}
$$

We can now generalize the previous result and find the probability that *x* of the next *n* customers will make a purchase. Here we will assume that *p* is the probability that a customer makes a purchase, $q = 1 - p$ is the probability that a customer does not make a purchase, and purchase decisions (trials) are independent. To generalize the probability that two out of the next three customers make a purchase, which equals

$$3(.4)^2(.6)$$

we note that

1 The 3 in this expression is the number of sample space outcomes (*SSF*, *SFS*, and *FSS*) that correspond to the event "two out of the next three customers make a purchase." Note that this number equals the number of ways we can arrange two successes among the three trials.

2 The .4 is *p*, the probability that a customer makes a purchase.

3 The .6 is $q = 1 - p$, the probability that a customer does not make a purchase.

Therefore, the probability that two of the next three customers make a purchase is

$$
\begin{pmatrix}
\text{Number of ways} \\
\text{to arrange 2 successes} \\
\text{among 3 trials}
\end{pmatrix}
p^2 q^1
$$

Now, notice that although each of the sample space outcomes *SSF*, *SFS*, and *FSS* represents a different arrangement of the two successes among the three trials, each of these sample space outcomes consists of two successes and one failure. For this reason, the probability of each of these sample space outcomes equals $(.4)^2(.6)^1 = p^2q^1$. It follows that p is raised to a power that equals the number of successes (2) in the three trials, and q is raised to a power that equals the number of failures (1) in the three trials.

In general, each sample space outcome describing the occurrence of x successes (purchases) in n trials represents a different arrangement of x successes in n trials. However, each outcome consists of x successes and $n - x$ failures. Therefore, the probability of each sample space outcome is p^xq^{n-x}. It follows by analogy that the probability that x of the next n trials are successes (purchases) is

$$\left(\begin{array}{c} \text{Number of ways} \\ \text{to arrange } x \text{ successes} \\ \text{among } n \text{ trials} \end{array} \right) p^xq^{n-x}$$

We can use the expression we have just arrived at to compute the probability of x successes in the next n trials if we can find a way to calculate the number of ways to arrange x successes among n trials. It can be shown that

Number of ways to arrange x successes among n trials $= \dfrac{n!}{x!(n-x)!}$ where $n!$ is pronounced "n factorial" and is calculated as $n! = n(n-1)(n-2) \cdots (1)$ and where (by definition) $0! = 1$.

For instance, using this formula, we can see that the number of ways to arrange $x = 2$ successes among $n = 3$ trials equals

$$\frac{n!}{x!(n-x)!} = \frac{3!}{2!(3-2)!} = \frac{3!}{2!1!} = \frac{3 \cdot 2 \cdot 1}{2 \cdot 1 \cdot 1} = 3$$

This could also be written as $3C2$ or $\binom{3}{2}$. Of course, we previously saw that the three ways to arrange $x = 2$ successes among $n = 3$ trials are *SSF*, *SFS*, and *FSS*.

Using the preceding formula, we obtain the following general result:

The Binomial Distribution

A **binomial experiment** has the following characteristics:

1 The experiment consists of n identical trials.

2 Each trial results in a *success* or a *failure*.

3 The probability of a success on any trial is p and remains constant from trial to trial. This implies that the probability of failure, q, on any trial is $1 - p$ and remains constant from trial to trial.

4 The trials are *independent* (that is, the results of the trials have nothing to do with each other).

Furthermore, if we define the random variable

x = Total number of successes in n trials of a binomial experiment

then we call x a **binomial random variable**, and the probability of obtaining x successes in n trials is

$$P(X = x) = \frac{n!}{x!(n-x)!}p^xq^{n-x}$$

Noting that we sometimes refer to the formula for $P(x)$ as the *binomial formula*, we illustrate the use of this formula in Example 4.9.

Example 4.9 More Sales Predictions in a Department Store

Consider the discount department store situation discussed in Example 4.8. In order to find the probability that three of the next five customers make purchases, we calculate

$$P(3) = \frac{5!}{3!(5-3)!}(.4)^3(.6)^{5-3} = \frac{5!}{3!2!}(.4)^3(.6)^2$$

$$= \frac{5 \cdot 4 \cdot 3 \cdot 2 \cdot 1}{(3 \cdot 2 \cdot 1)(2 \cdot 1)}(.4)^3(.6)^2$$

$$= 10(.064)(.36)$$

$$= .2304$$

Here we see that

1 $\frac{5!}{3!(5-3)!} = 10$ is the number of ways to arrange three successes among five trials. For instance, two ways to do this are described by the sample space outcomes *SSSFF* and *SFSSF*. There are eight other ways.

2 $(.4)^3(.6)^2$ is the probability of any sample space outcome consisting of three successes and two failures.

So far we have shown how to calculate binomial probabilities. We next give several examples that illustrate some practical applications of the binomial distribution. As we demonstrate in Example 4.10, the term *success* does not necessarily refer to a *desirable* experimental outcome. Rather, it refers to an outcome that we want to investigate.

Example 4.10 The Value of Investing in Lottery Tickets

Consider the lottery example discussed earlier. Although it is interesting to calculate the expected value of the average ticket, it is perhaps even more informative to calculate the probability of winning, given a particular number of tickets purchased. Based on the probabilities presented for each prize category, in Table 4.3, the probability of x, where x represents a winning ticket, is

$$P(x) = \frac{1}{13,983,816} + \frac{1}{2,330,636} + \frac{1}{55,492} + \frac{1}{1,033} + \frac{1}{56.70} + \frac{1}{81.20} = .0309$$

So the probability of any given lottery ticket winning a prize (ranging from $5 to the jackpot) is approximately 3 percent. If, on the eve of a particularly high jackpot, a woman decides to purchase 10 tickets, what is the probability that she will win on at least one of them?

To answer this question, we would need to calculate the probability of $x \geq 1$:

$$P(x \geq 1) = P(x = 1) + P(x = 2) + \cdots + P(x = 10)$$

Or, more simply, we could calculate the *complement* of $P(x \geq 1)$: $1 - P(x = 0)$:

$$P(x \geq 1) = 1 - P(x = 0) = 1 - \frac{10!}{0!10!}(.0309)^0(.9691)^{10} = .2694$$

In other words, if you purchase 10 Lotto 6/49 tickets, your probability of winning on at least one of them is 26.94 percent. If you purchase 100 Lotto 6/49 tickets, your probability of winning on a least one of them is

$$P(x \geq 1) = 1 - P(x = 0) = 1 - \frac{100!}{0!100!}(.0309)^0(.9691)^{100} = .9567$$

THEORY TO PRACTICE

Examples 4.7 and 4.10 illustrate the statistical reality that lottery ticket purchases are *not* good investments. The advertised jackpot must be in excess of $16 million for a $2 ticket purchase to represent a reasonable bet (i.e., for the expected value of the ticket to be equal to the ticket price, under several fairly liberal assumptions). Why then, do people spend money on lottery tickets? It is likely that some individuals purchase lottery tickets for the comparatively inexpensive flight of fancy that it affords (i.e., imagining the effect of winning the jackpot)—and lottery commercials leverage this tendency (advertisements like "imagine the freedom").

It is also likely that long-term lottery ticket purchasing behaviours are reinforced by the occasional wins that are likely to occur with chronic buying habits. As we note in Example 4.10, there is a 95.67 percent chance that an individual will have his or her ticket purchase reinforced at least once every 100 ticket purchases. Psychologists would term this type of reinforcement "variable ratio reinforcement"—and would note that it produces a high rate of behaviour and is difficult to extinguish. So, even though the average person probably knows, intellectually, that he is more likely to be struck by lightning than win the lottery, the reinforcement schedule is such that he will continue with his behaviour. In small doses, this is a comparatively inexpensive form of entertainment. The costs can, however, rapidly escalate when, for example, individuals add additional draws to their weekly purchases or participate in workplace ticket purchases.

Example 4.11   Phe-Mycin and Nausea

Antibiotics occasionally cause nausea as a side effect. A major drug company has developed a new antibiotic called Phe-Mycin. The company claims that, at most, 10 percent of all patients treated with Phe-Mycin would experience nausea as a side effect of taking the drug. Suppose that we randomly select $n = 4$ patients and treat them with Phe-Mycin. Each patient will either experience nausea (which we arbitrarily call a success) or will not experience nausea (a failure). We will assume that p, the true probability that a patient will experience nausea as a side effect, is .10, the maximum value of p claimed by the drug company. Furthermore, it is reasonable to assume that patients' reactions to the drug would be independent of each other. Let x denote the number of patients among the four who will experience nausea as a side effect. It follows that x is a binomial random variable, which can take on any of the potential values 0, 1, 2, 3, or 4. That is, anywhere between none of the patients and all four of the patients could potentially experience nausea as a side effect. Furthermore, we can calculate the probability associated with each possible value of x as shown in Table 4.7. For instance, the probability that none of the four randomly selected patients experiences nausea is

$$P(0) = P(x = 0) = \frac{4!}{0!(4 - 0)!}(.1)^0(.9)^{4-0}$$

$$= \frac{4!}{0!4!}(.1)^0(.9)^4$$

$$= \frac{4!}{(1)(4!)}(1)(.9)^4$$

$$= (.9)^4 = .6561$$

Because Table 4.7 lists each possible value of x and also gives the probability of each value, we say that this table gives the *binomial probability distribution of x.*

The binomial probabilities given in Table 4.7 do not need to be manually calculated. Excel can be used to calculate binomial probabilities. For instance, Figure 4.4(a) depicts the binomial probability distribution listed in Table 4.7. Figure 4.4(b) shows a graph of this distribution.

TABLE 4.7   The Binomial Probability Distribution of x, the Number of Four Randomly Selected Patients Who Will Experience Nausea as a Side Effect of Being Treated with Phe-Mycin

x (Number Who Experience Nausea)	$P(x) = \dfrac{n!}{x!(n-x)!}\, p^x (1-p)^{n-x}$
0	$P(0) = \dfrac{4!}{0!(4-0)!}(.1)^0(.9)^{4-0} = .6561$
1	$P(1) = \dfrac{4!}{1!(4-1)!}(.1)^1(.9)^{4-1} = .2916$
2	$P(2) = \dfrac{4!}{2!(4-2)!}(.1)^2(.9)^{4-2} = .0486$
3	$P(3) = \dfrac{4!}{3!(4-3)!}(.1)^3(.9)^{4-3} = .0036$
4	$P(4) = \dfrac{4!}{4!(4-4)!}(.1)^4(.9)^{4-4} = .0001$

FIGURE 4.4   The Binomial Probability Distribution with $p = .10$ and $n = 4$

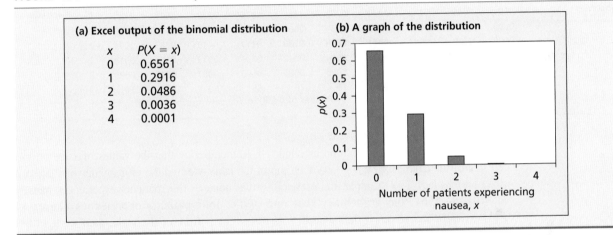

(a) Excel output of the binomial distribution

x	$P(X = x)$
0	0.6561
1	0.2916
2	0.0486
3	0.0036
4	0.0001

(b) A graph of the distribution

In order to interpret these binomial probabilities, consider administering the antibiotic Phe-Mycin to all possible samples of four randomly selected patients. Then, for example,

$$P(0) = .6561$$

says that none of the four sampled patients would experience nausea in 65.61 percent of all possible samples. Furthermore, as another example,

$$P(3) = .0036$$

says that three out of the four sampled patients would experience nausea in only .36 percent of all possible samples.

Another way to avoid manually calculating binomial probabilities is to use **binomial tables**, which have been constructed to give the probability of x successes in n trials. A table of binomial probabilities is given in Appendix A, Table A.1, at the back of this book. A portion of this table is reproduced in Table 4.8(a) and (b). Part (a) of this table gives binomial probabilities corresponding to $n = 4$ trials. Values of p, the probability of success, are listed across the top of the table (ranging from $p = .05$ to $p = .50$ in steps of .05), and more values of p (ranging from $p = .50$ to $p = .95$ in steps of .05) are listed across the bottom of the table.

When the value of p being considered is one of those across the top of the table, values of x (the number of successes in four trials) are listed down the left side of the table. For instance, to find the probabilities that we have computed in Table 4.7, we look in part (a) of Table 4.8

TABLE 4.8 A Portion of a Binomial Probability Table

(a) A Table for $n = 4$ Trials

		Values of p (.05 to .50)											
↓	.05	.10	.15	.20	.25	.30	.35	.40	.45	.50		
0	.8145	.6561	.5220	.4096	.3164	.2401	.1785	.1296	.0915	.0625	4	
1	.1715	.2916	.3685	.4096	.4219	.4116	.3845	.3456	.2995	.2500	3	
Number of 2	.0135	.0486	.0975	.1536	.2109	.2646	.3105	.3456	.3675	.3750	2	Number of
Successes 3	.0005	.0036	.0115	.0256	.0469	.0756	.1115	.1536	.2005	.2500	1	Successes
4	.0000	.0001	.0005	.0016	.0039	.0081	.0150	.0256	.0410	.0625	0	
	.95	.90	.85	.80	.75	.70	.65	.60	.55	.50	↑	

Values of p (.50 to .95) →

(b) A Table for $n = 8$ Trials

		Values of p (.05 to .50)											
↓	.05	.10	.15	.20	.25	.30	.35	.40	.45	.50		
0	.6634	.4305	.2725	.1678	.1001	.0576	.0319	.0168	.0084	.0039	8	
1	.2793	.3826	.3847	.3355	.2670	.1977	.1373	.0896	.0548	.0313	7	
2	.0515	.1488	.2376	.2936	.3115	.2965	.2587	.2090	.1569	.1094	6	
Number of 3	.0054	.0331	.0839	.1468	.2076	.2541	.2786	.2787	.2568	.2188	5	Number of
Successes 4	.0004	.0046	.0185	.0459	.0865	.1361	.1875	.2322	.2627	.2734	4	Successes
5	.0000	.0004	.0026	.0092	.0231	.0467	.0808	.1239	.1719	.2188	3	
6	.0000	.0000	.0002	.0011	.0038	.0100	.0217	.0413	.0703	.1094	2	
7	.0000	.0000	.0000	.0001	.0004	.0012	.0033	.0079	.0164	.0313	1	
8	.0000	.0000	.0000	.0000	.0000	.0001	.0002	.0007	.0017	.0039	0	
	.95	.90	.85	.80	.75	.70	.65	.60	.55	.50	↑	

Values of p (.50 to .95) →

($n = 4$) and read down the column labelled .10. Remembering that the values of x are on the left side of the table because $p = .10$ is on top of the table, we find the probabilities in Table 4.7 (they are shaded). For example, the probability that none of four patients experiences nausea is $P(0) = .6561$, the probability that one of the four patients experiences nausea is $P(1) = .2916$, and so on. If the value of p is across the bottom of the table, then we read the values of x from the right side of the table. As an example, if p equals .60, then the probability of two successes in four trials is $P(2) = .3456$ (we have shaded this probability).

ROADBLOCK

You cannot make linear interpolations within binomial tables

It's great to avoid manual calculations, but you will be able to do so only when your probability of success (p) is listed explicitly at the top of one of the columns in your binomial table. It's tempting to find the probability that lies between two values in the body of the binomial table, but this sort of linear interpolation does not work with the binomial equation.

Example 4.12　More on Phe-Mycin and Nausea

Suppose that we want to investigate whether p, the probability that a patient will experience nausea as a side effect of taking Phe-Mycin, is greater than .10, the maximum value of p claimed by the drug company. This assessment will be made by assuming, for the sake of argument, that p equals .10, and by using sample information to weigh the evidence against this assumption and in favour of the conclusion that p is greater than .10. Suppose that when a sample of $n = 4$ randomly selected patients is treated with Phe-Mycin, three of the four patients experience nausea. Because the fraction of patients in the sample that experience nausea is $3/4 = .75$, which is far greater than .10, we have some evidence contradicting the assumption that p equals .10. To evaluate the strength of this evidence, we calculate the probability that at least 3 out of 4 randomly selected patients would experience nausea as a side effect if, in fact, p equals .10. Using the binomial probabilities in Table 4.8(a), and realizing that the events $x = 3$ and $x = 4$ are mutually exclusive, we have

$$
\begin{aligned}
P(x \geq 3) &= P(x = 3 \text{ or } x = 4) \\
&= P(x = 3) + P(x = 4) \\
&= .0036 + .0001 \\
&= .0037
\end{aligned}
$$

This probability says that, if p equals .10, then in only .37 percent of all possible samples of four randomly selected patients would at least three of the four patients experience nausea as a side effect. This implies that, if we are to believe that p equals .10, then we must believe that we have observed a sample result that is so rare that it can be described as a 37 in 10,000 chance. Because observing such a result is very unlikely, we have very strong evidence that p does not equal .10 and is, in fact, greater than .10.

Next, suppose that we consider what our conclusion would have been if only one of the four randomly selected patients had experienced nausea. Because the sample fraction of patients who experienced nausea is $1/4 = .25$, which is greater than .10, we would have some evidence to contradict the assumption that p equals .10. To evaluate the strength of this evidence, we calculate the probability that at least one out of four randomly selected patients would experience nausea as a side effect of being treated with Phe-Mycin if, in fact, p equals .10. Using the binomial probabilities in Table 4.8(a), we have

$$
\begin{aligned}
P(x \geq 1) &= P(x = 1 \text{ or } x = 2 \text{ or } x = 3 \text{ or } x = 4) \\
&= P(x = 1) + P(x = 2) + P(x = 3) + P(x = 4) \\
&= .2916 + .0486 + .0036 + .0001 \\
&= .3439
\end{aligned}
$$

This probability says that, if p equals .10, then in 34.39 percent of all possible samples of four randomly selected patients, at least one of the four patients would experience nausea. Since it is not particularly difficult to believe that a 34.39 percent chance has occurred, we would not have much evidence against the claim that p equals .10.

Example 4.12 illustrates what is sometimes called the *rare event approach to making a statistical inference*. The idea of this approach is that if the probability of an observed sample result under a given assumption is small, then we have strong evidence that the assumption is false. Although there are no strict rules, many statisticians judge the probability of an observed sample result to be small if it is less than .05. The logic behind this will be explained more fully in Chapter 7.

Example 4.13   Probability of LCD TV Failure

The manufacturer of the ColourSmart-5000 television claims that 95 percent of its panels last at least five years without requiring a single repair. Suppose that we contact $n = 8$ randomly selected ColourSmart-5000 purchasers five years after they purchased their unit. Each panel will have needed no repairs (a success) or will have been repaired at least once (a failure). We will assume that p, the true probability that a purchaser's television will require no repairs within five years, is .95, as claimed by the manufacturer. Furthermore, it is reasonable to believe that purchaser repair records are independent of each other. Let x denote the number of the $n = 8$ randomly selected televisions that have lasted at least five years without a single repair. Then x is a binomial random variable that can take on any of the potential values 0, 1, 2, 3, 4, 5, 6, 7, or 8. The binomial distribution of x is listed in Table 4.9. Here we have obtained these probabilities from Table 4.8(b). To use the table, we look at the column corresponding to $p = .95$. Because $p = .95$ is listed at the bottom of the table, we read the values of x and their corresponding probabilities from bottom to top (we have shaded the probabilities). Notice that the values of x are listed on the right side of the table.

TABLE **4.9**   The Binomial Distribution of x, the Number of Eight ColourSmart-5000 Televisions That Have Lasted at Least Five Years without Needing a Single Repair, When $p = .95$

x, Number of Sets That Require No Repairs	$P(x) = \dfrac{8!}{x!(8-x)!}(.95)^x(.05)^{8-x}$
0	$P(0) = .0000$
1	$P(1) = .0000$
2	$P(2) = .0000$
3	$P(3) = .0000$
4	$P(4) = .0004$
5	$P(5) = .0054$
6	$P(6) = .0515$
7	$P(7) = .2793$
8	$P(8) = .6634$

FIGURE **4.5**   The Binomial Probability Distribution with $p = .95$ and $n = 8$

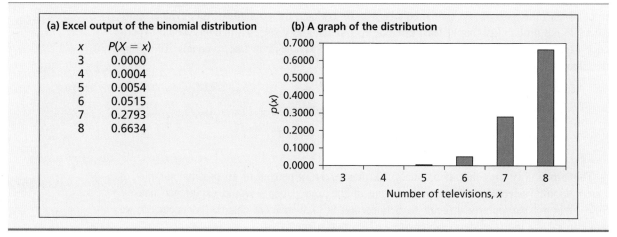

Figure 4.5(a) depicts the binomial distribution with $p = .95$ and $n = 8$ (that is, the binomial distribution of Table 4.9). This binomial distribution is graphed in Figure 4.5(b). Now, suppose that when we actually contact eight randomly selected purchasers, we find that five of the eight televisions owned by these purchasers have lasted at least five years without a single repair. Because the sample fraction, $5/8 = .625$, of television sets needing no repairs is less than .95, we have some evidence contradicting the manufacturer's claim that p equals .95. To evaluate the strength of this evidence, we will calculate the probability that five or fewer of the eight randomly selected televisions would last five years without a single repair if, in fact, p equals .95. Using the binomial probabilities in Table 4.9, we have

$$P(x \le 5) = P(x = 5 \text{ or } x = 4 \text{ or } x = 3 \text{ or } x = 2 \text{ or } x = 1 \text{ or } x = 0)$$
$$= P(x = 5) + P(x = 4) + P(x = 3) + P(x = 2) + P(x = 1) + P(x = 0)$$
$$= .0054 + .0004 + .0000 + .0000 + .0000 + .0000$$
$$= .0058$$

This probability says that, if p equals .95, then in only .58 percent of all possible samples of eight randomly selected ColourSmart-5000 televisions would five or fewer of the eight televisions last five years without a single repair. Therefore, if we are to believe that p equals .95, we must believe that a 58 in 10,000 chance has occurred. Since it is difficult to believe that such a small chance has occurred, we have strong evidence that p does not equal .95, and is, in fact, less than .95.

THEORY TO PRACTICE

Hopefully, you study for all of your exams, but if you've ever wondered about your probability of passing a multiple-choice exam by just guessing, you can use the binomial equations that we've just presented to figure out whether you'd better study instead. For a simple example, consider a pop quiz that consists of 10 true/false questions. Assuming that a pass is 60 percent, you would need to guess correctly the answers to at least 6 of these questions. In other words, you would need to guess 6, 7, 8, 9, or 10 questions correctly. The probabilities could be calculated as follows:

x, Number of Questions Guessed Correctly	$P(x) = \dfrac{10!}{x!(10-x)!}(.5)^x(.5)^{10-x}$
6	$P(6) = .20508$
7	$P(7) = .11719$
8	$P(8) = .04395$
9	$P(9) = .00977$
10	$P(10) = .00098$

So the probability that you will pass the exam by guessing at all of the answers is

$$.20508 + .11719 + .04395 + .00977 + .00098 = .37697 \text{(or } 37.7\%)$$

Now imagine that the quiz was multiple choice, with 5 options for each question. Assuming that there is only one correct answer per question and that a pass is still 60 percent, the exact probability calculation for each of the required values (6 through 10) is now

$$P(x) = \frac{10!}{x!(10-x)!}(.2)^x(.8)^{10-x}$$

The probability that you would pass this exam by guessing at all of the answers is .00637 (or .6 percent). In conclusion, it's usually a good idea to study.

In Examples 4.10, 4.11, and 4.13 we have illustrated binomial distributions with different values of n and p. The values of n and p are often called the *parameters* of the binomial distribution. Figure 4.6 shows several different binomial distributions. We see that, depending on the parameters, a binomial distribution can be skewed to the right, skewed to the left, or symmetrical.

We next consider calculating the mean, variance, and standard deviation of a binomial random variable. If we place the binomial probability formula into the expressions for the mean and variance of a discrete random variable (given in Section 4.2), we can derive formulas that allow us to easily compute μ_x, σ_x^2, and σ_x for a binomial random variable. Omitting the details of the derivation, we have the following results:

The Mean, Variance, and Standard Deviation of a Binomial Random Variable

If x is a binomial random variable, then

$$\mu_x = np \qquad \sigma_x^2 = npq \qquad \sigma_x = \sqrt{npq}$$

where n is the number of trials, p is the probability of success on each trial, and $q = 1 - p$ is the probability of failure on each trial.

As a simple example, again consider the television manufacturer, and recall that x is the number of eight randomly selected ColourSmart-5000 televisions that last five years without

FIGURE 4.6 Several Binomial Distributions

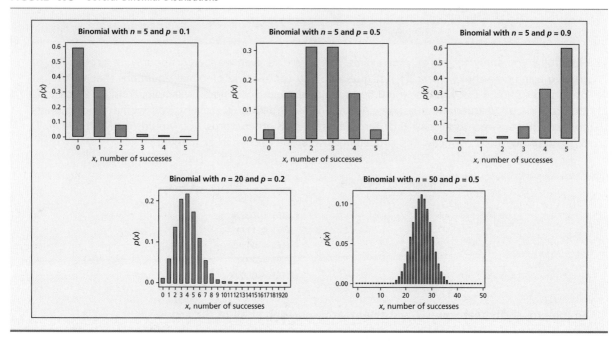

a single repair. If the manufacturer's claim that p equals .95 is true (which implies that q equals $1 - p = 1 - .95 = .05$), it follows that

$$\mu_x = np = 8(.95) = 7.6$$
$$\sigma_x^2 = npq = 8(.95)(.05) = .38$$
$$\sigma_x = \sqrt{npq} = \sqrt{.38} = .6164$$

To interpret $\mu_x = 7.6$, suppose that we were to randomly select all possible samples of eight ColourSmart-5000 televisions and record the number of sets in each sample that last five years without a repair. If we averaged all of our results, we would find that the average number of sets per sample that last five years without a repair is equal to 7.6.

In Section 4.5, we will discuss the hypergeometric distribution. This distribution is related to the binomial distribution. The main difference between the two distributions is that in the case of the hypergeometric distribution, the trials are not independent and the probabilities of success and failure change from trial to trial. This occurs when we sample without replacement from a finite population. However, when the finite population is large compared to the sample, the binomial distribution can be used to approximate the hypergeometric distribution. The details are explained in Section 4.5.

Exercises for Section **4.3**

CONCEPTS

4.19 List the four characteristics of a binomial experiment.

4.20 Suppose that x is a binomial random variable. Explain what the values of x represent. That is, how are the values of x defined?

4.21 Explain the logic behind the rare event approach to making statistical inferences.

METHODS AND APPLICATIONS

4.22 Suppose that x is a binomial random variable with $n = 5, p = .3$, and $q = .7$.
   a. Write the binomial formula for this situation and list the possible values of x.
   b. For each value of x, calculate $P(x)$, and graph the binomial distribution.
   c. Find $P(x = 3)$.
   d. Find $P(x \le 3)$.
   e. Find $P(x < 3)$.
   f. Find $P(x \ge 4)$.

g. Find $P(x > 2)$.

h. Use the probabilities you computed in part (b) to calculate the mean, μ_x, the variance, σ_x^2, and the standard deviation, σ_x, of this binomial distribution. Show that the formulas for μ_x, σ_x^2, and σ_x given in this section give the same results.

i. Calculate the interval $[\mu_x \pm 2\sigma_x]$. Use the probabilities of part (b) to find the probability that x will be in this interval.

4.23 Thirty percent of all customers who enter a store will make a purchase. Suppose that six customers enter the store and that these customers make independent purchase decisions.

  a. Let x = Number of the six customers who will make a purchase. Write the binomial formula for this situation.

  b. Use the binomial formula to calculate
   (1) The probability that exactly five customers make a purchase.
   (2) The probability that at least three customers make a purchase.
   (3) The probability that two or fewer customers make a purchase.
   (4) The probability that at least one customer makes a purchase.

4.24 The customer service department for a wholesale electronics outlet claims that 90 percent of all customer complaints are resolved to the satisfaction of the customer. In order to test this claim, a random sample of 15 customers who have filed complaints is selected.

  a. Let x = Number of sampled customers whose complaints were resolved to the customer's satisfaction. Assuming the claim is true, write the binomial formula for this situation.

  b. Use the binomial tables (see Appendix A, Table A.1) to find each of the following if we assume that the claim is true:
   (1) $P(x \le 13)$.
   (2) $P(x > 10)$.
   (3) $P(x \ge 14)$.
   (4) $P(9 \le x \le 12)$.
   (5) $P(x \le 9)$.

  c. Suppose that of the 15 customers selected, 9 have had their complaints resolved satisfactorily. Using part (b), do you believe the claim of 90 percent satisfaction? Explain.

4.25 The Royal Canadian Golf Association requires that the weight of a golf ball must not exceed 45.93 g. The association periodically checks golf balls sold in Canada by sampling specific brands stocked by pro shops. Suppose that a manufacturer claims that no more than 1 percent of its brand of golf balls exceeds 45.93 g. in weight. Suppose that 24 of this manufacturer's golf balls are randomly selected, and let x denote the number of the 24 randomly selected golf balls that exceed 45.93 g. Figure 4.7 gives part of an Excel output of the binomial distribution with n = 24, p = .01, and q =.99. (Note that, since $P(x)$ =.0000 for values of x from 6 to 24, we omit these probabilities.) Use this output to

  a. Find $P(x = 0)$, that is, find the probability that none of the randomly selected golf balls exceeds 45.93 g in weight.

FIGURE 4.7 Excel Output of the Binomial Distribution with n = 24, p = .01, and q = .99

Binomial distribution with n = 24 and p = .01	
x	$P(x)$
0	.7857
1	.1905
2	.0221
3	.0016
4	.0001
5	.0000

  b. Find the probability that at least one of the randomly selected golf balls exceeds 45.93 g in weight.

  c. Find $P(x \le 3)$.

  d. Find $P(x \ge 2)$.

  e. Suppose that 2 of the 24 randomly selected golf balls are found to exceed 45.93 g Using your result from part (d), do you believe the claim that no more than 1 percent of this brand of golf balls exceeds 45.93 g in weight?

4.26 An industry representative claims that 50 percent of all satellite dish owners subscribe to at least one premium movie channel. In an attempt to justify this claim, the representative will poll a randomly selected sample of dish owners.

  a. Suppose that the representative's claim is true, and suppose that a sample of four dish owners is randomly selected. Assuming independence, use an appropriate formula to compute
   (1) The probability that none of the dish owners in the sample subscribes to at least one premium movie channel.
   (2) The probability that more than two dish owners in the sample subscribe to at least one premium movie channel.

  b. Suppose that the representative's claim is true, and suppose that a sample of 20 dish owners is randomly selected. Assuming independence, what is the probability that
   (1) Nine or fewer dish owners in the sample subscribe to at least one premium movie channel?
   (2) More than 11 dish owners in the sample subscribe to at least one premium movie channel?
   (3) Fewer than five dish owners in the sample subscribe to at least one premium movie channel?

  c. Suppose that, when we survey 20 randomly selected dish owners, we find that 4 of the dish owners actually subscribe to at least one premium movie channel. Using a probability you found in this exercise as the basis for your answer, do you believe the industry representative's claim? Explain.

4.27 For each of the following, calculate μ_x, σ_x^2, and σ_x by using the formulas given in this section. Then (1) interpret the meaning of μ_x, and (2) find the probability that x falls in the interval $[\mu_x \pm 2\sigma_x]$.

  a. The situation in Exercise 4.23, where x = the number of the six customers who will make a purchase.

b. The situation in Exercise 4.24, where x = the number of 15 sampled customers whose complaints were resolved to the customer's satisfaction.

c. The situation in Exercise 4.25, where x = the number of the 24 randomly selected golf balls that exceed 45.93 g in weight.

4.28 The January 1986 mission of the space shuttle *Challenger* was the 25th such shuttle mission. It was unsuccessful due to an explosion caused by an O-ring seal failure.

a. According to NASA, the probability of such a failure in a single mission was 1/60,000. Using this value of p and assuming all missions are independent, calculate the probability of no mission failures in 25 attempts. Then calculate the probability of at least one mission failure in 25 attempts.

b. According to a study conducted for the U.S. Air Force, the probability of such a failure in a single mission was 1/35. Recalculate the probability of no mission failures in 25 attempts and the probability of at least one mission failure in 25 attempts.

c. Based on your answers to parts (a) and (b), which value of p seems more likely to be true? Explain.

d. How small must p be made in order to ensure that the probability of no mission failures in 25 attempts is .999?

4.4 THE POISSON DISTRIBUTION

We now discuss a discrete random variable that describes the number of occurrences of an event over a specified interval of time or space. For instance, we might want to describe (1) the number of customers who arrive at the checkout counters of a grocery store in one hour, or (2) the number of major fires in a city during the last two months, or (3) the number of dirt specks found in 1 square metre of plastic wrap.

LO4   Such a random variable can often be described by a **Poisson distribution**. We describe this distribution and give two assumptions needed for its use in the following boxed feature:

The Poisson Distribution

Consider the number of times an event occurs over an interval of time or space, and assume that

1 The probability of the event's occurrence is the same for any two intervals of equal length, and

2 Whether the event occurs in any interval is independent of whether the event occurs in any other nonoverlapping interval.

Then, the probability that the event will occur x times in a *specified interval* is

$$P(x) = \frac{e^{-\mu}\mu^x}{x!}$$

Here μ is the mean (or expected) number of occurrences of the event in the *specified interval*, and $e = 2.71828\ldots$ is the base of Napierian logarithms.

In theory, there is no limit to how large x might be. That is, theoretically speaking, the event under consideration could occur an indefinitely large number of times during any specified interval. This says that a **Poisson random variable** might take on any of the values 0, 1, 2, 3, . . . and so on (see Example 4.14).

Example 4.14 The Air Traffic Controller Example

Air traffic controllers are responsible for managing air traffic (i.e., the movement of aircraft in and out of an airport) in a highly stressful environment with extremely tight error tolerances. In this context, an "error" is defined as a situation in which a controller directs flights to fly on a path that is too close to another aircraft, based on standards that are determined by Transport Canada. Suppose that an air traffic control centre has been averaging 20.8 errors per year, and that the centre experiences 3 errors in a particular week. NAV CANADA must decide whether this occurrence is unusual enough to warrant an investigation as to the causes of the (possible) increase in errors. To investigate this possibility, we will find the probability distribution of x, the number of errors in a week, when we assume that the centre is still averaging 20.8 errors per year.

Arbitrarily choosing a time unit of one week, the average (or expected) number of errors per week is $20.8/52 = .4$. Therefore, we can use the Poisson formula (note that the Poisson assumptions are probably satisfied) to calculate the probability of no errors in a week to be

$$P(0) = P(x = 0) = \frac{e^{-\mu}\mu^0}{0!} = \frac{e^{-0.4}(.4)^0}{1} = .6703$$

Similarly, the probability of three errors in a week is

$$P(3) = P(x = 3) = \frac{e^{-.4}(.4)^3}{3!} = \frac{e^{-.4}(.4)^3}{3 \cdot 2 \cdot 1} = .0072$$

As with the binomial distribution, tables have been constructed that give Poisson probabilities. A table of these probabilities is given in Appendix A, Table A.2. A portion of this table is reproduced in Table 4.10. In this table, values of the mean number of occurrences, μ, are listed across the top of the table, and values of x (the number of occurrences) are listed down the left side of the table. In order to use the table in the traffic control situation, we look at the column in Table 4.10 corresponding to .4, and we find the probabilities of 0, 1, 2, 3, 4, 5, and 6 errors (we have shaded these probabilities). For instance, the probability of one error in a week is .2681. Also, note that the probability of any number of errors greater than 6 is so small that it is not listed in the table. Table 4.11 summarizes the Poisson distribution of x, the number of errors in a week. This table also shows how the probabilities associated with the different values of x are calculated.

Poisson probabilities can also be calculated in Excel. For instance, Figure 4.8(a) depicts the Poisson distribution presented in Table 4.10. This Poisson distribution is graphed in Figure 4.8(b).

TABLE **4.10** A Portion of a Poisson Probability Table

μ, Mean Number of Occurrences

x, Number of Occurrences	.1	.2	.3	.4	.5	.6	.7	.8	.9	1.0
0	.9048	.8187	.7408	.6703	.6065	.5488	.4966	.4493	.4066	.3679
1	.0905	.1637	.2222	.2681	.3033	.3293	.3476	.3595	.3659	.3679
2	.0045	.0164	.0333	.0536	.0758	.0988	.1217	.1438	.1647	.1839
3	.0002	.0011	.0033	.0072	.0126	.0198	.0284	.0383	.0494	.0613
4	.0000	.0001	.0003	.0007	.0016	.0030	.0050	.0077	.0111	.0153
5	.0000	.0000	.0000	.0001	.0002	.0004	.0007	.0012	.0020	.0031
6	.0000	.0000	.0000	.0000	.0000	.0000	.0001	.0002	.0003	.0005

μ, Mean Number of Occurrences

x, Number of Occurrences	1.1	1.2	1.3	1.4	1.5	1.6	1.7	1.8	1.9	2.0
0	.3329	.3012	.2725	.2466	.2231	.2019	.1827	.1653	.1496	.1353
1	.3662	.3614	.3543	.3452	.3347	.3230	.3106	.2975	.2842	.2707
2	.2014	.2169	.2303	.2417	.2510	.2584	.2640	.2678	.2700	.2707
3	.0738	.0867	.0998	.1128	.1255	.1378	.1496	.1607	.1710	.1804
4	.0203	.0260	.0324	.0395	.0471	.0551	.0636	.0723	.0812	.0902
5	.0045	.0062	.0084	.0111	.0141	.0176	.0216	.0260	.0309	.0361
6	.0008	.0012	.0018	.0026	.0035	.0047	.0061	.0078	.0098	.0120
7	.0001	.0002	.0003	.0005	.0008	.0011	.0015	.0020	.0027	.0034
8	.0000	.0000	.0001	.0001	.0001	.0002	.0003	.0005	.0006	.0009

Source: From Brooks/Cole © 1991.

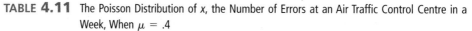

TABLE 4.11　The Poisson Distribution of x, the Number of Errors at an Air Traffic Control Centre in a Week, When $\mu = .4$

x, the Number of Errors in a Week	$P(x) = \dfrac{e^{-\mu}\mu^x}{x!}$
0	$P(0) = \dfrac{e^{-.4}(.4)^0}{0!} = .6703$
1	$P(1) = \dfrac{e^{-.4}(.4)^1}{1!} = .2681$
2	$P(2) = \dfrac{e^{-.4}(.4)^2}{2!} = .0536$
3	$P(3) = \dfrac{e^{-.4}(.4)^3}{3!} = .0072$
4	$P(4) = \dfrac{e^{-.4}(.4)^4}{4!} = .0007$
5	$P(5) = \dfrac{e^{-.4}(.4)^5}{5!} = .0001$
6	$P(6) = \dfrac{e^{-.4}(.4)^6}{6!} = .0000$

FIGURE 4.8　The Poisson Probability Distribution with $\mu = .4$

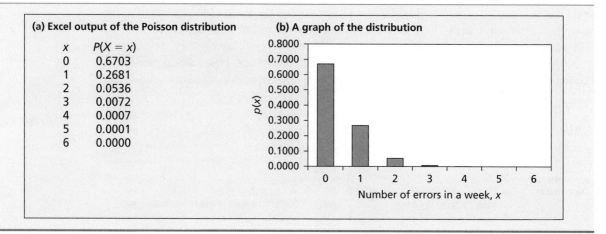

(a) Excel output of the Poisson distribution

x	$P(X = x)$
0	0.6703
1	0.2681
2	0.0536
3	0.0072
4	0.0007
5	0.0001
6	0.0000

(b) A graph of the distribution

Next, recall that there have been three errors at the air traffic control centre in the last week. This is considerably more errors than .4, the expected number of errors assuming the centre is still averaging 20.8 errors per year. Therefore, we have some evidence to contradict this assumption. To evaluate the strength of this evidence, we calculate the probability that at least three errors will occur in a week if, in fact, μ equals .4. Using the Poisson probabilities in Table 4.11 (for $\mu = .4$), we obtain

$$P(x \geq 3) = P(3) + P(4) + P(5) + P(6) = .0072 + .0007 + .0001 + .0000 = .008$$

This probability says that, if the centre is averaging 20.8 errors per year, then there would be three or more errors in a week in only .8 percent of all weeks. That is, if we are to believe that the control centre is averaging 20.8 errors per year, then we must believe that an 8 in 1,000 chance has occurred. Since it is very difficult to believe that such a rare event has occurred, we have strong evidence that the average number of errors per week has increased. Therefore, an investigation by NAV CANADA into the reasons for such an increase is probably justified.

Example 4.15 Probability of Errors in Computer Programs

Suppose that the number of errors per 1,000 lines of computer code is described by a Poisson distribution with a mean of four errors per 1,000 lines of code. If we want to find the probability of obtaining eight errors in 2,500 lines of computer code, we must adjust the mean of the Poisson distribution. To do this, we arbitrarily choose a *space unit* of one line of code, and we note that a mean of four errors per 1,000 lines of code is equivalent to 4/1,000 of an error per line of code. Therefore, the mean number of errors per 2,500 lines of code is $(4/1,000)(2,500) = 10$. It follows that

$$P(8) = \frac{e^{-\mu}\mu^8}{8!} = \frac{e^{-10}10^8}{8!} = .1126$$

The mean, μ, is often called the *parameter* of the Poisson distribution. Figure 4.9 shows several Poisson distributions. We see that, depending on its parameter (mean), a Poisson distribution can be very skewed to the right or can be quite symmetrical.

Finally, if we place the Poisson probability formula into the general expressions for μ_x, σ_x^2, and σ_x (from Section 4.2), we can derive formulas for calculating the mean, variance, and standard deviation of a Poisson distribution, as shown in the following boxed feature:

The Mean, Variance, and Standard Deviation of a Poisson Random Variable

Suppose that x is a Poisson random variable. If μ is the average number of occurrences of an event over the specified interval of time or space of interest, then

$$\mu_x = \mu \quad \sigma_x^2 = \mu \quad \sigma_x = \sqrt{\mu}$$

Here we see that both the mean and the variance of a Poisson random variable equal the average number of occurrences μ of the event of interest over the specified interval of time or space. For example, in the air traffic control situation, the Poisson distribution of x, the number of errors at the air traffic control centre in a week, has a mean of $\mu_x = .4$ and a standard deviation of $\sigma_x = \sqrt{.4} = .6325$.

FIGURE 4.9 Several Poisson Distributions

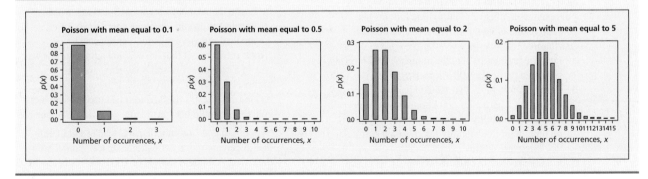

Exercises for Section 4.4

CONCEPTS

4.29 The values of a Poisson random variable are $x = 0, 1, 2, 3, \ldots$ Explain what these values represent.

4.30 Explain the assumptions that must be satisfied when a Poisson distribution adequately describes a random variable x.

METHODS AND APPLICATIONS

4.31 Suppose that x has a Poisson distribution with $\mu = 2$.
   a. Write the Poisson formula and describe the possible values of x.
   b. Starting with the smallest possible value of x, calculate $P(x)$ for each value of x until $P(x)$ becomes smaller than .001.
   c. Graph the Poisson distribution using your results from part(b).
   d. Find $P(x = 2)$.   **e.** Find $P(x \le 4)$.
   f. Find $P(x < 4)$.   **g.** Find $P(x \ge 1)$ and $P(x > 2)$.
   h. Find $P(1 \le x \le 4)$.   **i.** Find $P(2 < x < 5)$.
   j. Find $P(2 \le x \le 6)$.

4.32 Suppose that x has a Poisson distribution with $\mu = 2$.
   a. Use the formulas given in this section to compute the mean, μ_x, variance, σ_x^2, and standard deviation, σ_x.
   b. Calculate the intervals $[\mu_x \pm 2\sigma_x]$ and $[\mu_x \pm 3\sigma_x]$. Then use the probabilities you calculated in Exercise 4.31 to find the probability that x will be inside each of these intervals.

4.33 **THE CUSTOMER WAIT TIME EXAMPLE**

A bank manager wants to provide prompt service for customers at the bank's drive-up window. The bank currently can serve up to 10 customers per 15-minute period without significant delay. The average arrival rate is 7 customers per 15-minute period. Let x denote the number of customers arriving per 15-minute period. Assuming x has a Poisson distribution:
   a. Find the probability that 10 customers will arrive in a particular 15-minute period.
   b. Find the probability that 10 or fewer customers will arrive in a particular 15-minute period.
   c. Find the probability that there will be a significant delay at the drive-up window. That is, find the probability that more than 10 customers will arrive during a particular 15-minute period.

4.34 A telephone company's goal is to have no more than five monthly line failures on any 100 kilometres of line. The company currently experiences an average of two monthly line failures per 50 kilometres of line. Let x denote the number of monthly line failures per 100 kilometres of line. Assuming x has a Poisson distribution:
   a. Find the probability that the company will meet its goal on a particular 100 kilometres of line.
   b. Find the probability that the company will not meet its goal on a particular 100 kilometres of line.
   c. Find the probability that the company will have no more than five monthly failures on a particular 200 kilometres of line.
   d. Find the probability that the company will have more than 12 monthly failures on a particular 150 kilometres of line.

4.35 A local law enforcement agency claims that the number of times that a patrol car passes through a particular neighbourhood follows a Poisson process with a mean of three times per nightly shift. Let x denote the number of times that a patrol car passes through the neighbourhood during a nightly shift.

   a. Calculate the probability that no patrol cars pass through the neighbourhood during a nightly shift.
   b. Suppose that during a randomly selected night shift no patrol cars pass through the neighbourhood. Based on your answer from part (a), do you believe the agency's claim? Explain.
   c. Assuming that nightly shifts are independent and assuming that the agency's claim is correct, find the probability that exactly one patrol car will pass through the neighbourhood on each of four consecutive nights.

4.36 When the number of trials, n, is large, binomial probability tables may not be available. Furthermore, if a computer is not available, manual calculations will be tedious. As an alternative, the Poisson distribution can be used to approximate the binomial distribution when n is large and p is small. Here the mean of the Poisson distribution is taken to be $\mu = np$. That is, when n is large and p is small, we can use the Poisson formula with $\mu = np$ to calculate binomial probabilities; we will obtain results close to those we would obtain by using the binomial formula. A common rule is to use this approximation when $n/p \ge 500$.

To illustrate this approximation, in the movie *Coma*, a young female intern at a Boston hospital was very upset when her friend, a young nurse, went into a coma during routine anesthesia at the hospital. On investigation, she found that 10 of the last 30,000 healthy patients at the hospital had gone into comas during routine anesthesias. When she confronted the hospital administrator with this fact and the fact that the national average was 6 out of 100,000 healthy patients going into comas during routine anesthesias, the administrator replied that 10 out of 30,000 was still quite small and so not that unusual.
   a. Use the Poisson distribution to approximate the probability that 10 or more of 30,000 healthy patients would slip into comas during routine anesthesias, if in fact the true average at the hospital was 6 in 100,000. Hint: $\mu = np = 30,000(6/100,000) = 1.8$.
   b. Given the hospital's record and part (a), what conclusion would you draw about the hospital's medical practices regarding anesthesia?
   (Note: It turned out that the hospital administrator was part of a conspiracy to sell body parts and was purposely putting healthy adults into comas during routine anesthesias. If the intern had taken a statistics course, she could have avoided a great deal of danger.)

4.37 Suppose that an automobile parts wholesaler claims that .5 percent of the car batteries in a shipment are defective. A random sample of 200 batteries is taken, and four are found to be defective.
   a. Use the Poisson approximation discussed in Exercise 4.36 to find the probability that four or more car batteries in a random sample of 200 such batteries would be found to be defective, if we assume that the wholesaler's claim is true.
   b. Based on your answer to part (a), do you believe the claim? Explain.

4.5 THE HYPERGEOMETRIC DISTRIBUTION

Recall that a key property of the binomial distribution is that the probability of the event of interest remains constant between trials. The **hypergeometric distribution**, however, does not make this assumption—the trials are not independent and therefore the event probability changes from trial to trial. The most common situation in which this occurs is when we sample without replacement.

The Hypergeometric Distribution

Suppose that a population consists of N items and that r of these items are *successes* and $(N - r)$ of these items are *failures*. If we randomly select n of the N items without replacement, it can be shown that the probability that x of the n randomly selected items will be successes is given by the hypergeometric probability formula

$$p(x) = \frac{\binom{r}{x}\binom{N - r}{n - x}}{\binom{N}{n}}$$

Here $\binom{r}{x}$ is the number of ways x successes can be selected from the total of r successes in the population. As we discussed earlier, you can also write this as rCx. Likewise, $\binom{N - r}{n - x}$ is the number of ways $n - x$ failures can be selected from the total of $N - r$ failures in the population, and $\binom{N}{n}$ is the number of ways a sample of size n can be selected from a population of size N.

LO5

Example 4.16 Probability of Success in Stock Picking

Consider a population of $N = 6$ stocks that consists of $r = 4$ stocks having positive returns (that is, there are $r = 4$ *successes*) and $N - r = 6 - 4 = 2$ stocks having negative returns (that is, there are $N - r = 2$ *failures*). Suppose that we randomly select $n = 3$ of the six stocks in the population without replacement and that we define x to be the number of the three randomly selected stocks that give a positive return. Then, for example, the probability that $x = 2$ is

$$P(x = 2) = \frac{\binom{r}{x}\binom{N - r}{n - x}}{\binom{N}{n}} = \frac{\binom{4}{2}\binom{2}{1}}{\binom{6}{3}} = \frac{\left(\frac{4!}{2!2!}\right)\left(\frac{2!}{1!1!}\right)}{\left(\frac{6!}{3!3!}\right)} = \frac{(6)(2)}{20} = .6$$

Similarly, the probability that $x = 3$ is

$$P(x = 3) = \frac{\binom{4}{3}\binom{2}{0}}{\binom{6}{3}} = \frac{\left(\frac{4!}{3!1!}\right)\left(\frac{2!}{0!2!}\right)}{\frac{6!}{3!3!}} = \frac{(4)(1)}{20} = .2$$

It follows that the probability that at least two of the three randomly selected stocks will give a positive return is $P(x = 2) + P(x = 3) = .6 + .2 = .8$.

The above illustrates a fundamental difference between the binomial distribution and the hypergeometric distribution— namely that the binomial distribution is based on the assumption that the probability of the event of interest remains constant between trials. In this example, the probabilities are changing because the stocks are being sampled without replacement. Although this sampling method will always produce a measurable change in probability between trials, the change in probability will not be appreciable when the population is much larger than the sample. We will illustrate this in Example 4.17.

Example 4.17 More on the Probability of Success in Stock Picking

To illustrate the idea that sampling without replacement does not produce an appreciable change in probability between trials, consider a similar example using the Standard & Poor's 500 index, a market index that is based on the top 500 publicly traded American companies, as selected by a Standard & Poor's committee. Although the index maintains a generally upward trajectory when averaged across all of its constituent stocks, individual stocks within the index may show poor performance in any particular year. If 75 percent of the stocks are demonstrating positive returns in a given year and we randomly select 10 stocks from the population (without replacement), what is the probability that at least 8 of these stocks will be demonstrating a positive return?

The stocks have been selected from the population without replacement, so the probability will not be exactly constant between trials. Accordingly, we should use the hypergeometric probability formula:

$$P(x \geq 8) = P(x = 8) + P(x = 9) + P(x = 10)$$

$$P(x \geq 8) = \frac{\binom{375}{8}\binom{125}{2}}{\binom{500}{10}} + \frac{\binom{375}{9}\binom{125}{1}}{\binom{500}{10}} + \frac{\binom{375}{10}\binom{125}{0}}{\binom{500}{10}} = .525$$

The population ($N = 500$) is, however, substantially larger than the sample being drawn without replacement ($n = 10$), so it is likely that the sampling method will produce no appreciable effect on the outcome. This being the case, the binomial probability formula may be a reasonable approximation of the hypergeometric probability formula:

$$P(x \geq 8) = P(x = 8) + P(x = 9) + P(x = 10)$$

$$P(x \geq 8) = \frac{10!}{8!2!}(.75)^8(.25)^2 + \frac{10!}{9!1!}(.75)^9(.25)^1 + \frac{10!}{10!0!}(.75)^{10}(.25)^0 = .526$$

Although the probability derived from the hypergeometric probability formula is more precise, the probability derived from the binomial approximation is different by only .001. So, unless the probability of success is markedly different between trials, it is likely that the binomial approximation will produce acceptable probability estimates.

If we place the hypergeometric probability formula into the general expressions given in Section 4.2 for μ_x and σ_x^2, we can derive formulas for the mean and variance of the hypergeometric random variable.

The Mean and Variance of a Hypergeometric Random Variable

Suppose that x is a **hypergeometric random variable**. Then

$$\mu_x = n\left(\frac{r}{N}\right) \quad \text{and} \quad \sigma_x^2 = n\left(\frac{r}{N}\right)\left(1 - \frac{r}{N}\right)\left(\frac{N-n}{N-1}\right)$$

In the previous example, we have $N = 6$, $r = 4$, and $n = 3$. It follows that

$$\mu_x = n\left(\frac{r}{N}\right) = 3\left(\frac{4}{6}\right) = 2 \quad \text{and}$$

$$\sigma_x^2 = n\left(\frac{r}{N}\right)\left(1 - \frac{r}{N}\right)\left(\frac{N-n}{N-1}\right) = 3\left(\frac{4}{6}\right)\left(1 - \frac{4}{6}\right)\left(\frac{6-3}{6-1}\right) = .4$$

and that the standard deviation $\sigma_x = \sqrt{.4} = .6325$.

> **The fundamental difference between the hypergeometric distribution and the binomial distribution: the difference in sampling methods**
> One of the fundamental characteristics of the binomial distribution is that the probability remains absolutely consistent between trials. This means that items must be sampled with replacement. In our hypergeometric distribution calculations, we illustrate the calculation of probabilities when sampling without replacement.
>
> **ROADBLOCK**

Exercises for Section **4.5**

CONCEPTS

4.38 In the context of the hypergeometric distribution, explain the meanings of N, r, and n.

4.39 When can a hypergeometric distribution be approximated by a binomial distribution? Explain carefully what this means.

METHODS AND APPLICATIONS

4.40 Suppose that x has a hypergeometric distribution with $N = 8$, $r = 5$, and $n = 4$. Find

    a. $P(x = 0)$ **e.** $P(x = 4)$
    b. $P(x = 1)$ **f.** $P(x \geq 2)$
    c. $P(x = 2)$ **g.** $P(x < 3)$
    d. $P(x = 3)$ **h.** $P(x > 1)$

4.41 Suppose that x has a hypergeometric distribution with $N = 10$, $r = 4$, and $n = 3$.

    a. Write out the probability distribution of x.
    b. Find the mean μ_x, variance σ_x^2, and standard deviation σ_x of this distribution.

4.42 Among 12 metal parts produced in a machine shop, 3 are defective. If a random sample of three of these metal parts is selected, find

    a. The probability that this sample will contain at least two defectives.
    b. The probability that this sample will contain at most one defective.

4.43 Suppose that you randomly select and purchase 3 televisions from a production run of 10 televisions. Of the 10 televisions, 9 are destined to last at least five years without needing a single repair. What is the probability that all three of your TV sets will last at least five years without needing a single repair?

4.44 Suppose that you own an electronics store and purchase (assume random selection) 15 televisions from a production run of 500 televisions. Of the 500 televisions, 450 are destined to last at least five years without needing a single repair. Set up an expression using the hypergeometric distribution for the probability that at least 14 of your 15 televisions will last at least five years without needing a single repair. Then, using the binomial tables (see Appendix A, Table A.1), approximate this probability by using the binomial distribution. What justifies the approximation? Hint: $p = r/N = 450/500 = .9$.

CHAPTER SUMMARY

In this chapter, we began our study of random variables. We learned that a random variable represents an uncertain numerical outcome. We also learned that a random variable whose values can be listed is called a *discrete random variable*, while the values of a continuous random variable correspond to one or more intervals on the real number line. We saw that a probability distribution of a discrete random variable is a table, graph, or formula that gives the probability associated with each of the random variable's possible values. We also discussed several descriptive measures of a discrete random variable—its mean (or expected value), its variance, and its standard deviation.

We continued this chapter by studying two important, commonly used discrete probability distributions—the binomial distribution and the Poisson distribution—and we demonstrated how these distributions can be used to make statistical inferences. Finally, we studied a third important discrete probability distribution, the hypergeometric distribution.

KEY TERMS

binomial distribution
binomial experiment
binomial random variable
binomial tables
continuous random variable
discrete random variable
empirical rule
expected value (of a random variable)

hypergeometric distribution
hypergeometric random variable
Poisson distribution
Poisson random variable
probability distribution (of a discrete random variable)
random variable
standard deviation (of a random variable)
variance (of a random variable)

IMPORTANT FORMULAS

Properties of a discrete probability distribution

Mean (expected value) of a discrete random variable

Variance and standard deviation of a discrete random variable

Binomial probability formula

Mean, variance, and standard deviation of a binomial random variable

Poisson probability formula

Mean, variance, and standard deviation of a Poisson random variable

Hypergeometric probability formula

Mean and variance of a hypergeometric random variable

SUPPLEMENTARY EXERCISES

connect Practise and learn online with *Connect*. Items for which there are online data sets are marked with

4.45 An investor holds two stocks, each of which can rise (R), remain unchanged (U), or decline (D) on any particular day. Let x equal the number of stocks that rise on a particular day.
   a. Write the probability distribution of x assuming that all outcomes are equally likely.
   b. Write the probability distribution of x assuming that for each stock $P(R) = .6$, $P(U) = .1$, and $P(D) = .3$ and assuming that movements of the two stocks are independent.
   c. Write the probability distribution of x assuming that for the first stock

$$P(R) = .4, \quad P(U) = .2, \quad P(D) = .4$$

   and that for the second stock

$$P(R) = .8, \quad P(U) = .1, \quad P(D) = .1$$

   and assuming that movements of the two stocks are independent.

4.46 Repeat Exercise 4.45, letting x equal the number of stocks that decline on the particular day.

4.47 Using Exercise 4.45, let x equal the number of stocks that rise on the particular day. Find μ_x and σ_x for
   a. The probability distribution of x in Exercise 4.45(a).
   b. The probability distribution of x in Exercise 4.45(b).
   c. The probability distribution of x in Exercise 4.45(c).
   d. In which case is μ_x the largest? Interpret what this means in words.
   e. In which case is σ_x the largest? Interpret what this means in words.

4.48 Suppose that the probability distribution of a random variable x can be described by the formula

$$P(x) = \frac{(x - 3)^2}{55}$$

   for each of the values $x = -2, -1, 0, 1,$ and 2.
   a. Write the probability distribution of x.
   b. Show that the probability distribution of x satisfies the properties of a discrete probability distribution.
   c. Calculate the mean of x.
   d. Calculate the variance and standard deviation of x.

4.49 A rock concert promoter has scheduled an outdoor concert on July 1. If it does not rain, the promoter will make $30,000. If it does rain, the promoter will lose $15,000 in guarantees made to the band and other expenses. The probability of rain on July 1 is .4.

a. What is the promoter's expected profit? Is the expected profit a reasonable decision criterion? Explain.

b. How much should an insurance company charge to insure the promoter's full losses? Explain your answer.

4.50 The demand (in number of copies per day) for a city newspaper is listed below with corresponding probabilities:

x = Demand	P(x)
50,000	.1
70,000	.25
90,000	.4
110,000	.2
130,000	.05

a. Graph the probability distribution of x.

b. Find the expected demand. Interpret this value, and label it on the graph you've produced in part (a)

c. Using Chebyshev's theorem, find the minimum percentage of all possible daily demand values that will fall in the interval $[\mu_x \pm 2\sigma_x]$.

d. Calculate the interval $[\mu_x \pm 2\sigma_x]$. Illustrate this interval on the graph produced for part (a). According to the probability distribution of demand x previously given, what percentage of all possible daily demand values fall in the interval $[\mu_x \pm 2\sigma_x]$?

4.51 United Medicine, Inc., claims that a drug, Viro, significantly relieves the symptoms of a certain viral infection for 80 percent of all patients. Suppose that this drug is given to eight randomly selected patients who have been diagnosed with the viral infection.

a. Let x equal the number of the eight randomly selected patients whose symptoms are significantly relieved. What distribution describes the random variable x? Explain.

b. Assuming that the company's claim is correct, find $P(x \le 3)$.

c. Suppose that of the eight randomly selected patients, three have had their symptoms significantly relieved by Viro. Based on the probability in part (b), would you believe the claim of United Medicine, Inc.? Explain.

4.52 A consumer advocate claims that 80 percent of cable television subscribers are not satisfied with their cable service. In an attempt to justify this claim, a randomly selected sample of cable subscribers will be polled on this issue.

a. Suppose that the advocate's claim is true, and suppose that a random sample of five cable subscribers is selected. Assuming independence, use an appropriate formula to compute the probability that four or more subscribers in the sample are not satisfied with their service.

b. Suppose that the advocate's claim is true, and suppose that a random sample of 25 cable subscribers is selected. Assuming independence, find

(1) The probability that 15 or fewer subscribers in the sample are not satisfied with their service.

(2) The probability that more than 20 subscribers in the sample are not satisfied with their service.

(3) The probability that between 20 and 24 (inclusive) subscribers in the sample are not satisfied with their service.

(4) The probability that exactly 24 subscribers in the sample are not satisfied with their service.

c. Suppose that when we survey 25 randomly selected cable television subscribers, we find that 15 are actually not satisfied with their service. Using a probability you found in this exercise as the basis for your answer, do you believe the consumer advocate's claim? Explain.

4.53 A bank has implemented procedures aimed at reducing the number of NSF cheques deposited at ATMs. The bank's goal is to see no more than eight NSF cheques deposited per week. The average number of NSF cheques deposited is three per week. Let X denote the number of NSF cheques deposited per week. Assuming that X has a Poisson distribution:

a. Find the probability that the bank will not receive any NSF cheques in a particular week.

b. Find the probability that the bank will meet its goal during a particular week.

c. Find the probability that the bank will not meet its goal during a particular week.

d. Find the probability that the bank's ATMs will receive no more than 10 NSF cheques per two-week period.

e. Find the probability that the bank's ATMs will receive no more than five NSF cheques per three-week period.

4.54 Suppose that the number of accidents occurring in an industrial plant is described by a Poisson process as having an average of 1.5 accidents every three months. During the last three months, four accidents occurred.

a. Find the probability that no accidents will occur during the current three-month period.

b. Find the probability that fewer accidents will occur during the current three-month period than occurred during the last three-month period.

c. Find the probability that no more than 12 accidents will occur during a particular year.

d. Find the probability that no accidents will occur during a particular year.

4.55 A high-security government organization has installed four security systems to detect attempted break-ins. The four security systems operate independently of each other, and each has a .85 probability of detecting an attempted break-in. Assume an attempted break-in occurs. Use the binomial distribution to find the probability that at least one of the four security systems will detect it.

4.56   A new stain removal product claims to completely remove the stains on 90 percent of all stained garments. Assume that the product will be tested on 20 randomly selected stained garments, and let x denote the number of these garments from which the stains will be completely removed. Use the binomial distribution to find $P(x \leq 13)$ if the stain removal product's claim is correct. If x actually turns out to be 13, what do you think of the claim?

4.57   Consider Exercise 4.56, and find $P(x \leq 17)$ if the stain removal product's claim is correct. If x actually turns out to be 17, what do you think of the claim?

4.58   A province has averaged one small business failure per week over the past several years. Let x denote the number of small business failures in the next eight weeks. Use the Poisson distribution to find $P(x \geq 17)$ if the mean number of small business failures remains what it has been. If x actually turns out to be 17, what does this imply?

4.59   A candy company claims that its new chocolate almond bar averages 10 almonds per bar. Let x denote the number of almonds in the next bar that you buy. Use the Poisson distribution to find $P(x \leq 4)$ if the candy company's claim is correct. If x actually turns out to be 4, what do you think of the claim?

4.60   Consider Exercise 4.59, and find $P(x \leq 8)$ if the candy company's claim is true. If x actually turns out to be 8, what do you think of the claim?

4.61   **INTERNET EXERCISE**

Go to olg.ca/lotteries/index.jsp and, in the "Winning Numbers" section on the right-hand side of the screen, click on the gold button in the Lotto 6/49 listing (second from the top) to see the prizes that were won and the number of winning tickets for each prize that were sold in Canada. Using the techniques that you have learned in this chapter, calculate the expected value for a lottery ticket and calculate the standard deviation for this prize distribution. Is purchasing a ticket worthwhile? Why might this be a faulty way of considering the utility of a lottery ticket purchase?

CHAPTER 5
Continuous Random Variables

LEARNING OBJECTIVES

After reading this chapter, you should be able to

LO1 Explain the purpose of a continuous probability distribution

LO2 Compute probabilities using the uniform distribution

LO3 Describe the properties of the normal distribution

LO4 Compute probabilities using the normal distribution

LO5 Find population values that correspond to specified normal distribution probabilities

LO6 Approximate binomial probabilities using the normal distribution

LO7 Compute probabilities using the exponential distribution

CHAPTER OUTLINE

5.1 Continuous Probability Distributions

5.2 The Uniform Distribution

5.3 The Normal Probability Distribution

5.4 Approximating the Binomial Distribution by Using the Normal Distribution

5.5 The Exponential Distribution

In Chapter 4, we defined discrete and continuous random variables. We also discussed discrete probability distributions, which are used to compute the probabilities of values of discrete random variables. In this chapter, we discuss continuous probability distributions. These are used to find probabilities concerning continuous random variables. We begin by explaining the general idea behind a continuous probability distribution. Then we present three important continuous distributions—the uniform, normal, and exponential distributions. We also study when and how the normal distribution can be used to approximate the binomial distribution (which was discussed in Chapter 4).

5.1 CONTINUOUS PROBABILITY DISTRIBUTIONS

In Section 4.1, we noted that when a random variable might assume any numerical value in one or more intervals on the real number line, then the random variable is called a *continuous random variable*. For example, as discussed in Section 4.1, the combined city and highway fuel efficiency of a randomly selected midsized car is a continuous random variable. Furthermore, the temperature (in degrees Celsius) of a randomly selected cup of coffee at Tim Hortons is also a continuous random variable. We often want to compute probabilities about the range of values that a continuous random variable x might attain. For example, suppose that marketing research done by Tim Hortons indicates that coffee tastes best if its temperature is between 67°C and 75°C. The restaurant might then want to find the probability that x, the temperature of a randomly selected cup of coffee at the restaurant, will be between 67° and 75°. This probability would represent the proportion of coffee served by the restaurant that has a temperature between 67° and 75°. Moreover, one minus this probability would represent the proportion of coffee served by the restaurant that has a temperature outside the range 67° to 75°.

LO1   In general, to compute probabilities concerning a continuous random variable x, we assign probabilities to intervals of values by using a continuous probability distribution. To understand this idea, suppose that $f(x)$ is a continuous function of the numbers on the real line, and consider the continuous curve that results when $f(x)$ is graphed. Such a curve is illustrated in Figure 5.1 and defined in the following boxed feature.

> **Continuous Probability Distribution**
>
> The curve $f(x)$ is the **continuous probability distribution** of the random variable x if the probability that x will be in a specified interval of numbers is the area under the curve $f(x)$ corresponding to the interval. Sometimes we refer to a continuous probability distribution as a *probability curve* or as a *probability density function*.

An *area* under a continuous probability distribution (or probability curve) is a *probability*. For instance, consider the range of values on the number line from the number a to the number b—that is, the interval of numbers from a to b. If the continuous random variable x is described by the probability curve $f(x)$, then the area under $f(x)$ corresponding to the interval from a to b is the probability that x will be between a and b. Such a probability is illustrated as the shaded area in Figure 5.1. We write this probability as $P(a \leq x \leq b)$. For example, suppose that the continuous probability curve $f(x)$ in Figure 5.1 describes the random variable

FIGURE 5.1   An Example of a Continuous Probability Distribution $f(x)$

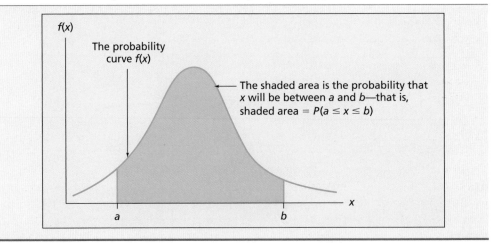

x, the temperature of a randomly selected cup of coffee at Tim Hortons. It then follows that $P(67 \leq x \leq 75)$—the probability that the temperature of a randomly selected cup of coffee will be between 67° and 75°—is the area under the curve $f(x)$ between 67 and 75.

We know that any probability is 0 or positive, and we also know that the probability assigned to all possible values of *x* must be 1. It follows that, similar to the conditions required for a discrete probability distribution, a probability curve must satisfy the following properties:

Properties of a Continuous Probability Distribution

The continuous probability distribution (or probability curve) *f(x)* of a random variable *x* must satisfy the following two conditions:

1 *f(x)* ≥ 0 for any value of *x*.

2 The total area under the curve *f(x)* is equal to 1.

Any continuous curve $f(x)$ that satisfies these two conditions is a valid continuous probability distribution. Such probability curves can have a variety of shapes—bell-shaped and symmetrical, skewed to the right, skewed to the left, or any other shape. In a practical problem, the shape of a probability curve would be estimated by looking at a frequency (or relative frequency) histogram of observed data (as we did in Chapter 2). Later in this chapter, we study probability curves that have several different shapes. For example, in the next section we introduce the *uniform distribution,* which has a rectangular shape.

We have seen that to calculate a probability concerning a continuous random variable, we must compute an appropriate area under the curve $f(x)$. In theory, such areas are calculated by calculus methods and/or numerical techniques. Because these methods are difficult, needed areas under commonly used probability curves have been compiled in statistical tables. As we need them, we show how to use the required statistical tables. Also, note that since there is no area under a continuous curve at a single point, the probability that a continuous random variable *x* will attain a single value is always equal to 0. It follows that in Figure 5.1 we have $P(x = a) = 0$ and $P(x = b) = 0$. Therefore, $P(a \leq x \leq b)$ equals $P(a < x < b)$ because each of the interval endpoints *a* and *b* has a probability that is equal to 0.

Defining the properties of your variable is crucial

ROADBLOCK

A continuous variable is easy to recognize when the data includes decimals and is reported with great precision. The distinguishing feature of a continuous variable is, however, found in its definition—not in your sample data. Consider the example of coffee temperatures: Even when the sample data is reported only in whole integers, the temperature of the coffee can, theoretically, take on any value along the temperature continuum. It is this theoretical continuity that makes a variable continuous.

5.2 THE UNIFORM DISTRIBUTION

Suppose that over a period of several days the manager of a large hotel has recorded the waiting times of 1,000 people waiting for an elevator in the lobby at dinnertime (5:00 P.M. to 7:00 P.M.). The observed waiting times range from zero to four minutes. Furthermore, when the waiting times are arranged into a histogram, the bars making up the histogram have approximately equal heights, giving the histogram a rectangular appearance. This implies that the relative frequencies of all waiting times from zero to four minutes are about the same. Therefore, it is reasonable to use the *uniform distribution* to describe the random variable *x,* the amount of

FIGURE **5.2**   The Uniform Distribution

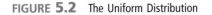

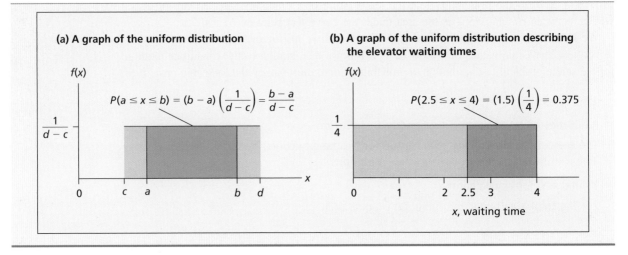

time a randomly selected hotel patron spends waiting for the elevator. In general, the equation that describes the uniform distribution is given in the following boxed feature, and this equation is graphed in Figure 5.2(a).

LO2

The Uniform Distribution

If c and d are numbers on the real line, the probability curve describing the **uniform distribution** is

$$f(x) = \begin{cases} \dfrac{1}{d-c} & \text{for } c \leq x \leq d \\ 0 & \text{otherwise} \end{cases}$$

Furthermore, the mean and the standard deviation of the population of all possible observed values of a random variable x that has a uniform distribution are

$$\mu_x = \frac{c+d}{2} \quad \text{and} \quad \sigma_x = \frac{d-c}{\sqrt{12}}$$

Notice that the total area under the uniform distribution is the area of a rectangle having a base equal to $(d - c)$ and a height equal to $1/(d - c)$. Therefore, the probability curve's total area is

$$\text{Base} \times \text{Height} = (d - c)\left(\frac{1}{d - c}\right) = 1$$

(remember that the total area under any continuous probability curve must equal 1). Furthermore, if a and b are numbers that are as illustrated in Figure 5.2(a), then the probability that x will be between a and b is the area of a rectangle with base $(b - a)$ and height $1/(d - c)$. That is,

$$P(a \leq x \leq b) = \text{Base} \times \text{Height}$$

$$= (b - a)\left(\frac{1}{d - c}\right)$$

$$= \frac{b - a}{d - c}$$

> **Even when your underlying variable is continuous, a histogram is useful when thinking about the continuous probability function**
> Recall that we construct a histogram by reporting the frequency of occurrence for each value within your data. When the variable reported along the *x*-axis is categorical, the histogram takes on its characteristic "boxy" appearance. When we consider that a continuous variable can (by definition) take on any value within the range of possible scores for the variable, we can see that this has the effect of "smoothing" the curve for the histogram. As the amount of data within the sample increases, the resulting graph will become increasingly smoother, until it more closely resembles the idealized continuous probability function that we see in the figures in this chapter.
>
> **ROADBLOCK**

Example 5.1 The Elevator Waiting Time Example

In the introduction to this section, we said that the amount of time, x, that a randomly selected hotel patron spends waiting for the elevator at dinnertime is uniformly distributed between zero and four minutes. In this case, $c = 0$ and $d = 4$. Therefore,

$$f(x) = \begin{cases} \dfrac{1}{d-c} = \dfrac{1}{4-0} = \dfrac{1}{4} & \text{for } 0 \le x \le 4 \\ 0 & \text{otherwise} \end{cases}$$

Noting that this equation is graphed in Figure 5.2(b), suppose that the hotel manager wants to find the probability that a randomly selected patron will spend at least 2.5 minutes waiting for the elevator. This probability is the area under the curve $f(x)$ that corresponds to the interval [2.5, 4]. As shown in Figure 5.2(b), this probability is the area of a rectangle having a base equal to $4 - 2.5 = 1.5$ and a height equal to $1/4$. That is,

$$P(x \ge 2.5) = P(2.5 \le x \le 4) = \text{Base} \times \text{Height} = 1.5 \times \frac{1}{4} = .375$$

Similarly, the probability that a randomly selected patron will spend less than one minute waiting for the elevator is

$$P(x < 1) = P(0 \le x \le 1) = \text{Base} \times \text{Height} = 1 \times \frac{1}{4} = .25$$

We next note that the mean waiting time for the elevator at dinnertime is

$$\mu_x = \frac{c+d}{2} = \frac{0+4}{2} = 2 \text{ (minutes)}$$

and that the standard deviation of this waiting time is

$$\sigma_x = \frac{d-c}{\sqrt{12}} = \frac{4-0}{\sqrt{12}} = 1.1547 \text{ (minutes)}$$

Therefore, because

$$\mu_x - \sigma_x = 2 - 1.1547 = .8453$$

and

$$\mu_x + \sigma_x = 2 + 1.1547 = 3.1547$$

the probability that the waiting time of a randomly selected patron will be within (plus or minus) one standard deviation of the mean waiting time is

$$P(.8453 \le x \le 3.1547) = (3.1547 - .8453) \times \frac{1}{4}$$

$$= .57735$$

Exercises for Sections **5.1** and **5.2**

CONCEPTS

5.1 A discrete probability distribution assigns probabilities to individual values. To what are probabilities assigned by a continuous probability distribution?

5.2 How do we use the continuous probability distribution (or probability curve) of a random variable x to find probabilities? Explain.

5.3 What two properties must be satisfied by a continuous probability distribution (or probability curve)?

5.4 Is the height of a probability curve over a given point a probability? Explain.

5.5 When is it appropriate to use the uniform distribution to describe a random variable x?

METHODS AND APPLICATIONS

5.6 Suppose that the random variable x has a uniform distribution with $c = 2$ and $d = 8$.
   a. Write the formula for the probability curve of x, and write an interval that gives the possible values of x.
   b. Graph the probability curve of x.
   c. Find $P(3 \leq x \leq 5)$.
   d. Find $P(1.5 \leq x \leq 6.5)$.
   e. Calculate the mean μ_x, variance σ^2_x, and standard deviation σ_x.
   f. Calculate the interval $[\mu_x \pm 2\sigma_x]$. What is the probability that x will be in this interval?

5.7 Consider the figure at right. Find the value h that makes the function $f(x)$ a valid continuous probability distribution.

5.8 Assume that the waiting time x for an elevator is uniformly distributed between zero and six minutes.
   a. Write the formula for the probability curve of x.
   b. Graph the probability curve of x.
   c. Find $P(2 \leq x \leq 4)$.
   d. Find $P(3 \leq x \leq 6)$.
   e. Find $P(\{0 \leq x \leq 2\} \text{ or} \{5 \leq x \leq 6\})$.

5.9 Refer to Exercise 5.8.
   a. Calculate the mean, μ_x, the variance, σ^2_x, and the standard deviation, σ_x.
   b. Find the probability that the waiting time of a randomly selected patron will be within one standard deviation of the mean.

5.10 Although there are probably "time of day" effects that impact on emergency room waiting times, these effects are likely to be substantially less than the effect of an arrival of a major trauma case or the effect of a highly complex (and acute) case. The remainder of the variability in waiting times is likely to be random. If you find that waiting times in a local emergency room range between 1 and 4 hours, find the mean and standard deviation for the waiting time at this hospital, under the assumption that all of the waiting times in this range are equally likely to occur. If you were to

calculate a range of values, centred around the mean of this distribution, between what two values would your waiting time fall 95 percent of the time? Between what two values (centred around the mean of the distribution) would your waiting time fall 90 percent of the time?

5.11 Suppose that WestJet quotes a flight time of 2 hours, 10 minutes between two cities. Furthermore, suppose that historical flight records indicate that the actual flight time between the two cities, x, is uniformly distributed between 2 hours and 2 hours, 20 minutes. Letting the time unit be one minute,
   a. Write the formula for the probability curve of x.
   b. Graph the probability curve of x.
   c. Find $P(125 \leq x \leq 135)$.
   d. Find the probability that a randomly selected flight between the two cities will be at least five minutes late.

5.12 Refer to Exercise 5.11.
   a. Calculate the mean flight time and the standard deviation of the flight time.
   b. Find the probability that the flight time will be within one standard deviation of the mean.

5.13 A weather forecaster predicts that the May rainfall in a local area will be between three and six centimetres but has no idea where within the interval the amount will be. Let x be the amount of May rainfall in the local area and assume that x is uniformly distributed over the interval three to six centimetres.
   a. Write the formula for the probability curve of x.
   b. Graph the probability curve of x.
   c. What is the probability that May rainfall will be at least four centimetres? At least five centimetres? At most 4.5 centimetres?

5.14 Refer to Exercise 5.13.
   a. Calculate the expected May rainfall.
   b. What is the probability that the observed May rainfall will fall within two standard deviations of the mean? Within one standard deviation of the mean?

5.15 Ever since residents of your community stopped using herbicides on their lawns, you have noticed that there is an increasing concentration of dandelions on your street. Because the seeds for these flowers are windborne, the number of dandelions on each lawn is entirely (and perfectly) random. You have determined, however, that the number of dandelions on each lawn ranges between 3 and 25 at any given time. Let x be the number of dandelions on a given lawn.
   a. Write the formula for the probability curve of x.
   b. What is the probability that there will be at least 10 dandelions on any given lawn? What is the probability that there will be no more than 15 dandelions on a randomly selected lawn? What is the probability that there will be less than 3 dandelions on a lawn?

5.3 THE NORMAL PROBABILITY DISTRIBUTION

The normal curve The bell-shaped appearance of the normal probability distribution is illustrated in Figure 5.3. The equation that defines this normal curve is given in the following box:

The Normal Probability Distribution

The **normal probability distribution** is defined by the equation

$$f(x) = \frac{1}{\sigma\sqrt{2\pi}}\, e^{-\frac{1}{2}\left(\frac{x-\mu}{\sigma}\right)^2} \text{ for all values of } x \text{ on the real line}$$

Here μ and σ are the mean and standard deviation of the population of all possible observed values of the random variable x under consideration. Furthermore, $\pi = 3.14159 \ldots$ and $e = 2.71828 \ldots$ is the base of natural logarithms.

LO3

The normal probability distribution has several important properties:

1 There is an entire family of normal probability distributions; the specific shape of each normal distribution is determined by its mean μ and its standard deviation σ.

2 The highest point on the normal curve is located at the mean, which is also the median and the mode of the distribution.

3 The normal distribution is symmetrical: The curve's shape to the left of the mean is the mirror image of its shape to the right of the mean.

4 The tails of the normal curve extend to infinity in both directions and never touch the horizontal axis. However, the tails get close enough to the horizontal axis quickly enough to ensure that the total area under the normal curve equals 1.

5 Since the normal curve is symmetrical, the area under the normal curve to the right of the mean (μ) equals the area under the normal curve to the left of the mean, and each of these areas equals .5 (see Figure 5.3).

FIGURE 5.3 The Normal Probability Curve

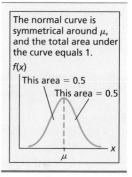

Intuitively, the mean μ positions the normal curve on the real line. This is illustrated in Figure 5.4(a). This figure shows two normal curves with different means μ_1 and μ_2 (where μ_1 is greater than μ_2) and with equal standard deviations. We see that the normal curve with mean μ_1 is centred farther to the right.

Both the variance (σ^2) and the standard deviation (σ) measure the spread of the normal curve. This is illustrated in Figure 5.4(b), which shows two normal curves with the same mean and two different standard deviations σ_1 and σ_2. Because σ_1 is greater than σ_2, the normal curve with standard deviation σ_1 is more spread out (flatter) than the normal curve with standard deviation σ_2. In general, larger standard deviations result in normal curves that are flatter and more spread out, while smaller standard deviations result in normal curves that have higher peaks and are less spread out.

Suppose that a random variable x is normally distributed with mean μ and standard deviation σ. If a and b are numbers on the real line, we consider the probability that x will be between a and b. That is, we consider

$$P(a \leq x \leq b)$$

which equals the area under the normal curve with mean (μ) and standard deviation (σ) corresponding to the interval $[a, b]$. Such an area is depicted in Figure 5.5. Later in this chapter, we will explain how to find such areas using a statistical table called a *normal table*. For now, we will discuss three important areas under a normal curve. These areas form the basis for the empirical rule for a normally distributed population.

FIGURE **5.4**   How the Mean μ and Standard Deviation σ Affect the Position and Shape of a Normal Probability Curve

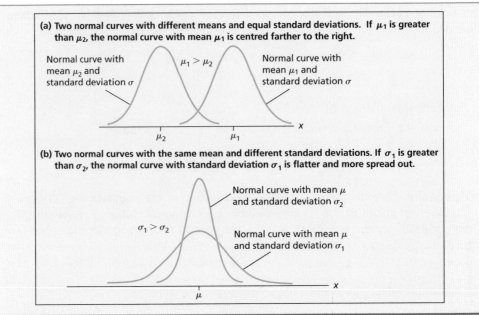

Specifically, if x is normally distributed with mean μ and standard deviation σ, it can be shown (using a normal table) that, as detailed in the following boxed feature and illustrated Figure 5.6:

Three Important Areas under the Normal Curve

1 $P(\mu - \sigma \leq x \leq \mu + \sigma) = .6826$

This means that 68.26 percent of all possible observed values of x are within (plus or minus) one standard deviation of μ.

2 $P(\mu - 2\sigma \leq x \leq \mu + 2\sigma) = .9544$

This means that 95.44 percent of all possible observed values of x are within (plus or minus) two standard deviations of μ.

3 $P(\mu - 3\sigma \leq x \leq \mu + 3\sigma) = .9973$

This means that 99.73 percent of all possible observed values of x are within (plus or minus) three standard deviations of μ.

FIGURE **5.5**   An Area under a Normal Curve Corresponding to the Interval [a, b]

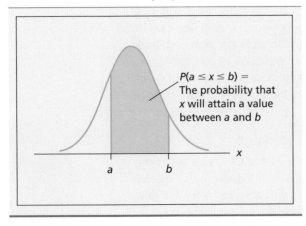

FIGURE **5.6**   Three Important Percentages Concerning a Normally Distributed Random Variable x with Mean μ and Standard Deviation σ

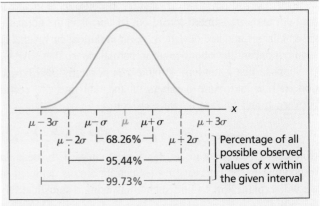

The normal distribution is symmetrical about the mean, but the distribution of values is not perfectly random
A key difference between the normal distribution and the uniform distribution lies in the level of randomness that we can ascribe to the data. The uniform distribution is useful in situations where you have no plausible rationale for expecting data to cluster around a particular value. In other words, there isn't any single point on the distribution that is more likely to occur than any other point (which is intuitive, given that all points on the distribution are equally likely), so the distribution of values is perfectly random. The normal distribution, on the other hand, is mound-shaped, owing to the fact that the values closest to the mean are more likely to occur than values that are farther away from the mean. In practical terms, this means that the values of the normal distribution are not distributed in a perfectly random fashion.

Finding normal curve areas There is a unique normal curve for every combination of μ and σ. Since there are many (theoretically, an unlimited number of) such combinations, we would like to have one table of normal curve areas that applies to all normal curves. There is such a table, and we can use it by thinking in terms of how many standard deviations a value of interest is from the mean. Specifically, consider a random variable x that is normally distributed with mean μ and standard deviation σ. Then the random variable

$$z = \frac{x - \mu}{\sigma}$$

LO4

expresses the number of standard deviations that x is from the mean μ. To understand this idea, notice that if x equals μ (that is, x is zero standard deviations from μ), then $z = (\mu - \mu)/\sigma = 0$. However, if x is one standard deviation above the mean (that is, if x equals $\mu + \sigma$), then $x - \mu = \sigma$ and $z = \sigma/\sigma = 1$. Similarly, if x is two standard deviations below the mean (that is, if x equals $\mu - 2\sigma$), then $x - \mu = -2\sigma$ and $z = -2\sigma/\sigma = -2$. Figure 5.7 illustrates that for values of x of, respectively, $\mu - 3\sigma$, $\mu - 2\sigma$, $\mu - \sigma$, μ, $\mu + \sigma$, $\mu + 2\sigma$, and $\mu + 3\sigma$, the corresponding values of z are -3, -2, -1, 0, 1, 2, and 3.

FIGURE 5.7   If x Is Normally Distributed with Mean μ and Standard Deviation σ, Then $z = \dfrac{x - \mu}{\sigma}$ Is Normally Distributed with Mean 0 and Standard Deviation 1

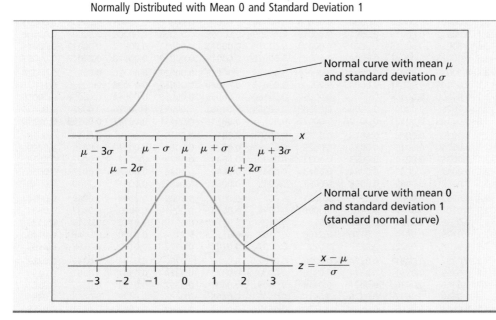

This figure also illustrates the following general result:

> ### The Standard Normal Distribution
>
> If a random variable x (or, equivalently, the population of all possible observed values of x) is normally distributed with mean μ and standard deviation σ, then the random variable
>
> $$z = \frac{x - \mu}{\sigma}$$
>
> (or, equivalently, the population of all possible observed values of z) is normally distributed with mean 0 and standard deviation 1. The distribution of these **z values** will be a normal distribution (or curve) with mean 0 and standard deviation 1, and is called a **standard normal distribution** (or **curve**).

Table A.4 in Appendix A is a table of *cumulative* areas under the standard normal curve. This table is called a *cumulative normal table,* and it is reproduced as Table 5.1. Specifically,

The **cumulative normal table** gives, for many different values of z, the area under the standard normal curve to the left of z.

Two such areas are shown next to Table 5.1—one with a negative z value and one with a positive z value. The values of z in the cumulative normal table range from -3.99 to 3.99 in increments of .01. As can be seen from Table 5.1, values of z accurate to the nearest tenth are given in the far left column (headed z) of the table. Further graduations to the nearest hundredth (.00, .01, .02,. . . , .09) are given across the top of the table. The areas under the normal curve are given in the body of the table, accurate to four (or sometimes five) decimal places.

TABLE 5.1　Cumulative Areas under the Standard Normal Curve

z	.00	.01	.02	.03	.04	.05	.06	.07	.08	.09
−3.9	0.00005	0.00005	0.00004	0.00004	0.00004	0.00004	0.00004	0.00004	0.00003	0.00003
−3.8	0.00007	0.00007	0.00007	0.00006	0.00006	0.00006	0.00006	0.00005	0.00005	0.00005
−3.7	0.00011	0.00010	0.00010	0.00010	0.00009	0.00009	0.00008	0.00008	0.00008	0.00008
−3.6	0.00016	0.00015	0.00015	0.00014	0.00014	0.00013	0.00013	0.00012	0.00012	0.00011
−3.5	0.00023	0.00022	0.00022	0.00021	0.00020	0.00019	0.00019	0.00018	0.00017	0.00017
−3.4	0.00034	0.00032	0.00031	0.00030	0.00029	0.00028	0.00027	0.00026	0.00025	0.00024
−3.3	0.00048	0.00047	0.00045	0.00043	0.00042	0.00040	0.00039	0.00038	0.00036	0.00035
−3.2	0.00069	0.00066	0.00064	0.00062	0.00060	0.00058	0.00056	0.00054	0.00052	0.00050
−3.1	0.00097	0.00094	0.00090	0.00087	0.00084	0.00082	0.00079	0.00076	0.00074	0.00071
−3.0	0.00135	0.00131	0.00126	0.00122	0.00118	0.00114	0.00111	0.00107	0.00103	0.00100
−2.9	0.0019	0.0018	0.0018	0.0017	0.0016	0.0016	0.0015	0.0015	0.0014	0.0014
−2.8	0.0026	0.0025	0.0024	0.0023	0.0023	0.0022	0.0021	0.0021	0.0020	0.0019
−2.7	0.0035	0.0034	0.0033	0.0032	0.0031	0.0030	0.0029	0.0028	0.0027	0.0026
−2.6	0.0047	0.0045	0.0044	0.0043	0.0041	0.0040	0.0039	0.0038	0.0037	0.0036
−2.5	0.0062	0.0060	0.0059	0.0057	0.0055	0.0054	0.0052	0.0051	0.0049	0.0048
−2.4	0.0082	0.0080	0.0078	0.0075	0.0073	0.0071	0.0069	0.0068	0.0066	0.0064
−2.3	0.0107	0.0104	0.0102	0.0099	0.0096	0.0094	0.0091	0.0089	0.0087	0.0084
−2.2	0.0139	0.0136	0.0132	0.0129	0.0125	0.0122	0.0119	0.0116	0.0113	0.0110
−2.1	0.0179	0.0174	0.0170	0.0166	0.0162	0.0158	0.0154	0.0150	0.0146	0.0143
−2.0	0.0228	0.0222	0.0217	0.0212	0.0207	0.0202	0.0197	0.0192	0.0188	0.0183
−1.9	0.0287	0.0281	0.0274	0.0268	0.0262	0.0256	0.0250	0.0244	0.0239	0.0233
−1.8	0.0359	0.0351	0.0344	0.0336	0.0329	0.0322	0.0314	0.0307	0.0301	0.0294
−1.7	0.0446	0.0436	0.0427	0.0418	0.0409	0.0401	0.0392	0.0384	0.0375	0.0367
−1.6	0.0548	0.0537	0.0526	0.0516	0.0505	0.0495	0.0485	0.0475	0.0465	0.0455
−1.5	0.0668	0.0655	0.0643	0.0630	0.0618	0.0606	0.0594	0.0582	0.0571	0.0559

(Table Continues)

TABLE 5.1 (Continued)

z	.00	.01	.02	.03	.04	.05	.06	.07	.08	.09
−1.4	0.0808	0.0793	0.0778	0.0764	0.0749	0.0735	0.0721	0.0708	0.0694	0.0681
−1.3	0.0968	0.0951	0.0934	0.0918	0.0901	0.0885	0.0869	0.0853	0.0838	0.0823
−1.2	0.1151	0.1131	0.1112	0.1093	0.1075	0.1056	0.1038	0.1020	0.1003	0.0985
−1.1	0.1357	0.1335	0.1314	0.1292	0.1271	0.1251	0.1230	0.1210	0.1190	0.1170
−1.0	0.1587	0.1562	0.1539	0.1515	0.1492	0.1469	0.1446	0.1423	0.1401	0.1379
−0.9	0.1841	0.1814	0.1788	0.1762	0.1736	0.1711	0.1685	0.1660	0.1635	0.1611
−0.8	0.2119	0.2090	0.2061	0.2033	0.2005	0.1977	0.1949	0.1922	0.1894	0.1867
−0.7	0.2420	0.2389	0.2358	0.2327	0.2296	0.2266	0.2236	0.2206	0.2177	0.2148
−0.6	0.2743	0.2709	0.2676	0.2643	0.2611	0.2578	0.2546	0.2514	0.2482	0.2451
−0.5	0.3085	0.3050	0.3015	0.2981	0.2946	0.2912	0.2877	0.2843	0.2810	0.2776
−0.4	0.3446	0.3409	0.3372	0.3336	0.3300	0.3264	0.3228	0.3192	0.3156	0.3121
−0.3	0.3821	0.3783	0.3745	0.3707	0.3669	0.3632	0.3594	0.3557	0.3520	0.3483
−0.2	0.4207	0.4168	0.4129	0.4090	0.4052	0.4013	0.3974	0.3936	0.3897	0.3859
−0.1	0.4602	0.4562	0.4522	0.4483	0.4443	0.4404	0.4364	0.4325	0.4286	0.4247
−0.0	0.5000	0.4960	0.4920	0.4880	0.4840	0.4801	0.4761	0.4721	0.4681	0.4641
0.0	0.5000	0.5040	0.5080	0.5120	0.5160	0.5199	0.5239	0.5279	0.5319	0.5359
0.1	0.5398	0.5438	0.5478	0.5517	0.5557	0.5596	0.5636	0.5675	0.5714	0.5753
0.2	0.5793	0.5832	0.5871	0.5910	0.5948	0.5987	0.6026	0.6064	0.6103	0.6141
0.3	0.6179	0.6217	0.6255	0.6293	0.6331	0.6368	0.6406	0.6443	0.6480	0.6517
0.4	0.6554	0.6591	0.6628	0.6664	0.6700	0.6736	0.6772	0.6808	0.6844	0.6879
0.5	0.6915	0.6950	0.6985	0.7019	0.7054	0.7088	0.7123	0.7157	0.7190	0.7224
0.6	0.7257	0.7291	0.7324	0.7357	0.7389	0.7422	0.7454	0.7486	0.7518	0.7549
0.7	0.7580	0.7611	0.7642	0.7673	0.7704	0.7734	0.7764	0.7794	0.7823	0.7852
0.8	0.7881	0.7910	0.7939	0.7967	0.7995	0.8023	0.8051	0.8078	0.8106	0.8133
0.9	0.8159	0.8186	0.8212	0.8238	0.8264	0.8289	0.8315	0.8340	0.8365	0.8389
1.0	0.8413	0.8438	0.8461	0.8485	0.8508	0.8531	0.8554	0.8577	0.8599	0.8621
1.1	0.8643	0.8665	0.8686	0.8708	0.8729	0.8749	0.8770	0.8790	0.8810	0.8830
1.2	0.8849	0.8869	0.8888	0.8907	0.8925	0.8944	0.8962	0.8980	0.8997	0.9015
1.3	0.9032	0.9049	0.9066	0.9082	0.9099	0.9115	0.9131	0.9147	0.9162	0.9177
1.4	0.9192	0.9207	0.9222	0.9236	0.9251	0.9265	0.9279	0.9292	0.9306	0.9319
1.5	0.9332	0.9345	0.9357	0.9370	0.9382	0.9394	0.9406	0.9418	0.9429	0.9441
1.6	0.9452	0.9463	0.9474	0.9484	0.9495	0.9505	0.9515	0.9525	0.9535	0.9545
1.7	0.9554	0.9564	0.9573	0.9582	0.9591	0.9599	0.9608	0.9616	0.9625	0.9633
1.8	0.9641	0.9649	0.9656	0.9664	0.9671	0.9678	0.9686	0.9693	0.9699	0.9706
1.9	0.9713	0.9719	0.9726	0.9732	0.9738	0.9744	0.9750	0.9756	0.9761	0.9767
→2.0	0.9772	0.9778	0.9783	0.9788	0.9793	0.9798	0.9803	0.9808	0.9812	0.9817
2.1	0.9821	0.9826	0.9830	0.9834	0.9838	0.9842	0.9846	0.9850	0.9854	0.9857
2.2	0.9861	0.9864	0.9868	0.9871	0.9875	0.9878	0.9881	0.9884	0.9887	0.9890
2.3	0.9893	0.9896	0.9898	0.9901	0.9904	0.9906	0.9909	0.9911	0.9913	0.9916
2.4	0.9918	0.9920	0.9922	0.9925	0.9927	0.9929	0.9931	0.9932	0.9934	0.9936
2.5	0.9938	0.9940	0.9941	0.9943	0.9945	0.9946	0.9948	0.9949	0.9951	0.9952
2.6	0.9953	0.9955	0.9956	0.9957	0.9959	0.9960	0.9961	0.9962	0.9963	0.9964
2.7	0.9965	0.9966	0.9967	0.9968	0.9969	0.9970	0.9971	0.9972	0.9973	0.9974
2.8	0.9974	0.9975	0.9976	0.9977	0.9977	0.9978	0.9979	0.9979	0.9980	0.9981
2.9	0.9981	0.9982	0.9982	0.9983	0.9984	0.9984	0.9985	0.9985	0.9986	0.9986
3.0	0.99865	0.99869	0.99874	0.99878	0.99882	0.99886	0.99889	0.99893	0.99897	0.99900
3.1	0.99903	0.99906	0.99910	0.99913	0.99916	0.99918	0.99921	0.99924	0.99926	0.99929
3.2	0.99931	0.99934	0.99936	0.99938	0.99940	0.99942	0.99944	0.99946	0.99948	0.99950
3.3	0.99952	0.99953	0.99955	0.99957	0.99958	0.99960	0.99961	0.99962	0.99964	0.99965
3.4	0.99966	0.99968	0.99969	0.99970	0.99971	0.99972	0.99973	0.99974	0.99975	0.99976
3.5	0.99977	0.99978	0.99978	0.99979	0.99980	0.99981	0.99981	0.99982	0.99983	0.99983
3.6	0.99984	0.99985	0.99985	0.99986	0.99986	0.99987	0.99987	0.99988	0.99988	0.99989
3.7	0.99989	0.99990	0.99990	0.99990	0.99991	0.99991	0.99992	0.99992	0.99992	0.99992
3.8	0.99993	0.99993	0.99993	0.99994	0.99994	0.99994	0.99994	0.99995	0.99995	0.99995
3.9	0.99995	0.99995	0.99996	0.99996	0.99996	0.99996	0.99996	0.99996	0.99997	0.99997

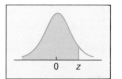

As an example, suppose that we want to find the area under the standard normal curve to the left of a z value of 2.00. This area is illustrated in Figure 5.8. To find this area, we start at the top of the leftmost column in Table 5.1 and scan down the column past the negative z values. We then scan through the positive z values until we find the z value 2.0—see the red arrow above. We now scan across the row in the table corresponding to the z value 2.0 until we find the column corresponding to the heading .00. The desired area (which we have shaded blue) is in the row corresponding to the z value 2.0 and in the column headed .00.

This area, which equals .9772, is the probability that the random variable z will be less than or equal to 2.00. That is, we have found that $P(z \leq 2) = .9772$. Note that, because there is no area under the normal curve at a single value of z, there is no difference between $P(z \leq 2)$ and $P(z < 2)$.

As another example, the area under the standard normal curve to the left of the z value 1.25 is found in the row corresponding to 1.2 and in the column corresponding to .05. We find that this area (also shaded blue) is .8944. That is, $P(z \leq 1.25) = .8944$ (see Figure 5.9).

We now show how to use the cumulative normal table to find several other kinds of normal curve areas. First, suppose that we want to find the area under the standard normal curve to the right of a z value of 2—that is, we want to find $P(z \geq 2)$. This area is illustrated in Figure 5.10 and is called a *right-hand tail area*. Since the total area under the normal curve equals 1, the area under the curve to the right of 2 equals 1 minus the area under the curve to the left of 2. Because Table 5.1 tells us that the area under the standard normal curve to the left of 2 is .9772, the area under the standard normal curve to the right of 2 is $1 - .9772 = .0228$. Said in an equivalent fashion, because $P(z \leq 2) = .9772$, it follows that $P(z \geq 2) = 1 - P(z \leq 2) = 1 - .9772 = .0228$.

Next, suppose that we want to find the area under the standard normal curve to the left of a z value of -2. That is, we want to find $P(z \leq -2)$. This area is illustrated in Figure 5.11 and is called a *left-hand tail area*. The needed area is found in the row of the cumulative normal table corresponding to -2.0 and in the column headed by .00. We find that $P(z \leq -2) = .0228$. Notice that the area under the standard normal curve to the left of -2 is equal to the area under this curve to the right of 2. This is true because of the symmetry of the normal curve.

Figure 5.12 illustrates how to find the area under the standard normal curve to the right of -2. Since the total area under the normal curve equals 1, the area under the curve to the right

FIGURE 5.8   Finding $P(z \leq 2)$

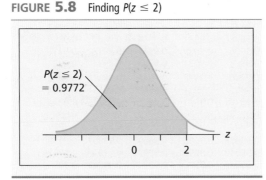

FIGURE 5.9   Finding $P(z \leq 1.25)$

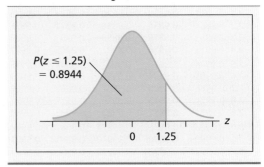

FIGURE 5.10   Finding $P(z \geq 2)$

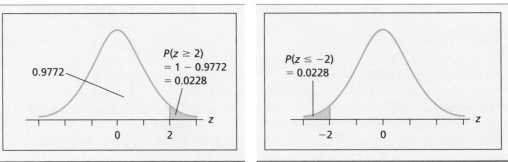

FIGURE 5.11   Finding $P(z \leq -2)$

FIGURE **5.12** Finding $P(z \geq -2)$ FIGURE **5.13** Finding $P(z \leq -3.99)$

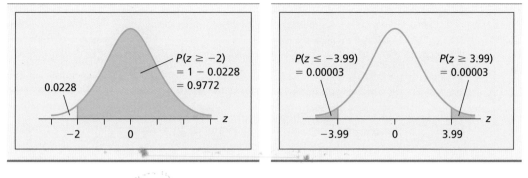

of −2 equals 1 minus the area under the curve to the left of −2. Because Table 5.1 tells us that the area under the standard normal curve to the left of −2 is .0228, the area under the standard normal curve to the right of −2 is 1 − .0228 = .9772. That is, because $P(z \leq -2) = .0228$, it follows that $P(z \geq -2) = 1 - P(z \leq -2) = 1 - .0228 = .9772$.

The smallest z value in Table 5.1 is −3.99, and the table tells us that the area under the standard normal curve to the left of −3.99 is .00003 (see Figure 5.13). Therefore, if we want to find the area under the standard normal curve to the left of any z value less than −3.99, the most we can say (without using a computer) is that this area is less than .00003. Similarly, the area under the standard normal curve to the right of any z value greater than 3.99 is also less than .00003 (see Figure 5.13).

Figure 5.14 illustrates how to find the area under the standard normal curve between 1 and 2. This area equals the area under the curve to the left of 2, which the normal table tells us is .9772, minus the area under the curve to the left of 1, which the normal table tells us is .8413. Therefore, $P(1 \leq z \leq 2) = .9772 - .8413 = .1359$.

To conclude our introduction to using the normal table, we will use this table to justify the empirical rule. Figure 5.15(a) illustrates the area under the standard normal curve between −1 and 1. This area equals the area under the curve to the left of 1, which the normal table tells us is .8413, minus the area under the curve to the left of −1, which the normal table tells us is .1587. Therefore, $P(-1 \leq z \leq 1) = .8413 - .1587 = .6826$. Now, suppose that a random variable x is normally distributed with mean μ and standard deviation σ, and remember that z is the number of standard deviations σ that x is from μ. It follows that when we say that $P(-1 \leq z \leq 1)$ equals .6826, we are saying that 68.26 percent of all possible observed values of x are between a point that is one standard deviation below μ (where z equals −1) and a point that is one standard deviation above μ (where z equals 1). That is, 68.26 percent of all possible observed values of x are within (plus or minus) one standard deviation of the mean μ.

FIGURE **5.14** Calculating $P(1 \leq z \leq 2)$

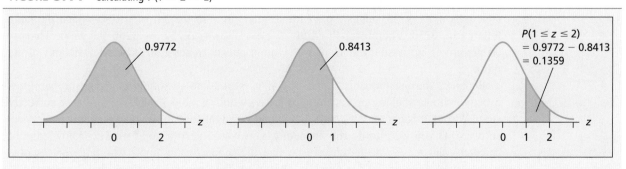

FIGURE 5.15   Some Areas under the Standard Normal Curve

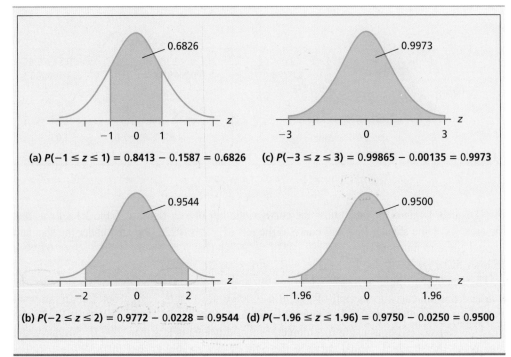

(a) $P(-1 \leq z \leq 1) = 0.8413 - 0.1587 = 0.6826$ (c) $P(-3 \leq z \leq 3) = 0.99865 - 0.00135 = 0.9973$

(b) $P(-2 \leq z \leq 2) = 0.9772 - 0.0228 = 0.9544$ (d) $P(-1.96 \leq z \leq 1.96) = 0.9750 - 0.0250 = 0.9500$

Figure 5.15(b) illustrates the area under the standard normal curve between -2 and 2. This area equals the area under the curve to the left of 2, which the normal table tells us is .9772, minus the area under the curve to the left of -2, which the normal table tells us is .0228. Therefore, $P(-2 \leq z \leq 2) = .9772 - .0228 = .9544$. That is, 95.44 percent of all possible observed values of x are within (plus or minus) two standard deviations of the mean μ.

Figure 5.15(c) illustrates the area under the standard normal curve between -3 and 3. This area equals the area under the curve to the left of 3, which the normal table tells us is .99865, minus the area under the curve to the left of -3, which the normal table tells us is .00135. Therefore, $P(-3 \leq z \leq 3) = .99865 - .00135 = .9973$. That is, 99.73 percent of all possible observed values of x are within (plus or minus) three standard deviations of the mean μ.

Although the empirical rule gives the percentages of all possible values of a normally distributed random variable x that are within one, two, and three standard deviations of the mean μ, we can use the normal table to find the percentage of all possible values of x that are within any particular number of standard deviations of μ. For example, in later chapters we will need to know the percentage of all possible values of x that are within plus or minus 1.96 standard deviations of μ. Figure 5.15(d) illustrates the area under the standard normal curve between -1.96 and 1.96. This area equals the area under the curve to the left of 1.96, which the normal table tells us is .9750, minus the area under the curve to the left of -1.96, which the table tells us is .0250. Therefore, $P(-1.96 \leq z \leq 1.96) = .9750 - .0250 = .9500$. That is, 95 percent of all possible values of x are within plus or minus 1.96 standard deviations of the mean μ.

By now, you are probably wondering if it is possible to simply calculate probabilities exactly, without looking up z scores (or areas) within a table—and have probably correctly surmised that it is not only possible, but is quite straight forward in most modern spreadsheet software. If you were to do this manually, you would need a good working knowledge of calculus—but these calculations are beyond the scope of this book. The table of z scores is, however, quite useful for quickly looking up the probability values that correspond to particular z scores. As you will see in Chapters 6 and 7, however, there are a few very commonly used z scores that you will probably commit to memory (however accidentally) over time:

$$P(z \geq 1.645) = .05$$

$$P(z \geq 1.96) = .025$$

$$P(z \geq 2.33) = .01$$

$$P(z \geq 2.575) = .005$$

Some practical applications We have seen how to use z values and the normal table to find areas under the standard normal curve. However, most practical problems are not stated in such terms. We now consider an example in which we must restate the problem in terms of the standard normal random variable z before using the normal table.

Example 5.2 Fuel Efficiency Claims

An automaker recently introduced a new midsized model, and wants to make claims about its fuel efficiency. To do so, it takes a sample of 50 of these vehicles and assesses the fuel efficiency of each. The company determines that distribution of fuel efficiencies are normally distributed, with a mean fuel efficiency equal to 7.50 L/100 km, and a standard deviation equal to .2 L/100 km.

Suppose that a competing automaker produces a midsized model that is somewhat smaller and less powerful. The competitor claims that its midsized model is more fuel efficient. Specifically, this competitor claims that the fuel efficiency of its vehicle is normally distributed with a mean fuel efficiency (μ) equal to 7.13 L/100 km and a standard deviation (σ) equal to .27 L/100 km. In the next example, we will consider one way to investigate the validity of this claim. In this example, we assume that the competitor's claim is true, and we calculate the probability that the fuel efficiency, x, of a randomly selected competitor's vehicle, will be between 6.75 and 7.49 L/100 km. That is, we want to find $P(6.75 \leq x \leq 7.49)$. As illustrated in Figure 5.16, this probability is the area between 6.75 and 7.49 under a normal curve having a mean (μ) of 7.13 and standard deviation $\sigma = .27$. In order to use the normal table, we must restate the problem in terms of the standard normal random variable z. The z value corresponding to 6.75 is

$$z = \frac{x - \mu}{\sigma} = \frac{6.75 - 7.13}{.27} = \frac{-.38}{.27} = -1.41$$

which says that the bottom end of this range of fuel efficiencies is 1.41 standard deviations below the mean ($\mu = 7.13$). The z value corresponding to 7.49 is

$$z = \frac{x - \mu}{\sigma} = \frac{7.49 - 7.13}{.27} = \frac{.36}{.27} = 1.33$$

which says that the upper end of this interval (7.49 L/100 km) is 1.33 standard deviations above the mean $\mu = 7.13$. Looking at Figure 5.16, we see that the area between 6.75 and 7.49 under the normal curve having mean $\mu = 7.13$ and standard deviation $\sigma = .27$ equals the area between -1.41 and 1.33 under the standard normal curve. This equals the area under the standard normal curve to the left of 1.33, which the normal table tells us is .9082, minus the area under the standard normal curve to the left of -1.41, which the normal table tells us is .0793.

This probability says that, if the competing automaker's claim is valid, then 82.89 percent of these vehicles will have fuel efficiencies that range between 6.75 and 7.49 L/100km.

FIGURE 5.16   Finding $P(6.75 \leq x \leq 7.49)$ When $\mu = 7.13$ and $\sigma = .27$ by Using a Normal Table

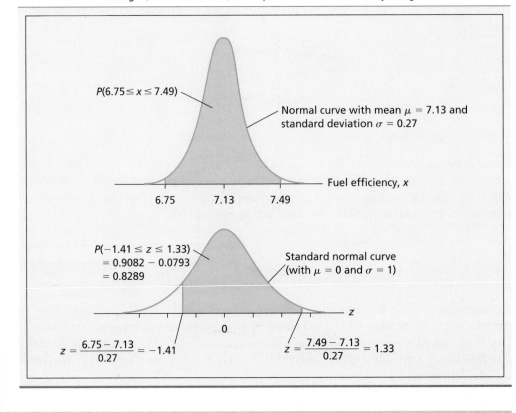

Example 5.2 illustrates the general procedure for finding a probability about a normally distributed random variable x. We summarize this procedure in the following box:

Finding Normal Probabilities

1 Formulate the problem in terms of the random variable x.

2 Calculate relevant z values and restate the problem in terms of the standard normal random variable

$$z = \frac{x - \mu}{\sigma}$$

3 Find the required area under the standard normal curve by using the normal table.

4 Note that it is always useful to draw a picture illustrating the needed area before using the normal table.

Example 5.3 More on Fuel Efficiency Claims

Consider the competing automakers in Example 5.2 again, one of whom is claiming that the fuel efficiency of its newest midsized vehicle is normally distributed with a mean of 7.13 and a standard deviation of .27. Suppose that an independent testing agency randomly selects one of these cars and finds that it has a fuel efficiency of 7.82 L/100 km when tested. Because this value is higher than the claimed mean of 7.13, we have some evidence that contradicts the automaker's claim. To evaluate the strength of this evidence, we will calculate the probability that the fuel efficiency, x, of a randomly selected midsized car would be *greater than or equal to* 7.82 if, in fact, the automaker's claim is true. To calculate $P(x \geq 7.82)$ under the assumption

FIGURE 5.17 Finding $P(x \geq 7.82)$ When $\mu = 7.13$ and $\sigma = .27$ by Using a Normal Table

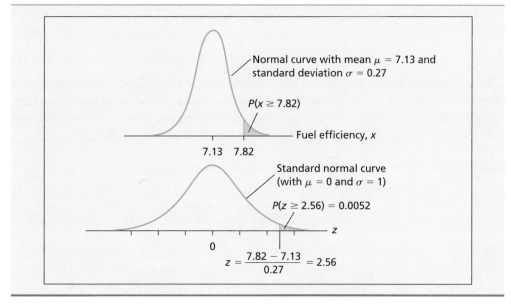

that the automaker's claim is true, we find the area to the right of 7.82 under a normal curve with $\mu = 7.13$ and $\sigma = .27$ (see Figure 5.17). In order to use the normal table, we must find the z value corresponding to 7.82. This z value is

$$z = \frac{7.82 - 7.13}{.27} = 2.56$$

which says that the fuel efficiency 7.82 L/100 km is 2.56 standard deviations worse than the mean fuel efficiency $\mu = 7.13$. Looking at Figure 5.17, we see that the area to the right of 7.82 under a normal curve with a mean of 7.13 and a standard deviation of .27 equals the area under the standard normal curve to the right of $z = 2.56$. The normal table tells us that the area under the standard normal curve to the right of 2.56 is .0052, as shown in Figure 5.17.

This probability says that, if the automaker's claim is valid, only 52 in 10,000 cars would obtain a fuel efficiency of 7.82 L/100 km or greater. Since it is very difficult to believe that a 52 in 10,000 chance has occurred, we have very strong evidence against the competing automaker's claim. It is probably true that μ is greater than 7.13 and/or σ is greater than .27 and/or the population of all fuel efficiencies is not normally distributed for this vehicle.

Example 5.4 The Coffee Temperature Example

Marketing research done by Tim Hortons indicates that coffee tastes best if its temperature is between 67°C and 75°C. The restaurant samples the coffee it serves and observes 24 temperature readings over a day. The temperature readings have a mean $\bar{x} = 71.1574$ and a standard deviation $s = 3.1495$ and are described by a bell-shaped distribution. Using $\bar{x}$ and s as point estimates of the mean and the standard deviation of the population of all possible coffee temperatures, we want to calculate the probability that x, the temperature of a randomly selected cup of coffee, is outside the customer requirements for best-testing coffee (that is, less than 67° or greater than 75°). In order to compute the probability $P(x < 67 \text{ or } x > 75)$ we compute the z values

$$z = \frac{67 - 71.1574}{3.1495} = -1.32 \quad \text{and} \quad z = \frac{75 - 71.1574}{3.1495} = 1.22$$

Because the events $\{x < 67\}$ and $\{x > 75\}$ are mutually exclusive, we have

$$P(x < 67 \text{ or } x > 75) = P(x < 67) + P(x > 75)$$
$$= P(z < -1.32) + P(z > 1.22)$$
$$= .0934 + .1112 = .2046$$

This calculation is illustrated in Figure 5.18. The probability of .2046 suggests that 20.46 percent of the coffee temperatures do not meet customer requirements. Therefore, if management believes that meeting this requirement is important, the coffee-making process must be improved.

FIGURE **5.18**   Finding $P(x < 67 \text{ or } x > 75)$ in the Coffee Temperature Case

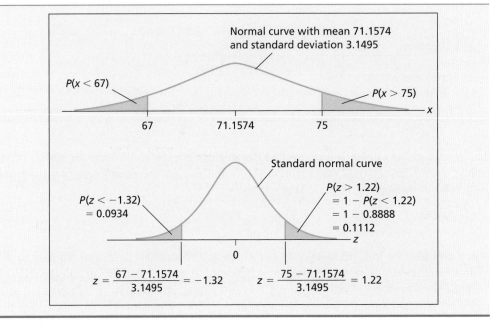

ROADBLOCK

Diagrams are useful in establishing the part of the z table that you should use
The z table that we will be using in this text has two sets of probabilities—one for the area under the curve *below z*, and one for the area under the curve *beyond z*. Most people find it easier to determine the appropriate area of interest when presented with a picture of the probability of interest (i.e., when presented with a normal curve with shading in the appropriate area of interest).

LO5   **Finding a point on the horizontal axis under a normal curve** In order to use many of the formulas given in later chapters, we must be able to find the z value so that the tail area to the right of z under the standard normal curve is a particular value. For instance, we might need to find the z value so that the tail area to the right of z under the standard normal curve is .025. This z value is denoted $z_{.025}$ and we illustrate $z_{.025}$ in Figure 5.19(a). We refer to $z_{.025}$ as *the point on the horizontal axis under the standard normal curve that gives a right-hand tail area equal to .025.* It is easy to use the cumulative normal table to find such a point. For instance, in order to find $z_{.025}$, we note from Figure 5.19(b) that the area under the standard normal curve to the left of $z_{.025}$ equals .975. Remembering that areas under the standard normal curve to the left of z are the four-digit (or five-digit) numbers given in the body of Table 5.1, we scan the body of the table and find the area .9750. We have shaded this area in Table 5.1 and we note that the area .9750 is in the row corresponding to a z of 1.9 and in the column

FIGURE 5.19   The Point $z_{.025} = 1.96$

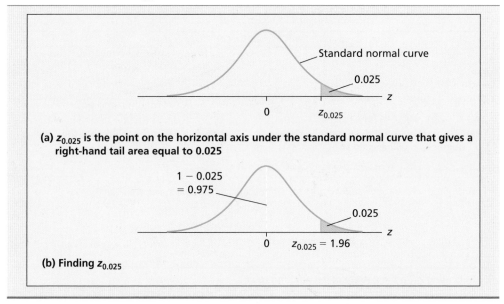

(a) $z_{0.025}$ is the point on the horizontal axis under the standard normal curve that gives a right-hand tail area equal to 0.025

(b) Finding $z_{0.025}$

headed by .06. It follows that the z value corresponding to .9750 is 1.96. Because the z value 1.96 gives an area under the standard normal curve to its left that equals .975, it also gives a right-hand tail area equal to .025. Therefore, $z_{.025} = 1.96$.

In general, we let the z_α **point** denote the point on the horizontal axis under the standard normal curve that gives a right-hand tail area equal to α. With this definition in mind, we consider Example 5.5.

Example 5.5 Demand for DVDs

A large discount store sells 50-packs of HX-150 blank DVDs and receives a shipment every Monday. Historical sales records indicate that the weekly demand, x, for HX-150 DVD 50-packs is normally distributed with a mean of $\mu = 100$ and a standard deviation of $\sigma = 10$. How many 50-packs should be stocked at the beginning of a week so that there is only a 5 percent chance that the store will run short during the week?

If we let st equal the number of 50-packs that will be stocked, then st must be chosen to allow only a .05 probability that weekly demand, x, will exceed st. That is, st must be chosen so that

$$P(x > st) = .05$$

Figure 5.20(a) shows that the number stocked, st, is located under the right-hand tail of the normal curve having mean $\mu = 100$ and standard deviation $\sigma = 10$. In order to find st, we need to determine how many standard deviations st must be above the mean in order to give a right-hand tail area that is equal to .05.

The z value corresponding to st is

$$z = \frac{st - \mu}{\sigma} = \frac{st - 100}{10}$$

and this z value is the number of standard deviations that st is from μ. This z value is illustrated in Figure 5.20(b), and it is the point on the horizontal axis under the standard normal curve that gives a right-hand tail area equal to .05. That is, the z value corresponding to st is $z_{.05}$. Since the area under the standard normal curve to the left of $z_{.05}$ is $1 - .05 = .95$—see Figure 5.20(b)—we look for .95 in the body of the normal table. In Table 5.1, we see that the areas closest to .95 are .9495, which has a corresponding z value of 1.64, and .9505, which has a corresponding z value of 1.65. Although it would probably be sufficient to use either of these

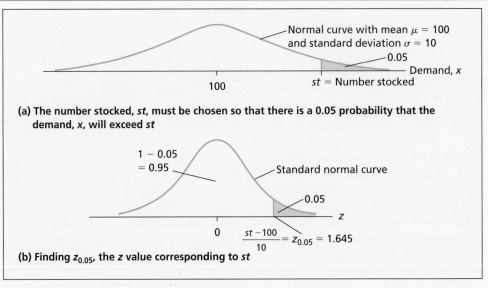

(a) The number stocked, *st*, must be chosen so that there is a 0.05 probability that the demand, *x*, will exceed *st*

(b) Finding $z_{0.05}$, the *z* value corresponding to *st*

z values, we will try to be a little more precise and interpolate halfway between them. This means that we will assume that $z_{.05}$ equals 1.645. To find *st*, we solve the equation

$$\frac{st - 100}{10} = 1.645$$

for *st*. Doing this yields

$$st - 100 = 1.645(10)$$

or

$$st = 100 + 1.645(10) = 116.45$$

This last equation says that *st* is 1.645 standard deviations ($\sigma = 10$) above the mean ($\mu = 100$). Rounding $st = 116.45$ up so that the store's chances of running short will be *no more* than 5 percent, the store should stock 117 of the 50-packs at the beginning of each week.

Sometimes we need to find the point on the horizontal axis under the standard normal curve that gives a particular left-hand tail area (say, for instance, an area of .025). Looking at Figure 5.21, it is easy to see that, if, for instance, we want a left-hand tail area of .025, the needed *z* value is $-z_{.025}$,

FIGURE 5.21   The *z* Value $-z_{.025} = -1.96$ Gives a Left-Hand Tail Area of .025 under the Standard Normal Curve

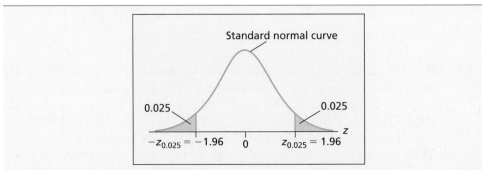

where $z_{.025}$ gives a right-hand tail area equal to .025. To find $-z_{.025}$, we look for .025 in the body of the normal table and find that the z value corresponding to .025 is -1.96. Therefore, $-z_{.025} = -1.96$. In general, the $-z_\alpha$ **point** *is the point on the horizontal axis under the standard normal curve that gives a left-hand tail area equal to* α.

THEORY TO PRACTICE

The normal curve is arguably one of the more useful concepts that you will learn about in this text. It can be used to describe the probability of values falling between particular points within a population, and as we will see, it can even be used to estimate the probability of occurrence for discrete variables. Furthermore, the normal curve is useful for describing data on a common scale—or as statisticians would say, using a "common metric. "For example, if you wanted to compare grades between two courses that you are taking, you might be concerned about the possibility that one course is easier than the other (and that this will produce a correspondingly higher mean score). If you simply compare the raw grades between the courses, you are not comparing the courses using a common metric—part of the reason that your grade in the easier course (or at least, your score in the course with the higher class average) will be higher than your grade in the other course is because grades are, on average, higher in that course. If you convert both grades to a z score, you can be assured that both distributions will have a mean of zero, and a standard deviation of 1—and can likewise be assured that the course in which you have the highest z score will be the course in which you did the best, relative to the other people in the course.

This is not, of course, limited to the comparison of academic grades: Any time you compare two values that are measured on different scales, you can convert them to z scores and evaluate the difference between these transformed ("re-scaled") values. In this way, it is possible to compare the sales records of individuals in different divisions (and account for departmental sales averages, differential sale prices, etc.), the salaries of individuals living in different cities (and account for regional differences in the cost of living), or customer satisfaction on products (and account for product categories that may not engender strong feelings among consumers).

In other words, and despite the adage admonishing us not to do so, it is possible to compare apples and oranges—you simply need to convert your variables to the same scale.

Example 5.6 Battery Life

Extensive testing indicates that the lifetime of the Everlast automobile battery is normally distributed with a mean of $\mu = 60$ months and a standard deviation of $\sigma = 6$ months. The Everlast's manufacturer has decided to offer a free replacement battery to any purchaser whose Everlast battery does not last at least as long as the minimum lifetime specified in its guarantee. How can the manufacturer establish the guarantee period so that only 1 percent of the batteries will need to be replaced free of charge?

If the battery will be guaranteed to last l months, l must be chosen to allow only a .01 probability that the lifetime, x, of an Everlast battery will be less than l. That is, we must choose l so that

$$P(x < l) = .01$$

Figure 5.22(a) shows that the guarantee period, l, is located under the left-hand tail of the normal curve having mean $\mu = 60$ and standard deviation $\sigma = 6$. In order to find l, we need to determine how many standard deviations l must be below the mean in order to give a left-hand tail area that equals .01. The z value corresponding to l is

$$z = \frac{l - \mu}{\sigma} = \frac{l - 60}{6}$$

FIGURE **5.22**   Finding the Guarantee Period, *l*, So That $P(x < l) = .01$ When $\mu = 60$ and $\sigma = 6$

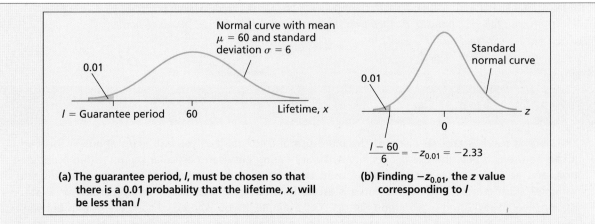

(a) The guarantee period, *l*, must be chosen so that there is a 0.01 probability that the lifetime, *x*, will be less than *l*

(b) Finding $-z_{0.01}$, the *z* value corresponding to *l*

and this *z* value is the number of standard deviations that *l* is from μ. This *z* value is illustrated in Figure 5.22(b) and it is the point on the horizontal axis under the standard normal curve that gives a left-hand tail area equal to .01. That is, the *z* value corresponding to *l* is $-z_{.01}$. To find $-z_{.01}$, we look for .01 in the body of the normal table. Doing this, we see that the area closest to .01 is .0099, which has a corresponding *z* value of -2.33. Therefore, $-z_{.01}$ is roughly -2.33. To find *l*, we solve the equation

$$\frac{l - 60}{6} = -2.33$$

for *l*. Doing this yields

$$l - 60 = -2.33(6)$$

or

$$l = 60 - 2.33(6) = 46.02$$

Note that this last equation says that *l* is 2.33 standard deviations ($\sigma = 6$) below the mean ($\mu = 60$). Rounding $l = 46.02$ down so that *no more* than 1 percent of the batteries will need to be replaced free of charge, it seems reasonable to guarantee the Everlast battery to last 46 months.

The intervals $[\mu \pm \sigma]$, $[\mu \pm 2\sigma]$, and $[\mu \pm 3\sigma]$ can be shown to contain, respectively, 68.26 percent, 95.44 percent, and 99.73 percent of the measurements in a normally distributed population having mean μ and standard deviation σ. In the following example, we demonstrate how to use the normal table to find the value *k* so that the interval $[\mu \pm k\sigma]$ contains any desired percentage of the measurements in a normally distributed population.

Example 5.7 Computing a Tolerance Interval

Consider computing a tolerance interval $[\mu \pm k\sigma]$ that contains 99 percent of the measurements in a normally distributed population having mean μ and standard deviation σ. As illustrated in Figure 5.23, we must find the value *k* so that the area under the normal curve having mean μ and standard deviation σ between $(\mu - k\sigma)$ and $(\mu + k\sigma)$ is .99. Because the total area under this normal curve is 1, the area under the normal curve that is not between $(\mu - k\sigma)$ and $(\mu + k\sigma)$ is $1 - .99 = .01$. This implies, as illustrated in Figure 5.23, that the area under the normal

FIGURE 5.23   Finding a Tolerance Interval [$\mu \pm k\sigma$] That Contains 99% of the Measurements in a Normally Distributed Population

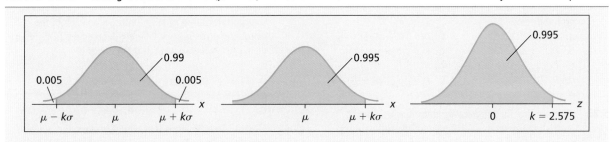

curve to the left of ($\mu - k\sigma$) is .01/2 = .005, and the area under the normal curve to the right of ($\mu + k\sigma$) is also .01/2 = .005. This further implies, as illustrated in Figure 5.23, that the area under the normal curve to the left of ($\mu + k\sigma$) is .995. Because the z value corresponding to a value of x tells us how many standard deviations x is from μ, the z value corresponding to ($\mu + k\sigma$) is obviously k. It follows that k is the point on the horizontal axis under the standard normal curve so that the area to the left of k is .995. Looking up .995 in the body of the normal table, we find that the values closest to .995 are .9949, which has a corresponding z value of 2.57, and .9951, which has a corresponding z value of 2.58. Although it would be sufficient to use either of these z values, we will interpolate halfway between them and we will assume that k equals 2.575. It follows that the interval [$\mu \pm 2.575\sigma$] contains 99 percent of the measurements in a normally distributed population having mean μ and standard deviation σ.

Whenever we use a normal table to find a z point corresponding to a particular normal curve area, we will use the *halfway interpolation* procedure illustrated in Examples 5.5 and 5.7 if the area we are looking for is exactly halfway between two areas in the table. Otherwise, as illustrated in Example 5.6, we will use the z value corresponding to the area in the table that is closest to the desired area.

Exercises for Section **5.3**

CONCEPTS

5.16 List five important properties of the normal probability curve.

5.17 Explain:
  a. What the mean, μ, tells us about a normal curve.
  b. What the standard deviation, σ, tells us about a normal curve.

5.18 If the random variable x is normally distributed, what percentage of all possible observed values of x will be
  a. Within one standard deviation of the mean?
  b. Within two standard deviations of the mean?
  c. Within three standard deviations of the mean?

5.19 Explain how to compute the z value corresponding to a value of a normally distributed random variable. What does the z value tell us about the value of the random variable?

5.20 Explain how x relates to the mean μ if the z value corresponding to x
  a. Equals zero.
  b. Is positive.
  c. Is negative.

5.21 Why do we compute z values when using the normal table? Explain.

METHODS AND APPLICATIONS

5.22 In each case, sketch the two specified normal curves on the same set of axes:
  a. A normal curve with $\mu = 20$ and $\sigma = 3$, and a normal curve with $\mu = 20$ and $\sigma = 6$.
  b. A normal curve with $\mu = 20$ and $\sigma = 3$, and a normal curve with $\mu = 30$ and $\sigma = 3$.
  c. A normal curve with $\mu = 100$ and $\sigma = 10$, and a normal curve with $\mu = 200$ and $\sigma = 20$.

5.23 Let x be a normally distributed random variable having mean $\mu = 30$ and standard deviation $\sigma = 5$. Find the z value for each of the following observed values of x:
  a. 25   **d.** 40
  b. 15   **e.** 50
  c. 30

In each case, explain what the z value tells us about how the observed value (x) compares to the mean (μ).

5.24 If the random variable z has a standard normal distribution, sketch and find each of the following probabilities:

 a. $P(0 \leq z \leq 1.5)$ **f.** $P(-1 \leq z \leq 1)$
 b. $P(z \geq 2)$ **g.** $P(-2.5 \leq z \leq .5)$
 c. $P(z \leq 1.5)$ **h.** $P(1.5 \leq z \leq 2)$
 d. $P(z \geq -1)$ **i.** $P(-2 \leq z \leq -.5)$
 e. $P(z \leq -3)$

5.25 Suppose that the random variable z has a standard normal distribution. Sketch each of the following z points, and use the normal table to find each z point.

 a. $z_{.01}$ **d.** $-z_{.01}$
 b. $z_{.05}$ **e.** $-z_{.05}$
 c. $z_{.02}$ **f.** $-z_{.10}$

5.26 Suppose that the random variable x is normally distributed with mean $\mu = 1{,}000$ and standard deviation $\sigma = 100$. Find each of the following probabilities:

 a. $P(1{,}000 \leq x \leq 1{,}200)$ **e.** $P(x \leq 700)$
 b. $P(x > 1{,}257)$ **f.** $P(812 \leq x \leq 913)$
 c. $P(x < 1{,}035)$ **g.** $P(x > 891)$
 d. $P(857 \leq x \leq 1{,}183)$ **h.** $P(1{,}050 \leq x \leq 1{,}250)$

5.27 Suppose that the random variable x is normally distributed with mean $\mu = 500$ and standard deviation $\sigma = 100$. For each of the following, use the normal table to find the needed value k.

 a. $P(x \geq k) = .025$ **f.** $P(x > k) = .95$
 b. $P(x \geq k) = .05$ **g.** $P(x \leq k) = .975$
 c. $P(x < k) = .025$ **h.** $P(x \geq k) = .0228$
 d. $P(x \leq k) = .015$ **i.** $P(x > k) = .9772$
 e. $P(x < k) = .985$

5.28 Stanford–Binet IQ test scores are normally distributed with a mean score of 100 and a standard deviation of 15.

 a. Sketch the distribution of Stanford–Binet IQ test scores.
 b. Write the equation that gives the z score corresponding to a Stanford–Binet IQ test score.
 c. Find the probability that a randomly selected person has an IQ test score
  (1) Over 140.
  (2) Under 88.
  (3) Between 72 and 128.
  (4) Within 1.5 standard deviations of the mean.
 d. Suppose you take the Stanford–Binet IQ test and receive a score of 136. What percentage of people would receive a score higher than yours?

5.29 Weekly demand at a grocery store for a brand of breakfast cereal is normally distributed with a mean of 800 boxes and a standard deviation of 75 boxes.

 a. What is the probability that weekly demand is
  (1) 959 boxes or less?
  (2) More than 1,004 boxes?
  (3) Less than 650 boxes or greater than 950 boxes?
 b. The store orders cereal from a distributor weekly. How many boxes should the store order for a week to have only a 2.5 percent chance of running short of this brand of cereal during the week?

5.30 The lifetimes of a particular brand of DVD player are normally distributed with a mean of eight years and a standard deviation of six months. Find each of the following probabilities where x denotes the lifetime in years. In each case, sketch the probability.

 a. $P(7 \leq x \leq 9)$ **e.** $P(x \leq 7)$
 b. $P(8.5 \leq x \leq 9.5)$ **f.** $P(x \geq 7)$
 c. $P(6.5 \leq x \leq 7.5)$ **g.** $P(x \leq 10)$
 d. $P(x \geq 8)$ **h.** $P(x > 10)$

5.31 United Motors claims that one of its cars, the Starbird 300, has a fuel efficiency of 7.84 L/100 km in the city, with a standard deviation of .26 L/100 km. Assume that the fuel efficiency for this vehicle is normally distributed within the population, and let x denote the fuel efficiency of a randomly selected Starbird 300.

 a. Assuming that United Motors' claim is correct, find $P(x \geq 8.71)$.
 b. If you purchase (randomly select) a Starbird 300 and your fuel efficiency is 8.71 L/100 km while driving in the city, what do you think of United Motors' claim? Explain your answer.

5.32 **THE INVESTMENT RETURN EXAMPLE**

An investment broker reports that the yearly returns on common shares are approximately normally distributed with a mean return of 12.4 percent and a standard deviation of 20.6 percent. On the other hand, the firm reports that the yearly returns on tax-free municipal bonds are approximately normally distributed with a mean return of 5.2 percent and a standard deviation of 8.6 percent. Find the probability that randomly selected

 a. Common shares will give a positive yearly return.
 b. Tax-free municipal bonds will give a positive yearly return.
 c. Common shares will give more than a 10 percent return.
 d. Tax-free municipal bonds will give more than a 10 percent return.
 e. Common shares will give a loss of at least 10 percent.
 f. Tax-free municipal bonds will give a loss of at least 10 percent.

5.33 A filling process is supposed to fill jars with 500 mL of grape jelly. Specifications state that each jar must contain between 498 mL and 502 mL of jelly. A jar is selected from the process every half hour until a sample of 100 jars is obtained. When the contents of the filled jars are measured, it is found that $\bar{x} = 500.075$ mL and $s = .97$. Using $\bar{x}$ and s as point estimates of μ and σ, estimate the probability that a randomly selected jar will have a fill, x, that is out of specification. Assume that the process is in control and that the population of all jar fills is normally distributed.

5.34 A tire company has developed a new type of steel-belted radial tire. Extensive testing indicates the population of kilometrage obtained by all tires of this new type is normally distributed with a mean of 60,000 kilometres and a standard deviation of 6,000 kilometres. The company wants to offer a guarantee providing a discount on a new set of tires if the original tires purchased do not exceed the kilometrage stated in the guarantee. What should the guaranteed kilometrage be if the tire company wants that no more than 2 percent of the tires will fail to meet the guarantee?

5.35 THE INVESTMENT RETURN EXAMPLE

Recall from Exercise 5.32 that yearly returns on common shares are normally distributed with a mean of 12.4 percent and a standard deviation of 20.6 percent.

a. What percentage of yearly returns are at or below the 10th percentile of the distribution of yearly returns? What percentage are at or above the 10th percentile? Find the 10th percentile of the distribution of yearly returns.

b. Find the first quartile, Q_1, and the third quartile, Q_3, of the distribution of yearly returns.

5.36 Two students take a college entrance exam known to have a normal distribution of scores. The students receive raw scores of 63 and 93, which correspond to z scores (often called the *standardized scores*) of -1 and 1.5, respectively. Find the mean and standard deviation of the distribution of raw exam scores.

5.37 THE TRASH BAG EXAMPLE

You are a manufacturer of trash bags, and want to determine the breaking strength of your products. A bag's breaking strength is the amount of a representative trash mix (in kilograms) that, when loaded into a bag suspended in the air, will cause the bag to rip or tear.

You take a sample of trash bags and measure the breaking strength of each bag. Suppose that a population of measurements is normally distributed with mean μ and standard deviation σ.

a. Write an expression (involving μ and σ) for a tolerance interval containing 98 percent of all the population measurements.

b. Estimate a tolerance interval containing 98 percent of all the trash bag breaking strengths by using the fact that a random sample of 40 breaking strengths has a mean of $\bar{x} = 50.575$ and a standard deviation of $s = 1.6438$.

5.38 THE INVESTMENT RETURN EXAMPLE

Consider the situation in Exercise 5.32.

a. Use the investment broker's report to estimate the maximum yearly return that might be obtained by investing in tax-free municipal bonds.

b. Find the probability that the yearly return obtained by investing in common shares will be higher than the maximum yearly return that might be obtained by investing in tax-free municipal bonds.

5.39 In his book *Advanced Managerial Accounting,* Robert P. Magee discusses monitoring cost variances. A *cost variance* is the difference between a budgeted cost and an actual cost. Magee describes the following situation:

Michael Bitner has responsibility for control of two manufacturing processes. Every week he receives a cost variance report for each of the two processes, broken down by labor costs, materials costs, and so on. One of the two processes, which we'll call process A, involves a stable, easily controlled production process with a little fluctuation in variances. Process

B involves more random events: the equipment is more sensitive and prone to breakdown, the raw material prices fluctuate more, and so on.

"It seems like I'm spending more of my time with process B than with process A," says Michael Bitner. "Yet I know that the probability of an inefficiency developing and the expected costs of inefficiencies are the same for the two processes. It's just the magnitude of random fluctuations that differs between the two, as you can see in the information below.

At present, I investigate variances if they exceed $2,500, regardless of whether it was process A or B. I suspect that such a policy is not the most efficient. I should probably set a higher limit for process B."

The means and standard deviations of the cost variances of processes A and B, when these processes are in control, are as follows:

	Process A	Process B
Mean cost variance (in control)	$ 0	$ 0
Standard deviation of cost variance (in control)	$5,000	$10,000

Furthermore, the means and standard deviations of the cost variances of processes A and B, when these processes are out of control, are as follows:

	Process A	Process B
Mean cost variance (out of control)	$7,500	$ 7,500
Standard deviation of cost variance (out of control)	$5,000	$10,000

a. Recall that the current policy is to investigate a cost variance if it exceeds $2,500 for either process. Assume that cost variances are normally distributed and that both Process A and Process B cost variances are in control. Find the probability that a cost variance for Process A will be investigated. Find the probability that a cost variance for Process B will be investigated. Which in-control process will be investigated more often?

b. Assume that cost variances are normally distributed and that both Process A and Process B cost variances are out of control. Find the probability that a cost variance for Process A will be investigated. Find the probability that a cost variance for Process B will be investigated. Which out-of-control process will be investigated more often?

c. If both Processes A and B are almost always in control, which process will be investigated more often?

d. Suppose that we want to reduce the probability that Process B will be investigated (when it is in control) to .3085. What cost variance investigation policy should be used? That is, how large a cost variance should trigger an investigation? Using this new policy, what is the probability that an out-of-control cost variance for Process B will be investigated?

5.40 You have been asked to audit the amount of sick time that employees within an organization are logging. Measured across the entire company, you find that the number of sick days ranged between 0 and 45 over the past 12 months. The mean is calculated to be 7.4, and the standard deviation is 3.2. Assume that "number of sick days" is a continuous variable (i.e., assume that employees can book off partial days due to illness).

a. What percentage have fewer than 5 sick days?
b. What percentage of employees have 5 to 10 sick days?

5.41 Suppose that the 33rd percentile of a normal distribution is equal to 656 and that the 97.5th percentile of this normal distribution is 896. Find the mean μ and the standard deviation σ of the normal distribution. Hint: Sketch these percentiles.

5.4 APPROXIMATING THE BINOMIAL DISTRIBUTION BY USING THE NORMAL DISTRIBUTION

LO6

Figure 5.24 illustrates several binomial distributions. In general, we can see that as n gets larger and as p gets closer to .5, the graph of a binomial distribution tends to have the symmetrical, bell-shaped appearance of a normal curve. It follows that, under conditions given in the following boxed feature, we can approximate the binomial distribution by using a normal distribution.

The Normal Approximation of the Binomial Distribution

Consider a binomial random variable x, where n is the number of trials performed and p is the probability of success in each trial. If n and p have values so that $np \geq 5$ and $n(1 - p) \geq 5$, then x is approximately normally distributed with mean $\mu = np$ and standard deviation $\sigma = \sqrt{npq}$, where $q = 1 - p$.

This approximation is often useful because binomial tables for large values of n are often unavailable. The conditions $np \geq 5$ and $n(1 - p) \geq 5$ must be met in order for the approximation to be appropriate. Note that if p is near 0 or near 1, then n must be larger for a good approximation, while if p is near .5, then n need not be as large.[1]

FIGURE 5.24   Several Binomial Distributions

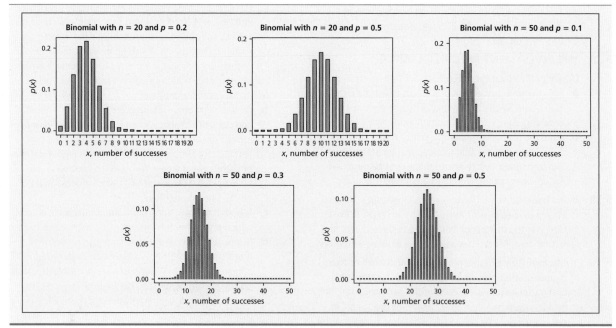

---

[1]As an alternative to the rule that both np and $n(1 - p)$ must be at least 5, some statisticians suggest using the more conservative rule that both np and $n(1 - p)$ must be at least 10.

When we say that we can approximate the binomial distribution by using a normal distribution, we are saying that we can compute binomial probabilities by finding corresponding areas under a normal curve (rather than by using the binomial formula). We illustrate how to do this in Example 5.8.

Example 5.8   Continuity Corrections for the Binomial Distribution

Consider the binomial random variable x with $n = 50$ trials and probability of success $p = .5$. This binomial distribution is one of those illustrated in Figure 5.24. Suppose we want to use the normal approximation to this binomial distribution to compute the probability of 23 successes in the 50 trials. That is, we want to compute $P(x = 23)$. Because $np = (50)(.5) = 25$ is at least 5, and $n(1 - p) = 50(1 - .5) = 25$ is also at least 5, we can appropriately use the approximation. Moreover, we can approximate the binomial distribution of x by using a normal distribution with mean $\mu = np = 50(.5) = 25$ and standard deviation $\sigma = \sqrt{npq} = \sqrt{50(.5)(1 - .5)} = 3.5355$.

To compute the needed probability, we must make a continuity correction because a discrete distribution (the binomial) is being approximated by a continuous distribution (the normal). Because there is no area under a normal curve at the single point $x = 23$, we must assign an area under the normal curve to the binomial outcome $x = 23$. It is logical to assign the area corresponding to the interval from 22.5 to 23.5 to the integer outcome $x = 23$. That is, the area under the normal curve corresponding to all values within .5 units of the integer outcome $x = 23$ is assigned to the value $x = 23$. So we approximate the binomial probability $P(x = 23)$ by calculating the normal curve area $P(22.5 \le x \le 23.5)$. This area is illustrated in Figure 5.25. Calculating the z values

$$z = \frac{22.5 - 25}{3.5355} = -.71 \quad \text{and} \quad z = \frac{23.5 - 25}{3.5355} = -.42$$

we find that $P(22.5 \le x \le 23.5) = P(-.71 \le z \le -.42) = .3372 - .2389 = .0983$. Therefore, we estimate that the binomial probability $P(x = 23)$ is .0983.

FIGURE **5.25** Approximating the Binomial Probability $P(x = 23)$ by Using the Normal Curve When
$\mu = np = 25$ and $\sigma = \sqrt{npq} = 3.5355$

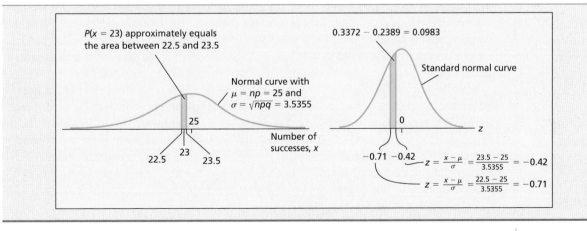

Making the proper continuity correction can sometimes be tricky. A good way to approach this is to list the numbers of successes that are included in the event for which the binomial probability is being calculated. Then assign the appropriate area under the normal curve to each number of successes in the list. Putting these areas together gives the normal curve area that must be calculated. For example, again consider the binomial random variable x with $n = 50$ and $p = .5$.

TABLE 5.2 Several Examples of the Continuity Correction ($n = 50$)

Binomial Probability	Numbers of Successes Included in Event	Normal Curve Area (with Continuity Correction)
$P(25 < x \leq 30)$	26, 27, 28, 29, 30	$P(25.5 \leq x \leq 30.5)$
$P(x \leq 27)$	0, 1, 2, . . . , 26, 27	$P(x \leq 27.5)$
$P(x > 30)$	31, 32, 33, . . . , 50	$P(x \geq 30.5)$
$P(27 < x < 31)$	28, 29, 30	$P(27.5 \leq x \leq 30.5)$

If we want to find $P(27 \leq x \leq 29)$, then the event $27 \leq x \leq 29$ includes 27, 28, and 29 successes. Because we assign the areas under the normal curve corresponding to the intervals [26.5, 27.5], [27.5, 28.5], and [28.5, 29.5] to the values 27, 28, and 29, respectively, then the area to be found under the normal curve is $P(26.5 \leq x \leq 29.5)$. Table 5.2 gives several other examples.

Example 5.9 The Cheese Spread Example

A food processing company markets a soft cheese spread that is sold in a plastic container with an "easy pour" spout. Although this spout works extremely well and is popular with consumers, it is expensive to produce. Because of the spout's high cost, the company has developed a new, less expensive spout. While the new, cheaper spout may alienate some purchasers, a company study shows that its introduction will increase profits if less than 10 percent of the cheese spread's current purchasers are lost. That is, if we let p be the true proportion of all current purchasers who would stop buying the cheese spread if the new spout was used, profits will increase as long as p is less than .10.

Suppose that (after trying the new spout) 63 of 1,000 randomly selected purchasers say that they would stop buying the cheese spread if the new spout was used. To assess whether p is less than .10, we will assume for the sake of argument that p equals .10, and we will use the sample information to weigh the evidence against this assumption and in favour of the conclusion that p is less than .10. Let the random variable x represent the number of the 1,000 purchasers who say they would stop buying the cheese spread. Assuming that p equals .10, then x is a binomial random variable with $n = 1,000$ and $p = .10$. Since the sample result of 63 is less than $\mu = np = 1,000(.1) = 100$, the expected value of x when p equals .10, we have some evidence to contradict the assumption that p equals .10. To evaluate the strength of this evidence, we calculate the probability that *63 or fewer* of the 1,000 randomly selected purchasers would say that they would stop buying the cheese spread if the new spout was used if, in fact, p equals .10.

Since both $np = 1,000(.10) = 100$ and $n(1 - p) = 1,000(1 - .10) = 900$ are at least 5, we can use the normal approximation to the binomial distribution to compute the needed probability. The appropriate normal curve has mean $\mu = np = 1,000(.10) = 100$ and standard deviation $\sigma = \sqrt{npq} = \sqrt{1,000(.10)(1 - .10)} = 9.4868$. In order to make the continuity correction, we note that the discrete value $x = 63$ is assigned the area under the normal curve corresponding to the interval from 62.5 to 63.5. It follows that the binomial probability $P(x \leq 63)$ is approximated by the normal probability $P(x \leq 63.5)$. This is illustrated in Figure 5.26. Calculating the z value for 63.5 to be

$$z = \frac{63.5 - 100}{9.4868} = -3.85$$

we find that

$$P(x \leq 63.5) = P(z \leq -3.85)$$

Using the normal table, we find that the area under the standard normal curve to the left of -3.85 is .00006. This says that, if p equals .10, then in only 6 in 100,000 of all possible

FIGURE **5.26** Approximating the Binomial Probability $P(x \leq 63)$ by Using the Normal Curve
When $\mu = np = 100$ and $\sigma = \sqrt{npq} = 9.4868$

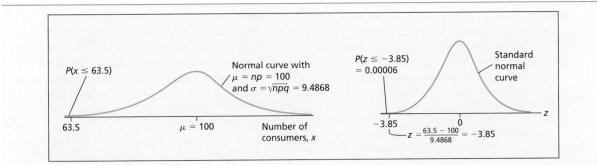

random samples of 1,000 purchasers would 63 or fewer say they would stop buying the cheese spread if the new spout was used. Since it is very difficult to believe that such a small chance (a .00006 chance) has occurred, we have very strong evidence that p does not equal .10 and is, in fact, less than .10. Therefore, it seems that using the new spout will be profitable.

ROADBLOCK

The difference between $<$ or $>$ and $\leq$ or $\geq$ is critical for the continuity correction
Be careful about the signs within the ranges that you are viewing. When a sign is "greater than" or "less than," the range will not include that value, so the continuity correction will be .5 less than the number (in the case of a "greater than" sign) or .5 larger than the number (in the case of a "less than" sign). When a sign is "greater than or equal to" or "less than or equal to," the range *will* include that value, so the continuity correction will be .5 larger than the number (in the case of a "greater than or equal to" sign) or .5 smaller than the number (in the case of a "less than or equal to" sign).

Exercises for Section **5.4**

CONCEPTS

5.42 Explain why it might be convenient to approximate binomial probabilities by using areas under an appropriate normal curve.

5.43 Under what condition can we use the normal approximation to the binomial distribution?

5.44 Explain how we make a continuity correction. Why is a continuity correction needed when we approximate a binomial distribution by a normal distribution?

METHODS AND APPLICATIONS

5.45 Suppose that x has a binomial distribution with $n = 200$ and $p = .4$.
  a. Show that the normal approximation to the binomial can appropriately be used to calculate probabilities for x.
  b. Make continuity corrections for each of the following, and then use the normal approximation to the binomial to find each probability:
  (1) $P(x = 80)$
  (2) $P(x \leq 95)$

  (3) $P(x < 65)$
  (4) $P(x \geq 100)$
  (5) $P(x > 100)$

5.46 Repeat Exercise 5.45 with $n = 200$ and $p = .5$.

5.47 An advertising agency conducted an ad campaign aimed at making consumers in the Maritimes aware of a new product. On completion of the campaign, the agency claimed that 20 percent of consumers in the area had become aware of the product. The product's distributor surveyed 1,000 consumers in the Maritimes and found that 150 were aware of the product.
  a. Assuming that the ad agency's claim is true:
  (1) Verify that we can use the normal approximation to the binomial.
  (2) Calculate the mean, μ, and the standard deviation, σ, we should use in the normal approximation.
  (3) Find the probability that 150 or fewer consumers in a random sample of 1,000 consumers would be aware of the product.
  b. Should the distributor believe the ad agency's claim? Explain.

5.48   To obtain additional information about respondents, some marketing researchers have used ultraviolet ink to precode questionnaires that promise confidentiality to respondents. Of 205 randomly selected marketing researchers who participated in an actual survey, 117 said that they disapprove of this practice. Suppose that, before the survey was taken, a marketing manager claimed that at least 65 percent of all marketing researchers would disapprove of the practice.

   a. Assuming that the manager's claim is correct, calculate the probability that 117 or fewer of 205 randomly selected marketing researchers would disapprove of the practice. Use the normal approximation to the binomial.

   b. Based on your result in part (a), do you believe the marketing manager's claim? Explain.

5.49   When a store uses electronic article surveillance (EAS) to combat shoplifting, it places a small sensor on each item of merchandise. When an item is legitimately purchased, the sales clerk is supposed to remove the sensor to prevent an alarm from sounding as the customer exits the store. In an actual survey of 250 consumers, 40 said that if they were to set off an EAS alarm because store personnel (mistakenly) failed to deactivate merchandise leaving the store, then they would never shop at that store again. A company marketing the alarm system claimed that no more than 5 percent of all consumers would say that they would never shop at that store again if they were subjected to a false alarm.

   a. Assuming that the company's claim is valid, use the normal approximation to the binomial to calculate the probability that at least 40 of the 250 randomly selected consumers would say that they would never shop at that store again if they were subjected to a false alarm.

   b. Do you believe the company's claim based on your answer to part (a)? Explain.

5.50   A department store will place a sale item in a special display for a one-day sale. Previous experience suggests that 20 percent of all customers who pass such a special display will purchase the item. If 2,000 customers will pass the display on the day of the sale, and if a one-item-per-customer limit is placed on the sale item, how many units of the sale item should the store stock in order to have at most a 1 percent chance of running short of the item on the day of the sale? Assume here that customers make independent purchase decisions.

5.51   You are in charge of the production of an integrated circuit for an electronics company. Based on your review of company data over the past year, you determine that approximately .01% of the integrated circuits that your company produces are defective. You need to determine the number of defective chips that your company will be selling over the next year.

   a. What is the smallest sample size that you can reasonably use in a binomial approximation of this probability function?

   b. Assume that your company makes 2 million of these chips each year. What is the probability that your company will make fewer than 175 defective chips per year?

   c. What is the probability that your company will make 225 to 250 (inclusive) defective chips in a year, again assuming that your company makes 2 million chips per year?

   d. The CEO wants to make a statement about the number of defective chips that are made (on average) per year, and wants to express this number as a range of values. If he wants to be 95 percent certain about his assertion, what range of values should he use in describing the number of defective chips that are manufactured each year?

5.5 THE EXPONENTIAL DISTRIBUTION

In Example 4.14 in Chapter 4, we considered an air traffic control centre where controllers occasionally misdirect pilots onto flight paths dangerously close to those of other aircraft. We found that the number of these controller errors in a given time period has a Poisson distribution and that the control centre is averaging 20.8 errors per year. However, rather than focusing on the number of errors occurring in a given time period, we could study the time elapsing between successive errors. If we let x denote the number of weeks elapsing between successive errors, then x is a continuous random variable that is described by what is called the *exponential distribution*. Moreover, because the control centre is averaging 20.8 errors per year, the centre is averaging a mean, denoted λ, of $20.8/52 = .4$ errors per week and thus a mean of $52/20.8 = 2.5$ (that is, $1/\lambda = 1/.4 = 2.5$) weeks between successive errors.

LO7   In general, if the number of events occurring per unit of time or space (for example, the number of controller errors per week or the number of imperfections per square metre of cloth) has a Poisson distribution with mean λ, then the number of units, x, of time or space between successive events has an *exponential distribution* with mean $1/\lambda$. The equation of the probability curve describing the exponential distribution is given in the following boxed feature.

The Exponential Distribution

If x is described by an **exponential distribution** with mean $1/\lambda$, then the equation of the probability curve describing x is

$$f(x) = \begin{cases} \lambda e^{-\lambda x} & \text{for } x \geq 0 \\ 0 & \text{otherwise} \end{cases}$$

Using this probability curve, it can be shown that

$$P(a \leq x \leq b) = e^{-\lambda a} - e^{-\lambda b}$$

In particular, since $e^0 = 1$ and $e^{-\infty} = 0$, this implies that

$$P(x \leq b) = 1 - e^{-\lambda b} \quad \text{and} \quad P(x \geq a) = e^{-\lambda a}$$

Furthermore, both the mean and the standard deviation of the population of all possible observed values of a random variable x that has an exponential distribution are equal to $1/\lambda$. That is, $\mu_x = \sigma_x = 1/\lambda$.

The graph of the equation describing the exponential distribution and the probability $P(a \leq x \leq b)$ where x is described by this exponential distribution is illustrated in Figure 5.27.

We illustrate the use of the exponential distribution in the following examples.

Example 5.10 The Air Traffic Controller Example

We have seen in the air traffic control example that the control centre is averaging $\lambda = .4$ errors per week and $1/\lambda = 1/.4 = 2.5$ weeks between successive errors. It follows that the equation of the exponential distribution describing x is $f(x) = \lambda e^{-\lambda x} = .4e^{-.4x}$. For example, the probability that the time between successive errors will be between 1 and 2 weeks is

$$P(1 \leq x \leq 2) = e^{-\lambda a} - e^{-\lambda b} = e^{-\lambda(1)} - e^{-\lambda(2)}$$
$$= e^{-.4(1)} - e^{-.4(2)} = e^{-.4} - e^{-.8}$$
$$= .6703 - .4493 = .221$$

FIGURE 5.27 A Graph of the Exponential Distribution $f(x) = \lambda e^{-\lambda x}$

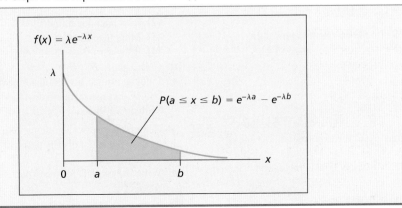

Example 5.11   The Hospital Waiting Time Example

Suppose that the number of people who arrive at a hospital emergency room during a given time period has a Poisson distribution. It follows that the time, x, between successive arrivals of people to the emergency room has an exponential distribution. Furthermore, historical records indicate that the mean time between successive arrivals of people to the emergency room is seven minutes. Therefore, $\mu_x = 1/\lambda = 7$, which implies that $\lambda = 1/7 = .14286$. Noting that $\sigma_x = 1/\lambda = 7$, it follows that

$$\mu_x - \sigma_x = 7 - 7 = 0 \text{ and } \mu_x + \sigma_x = 7 + 7 = 14$$

Therefore, the probability that the time between successive arrivals of people to the emergency room will be within (plus or minus) one standard deviation of the mean inter-arrival time is

$$
\begin{aligned}
P(0 \leq x \leq 14) &= e^{-\lambda a} - e^{-\lambda b} \\
&= e^{-(.14286)(0)} - e^{-(.14286)(14)} \\
&= 1 - .1353 \\
&= .8647
\end{aligned}
$$

To conclude this section we note that the exponential and related Poisson distributions are useful in analyzing waiting lines, or queues. In general, **queueing theory** attempts to determine the number of servers (for example, doctors in an emergency room) that strikes an optimal balance between the time customers wait for service and the cost of providing service. The reader is referred to any textbook on management science or operations research for a discussion of queueing theory.

Exercises for Section **5.5**

CONCEPTS

5.52 Give two examples of situations in which the exponential distribution might be used appropriately. In each case, define the random variable having an exponential distribution.

5.53 State the formula for the exponential probability curve. Define each symbol in the formula.

5.54 Explain the relationship between the Poisson and exponential distributions.

METHODS AND APPLICATIONS

5.55 Suppose that the random variable x has an exponential distribution with $\lambda = 2$.
   a. Write the formula for the exponential probability curve of x. What are the possible values of x?
   b. Sketch the probability curve.
   c. Find $P(x \leq 1)$.
   d. Find $P(.25 \leq x \leq 1)$.
   e. Find $P(x \geq 2)$.
   f. Calculate the mean, μ_x, the variance, σ_x^2, and the standard deviation, σ_x, of the exponential distribution of x.
   g. Find the probability that x will be in the interval $[\mu_x \pm 2\sigma_x]$.

5.56 Repeat Exercise 5.55 with $\lambda = 3$.

5.57 **THE CUSTOMER WAIT TIME EXAMPLE**
   Recall in Exercise 4.33 in Chapter 4 that the number of customer arrivals at a bank's drive-up window in a 15-minute period is Poisson distributed with a mean of seven customer arrivals per 15-minute period. Define the random variable x to be the time (in minutes) between successive customer arrivals at the bank's drive-up window.
   a. Write the formula for the exponential probability curve of x.
   b. Sketch the probability curve of x.
   c. Find the probability that the time between arrivals is
      (1) Between one and two minutes.
      (2) Less than one minute.
      (3) More than three minutes.
      (4) Between 1/2 and $3\frac{1}{2}$ minutes.
   d. Calculate μ_x, σ_x^2, and σ_x.
   e. Find the probability that the time between arrivals falls within one standard deviation of the mean. Within two standard deviations of the mean.

5.58 The length of a particular telemarketing phone call, x, has an exponential distribution with mean equal to 1.5 minutes.
   a. Write the formula for the exponential probability curve of x.
   b. Sketch the probability curve of x.

c. Find the probability that the length of a randomly selected call will be
  (1) No more than three minutes.
  (2) Between one and two minutes.
  (3) More than four minutes.
  (4) Less than 30 seconds.

5.59 The maintenance department in a factory claims that the number of breakdowns of a particular machine follows a Poisson distribution with a mean of two breakdowns every 500 hours. Let x denote the time (in hours) between successive breakdowns.
  a. Find λ and μ_x.
  b. Write the formula for the exponential probability curve of x.
  c. Sketch the probability curve.
  d. Assuming that the maintenance department's claim is true, find the probability that the time between successive breakdowns is at most five hours.
  e. Assuming that the maintenance department's claim is true, find the probability that the time between successive breakdowns is between 100 and 300 hours.
  f. Suppose that the machine breaks down five hours after its most recent breakdown. Based on your answer to part (d), do you believe the maintenance department's claim? Explain.

5.60 Suppose that the number of accidents occurring in an industrial plant is described by a Poisson distribution with an average of one accident per month. Let x denote the time (in months) between successive accidents.
  a. Find the probability that the time between successive accidents is
  (1) More than two months.
  (2) Between one and two months.
  (3) Less than one week (1/4 of a month).
  b. Suppose that an accident occurs less than one week after the plant's most recent accident. Would you consider this event unusual enough to warrant special investigation? Explain.

CHAPTER SUMMARY

In this chapter, we discussed continuous probability distributions. We began by learning that a continuous probability distribution is described by a continuous probability curve and that in this context, probabilities are areas under the probability curve. We next studied several important continuous probability distributions— the uniform distribution, the normal distribution, and the exponential distribution. In particular, we concentrated on the normal distribution, which is the most important continuous probability distribution.

We learned about the properties of the normal curve, and we saw how to use a normal table to find various areas under a normal curve. We also saw that the normal curve can be employed to approximate binomial probabilities, and we demonstrated how we can use a normal curve probability to make a statistical inference.

KEY TERMS

continuous probability distributions (or probability curves)
cumulative normal table
exponential distribution
normal probability distribution
queueing theory

standard normal distribution (or curve)
uniform distribution
z_α point
$-z_\alpha$ point
z value

IMPORTANT FORMULAS

Uniform probability curve

Mean and standard deviation of a uniform distribution

Normal probability curve

z values

Finding normal probabilities

Normal approximation to the binomial distribution

Exponential probability curve

Mean and standard deviation of an exponential distribution

SUPPLEMENTARY EXERCISES

Connect   Practise and learn online with *Connect*. Items for which there are online data sets are marked with.

5.61   In a bottle-filling process, the amount of drink injected into 500 mL bottles is normally distributed with a mean of 500 mL and a standard deviation of .8 mL. Bottles containing less than 498 mL do not meet the bottler's quality standard. What percentage of filled bottles do not meet the standard?

5.62   In a murder trial in Vancouver, a shoe expert stated that the range of heights of men with a size 12 shoe is 1.800 metres to 1.940 metres. Suppose the heights of all men wearing size 12 shoes are normally distributed with a mean of 1.870 metres and a standard deviation of .028 metres. What is the probability that a randomly selected man who wears a size 12 shoe

  a.   Has a height outside the range 1.800 metres to 1.930 metres?

  b.   Is 1.884 metres or taller?

  c.   Is shorter than 1.786 metres?

5.63   In the movie *Forrest Gump,* the public school required an IQ of at least 80 for admittance.

  a.   If IQ test scores are normally distributed with mean 100 and standard deviation 15, what percentage of people would qualify for admittance to the school?

  b.   If the public school wants 95 percent of all children to qualify for admittance, what minimum IQ test score should be required for admittance?

5.64   The amount of sales tax paid on a purchase is rounded to the nearest cent. Assume that the round-off error is uniformly distributed in the interval $-.5$ to .5 cents.

  a.   Write the formula for the probability curve describing the round-off error.

  b.   Graph the probability curve describing the round-off error.

  c.   What is the probability that the round-off error exceeds .3 cents or is less than $-.3$ cents?

  d.   What is the probability that the round-off error exceeds .1 cent or is less than $-.1$ cent?

  e.   Find the mean and the standard deviation of the round-off error.

  f.   Find the probability that the round-off error will be within one standard deviation of the mean.

5.65   A *consensus forecast* is the average of a large number of individual analysts' forecasts. Suppose the individual forecasts for a particular interest rate are normally distributed with a mean of 5.0 percent and a standard deviation of 1.2 percent. A single analyst is randomly selected. Find the probability that his or her forecast is

  a.   At least 3.5 percent.

  b.   At most 6 percent.

  c.   Between 3.5 percent and 6 percent.

5.66 Recall from Exercise 5.65 that individual forecasts of a particular interest rate are normally distributed with a mean of 5 percent and a standard deviation of 1.2 percent.
   a. What percentage of individual forecasts are at or below the 10th percentile of the distribution of forecasts? What percentage are at or above the 10th percentile? Find the 10th percentile of the distribution of individual forecasts.
   b. Find the first quartile, Q_1, and the third quartile, Q_3, of the distribution of individual forecasts.

5.67 The scores on the entrance exam at a well-known, exclusive law school are normally distributed with a mean score of 200 and a standard deviation equal to 50. At what value should the lowest passing score be set if the school wants only 2.5 percent of those taking the test to pass?

5.68 A machine is used to cut a metal automobile part to its desired length. The machine can be set so that the mean length of the part will be any value that is desired. The standard deviation of the lengths always runs at .02 centimetres. Where should the mean be set if we want only .4 percent of the parts cut by the machine to be shorter than 15 centimetres long?

5.69 A motel accepts 325 reservations for 300 rooms on July 1, expecting 10 percent no-shows on average from past records. Use the normal approximation to the binomial to find the probability that all guests who arrive on July 1 will receive a room.

5.70 Suppose a software company finds that the number of errors in its software per 1,000 lines of code is described by a Poisson distribution. Furthermore, it is found that there is an average of four errors per 1,000 lines of code. Letting x denote the number of lines of code between successive errors:
   a. Find the probability that there will be at least 400 lines of code between successive errors in the company's software.
   b. Find the probability that there will be no more than 100 lines of code between successive errors in the company's software.

5.71 The daily water consumption of an Ontario community is normally distributed with a mean consumption of 800,000 litres and a standard deviation of 80,000 litres. The community water system will experience a noticeable drop in water pressure when the daily water consumption exceeds 984,000 litres. What is the probability of experiencing such a drop in water pressure?

5.72 Suppose the times required for a cable company to fix cable problems in its customers' homes are uniformly distributed between 10 minutes and 25 minutes. What is the probability that a randomly selected cable repair visit will take at least 15 minutes?

5.73 Suppose the waiting time to get food after placing an order at a fast-food restaurant is exponentially distributed with a mean of 60 seconds. If a randomly selected customer orders food at the restaurant, what is the probability that the customer will wait at least
   a. 90 seconds?
   b. Two minutes?

5.74 Net interest margin—often referred to as *spread*—is the difference between the rate that banks pay on deposits and the rate they charge for loans. Suppose that the net interest margins for all Canadian banks are normally distributed with a mean of 4.15 percent and a standard deviation of .5 percent.
   a. Find the probability that a randomly selected Canadian bank will have a net interest margin that exceeds 5.40 percent.
   b. Find the probability that a randomly selected Canadian bank will have a net interest margin less than 4.40 percent.
   c. A bank wants its net interest margin to be less than the net interest margins of 95 percent of all Canadian banks. Where should the bank's net interest margin be set?

5.75 In an article in the November 11, 1991, issue of *Advertising Age,* Nancy Giges studied global spending patterns. Giges presented data concerning the percentage of adults in various countries who purchased various consumer items (such as soft drinks, athletic footwear, blue jeans, beer, and so on) in the previous three months.
   a. Suppose we want to justify the claim that less than 50 percent of adults in Germany have purchased blue jeans in the past three months. The survey reported by Giges found that 45 percent of the respondents in Germany had purchased blue jeans in the previous three months.[2]

   Assume that a random sample of 400 German adults was selected, and let p be the proportion of all German adults who have purchased blue jeans in the past three months. If, for the sake of argument, we assume that $p = .5$, use the normal approximation to the binomial distribution to calculate the probability that 45 percent or less of 400 randomly selected German adults would have purchased blue jeans in the past three months. Note: Because 45 percent of 400 is 180, you should calculate the probability that 180 or fewer of 400 randomly selected German adults would have purchased blue jeans in the past three months.
   b. Based on the probability you computed in part (a), would you conclude that p is really less than .5? That is, would you conclude that less than 50 percent of adults in Germany have purchased blue jeans in the past three months? Explain.

5.76 Assume that the ages for first marriages are normally distributed with a mean of 26 years and a standard deviation of 4 years. What is the probability that a person getting married for the first time is in his or her twenties?

5.77 **INTERNET EXERCISE**

Beckstead, Brown, Guo, and Newbold present an interesting analysis of urban and rural income disparity in Canada in their article "Growth: Earnings Levels Across Urban and Rural Areas: The Role of Human Capital" (2010), published on the Statistics Canada website. In this article, they focus on the effects of education levels and work experience on this income gap, and note that this income disparity may be largely due to these factors.

   The data presented in this article was collected as part of the 2001 Census. Some of the more detailed information

---
[2]Source: N. Giges, "Global Spending Patterns Emerge," *Advertising Age* (November 11, 1991), p. 64.

was collected as a supplemental questionnaire that targeted approximately 1 in 5 Canadians, for a total of approximately 6.08 million individuals. Because of the nature of the analyses conducted by Beckstead and his colleagues, only those individuals that (a) were working in 2000 and (b) worked in the same urban/rural regional classification throughout 2000 were included in the sample.

On the article's main web page (statcan.gc.ca/pub/ 11-622-m/11-622-m2010020-eng.htm), click on "Tables," to access the data that we will be looking at in this example. The table we are interested in is Table 3, "Average weekly earnings levels, by employed worker characteristics," which presents means and standard deviations for a variety of demographic characteristics. We are going to look at the statistics presented for income disparity between men and women, between visible minorities and individuals that are not from a visible minority, and between individuals who were born in Canada and individuals who immigrated to Canada. These data have been extracted from the online report, and are presented in Table 5.3.

We can use this information to come up with a fairly accurate picture of income patterns among Canadians. Using the above data we can, for example, estimate the range of incomes that we would expect for men and women. Using our standard normal table, we can look up the z scores that bound a range of the distribution that represents approximately 95 percent of the data—this z score would be ± 1.96. We can then use these z scores to derive the raw score values that would bound this region.

For example, in men, the lower bound for this range would be calculated as follows:

$$z = \frac{x_{lower} - \mu}{\sigma}$$

$$-1.96 = \frac{x_{lower} - 983}{3.660}$$

$$\bar{x}_{lower} = 983 - 1.96(3.660)$$

$$\bar{x}_{lower} = 975.83$$

with the upper bound being

$$z = \frac{x_{upper} - \mu}{\sigma}$$

$$1.96 = \frac{x_{upper} - 983}{3.660}$$

$$\bar{x}_{upper} = 983 + 1.96(3.660)$$

$$\bar{x}_{upper} = 990.17$$

95 percent of the men in this population, therefore, had weekly incomes that ranged from $975.83 to $990.17 per week.

If you perform the sample calculation for the women in this population, you will find that weekly incomes ranged from $660.41 to $669.59 for about 95 percent of the data.

Later in this textbook, we will examine methods for testing the difference between samples, but for now, calculate the range of values that would be expected for a description of 95 percent of the data for all of the other demographic categories.

TABLE 5.3   Means and Standard Deviations for Weekly Incomes of Canadians Living in Both Urban and Rural Settings

	Mean	Standard Deviation
Men	983	3.660
Women	665	2.344
Minority	753	2.547
Non-minority	851	3.271
Canadian-born	831	3.077
Immigrant	853	3.389

CHAPTER **6**
Sampling Distributions

LEARNING OBJECTIVES

After reading this chapter, you should be able to

LO1 Demonstrate the sampling distribution of the sample mean

LO2 Explain the central limit theorem

LO3 Use the sampling distribution of the sample proportion

CHAPTER OUTLINE

6.1 The Sampling Distribution of the Sample Mean

6.2 The Sampling Distribution of the Sample Proportion

In Chapter 1, we introduced random sampling. In this chapter, we continue our discussion of random sampling by discussing two probability distributions that are related to random sampling: *the sampling distribution of the sample mean* and *the sampling distribution of the sample proportion.* These sampling distributions employ a *point estimate* to identify the likely centre of the population distribution, and *standard error* to capture the dispersion about this measure of central tendency. As we will see, these sampling distributions are critical for drawing statistical inferences.

6.1 THE SAMPLING DISTRIBUTION OF THE SAMPLE MEAN

Introductory ideas and basic properties Suppose that we are about to randomly select a sample of n elements (for example, cars) from a population of elements. Also, suppose that for each sampled element, we will measure the value of a characteristic of interest (for example, we might measure the fuel efficiency of each sampled car). The characteristics of this sample can be described using measures of central tendency (the mean, median, and mode), or measures of dispersion (range, standard deviation, and variance), and the sample itself is described with the sample distribution. The sample distribution is the set of values that you selected for measurement within your experiment.

Before we actually select the sample, however, there are many different samples of n elements and corresponding measurements that we might potentially obtain. Because different samples of measurements generally have different sample means, there are many different sample means that we might potentially obtain. It follows that, *before we draw the sample, the sample mean $\bar{x}$ is a random variable.*

LO1

The **sampling distribution of the sample mean $\bar{x}$** is the probability distribution of the population of all possible sample means that could be obtained from all possible samples of the same size.

Example 6.1 Fuel Efficiency

This is the first year that the automaker has offered its new midsized model for sale to the public. Last year, however, the automaker made six preproduction cars of this new model. Two of these six cars were randomly selected for testing, and the other four were sent to auto shows at which the new model was introduced to the news media and the public. As is standard industry practice, the automaker did not test the four auto show cars before or during the five months these auto shows were held, because testing can potentially harm the appearance of the cars.

To obtain a preliminary estimate of the midsized model's combined city and highway driving fuel efficiency—to be reported at the auto shows—the automaker subjected the two cars selected for fuel efficiency testing to the Federal Test Procedure endorsed by Transport Canada. When this was done, the cars obtained fuel efficiency ratings of 7.5 L/100 km, and 7.3 L/100 km. The mean of this sample is

$$\bar{x} = \frac{7.5 + 7.3}{2} = 7.4 \text{ L/100 km}$$

This sample mean is the point estimate of the mean (μ) fuel efficiency for the population of six preproduction cars and is the preliminary fuel efficiency estimate for the new midsized model that was reported at the auto shows.

When the auto shows were over, the automaker decided to further study the new midsized model by subjecting the four auto show cars to various tests. When the fuel efficiency test was performed, the four cars obtained ratings (in L/100 km) of 6.9, 7.1, 7.7, and 7.9. So the fuel efficiency test results obtained by the six preproduction cars were (in L/100 km) 6.9, 7.1, 7.3, 7.5, 7.7, and 7.9. The probability distribution of this population of six individual car fuel efficiency ratings is given in Table 6.1 and graphed in Figure 6.1(a). The mean of the population of fuel efficiency ratings is

$$\mu = \frac{6.9 + 7.1 + 7.3 + 7.5 + 7.7 + 7.9}{6} = 7.4 \text{ L/100 km}$$

Note that although the point estimate that was reported at the auto shows is exactly the same as the true population mean (μ) of 7.4 L/100 km, different samples of two cars would have given different sample means. There are, in total, 15 samples of two cars that could have been obtained by randomly selecting two cars from the population of six cars and subjecting the

TABLE 6.1 A Probability Distribution Describing the Population of Six Individual Fuel Efficiency Ratings

Individual Car Fuel Efficiency Ratings	6.9	7.1	7.3	7.5	7.7	7.9
Probability	1/6	1/6	1/6	1/6	1/6	1/6

FIGURE 6.1 A Comparison of Individual Fuel Efficiencies and Sample Means

(a) A graph of the probability distribution describing the population of six individual fuel efficiencies

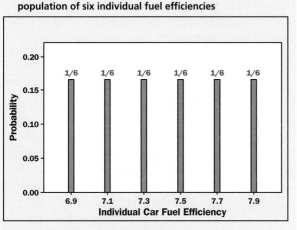

(b) A graph of the probability distribution describing the population of 15 sample means

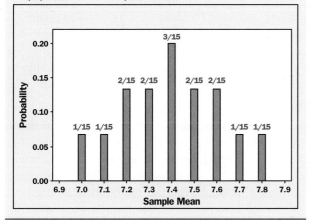

TABLE 6.2 The Population of Sample Means

(a) The population of the 15 samples of $n = 2$ car fuel efficiencies and corresponding sample means

Sample	Car Fuel Efficiency Ratings	Sample Mean
1	7.9, 7.7	7.8
2	7.9, 7.5	7.7
3	7.9, 7.3	7.6
4	7.9, 7.1	7.5
5	7.9, 6.9	7.4
6	7.7, 7.5	7.6
7	7.7, 7.3	7.5
8	7.7, 7.1	7.4
9	7.7, 6.9	7.3
10	7.5, 7.3	7.4
11	7.5, 7.1	7.3
12	7.5, 6.9	7.2
13	7.3, 7.1	7.2
14	7.3, 6.9	7.1
15	7.1, 6.9	7.0

(b) A probability distribution describing the population of 15 sample means: the sampling distribution of the sample mean

Sample Mean	Frequency	Probability
7.0	1	1/15
7.1	1	1/15
7.2	2	2/15
7.3	2	2/15
7.4	3	3/15
7.5	2	2/15
7.6	2	2/15
7.7	1	1/15
7.8	1	1/15

cars to the Federal Test Procedure. These samples correspond to the 15 combinations of two fuel efficiencies that can be selected from the six values listed previously: 6.9, 7.1, 7.3, 7.5, 7.7, and 7.9. The samples are given, along with their means, in Table 6.2(a).

To find the probability distribution of the population of sample means, note that different sample means correspond to different numbers of samples. For example, since the sample mean of 7.3 L/100 km corresponds to 2 out of 15 samples—the sample (7.1, 7.5) and the sample (6.9, 7.7)—the probability of obtaining a sample mean of 7.3 L/100 km is 2/15. If we analyze all of the sample means in a similar fashion, we find that the probability distribution of the population of sample means is as given in Table 6.2(b). This distribution is the *sampling distribution of the sample mean*. A graph of this distribution is shown in Figure 6.1(b) and illustrates the accuracies of the different possible sample means as point estimates of the population mean. For example, while 3 out of 15 sample means exactly equal the population mean of 7.4 L/100 km, other sample means differ from the population mean by amounts varying from .1 L/100 km to .5 L/100 km.

> **ROADBLOCK**
>
> **The difference between the sample distribution and the sampling distribution is subtle, but important**
> Before progressing to the remainder of this chapter, ensure that you truly understand the conceptual difference between the sample distribution and the sampling distribution because, as you will see, the sampling distribution lies at the heart of the inferential statistics that we will be introducing in subsequent chapters. The sample distribution is the set of measurements that you have taken from the population, while the sampling distribution is the set of all sample means that could have been calculated, on all of the samples that you could have drawn from your population. Put another way, the sample distribution is a distribution of measurements that are taken on individuals or items that you *have drawn* from the population, while the sampling distribution is a theoretical distribution of all of the samples of a particular sample size that you *could have drawn*, from your population.

As illustrated in Example 6.1, one of the purposes of the sampling distribution of the sample mean is to tell us how accurate the sample mean is likely to be as a point estimate of the population mean. Because the population of six individual fuel efficiencies in Example 6.1 is small, we were able (after the auto shows were over) to test all six cars, determine the fuel efficiencies of the six cars, and calculate the population mean. Often, however, the population of individual measurements under consideration is very large—either a large finite population or an infinite population. In this case, it would be impractical or impossible to determine the values of all of the population measurements and calculate the population mean. Instead, we randomly select a sample of individual measurements from the population and use the mean of this sample as the point estimate of the population mean.

Moreover, although it would be impractical or impossible to list all of the many (perhaps trillions of) different possible sample means that could be obtained if the sampled population is very large, statisticians know various theoretical properties about the sampling distribution of these sample means. Some of these theoretical properties are intuitively illustrated by the sampling distribution of the 15 sample means in Example 6.1. Specifically, suppose that we will randomly select a sample of n individual measurements from a population of individual measurements having mean μ and standard deviation σ. Then, it can be shown that

- **In many situations, the distribution of the population of all possible sample means looks, at least roughly, like a normal curve.** For example, consider Figure 6.1. This figure shows that, while the distribution of the population of six individual fuel efficiencies is a uniform distribution, the distribution of the population of 15 sample means has a somewhat bell-shaped appearance. Noting, however, that this rough bell-shaped appearance is not identical to the appearance of a normal curve, we want to know when the distribution of all possible sample means is exactly or approximately normally distributed.

- **If the population from which we will select the sample is normally distributed, then for any sample size n the population of all possible sample means is also normally distributed.** For example, consider the population of the fuel efficiencies for all of the new midsized cars that could potentially be produced by this year's manufacturing process. As discussed in Chapter 1, we consider this population to be an infinite population, because the automaker could always make "one more car." Moreover, assume that (as will be verified in a later example) this infinite population of all individual fuel efficiencies is normally distributed (see Figure 6.2), and assume that the automaker will randomly select a sample of $n = 5$ cars, test them as prescribed by the Federal Testing Procedure, and calculate the mean of the resulting sample of fuel efficiencies. It then follows that the population of all possible sample means that the automaker might obtain is also normally distributed (again, see Figure 6.2). Note that there is nothing special about the sample size $n = 5$. The above boldfaced result holds—as it states—for any sample size n. Moreover, in the next subsection we will see that, even if the population from which we will select the sample is *not* normally distributed, the population of all possible sample means is *approximately normally*

FIGURE **6.2** The Normally Distributed Population of All Individual Fuel Efficiencies and the Normally Distributed Population of All Possible Sample Means

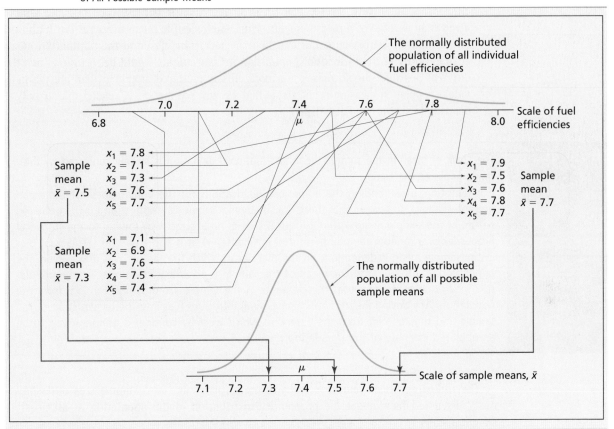

distributed if the sample size n is large (say, at least 30). Finally, note that to make Figure 6.2 easier to understand, we have hypothetically assumed that the true value of the population mean fuel efficiency (μ) of all of the new midsized cars is 7.4 L/100 km. Of course, no one can know the true value of μ. **Our objective is to estimate μ.**

- **The mean of the population of all possible sample means ($\mu_{\bar{x}}$) is equal to μ, the mean of the population from which we will select the sample.** For example, the mean, $\mu_{\bar{x}}$, of the population of 15 sample means in Table 6.2(a) can be calculated by adding up the 15 sample means, which gives 111, and dividing by 15. That is, $\mu_{\bar{x}} = 111/15 = 7.4$, which is the same as μ, the mean of the population of six individual car fuel efficiencies in Table 6.1. The fact that $\mu_{\bar{x}}$ equals μ is graphically illustrated in Figure 6.1, which shows that the distribution of the six individual fuel efficiencies and the distribution of the 15 sample means are centred over the same mean of 7.4 L/100 km. The fact that $\mu_{\bar{x}}$ equals μ is also graphically illustrated in Figure 6.2, which shows that the normal distribution describing the fuel efficiencies of all individual cars that could be produced this year and the normal distribution describing all possible sample means are centred over the same mean of 7.4 L/100 km. Furthermore, because $\mu_{\bar{x}}$ equals μ, we call the sample mean an *unbiased point estimate* of the population mean. This unbiasedness property says that, although most of the possible sample means that we might obtain are either above or below the population mean, there is no systematic tendency for the sample mean to overestimate or underestimate the population mean. That is, although we will randomly select only one sample, the unbiased sample mean is correct "on the average" when measured across all possible samples.

- **The standard deviation, $\sigma_{\bar{x}}$, of the population of all possible sample means is less than σ, the standard deviation of the population from which we will select the sample.**

This is illustrated in both Figures 6.1 and 6.2. That is, in each figure the distribution of all possible sample means is less spread out than the distribution of all individual fuel efficiencies. Intuitively, we see that $\sigma_{\bar{x}}$ is smaller than σ because each possible sample mean is an average of n measurements. Thus, **each sample mean** *averages out* **high and low sample measurements and can be expected to be closer to the population mean μ than many of the individual population measurements would be.** It follows that the different possible sample means are more closely clustered around μ than are the individual population measurements. (Note that we will see that $\sigma_{\bar{x}}$ is smaller than σ only if the sample size n is greater than 1.)

ROADBLOCK

The "lack of bias" in the sample mean and standard deviation is largely conferred by the randomness of the sample

It is tempting, after reading the numerical justifications for the unbiasedness of the mean presented above, to assume that there is a strictly mathematical justification for the unbiased nature of the sample mean. Although this is true in an abstract way (owing to the statistical properties of a random sample, presented in Chapter 1), it is also true that the lack of bias in the sample mean is dependent on the manner in which the sample was drawn from the population. In other words, the mean of the sample is an unbiased estimate of the population mean due to the fact that the elements of the sample are drawn at random from the population. Any deviations from randomness will introduce bias into the construction of the sample and thus detract from the extent to which we may consider a sample mean to be an unbiased estimate of the population mean.

The following boxed feature gives a formula for $\sigma_{\bar{x}}$ and also summarizes other previously discussed facts about the probability distribution of the population of all possible sample means.

The Sampling Distribution of $\bar{x}$

Assume that the population from which we will randomly select a sample of n measurements has mean μ and standard deviation σ. Then, the population of all possible sample means

1   Has a normal distribution, if the sampled population has a normal distribution.

2   Has mean $\mu_{\bar{x}} = \mu$.

3   Has standard deviation $\sigma_{\bar{x}} = \dfrac{\sigma}{\sqrt{n}}$. The standard deviation of the sampling distribution is also called the *standard error.*

The formula for $\sigma_{\bar{x}}$ in (3) holds exactly if the sampled population is infinite. If the sampled population is finite, this formula holds approximately under conditions to be discussed later in this section.

Stated equivalently, the sampling distribution of $\bar{x}$ has mean $\mu_{\bar{x}} = \mu$, has standard deviation $\sigma_{\bar{x}} = \sigma/\sqrt{n}$ (if the sampled population is infinite), and is a normal distribution (if the sampled population has a normal distribution).[1]

The third result in the boxed feature says that, if the sampled population is infinite, then

$$\sigma_{\bar{x}} = \frac{\sigma}{\sqrt{n}}$$

In words, **standard error** $(\sigma_{\bar{x}})$, the standard deviation of the population of all possible sample means, equals σ, the standard deviation of the population, divided by the square root of the sample size n. Furthermore, in addition to showing that $\sigma_{\bar{x}}$ is smaller than σ (assuming that

---

[1]In Appendix C (Part 3) on *Connect*, we derive the formulas $\mu_{\bar{x}} = \mu$ and $\sigma_{\bar{x}} = \sigma/\sqrt{n}$.

the sample size n is larger than one), this formula for $\sigma_{\bar{x}}$ also says that $\sigma_{\bar{x}}$ decreases as n increases. That is, intuitively, when the sample size is larger, each possible sample averages more observations. Therefore, the resulting different possible sample means will differ from each other by less and thus will become more closely clustered around the population mean. It follows that, if we take a larger sample, we are more likely to obtain a sample mean that is near the population mean.

In Example 6.2, we will illustrate the formula for $\sigma_{\bar{x}}$. In this and several other examples we will assume that, although we do not know the true value of the population mean μ, we do know the true value of the population standard deviation σ. Here, knowledge of σ might be based on theory or history related to the population under consideration. For example, because the automaker has been working to improve fuel efficiency, we cannot assume that we know the true value of the population mean (μ) for the new midsized model. However, engineering data might indicate that the spread of individual fuel efficiencies for the automaker's midsized cars is the same from model to model and year to year. Therefore, if the fuel efficiencies for previous models had a standard deviation equal to .1 L/100 km., it might be reasonable to assume that the standard deviation of the fuel efficiency for the new model will also equal .1. Such an assumption would, of course, be questionable, and in most real-world situations there would probably not be an actual basis for knowing σ. However, assuming that σ is known will help us to illustrate sampling distributions, and in later chapters we will see what to do when σ is unknown.

ROADBLOCK

Despite our use of population parameters in the definition of the sampling distribution, sample statistics are very important

We note in our definition of the sampling distribution that the centre of our sampling distribution is equal to the mean of the population (μ), and this is true. We also note that the standard deviation of the sampling distribution is derived by dividing the standard deviation of the population (σ) by the square root of the sample—and this is also true. It is important to remember, however, that the sample mean is considered to be an unbiased estimate of the population mean, so, even though the centre of the sampling distribution is defined as being equal to the population mean, it is (in practice) equal to our sample mean.

Furthermore, as we will see in subsequent chapters (particularly in Chapter 8), the standard deviation of the sample may be used in place of the standard deviation of the population, when it is computed with a denominator of $n - 1$, as this computational practice makes the sample standard deviation an unbiased estimate of the population standard deviation.

Example 6.2 Fuel Efficiency

Part 1: Basic concepts Consider the infinite population of the fuel efficiencies for all of the new midsized cars that could potentially be produced by this year's manufacturing process. If we assume that this population is normally distributed with mean μ and standard deviation $\sigma = .1$ (see Figure 6.3[a]), and if the automaker will randomly select a sample of n cars and test them as prescribed by the Federal Test Procedure, it follows that the population of all possible sample means is normally distributed with mean $\mu_{\bar{x}} = \mu$ and standard deviation $\sigma_{\bar{x}} = \sigma/\sqrt{n} = .1/\sqrt{n}$. In order to show that a larger sample is more likely to give a more accurate point estimate $\bar{x}$ of μ, compare taking a sample of size $n = 5$ with taking a sample of size $n = 50$. If $n = 5$, then

$$\sigma_{\bar{x}} = \frac{\sigma}{\sqrt{n}} = \frac{.1}{\sqrt{5}} = 0.447$$

FIGURE **6.3**   A Comparison of (1) the Population of All Individual Fuel Efficiencies, (2) the Sampling Distribution of the Sample Mean $\bar{x}$ When $n = 5$, and (3) the Sampling Distribution of the Sample Mean $\bar{x}$ When $n = 50$

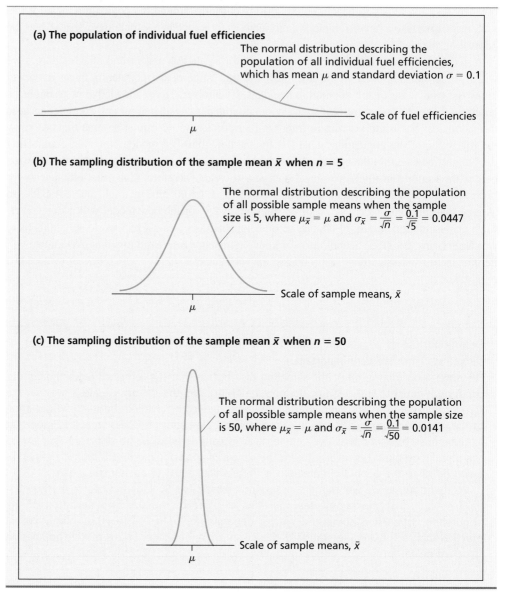

and it follows (by the empirical rule) that 95.44 percent of all possible sample means are within plus or minus $2\sigma_{\bar{x}} = 2(.0447) = .0894$ L/100 km of the population mean μ. If $n = 50$, then

$$\sigma_{\bar{x}} = \frac{\sigma}{\sqrt{n}} = \frac{.1}{\sqrt{50}} = .0141$$

and it follows that 95.44 percent of all possible sample means are within plus or minus $2\sigma_{\bar{x}} = 2(.0141) = .0282$ L/100 km of the population mean μ. Therefore, if $n = 50$, the different possible sample means that the automaker might obtain will be more closely clustered around μ than they will be if $n = 5$ (see Figures 6.3[b] and [c]). This implies that the larger sample of size $n = 50$ is more likely to give a sample mean $\bar{x}$ that is close to μ.

Part 2: Statistical inference Imagine that an automaker randomly selects a sample of $n = 50$ fuel efficiencies that has a mean $(\bar{x})$ of 7.47 L/100 km. We can now ask the following question: If the population mean fuel efficiency (μ) is exactly 7.40 L/100 km, what is the probability of

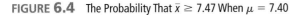

FIGURE 6.4   The Probability That $\bar{x} \geq 7.47$ When $\mu = 7.40$

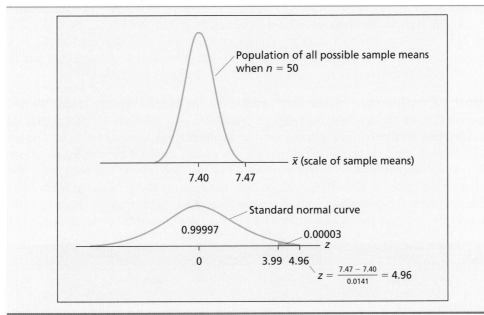

observing a sample mean fuel efficiency that is greater than or equal to 7.47 L/100 km? If we assume that the population of all individual fuel efficiencies is normally distributed and further assume that the population standard deviation (σ) is known to equal .1 L/100 km, it follows that the sampling distribution of the sample mean ($\bar{x}$) is a normal distribution, with mean ($\mu_{\bar{x}} = \mu$) and standard deviation $\sigma_{\bar{x}} = \sigma/\sqrt{n} = .1/\sqrt{50} = .0141$. Therefore,

$$P(\bar{x} \geq 7.47 \text{ if } \mu = 7.4) = P\left(z \geq \frac{7.47 - \mu_{\bar{x}}}{\sigma_{\bar{x}}}\right) = P\left(z \geq \frac{7.47 - 7.40}{.0141}\right)$$

$$= P(z \geq 4.96)$$

To find $P(z \geq 4.96)$, notice that the largest z value given in Table A.4 in Appendix A is 3.99, which gives a right-hand tail area of .00003. Therefore, since $P(z \geq 3.99) = .00003$, it follows that $P(z \geq 4.96)$ is less than .00003 (see Figure 6.4). The fact that this probability is less than .00003 says that, if μ equals 7.4, then fewer than 3 in 100,000 of all possible sample means are at least as large as the sample mean $\bar{x} = 7.47$ that we have actually observed. Therefore, if we are to believe that μ equals 7.4, then we must believe that we have observed a sample mean that can be described as a smaller than 3 in 100,000 chance. Since it is extremely difficult to believe that such a small chance would occur, we have extremely strong evidence that μ does not equal 7.4 and that μ is, in fact, larger than 7.4.

To conclude this subsection, it is important to make two comments. First, the formula $\sigma_{\bar{x}} = \sigma/\sqrt{n}$ follows, in theory, from the formula for $\sigma_{\bar{x}}^2$, the variance of the population of all possible sample means. The formula for $\sigma_{\bar{x}}^2$ is $\sigma_{\bar{x}}^2 = \sigma^2/n$. Second, in addition to holding exactly if the sampled population is infinite, **the formula $\sigma_{\bar{x}} = \sigma/\sqrt{n}$ holds approximately if the population is finite and much larger than (say, at least 20 times) the size of the sample.** For example, if we define the population of the fuel efficiencies of all new midsized cars to be the population of the fuel efficiencies of all cars that will actually be produced this year, then the population is finite. However, the population would be very large—certainly at least as large as 20 times any reasonable sample size. For example, if the automaker produces 100,000 new midsized cars this year, and if we randomly select a sample of $n = 50$ of these cars, then the population size of 100,000 is larger than 20 times the sample size of 50 (which is 1,000).

It follows that, even though the population is finite and therefore the formula $\sigma_{\bar{x}} = \sigma/\sqrt{n}$ would not hold exactly, this formula would hold approximately. The exact formula for $\sigma_{\bar{x}}$ when the sampled population is finite is given in a technical note at the end of this section. It is important to use this exact formula if the sampled population is finite and less than 20 times the size of the sample. However, with the exception of the populations considered in the technical note, we will assume that all of the remaining populations to be discussed in this book are either infinite or finite and at least 20 times the size of the sample. Therefore, it will be appropriate to use the formula $\sigma_{\bar{x}} = \sigma/\sqrt{n}$.

LO2   **Sampling a non-normally distributed population: the central limit theorem** We now consider what can be said about the sampling distribution of $\bar{x}$ when the sampled population is not normally distributed. First, as previously stated, the fact that $\mu_{\bar{x}} = \mu$ is still true. Second, as also previously stated, the formula $\sigma_{\bar{x}} = \sigma/\sqrt{n}$ is exactly correct if the sampled population is infinite and is approximately correct if the sampled population is finite and much larger than (say, at least 20 times as large as) the sample size. Third, an extremely important result called the **central limit theorem** tells us that, if the sample size n is large, then the sampling distribution of $\bar{x}$ is approximately normal, even if the sampled population is not normally distributed.

The Central Limit Theorem

If the sample size n is sufficiently large, then the population of all possible sample means is approximately normally distributed (with mean $\mu_{\bar{x}} = \mu$ and standard deviation $\sigma_{\bar{x}} = \sigma/\sqrt{n}$), no matter what probability distribution describes the sampled population. Furthermore, the larger the sample size n is, the more nearly normally distributed is the population of all possible sample means.

The central limit theorem is illustrated in Figure 6.5 for several population shapes. Notice that as the sample size increases (from 2 to 6 to 30), the populations of all possible sample

FIGURE 6.5   The Central Limit Theorem Says That the Larger the Sample Size Is, the More Nearly Normally Distributed Is the Population of All Possible Sample Means

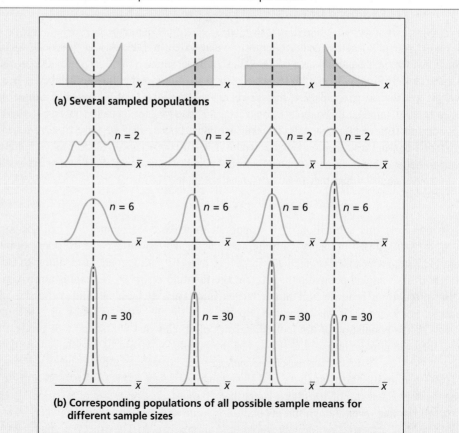

(a) Several sampled populations

(b) Corresponding populations of all possible sample means for different sample sizes means become more nearly normally distributed. This figure also illustrates that, as the sample size increases, the spread of the distribution of all possible sample means decreases (remember that this spread is measured by $\sigma_{\bar{x}}$, which decreases as the sample size increases).

How large must the sample size be for the sampling distribution of $\bar{x}$ to be approximately normal? In general, the more skewed the probability distribution of the sampled population, the larger the sample size must be for the population of all possible sample means to be approximately normally distributed. For some sampled populations, particularly those described by symmetric distributions, the population of all possible sample means is approximately normally distributed for a fairly small sample size. In addition, studies indicate that, **if the sample size is at least 30, then for most sampled populations the population of all possible sample means is approximately normally distributed.** In this book, whenever the sample size n is at least 30, we will assume that the sampling distribution of $\bar{x}$ is approximately a normal distribution. Of course, if the sampled population is exactly normally distributed, the sampling distribution of $\bar{x}$ is exactly normal for any sample size.

THEORY TO PRACTICE

Is 30 a magic number?

The central limit theorem is often invoked in the justification of one's choice of sample size when conducting experiments that require inferential statistics for their interpretation. As discussed in this section (and graphically depicted in Figure 6.5), there is a tendency for sampling distributions to become "more normal" as the sample size increases—and the central limit theorem does indeed suggest that most sampling distributions approach normality when the sample size (n) is at least 30. The degree of non-normality in the population will, however, impact on the sample size required for a normally distributed sampling distribution, with more profoundly non-normal populations requiring larger samples.

Furthermore, although the normality of the sampling distribution appears in this section of the textbook to be the most important outcome of increasing n size, it is by no means the only benefit that can be seen from increasing sample size. As noted in this first section of the chapter, the standard error will become smaller as the sample size increases, thus decreasing the amount of sampling error in our sample. As we will see in subsequent chapters, reducing the sampling error in a statistic will increase the ability of the statistic to identify real effects in the data. So, although having a sample size of *at least* 30 is a good place to start, in practice, we need to take into account a number of factors in determining the required size of our sample. Intuitively, this includes (1) the amount of error that is acceptable in our experiment (in other words, what are the consequences of drawing incorrect conclusions in our experiment) and (2) the size of the effect that we are likely to see in our experiment—or perhaps, the size of the effect that would be meaningful. Small effects will be apparent only in large samples, and conversely, small samples are really useful only in the identification (and quantification) of large effects.

Example 6.3 The Payment Time Example

A management consulting firm has installed a new electronic billing system in a cross-Canada trucking company. Because of the advantages of the new billing system, and because the trucking company's clients are receptive to using this system, the management consulting firm believes that the new system will reduce the mean bill payment time by more than 50 percent. The mean payment time using the old billing system was approximately equal to, but no less than, 39 days. Therefore, if μ denotes the new mean payment time, the consulting firm believes that μ will be less than 19.5 days. To assess whether μ is less than 19.5 days, the consulting firm has randomly selected a sample of $n = 65$ invoices processed using the new billing system and has determined the payment times for these invoices. The mean of the 65 payment times is $\bar{x} = 18.1077$ days, which is less than 19.5 days. Therefore, we ask the following

question: If the population mean payment time is 19.5 days, what is the probability of observing a sample mean payment time that is less than or equal to 18.1077 days? The central limit theorem tells us that, because the sample size $n = 65$ is large, the sampling distribution of $\bar{x}$ will approximate a normal distribution with mean $\mu_{\bar{x}} = \mu$ and standard deviation $\sigma_{\bar{x}} = \sigma/\sqrt{n}$.

Consider also that although this is the first time that the consulting company has installed an electronic billing system in a trucking company, the firm has installed electronic billing systems in other types of companies. Analysis of results from these other companies shows that, although the population mean payment time μ varies from company to company, the population standard deviation σ of payment times is the same for different companies and equals 4.2 days. Assuming that σ also equals 4.2 days for the trucking company, it follows that $\sigma_{\bar{x}}$ equals $4.2/\sqrt{65} = .5209$ and that

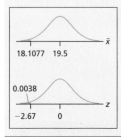

$$P(\bar{x} \leq 18.1077 \text{ if } \mu = 19.5) = P\left(z \leq \frac{18.1077 - 19.5}{.5209}\right) = P(z \leq -2.67)$$

which is the area under the standard normal curve to the left of -2.67. The normal table tells us that this area equals .0038. This probability says that, if μ equals 19.5, then only .0038 of all possible sample means are at least as small as the sample mean $\bar{x} = 18.1077$ that we have actually observed. Therefore, if we are to believe that μ equals 19.5, we must believe that we have observed a sample mean that can be described as a 38 in 10,000 chance. It is very difficult to believe that such a small chance would occur, so we have very strong evidence that μ does not equal 19.5 and is, in fact, less than 19.5. We conclude that the new billing system has reduced the mean bill payment time by more than 50 percent.

Unbiasedness and minimum-variance estimates Recall that a sample statistic is any descriptive measure of the sample measurements. For instance, the sample mean $\bar{x}$ is a statistic, and so are the sample median, the sample variance s^2, and the sample standard deviation s. Not only do different samples give different values of $\bar{x}$, different samples also give different values of the median, s^2, s, or any other statistic. It follows that, *before we draw the sample, any sample statistic is a random variable,* and

The **sampling distribution of a sample statistic** is the probability distribution of the population of all possible values of the sample statistic.

In general, we want to estimate a population parameter by using a sample statistic that is what we call an *unbiased point estimate* of the parameter.

A sample statistic is an **unbiased point estimate** of a population parameter if the mean of the population of all possible values of the sample statistic equals the population parameter.

For example, we use the sample mean $\bar{x}$ as the point estimate of the population mean μ because $\bar{x}$ is an unbiased point estimate of μ. That is, $\mu_{\bar{x}} = \mu$. In words, the average of all possible sample means (that we could obtain from all the different possible samples) equals μ.

Although we want a sample statistic to be an unbiased point estimate of the population parameter of interest, we also want the statistic to have a small standard deviation (and variance). That is, we want the different possible values of the sample statistic to be closely clustered around the population parameter. If this is the case, when we actually randomly select one sample and compute the sample statistic, its value is likely to be close to the value of the population parameter. Furthermore, some general results apply to estimating the mean μ of a normally distributed population. In this situation, it can be shown that both the sample mean and the sample median are unbiased point estimates of μ. In fact, there are many unbiased point estimates of μ. However, it can be shown that the variance of the population of all possible sample means is smaller than the variance of the population of all possible values of any other unbiased point estimate of μ. For this reason, we call the sample mean a **minimum-variance unbiased point estimate** of μ. When we use the sample mean as the point estimate of μ, we are more likely to obtain a point estimate close to μ than if we used any other un-biased sample statistic as the point estimate of μ. This is one reason why we use the sample mean as the point estimate of the population mean.

We next consider estimating the population variance σ^2. It can be shown that if the sampled population is infinite, then s^2 is an unbiased point estimate of σ^2. That is, the average of all the different possible sample variances that we could obtain (from all of the different possible samples) is equal to σ^2. This is why we use a divisor equal to $n - 1$ rather than n when we estimate σ^2. It can be shown that, if we used n as the divisor when estimating σ^2, we would not obtain an unbiased point estimate of σ^2. When the population is finite, s^2 may be regarded as an approxi-mately unbiased estimate of σ^2 as long as the population is fairly large (which is usually the case).

It would seem logical to think that, because s^2 is an unbiased point estimate of σ^2, s should be an unbiased point estimate of σ. This seems plausible, but it is not the case. There is no easy way to calculate an unbiased point estimate of σ. Because of this, the usual practice is to use s as the point estimate of σ (even though it is not an unbiased estimate).

This ends our discussion of the theory of point estimation. It suffices to say that in this book we estimate population parameters by using sample statistics that statisticians generally agree are best. Whenever possible, these sample statistics are unbiased point estimates and have small variances.

Technical note If we randomly select a sample of size n without replacement from a finite population of size N, then it can be shown that $\sigma_{\bar{x}} = (\sigma/\sqrt{n})\sqrt{(N - n)/(N - 1)}$, where the quantity $\sqrt{(N - n)/(N - 1)}$ is called the *finite population multiplier*. If the size of the sampled population is at least 20 times the size of the sample (that is, if $N \geq 20n$), then the finite population multiplier is approximately equal to one, and $\sigma_{\bar{x}}$ approximately equals $\sigma/\sqrt{n}$. However, if the population size N is smaller than 20 times the size of the sample, then the finite population multiplier is substantially less than one, and we must include this multiplier in the calculation of $\sigma_{\bar{x}}$. For instance, in Example 6.1, where the standard deviation σ of the population of $N = 6$ fuel efficiencies can be calculated to be .3416, and where $N = 6$ is only three times the sample size $n = 2$, it follows that

$$\sigma_{\bar{x}} = \frac{\sigma}{\sqrt{n}}\sqrt{\frac{N - n}{N - 1}} = \left(\frac{.3416}{\sqrt{2}}\right)\sqrt{\frac{6 - 2}{6 - 1}} = .2415(.8944) = .2160$$

Exercises for Section **6.1**

CONCEPTS

6.1 Suppose that we randomly select a sample of four measurements from a larger population of measurements. The sampling distribution of the sample mean $\bar{x}$ is the probability distribution of a population. In your own words, describe the elements in this population.

6.2 What does the central limit theorem tell us about the sampling distribution of the sample mean?

METHODS AND APPLICATIONS

6.3 Suppose that we take a random sample of size n from a population having mean μ and standard deviation σ. For each of the following situations, find the mean, variance, and standard deviation of the sampling distribution of the sample mean $\bar{x}$:
   a. $\mu = 10, \sigma = 2, n = 25$
   b. $\mu = 500, \sigma = .5, n = 100$
   c. $\mu = 3, \sigma = .1, n = 4$
   d. $\mu = 100, \sigma = 1, n = 1,600$

6.4 For each situation in Exercise 6.3, find an interval that contains (approximately or exactly) 99.73 percent of all the possible sample means. In which cases must we assume that the population is normally distributed? Why?

6.5 Suppose that we randomly select a sample of 64 measurements from a population having a mean equal to 20 and a standard deviation equal to 4.
   a. Describe the shape of the sampling distribution of the sample mean $\bar{x}$. Do we need to make any assumptions about the shape of the population? Why or why not?
   b. Find the mean and the standard deviation of the sampling distribution of the sample mean $\bar{x}$.
   c. Calculate the probability that we will obtain a sample mean greater than 21; that is, calculate $P(\bar{x} > 21)$. Hint: Find the z value corresponding to 21 by using $\mu_{\bar{x}}$ and $\sigma_{\bar{x}}$ because we want to calculate a probability about $\bar{x}$. Then sketch the sampling distribution and the probability.
   d. Calculate the probability that we will obtain a sample mean less than 19.385; that is, calculate $P(\bar{x} < 19.385)$.

EXERCISES 6.6 THROUGH 6.10 ARE BASED ON THE FOLLOWING SITUATION.

Congratulations! You have just won the question-and-answer portion of a popular game show and will now be given an opportunity to select a grand prize. The game show host shows you a large revolving drum containing four identical white envelopes that have been thoroughly mixed in the drum. Each of the envelopes contains one of four cheques made out for grand prizes of $20,000, $40,000, $60,000, and $80,000. Usually, a contestant reaches into the drum, selects an envelope, and receives the grand prize in the envelope. Today, however, is a special day. You will be given the choice of either selecting one envelope or selecting two envelopes and receiving the average of the grand prizes in the two envelopes. If you select one envelope, the probability is 1/4 that you will receive any one of the individual grand prizes of $20,000, $40,000, $60,000, and $80,000. To see what could happen if you select two envelopes, do Exercises 6.6 through 6.10.

6.6   There are six combinations, or samples, of two grand prizes that can be randomly selected from the four grand prizes of $20,000, $40,000, $60,000, and $80,000. Four of these samples are (20, 40), (20, 60), (20, 80), and (40, 60). Find the other two samples.

6.7   Find the mean of each sample in Exercise 6.6.

6.8   Find the probability distribution of the population of six sample mean grand prizes.

6.9   If you select two envelopes, what is the probability that you will receive a sample mean grand prize of at least $50,000?

6.10   Compare the probability distribution of the four individual grand prizes with the probability distribution of the six sample mean grand prizes. Would you select one or two envelopes? Why? Note: There is no one correct answer. It is a matter of opinion.

6.11   THE CUSTOMER WAIT TIME EXAMPLE

A bank manager wants to show that her branch's new system reduces typical customer waiting times to less than six minutes. One way to do this is to demonstrate that the mean of the population of all customer waiting times is less than 6. Letting this mean be μ, in this exercise we want to investigate whether the sample of 100 waiting times provides evidence to support the claim that μ is less than 6.

For the sake of argument, we will begin by assuming that μ equals 6, and we will then attempt to use the sample to contradict this assumption in favour of the conclusion that μ is less than 6. Recall that the mean of the sample of 100 waiting times is $\bar{x} = 5.46$ and assume that σ, the standard deviation of the population of all customer waiting times, is known to be 2.47.

a.   Consider the population of all possible sample means obtained from random samples of 100 waiting times. What is the shape of this population of sample means? That is, what is the shape of the sampling distribution of $\bar{x}$? Why is this true?

b.   Find the mean and standard deviation of the population of all possible sample means when we assume that μ equals 6.

c.   The sample mean that we have actually observed is $\bar{x} = 5.46$. Assuming that μ equals 6, find the probability of observing a sample mean that is less than or equal to $\bar{x} = 5.46$.

d.   If μ equals 6, what percentage of all possible sample means are less than or equal to 5.46? Since we have actually observed a sample mean of $\bar{x} = 5.46$, is it more reasonable to believe that (1) μ equals 6 and we have observed one of the sample means that is less than or equal to 5.46 when μ equals 6, or (2) that we have observed a sample mean less than or equal to 5.46 because μ is less than 6? Explain. What do you conclude about whether the new system has reduced the typical customer waiting time to less than six minutes?

6.12   THE VIDEO GAME SATISFACTION RATING EXAMPLE

A customer is considered to be very satisfied with his or her XYZ-Box video game system if the composite score on a survey instrument is at least 42. So one way to show that customers are typically very satisfied is to show that the mean of the population of all satisfaction ratings is at least 42. Letting this mean be μ, in this exercise we want to investigate whether the sample of 65 satisfaction ratings provides evidence to support the claim that μ exceeds 42 (and, therefore, is at least 42).

We begin by assuming that μ equals 42, and we then attempt to use the sample to contradict this assumption in favour of the conclusion that μ exceeds 42. The mean of the sample of 65 satisfaction ratings is $\bar{x} = 42.95$. Assume that σ, the standard deviation of the population of all satisfaction ratings, is known to be 2.64.

a.   Consider the sampling distribution of $\bar{x}$ for random samples of 65 customer satisfaction ratings. Use the properties of this sampling distribution to find the probability of observing a sample mean greater than or equal to 42.95 when we assume that μ equals 42.

b.   If μ equals 42, what percentage of all possible sample means are greater than or equal to 42.95? Since we have actually observed a sample mean of $\bar{x} = 42.95$, is it more reasonable to believe that (1) μ equals 42 and we have observed a sample mean that is greater than or equal to 42.95 when μ equals 42, or (2) that we have observed a sample mean that is greater than or equal to 42.95 because μ is greater than 42? Explain. What do you conclude about whether customers are typically very satisfied with the XYZ-Box video game system?

6.13   In an article in the *Journal of Management,* Joseph Martocchio studied and estimated the costs of employee absences. Based on a sample of 176 blue-collar workers, Martocchio estimated that the mean amount of paid time lost during a three-month period was 1.4 days per employee with a standard deviation of 1.3 days. Martocchio also estimated that the mean amount of unpaid time lost during a three-month period was 1.0 day per employee with a standard deviation of 1.8 days.

Suppose we randomly select a sample of 100 blue-collar workers. Based on Martocchio's estimates:

a.   What is the probability that the average amount of paid time lost during a three-month period for the 100 blue-collar workers will exceed 1.5 days?

b. What is the probability that the average amount of unpaid time lost during a three-month period for the 100 blue-collar workers will exceed 1.5 days?

c. Suppose we randomly select a sample of 100 blue-collar workers, and suppose the sample mean amount of unpaid time lost during a three-month period actually exceeds 1.5 days. Would it be reasonable to conclude that the mean amount of unpaid time lost has increased above the previously estimated 1.0 days? Explain.

6.14 When a pizza restaurant's delivery process is operating effectively, pizzas are delivered in an average of 45 minutes with a standard deviation of 6 minutes. To monitor its delivery process, the restaurant randomly selects five pizzas each night and records their delivery times.

a. For the sake of argument, assume that the population of all delivery times on a given evening is normally distributed with a mean of $\mu = 45$ minutes and a standard deviation of $\sigma = 6$ minutes. (That is, we assume that the delivery process is operating effectively.) Find the mean and the standard deviation of the population of all possible sample means, and calculate an interval containing 99.73 percent of all possible sample means.

b. Suppose that the mean of the five sampled delivery times on a particular evening is $\bar{x} = 55$ minutes. Using the interval that you calculated in part (a), what would you conclude about whether the restaurant's delivery process is operating effectively? Why?

6.2 THE SAMPLING DISTRIBUTION OF THE SAMPLE PROPORTION

The first half of this chapter has been oriented toward the identification of the sampling distribution of the mean. In the second half of this chapter, we turn our attention to another commonly used summary statistic—the proportion. Proportions are used to describe the outcomes of binomial experiments, in which there are only two possible outcomes. The population parameter for a proportion is considered to equal the frequency of an outcome of interest (in this binomial experiment) divided by the total number of outcomes. It is typically given the symbol p, and the standard deviation of a population with a mean of p is $\sqrt{p(1-p)}$. The sample statistic for a proportion is typically indicated with the symbol $\hat{p}$, and the standard deviation of the sample distribution is equal to $\sqrt{\hat{p}(1-\hat{p})}$. As we will see in this section, despite differing in some calculation specifics, both the sample and the sampling distributions of the proportion bear a striking resemblance to the corresponding distributions of the mean.

LO3

A food processing company markets a soft cheese spread that is sold in a plastic container with an "easy pour" spout. Although this spout works extremely well and is popular with consumers, it is expensive to produce. Because of the spout's high cost, the company has developed a new, less expensive spout. While the new, cheaper spout may alienate some purchasers, a company study shows that its introduction will increase profits if less than 10 percent of the cheese spread's current purchasers are lost. That is, if we let p be the true proportion of all current purchasers who would stop buying the cheese spread if the new spout was used, profits will increase as long as p is less than .10.

Suppose that after trying the new spout, 63 of 1,000 randomly selected purchasers say that they would stop buying the cheese spread if the new spout was used. The point estimate of the population proportion p is the sample proportion $\hat{p} = 63/1,000 = .063$. This sample proportion says that we estimate that 6.3 percent of all current purchasers would stop buying the cheese spread if the new spout was used. Since $\hat{p}$ equals .063, we have some evidence that the population proportion p is less than .10. In order to determine the strength of this evidence, we need to consider the sampling distribution of $\hat{p}$. In general, assume that we will randomly select a sample of n elements from a population, and assume that a proportion p of all of the elements in the population fall into a particular category (for instance, the category of consumers who would stop buying the cheese spread). Before we actually select the sample, there are many different samples of n elements that we might potentially obtain.

The number of elements that fall into the category in question will vary from sample to sample, so the sample proportion of elements falling into the category will also vary from sample to sample. For example, if three possible random samples of 1,000 soft cheese spread purchasers had, respectively, 63, 58, and 65 purchasers say that they would stop buying the cheese spread if the new spout was used, then the sample proportions given by the three samples would be $\hat{p} = 63/1{,}000 = .063$, $\hat{p} = 58/1{,}000 = .058$, and $\hat{p} = 65/1{,}000 = .065$. In general, before we randomly select the sample, there are many different possible sample proportions that we might obtain, so the sample proportion $\hat{p}$ is a random variable. In the following boxed feature, we give the properties of the probability distribution of this random variable, which is called the **sampling distribution of the sample proportion $\hat{p}$**.

The Sampling Distribution of the Sample Proportion $\hat{p}$

The population of all possible sample proportions

1   Approximately has a normal distribution, if the sample size n is large.

2   Has mean $\mu_{\hat{p}} = p$.

3   Has standard deviation[2] $\sigma_{\hat{p}} = \sqrt{\dfrac{p(1-p)}{n}}$.

Stated equivalently, the sampling distribution of $\hat{p}$ has mean $\mu_{\hat{p}} = p$, has standard deviation

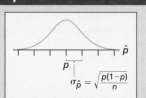

$\sigma_{\hat{p}} = \sqrt{p(1-p)/n}$, and is approximately a normal distribution (if the sample size n is large).[3]

Property 1 in the boxed feature says that, if n is large, then the population of all possible sample proportions approximately has a normal distribution. Here, it can be shown that **n should be considered large if both np and $n(1 - p)$ are at least 5.**[4] Property 2 says that $\mu_{\hat{p}} = p$ is valid for any sample size and tells us that $\hat{p}$ is an unbiased estimate of p. That is, although the sample proportion $\hat{p}$ that we calculate probably does not equal p, the average of all of the different sample proportions that we could have calculated (from all the different possible samples) is equal to p. Property 3, which says that the standard error for a test of proportions is

$$\sigma_{\hat{p}} = \sqrt{\frac{p(1-p)}{n}}$$

is *exactly* correct if the sampled population is infinite and is *approximately correct* if the sampled population is finite and much larger than (say, at least 20 times as large as) the sample size. Property 3 tells us that the standard deviation of the population of all possible sample proportions decreases as the sample size increases. That is, the larger n is, the more closely clustered are all of the different sample proportions around the true population proportion. Finally, note the similarities between the standard deviation of the sampling distribution of the sample proportion and the standard deviation of the sampling distribution of the sample mean. Recall from the introduction to this section that the standard deviation of the population is equal to $\sqrt{p(1-p)}$. So, as we can see from Property 3 in the boxed feature, the standard deviation of both of these sampling distributions (mean and proportion) is equal to the standard deviation of the population divided by the square root of the sample size.

Example 6.4   The Cheese Spread Example

In the cheese spread example, the food processing company must decide whether p, the proportion of all current purchasers who would stop buying the cheese spread if the new spout were used, is less than .10. In order to do this, remember that when 1,000 purchasers of the cheese spread are randomly selected, 63 of these purchasers say they would stop buying the cheese spread if the new spout were used. Noting that the sample proportion $\hat{p} = .063$ is less than .10, we ask the following question. If the true population proportion is .10, what is the probability of observing a sample proportion that is less than or equal to .063?

---

[2]Note that the formula for $\sigma_{\hat{p}}$ follows, in theory, from the formula for $\sigma_{\hat{p}}^2$, the variance of the population of all possible sample proportions. The formula for $\sigma_{\hat{p}}^2$ is $\sigma_{\hat{p}}^2 = p(1 - p)/n$.

[3]In Appendix C (Part 3) on *Connect*, we derive the formulas for $\mu_{\hat{p}}$ and $\sigma_{\hat{p}}$.

[4]Some statisticians suggest using the more conservative rule that both np and $n(1 - p)$ must be at least 10.

If p equals .10, we can assume that the sampling distribution of $\hat{p}$ is approximately a normal distribution, because both $np = 1{,}000(.10) = 100$ and $n(1 - p) = 1{,}000(1 - .10) = 900$ are at least 5. Furthermore, the mean and standard deviation of the sampling distribution of $\hat{p}$ are $\mu_{\hat{p}} = p = .10$ and

$$\sigma_{\hat{p}} = \sqrt{\frac{p(1 - p)}{n}} = \sqrt{\frac{(.10)(.90)}{1{,}000}} = .0094868$$

Therefore,

$$P(\hat{p} \le .063 \text{ if } p = .10) = P\!\left(z \le \frac{.063 - \mu_{\hat{p}}}{\sigma_{\hat{p}}}\right) = P\!\left(z \le \frac{.063 - .10}{.0094868}\right)$$

$$= P(z \le -3.90)$$

which is the area under the standard normal curve to the left of -3.90. The normal table tells us that this area equals .00005. This probability says that, if p equals .10, then only 5 in 100,000 of all possible sample proportions are at least as small as the sample proportion $\hat{p} = .063$ that we have actually observed. That is, if we are to believe that p equals .10, we must believe that we have observed a sample proportion that can be described as a 5 in 100,000 chance. It follows that we have extremely strong evidence that p does not equal .10 and is, in fact, less than .10. In other words, we have extremely strong evidence that less than 10 percent of current purchasers would stop buying the cheese spread if the new spout was used. It seems that introducing the new spout will be profitable.

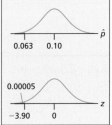

Exercises for Section **6.2**

CONCEPTS

6.15 What population is described by the sampling distribution of $\hat{p}$?

6.16 Suppose that we randomly select a sample of n elements from a population and that we compute the sample proportion $\hat{p}$ of these elements that fall into a category of interest. If we consider the sampling distribution of $\hat{p}$:
  a. If the sample size n is large, the sampling distribution of $\hat{p}$ is approximately a normal distribution. What condition must be satisfied to guarantee that n is large enough to say that $\hat{p}$ is normally distributed?
  b. Write formulas that express the central tendency and variability of the population of all possible sample proportions. Explain what each of these formulas means in your own words.

6.17 Describe the effect of increasing the sample size on the population of all possible sample proportions.

METHODS AND APPLICATIONS

6.18 In each of the following cases, determine whether the sample size n is large enough to say that the sampling distribution of $\hat{p}$ is a normal distribution.
  a. $p = .4, n = 100$ **d.** $p = .8, n = 400$
  b. $p = .1, n = 10$ **e.** $p = .98, n = 1{,}000$
  c. $p = .1, n = 50$ **f.** $p = .99, n = 400$

6.19 In each of the following cases, find the mean, variance, and standard deviation of the sampling distribution of the sample proportion $\hat{p}$.
  a. $p = .5, n = 250$ **c.** $p = .8, n = 400$
  b. $p = .1, n = 100$ **d.** $p = .98, n = 1{,}000$

6.20 For each situation in Exercise 6.19, find an interval that contains approximately 95.44 percent of all of the possible sample proportions.

6.21 Suppose that we randomly select a sample of $n = 100$ elements from a population and that we compute the sample proportion $\hat{p}$ of these elements that fall into a category of interest. If the true population proportion p equals .9:
  a. Describe the shape of the sampling distribution of $\hat{p}$. Why can we validly describe the shape?
  b. Find the mean and the standard deviation of the sampling distribution of $\hat{p}$.

6.22 For the situation in Exercise 6.21, calculate the following probabilities. In each case, sketch the sampling distribution and the probability.
  a. $P(\hat{p} \ge .96)$
  b. $P(.855 \le \hat{p} \le .945)$
  c. $P(\hat{p} \le .915)$

6.23 **THE CONTENT SCREENING EXAMPLE**

Consider again the use of iTunes content ratings for restricting children's television viewing (i.e., to block movies and TV shows with ratings at or above a particular "rating threshold," such as PG-13 or R). You conduct a survey of Canadian families that have access to an iTunes-capable device (be it a computer or an Apple TV) and ask whether the parents use this functionality to control the television viewing habits of their children.
  a. Suppose that we want to use your results to justify the claim that less than 20 percent of parents with access to this technology utilize content ratings in this fashion. If you actually found that 17 percent of the parents that

you polled used this functionality to restrict television viewing habits in their household, and if you surveyed 1,000 parents, calculate the probability of observing a sample proportion of .17 or less when the population is assumed to have a proportion of .20.

b. Based on the probability you computed in part (a), would you conclude that less than 20 percent of parents utilize content ratings in this fashion? Explain.

6.24 Consider a poll that was done to evaluate Canadian attitudes toward the 2010 Winter Olympic Games in Vancouver. The poll results were based on telephone interviews with a randomly selected national sample of 1,011 adults, 18 years and older.

a. Suppose we want to use the poll's results to justify the claim that more than 30 percent of Canadians (18 years or older) say that figure skating is their favourite Winter Olympic event. The poll actually found that 32 percent of respondents reported that figure skating was their favourite event. If, for the sake of argument, we assume that 30 percent of Canadians (18 years or older) say figure skating is their favourite event (that is, $p = .3$), calculate the probability of observing a sample proportion of .32 or more; that is, calculate $P(\hat{p} \geq .32)$.

b. Based on the probability you computed in part (a), would you conclude that more than 30 percent of Canadians (18 years or older) say that figure skating is their favourite Winter Olympic event?

6.25 THE BANK CUSTOMER SATISFACTION EXAMPLE

The Alliance Bank of Canada is interested in evaluating gains in customer satisfaction and loyalty that it has made over the past two years. A key measure of customer satisfaction is the response (on a scale from 1 to 10) to the question: "Considering all the business you do with our bank, what is your overall satisfaction with the Alliance Bank of Canada?" Here, a response of 9 or 10 represents "customer delight."

a. Historically, the percentage of Alliance Bank customers expressing customer delight has been 48 percent. Suppose that we want to use the results of a survey of 350 Alliance Bank customers to justify the claim that more than 48 percent of all current customers would express customer delight. The survey finds that 189 of 350 randomly selected customers express customer delight. If, for the sake of argument, we assume that the proportion of customer delight is $p = .48$, calculate the probability of observing a sample proportion greater than or equal to 189/350 = .54. That is, calculate $P(\hat{p} \geq .54)$.

b. Based on the probability you computed in part (a), would you conclude that more than 48 percent of current Alliance Bank customers express customer delight? Explain.

6.26 THE BANK CUSTOMER SATISFACTION EXAMPLE

Again consider the survey of 350 Alliance Bank customers discussed in Exercise 6.25, and assume that 48 percent of customers would currently express delight. That is, assume $p = .48$. Find

a. The probability that the sample proportion obtained from the sample of 350 Alliance Bank customers would be within three percentage points of the population proportion. That is, find $P(.45 \leq \hat{p} \leq .51)$.

b. The probability that the sample proportion obtained from the sample of 350 Alliance Bank customers would be within six percentage points of the population proportion. That is, find $P(.42 \leq \hat{p} \leq .54)$.

6.27 THE BANK CUSTOMER SATISFACTION EXAMPLE

Based on your results in Exercise 6.26, would it be reasonable to state that the survey's "margin of error" is ± 3 percentage points? ± 6 percentage points? Explain.

6.28 A special advertising section in the July 20, 1998, issue of *Fortune* magazine discusses "outsourcing." According to the article, outsourcing is "the assignment of critical, but noncore, business functions to outside specialists." This allows a company to immediately bring operations up to best-in-world standards while avoiding huge capital investments. The article includes the results of a poll of business executives addressing the benefits of outsourcing.

a. Suppose we want to use the poll's results to justify the claim that less than 26 percent of business executives feel that the benefits of outsourcing are either "less or much less than expected." The poll actually found that 15 percent of the respondents felt that the benefits of outsourcing were either "less or much less than expected."[5] If 1,000 randomly selected business executives were polled, and if for the sake of argument, we assume that 20 percent of all business executives feel that the benefits of outsourcing are either less or much less than expected (that is, $p = .20$), calculate the probability of observing a sample proportion of .15 or less. That is, calculate $P(\hat{p} \leq .15)$.

b. Based on the probability you computed in part (a), would you conclude that less than 20 percent of business executives feel that the benefits of outsourcing are either "less or much less than expected"? Explain.

6.29 The July 20, 1998, issue of *Fortune* magazine reported the results of a survey on executive training that was conducted by the Association of Executive Search Consultants. The survey showed that 75 percent of 300 polled CEOs believe that companies should have "fast-track training programs" for developing managerial talent.[6]

a. Suppose we want to use the results of this survey to justify the claim that more than 70 percent of CEOs believe that companies should have fast-track training programs. Assuming that the 300 surveyed CEOs were randomly selected, and assuming, for the sake of argument, that 70 percent of CEOs believe that companies should have fast-track training programs (that is, $p = .70$), calculate the probability of observing a sample proportion of .75 or more. That is, calculate $P(\hat{p} \geq .75)$.

b. Based on the probability you computed in part (a), would you conclude that more than 70 percent of CEOs believe that companies should have fast-track training programs? Explain.

[5]Source: M. R. Ozanne and M. F. Corbette, "Outsourcing 98," *Fortune* (July 20, 1998), p. 510.

[6]Source: E. P. Gunn, "The Fast Track Is Where to Be, If You Can Find It," *Fortune* (July 20, 1998), p. 152.

CHAPTER SUMMARY

In this chapter, we discussed sampling distributions, and the practical uses to which these distributions can be put, in the context of testing statistical inference. A sampling distribution is the probability distribution that describes the population of all possible values of a sample statistic. We studied the properties of two important sampling distributions—the sampling distribution of the sample mean, $\bar{x}$, and the sampling distribution of the sample proportion, $\hat{p}$.

Because different samples that can be randomly selected from a population give different sample means, there is a population of sample means corresponding to a particular sample size. The probability distribution describing the population of all possible sample means is called the *sampling distribution of the sample mean*, $\bar{x}$. We studied the properties of this sampling distribution when the sampled population is and is not normally distributed. We found that, when the sampled population has a normal distribution, then the sampling distribution of the sample mean is a normal distribution. Furthermore, the central limit theorem tells us that, if the sampled population is not normally distributed, then the sampling distribution of the sample mean is approximately a normal distribution when the sample size is large (at least 30).

We also saw that the mean of the sampling distribution of $\bar{x}$ always equals the mean of the sampled population, and we presented formulas for the variance and the standard deviation of this sampling distribution. Finally, we explained that the sample mean is a minimum-variance unbiased point estimate of the mean of a normally distributed population.

We studied the properties of the sampling distribution of the sample proportion $\hat{p}$ and found that, if the sample size is large, then this sampling distribution is approximately a normal distribution, and we gave a rule for determining whether the sample size is large. We found that the mean of the sampling distribution of $\hat{p}$ is the population proportion p, and we gave formulas for the variance and the standard deviation of this sampling distribution.

Throughout our discussions of sampling distributions, we demonstrated that knowing the properties of sampling distributions can help us make statistical inferences about population parameters. In fact, we will see that the properties of various sampling distributions provide the foundation for most of the techniques to be discussed in future chapters.

KEY TERMS

central limit theorem
minimum-variance unbiased point estimate
sampling distribution of a sample statistic
sampling distribution of the sample mean $\bar{x}$

sampling distribution of the sample proportion $\hat{p}$
standard error
unbiased point estimate

IMPORTANT FORMULAS

Sampling distribution of the sample mean

Standard deviation of the sampling distribution of the sample mean

Central limit theorem

Sampling distribution of the sample proportion

Standard deviation of the sampling distribution of the sample proportion

SUPPLEMENTARY EXERCISES

connect Practise and learn online with *Connect*. Items for which there are online data sets are marked with ⟋.

6.30 Each day a manufacturing plant receives a large shipment of containers of Chemical ZX-900. These containers are supposed to have a mean fill of 50 litres, while the fills have a standard deviation known to be .6 litres.

  a. Suppose that the mean fill for the shipment is actually 50 litres. If we draw a random sample of 100 containers from the shipment, what is the probability that the average fill for the 100 containers is between 49.88 litres and 50.12 litres?

  b. The plant manager is worried that the containers of Chemical ZX-900 are underfilled. Because of this, she decides to draw a sample of 100 containers from each daily shipment and will reject the shipment (send it back to the supplier) if the average fill for the 100 containers is less than 49.85 litres. Suppose that a shipment that actually has a mean fill of 50 litres is

received. What is the probability that this shipment will be rejected and sent back to the supplier?

6.31 The Toronto Stock Exchange suffered its largest point drop in history on Monday, September 29, 2008. Four years later (i.e., late September of 2012), you conduct a poll of 1,250 Canadian investors, investigating the stock market's current appeal to investors.

  Assume that 50 percent of all Canadian investors in 2012 found the stock market less attractive than it was in early 2008 (that is, $p = .5$). Find the probability that the sample proportion obtained from the sample of 1,250 investors would be:

  a. Within 4 percentage points of the population proportion—that is, find $P(.46 \leq \hat{p} \leq .54)$.

  b. Within 2 percentage points of the population proportion.

c. Within 1 percentage point of the population proportion.

d. Based on these probabilities, would it be reasonable to claim a ± 2 percentage point margin of error? A ± 1 percentage point margin of error? Explain.

6.32 Again consider the stock market poll discussed in Exercise 6.31.

a. Suppose we want to use the poll's results to justify the claim that less than 50 percent of Canadian investors in 2012 found the stock market less attractive than in 2008. The poll actually found that 41 percent of the respondents said the stock market was less attractive than in early 2008. If, for the sake of argument, we assume that $p = .5$, calculate the probability of observing a sample proportion of .41 or less. That is, calculate $P(\hat{p} \leq .41)$.

b. Based on the probability you computed in part (b), would you conclude that less than 50 percent of Canadian investors in 2012 found the stock market to be less attractive than in early 2008? Explain.

6.33 Acme Heating and Cooling, Inc. advertises that any customer buying an air conditioner during the first 16 days of July will receive a 25 percent discount if the average high temperature for this 16-day period is more than 1.5 degrees Celsius above normal.

a. If daily high temperatures in July are normally distributed with a mean of 29 degrees Celsius and a standard deviation of 3 degrees, what is the probability that Acme Heating and Cooling will have to give its customers the 25 percent discount?

b. Based on the probability you computed in part (a), do you think that Acme's promotion is ethical? Write a paragraph justifying your opinion.

6.34 THE TRASH BAG EXAMPLE

A trash bag manufacturer has concluded that its new 100-litre bag will be the strongest such bag on the market if its mean breaking strength is at least 25 kilograms. To provide statistical evidence that the mean breaking strength of the new bag is at least 25 kilograms, the manufacturer randomly selects a sample of n bags and calculates the mean $\bar{x}$ of the breaking strengths of these bags. If the sample mean so obtained is at least 25 kilograms, some evidence is provided that the mean breaking strength of all new bags is at least 25 kilograms.

Suppose that (unknown to the manufacturer) the breaking strengths of the new 100-litre bag are normally distributed with a mean of $\mu = 25.3$ kilograms and a standard deviation of $\sigma = .81$ kilograms.

a. Find an interval containing 95.44 percent of all possible sample means if the sample size employed is $n = 5$.

b. Find an interval containing 95.44 percent of all possible sample means if the sample size employed is $n = 40$.

c. If the trash bag manufacturer hopes to obtain a sample mean that is at least 25 kilograms (so that it can provide evidence that the population mean breaking strength of the new bags is at least 25), which sample size ($n = 5$ or $n = 40$) would be best? Explain why.

6.35 The year 1987 featured extreme volatility on the U.S. stock market, including a loss of over 20 percent of the market's value on a single day. Figure 6.6(a) shows the percent frequency histogram of the percentage returns for the entire year 1987 for the population of all 1,815 stocks listed on the New York Stock Exchange. The mean and the standard deviation of the population of percentage returns are −3.5 percent and 26 percent, respectively.

FIGURE 6.6 The New York Stock Exchange in 1987: A Comparison of Individual Stock Returns and Sample Mean Returns

(a) The percent frequency histogram describing the population of individual stock returns

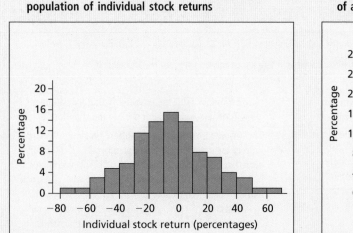

(b) The percent frequency histogram describing the population of all possible sample mean returns when $n = 5$

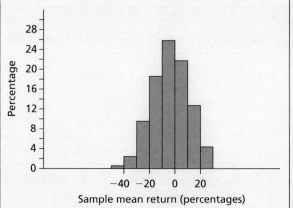

Figure 6.6 is adapted with permission from John K. Ford, "A Method for Grading 1987 Stock Recommendations," *The American Association of Individual Investors Journal,* March 1988, pp. 16–17.

Consider drawing a random sample of $n = 5$ stocks from the population of 1,815 stocks and calculating the mean return, $\bar{x}$, of the sampled stocks. If we use a computer, we can generate all of the different samples of five stocks that can be obtained (there are trillions of such samples) and calculate the corresponding sample mean returns.

A percent frequency histogram describing the population of all possible sample mean returns is given in Figure 6.6(b). Comparing Figures 6.6(a) and (b), we see that, although the histogram of individual stock returns and the histogram of sample mean returns are both bell-shaped and centred over the same mean of -3.5 percent, the histogram of sample mean returns looks *less spread out* than the histogram of individual returns. A sample of 5 stocks is a portfolio of stocks, where the average return of the 5 stocks is the portfolio's return if we invest equal amounts of money in each of the 5 stocks. Because the sample mean returns are less spread out than the individual stock returns, we have illustrated that diversification reduces risk. Find the standard deviation of the population of all sample mean returns, and assuming that this population is normally distributed, find an interval that contains 95.44 percent of all sample mean returns.

6.36 Suppose that we want to assess whether more than 60 percent of all Canadian households purchased life insurance in 2012. That is, we want to assess whether the proportion, p, of all Canadian households that have purchased life insurance in 2012 exceeds .60. Assume that the survey is based on 1,000 randomly selected households and that 640 of these households purchased life insurance in 2012.

    a. Assuming that p equals .60 and the sample size is 1,000, what is the probability of observing a sample proportion that is at least .64?

    b. Based on your answer in part (a), do you think more than 60 percent of all Canadian households purchased life insurance in 2012? Explain.

6.37 **INTERNET EXERCISE**

The best way to observe first-hand the concepts of sampling distributions is to conduct sampling experiments with real data. However, sampling experiments can be prohibitively time-consuming and tedious. An excellent alternative is to conduct computer-assisted sampling experiments or simulations. The Wolfram Demonstrations Project has a number of interactive demonstrations that are helpful in developing an understanding of basic concepts like the sampling distribution of the mean. Go to demonstrations. wolfram.com/SamplingDistributionOfTheSampleMean

Unless you previously installed the free Wolfram CDF Player, you will need to click on the orange rectangle in the centre of the Wolfram Demonstrations main page. Clicking on this box will take you to a download window, where you will be asked to provide information about your college or university and your e-mail address. After you have done this, the appropriate software for your browser (and computer platform) will begin to download. Double-click the file that you have downloaded in order to install the software, and relaunch your browser.

You will now be able to interact with the sampling distribution on your screen. Notice how increasing the n size of your sample decreases the standard deviation of your sampling distribution. Recall that this is due to the fact that the standard error of the sampling distribution is equal to the standard deviation of the population divided by the square root of the n size. You should see a similar effect when you reduce the standard deviation.

CHAPTER **7**

Hypothesis Testing

Hypothesis testing is a statistical procedure used to provide evidence in favour of some statement (called a *hypothesis*). Hypothesis testing might be used to assess whether a population parameter, such as a population mean, differs from a specified standard or previous value. It may also be used to determine whether two populations differ from each other. In this chapter, we introduce a formal method for testing hypotheses about population means and proportions, and discuss the errors that can be made when making a determination as to whether these parameters are sufficiently different from expectation as to be declared "significantly different." Finally, we introduce the concept of effect size, and discuss this concept in the context of Type II error and power.

7.1 THE NULL AND ALTERNATIVE HYPOTHESES AND ERRORS IN HYPOTHESIS TESTING

One of the key responsibilities of the standards and practices division in a television network is to reduce the chances that advertisers will make false claims in commercials run on the network. It is possible to use a statistical methodology called *null hypothesis significance testing* (or *hypothesis testing*, for short) to do this. To see how this might be done, suppose that a company wants to advertise a claim on the television network. To evaluate this claim, the hypothesis testing procedure that we will outline in this chapter requires that the network first assume that the claim is not valid. This assumption is called the *null hypothesis*. The statement that *the claim is valid* is called the *alternative* (or *research*) *hypothesis*. The network will run the commercial only if the company making the claim provides sufficient sample evidence to reject the null hypothesis that the claim is not valid, in favour of the alternative hypothesis that the claim is valid. Explaining the exact meaning of *sufficient sample evidence* is quite involved and will be discussed as we proceed through this chapter.

LO1

The Null Hypothesis and the Alternative Hypothesis

In hypothesis testing:

1 The **null hypothesis,** denoted H_0, is the statement being tested. Often (but not always), the null hypothesis is a statement of "no difference" or "no effect." The null hypothesis is not rejected unless there is convincing sample evidence that it is false.

2 The **alternative,** or **research, hypothesis,** denoted H_a, is a statement that will be accepted only if there is convincing sample evidence that it is true.

Setting up the null and alternative hypotheses in a practical situation can be tricky. In some situations, there is a statement about a population parameter (such as a population mean) for which we need to find supportive evidence. If the statement indicates an interest in testing to see if a parameter is "greater than" a particular number, or if the parameter is "less than" a particular number, then (for reasons to be discussed later) this statement will be used to create our alternative hypothesis, H_a. Counterintuitive though it might seem, the *alternative hypothesis* generally represents the research question that we want to investigate. The situation that would exist if this statement turns out to be incorrect is termed the *null hypothesis*, H_0. We illustrate these ideas in Examples 7.1 and 7.2.

Example 7.1 The Trash Bag Example

A leading manufacturer of trash bags produces the strongest trash bags on the market. The company has developed a new 100-litre bag using a specially formulated plastic that is stronger and more biodegradable than other plastics. This plastic's increased strength allows the

bag's thickness to be reduced, and the resulting cost savings will enable the company to lower its bag price by 25 percent. The company also believes the new bag is stronger than its current 100-litre bag.

The manufacturer wants to advertise the new bag on a major television network. In addition to promoting its price reduction, the company also wants to claim the new bag is better for the environment and stronger than its current bag. The network is convinced of the bag's environmental advantages because, in addition to being stronger, its specially formulated plastic is more biodegradable than other plastics and also the bag's thickness has been reduced, so less plastic is used. However, the network questions the company's claim of increased strength, and requires the company to present statistical evidence that supports this claim. The manufacturer and the network agree to use breaking strength, which is the amount of a representative trash mix (in kilograms) that, when loaded into a bag suspended in the air, will cause the bag to rip or tear.

Tests show that the current bag has a mean breaking strength that is very close to (but does not exceed) 25 kilograms. The new bag's mean breaking strength μ is unknown and in question. Because the trash bag manufacturer wants to show that μ *is greater than 25 kilograms*, we formulate our alternative hypothesis (H_a) from the statement μ *is greater than 25 kilograms*. This means that our null hypothesis (H_0) will be formed from the statement μ *is less than or equal to 25 kilograms*. In this way, the null hypothesis posits that the new trash bag is *not stronger* than the former bag.

We can summarize the null and alternative hypotheses by saying that we are testing

$$H_0: \mu \le 25 \text{ versus } H_a: \mu > 25$$

The network will run the manufacturer's commercial if a random sample of n new bags provides sufficient evidence to reject $H_0: \mu \le 25$ in favour of $H_a: \mu > 25$.

Example 7.2 The Billing Time Example

Recall the management consulting firm that installed a new electronic billing system for a trucking company. Because of the system's advantages and because the trucking company's clients are receptive to using this system, the management consulting firm believes that the new system will reduce the mean bill payment time by more than 50 percent. The mean payment time using the old billing system was approximately equal to, but no less than, 39 days. Therefore, if μ denotes the mean payment time using the new system, the consulting firm believes and wants to show that μ *is less than 19.5 days*. It follows that we should formulate our alternative hypothesis (H_a) from the statement μ *is less than 19.5 days*. Our null hypothesis (H_0), therefore, is drawn from the statement that μ *is greater than or equal to 19.5 days*.

The consulting firm will randomly select a sample of n invoices and determine if the payment times provide sufficient evidence to reject $H_0: \mu \ge 19.5$ in favour of $H_a: \mu < 19.5$. If such evidence exists, the consulting firm will conclude that the new electronic billing system has reduced the trucking company's mean bill payment time by more than 50 percent. This conclusion will be used to help demonstrate the benefits of the new billing system both to the company and to other trucking companies that are considering using such a system.

In some situations we need to evaluate a statement that says that a population parameter exactly equals a particular number. It then follows that we make the statement that the population parameter *equals* the particular number, the *null hypothesis, H_0,* and we make the statement that the population parameter *does not equal* the particular number, the *alternative hypothesis, H_a.* We demonstrate this in Example 7.3.

Example 7.3 Assessing Demand for a Seasonal Box of Chocolates

A candy company annually markets a special 500-g box of assorted chocolates to large retail stores for Valentine's Day. This year the candy company has designed an extremely attractive new valentine box and will fill the box with an especially appealing assortment of chocolates. For this reason, the candy company subjectively projects—based on past experience and knowledge of the candy market—that sales of its valentine box will be 10 percent higher than last year. However, since the candy company must decide how many valentine boxes to produce, the company needs to assess whether it is reasonable to plan for a 10 percent increase in sales.

Before the beginning of each Valentine's Day sales season, the candy company sends large retail stores information about its newest valentine box of assorted chocolates. This information includes a description of the box of chocolates, as well as a preview of advertising displays that the candy company will provide to help retail stores sell the chocolates. Each retail store then places a single (nonreturnable) order of valentine boxes to satisfy its anticipated customer demand for the Valentine's Day sales season.

Last year the mean order quantity of large retail stores was 300 boxes per store. If the projected 10 percent sales increase occurs, the mean order quantity, μ, of large retail stores this year will *equal* 330 boxes per store. Therefore, the candy company will test the *null hypothesis* H_0: $\mu = 330$ versus the *alternative hypothesis* H_a: $\mu \neq 330$. Here, the alternative hypothesis H_a says that μ might be greater than or less than 330 boxes. If μ turns out to be greater than 330 boxes and the candy company bases its production on a projected mean order quantity of 330 boxes, the company will fail to satisfy demand for its valentine box. If μ turns out to be less than 330 boxes and the candy company bases its production on a projected mean order quantity of 330 boxes, the company will produce more valentine boxes than it can sell.

To perform the hypothesis test, the candy company will randomly select a sample of n large retail stores and will make an early mailing to these stores promoting this year's valentine box. The candy company will then ask each retail store to report how many valentine boxes it anticipates ordering. If the sample data do not provide sufficient evidence to reject H_0: $\mu = 330$ in favour of H_a: $\mu \neq 330$, the candy company will base its production on the projected 10 percent sales increase. On the other hand, if there is sufficient evidence to reject H_0: $\mu = 330$, the candy company will change its production plans.

Let's summarize the sets of null and alternative hypotheses that we have considered so far:

$$H_0: \mu \leq 25 \qquad H_0: \mu \geq 19.5 \qquad H_0: \mu = 330$$
$$\text{versus} \qquad\quad \text{versus} \qquad\quad \text{versus}$$
$$H_a: \mu > 25 \qquad H_a: \mu < 19.5 \qquad H_a: \mu \neq 330$$

The **one-sided alternative hypothesis** H_a: $\mu > 25$ is called a one-sided **greater than alternative** hypothesis, whereas the one-sided alternative hypothesis H_a: $\mu < 19.5$ is called a one-sided **less than alternative** hypothesis. Similarly, the **two-sided alternative hypothesis** H_a: $\mu \neq 330$ is called a two-sided, **not equal to alternative** hypothesis. All of the alternative hypotheses that we consider in this book are one of these three types. Also, note that each null hypothesis we have considered involves an *equality*. For example, the null hypothesis H_0: $\mu \leq 25$ says that μ is either less than or *equal to* 50. We will see that, in general, the approach we use to test a null hypothesis versus an alternative hypothesis requires that the null hypothesis involve an equality. For this reason, **we always formulate the null and alternative hypotheses so that the null hypothesis involves an equality.**

The idea of a test statistic Suppose that in the trash bag case, the manufacturer randomly selects a sample of $n = 40$ new trash bags. Each of these bags is tested for breaking strength, and the sample mean $\bar{x}$ of the 40 breaking strengths is calculated to be 25.575 kg. This suggests that we have evidence to suggest that the breaking strength of the new trash bags has increased from previous generations of the bag (which had a breaking strength of 25 kg). Does this, on its own, provide us with sufficient evidence to make a claim of greater breaking strength for the new bag? Intuitively, we know that it does not. It may be possible to account for the difference in breaking strength between the new bag and the old bag by considering random fluctuations in our measurement of this parameter. In other words, we need to take into account the variability in breaking strength that is demonstrated within the population of new trash bags. Furthermore, we know from our discussion of sampling distributions in Chapter 6, that we must take the sample size into account when identifying the likelihood of drawing this sample. Taken together, this suggests that we must consider both the standard deviation of the breaking strengths of the trash bags, and the sample size ($n = 40$) that we drew in identifying our point estimate of the breaking strength of the new trash bags. We must, therefore, scale the difference between our sample mean (25.575 kg) and our null hypothesis test value (the breaking strength of previous generations of the bag, 25 kg), in terms of the standard error, $\sigma_{\bar{x}}$. So, in order to test H_0: $\mu \leq 25$ versus H_a: $\mu > 25$, we utilize the test statistic

$$z = \frac{\bar{x} - 25}{\sigma_{\bar{x}}} = \frac{\bar{x} - 25}{\sigma/\sqrt{n}}$$

The test statistic z measures the distance between the sample mean ($\bar{x}$) and 25. The division by the standard error, $\sigma_{\bar{x}}$, says that this distance is measured in units of the standard deviation of all possible sample means. For example, a value of z equal to, say, 2.4 would tell us that $\bar{x}$ is 2.4 such standard deviations above 25. In general, a value of the test statistic that is less than or equal to zero results when $\bar{x}$ is less than or equal to 25. Because we are testing a one-sided greater-than alternative hypothesis, this provides no evidence to support rejecting H_0 in favour of H_a, because the point estimate $\bar{x}$ indicates that μ is probably less than or equal to 25. However, a value of the test statistic that is greater than zero results when $\bar{x}$ is greater than 25. This provides evidence to support rejecting H_0 in favour of H_a, because the point estimate $\bar{x}$ indicates that μ might be greater than 25. Furthermore, the farther the value of the test statistic is above 0 (the farther $\bar{x}$ is above 25), the stronger the evidence to support rejecting H_0 in favour of H_a.

Hypothesis testing and the legal system If the value of the test statistic z is far enough away from zero, we reject H_0 in favour of H_a. To see how large z must be in order to reject H_0, we must understand that **a hypothesis test rejects a null hypothesis H_0 only if there is strong statistical evidence against H_0.** This is similar to our legal system, which rejects the innocence of the accused only if evidence of guilt is beyond a reasonable doubt. For instance, the network will reject H_0: $\mu \leq 25$ and run the trash bag commercial only if the test statistic z is far enough above zero to show beyond a reasonable doubt that H_0: $\mu \leq 25$ is false and H_a: $\mu > 25$ is true. A test statistic that is only slightly different from zero might not be convincing enough. However, because such a test statistic would result from a sample mean $\bar{x}$ that is slightly greater than 25, it would provide some evidence to support rejecting H_0: $\mu \leq 25$, and it certainly would not provide strong evidence supporting H_0: $\mu \leq 25$. Therefore, if the value of the test statistic is not large enough to convince us to reject H_0, **we do not say that we accept H_0. Rather, we say that we do not reject H_0** because the evidence against H_0 is not strong enough. Again, this is similar to our legal system, where the lack of evidence of guilt beyond a reasonable doubt results in a verdict of not guilty, but does not prove that the accused is innocent.

ROADBLOCK

Our hypothesis statements are evaluating a theoretical population parameter
It is important to remember, when setting up your hypothesis statements, that you are evaluating a statement about the centre of your population. This means that you are setting the parameter to be equal to a particular value of interest (usually some historical value—as was the case in the trash bag example—or a value that has some intrinsic meaning—as was the case in the Valentine's Day candy example). When you evaluate this population parameter in your test statistic, you are attempting to amass evidence that the parameter is actually different from expectation. In this way, we are always attempting to *reject* or *fail to reject* the null hypothesis. As we mentioned previously, we never *accept* the null hypothesis.

TABLE 7.1 Type I and Type II Errors

	State of Nature	
Decision	H_0: $\mu \leq 25$ **True**	H_0: $\mu \leq 25$ **False**
Reject H_0: $\mu \leq 25$	Type I error	Correct decision
Do not reject H_0: $\mu \leq 25$	Correct decision	Type II error

TABLE 7.2 The Implications of Type I and Type II Errors in the Trash Bag Example

	State of Nature	
Decision	**Claim False**	**Claim True**
Advertise the claim	Advertise a false claim	Advertise a true claim
Do not advertise the claim	Do not advertise a false claim	Do not advertise a true claim

Type I and Type II errors and their probabilities To determine exactly how much statistical evidence is required to reject H_0, we consider the errors and the correct decisions that can be made in hypothesis testing. These errors and correct decisions, as well as their implications in the trash bag advertising example, are summarized in Tables 7.1 and 7.2. Across the top of each table are listed the two possible "states of nature": Either H_0: $\mu \leq 25$ is true, which means that the manufacturer's claim that μ is greater than 25 is false, or H_0 is false, which means that the claim is true. Down the left side of each table are listed the two possible decisions we can make in the hypothesis test. Using the sample data, we will either reject H_0: $\mu \leq 25$, which implies that the claim will be advertised, or we will not reject H_0, which implies that the claim will not be advertised.

In general, the two types of errors that can be made in hypothesis testing are defined as follows:

LO2

Type I and Type II Errors

If we reject H_0 when it is true, this is a **Type I error**.
If we do not reject H_0 when it is false, this is a **Type II error**.

As can be seen by comparing Tables 7.1 and 7.2, if we commit a Type I error, we will advertise a false claim. If we commit a Type II error, we will fail to advertise a true claim.

We now let the symbol α (pronounced *alpha*) denote the probability of a Type I error, and we let β (pronounced *beta*) denote the probability of a Type II error. Obviously, we would like both α and β to be small. A common (but not the only) procedure is to base a hypothesis test on taking a sample of a fixed size (for example, $n = 40$ trash bags) and on setting α equal to a small prespecified value. Setting α low means there is only a small chance of rejecting H_0 when it is true. This implies that we are requiring strong evidence against H_0 before we reject it.

We sometimes choose α as high as .10, but we usually choose α between .05 and .01. A frequent choice for α is .05. In the context of our trash bag example, then, the network in question may have a policy of testing claims against an alpha of .05. Since a Type I error refers to a decision that a claim is valid when it is not, the policy of setting α equal to .05 says that, in the long run, the network will advertise only 5 percent of the invalid claims that could be made by advertisers.

One might wonder why the network does not set α lower—say at .01. One reason is that it can be shown that, for a fixed sample size, the lower we set α, the higher β is, and the higher we set α, the lower β is. Setting α at .05 means that β, the probability of failing to advertise a true claim (a Type II error), will be smaller than it would be if α was set at .01. As long as (1) the claim to be advertised is plausible and (2) the consequences of advertising the claim even if it is false are not terribly serious, then it is reasonable to set α equal to .05. However, if either (1) or (2) is not true, then we might set α lower than .05. For example, suppose a pharmaceutical company wants to advertise that it has developed an effective treatment for a disease that has formerly been very resistant to treatment. Such a claim is perhaps difficult to believe. Moreover, if the claim is false, patients suffering from the disease would be subjected to false hope and needless expense. In such a case, it might be reasonable for the network to set α at .01 because this would lower the chance of advertising the claim if it is false. We usually do not set α lower than .01 because doing so often leads to an unacceptably large value of β. We explain some methods for computing the probability of a Type II error in Section 7.6. However, β can be difficult or impossible to calculate in many situations, and we often must rely on our intuition when deciding how to set α.

Exercises for Section **7.1**

CONCEPTS

7.1   Define each of the following: Type I error, α, Type II error, β.

7.2   When testing a hypothesis, why don't we set the probability of a Type I error to be extremely small? Explain.

METHODS AND APPLICATIONS

7.3   THE VIDEO GAME SATISFACTION RATING EXAMPLE

Recall that "very satisfied" customers give the XYZ-Box video game system a rating that is at least 42. Suppose that the manufacturer of the XYZ-Box wants to use the 65 satisfaction ratings to provide evidence supporting the claim that the mean composite satisfaction rating for the XYZ-Box exceeds 42.

a. Letting μ represent the mean composite satisfaction rating for the XYZ-Box, set up the null and alternative hypotheses needed if we want to attempt to provide evidence supporting the claim that μ exceeds 42.

b. In the context of this situation, interpret making a Type I error; interpret making a Type II error.

7.4   THE CUSTOMER WAIT TIME EXAMPLE

Recall that a bank manager has developed a new system to reduce the time customers spend waiting for teller service during peak hours. The manager hopes the new system will reduce waiting times from the current 9 to 10 minutes to less than 6 minutes.

Suppose the manager wants to use the 100 waiting times to support the claim that the mean waiting time under the new system is shorter than 6 minutes.

a. Letting μ represent the mean waiting time under the new system, set up the null and alternative hypotheses needed if we want to attempt to provide evidence supporting the claim that μ is shorter than 6 minutes.

b. In the context of this situation, interpret making a Type I error; interpret making a Type II error.

7.5   THE AUTO PARTS PRODUCTION EXAMPLE

An automobile parts supplier owns a machine that produces a cylindrical engine part. This part is supposed to have an outside diameter of three centimetres. Parts with diameters that are too small or too large do not meet customer requirements and must be rejected. Lately, the company has experienced problems meeting customer requirements. The technical staff feels that the

mean diameter produced by the machine is off target. In order to verify this, a special study will randomly sample 100 parts produced by the machine. The 100 sampled parts will be measured, and if the results obtained cast a substantial amount of doubt on the hypothesis that the mean diameter equals the target value of three centimetres, the company will assign a problem-solving team to intensively search for the causes of the problem.

a. The parts supplier wants to set up a hypothesis test so that the problem-solving team will be assigned when the null hypothesis is rejected. Set up the null and alternative hypotheses for this situation.

b. In the context of this situation, interpret making a Type I error; interpret making a Type II error.

7.6   THE BOTTLE FILLING EXAMPLE

The Black Fly Beverage Company has just installed a new bottling process that will fill 500-mL bottles of its popular margarita beverage. Both overfilling and underfilling bottles are undesirable: Underfilling leads to customer complaints and overfilling costs the company a considerable amount of money. To verify that the filler is set up correctly, the company wants to see whether the mean bottle fill, μ, is close to the target fill of 500 mL. To this end, a random sample of 36 filled bottles is selected from the output of a test filler run. If the sample results cast a substantial amount of doubt on the hypothesis that the mean bottle fill is the desired 500 mL, the filler's initial setup will be readjusted.

a. The bottling company wants to set up a hypothesis test so that the filler will be readjusted if the null hypothesis is rejected. Set up the null and alternative hypotheses for this hypothesis test.

b. In the context of this situation, interpret making a Type I error; interpret making a Type II error.

7.7   THE WASTE WATER EXAMPLE

Atlantic Power, a large electric power utility, has just built a modern nuclear power plant. This plant discharges waste water that is allowed to flow into the Atlantic Ocean. Environment Canada has ordered that the waste water must not be excessively warm, so that thermal pollution of the marine environment near the plant can be avoided. Because of this order, the waste water is allowed to cool in specially constructed ponds and is then released into the ocean. This cooling system works properly if the mean temperature of waste water discharged is 15°C or cooler. Atlantic Power is required to monitor the temperature of the waste water. A sample of 100 temperature readings will be obtained each day, and if the sample results cast a substantial amount of doubt on the hypothesis that the cooling system is working properly (i.e., the mean temperature of waste water discharged is 15°C or cooler), then the plant must be shut down and appropriate actions must be taken to correct the problem.

a. Atlantic Power wants to set up a hypothesis test so that the power plant will be shut down when the null hypothesis is rejected. Set up the null and alternative hypotheses that should be used.

b. In the context of this situation, interpret making a Type I error; interpret making a Type II error.

c. Environment Canada periodically conducts spot checks to determine whether the waste water being discharged is too warm. Suppose that Environment Canada has the power to impose very severe penalties (for example, very heavy fines) when the waste water is excessively warm. All else being equal, should Atlantic Power set the probability of a Type I error equal to $\alpha = .01$ or $\alpha = .05$? Explain.

7.2 SINGLE-SAMPLE TESTS OF A POPULATION MEAN WHEN σ IS KNOWN

LO3

In this section, we discuss hypothesis tests about a population mean that are *based on the normal distribution*. These tests are called *z tests*, and they require that the *true value of the population standard deviation σ is known*. In most real-world situations, of course, the true value of σ is not known. However, the concepts and calculations of hypothesis testing are most easily illustrated using the normal distribution. Therefore, in this section we will assume that—through theory or history related to the population under consideration—we know σ. When σ is unknown, we test hypotheses about a population mean by using the *t distribution*. We will study *t* tests in Chapter 8, and we will revisit the examples of this section with the assumption that σ is unknown.

Testing a "greater than" alternative hypothesis by using a critical value rule In Section 7.1 we explained how to set up appropriate null and alternative hypotheses. We also discussed how to specify a value for α, the probability of a Type I error (also called the *level of significance*) of the hypothesis test, and we introduced the idea of a test statistic. We can use these concepts to begin developing a five-step hypothesis testing procedure. We will introduce these steps in the context of the trash bag case and testing a "greater than" alternative hypothesis.

Step 1: State the null hypothesis H_0 and the alternative hypothesis H_a. In the trash bag case, we will test H_0: $\mu \leq 25$ versus H_a: $\mu > 25$. Here, μ is the mean breaking strength of the new trash bag.

Step 2: Specify the level of significance α. The television network will run the commercial stating that the new trash bag is stronger than the former bag if we can reject H_0: $\mu \leq 25$ in favour of H_a: $\mu > 25$ by setting α equal to .05.

Step 3: Select the test statistic. In order to test H_0: $\mu \leq 25$ versus H_a: $\mu > 25$, we will test the modified null hypothesis H_0: $\mu = 25$ versus H_a: $\mu > 25$. The idea here is that if there is sufficient evidence to reject the hypothesis that μ equals 25 in favour of $\mu > 25$, then there is certainly also sufficient evidence to reject the hypothesis that μ is less than or equal to 25. In order to test H_0: $\mu = 25$ versus H_a: $\mu > 25$, we will randomly select a sample of $n = 40$ new trash bags and calculate the mean $\bar{x}$ of the breaking strengths of these bags. We will then utilize the test statistic

$$z = \frac{\bar{x} - 25}{\sigma_{\bar{x}}} = \frac{\bar{x} - 25}{\sigma / \sqrt{n}}$$

A positive value of this test statistic results from an $\bar{x}$ that is greater than 25 and therefore provides evidence against H_0: $\mu = 25$ and in favour of H_a: $\mu > 25$. Moreover, the manufacturer has improved its trash bags multiple times in the past. Studies show that the population standard deviation σ of individual trash bag breaking strengths has remained constant for each of these updates and equals 1.65 kilograms.

FIGURE 7.1   The Critical Value for Testing H_0: $\mu = 25$ versus H_a: $\mu > 25$ by Setting $\alpha = .05$

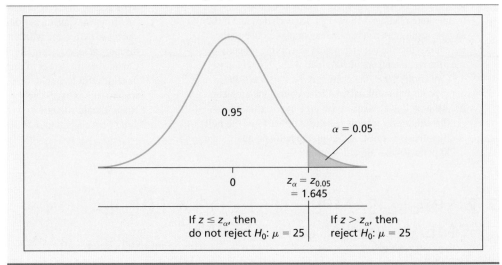

Step 4: Determine the critical value rule for deciding whether to reject H_0. To decide how large the test statistic z must be to reject H_0 in favour of H_a by setting the probability of a Type I error equal to α, we note that different samples would give different sample means and therefore different values of z. Because the sample size $n = 40$ is large, the central limit theorem tells us that the sampling distribution of z is (approximately) a standard normal distribution if the null hypothesis H_0: $\mu = 25$ is true. Therefore, we do the following:

- Place the probability of a Type I error, α, in the right-hand tail of the standard normal curve and use the normal table (see Table A.4) to find the normal point z_α. Here z_α, which we call a **critical value,** is the point on the horizontal axis under the standard normal curve that gives a right-hand tail area equal to α.

- **Reject H_0: $\mu = 25$ in favour of H_a: $\mu > 25$ if and only if the test statistic z is greater than the critical value z_α.** (This is the *critical value rule.*)

Figure 7.1 illustrates that since we have set α equal to .05, we should use the critical value $z_\alpha = z_{.05} = 1.645$ (see Table A.4). This says that we should reject H_0 if $z > 1.645$ and we should not reject H_0 if $z \leq 1.645$. To better understand the critical value rule, consider the .05 area in the right-hand tail of the standard normal curve in Figure 7.1. This .05 area is the probability of a Type I error and says that, if H_0: $\mu = 25$ is true, then only 5 percent of all possible values of the test statistic z are greater than 1.645 and therefore would cause us to wrongly reject H_0. Therefore, if the sample that we will actually select gives a value of the test statistic z that is greater than 1.645 and thus causes us to reject H_0: $\mu = 25$, we can be intuitively confident that we have made the right decision because we will have rejected H_0 by using a test that allows only a 5 percent chance of wrongly rejecting H_0. In general, if we can reject a null hypothesis in favour of an alternative hypothesis by setting the probability of a Type I error equal to α, we say that we have *statistical significance at the α level.*

Step 5: Collect the sample data, compute the value of the test statistic, and decide whether to reject H_0. Interpret the statistical results. When the sample of $n = 40$ new trash bags is randomly selected, the mean of the breaking strengths is calculated to be $\bar{x} = 25.575$ kilograms. Assuming that σ is 1.65 kilograms, the value of the test statistic is

$$z = \frac{\bar{x} - 25}{\sigma/\sqrt{40}} = \frac{25.575 - 25}{1.65/\sqrt{40}} = 2.20$$

Because $z = 2.20$ is greater than the critical value $z_{.05} = 1.645$, we can reject H_0: $\mu = 25$ in favour of H_a: $\mu > 25$ by setting α equal to .05. Therefore, we conclude (at an α of .05) that the mean breaking strength of the new trash bag exceeds 25 kilograms. Furthermore, this conclusion has practical importance to the trash bag manufacturer because it means that the television network will approve running commercials claiming that the new trash bag is stronger than the former bag. Note, however, that the point estimate of μ, $\bar{x} = 25.575$, indicates that μ is not much larger than 25. Therefore, the trash bag manufacturer can claim only that its new bag is slightly stronger than its former bag. Of course, this might be practically important to consumers who feel that, because the new bag is 25 percent less expensive and is more environmentally sound, it is definitely worth purchasing if it has any strength advantage. However, to customers who are looking only for a substantial increase in bag strength, the statistical results would not be practically important. Notice that the point estimate of the parameter involved in a hypothesis test can help us to assess practical importance.

A p-value for testing a "greater than" alternative hypothesis To decide whether to reject the null hypothesis H_0 at level of significance α, Steps 4 and 5 of the five-step hypothesis testing procedure compare the test statistic value to a critical value. Another way to make this decision is to calculate a p-value, which measures the likelihood of the sample results if the null hypothesis H_0 is true. **Sample results that are not likely if H_0 is true are evidence that H_0 is not true.** To test H_0 by using a p-value, we use the following Steps 4 and 5:

Step 4: Collect the sample data, compute the value of the test statistic, and compute the p-value. The p-value for testing a null hypothesis H_0 versus an alternative hypothesis H_a is defined as follows:

The **p-value** is the probability, computed assuming that the null hypothesis H_0 is true, of observing a value of the test statistic that is at least as contradictory to H_0 and supportive of H_a as the value actually computed from the sample data.

In the trash bag case, the value of the test statistic computed from the sample data is $z = 2.20$. Because we are testing H_0: $\mu = 25$ versus the greater than alternative hypothesis H_a: $\mu > 25$, this positive test statistic value contradicts H_0 and supports H_a. A value of the test statistic that is at least as contradictory to H_0 and supportive of H_a as $z = 2.20$ is a value of the test statistic that is greater than or equal to $z = 2.20$. Therefore, the p-value is the probability, computed assuming that H_0: $\mu = 25$ is true, of observing a value of the test statistic that is greater than or equal to $z = 2.20$. As illustrated in Figure 7.2(b), this p-value is the area under the standard normal curve to the right of $z = 2.20$ and equals $1 - .9861 = .0139$ (see Table A.4).

FIGURE 7.2   The p-Value for Testing H_0: $\mu = 25$ versus H_a: $\mu > 25$

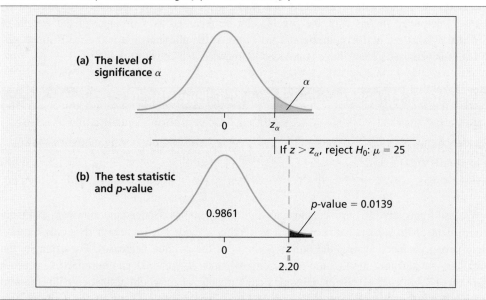

The p-value of .0139 says that, if H_0: $\mu = 25$ is true, then only 139 in 10,000 of all possible test statistic values are at least as large, or contradictory to H_0, as the value $z = 2.20$. That is, if we are to believe that H_0 is true, we must believe that we have observed a test statistic value that can be described as having a 139 in 10,000 chance. Because it is difficult to believe that we have observed a 139 in 10,000 chance, we intuitively have evidence that H_0: $\mu = 25$ is false and H_a: $\mu > 25$ is true. Is this evidence strong enough to reject H_0: $\mu = 25$ and run the trash bag commercial? As discussed in Step 5, this depends on the level of significance α used by the television network.

Step 5: Reject H_0 if the p-value is less than α. Interpret the statistical results. Consider the two normal curves in Figures 7.2(a) and (b). These normal curves show that if the p-value of .0139 is less than a particular level of significance α, the test statistic value $z = 2.20$ is greater than the critical value z_α, so we can reject H_0: $\mu = 25$ at level of significance α. For example, recall that the television network has set α equal to .05. Then, because the p-value of .0139 is less than the α of .05, we would reject H_0: $\mu = 25$ at level of significance .05 and run the trash bag commercial on the network.

Comparing the critical value and p-value methods   So far we have seen that we can reject H_0: $\mu = 25$ in favour of H_a: $\mu > 25$ at level of significance α if the test statistic z is greater than the critical value z_α, or equivalently, if the p-value is less than α. Because different television networks sometimes have different policies for evaluating an advertising claim, different television networks sometimes use different values of α when evaluating the same advertising claim. For example, whereas the network of the previous example used an α value of .05 to evaluate the trash bag claim, three other networks might use three different α values—say, .04, .025, and .01—to evaluate this claim. If we use the critical value method to test H_0: $\mu = 25$ versus H_a: $\mu > 25$ at each of these α values, we would have to look up a different critical value z_α for each different α value. On the other hand, the p-value of .0139 immediately tells us whether we can reject H_0 at each different α value. Specifically, because the p-value of .0139 is less than each of the α values .05, .04, and .025, we would reject H_0 and run the trash bag commercial on the networks using these α values. However, because the p-value of .0139 is greater than the α value .01, we would not reject H_0 and so would not run the trash bag commercial on the network using this α value.

The above discussion illustrates that, if there are different decision makers who want to test a particular null hypothesis by using different α values, the most efficient way to test the hypothesis is to use the p-value method. In addition, as originally defined, the p-value is a probability that measures the likelihood of the sample results if the null hypothesis H_0 is true. The smaller the p-value is, the less likely are the sample results if the null hypothesis H_0 is true. Therefore, the stronger the evidence is that H_0 is false and that the alternative hypothesis H_a is true. Interpreted in this way, the p-value can be regarded as a measure of the weight of evidence against the null hypothesis and in favour of the alternative hypothesis. Through statistical practice, statisticians have concluded (somewhat subjectively) that:

Interpreting the Weight of Evidence against the Null Hypothesis

If the p-value for testing H_0 is less than

- .10, we have **some evidence** that H_0 is false.

- .05, we have **strong evidence** that H_0 is false.

- .01, we have **very strong evidence** that H_0 is false.

- .001, we have **extremely strong evidence** that H_0 is false.

We will frequently use these conclusions in future examples. Understand, however, that there are really no sharp borders between different weights of evidence. Rather, there is only increasingly strong evidence against the null hypothesis as the p-value decreases. For example, the trash bag manufacturer, in addition to deciding whether H_0: $\mu = 25$ can be rejected in favour of H_a: $\mu > 25$ at each television network's chosen value of α, would almost certainly want to know how much evidence there is that its new trash bag is stronger than its former trash bag.

The p-value for testing H_0: $\mu = 25$ is .0139, which is less than .05 but not quite less than .01. Therefore, we have strong evidence, and almost—but not quite—very strong evidence, that H_0: $\mu = 25$ is false and H_a: $\mu > 25$ is true. That is, we have strong evidence that the mean breaking strength of the new trash bag exceeds 25 kilograms.

Note also that, on its own, the p-value does not provide us with any information about the magnitude of the effect. A smaller p-value *suggests* that there is likely to be a larger difference between our sample mean and our null hypothesis mean, but it is also influenced by the size of the standard error, which means that parameters with smaller standard deviations will result in statistical tests with smaller p-values. It also means that, since the standard error becomes smaller as the sample size becomes larger, larger sample sizes will result in statistical tests with smaller p-values. For this reason, we will need to consider effect size—a topic that will be introduced later in this chapter.

In the real world, where statistical analysis is almost invariably done using computer programs, the vast majority of statistical decisions are made on the basis of p-values. This is probably due to the fact that p-values can be computed directly from sample statistics, using calculus, and so they are readily available in the output produced by these programs. When statistical software is not readily available (but statistical tables are), you can rely on critical value rules to give accurate information. So, throughout this book, we will continue to present both the critical value and the p-value approaches to hypothesis testing.

ROADBLOCK

Don't confuse *p*-values with alpha

Remember that we are comparing p-values with alpha—we are not computing exact values of alpha when we look up the area under the curve that is associated with a particular z. This is a frequent error committed by students and scientists alike, as we tend to lower our "comparison alpha" in tandem with our demonstration of smaller p-values. For example, in the trash bag example, we demonstrated that our sample mean is associated with a p-value of .0139, so it is tempting to say that this p-value is less than an alpha of .0140.

Although this is technically true, it obscures the purpose of the p-value in this context, which is to be used in a comparison that results in a rejection or a non-rejection of the null hypothesis. From this standpoint, we can never demonstrate that a null hypothesis is "more rejected" or "less rejected"—it is just "rejected" or "not rejected." Furthermore, if you look at the ordering of the steps in the five-step hypothesis testing procedure, you will note that the comparison alpha is set in Step 2—before we actually calculate the test statistic. To set one's alpha after the data have been analyzed opens the door for criticisms about experimenter bias (i.e., setting the error criterion to generate the most favourable results). For information about the magnitude of the effect, we must calculate an effect size.

Testing a "less than" alternative hypothesis We next consider the payment time case and testing a "less than" alternative hypothesis. Recall that the management consulting firm has gathered a sample of 65 invoices, and wants to test to see if the new billing system has reduced the bill payment time (formerly 39 days) by more than 50 percent.

Step 1: State the null hypothesis H_0 and the alternative hypothesis H_a. To study whether the new electronic billing system reduces the mean bill payment time by more than 50 percent, the management consulting firm will test H_0: $\mu \geq 19.5$ versus H_a: $\mu < 19.5$.

Step 2: Specify the level of significance α. The management consulting firm wants to be very sure that it truthfully describes the benefits of the new system both to the company in which it has been installed and to other companies that are considering installing such a system. Therefore, the firm will require very strong evidence to conclude that μ is less than 19.5, which implies that it will test H_0: $\mu \geq 19.5$ versus H_a: $\mu < 19.5$ by setting α equal to .01.

Step 3: Select the test statistic. In order to test H_0: $\mu \geq 19.5$ versus H_a: $\mu < 19.5$, we will test the modified null hypothesis H_0: $\mu = 19.5$ versus H_a: $\mu < 19.5$. To do this, we will randomly select a sample of $n = 65$ invoices paid using the billing system and calculate the mean

$\bar{x}$ of the payment times of these invoices. Since the sample size is large, the central limit theorem applies, and we will utilize the test statistic

$$z = \frac{\bar{x} - 19.5}{\sigma / \sqrt{n}}$$

A value of the test statistic z that is less than zero results when $\bar{x}$ is less than 19.5. This provides evidence to support rejecting H_0 in favour of H_a because the point estimate $\bar{x}$ indicates that μ might be less than 19.5.

Step 4: Determine a critical value rule for deciding whether to reject H_0. To decide how much less than zero the test statistic must be to reject H_0 in favour of H_a by setting the probability of a Type I error equal to α, we do the following:

- Place the probability of a Type I error, α, in the left-hand tail of the standard normal curve and use the normal table to find the critical value $-z_\alpha$. Here $-z_\alpha$ is the negative of the normal point z_α. That is, $-z_\alpha$ is the point on the horizontal axis under the standard normal curve that gives a left-hand tail area equal to α.

- **Reject H_0: $\mu = 19.5$ in favour of H_a: $\mu < 19.5$ if and only if the test statistic z is less than the critical value $-z_\alpha$.** Because α equals .01, the critical value $-z_\alpha$ is $-z_{.01} = -2.33$ (see Figure. 7.3[a]).

Step 4: Collect the sample data, compute the value of the test statistic, and decide whether to reject H_0. Interpret the statistical results. When the sample of $n = 65$ invoices is randomly selected, the mean of the payment times of these invoices is calculated to be $\bar{x} = 18.1077$ days. Assuming that the population standard deviation σ of payment times for the new electronic billing system is 4.2 days, the value of the test statistic is

$$z = \frac{\bar{x} - 19.5}{\sigma / \sqrt{n}} = \frac{18.1077 - 19.5}{4.2 / \sqrt{65}} = -2.67$$

Because $z = -2.67$ is less than the critical value $-z_{.01} = -2.33$, we can reject H_0: $\mu = 19.5$ in favour of H_a: $\mu < 19.5$ by setting α equal to .01. Therefore, we conclude (at an α of .01) that the mean payment time for the new electronic billing system is less than 19.5 days. This, along with the fact that the sample mean $\bar{x} = 18.1077$ is slightly less than 19.5, implies that it is reasonable for the management consulting firm to conclude that the new electronic billing system has reduced the mean payment time by more than 50 percent (a substantial improvement over the old system).

A p-value for testing a "less than" alternative hypothesis To test H_0: $\mu = 19.5$ versus H_a: $\mu < 19.5$ in the payment time case by using a p-value, we use the following Steps 4 and 5:

Step 4: Collect the sample data, compute the value of the test statistic, and compute the p-value. In the payment time case, the value of the test statistic computed from the sample data is $z = -2.67$. Because we are testing H_0: $\mu = 19.5$ versus the *less than* alternative hypothesis H_a: $\mu < 19.5$, a value of the test statistic that is at least as contradictory to H_0 and supportive of H_a as $z = -2.67$ is a value of the test statistic that is *less than or equal to $z = -2.67$*. Therefore, the p-value is the probability, computed assuming that H_0: $\mu = 19.5$ is true, of observing a value of the test statistic that is less than or equal to $z = -2.67$. As illustrated in Figure 7.3(b), this p-value is the area under the standard normal curve to the left of $z = -2.67$ and equals .0038 (see Table A.4). The p-value of .0038 says that, if H_0: $\mu = 19.5$ is true, then only 38 in 10,000 of all possible test statistic values are at least as negative, or contradictory to H_0, as the value $z = -2.67$. That is, if we are to believe that H_0 is true, we must believe that we have observed a test statistic value that can be described as having a 38 in 10,000 chance.

Step 5: Reject H_0 if the p-value is less than α. Interpret the statistical results. The management consulting firm has set α equal to .01. The p-value of .0038 is less than the α of .01. Therefore, we can reject H_0 by setting α equal to .01. Moreover, because the p-value of .0038 is between .01 and .001, we have very strong evidence, but not extremely strong evidence, that H_0: $\mu = 19.5$

FIGURE **7.3** Testing H_0: $\mu = 19.5$ versus H_a: $\mu < 19.5$ by Using Critical Values and the p-Value

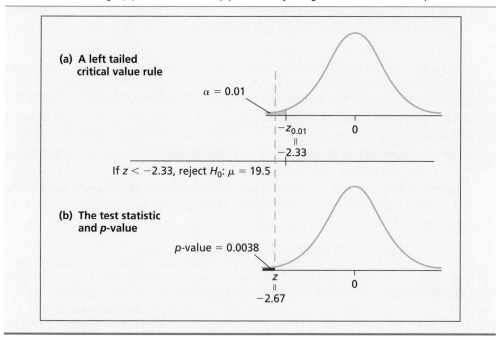

(a) **A left tailed critical value rule**

$\alpha = 0.01$

$-z_{0.01}$
$=$
-2.33

0

If $z < -2.33$, reject H_0: $\mu = 19.5$

(b) **The test statistic and p-value**

p-value $= 0.0038$

z
$=$
-2.67

0

is false and H_a: $\mu < 19.5$ is true. That is, we have very strong evidence that the new billing system has reduced the mean payment time by more than 50 percent.

Testing a "not equal to" alternative hypothesis We next consider the Valentine's Day chocolate example and testing a "not equal to" alternative hypothesis.

Step 1: State the null hypothesis H_0 and the alternative hypothesis H_a. To assess whether this year's sales of its valentine box of assorted chocolates will be 10 percent higher than last year's, the candy company will test H_0: $\mu = 330$ versus H_a: $\mu \neq 330$. Here, μ is the mean order quantity of this year's valentine box by large retail stores.

Step 2: Specify the level of significance α. If the candy company does not reject H_0: $\mu = 330$ and H_0: $\mu = 330$ is false—a Type II error—the candy company will base its production of valentine boxes on a 10 percent projected sales increase that is not correct. Since the candy company wants to have a reasonably small probability of making this Type II error, the company will set α equal to .05. Setting α equal to .05 rather than .01 makes the probability of a Type II error smaller than it would be if α was set at .01. Therefore, if the candy company ends up not rejecting H_0: $\mu = 330$ and therefore decides to base its production of valentine boxes on the 10 percent projected sales increase, the company can be intuitively confident that it has made the right decision.

Step 3: Select the test statistic. The candy company will randomly select $n = 100$ large retail stores and will make an early mailing to these stores promoting this year's valentine box of assorted chocolates. The candy company will then ask each sampled retail store to report its anticipated order quantity of valentine boxes and will calculate the mean $\bar{x}$ of the reported order quantities. Since the sample size is large, the central limit theorem applies, and we will utilize the test statistic

$$z = \frac{\bar{x} - 330}{\sigma / \sqrt{n}}$$

A value of the test statistic that is greater than 0 results when $\bar{x}$ is greater than 330. This provides evidence to support rejecting H_0 in favour of H_a because the point estimate $\bar{x}$ indicates that μ might be greater than 330. Similarly, a value of the test statistic that is less than 0 results when $\bar{x}$ is less than 330. This also provides evidence to support rejecting H_0 in favour of H_a because the point estimate $\bar{x}$ indicates that μ might be less than 330.

Step 4: Determine a critical value rule for deciding whether to reject H_0. To decide how different from zero (positive or negative) the test statistic must be in order to reject H_0 in favour of H_a by setting the probability of a Type I error equal to α, we do the following:

- Divide the probability of a Type I error, α, into two equal parts and place the area $\alpha/2$ in the right-hand tail of the standard normal curve and the area $\alpha/2$ in the left-hand tail of the standard normal curve. Then use the normal table to find the rejection points $z_{\alpha/2}$ and $-z_{\alpha/2}$. Here $z_{\alpha/2}$ is the point on the horizontal axis under the standard normal curve that gives a right-hand tail area equal to $\alpha/2$, and $-z_{\alpha/2}$ is the point giving a left-hand tail area equal to $\alpha/2$.

- **Reject H_0: $\mu = 330$ in favour of H_a: $\mu \neq 330$ if and only if the test statistic z is greater than the critical value $z_{\alpha/2}$ or less than the critical value $-z_{\alpha/2}$.** Note that this is equivalent to saying that we should **reject H_0 if and only if the absolute value of the test statistic, $|z|$, is greater than the critical value $z_{\alpha/2}$.** Because α equals .05, the critical values are (see Figure 7.4[a])

$$z_{\alpha/2} = z_{.05/2} = z_{.025} = 1.96 \quad \text{and} \quad -z_{\alpha/2} = -z_{.025} = -1.96$$

Step 5: Collect the sample data, compute the value of the test statistic, and decide whether to reject H_0. Interpret the statistical results. When the sample of $n = 100$ large retail stores is randomly selected, the mean of their reported order quantities is calculated to be $\bar{x} = 326$ boxes. Assuming that the population standard deviation σ of large retail store order quantities for this year's valentine box will be 40 boxes (the same as it was for previous years' valentine boxes), the value of the test statistic is

$$z = \frac{\bar{x} - 330}{\sigma/\sqrt{n}} = \frac{326 - 330}{40/\sqrt{100}} = -1$$

Because $z = -1$ is between the critical values $-z_{.025} = -1.96$ and $z_{.025} = 1.96$ (or, equivalently, because $|z| = 1$ is less than $z_{.025} = 1.96$), we cannot reject H_0: $\mu = 330$ in favour of H_a: $\mu \neq 330$ by setting α equal to .05. Therefore, we cannot conclude (at an α of .05) that the mean order quantity of this year's valentine box by large retail stores will differ from 330 boxes. It follows that the candy company will base its production of valentine boxes on the 10 percent projected sales increase.

FIGURE **7.4**   Testing H_0: $\mu = 330$ versus H_a: $\mu \neq 330$ by Using Critical Values and the p-Value

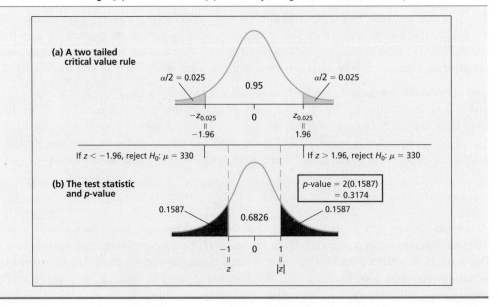

A p-value for testing a "not equal to" alternative hypothesis To test H_0: $\mu = 330$ versus H_a: $\mu \neq 330$ in the Valentine's Day chocolate example by using a p-value, we use the following Steps 4 and 5:

Step 4: Collect the sample data, compute the value of the test statistic, and compute the p-value. In the Valentine's Day chocolate example, the value of the test statistic computed from the sample data is $z = -1$. Because the alternative hypothesis H_a: $\mu \neq 330$ says that μ might be greater or less than 330, both positive and negative test statistic values contradict H_0: $\mu = 330$ and support H_a: $\mu \neq 330$. It follows that a value of the test statistic that is at least as contradictory to H_0 and supportive of H_a as $z = -1$ is a value of the test statistic that is greater than or equal to 1 or less than or equal to -1. Therefore, the p-value is the probability, computed assuming that H_0: $\mu = 330$ is true, of observing a value of the test statistic that is greater than or equal to 1 or less than or equal to -1. As illustrated in Figure 7.4(b), this p-value equals the area under the standard normal curve to the right of 1, plus the area under this curve to the left of -1. But, by the symmetry of the normal curve, the sum of these two areas, and therefore the p-value, is twice the area under the standard normal curve to the right of $|z| = 1$, the absolute value of the test statistic. Because the area under the standard normal curve to the right of $|z| = 1$ is $1 - .8413 = .1587$ (see Table A.4,), the p-value is $2(.1587) = .3174$. The p-value of .3174 says that, if H_0: $\mu = 330$ is true, then 31.74 percent of all possible test statistic values are at least as contradictory to H_0 as $z = -1$. That is, if we are to believe that H_0 is true, we must believe that we have observed a test statistic value that can be described as having a 31.74 percent chance.

Step 5: Reject H_0 if the p-value is less than α. Interpret the statistical results. The candy company has set α equal to .05. The p-value of .3174 is greater than the α of .05. Therefore, we cannot reject H_0 by setting α equal to .05. Moreover, because the p-value is larger than .10, we have little evidence that H_0: $\mu = 330$ is false and H_a: $\mu \neq 330$ is true. That is, we have little evidence that the increase in the mean order quantity of large retail stores will differ from 10 percent.

ROADBLOCK

It is helpful to think about the sampling distribution as having "rejection regions"
Regardless of whether you are comparing the obtained value of your statistic (i.e., derived from your sample mean) to a critical value or comparing a p-value to a target alpha, you are making a decision about whether you have sufficient evidence (based on the level of error that you consider acceptable) to reject the null hypothesis. It is helpful, therefore, to consider the area defined by your critical value and/or your alpha as a "rejection region." When a statistic or p-value falls within this area, we know that we have sufficient evidence to reject the null hypothesis. For example, consider Figure 7.3—the area defined by the critical value of z associated with an alpha of .01 is bounded by $z = -2.33$. This means that the rejection region includes all of the area below $z = -2.33$. Similarly, the rejection region could be described as having an area of .01. In this way, we know that, because our obtained value of z (-2.67) falls in the rejection region (see Figure 7.3), the appropriate statistical decision is to reject the null hypothesis.

   The use of "rejection regions" becomes even more intuitively useful when considering "not-equal-to" alternative hypotheses. As illustrated in Figure 7.4, we now have two rejection regions—one above the mean, and one below the mean. If the obtained value falls in either region, we conclude that there is sufficient evidence to reject the null hypothesis. Due to the fact that rejection regions always fall in the "tails" of the distribution, statisticians frequently call "greater than" and "less than" alternative hypothesis tests *one-tailed tests*, and they call the "not equal to" alternative hypothesis test a *two-tailed test*. Alternatively, one-tailed tests can be referred to as *upper tailed tests* (when referring to a "greater than" alternative hypothesis test), or *lower tailed tests* (when referring to a "less than" alternative hypothesis test).

FIGURE 7.5   A Summary Box for Testing a Hypothesis about a Population Mean and the Five-Step Hypothesis Testing Procedure

---

Testing a Hypothesis about a Population Mean When σ Is Known

Define the test statistic

$$z = \frac{\bar{x} - \mu_0}{\sigma/\sqrt{n}}$$

and assume that the population sampled is normally distributed or that the sample size n is large. We can test $H_0: \mu = \mu_0$ versus a particular alternative hypothesis at level of significance α by using the appropriate critical value rule, or equivalently, the corresponding p-value.

Alternative Hypothesis	Critical Value Rule: Reject H_0 if	p-Value (Reject H_0 if p-Value $< \alpha$)
$H_a: \mu > \mu_0$	$z > z_\alpha$	The area under the standard normal curve to the right of z
$H_a: \mu < \mu_0$	$z < -z_\alpha$	The area under the standard normal curve to the left of z
$H_a: \mu \neq \mu_0$	$\|z\| > z_{\alpha/2}$—that is, $z > z_{\alpha/2}$ or $z < -z_{\alpha/2}$	Twice the area under the standard normal curve to the right of $\|z\|$

The Five Steps of Hypothesis Testing

1   State the null hypothesis H_0 and the alternative hypothesis H_a.
2   Specify the level of significance α.
3   Select the test statistic.

Using a critical value rule:

4   Use the summary box to find the critical value rule corresponding to the alternative hypothesis. Use the specified value of α to find the critical value given in the critical value rule.
5   Collect the sample data, compute the value of the test statistic, and decide whether to reject H_0. Interpret the statistical results.

Using a p-value:

4   Collect the sample data, compute the value of the test statistic, and compute the p-value. (Use the summary box to find the p-value corresponding to the alternative hypothesis.)
5   Reject H_0 at level of significance α if the p-value is less than α. Interpret the statistical results.

A general procedure for testing a hypothesis about a population mean In the trash bag case, we tested $H_0: \mu \leq 25$ versus $H_a: \mu > 25$ by testing $H_0: \mu = 25$ versus $H_a: \mu > 25$. In the payment time case, we tested $H_0: \mu \geq 19.5$ versus $H_a: \mu < 19.5$ by testing $H_0: \mu = 19.5$ versus $H_a: \mu < 19.5$. In general, the usual procedure for testing a "less than or equal to" null hypothesis or a "greater than or equal to" null hypothesis is to change the null hypothesis to an equality. We then test the "equal to" null hypothesis versus the alternative hypothesis. Furthermore, the critical value and p-value procedures for testing a null hypothesis versus an alternative hypothesis depend on whether the alternative hypothesis is a "greater than," a "less than," or a "not equal to" alternative hypothesis. The summary box in Figure 7.5 gives the appropriate procedures. Specifically, letting μ_0 be a particular number, the summary box shows how to test $H_0: \mu = \mu_0$ versus $H_a: \mu < \mu_0$, $H_a: \mu > \mu_0$, or $H_a: \mu \neq \mu_0$. Below the summary box, the five-step hypothesis testing procedure is presented in a way that emphasizes how to determine an appropriate critical value rule and an appropriate p-value by using the summary box.

Exercises for Section 7.2

CONCEPTS

7.8   Explain what a critical value is, and explain how it is used to test a hypothesis.

7.9   Explain what a p-value is, and explain how it is used to test a hypothesis.

METHODS AND APPLICATIONS

7.10   Suppose that we want to test $H_0: \mu = 80$ versus $H_a: \mu > 80$, where σ is known to equal 20. Also, suppose that a sample of $n = 100$ measurements randomly selected from the population has a mean of $\bar{x} = 85$.

a.   Calculate the value of the test statistic z.
b.   By comparing z with a critical value, test H_0 versus H_a at $\alpha = .05$.
c.   Calculate the p-value for testing H_0 versus H_a.
d.   Use the p-value to test H_0 versus H_a at each of $\alpha = .10, .05, .01$, and $.001$.
e.   How much evidence is there that $H_0: \mu = 80$ is false and $H_a: \mu > 80$ is true?

7.11   Suppose that we want to test $H_0: \mu = 20$ versus $H_a: \mu > 20$, where σ is known to equal 7. Also, suppose that a sample of $n = 49$ measurements randomly selected from the population has a mean of $\bar{x} = 18$.

a. Calculate the value of the test statistic z.

b. By comparing z with a critical value, test H_0 versus H_a at $\alpha = .01$.

c. Calculate the p-value for testing H_0 versus H_a.

d. Use the p-value to test H_0 versus H_a at each of $\alpha = .10, .05, .01,$ and $.001$.

e. How much evidence is there that H_0: $\mu = 20$ is false and H_a: $\mu < 20$ is true?

7.12 Suppose that we want to test H_0: $\mu = 40$ versus H_a: $\mu \neq 40$, where σ is known to equal 18. Also, suppose that a sample of $n = 81$ measurements randomly selected from the population has a mean of $\bar{x} = 35$.

a. Calculate the value of the test statistic z.

b. By comparing z with a critical value, test H_0 versus H_a at $\alpha = .05$.

c. Calculate the p-value for testing H_0 versus H_a.

d. Use the p-value to test H_0 versus H_a at each of $\alpha = .10, .05, .01,$ and $.001$.

e. How much evidence is there that H_0: $\mu = 40$ is false and H_a: $\mu \neq 40$ is true?

7.13 **THE VIDEO GAME SATISFACTION RATING EXAMPLE**

Recall that "very satisfied" customers give the XYZ-Box video game system a rating that is at least 42. Suppose that the manufacturer of the XYZ-Box wants to use the random sample of 65 satisfaction ratings to provide evidence supporting the claim that the mean composite satisfaction rating for the XYZ-Box exceeds 42.

a. Letting μ represent the mean composite satisfaction rating for the XYZ-Box, set up the null hypothesis H_0 and the alternative hypothesis H_a needed if we want to attempt to provide evidence supporting the claim that μ exceeds 42.

b. The random sample of 65 satisfaction ratings yields a sample mean of $\bar{x} = 42.954$. Assuming that σ equals 2.64, use critical values to test H_0 versus H_a at each of $\alpha = .10, .05, .01,$ and $.001$.

c. Using the information in part (b), calculate the p-value and use it to test H_0 versus H_a at each of $\alpha = .10, .05, .01,$ and $.001$.

d. How much evidence is there that the mean composite satisfaction rating exceeds 42?

7.14 **THE CUSTOMER WAIT TIME EXAMPLE**

Recall that a bank manager has developed a new system to reduce the time that customers spend waiting for teller service during peak hours. The manager hopes the new system will reduce waiting times from the current 9 to 10 minutes to less than 6 minutes.

Suppose the manager wants to use the random sample of 100 waiting times to support the claim that the mean waiting time under the new system is shorter than six minutes.

a. Letting μ represent the mean waiting time under the new system, set up the null and alternative hypotheses needed if we want to attempt to provide evidence supporting the claim that μ is shorter than six minutes.

b. The random sample of 100 waiting times yields a sample mean of $\bar{x} = 5.46$ minutes. Assuming that $\sigma = 2.47$ minutes, use critical values to test H_0 versus H_a at each of $\alpha = .10, .05, .01,$ and $.001$.

c. Using the information in part (b), calculate the p-value and use it to test H_0 versus H_a at each of $\alpha = .10, .05, .01,$ and $.001$.

d. How much evidence is there that the new system has reduced the mean waiting time to below six minutes?

7.15 **THE WASTE WATER EXAMPLE**

Recall Atlantic Power, a large electric power utility, that has just built a modern nuclear power plant. This plant discharges waste water that is allowed to flow into the Atlantic Ocean. Environment Canada has ordered that the waste water must not be excessively warm so that thermal pollution of the marine environment near the plant can be avoided. Because of this order, the waste water is allowed to cool in specially constructed ponds and is then released into the ocean. This cooling system works properly if the mean temperature of waste water discharged is 15°C or cooler. Atlantic Power is required to monitor the temperature of the waste water. A sample of 100 temperature readings will be obtained each day, and if the sample results cast a substantial amount of doubt on the hypothesis that the cooling system is working properly (the mean temperature of waste water discharged is 15°C or cooler), then the plant must be shut down and appropriate actions must be taken to correct the problem.

a. Atlantic Power wants to set up a hypothesis test so that the power plant will be shut down when the null hypothesis is rejected. Set up the null hypothesis H_0 and the alternative hypothesis H_a that should be used.

b. Suppose that Atlantic Power decides to use a level of significance of $\alpha = .05$, and suppose a random sample of 100 temperature readings is obtained. If the sample mean of the 100 temperature readings is 15.482, test H_0 versus H_a and determine whether the power plant should be shut down and the cooling system repaired. Perform the hypothesis test by using a critical value and a p-value. Assume $\sigma = 2$.

7.16 Do part (b) of Exercise 7.15 again, with a sample mean of 15.262.

7.17 Do part (b) of Exercise 7.15 again, with a sample mean of 15.618.

7.18 **THE AUTO PARTS PRODUCTION EXAMPLE**

Recall the automobile parts supplier that produces a cylindrical engine part with an outside diameter of three centimetres. Parts with diameters that are too small or too large do not meet customer requirements and must be rejected. Lately, the company has experienced problems meeting customer requirements. The technical staff feels that the mean diameter produced by the machine is off target. In order to verify this, a special study will randomly sample 100 parts produced by the machine. The 100 sampled parts will be measured, and if the results obtained cast a substantial amount of doubt on the hypothesis that the mean diameter equals the target value of three centimetres, the company will assign a problem-solving team to intensively search for the causes of the problem.

a. The parts supplier wants to set up a hypothesis test so that the problem-solving team will be assigned when the null hypothesis is rejected. Set up the null and alternative hypotheses for this situation.

b. A sample of 40 parts yields a sample mean diameter of $\bar{x} = 3.006$ centimetres. Assuming σ equals .016, use a critical value and a p-value to test H_0 versus H_a by setting α equal to .05. Should the problem-solving team be assigned?

7.19 THE BOTTLE FILLING EXAMPLE

Recall the new bottling process that was installed by the Black Fly Beverage Company, intended to fill 500-mL bottles of its popular margarita beverage. Both overfilling and underfilling bottles are undesirable: Underfilling leads to customer complaints and overfilling costs the company a considerable smount of money. To verify that the filler is set up correctly, the company wants to see whether the mean bottle fill, μ, is close to the target fill of 500 mL. To this end, a random sample of 36 filled bottles is selected from the output of a test filler run. If the sample results cast a substantial amount of doubt on the hypothesis that the mean bottle fill is the desired 500 mL, then the filler's initial setup will be readjusted.

a. The bottling company wants to set up a hypothesis test so that the filler will be readjusted if the null hypothesis is rejected. Set up the null and alternative hypotheses for this hypothesis test.

b. Suppose that the company decides to use a level of significance of $\alpha = .01$, and suppose that a random sample of 36 bottle fills is obtained from a test run of the filler. For each of the following four sample means—501.56, 498.75, 500.63, and 498.125—determine whether the filler's initial setup should be readjusted. In each case, use a critical value, a p-value, and a confidence interval. Assume that σ equals 3.12 mL.

7.20 THE DISC BRAKE SYSTEM EXAMPLE

National Motors has equipped the ZX-900 with a new disc brake system. We define μ to be the mean stopping distance (from a speed of 55 km/h) of all ZX-900s. National Motors would like to claim that the ZX-900 achieves a shorter mean stopping distance than the 20 metres claimed by a competitor.

a. Set up the null and alternative hypotheses needed to support National Motors' claim.

b A television network will allow National Motors to advertise its claim if the appropriate null hypothesis can be rejected at $\alpha = .05$. If a random sample of 81 ZX-900s have a mean stopping distance of 19.27 metres, will National Motors be allowed to advertise the claim? Assume that $\sigma = 2$ m and justify your answer using both a critical value and a p-value.

7.3 SINGLE-SAMPLE TESTS OF A PROPORTION

LO4

In this section, we study a large sample hypothesis test about a population proportion (that is, about the fraction of population elements that possesses some characteristic). We begin with Example 7.4.

Example 7.4 The Cheese Spread Example

Recall that the soft cheese spread producer has decided that replacing the current spout with the new spout is profitable only if p, the true proportion of all current purchasers who would stop buying the cheese spread if the new spout was used, is less than .10. The producer feels that it is unwise to change the spout unless there is very strong evidence that p is less than .10. Therefore, the spout will be changed if and only if the null hypothesis H_0: $p = .10$ can be rejected in favour of the alternative hypothesis H_a: $p < .10$ at the .01 level of significance.

To see how to test this kind of hypothesis, remember that when n is large, the sampling distribution of

$$\frac{\hat{p} - p}{\sqrt{\dfrac{p(1 - p)}{n}}}$$

is approximately a standard normal distribution. Let p_0 denote a specified value between 0 and 1 (its exact value will depend on the problem) and consider testing the null hypothesis H_0: $p = p_0$. We then have the following result:

A Large Sample Test about a Population Proportion

Define the test statistic

$$z = \frac{\hat{p} - p_0}{\sqrt{\dfrac{p_0(1 - p_0)}{n}}}$$

If the sample size n is large, we can test H_0: $p = p_0$ versus a particular alternative hypothesis at level of significance α by using the appropriate critical value rule, or, equivalently, the corresponding p-value.

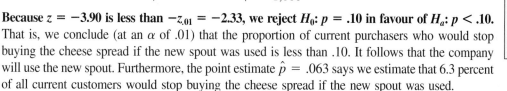

Alternative Hypothesis	Critical Value Rule: Reject H_0 if	p-Value (Reject H_0 if p-Value $< \alpha$)
$H_a: p > p_0$	$z > z_\alpha$	The area under the standard normal curve to the right of z
$H_a: p < p_0$	$z < -z_\alpha$	The area under the standard normal curve to the left of z
$H_a: p \neq p_0$	$|z| > z_{\alpha/2}$—that is, $z > z_{\alpha/2}$ or $z < -z_{\alpha/2}$	Twice the area under the standard normal curve to the right of $|z|$

Here n should be considered large if both np_0 and $n(1 - p_0)$ are at least 5.[1]

We have seen that the cheese spread producer wants to test H_0: $p = .10$ versus H_a: $p < .10$, where p is the proportion of all current purchasers who would stop buying the cheese spread if the new spout was used. The producer will use the new spout if H_0 can be rejected in favour of H_a at the .01 level of significance. To perform the hypothesis test, we will randomly select $n = 1,000$ current purchasers of the cheese spread, find the proportion $(\hat{p})$ of these purchasers who would stop buying the cheese spread if the new spout was used, and calculate the obtained value of the test statistic z. Then, since the alternative hypothesis H_a: $p < .10$ is of the form H_a: $p < p_0$, we will reject H_0: $p = .10$ if the value of z is less than $-z_\alpha = -z_{.01} = -2.33$. (Note that using this procedure is valid because $np_0 = 1,000(.10) = 100$ and $n(1 - p_0) = 1,000(1 - .10) = 900$ are both at least 5.) Suppose that when the sample is randomly selected, we find that 63 of the 1,000 current purchasers say they would stop buying the cheese spread if the new spout was used. Since $\hat{p} = 63/1,000 = .063$, the value of the test statistic is

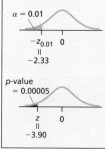

$$z = \frac{\hat{p} - p_0}{\sqrt{\dfrac{p_0(1 - p_0)}{n}}} = \frac{.063 - .10}{\sqrt{\dfrac{.10(1 - .10)}{1,000}}} = -3.90$$

Because $z = -3.90$ is less than $-z_{.01} = -2.33$, we reject H_0: $p = .10$ in favour of H_a: $p < .10$. That is, we conclude (at an α of .01) that the proportion of current purchasers who would stop buying the cheese spread if the new spout was used is less than .10. It follows that the company will use the new spout. Furthermore, the point estimate $\hat{p} = .063$ says we estimate that 6.3 percent of all current customers would stop buying the cheese spread if the new spout was used.

Although the cheese spread producer has made its decision by setting α equal to a single, prechosen value (.01), it would probably also want to know the weight of evidence against H_0 and in favour of H_a. The p-value is the area under the standard normal curve to the left of $z = -3.90$. Table A.4 tells us that this area is .00005. Because this p-value is less than .001, we have extremely strong evidence that H_a: $p < .10$ is true. That is, we have extremely strong evidence that less than 10 percent of current purchasers would stop buying the cheese spread if the new spout was used.

ROADBLOCK

The single-sample z test of proportions is not a new formula
Rather than viewing the single-sample z test of proportions as a new formula that must be memorized, note that it follows the same form as our now-familiar z test of means. The numerator consists of a difference between our *observed value* (the sample statistic) and our *test value* (the value presented in our hypothesis statements)—with the familiar means being replaced with the slightly less familiar sample and population proportions. The denominator is still the standard deviation of the sampling distribution—again, the statistic refers to the sampling distribution for proportions, rather than the sampling distribution for means. So our obtained value of z is still calculated as the ratio of a difference score to the standard error for that difference score. This is an important generalization—as you will see, this format holds true for virtually all parametric statistics.

[1]Some statisticians suggest using the more conservative rule that both np_0 and $n(1 - p_0)$ must be at least 10.

Example 7.5   Evaluating the Relative Effectiveness of Two Medications

Recent medical research has sought to develop drugs that lessen the severity and duration of viral infections. Virol, a relatively new drug, has been shown to provide relief for 70 percent of all patients suffering from viral upper respiratory infections. A major drug company is developing a competing drug called Phantol. The drug company wants to investigate whether Phantol is more effective than Virol. To do this, the drug company will test a hypothesis about the true proportion, p, of all patients whose symptoms would be relieved by Phantol.

The null hypothesis to be tested is H_0: $p = .70$ and the alternative hypothesis is H_a: $p > .70$. If H_0 can be rejected in favour of H_a at the .05 level of significance, the drug company will conclude that Phantol helps more than the 70 percent of patients helped by Virol. To perform the hypothesis test, we will randomly select $n = 300$ patients having viral upper respiratory infections, find the proportion $(\hat{p})$ of these patients whose symptoms are relieved by Phantol, and calculate the obtained value of the test statistic z. Then, since the alternative hypothesis H_a: $p > .70$ is of the form H_a: $p > p_0$, we will reject H_0: $p = .70$ if the value of z is greater than $z_\alpha = z_{.05} = 1.645$. (Note that using this procedure is valid because $np_0 = 300(.70) = 210$ and $n(1 - p_0) = 300(1 - .70) = 90$ are both at least 5.)

Suppose that when the sample is randomly selected, we find that Phantol provides relief for 231 of the 300 patients. Since $\hat{p} = 231/300 = .77$, the value of the test statistic is

$$z = \frac{\hat{p} - p_0}{\sqrt{\dfrac{p_0(1 - p_0)}{n}}} = \frac{.77 - .70}{\sqrt{\dfrac{(.70)(1 - .70)}{300}}} = 2.65$$

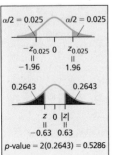

Because $z = 2.65$ is greater than $z_{.05} = 1.645$, we reject H_0: $p = .70$ in favour of H_a: $p > .70$. That is, we conclude (at an α of .05) that Phantol will provide relief for more than 70 percent of all patients suffering from viral upper respiratory infections. More specifically, the point estimate $\hat{p} = .77$ of p says that we estimate that Phantol will provide relief for 77 percent of all such patients. Comparing this estimate to the 70 percent of patients whose symptoms are relieved by Virol, we conclude that Phantol is more effective.

We can draw the same conclusion when using the p-value method of testing hypotheses. The p-value for testing H_0: $p = .70$ versus H_a: $p > .70$ is the area under the standard normal curve to the right of $z = 2.65$. This p-value is $(1.0 - .9960) = .004$ (see Table A.4), and it provides very strong evidence against H_0: $p = .70$ and in favour of H_a: $p > .70$. That is, we have very strong evidence that Phantol will provide relief for more than 70 percent of all patients suffering from viral upper respiratory infections.

Example 7.6   Evaluating the Effects of a Theft Deterrent System

A sports equipment discount store is considering installing an electronic article surveillance device and is concerned about the proportion, p, of all consumers who would never shop in the store again if the device subjected them to a false alarm. Suppose that industry data for general discount stores say that 15 percent of all consumers say that they would never shop in a store again if the device subjected them to a false alarm. To determine whether this percentage is different for the sports equipment discount store, the store will test the null hypothesis H_0: $p = .15$ versus the alternative hypothesis H_a: $p \neq .15$ at the .05 level of significance.

To perform the hypothesis test, the store will randomly select $n = 500$ consumers, find the proportion $\hat{p}$ of these consumers who say that they would never shop in the store again if the device subjected them to a false alarm, and calculate the value of the test statistic z. Then, since the alternative hypothesis H_a: $p \neq .15$ is of the form H_a: $p \neq p_0$, we will reject H_0: $p = .15$ if $|z|$, the absolute value of the test statistic z, is greater than $z_{\alpha/2} = z_{.025} = 1.96$.

(Note that using this procedure is valid because $np_0 = (500)(.15) = 75$ and $n(1 - p_0) = (500)$ $(1 - .15) = 425$ are both at least 5.)

Suppose that when the sample is randomly selected, we find that 70 out of 500 consumers say that they would never shop in the store again if the device subjected them to a false alarm. Since $\hat{p} = 70/500 = .14$, the value of the test statistic is

$$z = \frac{\hat{p} - p_0}{\sqrt{\dfrac{p_0(1 - p_0)}{n}}} = \frac{.14 - .15}{\sqrt{\dfrac{.15(1 - .15)}{500}}} = -.63$$

Because $|z| = .63$ is less than $z_{.025} = 1.96$, we cannot reject H_0: $p = .15$ in favour of H_a: $p \neq .15$. That is, we cannot conclude (at an α of .05) that the percentage of people who would never shop in the sports discount store again if the device subjected them to a false alarm differs from the general discount store percentage of 15 percent.

The p-value for testing H_0: $p = .15$ versus H_a: $p \neq .15$ is twice the area under the standard normal curve to the right of $|z| = .63$. Because the area under the standard normal curve to the right of $|z| = .63$ is $(1 - .7357) = .2643$ (see Table A.3), the p-value is $2(.2643) = .5286$. This p-value is large and provides little evidence against H_0: $p = .15$ and in favour of H_a: $p \neq .15$. That is, we have little evidence that the percentage of people who would never shop in the sports discount store again if the device subjected them to a false alarm differs from the general discount store percentage of 15 percent.

Technical note Some statistical packages or subroutines (e.g., Excel) express very small p-values in scientific notation. For example, suppose that the test statistic z for testing a "greater than" alternative hypothesis about a population proportion equalled 7.98. If you were to calculate the p-value for the hypothesis test—the area under the standard normal curve to the right of $z = 7.98$—the program might express the p-value as 7.77 E−16. To get the decimal point equivalent, the "E−16" says that we must move the decimal point 16 places to the left. Therefore, the p-value is .000000000000000777. Still other statistical packages (e.g., SPSS) will truncate p-values after a certain number of decimal places. In this way, $z = 7.98$ might have a reported p-value of .000.

The corollary to our earlier admonishment to never accept the null hypothesis is that p-values can never be 0. They can be very small (and 7.77×10^{-16} is *very* small), but given that z ranges from negative infinity to positive infinity, they can always be smaller!

Exercises for Section **7.3**

CONCEPTS

7.21 If we want to test a hypothesis to provide evidence supporting the claim that less than 5 percent of the units produced by a process are defective, formulate the null and alternative hypotheses.

7.22 What condition must be satisfied in order to appropriately use the methods of this section?

METHODS AND APPLICATIONS

7.23 Suppose we test H_0: $p = .3$ versus H_a: $p \neq .3$ and that a random sample of $n = 100$ gives a sample proportion $\hat{p} = .20$.
a. Test H_0 versus H_a at the .01 level of significance by using a critical value. What do you conclude?
b. Find the p-value for this test.

c. Use the p-value to test H_0 versus H_a by setting α equal to .10, .05, .01, and .001. What do you conclude at each value of α?

7.24 THE MARKETING ETHICS EXAMPLE

A group of researchers presented 205 research participants (all of whom were marketing researchers) with a series of scenarios involving ethical issues such as confidentiality, conflict of interest, and social acceptability. One of the scenarios presented to the participants was as follows:

> A marketing testing firm to which X Company gives most of its business recently went public. The marketing research director of X Company had been looking for a good investment and proceeded to buy some $20,000 of their stock. The firm continues as X Company's leading supplier for testing.

Of the 205 marketing researchers who participated in the ethics survey, 111 said that they disapproved of the actions taken in the scenario.

a. Let p be the proportion of all marketing researchers who disapprove of the actions taken in the conflict of interest scenario. Set up the null and alternative hypotheses needed to attempt to provide evidence supporting the claim that a majority (more than 50 percent) of all marketing researchers disapprove of the actions taken.

b. Assuming that the sample of 205 marketing researchers has been randomly selected, use critical values and the previously given sample information to test the hypotheses you set up in part (a) at the .10, .05, .01, and .001 levels of significance. How much evidence is there that a majority of all marketing researchers disapprove of the actions taken?

c. Suppose a random sample of 1,000 marketing researchers reveals that 540 of the researchers disapprove of the actions taken in the conflict of interest scenario. Use critical values to determine how much evidence there is that a majority of all marketing researchers disapprove of the actions taken.

d. Note that in parts (b) and (c) the sample proportion $\hat{p}$ is essentially the same. Explain why the results of the hypothesis tests in parts (b) and (c) differ.

7.25 Last year, television station WXYZ's share of the 11 P.M. news audience was approximately equal to, but no greater than, 25 percent. The station's management believes that the current audience share is higher than last year's 25 percent share. In an attempt to substantiate this belief, the station surveyed a random sample of 400 11 P.M. news viewers and found that 146 watched WXYZ.

a. Let p be the current proportion of all 11 P.M. news viewers who watch WXYZ. Set up the null and alternative hypotheses needed to attempt to provide evidence supporting the claim that the current audience share for WXYZ is higher than last year's 25 percent share.

b. Use critical values to test the hypotheses you set up in part (a) at the .10, .05, .01, and .001 levels of significance. How much evidence is there that the current audience share is higher than last year's 25 percent share?

c. Find the p-value for the hypothesis test in part (b). Use the p-value to carry out the test by setting α equal to .10, .05, .01, and .001. Interpret your results.

d. Do you think that the result of the station's survey has practical importance? Why or why not?

7.26 In the book *Essentials of Marketing Research,* William R. Dillon, Thomas J. Madden, and Neil H. Firtle discuss a marketing research proposal to study day-after recall for a brand of mouthwash. To quote the authors:

> The ad agency has developed a TV ad for the introduction of the mouthwash. The objective of the ad is to create awareness of the brand. The objective of this research is to evaluate the awareness generated by the ad measured by aided- and unaided-recall scores.

> A minimum of 200 respondents who claim to have watched the TV show in which the ad was aired the night before will be contacted by telephone in 20 cities.

> The study will provide information on the incidence of unaided and aided recall.

Suppose a random sample of 200 respondents showed that 46 of the people interviewed were able to recall the commercial without any prompting (unaided recall).

a. For the ad to be considered successful, the percentage of unaided recall must be above the category norm for a TV commercial for the product class. If this norm is 18 percent, set up the null and alternative hypotheses needed to attempt to provide evidence that the ad is successful.

b. Use the previously given sample information to compute the p-value for the hypothesis test you set up in part (a). Use the p-value to carry out the test by setting α equal to .10, .05, .01, and .001. How much evidence is there that the TV commercial is successful?

c. Do you think the result of the ad agency's survey has practical importance? Explain your opinion.

7.27 An airline's data indicate that 50 percent of people who begin the online process of booking a flight never complete the process and pay for the flight. To reduce this percentage, the airline is considering changing its website so that the entire booking process, including flight and seat selection and payment, can be done on two simple pages rather than the current four pages. A random sample of 300 customers who begin the booking process are provided with the new system, and 117 of them do not complete the process. Formulate the null and alternative hypotheses needed to attempt to provide evidence that the new system has reduced the noncompletion percentage. Use critical values and a p-value to perform the hypothesis test by setting α equal to .10, .05, .01, and .001.

7.28 Suppose that a national survey finds that 73 percent of restaurant employees say that work stress has a negative impact on their personal lives. A random sample of 200 employees of a large restaurant chain finds that 141 employees say that work stress has a negative impact on their personal lives. Formulate the null and alternative hypotheses needed to attempt to provide evidence that the percentage of work-stressed employees of the restaurant chain differs from the national percentage. Use critical values and a p-value to perform the hypothesis test by setting α equal to .10, .05, .01, and .001.

7.29   THE TELEVISION REPAIR EXAMPLE

The manufacturer of the ColourSmart-5000 television claims that 95 percent of its televisions last at least five years without needing a single repair. In order to test this claim, a consumer group randomly selects 400 consumers who have owned a ColourSmart-5000 television for five years. Of these 400 consumers, 316 say that their ColourSmart-5000 television did not need repair during this time, while 84 say that their ColourSmart-5000 television did need at least one repair.

a. Letting p be the proportion of ColourSmart-5000 televisions that last five years without a single repair, set up the null and alternative hypotheses that the consumer group should use to attempt to show that the manufacturer's claim is false.

b. Use critical values and the previously given sample information to test the hypotheses you set up in

part (a) by setting α equal to .10, .05, .01, and .001. How much evidence is there that the manufacturer's claim is false?

c. Do you think the results of the consumer group's survey have practical importance? Explain your opinion.

7.4 TWO-SAMPLE TESTS OF MEAN DIFFERENCES WHEN σ IS KNOWN

Up to this point in the chapter, we have evaluated the hypothesis that a value has changed from some theoretical or historical value, and we have seen that this can be useful in measuring changes over time or in determining the extent to which a required production value is seen in practice. Across all of the examples that we have evaluated, one value (the comparison value) remains unchanged. It is not difficult, however, to imagine the utility of comparing two populations that can change independently. For example, to increase consumer awareness of a product or service, it might be necessary to compare different types of advertising campaigns. Or to offer more profitable investments to its customers, an investment firm might compare the profitability of different investment portfolios. As a third example, a manufacturer might compare different production methods in order to minimize or eliminate out-of-specification product. In all of these situations, we need to use a hypothesis test to determine whether the difference between the populations is sufficiently large as to be considered statistically significant. Although the sampling distribution on which this statistical test is based is slightly different from the sampling distribution that we discussed in our earlier treatment of single-sample hypothesis tests, the hypothesis testing procedure is very similar—and as was the case previously, we can employ a *z test* when the population variances are known.

Using a *z* test to compare two independent samples when variances are known   **LO5**

A bank manager has developed a new system to reduce the time customers spend waiting to be served by tellers during peak business hours. We let μ_1 denote the mean customer waiting time during peak business hours under the current system. To estimate μ_1, the manager randomly selects $n_1 = 100$ customers and records the length of time each customer spends waiting for service. The manager finds that the sample mean waiting time for these 100 customers is $\bar{x}_1 = 8.79$ minutes. We let μ_2 denote the mean customer waiting time during peak business hours for the new system. During a trial run, the manager finds that the mean waiting time for a random sample of $n_2 = 100$ customers is $\bar{x}_2 = 5.14$ minutes.

To compare μ_1 and μ_2, the manager estimates $\mu_1 - \mu_2$, the difference between μ_1 and μ_2. Intuitively, a logical point estimate of $\mu_1 - \mu_2$ is the difference between the sample means

$$\bar{x}_1 - \bar{x}_2 = 8.79 - 5.14 = 3.65 \text{ minutes}$$

This says we estimate that the current mean waiting time is 3.65 minutes longer than the mean waiting time under the new system. That is, we estimate that the new system reduces the mean waiting time by 3.65 minutes.

To test a hypothesis about $\mu_1 - \mu_2$, we need to know the properties of the sampling distribution of $\bar{x}_1 - \bar{x}_2$. To understand this sampling distribution, consider randomly selecting a sample of n_1 measurements from a population having mean μ_1 and variance σ_1^2. Let $\bar{x}_1$ be the mean of this sample. Also consider randomly selecting a sample of n_2 measurements from another population having mean μ_2 and variance σ_2^2. Let $\bar{x}_2$ be the mean of this sample. Different samples from the first population would give different values of $\bar{x}_1$, and different samples from the second population would give different values of $\bar{x}_2$—so different pairs of samples from the two populations would give different values of $\bar{x}_1 - \bar{x}_2$. In the following boxed feature, we describe the **sampling distribution of $\bar{x}_1 - \bar{x}_2$,** which is the probability distribution of all possible values of $\bar{x}_1 - \bar{x}_2$.

The Sampling Distribution of $\bar{x}_1 - \bar{x}_2$

If the randomly selected samples are independent of each other,[2] then the population of all possible values of $\bar{x}_1 - \bar{x}_2$

1   Has a normal distribution if each sampled population has a normal distribution, or has an approximately normal distribution if the sampled

populations are not normally distributed and each of the sample sizes n_1 and n_2 is large.

2   Has mean $\mu_{\bar{x}_1 - \bar{x}_2} = \mu_1 - \mu_2$

3   Has standard deviation $\sigma_{\bar{x}_1 - \bar{x}_2} = \sqrt{\dfrac{\sigma_1^2}{n_1} + \dfrac{\sigma_2^2}{n_2}}$

FIGURE **7.6**   The Sampling Distribution of $\bar{x}_1 - \bar{x}_2$ Has Mean $\mu_1 - \mu_2$ and Standard Deviation $\sigma_{\bar{x}_1 - \bar{x}_2}$

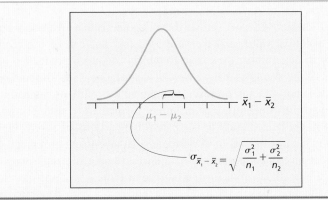

Figure 7.6 illustrates the sampling distribution of $\bar{x}_1 - \bar{x}_2$. Using this sampling distribution, we can test a hypothesis about $\mu_1 - \mu_2$. As we discussed in Section 7.2, although the *z test* requires you to assume that the true values of the population variances σ_1^2 and σ_2^2 are known, they provide a simple introduction to the basic idea of comparing two population means. In Chapter 8, we will present methods for evaluating differences between means when population variances are unknown.

Example 7.7   Customer Waiting Time Example

Consider the bank customer waiting time example again. Suppose the random sample of 100 waiting times observed under the current system gives a sample mean of 8.79, and the random sample of 100 waiting times observed during the trial run of the new system yields a sample mean of 5.14. Assume that the population variance is 4.7 for the wait times under the current system and 1.9 for wait times under the new system, and further assume that the populations are normally distributed. In the following boxed feature, we describe how we might test a hypothesis about the difference between these two populations. Here we test the null hypothesis $H_0: \mu_1 - \mu_2 = D_0$, where D_0 is a number whose value varies depending on the situation.

Often D_0 will be the number 0. In such a case, the null hypothesis $H_0: \mu_1 - \mu_2 = 0$ says there is no difference between the population means μ_1 and μ_2. For example, in the bank customer waiting time situation, the null hypothesis $H_0: \mu_1 - \mu_2 = 0$ says there is no difference between the mean customer waiting times under the current and new systems. When D_0 is 0, each alternative hypothesis in the box implies that the population means μ_1 and μ_2 differ. For instance, in the bank waiting time situation, the alternative hypothesis $H_a: \mu_1 - \mu_2 > 0$ says that the current mean customer waiting time is longer than the new mean customer waiting time. That is, this alternative hypothesis says that the new system reduces the mean customer waiting time. When D_0 is equal to a non-zero value, the alternative hypothesis is formed

---

[2]This means that there is no relationship between the measurements in one sample and the measurements in the other sample.

A z Test about the Difference between Two Population Means When σ_1 and σ_2 Are Known

Let $\bar{x}_1$ be the mean of a sample of size n_1 that has been randomly selected from a population with mean μ_1 and standard deviation σ_1, and let $\bar{x}_2$ be the mean of a sample of size n_2 that has been randomly selected from a population with mean μ_2 and standard deviation σ_2. As was the case in the single-sample case (for tests of both means and proportions), we can evaluate the statistical significance of the difference between observation and expectation by dividing it by the standard deviation for the sampling distribution of $\bar{x}_1 - \bar{x}_2$ (the standard error

for the difference between two means). The formula is, therefore,

$$z = \frac{(\bar{x}_1 - \bar{x}_2) - D_0}{\sqrt{\dfrac{\sigma_1^2}{n_1} + \dfrac{\sigma_2^2}{n_2}}}$$

We can test H_0: $\mu_1 - \mu_2 = D_0$ versus a particular alternative hypothesis at level of significance α by using the appropriate critical value rule, or, equivalently, the corresponding p-value.

Alternative Hypothesis	Critical Value Rule: Reject H_0 if	p-Value (reject H_0 if p-value $< \alpha$)
H_a: $\mu_1 - \mu_2 > D_0$	$z > z_\alpha$	The area under the standard normal curve to the right of z
H_a: $\mu_1 - \mu_2 < D_0$	$z < -z_\alpha$	The area under the standard normal curve to the left of z
H_a: $\mu_1 - \mu_2 \neq D_0$	$\|z\| > z_{\alpha/2}$—that is, $z > z_{\alpha/2}$ or $z < -z_{\alpha/2}$	Twice the area under the standard normal curve to the right of $\|z\|$

in such a way as to denote the extent to which the means differ. For example, if the bank manager had wanted to be certain that the difference between the old system and the new system was at least 3 minutes (perhaps because this difference constituted a sufficiently meaningful difference to warrant the expense of changing systems), then he might have set the alternative hypothesis to be H_a: $\mu_1 - \mu_2 > 3$, which would allow him to test the hypothesis that the current mean customer waiting time is 3 minutes longer than the new mean customer waiting time.

In an attempt to provide evidence supporting the claim that the new system reduces the mean bank customer waiting time, we will test H_0: $\mu_1 - \mu_2 = 0$ versus H_a: $\mu_1 - \mu_2 > 0$ at the .05 level of significance. To perform the hypothesis test, we will use the sample information in Example 7.7 to calculate the value of the test statistic z. Then, since H_a: $\mu_1 - \mu_2 > 0$ is of the form H_a: $\mu_1 - \mu_2 > D_0$, we will reject H_0: $\mu_1 - \mu_2 = 0$ if the value of z is greater than $z_\alpha = z_{.05} = 1.645$. Assuming that $\sigma_1^2 = 4.7$ and $\sigma_2^2 = 1.9$, the obtained value of the test statistic is

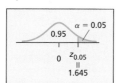

$$z = \frac{(\bar{x}_1 - \bar{x}_2) - D_0}{\sqrt{\dfrac{\sigma_1^2}{n_1} + \dfrac{\sigma_2^2}{n_2}}} = \frac{(8.79 - 5.14) - 0}{\sqrt{\dfrac{4.7}{100} + \dfrac{1.9}{100}}} = \frac{3.65}{.2569} = 14.21$$

Because $z = 14.21$ is greater than $z_{.05} = 1.645$, we reject H_0: $\mu_1 - \mu_2 = 0$ in favour of H_a: $\mu_1 - \mu_2 > 0$. We conclude (at an α of .05) that $\mu_1 - \mu_2$ is greater than 0 and, therefore, that the new system reduces the mean customer waiting time. Furthermore, the point estimate $\bar{x}_1 - \bar{x}_2 = 3.65$ says we estimate that the new system reduces mean waiting time by 3.65 minutes. The p-value for the test is the area under the standard normal curve to the right of $z = 14.21$. Because this p-value is less than .00003, it provides extremely strong evidence that H_0 is false and that H_a is true. That is, we have extremely strong evidence that $\mu_1 - \mu_2$ is greater than 0 and, therefore, that the new system reduces the mean customer waiting time.

Next, suppose that because of cost considerations, the bank manager wants to implement the new system only if it reduces mean waiting time by more than 3 minutes. In order to demonstrate that $\mu_1 - \mu_2$ is greater than 3, the manager (setting D_0 equal to 3) will attempt to reject the null hypothesis H_0: $\mu_1 - \mu_2 = 3$ in favour of the alternative hypothesis H_a: $\mu_1 - \mu_2 > 3$ at the .05 level of significance. To perform the hypothesis test, we compute

$$z = \frac{(\bar{x}_1 - \bar{x}_2) - 3}{\sqrt{\dfrac{\sigma_1^2}{n_1} + \dfrac{\sigma_2^2}{n_2}}} = \frac{(8.79 - 5.14) - 3}{\sqrt{\dfrac{4.7}{100} + \dfrac{1.9}{100}}} = \frac{.65}{.2569} = 2.53$$

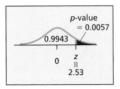

Because $z = 2.53$ is greater than $z_{.05} = 1.645$, we can reject H_0: $\mu_1 - \mu_2 = 3$ in favour of H_a: $\mu_1 - \mu_2 > 3$. The p-value for the test is the area under the standard normal curve to the right of $z = 2.53$. Table A.3 tells us that this area is $1 - .9943 = .0057$. Therefore, we have very strong evidence against H_0: $\mu_1 - \mu_2 = 3$ and in favour of H_a: $\mu_1 - \mu_2 > 3$. In other words, we have very strong evidence that the new system reduces mean waiting time by more than three minutes.

ROADBLOCK

The null hypothesis does not need to be a nil hypothesis

Example 7.7 illustrates an important point about the null hypothesis—namely that the centre of the sampling distribution does not need to be zero when looking at the difference between two groups. When D_0 equals zero, we are looking to see if there is any difference between groups—it could be termed a nil hypothesis. When D_0 is set to any other value, however, we can look for differences of particular magnitudes. This is particularly important when we are looking to demonstrate differences that are conceptually (or financially) meaningful—and determining the magnitude of group difference that is meaningful is an important part of the experimental planning process. As we have seen, increasing the n size of one's sample will reduce the size of the standard error and will increase the size of our test statistic, so we can demonstrate statistical significance for any group difference if we have a sufficiently large sample. Careful specification of our null hypothesis is a key component to engaging in meaningful statistical decision making.

Exercises for Section **7.4**

CONCEPTS

7.30 Suppose we compare two population means, μ_1 and μ_2, and consider the difference $\mu_1 - \mu_2$. In each case, is μ_1 greater than, less than, equal to, or not equal to μ_2?
  a. $\mu_1 - \mu_2 < 0$ **d.** $\mu_1 - \mu_2 > 0$
  b. $\mu_1 - \mu_2 = 0$ **e.** $\mu_1 - \mu_2 > 20$
  c. $\mu_1 - \mu_2 < -10$ **f.** $\mu_1 - \mu_2 \neq 0$

7.31 To use the formulas and tests in this section, the samples that have been randomly selected from the populations being compared must be independent of each other. In such a case, we say that we are performing an **independent samples experiment.** In your own words, explain what it means when we say that samples are independent of each other.

7.32 Describe the assumptions that must be met in order to validly use the methods discussed in Section 7.4.

METHODS AND APPLICATIONS

7.33 Suppose we randomly select two independent samples from populations having means μ_1 and μ_2. If $\bar{x}_1 = 25$, $\bar{x}_2 = 20$, $\sigma_1 = 3$, $\sigma_2 = 4$, $n_1 = 100$, and $n_2 = 100$:
  a. Test the null hypothesis H_0: $\mu_1 - \mu_2 = 0$ versus H_a: $\mu_1 - \mu_2 > 0$ by setting $\alpha = .05$. What do you conclude about how μ_1 compares to μ_2?

  b. Find the p-value for testing H_0: $\mu_1 - \mu_2 = 4$ versus H_a: $\mu_1 - \mu_2 > 4$. Use the p-value to test these hypotheses by setting α equal to .10, .05, .01, and .001.

7.34 Suppose we select two independent random samples from populations having means μ_1 and μ_2. If $\bar{x}_1 = 151$, $\bar{x}_2 = 162$, $\sigma_1 = 6$, $\sigma_2 = 8$, $n_1 = 625$, and $n_2 = 625$:
  a. Test the null hypothesis H_0: $\mu_1 - \mu_2 = -10$ versus H_a: $\mu_1 - \mu_2 < -10$ by setting $\alpha = .05$. What do you conclude?
  b. Test the null hypothesis H_0: $\mu_1 - \mu_2 = -10$ versus H_a: $\mu_1 - \mu_2 \neq -10$ by setting α equal to .01. What do you conclude?
  c. Find the p-value for testing H_0: $\mu_1 - \mu_2 = -10$ versus H_a: $\mu_1 - \mu_2 \neq -10$. Use the p-value to test these hypotheses by setting α equal to .10, .05, .01, and .001.

7.35 In an article in *Accounting and Business Research*, Carslaw and Kaplan study the effect of control (owner versus manager control) on audit delay (the length of time from a company's financial year-end to the date of the auditor's report) in public companies. Suppose a random sample of 100 public owner-controlled companies yields a mean audit delay of

$\bar{x}_1 = 82.6$ days, while a random sample of 100 public manager-controlled companies has a mean audit delay of $\bar{x}_2 = 93$. Assuming the samples are independent and that $\sigma_1 = 32.83$ and $\sigma_2 = 37.18$:

a. Consider testing the null hypothesis $H_0: \mu_1 - \mu_2 = 0$ versus $H_a: \mu_1 - \mu_2 < 0$. Interpret (in writing) the meaning (in practical terms) of each of H_0 and H_a.

b. Use a critical value to test the null hypothesis $H_0: \mu_1 - \mu_2 = 0$ versus $H_a: \mu_1 - \mu_2 < 0$ at the .05 level of significance. Based on this test, what do you conclude about how μ_1 and μ_2 compare? Write your conclusion in practical terms.

c. Find the p-value for testing $H_0: \mu_1 - \mu_2 = 0$ versus $H_a: \mu_1 - \mu_2 < 0$. Use the p-value to test H_0 versus H_a by setting α equal to .10, .05, .025, .01, and .001. How much evidence is there that μ_1 is less than μ_2?

7.36 In an article in the *Journal of Management,* Wright and Bonett study the relationship between voluntary organizational turnover and such factors as work performance, work satisfaction, and length of employment with the company. As part of the study, the authors compare work performance ratings for "stayers" (employees who stay with their organization) and "leavers" (employees who voluntarily quit their jobs). Suppose that a random sample of 175 stayers has a mean performance rating (on a 20-point scale) of $\bar{x}_1 = 12.8$, and that a random sample of 140 leavers has a mean performance rating of $\bar{x}_2 = 14.7$. Assuming these random samples are independent and that $\sigma_1 = 3.7$ and $\sigma_2 = 4.5$:

a. Set up the null and alternative hypotheses needed to try to establish that the mean performance rating for leavers is higher than the mean performance rating for stayers.

b. Use critical values to test the hypotheses you set up in part (a) by setting α equal to .10, .05, .01, and .001. How much evidence is there that leavers have a higher mean performance rating than do stayers?

7.37 The University of Western Ontario wants to demonstrate that car ownership is detrimental to academic achievement. A random sample of 100 students who do not own cars had a mean grade point average (GPA) of 2.68, while a random sample of 100 students who own cars had a mean GPA of 2.55.

a. Set up the null and alternative hypotheses that should be used to attempt to justify that the mean GPA for non-car owners is higher than the mean GPA for car owners.

b. Test the hypotheses that you set up in part (a) with $\alpha = .05$. Assume that $\sigma_1 = .7$ and $\sigma_2 = .6$ and interpret the results of your test. That is, what do your results say about whether car ownership is associated with decreased academic achievement?

7.38 **THE VEHICLE REPLACEMENT EXAMPLE**

In the *Journal of Marketing,* Bayus studied differences between "early replacement buyers" and "late replacement buyers." Suppose that a random sample of 800 early replacement buyers yields a mean number of dealers visited of $\bar{x}_1 = 3.3$, and that a random sample

of 500 late replacement buyers yields a mean number of dealers visited of $\bar{x}_2 = 4.5$. Assuming that the standard deviation for early replacement buyers is .66, and the standard deviation for late replacement buyers is .71, and assuming that the samples are independent:

a. Set up the null and alternative hypotheses needed to attempt to show that the mean number of dealers visited by late replacement buyers exceeds the mean number of dealers visited by early replacement buyers by more than 1.

b. Test the hypotheses you set up in part (a) by using critical values and by setting α equal to .10, .05, .01, and .001. How much evidence is there that H_0 should be rejected?

c. Find the p-value for testing the hypotheses you set up in part (a). Use the p-value to test these hypotheses with α equal to .10, .05, .01, and .001. How much evidence is there that H_0 should be rejected? Explain your conclusion in practical terms.

d. Do you think that the results of the hypothesis tests in parts (b) and (c) have practical significance? Explain and justify your answer.

7.39 In the book *Essentials of Marketing Research,* William R. Dillon, Thomas J. Madden, and Neil H. Firtle discuss a corporate image study designed to find out whether perceptions of technical support services vary depending on the position of the respondent in the organization. The management of a company that supplies telephone cable to telephone companies commissioned a media campaign primarily designed to (1) increase awareness of the company and (2) create favourable perceptions of the company's technical support. The campaign was targeted to purchasing managers and technical managers at independent telephone companies with greater than 10,000 trunk lines.

Perceptual ratings were measured with a nine-point agree−disagree scale. Suppose the results of a telephone survey of 175 technical managers and 125 purchasing managers reveal that the mean perception score for technical managers is 7.3 and that the mean perception score for purchasing managers is 8.2.

a. Let μ_1 be the mean perception score for all purchasing managers, and let μ_2 be the mean perception score for all technical managers. Set up the null and alternative hypotheses needed to establish whether the mean perception scores for purchasing managers and technical managers differ.

b. Assuming that the samples of 175 technical managers and 125 purchasing managers are independent random samples, test the hypotheses you set up in part (a) by using a critical value with $\alpha = .05$. Assume here that $\sigma_1 = 1.6$ and $\sigma_2 = 1.4$. What do you conclude about whether the mean perception scores for purchasing managers and technical managers differ?

c. Find the p-value for testing the hypotheses you set up in part (a) Use the p-value to test these hypotheses by setting α equal to .10, .05, .01, and .001. How much evidence is there that the mean perception scores for purchasing managers and technical managers differ?

7.5 TWO-SAMPLE TESTS OF A DIFFERENCE BETWEEN PROPORTIONS

LO6

Example 7.8 Measuring the Effects of Advertising

Suppose a new product was test marketed in the Vancouver and Toronto metropolitan areas. Equal amounts of money were spent on advertising in the two areas. However, different advertising media were used in the two areas. Advertising in the Vancouver area was done entirely on television, while advertising in the Toronto area consisted of a mixture of television, radio, newspaper, and magazine ads. Two months after the advertising campaigns commenced, surveys were conducted to estimate consumer awareness of the product. In the Vancouver area, 631 of 1,000 randomly selected consumers were aware of the product, whereas in the Toronto area 798 of 1,000 randomly selected consumers were aware of the product. We define p_1 to be the true proportion of consumers in the Vancouver area who were aware of the product and p_2 to be the true proportion of consumers in the Toronto area who were aware of the product. It follows that, since the sample proportions of consumers who were aware of the product in the Vancouver and Toronto areas were

$$\hat{p}_1 = \frac{631}{1,000} = .631$$

and

$$\hat{p}_2 = \frac{798}{1,000} = .798$$

then a point estimate of $p_1 - p_2$ was

$$\hat{p}_1 - \hat{p}_2 = .631 - .798 = -.167$$

This says we estimated that p_1 was .167 less than p_2. That is, we estimated that the percentage of consumers who were aware of the product in the Toronto area was 16.7 percentage points higher than the percentage in the Vancouver area.

To carry out a hypothesis test about $p_1 - p_2$, we need to know the properties of the sampling distribution of $\hat{p}_1 - \hat{p}_2$. In general, therefore, consider randomly selecting n_1 elements from a population, and assume that a proportion p_1 of all the elements in the population fall into a particular category. Let $\hat{p}_1$ denote the proportion of elements in the sample that fall into the category. Also, consider randomly selecting a sample of n_2 elements from a second population, and assume that a proportion p_2 of all the elements in this population fall into the particular category. Let $\hat{p}_2$ denote the proportion of elements in the second sample that fall into the category. The following boxed feature defines the **sampling distribution of $\hat{p}_1 - \hat{p}_2$**.

The Sampling Distribution of $\hat{p}_1 - \hat{p}_2$

If the randomly selected samples are independent of each other, then the population of all possible values of $\hat{p}_1 - \hat{p}_2$

1 Approximately has a normal distribution if each of the sample sizes n_1 and n_2 is large. Here n_1 and n_2 are large enough if $n_1 p_1$, $n_1(1 - p_1)$, $n_2 p_2$, and $n_2(1 - p_2)$ are all at least 5.

2 Has mean $\mu_{\hat{p}_1 - \hat{p}_2} = p_1 - p_2$

3 Has standard deviation

$$\sigma_{\hat{p}_1 - \hat{p}_2} = \sqrt{\frac{p_1(1 - p_1)}{n_1} + \frac{p_2(1 - p_2)}{n_2}}$$

Recall that 631 of 1,000 randomly selected consumers in Vancouver were aware of the new product, while 798 of 1,000 randomly selected consumers in Toronto were aware of the new product. Also recall that

$$\hat{p}_1 = \frac{631}{1,000} = .631$$

and

$$\hat{p}_2 = \frac{798}{1,000} = .798$$

Because $n_1\hat{p}_1 = 1,000(.631) = 631$, $n_1(1 - \hat{p}_1) = 1,000(1 - .631) = 369$, $n_2\hat{p}_2 = 1,000(.798) = 798$, and $n_2(1 - \hat{p}_2) = 1,000(1 - .798) = 202$ are all at least 5, both n_1 and n_2 can be considered to be large.

To test the null hypothesis H_0: $p_1 - p_2 = D_0$, we use the test statistic

$$z = \frac{(\hat{p}_1 - \hat{p}_2) - D_0}{\sigma_{\hat{p}_1 - \hat{p}_2}}$$

A commonly used special case of this hypothesis test is obtained by setting D_0 equal to 0. In this case, the null hypothesis H_0: $p_1 - p_2 = 0$ says there is no difference between the population proportions p_1 and p_2. When $D_0 = 0$, the best estimate of the common population proportion $p = p_1 = p_2$ is obtained by computing

$$\hat{p} = \frac{\text{Total number of elements in the two samples that fall into the category of interest}}{\text{Total number of elements in the two samples}}$$

Therefore, the point estimate of $\sigma_{\hat{p}_1 - \hat{p}_2}$ is

$$s_{\hat{p}_1 - \hat{p}_2} = \sqrt{\frac{\hat{p}(1 - \hat{p})}{n_1} + \frac{\hat{p}(1 - \hat{p})}{n_2}}$$

$$= \sqrt{\hat{p}(1 - \hat{p})\left(\frac{1}{n_1} + \frac{1}{n_2}\right)}$$

For the case where $D_0 \neq 0$, the point estimate of $\sigma_{\hat{p}_1 - \hat{p}_2}$ is obtained by estimating p_1 by $\hat{p}_1$ and p_2 by $\hat{p}_2$. With these facts in mind, we present the following procedure for testing H_0: $p_1 - p_2 = D_0$:

A Hypothesis Test about the Difference between Two Population Proportions

Let $\hat{p}$ be as just defined and let $\hat{p}_1$, $\hat{p}_2$, n_1, and n_2 be as defined in the boxed feature "The Sampling Distribution of $\hat{p}_1 - \hat{p}_2$." Furthermore, define the test statistic

$$z = \frac{(\hat{p}_1 - \hat{p}_2) - D_0}{\sigma_{\hat{p}_1 - \hat{p}_2}}$$

and assume that each of the sample sizes n_1 and n_2 is large. Then, if the samples are independent of each other, we can test H_0: $p_1 - p_2 = D_0$ versus a particular alternative hypothesis at level of significance α by using the appropriate critical value rule, or, equivalently, the corresponding p-value.

Alternative Hypothesis	Critical Value Rule: Reject H_0 if	p-Value (reject H_0 if p-value $< \alpha$)
H_a: $p_1 - p_2 > D_0$	$z > z_\alpha$	The area under the standard normal curve to the right of z
H_a: $p_1 - p_2 < D_0$	$z < -z_\alpha$	The area under the standard normal curve to the left of z
H_a: $p_1 - p_2 \neq D_0$	$|z| > z_{\alpha/2}$—that is, $z > z_{\alpha/2}$ or $z < -z_{\alpha/2}$	Twice the area under the standard normal curve to the right of $|z|$

[handwritten annotations: "fail to we don't reject" and "$z < z_\alpha$"]

Note:

1 If $D_0 = 0$, we estimate $\sigma_{\hat{p}_1 - \hat{p}_2}$ by

$$s_{\hat{p}_1 - \hat{p}_2} = \sqrt{\hat{p}(1 - \hat{p})\left(\frac{1}{n_1} + \frac{1}{n_2}\right)}$$

2 If $D_0 \neq 0$, we estimate $\sigma_{\hat{p}_1 - \hat{p}_2}$ by

$$s_{\hat{p}_1 - \hat{p}_2} = \sqrt{\frac{\hat{p}_1(1 - \hat{p}_1)}{n_1} + \frac{\hat{p}_2(1 - \hat{p}_2)}{n_2}}$$

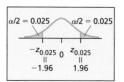

To test for the equality of the proportions of consumers aware of the product in these two metropolitan areas, we will test H_0: $p_1 - p_2 = 0$ versus H_a: $p_1 - p_2 \neq 0$ at the .05 level of significance. Because both of the Vancouver and Toronto samples are large, we will calculate the value of the test statistic z where $D_0 = 0$. Since H_a: $p_1 - p_2 \neq 0$ is of the form H_a: $p_1 - p_2 \neq D_0$, we will reject H_0: $p_1 - p_2 = 0$ if the absolute value of z is greater than $z_{\alpha/2} = z_{.05/2} = z_{.025} = 1.96$. Because 631 of 1,000 randomly selected Vancouver residents were aware of the product and 798 of 1,000 randomly selected Toronto residents were aware of the product, the estimate of $p = p_1 = p_2$ is

$$\hat{p} = \frac{631 + 798}{1,000 + 1,000} = \frac{1,429}{2,000} = .7145$$

and the value of the test statistic is

$$z = \frac{(\hat{p}_1 - \hat{p}_2) - D_0}{\sqrt{\hat{p}(1 - \hat{p})\left(\dfrac{1}{n_1} + \dfrac{1}{n_2}\right)}} = \frac{(.631 - .798) - 0}{\sqrt{(.7145)(.2855)\left(\dfrac{1}{1,000} + \dfrac{1}{1,000}\right)}} = \frac{-.167}{.0202} = -8.2673$$

Because $|z| = 8.2673$ is greater than 1.96, we can reject H_0: $p_1 - p_2 = 0$ in favour of H_a: $p_1 - p_2 \neq 0$. We conclude (at an α of .05) that the proportions of consumers who were aware of the product in Vancouver and Toronto differed. Furthermore, the point estimate $\hat{p}_1 - \hat{p}_2 = .631 - .798 = -.167$ says we estimated that the percentage of consumers who were aware of the product in Toronto was 16.7 percentage points higher than the percentage of consumers who were aware of the product in Vancouver. The p-value for this test was twice the area under the standard normal curve to the right of $|z| = 8.2673$. Since the area under the standard normal curve to the right of 3.99 is .00003, the p-value for testing H_0 was less than $2(.00003) = .00006$. It follows that we have extremely strong evidence that H_0: $p_1 - p_2 = 0$ should be rejected in favour of H_a: $p_1 - p_2 \neq 0$. That is, this small p-value provides extremely strong evidence that p_1 and p_2 differ.

Example 7.9 Drawing Inferences about Intercity Differences in the Effects of Advertising

Consider the advertising data presented in Examples 7.7 and 7.8. You have historical company data suggesting that your products tend to be more well-known in the Toronto market than in the Vancouver market. Averaging across the other products that the company advertises in these two markets, you find that the Toronto market tends to be 10 percent more familiar with your products than the Vancouver market. Bearing this in mind, evaluate the sample data that you gathered in your advertising study, and determine whether the Toronto marketing strategy is more effective than the Vancouver marketing strategy, assuming an alpha of .05.

The sample data have not, of course, changed:

$$\hat{p} = .631 \quad \text{and} \quad \hat{p} = .798$$

but the framing of the hypothesis test (and therefore the calculation of the z statistic) is slightly different. We are interested in testing to see if product awareness between these two markets is more than 10 percent different—and specifically, whether product awareness is more than 10 percent greater in the Toronto market. So we are looking at a one-sided, greater-than alternative hypothesis, with D_0 equal to .10. Since H_a: $p_1 - p_2 > 0$ is of the form H_a: $p_1 - p_2 > D_0$, we will reject H_0: $p_1 - p_2 \leq 0$ if the absolute value of z is greater than $z_\alpha = z_{.05} = 1.645$.

Our test statistic still takes the form

$$z = \frac{(\hat{p}_1 - \hat{p}_2) - D_0}{\sigma_{\hat{p}_1 - \hat{p}_2}}$$

but because D_0 is not equal to 0, we must estimate the standard error using

$$s_{\hat{p}_1 - \hat{p}_2} = \sqrt{\frac{\hat{p}_1(1 - \hat{p}_1)}{n_1} + \frac{\hat{p}_2(1 - \hat{p}_2)}{n_2}}$$

Our test statistic is therefore computed to be

$$z = \frac{(\hat{p}_1 - \hat{p}_2) - D_0}{\sqrt{\dfrac{\hat{p}_1(1 - \hat{p}_1)}{n_1} + \dfrac{\hat{p}_2(1 - \hat{p}_2)}{n_2}}} = \frac{(.798 - .631) - .1}{\sqrt{\dfrac{.798(1 - .798)}{1000} + \dfrac{.631(1 - .631)}{1000}}} = 3.38$$

Because $z = 3.38$ is larger than $z = 1.645$, we can conclude that we have evidence to suggest that the percentage of consumers that are aware of the product in the Toronto market is significantly more than 10 percent higher than the percentage of consumers that are aware of the product in the Vancouver market.

Exercises for Section **7.5**

CONCEPTS

7.40 Explain what population is described by the sampling distribution of $\hat{p}_1 - \hat{p}_2$.

7.41 What assumptions must be satisfied in order to use the methods presented in this section?

METHODS AND APPLICATIONS

In Exercises 7.42 and 7.43, we assume that we have selected two independent random samples from populations having proportions p_1 and p_2 and that $\hat{p}_1 = 800/1{,}000 = .8$ and $\hat{p}_2 = 950/1{,}000 = .95$.

7.42 Test $H_0: p_1 - p_2 = 0$ versus $H_a: p_1 - p_2 \neq 0$ by using critical values and by setting α equal to .10, .05, .01, and .001. How much evidence is there that p_1 and p_2 differ? Explain. Hint: $z_{.0005} = 3.29$.

7.43 Test $H_0: p_1 - p_2 \geq -.12$ versus $H_a: p_1 - p_2 < -.12$ by using a p-value and by setting α equal to .10, .05, .01, and .001. How much evidence is there that p_2 exceeds p_1 by more than .12? Explain.

7.44 In an article in the *Journal of Advertising*, Weinberger and Spotts compare the use of humour in television ads in the United States and in the United Kingdom. Suppose that independent random samples of television ads are taken in the two countries. A random sample of 400 television ads in the United Kingdom reveals that 142 use humour, while a random sample of 500 television ads in the United States reveals that 122 use humour.
   a. Set up the null and alternative hypotheses needed to determine whether the proportion of ads using humour in the United Kingdom differs from the proportion of ads using humour in the United States.
   b. Test the hypotheses you set up in part (a) by using critical values and by setting α equal to .10, .05, .01, and .001. How much evidence is there that the proportions of U.K. and U.S. ads using humour are different?
   c. Set up the hypotheses needed to attempt to establish that the difference between the proportions of U.K. and U.S. ads using humour is more than .05 (5 percentage points). Test these hypotheses by using a p-value and by setting α equal to .10, .05, .01, and .001. How much evidence is there that the difference between the proportions exceeds .05?

7.45 In the book *Essentials of Marketing Research*, William R. Dillon, Thomas J. Madden, and Neil H. Firtle discuss a research proposal in which a telephone company wants to determine whether the appeal of a new security system varies between homeowners and renters. Independent samples of 140 homeowners and 60 renters are randomly selected. Each respondent views a TV pilot in which a test ad for the new security system is embedded twice. Afterward, each respondent is interviewed to find out whether he or she would purchase the security system.
   Results show that 25 out of the 140 homeowners definitely would buy the security system, while 9 out of the 60 renters definitely would buy the system.
   a. Letting p_1 be the proportion of homeowners who would buy the security system, and letting p_2 be the proportion of renters who would buy the security system, set up the null and alternative hypotheses needed to determine whether the proportion of homeowners who would buy the security system differs from the proportion of renters who would buy the security system.
   b. Find the test statistic z and the p-value for testing the hypotheses of part (a). Use the p-value to test the hypotheses with α equal to .10, .05, .01, and .001. How much evidence is there that the proportions of homeowners and renters differ?

7.46 In the book *Cases in Finance*, Nunnally and Plath (1995) present a case in which the estimated percentage of uncollectable accounts varies with the age of the account. Here the age of an unpaid account is the number of days elapsed since the invoice date.
   An accountant believes that the percentage of accounts that will be uncollectable increases as the ages of the accounts increase. To test this theory, the accountant randomly selects independent samples of 500 accounts with ages between 31 and 60 days and 500 accounts with ages between 61 and 90 days from the accounts receivable ledger dated one year ago. When the sampled accounts are examined, it is found that 10 of the 500 accounts with ages between 31 and 60 days were eventually classified as uncollectable, while 27 of the 500 accounts with ages between 61 and 90 days were eventually classified as uncollectable. Let p_1 be the proportion of accounts with ages between 31 and 60 days that will be uncollectable, and let p_2 be the proportion of accounts with ages between 61 and 90 days that will be uncollectable. Determine how much evidence there is that we should reject $H_0: p_1 - p_2 = 0$ in favour of $H_a: p_1 - p_2 \neq 0$.

7.47 In July 2012, Angus Reid conducted a poll[3] that asked about the positive feelings that residents of four countries (Australia, Canada, Britain, and the United States) held toward the economy of their respective countries (see Table 7.3). The sample composition in the four countries was as follows:

Australia	$n = 1,505$
Britain	$n = 2,033$
Canada	$n = 1,003$
United States	$n = 1,005$

a. Is there a significant difference between Canada and the United States, in terms of respondent ratings of the current economic conditions? How about Canada and Britain? Canada and Australia? Consider the results of an appropriate test of statistical significance for each of these questions ($\alpha = 0.001$).

b. If we consider the first question in the table to be reflective of an individual's perception of "current reality" and the second question to be reflective of an individual's level of "optimism for the future," which country demonstrates the greatest difference

---
[3]Angus Reid Global, *Economic Optimism Higher in Australia and Canada, Compared to Britain and U.S.*, July 25, 2012.

between its ratings of current conditions, and its optimism for the future? Calculate appropriate tests of statistical significance in each country to determine the difference between the two questions.

7.48 The poll referenced in Exercise 7.47 also asked respondents what they would do if they were given $/£1,000. Poll respondents were given several options, and asked to allocate an amount for each activity. The money values associated with each economic activity are reported in Table 7.4.

a. Is there a difference between Canada and the United States in terms of debt repayment? How about Canada and Britain? Canada and Australia? Consider the results of an appropriate test of statistical significance for each of these questions.

b. One way to look at these data might be to consider the amount spent or invested (not including daily expenses) as indicative of consumer optimism, and the amount saved or spent in debt repayment as being indicative of consumer pessimism. Compare "consumer optimism" between Canada and each of the other three countries. How do these findings compare with the actual ratings of consumer optimism in Exercise 7.47?

TABLE 7.3. Economic Optimism in Australia, Britain, Canada, and the United States

	% of Respondents Selecting "Good" or "Very Good"			
	Australia	Britain	Canada	United States
How would you rate the economic conditions in your country today?	57%	12%	58%	21%

	% of Respondents Selecting "Very Optimistic" or "Moderately Optimistic"			
	Australia	Britain	Canada	United States
All things considered, are you optimistic or pessimistic about the future	69%	43%	67%	52%

TABLE 7.4 "If you were given $/£1,000 today, what would you do with it?"

	Australia	Britain	Canada	United States
Invest in individual stocks	23	42	26	26
Invest in mutual funds	20	37	32	37
Pay down debt	301	112	377	284
Save (in a bank account)	236	120	200	269
Spend on a holiday	155	187	89	51
Put toward a big purchase (like a car, or home renovations)	75	166	72	61
Spend on personal items (gifts, special treats, etc.)	81	111	68	69
Cover daily expenses (groceries, gas, etc.)	109	225	136	203

7.6 TYPE II ERROR PROBABILITIES AND SAMPLE SIZE DETERMINATION

LO7

As we have seen, we often take action (for example, advertise a claim) on the basis of having rejected the null hypothesis. In this case, we know the chances that the action has been taken erroneously because we have prespecified α, the probability of rejecting a true null hypothesis. However, sometimes we must act (for example, decide how many Valentine's Day boxes of chocolates to produce) on the basis of *not* rejecting the null hypothesis. If we must do this, it is best to know the probability of not rejecting a false null hypothesis (a Type II error). If this probability is not small enough, we might change the hypothesis testing procedure. In order to discuss this further, we must first see how to compute the probability of a Type II error.

As an example, the Office of Consumer Affairs (OCA; a division of Industry Canada) might be interested in testing claims that companies make about their products. Suppose coffee is being sold in cans that are labelled as containing three kilograms, and also suppose that the OCA wants to determine if the mean amount of coffee μ in all such cans is at least three kilograms. To do this, the OCA tests $H_0: \mu \geq 3$ (or $\mu = 3$) versus $H_a: \mu < 3$ by setting $\alpha = .05$. Suppose that a sample of 35 coffee cans yields $\bar{x} = 2.9973$. Assuming that σ is known to equal .0147, we see that because

$$z = \frac{2.9973 - 3}{.0147/\sqrt{35}} = -1.09$$

is not less than $-z_{.05} = -1.645$, we cannot reject $H_0: \mu \geq 3$ by setting $\alpha = .05$. Since we cannot reject H_0, we cannot have committed a Type I error, which is the error of rejecting a true H_0. However, we might have committed a Type II error, which is the error of not rejecting a false H_0. Therefore, before we make a final conclusion about μ, we should calculate the probability of a Type II error.

A Type II error is not rejecting $H_0: \mu \geq 3$ when H_0 is false. Because any value of μ that is less than 3 makes H_0 false, there is a different Type II error (and, therefore, a different Type II error probability) associated with each value of μ that is less than 3. In order to demonstrate how to calculate these probabilities, we will calculate the probability of not rejecting $H_0: \mu \geq 3$ when in fact μ equals 2.995. This is the probability of failing to detect an average underfill of .005 kilograms. For a fixed sample size (for example, $n = 35$ coffee can fills), the value of β, the probability of a Type II error, depends on how we set α, the probability of a Type I error. Since we have set $\alpha = .05$, we reject H_0 if

$$\frac{\bar{x} - 3}{\sigma/\sqrt{n}} < -z_{.05}$$

or, equivalently, if

$$\bar{x} < 3 - z_{.05}\frac{\sigma}{\sqrt{n}}$$

$$\bar{x} < 3 - 1.645\left(\frac{.0147}{\sqrt{35}}\right)$$

$$\bar{x} < 2.9959126$$

Therefore, we do not reject H_0 if $\bar{x} \geq 2.9959126$. It follows that β, the probability of not rejecting $H_0: \mu \geq 3$ when μ equals 2.995, is

$$\beta = P(\bar{x} \geq 2.9959126 \text{ when } \mu = 2.995)$$

$$= P\left(z \geq \frac{2.9959126 - 2.995}{.0147/\sqrt{35}}\right)$$

$$= P(z \geq .37) = 1 - .6443 = .3557$$

In other words, the probability that we will incorrectly conclude that the coffee cans are (on average) filled appropriately when they are, in fact, underfilled by .005 kg, is 0.3557 (35.57 percent). This calculation is illustrated in Figure 7.7. Similarly, it follows that β, the probability of not rejecting $H_0: \mu \geq 3$ when μ equals 2.99, is

$$\beta = P(\bar{x} \geq 2.9959126 \text{ when } \mu = 2.99)$$

$$= P\left(z \geq \frac{2.9959126 - 2.99}{.0147/\sqrt{35}}\right)$$

$$= P(z \geq 2.38) = 1 - .9913 = .0087$$

FIGURE 7.7   Calculating β When μ Equals 2.995

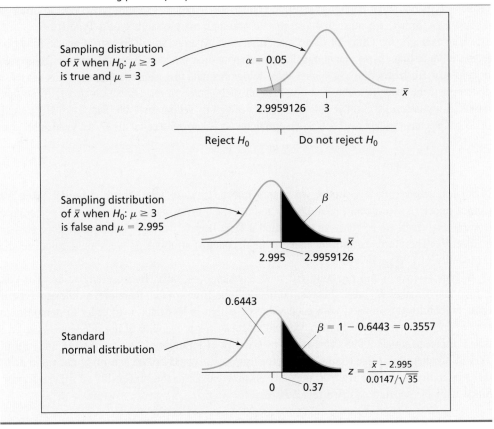

It also follows that β, the probability of not rejecting H_0: $\mu \geq 3$ when μ equals 2.985, is

$$\beta = P(\bar{x} \geq 2.9959126 \text{ when } \mu = 2.985)$$

$$= P\left(z \geq \frac{2.9959126 - 2.985}{.0147/\sqrt{35}}\right)$$

$$= P(z \geq 4.39)$$

This probability is less than .00003 (because z is greater than 3.99).

In Figure 7.8 we illustrate the values of β that we have calculated. Notice that the closer an alternative value of μ is to 3 (the value specified by H_0: $\mu = 3$), the larger is the associated value of β. Although alternative values of μ that are closer to 3 have larger associated probabilities of Type II errors, these values of μ have associated Type II errors with less serious consequences. For example, we are more likely not to reject H_0: $\mu = 3$ when $\mu = 2.995$ ($\beta = .3557$) than we are not to reject H_0: $\mu = 3$ when $\mu = 2.99$ ($\beta = .0087$). However, not rejecting H_0: $\mu = 3$ when $\mu = 2.995$, which means that we are failing to detect an average underfill of .005 kilograms, is less serious than not rejecting H_0: $\mu = 3$ when $\mu = 2.99$, which means that we are failing to detect a larger average underfill of .01 kilograms.

In order to decide whether a particular hypothesis test adequately controls the probability of a Type II error, we must determine which Type II errors are serious, and then we must decide whether the probabilities of these errors are small enough. For example, suppose that the OCA and the coffee producer agree that failing to reject H_0: $\mu = 3$ when μ equals 2.99 is a serious error, but that failing to reject H_0: $\mu = 3$ when μ equals 2.995 is not a particularly serious error. Then, since the probability of not rejecting H_0: $\mu = 3$ when μ equals 2.99 is .0087, which is quite small, we might decide that the hypothesis test adequately controls the probability of a Type II error. To understand the implication of this, recall that the sample of 35 coffee cans, which has $\bar{x} = 2.9973$, does not provide enough evidence to reject H_0: $\mu \geq 3$ by setting $\alpha = .05$.

FIGURE **7.8** How β Changes as the Alternative Value of μ Changes

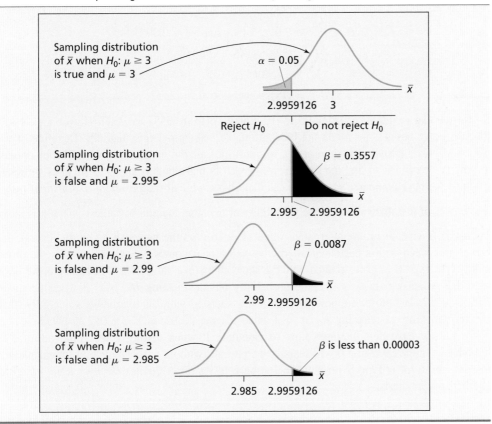

We have just shown that the probability that we have failed to detect a serious underfill is quite small (.0087), so the OCA might decide that no action should be taken against the coffee producer. Of course, this decision should also be based on the variability of the fills of the individual cans. Because $\bar{x} = 2.9973$ and $\sigma = .0147$, we estimate that 99.73 percent of all individual coffee can fills are contained in the interval $[\bar{x} \pm 3\sigma] = [2.9973 \pm 3(.0147)] = [2.9532, 3.0414]$. If the OCA believes it is reasonable to accept fills as low as (but no lower than) 2.9532 kilograms, this evidence also suggests that no action against the coffee producer is needed.

Suppose, instead, that the OCA and the coffee producer had agreed that failing to reject $H_0: \mu \geq 3$ when μ equals 2.995 is a serious mistake. The probability of this Type II error is .3557, which is large. Therefore, we might conclude that the hypothesis test is not adequately controlling the probability of a serious Type II error. In this case, we have two possible courses of action. First, we have previously said that, for a fixed sample size, the lower we set α, the higher is β, and the higher we set α, the lower is β. Therefore, if we keep the sample size fixed at $n = 35$ coffee cans, we can reduce β by increasing α. To demonstrate this, suppose we increase α to .10. In this case we reject H_0 if

$$\frac{\bar{x} - 3}{\sigma/\sqrt{n}} < -z_{.10}$$

or, equivalently, if

$$\bar{x} < 3 - z_{.10}\frac{\sigma}{\sqrt{n}}$$

$$\bar{x} < 3 - 1.282\left(\frac{.0147}{\sqrt{35}}\right)$$

$$\bar{x} < 2.9968145$$

Therefore, we do not reject H_0 if $\bar{x} > 2.9968145$. It follows that β, the probability of not rejecting $H_0: \mu \geq 3$ when μ equals 2.995, is

$$\beta = P(\bar{x} \geq 2.9968145 \text{ when } \mu = 2.995)$$

$$= P\left(z \geq \frac{2.9968145 - 2.995}{.0147/\sqrt{35}}\right)$$

$$= P(z \geq .73) = 1 - .7673 = .2327$$

So we see that increasing α from .05 to .10 reduces β from .3557 to .2327. However, β is still too large, and, besides, we might not be comfortable making α larger than .05. Therefore, if we want to decrease β and maintain α at .05, we must increase the sample size. We will soon present a formula we can use to find the sample size needed to make both α and β as small as we want.

Once we have computed β, we can calculate what we call the *power of a statistical test*.

The **power of a statistical test** is the probability of rejecting the null hypothesis when it is false.

Just as β depends on the alternative value of μ, so does the power of a test. In general, the power associated with a particular alternative value of μ equals $1 - \beta$, where β is the probability of a Type II error associated with the same alternative value of μ. For example, we have seen that, when we set $\alpha = .05$, the probability of not rejecting $H_0: \mu \geq 3$ when μ equals 2.99 is .0087. Therefore, the power of the test associated with the alternative value 2.99 (that is, the probability of rejecting $H_0: \mu \geq 3$ when μ equals 2.99) is $1 - .0087 = .9913$.

So far we have demonstrated how to calculate β when testing a *less than* alternative hypothesis. In the following boxed feature, we present (without proof) a method for calculating the probability of a Type II error when testing a *less than*, a *greater than*, or a *not equal to* alternative hypothesis.

Calculating the Probability of a Type II Error

Assume that the sampled population is normally distributed, or that a large sample will be taken. Consider testing $H_0: \mu = \mu_0$ versus one of $H_a: \mu > \mu_0$, $H_a: \mu < \mu_0$, or $H_a: \mu \neq \mu_0$. Then, if we set the probability of a Type I error equal to α and randomly select a sample of size n, the probability, β, of a Type II error corresponding to the alternative value μ_a of μ is (exactly or approximately) equal to the area under the standard normal curve to the left of

$$z^* - \frac{|\mu_0 - \mu_a|}{\sigma/\sqrt{n}}$$

Here z^* equals z_α if the alternative hypothesis is one-sided ($\mu > \mu_0$ or $\mu < \mu_0$), in which case the method for calculating β is exact. Furthermore, z^* equals $z_{\alpha/2}$ if the alternative hypothesis is two-sided ($\mu \neq \mu_0$), in which case the method for calculating β is approximate.

Example 7.10 Drawing Inferences about Demand for a Seasonal Box of Chocolates

Recall from Example 7.3 that we were interested in determining whether order quantities for a particular box of candy would be equal to 330. We did this by testing $H_0: \mu = 330$ versus $H_a: \mu \neq 330$, and setting $\alpha = .05$. We have seen that the mean of the reported order quantities of a random sample of $n = 100$ retail stores is $\bar{x} = 326$. Assuming that σ equals 40, it follows that because

$$z = \frac{326 - 330}{40/\sqrt{100}} = -1$$

is between $-z_{.025} = -1.96$ and $z_{.025} = 1.96$, we cannot reject $H_0: \mu = 330$ by setting $\alpha = .05$. Since we cannot reject H_0, we might have committed a Type II error. Suppose that the candy company decides that failing to reject H_0: $\mu = 330$ when μ differs from 330 by as many as 15 valentine boxes (that is, when μ is 315 or 345) is a serious Type II error. Because we have set α equal to .05, β for the alternative value $\mu_a = 315$ (that is, the probability of not rejecting H_0: $\mu = 330$ when μ equals 315) is the area under the standard normal curve to the left of

$$z^* - \frac{|\mu_0 - \mu_a|}{\sigma/\sqrt{n}} = z_{.025} - \frac{|\mu_0 - \mu_a|}{\sigma/\sqrt{n}}$$

$$= 1.96 - \frac{|330 - 315|}{40/\sqrt{100}}$$

$$= -1.79$$

Here $z^* = z_{\alpha/2} = z_{.05/2} = z_{.025}$ since the alternative hypothesis ($\mu \neq 330$) is two-sided. The area under the standard normal curve to the left of -1.79 is $1 - .9633 = .0377$. Therefore, β for the alternative value $\mu_a = 315$ is .0377. Similarly, it can be verified that β for the alternative value $\mu_a = 345$ is .0377. It follows, because we cannot reject H_0: $\mu = 330$ by setting $\alpha = .05$, and because we have just shown that there is a reasonably small (.0377) probability that we have failed to detect a serious (that is, a 15 valentine box) deviation of μ from 330, that it is reasonable for the candy company to base this year's production of valentine boxes on the projected mean order quantity of 330 boxes per large retail store.

In the following boxed feature, we present (without proof) a formula that tells us the sample size needed to make both the probability of a Type I error and the probability of a Type II error as small as we want.

Calculating the Sample Size Needed to Achieve Specified Values of α and β

Assume that the sampled population is normally distributed, or that a large sample will be taken. Consider testing H_0: $\mu = \mu_0$ versus one of H_a: $\mu > \mu_0$, H_a: $\mu < \mu_0$, or H_a: $\mu \neq \mu_0$. Then, in order to make the probability of a Type I error equal to α and the probability of a Type II error corresponding to the alternative value μ_a of μ equal to β, we should take a sample of size

$$n = \frac{(z^* + z_\beta)^2 \sigma^2}{(\mu_0 - \mu_a)^2}$$

Here z^* equals z_α if the alternative hypothesis is one-sided ($\mu > \mu_0$ or $\mu < \mu_0$), and z^* equals $z_{\alpha/2}$ if the alternative hypothesis is two-sided ($\mu \neq \mu_0$). Also, z_β is the point on the scale of the standard normal curve that gives a right-hand tail area equal to β.

Example 7.11   Testing Production Values for a Standardized Coffee Fill

Again consider the coffee fill example and suppose we want to test H_0: $\mu \geq 3$ (or $\mu = 3$) versus H_a: $\mu < 3$. If we want α to be .05 and β for the alternative value $\mu_a = 2.995$ of μ to be .05, we should take a sample of size

$$n = \frac{(z^* + z_\beta)^2 \sigma^2}{(\mu_0 - \mu_a)^2} = \frac{(z_\alpha + z_\beta)^2 \sigma^2}{(\mu_0 - \mu_a)^2}$$

$$= \frac{(z_{.05} + z_{.05})^2 \sigma^2}{(\mu_0 - \mu_a)^2}$$

$$= \frac{(1.645 + 1.645)^2 (.0147)^2}{(3 - 2.995)^2}$$

$$= 93.5592 = 94 \text{ (rounding up)}$$

Here, $z^* = z_\alpha = z_{.05} = 1.645$ because the alternative hypothesis ($\mu < 3$) is one-sided, and $z_\beta = z_{.05} = 1.645$.

Although we have set both α and β equal to the same value in the coffee fill situation, it is not necessary for α and β to be equal. As an example, again consider the Valentine's Day chocolate example, in which we are testing H_0: $\mu = 330$ versus H_a: $\mu \neq 330$. Suppose that the candy company decides that failing to reject H_0: $\mu = 330$ when μ differs from 330 by as many as 15 valentine boxes (that is, when μ is 315 or 345) is a serious Type II error. Furthermore, suppose that it is also decided that this Type II error is more serious than a Type I error. Therefore, α will be set equal to .05 and β for the alternative value $\mu_a = 315$ (or $\mu_a = 345$) of μ will be set equal to .01. It follows that the candy company should take a sample of size

$$
\begin{aligned}
n &= \frac{(z^* + z_\beta)^2 \sigma^2}{(\mu_0 - \mu_a)^2} = \frac{(z_{\alpha/2} + z_\beta)^2 \sigma^2}{(\mu_0 - \mu_a)^2} \\
&= \frac{(z_{.025} + z_{.01})^2 \sigma^2}{(\mu_0 - \mu_a)^2} \\
&= \frac{(1.96 + 2.326)^2 (40)^2}{(330 - 315)^2} \\
&= 130.62 = 131 \text{ (rounding up)}
\end{aligned}
$$

Here, $z^* = z_{\alpha/2} = z_{.05/2} = z_{.025} = 1.96$ because the alternative hypothesis ($\mu \neq 330$) is two-sided, and $z_\beta = z_{.01} = 2.326$ (see the bottom row of the t table in Appendix A).

The methods we have presented for calculating the probability of a Type II error and determining sample size can be extended to other hypothesis tests that utilize the normal distribution. We will not, however, present the extensions in this book.

Exercises for Section **7.6**

CONCEPTS

7.49 We usually take action on the basis of having rejected the null hypothesis. When we do this, we know the chances that the action has been taken erroneously because we have prespecified α, the probability of rejecting a true null hypothesis. Here, it is obviously important to know (prespecify) α, the probability of a Type I error. When is it important to know the probability of a Type II error? Explain why.

7.50 Explain why we are able to compute many different values of β, the probability of a Type II error, for a single hypothesis test.

7.51 Explain what is meant by
 a. A serious Type II error.
 b. The power of a statistical test.

7.52 In general, do we want the power corresponding to a serious Type II error to be near 0 or near 1? Explain.

METHODS AND APPLICATIONS

7.53   THE WASTE WATER EXAMPLE

Again consider the Atlantic Power waste water situation. Remember that the power plant will be shut down and corrective action will be taken on the cooling

system if the null hypothesis H_0: $\mu \leq 15$ is rejected in favour of H_a: $\mu > 15$. In this exercise, we calculate probabilities of various Type II errors in the context of this situation.

 a. Recall that Atlantic Power's hypothesis test is based on a sample of $n = 100$ temperature readings and assume that σ equals 2. If the power company sets $\alpha = .025$, calculate the probability of a Type II error for each of the following alternative values of μ: 15.1, 15.2, 15.3, 15.4, 15.5, 15.6, 15.7, 15.8, 15.9, 16.

 b. If we want the probability of making a Type II error when μ equals 15.5 to be very small, is Atlantic Power's hypothesis test adequate? Explain why or why not. If not, and if we want to maintain the value of α at .025, what must be done?

 c. The power curve for a statistical test is a plot of the power $= 1 - \beta$ on the vertical axis versus values of μ that make the null hypothesis false on the horizontal axis. Plot the power curve for Atlantic Power's test of H_0: $\mu \leq 15$ versus H_a: $\mu > 15$ by plotting power $= 1 - \beta$ for each of the alternative values of μ in part a. What happens to the power of the test as the alternative value of μ moves away from 15?

7.54 THE AUTO PARTS PRODUCTION EXAMPLE

Again consider the automobile parts supplier situation. Remember that a problem-solving team will be assigned to rectify the process producing the cylindrical engine parts if the null hypothesis H_0: $\mu = 3$ is rejected in favour of H_a: $\mu \neq 3$. In this exercise we calculate probabilities of various Type II errors in the context of this situation.

a. Suppose that the parts supplier's hypothesis test is based on a sample of $n = 100$ diameters and that σ equals .023. If the parts supplier sets $\alpha = .05$, calculate the probability of a Type II error for each of the following alternative values of μ: 2.990, 2.995, 3.005, 3.010.

b. If we want both the probabilities of making a Type II error when μ equals 2.995 and when μ equals 3.005 to be very small, is the parts supplier's hypothesis test adequate? Explain why or why not. If not, and if we want to maintain the value of α at .05, what must be done?

c. Plot the power of the test versus the alternative values of μ in part (a). What happens to the power of the test as the alternative value of μ moves away from 3?

7.55 THE WASTE WATER EXAMPLE

In the Atlantic Power hypothesis test of H_0: $\mu \leq 15$ versus H_a: $\mu > 15$ (as discussed in Exercise 7.53) find the sample size needed to make the probability of a Type I error equal to .025 and the probability of a Type II error corresponding to the alternative value $\mu_a = 15.5$ equal to .025. Here, assume σ equals 2.

7.56 THE AUTO PARTS PRODUCTION EXAMPLE

In the automobile parts supplier's hypothesis test of H_0: $\mu = 3$ versus H_a: $\mu \neq 3$ (as discussed in Exercise 7.54) find the sample size needed to make the probability of a Type I error equal to .05 and the probability of a Type II error corresponding to the alternative value $\mu_a = 3.005$ equal to .05. Here, assume σ equals .023.

7.7 STANDARDIZED EFFECT SIZE ESTIMATION FOR MEAN DIFFERENCES

In this final section, we will introduce statistics for estimating the magnitude of an effect in tests of means (for both the single-sample and two-sample cases). On the surface, this appears to be a rather straightforward process. Given that we are considering the difference between two values (whether it is a difference between a sample mean and a hypothetical value, or a difference between two sample means), it would seem logical to simply calculate the difference between values and use this value to quantify the difference between the groups. And this does, in fact, provide us with some information as to the difference between the values under study.

LO8

The problem with this method for quantifying the magnitude of an effect is, however, the interpretation of the difference score. If, for example, we are asked to provide an estimate of the magnitude of the difference between the two different generations of trash bag, we could use a simple difference score and suggest that the new product has (on average) a breaking strength that is .575 kg greater than the old product. To an industry insider, this might provide adequate information, but to a consumer (or even a manager), it provides little practical information. Interpretation is aided considerably through the use of standardized effect size estimates, as this allows us to express the difference between means in terms of standard deviations.

For example, let's reconsider the trash bag example. In our sample of 40 bags, we found a sample mean of 25.575, and were given to expect a population standard deviation of 1.65. In our calculation of a hypothesis test around our null hypothesized population mean of 25, we computed a z test as follows:

$$z = \frac{\bar{x} - \mu}{\sigma / \sqrt{n}} = \frac{25.575 - 25}{1.65 / \sqrt{40}} = 2.20$$

This provides us with the evidence that we need in order to determine whether the difference from expectation is statistically significant, but does not provide us with information that we need in order to determine the magnitude of the effect. In particular, this statistic is heavily influenced by the sample size—as the sample size increases, the standard error in the denominator decreases and the statistic increases. This is a problem for the estimation of effect size, as it is intended to represent practical or substantive significance and should therefore be invariant with sample size. To generate a standardized effect size estimate, we need a new statistic that will provide us with a common metric for use in describing the magnitude of observed effects within tests of means. For situations in which the population variance is known, a good statistic to use is Cohen's d.

The numerator of Cohen's d may be considered to be the difference between the sample mean (or mean difference) and the null hypothesized mean (or mean difference). The denominator of Cohen's d is the standard deviation of the population under study (in the single-sample case), or the square root of the average of the two variances (in the two-sample case). Accordingly, the formulas for Cohen's d that we will consider in this section are the single-sample test of means and the two-sample test of means.

Single-Sample Test of Means

$$d = \left| \frac{\bar{x} - \mu}{\sigma} \right|$$

Two-Sample Test of Means

$$d = \left| \frac{\bar{x}_1 - \bar{x}_2}{\sqrt{\dfrac{\sigma_1^2 + \sigma_2^2}{2}}} \right|$$

Cohen suggested that we can describe the magnitude of an effect on a simple scale ranging from small to large, and proposed some rough descriptors of these effect sizes (see Table 7.5).[4] The distance between small and medium effects was proposed to be equal to the distance between medium and large, in an effort to make the scale for this statistic as close to a ratio scale as possible.

TABLE 7.5   Qualitative Descriptors for Different Magnitudes of Cohen's d

Effect Size	Cohen's d	Description
Small	.2	An effect that is small enough to require specialized equipment to detect it.
Medium	.5	An effect that is large enough to be visible to the naked eye of the careful observer.
Large	.8	An effect that is large enough to be visible to the naked eye of a layperson.

Example 7.12   Measuring Effect Size in the Trash Bag Example

The trash bag example presented earlier in the chapter involved testing a sample of 40 bags that were purported to be stronger than previous generations of the product. This sample of bags demonstrated a breaking strength of 25.575 kg, as compared with the previous generation of the product that had a breaking strength of 25 kg (and a standard deviation of 1.65). Although our product testing suggests a statistically significant difference when comparing the new product to the old product (as $z = 2.20$ was larger than our critical value of $z = 1.645$ for a one-tailed hypothesis test at an alpha of 0.05), we would like to present a standardized effect size estimate.

$$d = \left| \frac{\bar{x} - \mu}{\sigma} \right| = \left| \frac{25.575 - 25}{1.65} \right| = .35$$

This suggests that the new trash bags are, on average, 0.35 standard deviations stronger than the old trash bags. It also suggests that the difference between the new and the old bags is a *small to medium* effect. So, although it is true that the new bags are stronger than the previous generation of bags, it is likely that this effect will go unnoticed by the majority of consumers.

---

[4]Cohen's description of effect sizes was intended to allow researchers to use these values as rough approximations in sample size and power calculations.

Example 7.13 Measuring Effect Size in the Waiting Time Example

Now let's revisit the customer waiting time example, where a bank implements a new system that is intended to significantly reduce customer waiting time. In this example, the wait time for 200 customers is carefully tracked—100 customers are tracked with the old system, and 100 are tracked with a pilot testing of the new system. The mean waiting time under the old system was 8.79 minutes and the mean waiting time under the new system is 5.14 minutes. The variance of the population of all waiting times was 4.7 minutes under the old system and 1.9 minutes under the new system. Using the standardized effect size estimate introduced earlier, we can calculate Cohen's d to be

$$d = \left| \frac{\bar{x}_1 - \bar{x}_2}{\sqrt{\dfrac{\sigma_1^2 + \sigma_2^2}{2}}} \right| = \left| \frac{8.79 - 5.14}{\sqrt{\dfrac{4.7 + 1.9}{2}}} \right| = 2.01$$

This suggests that the new system is markedly better than the old system, with the average waiting time under the new system being 2.01 standard deviations faster than the average waiting time under the old system. Cohen would term this a *strong* effect (or even a *very strong* effect), and we could expect that the improvement should be qualitatively obvious to all.

The simplicity of these calculations belies their importance in the practical interpretation of data. Frequently, we can demonstrate a statistically significant difference that is, in practical terms, of little importance. Consider, for the final time in this chapter, the trash bag example, noting that the effect size estimate is 0.35, indicating that it is a *small to medium* effect. The experiment described in this chapter involved the sampling of 40 trash bags and (as reiterated at the outset of this section) resulted in a z test of 2.20. All else being equal, if this experiment had been conducted with a sample of 400 trash bags, the z test would have been

$$z = \frac{\bar{x} - \mu}{\sigma / \sqrt{n}} = \frac{25.575 - 25}{1.65 / \sqrt{400}} = 6.97$$

This dramatic change in the z *test* was accomplished solely through an increase in sample size—the magnitude of the effect remained the same, so the practical significance of the finding remains unchanged. It is important, therefore, to include an effect size estimate whenever you present a statistical test. In Chapter 9, we will introduce another method for addressing the substantive significance of a finding—the confidence interval.

Exercises for Section **7.7**

CONCEPTS

7.57 What is an effect size?

7.58 Why might we want to include a measure of effect size along with our statistical analysis?

7.59 Why is the z *test* inappropriate for use as a standardized measure of effect size?

METHODS AND APPLICATIONS

7.60 For each of the following scenarios, indicate the effect magnitude (both qualitatively and quantitatively):
a. $\bar{x} = 36; \mu = 40; \sigma = 5$
b. $\bar{x} = 115; \mu = 111; \sigma = 20$
c. $\bar{x} = 75; \mu = 60; \sigma = 30$
d. $\bar{x}_1 = 120; \bar{x}_2 = 115; \sigma_1^2 = 90; \sigma_2^2 = 110$
e. $\bar{x}_1 = 4.5; \bar{x}_2 = 5.8; \sigma_1^2 = 1.2; \sigma_2^2 = 4.1$
f. $\bar{x}_1 = 53.26; \bar{x}_2 = 52.89; \sigma_1^2 = 2.7; \sigma_2^2 = 4.2$

7.61 Your division's sales have, on average, risen by 2.5 percent this quarter and you want to emphasize the significance of this outcome to the vice-president of your company. Unfortunately, he is impressed only by tests of statistical significance, and your division has only 5 salespeople (meaning that the change is not statistically significant). If your baseline sales were $200,000 and the standard deviation across the 5 people in your division is $10,000, present an effect size estimate that captures the substantive significance of your division's accomplishment.

7.62 THE BOTTLE FILLING EXAMPLE

Consider again the bottle filling process under evaluation by the Black Fly Beverage Company. Calculate the effect sizes for each of its four test runs of 36 bottles: 501.56 mL, 498.75 mL, 500.63 mL, and 498.125 mL. Do these discrepancies represent meaningful discrepancies from the intended fill (500 mL)? Assume that σ equals 3.12 mL.

7.63 THE DISC BRAKE SYSTEM EXAMPLE

Recall that National Motors has equipped the ZX-900 with a new disc brake system. The company would like to claim that the ZX-900 achieves a shorter mean stopping distance than the 20 metres claimed by a competitor. Calculate and evaluate the effect size for a random sample of 81 ZX-900s with a mean stopping distance of 19.27 m. Assume that the standard deviation is 2 m.

7.64 You are evaluating the number of sick days taken by two divisions in your company. They appear to be roughly equivalent when you evaluate the average number of sick days taken in each group (20 in the Marketing Department and 18 in the Accounting Department). If the variance for the Marketing Department is 12 days and the variance for the Accounting Department is 16 days, compute a standardized effect size estimate for the difference in sick time taken by the two departments. Is this likely to be a meaningful difference between groups?

THEORY TO PRACTICE

Throughout this chapter, we have presented methods for identifying whether we can use statistical evidence to support business decision making in a variety of contexts. In all of these cases, we have relied on the demonstration that a sample mean or proportion is unlikely to occur due to chance, and used this probabilistic statement to support our rejecting (or failing to reject) the null hypothesis. A subtle flaw in this process can be found, however, in the fact that it is possible to demonstrate a statistically significant difference between any two numbers (whether they are means or proportions) if you ask the question using a sufficiently large sample. The population parameter has always changed from its historical value, because all parameters are in constant flux, meaning that no parameter can ever truly be a constant. In the same way that no two individuals (or objects) are ever identical in every way, it is exceedingly unlikely (perhaps impossible) that any two groups of individuals or objects will ever be identical. In other words, everything is different from everything else.

This does not mean that there is no point to hypothesis testing—and this does not negate the importance of statistical analysis. What it does mean, however, is that there is tremendous value in systematically quantifying differences between values through the identification of effect sizes. It also suggests that our best hypothesis tests are not designed just to see if two values "are different," but rather they are designed to determine the extent to which two values "are different to a meaningful degree." Consider the trash bag example and recall that the company claimed that the trash bags are stronger. If the company truly wants to serve its customers faithfully, it would attempt to determine the amount of additional strength that a bag would need to possess before the bag is more useful. If you test enough individual bags, you can demonstrate that an increase of 0.01 kg in breaking strength represents a statistically significant improvement in breaking strength—but it is unlikely that this will result in a qualitative improvement that will improve the utility of the bags for the consumer.

These judgments about substantive or practical significance cannot be made numerically, but they are critical for the task of placing our statistical analyses in proper context.

With our discussion of effect sizes, we have started the process of considering practical significance in this chapter. Many of these questions are, however, addressed through the identification of a confidence interval—a topic that has been foreshadowed in previous chapters but is addressed in detail in Chapter 9.

CHAPTER SUMMARY

We began this chapter by learning about the two hypotheses that make up the structure of a hypothesis test. The null hypothesis is the statement being tested. The null hypothesis is often a statement of "no difference" or "no effect," and it is not rejected unless there is convincing sample evidence that it is false. The alternative, or, research, hypothesis is a statement that is accepted only if there is convincing sample evidence that it is true and that the null hypothesis is false. In some situations, the alternative hypothesis is a statement for which we need to attempt to find supportive evidence. We also learned that two types of errors can be made in a hypothesis test: A Type I error occurs when we reject a true null hypothesis, and a Type II error occurs when we do not reject a false null hypothesis.

We studied two commonly used ways to conduct a hypothesis test. The first involves comparing the value of a test statistic with what is called a *critical value*, and the second employs what is called a *p-value*. The *p*-value measures the weight of evidence against the null hypothesis. The smaller the *p*-value, the more we doubt the null hypothesis.

The mean difference tests that we covered in this chapter all dealt with the situation in which the population standard deviation σ is known. We also discussed tests that evaluate the population proportion, based on the normal distribution. Finally, we studied Type II error probabilities, and we showed how we can find the sample size needed to make both the probability of a Type I error and the probability of a serious Type II error as small as we want.

KEY TERMS

alternative (research) hypothesis
critical value
greater than alternative
independent samples experiment
less than alternative
not equal to alternative
null hypothesis
one-sided alternative hypothesis

p-value (probability value)
power of a statistical test
sampling distribution of $\hat{p}_1 - \hat{p}_2$
sampling distribution of $\bar{x}_1 - \bar{x}_2$
test statistic
two-sided alternative hypothesis
Type I error
Type II error

IMPORTANT FORMULAS AND TESTS

Hypothesis testing steps

Hypothesis test about a population mean (σ known)

Large-sample hypothesis test about a population proportion

Calculating the probability of a Type II error

Sample-size determination to achieve specified values of α and β

Statistical inference about a population variance

SUPPLEMENTARY EXERCISES

connect Practise and learn online with *Connect*. Items for which there are online data sets are marked with ✐.

7.65 The auditor for a large corporation routinely monitors cash disbursements. As part of this process, the auditor examines cheque request forms to determine whether they have been properly approved. Improper approval can occur in several ways. For instance, the cheque might not have received approval, the cheque request might be missing, the approval might be written by an unauthorized person, or the dollar limit of the authorizing person might be exceeded.
   a. Last year the corporation experienced a 5 percent improper cheque request approval rate. Since this was considered unacceptable, efforts were made to reduce the rate of improper approvals. Letting *p* be the proportion of all cheques that are now improperly approved, set up the null and alternative hypotheses needed to attempt to demonstrate that the current rate of improper approvals is lower than last year's rate of 5 percent.
   b. Suppose that the auditor selects a random sample of 625 cheques that have been approved in the last month. The auditor finds that 18 of these 625 cheques have been improperly approved. Use critical values and this sample

information to test the hypotheses you set up in part (a) at the .10, .05, .01, and .001 levels of significance. How much evidence is there that the rate of improper approvals has been reduced below last year's 5 percent rate?
   c. Find the *p*-value for the test of part (b). Use the *p*-value to carry out the test by setting α equal to .10, .05, .01, and .001. Interpret your results.
   d. Suppose the corporation incurs a $10 cost to detect and correct an improperly approved cheque. If the corporation disburses at least 2 million cheques per year, does the observed reduction of the rate of improper approvals seem to have practical importance? Explain your opinion.

7.66 A consumer electronics firm has developed a new type of remote control button that is designed to operate longer before becoming intermittent. A random sample of 35 of the new buttons is selected and each is tested in continuous operation until it becomes intermittent. The resulting lifetimes are found to have a sample mean of $\bar{x} = 1{,}241.2$ hours. The population standard deviation is known to be 110.8.

a. Independent tests reveal that the mean lifetime (in continuous operation) of the best remote control button on the market is 1,200 hours. Letting μ be the mean lifetime of the population of all new remote control buttons that will or could potentially be produced, set up the null and alternative hypotheses needed to attempt to provide evidence that the new button's mean lifetime exceeds the mean lifetime of the best remote button currently on the market.

b. Using the previously given sample results, use critical values to test the hypotheses you set up in part (a) by setting α equal to .10, .05, .01, and .001. What do you conclude for each value of α?

c. Suppose that $\bar{x} = 1,241.2$ had been obtained by testing a sample of 100 buttons. Use critical values to test the hypotheses you set up in part (a) by setting α equal to .10, .05, .01, and .001. Which sample (the sample of 35 or the sample of 100) gives a more statistically significant result? That is, which sample provides stronger evidence that H_a is true?

d. If we define *practical importance* to mean that μ exceeds 1,200 by an amount that would be clearly noticeable to most consumers, do you think that the result has practical importance? Explain why the samples of 35 and 100 both indicate the same degree of practical importance.

7.67 Again consider the remote control button lifetime situation discussed in Exercise 7.66. Using the sample information given in the introduction to that exercise, the p-value for testing H_0 versus H_a can be calculated to be .0139.

a. Determine whether H_0 would be rejected at each of $\alpha = .10$, $\alpha = .05$, $\alpha = .01$, and $\alpha = .001$.

b. Describe how much evidence we have that the new button's mean lifetime exceeds the mean lifetime of the best remote button currently on the market.

7.68 Several industries located along the St. Lawrence River discharge the toxic substance carbon tetrachloride into the river. Environment Canada monitors the amount of carbon tetrachloride pollution in the river and requires that the carbon tetrachloride contamination must average no more than 10 parts per million. In order to monitor the carbon tetrachloride contamination in the river, it takes a daily sample of 100 pollution readings at a specified location. If the mean carbon tetrachloride reading for this sample casts substantial doubt on the hypothesis that the average amount of carbon tetrachloride contamination in the river is at most 10 parts per million, Environment Canada will issue a shutdown order. In the event of such a shutdown order, industrial plants along the river must be closed until the carbon tetrachloride contamination is reduced to a more acceptable level. Assume that Environment Canada decides to issue a shutdown order if a sample of 100 pollution readings implies that $H_0: \mu \leq 10$ can be rejected in favour of $H_a: \mu > 10$ by setting $\alpha = .01$. If σ equals 2, calculate the probability of a Type II error for each of the following alternative values of μ: 10.1, 10.2, 10.3, 10.4, 10.5, 10.6, 10.7, 10.8, 10.9, and 11.0.

7.69 Assume that an insurance survey is based on 1,000 randomly selected Canadian households and that 640 of these households spent money to buy life insurance in 2012.

a. If p denotes the proportion of all Canadian households that spent money to buy life insurance in 2012, set up the null and alternative hypotheses needed to attempt to justify the claim that more than 60 percent of Canadian households spent money to buy life insurance in 2012.

b. Test the hypotheses you set up in part (a) by setting $\alpha = .10$, .05, .01, and .001. How much evidence is there that more than 60 percent of Canadian households spent money to buy life insurance in 2012?

7.70 *Consumer Reports* (January 2005) indicates that profit margins on extended warranties are much greater than on the purchase of most products.[5] In this exercise we consider a major electronics retailer that wants to increase the proportion of customers who buy extended warranties on digital cameras. Historically, 20 percent of digital camera customers have purchased the retailer's extended warranty. To increase this percentage, the retailer has decided to offer a new warranty that is less expensive and more comprehensive. Suppose that three months after starting to offer the new warranty, a random sample of 500 customer sales invoices shows that 152 out of 500 digital camera customers purchased the new warranty. Letting p denote the proportion of all digital camera customers who have purchased the new warranty, calculate the p-value for testing $H_0: p = .20$ versus $H_a: p > .20$. How much evidence is there that p exceeds .20? Does the difference between $\hat{p}$ and .2 seem to be practically important? Explain your opinion.

7.71 In its February 2, 1998, issue, *Fortune* magazine published the results of a Yankelovich Partners survey of 600 adults that investigated their ideas about marriage, divorce, and the contributions of the corporate wife. The survey results are shown in Figure 7.9. For each statement in the figure, the proportions of men and women who agreed with the statement are given. Assume that the survey results were obtained from independent random samples of 300 men and 300 women and, for each statement, carry out a hypothesis test that tests the equality of the population proportions of men and women who agree with the statement. Use α equal to .10, .05, .01, and .001. How much evidence is there that the population proportions of men and women who agree with each statement differ? If this survey was given again today, do you think that the results would change significantly?

7.72 In the book *Essentials of Marketing Research*, William R. Dillon, Thomas J. Madden, and Neil H. Firtle discuss evaluating the effectiveness of a test coupon. Samples of 500 test coupons and 500 control coupons were randomly delivered to shoppers. The results indicated that 35 of the 500 control coupons were redeemed, while 50 of the 500 test coupons were redeemed.

a. In order to consider the test coupon for use, the marketing research organization required that the proportion of all shoppers who would redeem the test coupon be statistically shown to be greater than the proportion of all shoppers who would redeem the control coupon. Assuming that the two samples of shoppers are independent, carry out a hypothesis test at the .01 level of significance that will show whether this requirement is met by the test coupon. Explain your conclusion.

b. Carry out the test of part (a) at the .10 level of significance. What do you conclude? Is your result statistically significant?

---

[5]*Consumer Reports*, "Extended Warranties Say Yes, Sometimes," January 1, 2005, p. 51.

FIGURE 7.9 The Results of a Yankelovich Partners Survey of 600 Adults on Marriage, Divorce, and the Contributions of the Corporate Wife (All Respondents with Income $50,000 or More)

People were magnanimous on the general proposition:

- In a divorce in a long-term marriage where the husband works outside the home and the wife is not employed for pay, the wife should be entitled to half the assets accumulated during the marriage.

    93% of women agree
    85% of men agree

But when we got to the goodies, a gender gap began to appear . . .

- The pension accumulated during the marriage should be split evenly.

    80% of women agree
    68% of men agree

- Stock options granted during the marriage should be split evenly.

    77% of women agree
    62% of men agree

. . . and turned into a chasm over the issue of how important a stay-at-home wife is to a husband's success.

- Managing the household and child rearing are extremely important to a husband's success.

    57% of women agree
    41% of men agree

- A corporate wife who also must travel, entertain, and act as a sounding board is extremely important to the success of a high-level business executive.

    51% of women agree
    28% of men agree

- The lifestyle of a corporate wife is more of a job than a luxury.

    73% of women agree
    57% of men agree

Source: Reprinted from the February 2, 1998, issue of *Fortune*. Copyright 1998 Time, Inc. Reprinted by permission.

7.73 INTERNET EXERCISE

Chances are that you're too young to remember much of the controversy over the 1995 Quebec referendum, but it remains an important part of Canada's history nonetheless. The following question was asked of residents of Quebec, on October 30, 1995:

> *Do you agree that Quebec should become sovereign after having made a formal offer to Canada for a new economic and political partnership within the scope of the bill respecting the future of Quebec and of the agreement signed on June 12, 1995?*

This textbook is probably not the most appropriate venue to revisit the referendum in any great detail, but there is an excellent description of the referendum (and the controversies associated with it) at wikipedia.org/wiki/1995_Quebec_referendum. All of the data used in this example comes from this web page.

One of the prominent features of the public commentary of the time was a focus on the narrowness of the margin between the two options on the ballot: 50.58 percent of participants voted "no" and 49.42 percent of participants voted "yes." [6] Specifically, there was significant concern over whether this was a "significant difference." The question of whether this difference is "substantively significant" or "meaningful" is open to interpretation. We can, however, calculate the statistical significance of this difference using the procedures outlined in Section 7.5.

[6]One of the controversies related to the referendum was about the rejected ballots—amounting to 1.82 percent of the vote. Proponents of secession noted that the margin of victory was small enough to make these votes potentially important in determining the outcome of the referendum. The calculations presented here use only the "valid votes" as counted in the referendum.

Of the 4,671,008 valid votes, 2,362,648 were cast in opposition to secession (i.e., voted "no") and 2,308,360 were cast in support of secession (i.e., voted "yes"). If we are interested in determining whether the percentage of valid votes is different across categories, we are testing to see if there is a significant difference between the percentage of valid votes in either category, and $p = 0.50$. This should be apparent from the fact that when $p_1 = p_2$, the only way that $p_1 + p_2$ can equal 1.0 is to have both proportions equal 0.50. So our null hypothesized proportion is .50, and the statistical significance of the difference between these two proportions would be tested as follows:

$$z = \frac{\hat{p} - p}{\frac{p(1-p)}{\sqrt{n}}}$$

$$z = \frac{\left(\frac{2{,}362{,}648}{4{,}671{,}008}\right) - .5}{\frac{.5(1-.5)}{\sqrt{4{,}671{,}008}}} = 50.2376$$

If you were to attempt to calculate the *p*-value associated with $z = 50.2376$, you would find a number so infinitesimally small that most statistical packages would fail to compute it (even using scientific notation). In other words, the probability of deriving a difference of 1.16 percent between two groups in a total sample of 4.671 million people, when there is truly no difference between groups, is virtually nil.

This is not to say that there is no reasonable argument to be made in favour of systematic bias existing in the method of counting (or discounting) votes, or in any number of other *methodological flaws*. It is clear from this calculation, however, that the difference between these groups is inarguably "real" (or at least "statistically significant") in the context of the referendum methodology that was employed.

CHAPTER **8**

Comparing Population Means and Variances Using *t* Tests and *F* Ratios

LEARNING OBJECTIVES

After reading this chapter, you should be able to

LO1 Use critical values and *p*-values to perform a *t* test about a population mean when σ is unknown

LO2 Compare two population means when the samples are independent and the population variances are unknown

LO3 Recognize when data come from independent samples and when they are paired

LO4 Compare two population means when the data are paired

LO5 Describe the properties of the *F* distribution

LO6 Use an *F* table

LO7 Compare two population variances when the samples are independent

CHAPTER OUTLINE

8.1 Single-Sample Tests of a Population Mean When σ Is Unknown

8.2 Comparing Two Population Means by Using Independent Samples: Variances Unknown

8.3 Paired Difference Experiments

8.4 Comparing Two Population Variances by Using Independent Samples

In this chapter, we continue our discussion of using hypothesis tests to make comparisons between historical values and present information, and between two populations of values, but introduce the idea of making these comparisons when the population variance is unknown. As will become apparent, this extension of the information presented in Chapter 7 has tremendous practical import, given that the population variance is rarely known with any certainty, so the calculation of inferential statistics based on sample information is critical. We conclude the chapter with a discussion of variance comparisons that foreshadows the use of this statistical technique in widely used techniques such as analysis of variance (a concept that will be introduced in Chapter 10).

8.1 SINGLE-SAMPLE TESTS OF A POPULATION MEAN WHEN σ IS UNKNOWN

Recall from Chapter 7 that we can use a z test to evaluate a hypothesis about the difference between a current population mean and some historical (or hypothetical) value, using the following equation:

LO1

$$z = \frac{\bar{x} - \mu}{\sigma / \sqrt{n}}$$

Our best estimate of the population mean is represented in this formula by the value of the sample mean, and the standard error of the sampling distribution is computed by dividing the standard deviation of the population by the square root of the sample size.

A key assumption required for the use of the z test is, therefore, the assumption that the standard deviation of the population is known. If we do not know σ (which is usually the case), we are left estimating the standard deviation of the population with the standard deviation of the sample. So we can reformulate our hypothesis test as follows:

$$\frac{\bar{x} - \mu}{s / \sqrt{n}}$$

If the sampled population is normally distributed (or if the sample size is large—at least 30), then this sampling distribution is exactly (or approximately) a t distribution having $n - 1$ **degrees of freedom**.

The curve of the t distribution has a shape similar to that of the standard normal curve. Two t curves and a standard normal curve are illustrated in Figure 8.1. The t distribution is symmetrical about zero, which is the mean of any t distribution. However, the t distribution is more spread out, or variable, than the standard normal distribution. Since the above t statistic is a function of two random variables, $\bar{x}$ and s, it is logical that the sampling distribution of this statistic is more variable than the sampling distribution of the z statistic, which is a function of only one random variable, $\bar{x}$. The exact spread, or standard deviation, of the t distribution depends on a parameter that is called the *number of degrees of freedom* (denoted df). The number of degrees of freedom df varies depending on the problem. In the present situation, the sampling distribution of t has a number of degrees of freedom that equals the sample size minus 1. We say that this sampling distribution is a t *distribution with $n - 1$ degrees of freedom*. As the sample size n (and thus the number of degrees of freedom) increases, the spread of the t distribution decreases (see Figure 8.1). Furthermore, as the number of degrees of freedom approaches infinity, the curve of the t distribution approaches (that is, becomes shaped more and more like) the curve of the standard normal distribution.

FIGURE 8.1   As the Number of Degrees of Freedom Increases, the Spread of the t Distribution Decreases and the t Curve Approaches the Standard Normal Curve

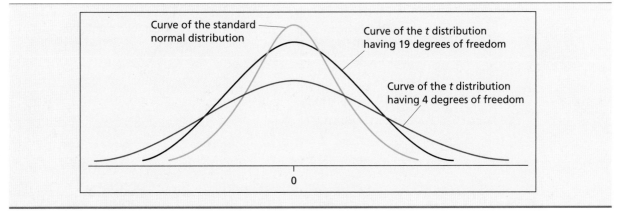

FIGURE 8.2 An Example of a *t* Point Giving a Specified Right-Hand Tail Area (This *t* Point Gives a Right-Hand Tail Area Equal to α)

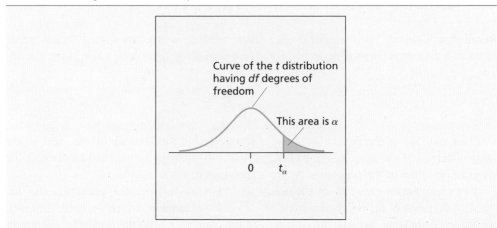

To use the *t* distribution, we employ a *t* point that is denoted t_α. As illustrated in Figure 8.2, t_α is the point on the horizontal axis under the curve of the *t* distribution that gives a right-hand tail area equal to α. The value of t_α in a particular situation depends on the right-hand tail area α and the number of degrees of freedom of the *t* distribution. Values of t_α are tabulated in a *t* table. Such a table is given in Table A.5 in Appendix A at the back of this book, and a portion of Table A.5 is reproduced below as Table 8.1. In this *t* table, the rows correspond to the different numbers of degrees of freedom (which are denoted as *df*). The values of *df* are listed down the left side of the table, while the columns designate the right-hand tail area α. For example, suppose we want to find the *t* point that gives a right-hand tail area of .025 under a *t* curve having *df* = 14 degrees of freedom. To do this, we look in Table 8.1 at the row labelled 14 and the column labelled $t_{.025}$. We find that this $t_{.025}$ point is 2.145 (also see Figure 8.3). Similarly, when there are *df* = 14 degrees of freedom, we find that $t_{.005}$ = 2.977 (see Table 8.1 and Figure 8.4).

Finally, when we are looking at a two-tailed test of significance, we need to split α between the two tails. This means that the area under the curve in the right-hand tail area is actually α/2 (see Figure 8.5) and it also means that the area under the curve in a two-tailed test of significance will always be smaller than the comparable area in a one-tailed test of significance.

FIGURE 8.3 The *t* Point Giving a Right-Hand Tail Area of .025 under the *t* Curve Having 14 Degrees of Freedom: $t_{.025}$ = 2.145

FIGURE 8.4 The *t* Point Giving a Right-Hand Tail Area of .005 under the *t* Curve Having 14 Degrees of Freedom: $t_{.005}$ = 2.977

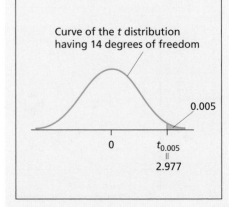

TABLE 8.1 A *t* Table

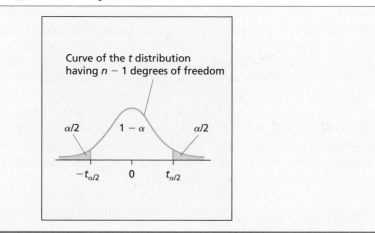

df	$t_{.100}$	$t_{.050}$	$t_{.025}$	$t_{.01}$	$t_{.005}$	$t_{.001}$	$t_{.0005}$
1	3.078	6.314	12.706	31.821	63.657	318.31	636.62
2	1.886	2.920	4.303	6.965	9.925	22.326	31.598
3	1.638	2.353	3.182	4.541	5.841	10.213	12.924
4	1.533	2.132	2.776	3.747	4.604	7.173	8.610
5	1.476	2.015	2.571	3.365	4.032	5.893	6.869
6	1.440	1.943	2.447	3.143	3.707	5.208	5.959
7	1.415	1.895	2.365	2.998	3.499	4.785	5.408
8	1.397	1.860	2.306	2.896	3.355	4.501	5.041
9	1.383	1.833	2.262	2.821	3.250	4.297	4.781
10	1.372	1.812	2.228	2.764	3.169	4.144	4.587
11	1.363	1.796	2.201	2.718	3.106	4.025	4.437
12	1.356	1.782	2.179	2.681	3.055	3.930	4.318
13	1.350	1.771	2.160	2.650	3.012	3.852	4.221
14	1.345	1.761	2.145	2.624	2.977	3.787	4.140
15	1.341	1.753	2.131	2.602	2.947	3.733	4.073
16	1.337	1.746	2.120	2.583	2.921	3.686	4.015
17	1.333	1.740	2.110	2.567	2.898	3.646	3.965
18	1.330	1.734	2.101	2.552	2.878	3.610	3.922
19	1.328	1.729	2.093	2.539	2.861	3.579	3.883
20	1.325	1.725	2.086	2.528	2.845	3.552	3.850
21	1.323	1.721	2.080	2.518	2.831	3.527	3.819
22	1.321	1.717	2.074	2.508	2.819	3.505	3.792
23	1.319	1.714	2.069	2.500	2.807	3.485	3.767
24	1.318	1.711	2.064	2.492	2.797	3.467	3.745
25	1.316	1.708	2.060	2.485	2.787	3.450	3.725
26	1.315	1.706	2.056	2.479	2.779	3.435	3.707
27	1.314	1.703	2.052	2.473	2.771	3.421	3.690
28	1.313	1.701	2.048	2.467	2.763	3.408	3.674
29	1.311	1.699	2.045	2.462	2.756	3.396	3.659
30	1.310	1.697	2.042	2.457	2.750	3.385	3.646
40	1.303	1.684	2.021	2.423	2.704	3.307	3.551
60	1.296	1.671	2.000	2.390	2.660	3.232	3.460
120	1.289	1.658	1.980	2.358	2.617	3.160	3.373
∞	1.282	1.645	1.960	2.326	2.576	3.090	3.291

FIGURE 8.5 The Point $t_{\alpha/2}$ with $n - 1$ Degrees of Freedom

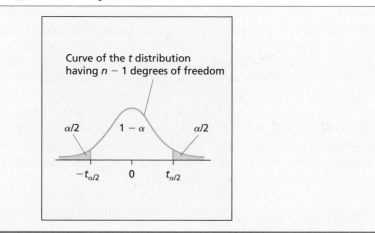

Table 8.1 gives *t* points for degrees of freedom *df* from 1 to 30. The table also gives *t* points for 40, 60, 120, and an infinite number of degrees of freedom. Looking at this table, it is useful to realize that the normal points giving the various right-hand tail areas are listed in the row of the *t* table corresponding to an infinite (∞) number of degrees of freedom. Looking at the row corresponding to ∞, we see that, for example, $z_{.025} = 1.96$. Therefore, we can use this row in the *t* table as an alternative to using the normal table when we need to find normal points.

The *t* Test for a Population Mean When σ Is Unknown

Define the test statistic

$$t = \frac{\bar{x} - \mu_0}{s/\sqrt{n}}$$

and assume that the population sampled is normally distributed or the sample size is large (at least 30).

We can test $H_0: \mu = \mu_0$ versus a particular alternative hypothesis at level of significance α by using the appropriate critical value rule, or, equivalently, the corresponding *p*-value. Here, t_α, $t_{\alpha/2}$, and the *p*-values are based on $n - 1$ degrees of freedom.

Alternative Hypothesis	Critical Value Rule: Reject H_0 if	*p*-Value (reject H_0 if *p*-value $< \alpha$)
$H_a: \mu > \mu_0$	$t > t_\alpha$	The area under the *t* distribution curve to the right of *t*
$H_a: \mu < \mu_0$	$t < -t_\alpha$	The area under the *t* distribution curve to the left of *t*
$H_a: \mu \neq \mu_0$	$\lvert t \rvert > t_{\alpha/2}$—that is, $t > t_{\alpha/2}$ or $t < -t_{\alpha/2}$	Twice the area under the *t* distribution curve to the right of $\lvert t \rvert$

In the rest of this chapter, we will follow the five hypothesis testing steps given in the previous section, but will not formally number each hypothesis testing step. Rather, for each of the five steps, we will set in boldfaced font a key phrase that indicates that the step is being carried out. After this chapter, we will use the five steps more informally.

Example 8.1   Using Debt-to-Equity Ratio to Limit Risk in Bank Loans

One measure of a company's financial health is its *debt-to-equity ratio*. This quantity is defined to be the ratio of the company's corporate debt to the company's equity. If this ratio is too high, it is one indication of financial instability. For obvious reasons, banks often monitor the financial health of companies to which they have extended commercial loans. Suppose that, in order to reduce risk, a large bank has decided to initiate a policy limiting the mean debt-to-equity ratio for its portfolio of commercial loans to being less than 1.5. In order to assess whether the mean debt-to-equity ratio μ of its current commercial loan portfolio is less than 1.5, the bank will test the **null hypothesis $H_0: \mu = 1.5$ versus the alternative hypothesis $H_a: \mu < 1.5$.** In this situation, a Type I error—rejecting $H_0: \mu = 1.5$ when $H_0: \mu = 1.5$ is true—would result in the bank concluding that the mean debt-to-equity ratio of its commercial loan portfolio is less than 1.5 when it is not. Because the bank wants to be very sure that it does not commit this Type I error, it will test H_0 versus H_a by using a .01 level of significance. Furthermore, since $H_a: \mu < 1.5$ is of the form $H_a: \mu < \mu_0$, we should **reject $H_0: \mu = 1.5$ if the value of *t* is less than the critical value $-t_\alpha = -t_{.01} = -2.624$.** Here, $-t_{.01} = -2.624$ is based on $n - 1 = 15 - 1 = 14$ degrees of freedom, and this critical value is illustrated in Figure 8.6.

FIGURE 8.6   Testing H_0: $\mu = 1.5$ versus H_a: $\mu < 1.5$ by Using a Critical Value and the p-Value

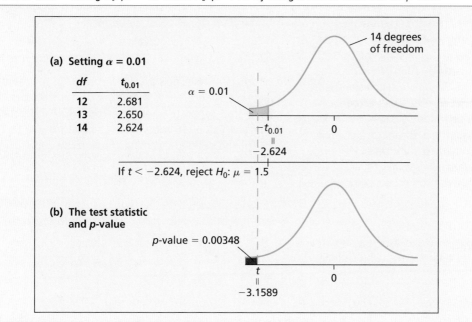

To perform the hypothesis test, the bank randomly selects a sample of 15 of its commercial loan accounts. Audits of these companies result in the following debt-to-equity ratios (arranged in increasing order): 1.05, 1.11, 1.19, 1.21, 1.22, 1.29, 1.31, 1.32, 1.33, 1.37, 1.41, 1.45, 1.46, 1.65, and 1.78. The mound-shaped stem-and-leaf display of these ratios is given in the figure in the page margin and indicates that the population of all debt-to-equity ratios is (approximately) normally distributed. To evaluate the difference between the sample mean and the mean of the sampling distribution, we must **calculate the value of the test statistic** *t.* Since the mean of the sample is $\bar{x} = 1.3433$ and the standard deviation is $s = .1921$, the value of the test statistic is

1.0	5
1.1	1 9
1.2	1 2 9
1.3	1 2 3 7
1.4	1 5 6
1.5	
1.6	5
1.7	8

$$t = \frac{\bar{x} - 1.5}{s/\sqrt{n}} = \frac{1.3433 - 1.5}{.1921/\sqrt{15}} = -3.1589$$

Since $t = -3.1589$ **is less than** $-t_{.01} = -2.624$, **we reject** H_0: $\mu = 1.5$ **in favour of** H_a: $\mu < 1.5$. That is, we conclude (at an α of .01) that the mean debt-to-equity ratio of the bank's commercial loan portfolio is less than 1.5. This, along with the fact that the sample mean $\bar{x} = 1.3433$ is slightly less than 1.5, implies that it is reasonable for the bank to conclude that the mean debt-to-equity ratio of its commercial loan portfolio is slightly less than 1.5.

The p-value for testing H_0: $\mu = 1.5$ versus H_a: $\mu < 1.5$ is the area under the curve of the *t* distribution having 14 degrees of freedom to the left of $t = -3.1589$. Tables of *t* points (such as Table A.5) are not complete enough to give such areas for most *t* statistic values, so we use computer software to calculate p-values that are based on the *t* distribution. For example, we can use Excel to determine that the p-value for testing H_0: $\mu = 1.5$ versus H_a: $\mu < 1.5$ is .00348. The p-value of .00348 says that if we are to believe that H_0 is true, we must believe that we have observed a test statistic value that can be described as having a 348 in 100,000 chance. Moreover, because the p-value of .00348 is between .01 and .001, we have very strong evidence, but not extremely strong evidence, that H_0: $\mu = 1.5$ is false and H_a: $\mu < 1.5$ is true. That is, we have very strong evidence that the mean debt-to-equity ratio of the bank's commercial loan portfolio is less than 1.5.

Effect Size Estimation When σ Is Unknown

As we discussed in Chapter 7, it is important to present information concerning the magnitude of an effect when presenting the results of a hypothesis test. When we know the standard deviation of the population (σ), we are able to use Cohen's *d*, as the standard deviation in this standardized effect size estimate is the population standard deviation. This is true even in cases when we are considering a difference between two populations, as Cohen's *d* also relies on the assumption that the population standard deviations are equal in the case of a two-group comparison.

$$d = \left|\frac{\bar{x} - \mu}{\sigma}\right|$$

When σ is unknown, however, we make a slight modification in our effect size estimate by incorporating the standard deviation of the sample:

$$g = \left|\frac{\bar{x} - \mu}{s}\right|$$

Cohen's *d* and Hedge's *g* are interpreted in the same way—both represent the number of standard deviations that separate your observed value and your expected value. So we would calculate the effect size for the debt-to-equity example to be

$$g = \left|\frac{\bar{x} - \mu}{s}\right| = \left|\frac{1.3433 - 1.5}{.1921}\right| = .82$$

This suggests that the current portfolio is .82 standard deviations below the risk threshold set in the new policy.

Recall that in three examples discussed in Chapter 7, we tested hypotheses by assuming that the population standard deviation σ was known and by using z tests. If σ is actually not known in cases such as these (which would probably be true), we should test the hypotheses under consideration by using t tests. Furthermore, recall that in each case, the sample size was large (at least 30). **In general, it can be shown that if the sample size is large, the t test is approximately valid even if the sampled population is not normally distributed (or mound-shaped).** Therefore, consider the Valentine's Day chocolate example and testing H_0: $\mu = 330$ versus H_a: $\mu \neq 330$ at the .05 level of significance. To perform the hypothesis test, assume that we will randomly select $n = 100$ large retail stores and use their anticipated order quantities to calculate the value of the **test statistic t.** Then, since the alternative hypothesis H_a: $\mu \neq 330$ is of the form H_a: $\mu \neq \mu_0$, we will **reject H_0: $\mu = 330$ if the absolute value of t is greater than $t_{\alpha/2} = t_{.025} = 1.984$ (based on $n - 1 = 99$ degrees of freedom)**—see Figure 8.7. Suppose that when the sample is randomly selected, the mean and the standard deviation of the $n = 100$ reported order quantities are calculated to be $\bar{x} = 326$ and $s = 39.1$. The **value of the test statistic is**

$$t = \frac{\bar{x} - 330}{s/\sqrt{n}} = \frac{326 - 330}{39.1/\sqrt{100}} = -1.023$$

Since $|t| = 1.023$ is less than $t_{.025} = 1.984$, we cannot reject H_0: $\mu = 330$ by setting α equal to .05. It follows that we cannot conclude (at an α of .05) that this year's mean order quantity of the valentine box by large retail stores will differ from 330 boxes. Therefore, the candy company will base its production of valentine boxes on the 10 percent projected sales increase. The p-value for the hypothesis test is twice the area under the t distribution curve having 99 degrees of freedom to the right of $|t| = 1.023$. Using a computer, we find that this p-value is .3088 (see Figure 8.7[b]), which provides little evidence against H_0: $\mu = 330$ and in favour of H_a: $\mu \neq 330$. Furthermore, the standardized effect size estimate would be computed to be

$$g = \left|\frac{\bar{x} - \mu}{s}\right| = \left|\frac{326 - 330}{39.1}\right| = .10$$

suggesting that the average number of boxes ordered will be .10 standard deviations different from a projected 10 percent sales increase.

FIGURE 8.7 Testing H_0: $\mu = 330$ versus H_a: $\mu = 330$ by Using Critical Values and the p-Value

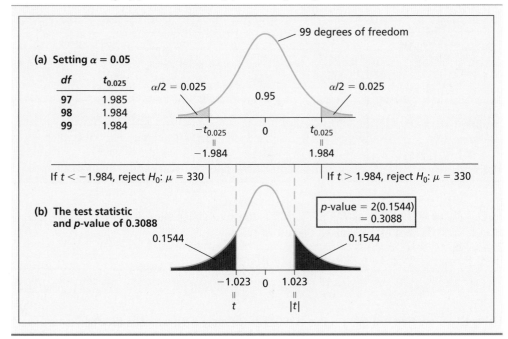

Don't forget to consider both tails of your hypothesis test

A common mistake when computing p-values for two-tailed hypothesis tests (i.e., when the alternative hypothesis is set to be "not equal to" the mean of your sampling distribution) is to forget to include the area in both ends of the distribution. Because there are two rejection regions for your hypothesis test, you need to consider the area under the curve in both ends of the distribution. This is illustrated in Figure 8.7.

ROADBLOCK

Consider also the trash bag example and note that the sample of $n = 40$ trash bag breaking strengths has mean $\bar{x} = 25.575$ and standard deviation $s = 1.6438$. The p-value for testing H_0: $\mu = 25$ versus H_a: $\mu > 25$ is the area under the t distribution curve having $n - 1 = 39$ degrees of freedom to the right of

$$t = \frac{\bar{x} - 25}{\frac{s}{\sqrt{n}}} = \frac{25.575 - 25}{\frac{1.6438}{\sqrt{40}}} = 2.2123$$

Using Excel, we find that this p-value is .0164 (see Figure 8.8), which provides strong evidence against H_0: $\mu = 25$ and in favour of H_a: $\mu > 25$. In particular, suppose that most television networks would evaluate the claim that the new trash bag has a mean breaking strength that exceeds 25 kilograms by choosing an α value between .02 and .05. It follows that, since the p-value of .0164 is less than all these α values, most networks would allow the trash bag claim to be advertised. Furthermore, the effect size estimate would be

$$g = \left| \frac{\bar{x} - \mu}{s} \right| = \left| \frac{25.575 - 25}{1.6438} \right| = .35$$

suggesting that the new trash bags have a breaking strength that is .35 standard deviations higher than the old bags.

As a third example, consider the payment time example and note that the sample of $n = 65$ payment times has mean $\bar{x} = 18.1077$ and standard deviation $s = 3.9612$. The p-value for

FIGURE 8.8   The *p*-Value for Testing H_0: $\mu = 25$ versus H_a: $\mu > 25$

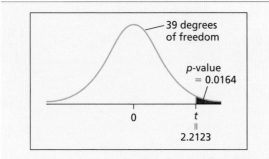

39 degrees of freedom

p-value = 0.0164

0   *t* ‖ 2.2123

FIGURE 8.9   The *p*-Value for Testing H_0: $\mu = 19.5$ versus H_a: $\mu < 19.5$

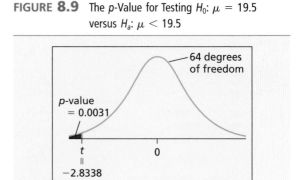

64 degrees of freedom

p-value = 0.0031

t ‖ −2.8338   0

testing H_0: $\mu = 19.5$ versus H_a: $\mu < 19.5$ is the area under the *t* distribution curve having $n - 1 = 64$ degrees of freedom to the left of

$$t = \frac{\bar{x} - 19.5}{\frac{s}{\sqrt{n}}} = \frac{18.1077 - 19.5}{\frac{3.9612}{\sqrt{65}}} = -2.8338$$

Using Excel, we find that this *p*-value is .0031 (see Figure 8.9), which is less than the management consulting firm's α value of .01. It follows that the consulting firm will claim that the new electronic billing system has reduced the trucking company's mean bill payment time by more than 50 percent—and that the new billing system will result in an average payment time that is .35 standard deviations shorter than the payment time under the former system:

$$g = \left| \frac{\bar{x} - \mu}{s} \right| = \left| \frac{18.1077 - 19.5}{3.9612} \right| = .35$$

To conclude this section, note that if the sample size is small (<30) and the sampled population is not approximately normally distributed (that is, is not mound-shaped or is highly skewed), then it might be appropriate to use a nonparametric test about the population median. Such a test is discussed in Chapter 13.

ROADBLOCK   **You cannot easily perform manual calculations or find reference tables for *t* tests**
Unlike the *z* distribution, the *t* distribution is dependent on the sample size. In practical terms, this means that there is a single *z* table in which you can look up the area under the curve for particular values of *z*, but no such singular resource for values of *t*. This means that you will need to use calculus or a computer program (such as Excel) to compute the *p*-value associated with a particular *t*. We will not present the calculus required for evaluating the probability density functions of *t*, but we do present information about the use of Excel's MegaStat throughout this textbook.

Exercises for Section **8.1**

CONCEPTS

8.1 What assumptions must be met in order to carry out the test about a population mean based on the *t* distribution?

8.2 How do we decide whether to use a *z* test or a *t* test when testing a hypothesis about a population mean?

8.3 How is Hedge's *g* different from Cohen's *d*?

METHODS AND APPLICATIONS

8.4 Suppose that a random sample of 16 measurements from a normally distributed population gives a sample mean of $\bar{x} = 13.5$ and a sample standard deviation of $s = 6$. Use critical values to test H_0: $\mu \leq 10$ versus H_a: $\mu > 10$ using levels of significance $\alpha = .10$, $\alpha = .05$, $\alpha = .01$, and $\alpha = .001$. What do you conclude at each value of α?

8.5 Suppose that a random sample of nine measurements from a normally distributed population gives a sample mean of $\bar{x} = 2.57$ and a sample standard deviation of $s = .3$. Use critical values to test $H_0: \mu = 3$ versus $H_a: \mu \neq 3$ using levels of significance $\alpha = .10$, $\alpha = .05$, $\alpha = .01$, and $\alpha = .001$. What do you conclude at each value of α?

8.6 THE AIR TRAFFIC CONTROLLER EXAMPLE

It is hoped that the mean alert time, μ, using a new air traffic controlling display panel is less than eight seconds. Formulate the null hypothesis (H_0) and the alternative hypothesis (H_a) that would be used to attempt to provide evidence that μ is less than eight seconds. Discuss the meanings of a Type I error and a Type II error in this situation. The mean and the standard deviation of the sample of $n = 15$ alert times are $\bar{x} = 7.4$ and $s = 1.0261$. Perform a t test of H_0 versus H_a by setting α equal to .05 and using a critical value. Interpret the results of the test, and present a standardized effect size estimate. Assume (as before) that the population of all alert times using the new display panel is approximately normally distributed.

8.7 The p-value for the hypothesis test of Exercise 8.6 can be computer-calculated to be .0200. How much evidence is there that μ is less than eight seconds?

8.8 THE DEBT RATIO EXAMPLE

The *bad debt ratio* for a financial institution is defined to be the dollar value of loans defaulted divided by the total dollar value of all loans made. Suppose that a random sample of seven Manitoba credit unions is selected, and that the bad debt ratios (written as percentages) are 7%, 4%, 6%, 7%, 5%, 4%, and 9%.

a. Officials claim that the mean bad debt ratio for all Canadian credit unions is 3.5 percent and that the mean bad debt ratio for Manitoba credit unions is higher. Set up the null and alternative hypotheses needed to attempt to provide evidence supporting the claim that the mean bad debt ratio for Manitoba credit unions exceeds 3.5 percent. Discuss the meanings of a Type I error and a Type II error in this situation.

b. Assuming that bad debt ratios for Manitoba credit unions are approximately normally distributed, use critical values and the given sample information to test the hypotheses you set up in part (a) by setting α equal to .01. Provide an appropriate standardized effect size estimate.

c. Are you qualified to decide whether we have a practically important result? Who would be? How might practical importance be defined in this situation?

d. The p-value for the hypothesis test of part (b) can be calculated to be .006. What does this p-value say about whether the mean bad debt ratio for Manitoba credit unions exceeds 3.5 percent?

8.9 THE VIDEO GAME SATISFACTION RATING EXAMPLE

Recall that "very satisfied" customers give the XYZ-Box video game system a rating that is at least 42.

Suppose that the manufacturer of the XYZ-Box wants to use the random sample of 65 satisfaction ratings to provide evidence supporting the claim that the mean composite satisfaction rating for the XYZ-Box exceeds 42.

a. Letting μ represent the mean composite satisfaction rating for the XYZ-Box, set up the null and alternative hypotheses needed if we want to attempt to provide evidence supporting the claim that μ exceeds 42.

b. The mean and the standard deviation of the sample of $n = 65$ customer satisfaction ratings are $\bar{x} = 42.95$ and $s = 2.6424$. Use a critical value to test the hypotheses you set up in part (a) by setting α equal to .01. Present a standardized effect size estimate along with your hypothesis test.

8.10 THE CUSTOMER WAIT TIME EXAMPLE

Recall the bank manager who developed a new system to reduce the time customers spend waiting for teller service during peak hours. The manager hopes the new system will reduce waiting times from the current 9 to 10 minutes to less than 6 minutes.

Suppose the manager wants to use a random sample of 100 waiting times to support the claim that the mean waiting time under the new system is shorter than six minutes.

a. Letting μ represent the mean waiting time under the new system, set up the null and alternative hypotheses needed if we want to attempt to provide evidence supporting the claim that μ is shorter than six minutes.

b. The mean and the standard deviation of the sample of 100 bank customer waiting times are $\bar{x} = 5.46$ and $s = 2.475$. Use a critical value to test the hypotheses you set up in part (a) by setting α equal to .05. Present a standardized effect size estimate along with your hypothesis test.

8.11 THE CHEMICAL CATALYST EXAMPLE

Consider a chemical company that wants to determine whether a new catalyst, Catalyst XA-100, changes the mean hourly yield of its chemical process from the historical process mean of 750 kilograms per hour. When five trial runs are made using the new catalyst, the following yields (in kilograms per hour) are recorded: 801, 814, 784, 836, and 820.

a. Letting μ be the mean of all possible yields using the new catalyst, set up the null and alternative hypotheses needed if we want to attempt to provide evidence that μ differs from 750 kilograms.

b. The mean and the standard deviation of the sample of five catalyst yields are $\bar{x} = 811$ and $s = 19.647$. Using a critical value and assuming approximate normality, test the hypotheses you set up in part (a) by setting α equal to .01. The p-value for the hypothesis test is given in the Excel output on the page margin. Interpret this p-value. Present a standardized effect size estimate to accompany the hypothesis test.

t statistic
6.942585
p-value
0.002261

8.12   THE VEHICLE REPLACEMENT EXAMPLE

Recall from Exercise 7.38 that Bayus studied the mean numbers of auto dealers visited by early and late replacement buyers. Letting μ be the mean number of dealers visited by late replacement buyers, set up the null and alternative hypotheses needed if we want to attempt to provide evidence that μ differs from 4 dealers. A random sample of 100 late replacement buyers yields a mean and a standard deviation of the number of dealers visited of $\bar{x} = 4.32$ and $s = .67$. Use critical values to test the hypotheses you set up by setting α equal to .10, .05, .01, and .001. Do we have evidence to suggest that μ is less than 4 or greater than 4? Present a standardized effect size estimate along with your hypothesis test.

8.13   The controller of a large retail chain is concerned about a possible slowdown in payments by customers. The controller randomly selects a sample of 25 accounts and finds that the mean and the standard deviation of the number of days that the accounts have remained unpaid are $\bar{x} = 54$ and $s = 8$. Using critical values and assuming approximate normality, determine if this sample evidence allows us to conclude that the current

population mean of the number of days that accounts have remained unpaid exceeds 50 days, the historical average for the company. Perform the hypothesis test by setting α equal to .10, .05, .01, and .001. Present a standardized effect size estimate along with your hypothesis tests.

8.14   In 1991 the average interest rate charged by Canadian credit card issuers was 18.8 percent. Since that time, there has been a proliferation of new credit cards affiliated with retail stores, oil companies, alumni associations, and so on. A financial officer wants to study whether the increased competition in the credit card business has reduced interest rates. To do this, the officer will test a hypothesis about the current mean interest rate, μ, charged by Canadian credit card issuers. To perform the hypothesis test, the officer randomly selects $n = 15$ credit cards and obtains the following interest rates (arranged in increasing order): 14.0, 14.6, 15.3, 15.6, 15.8, 16.4, 16.6, 17.0, 17.3, 17.6, 17.8, 18.1, 18.4, 18.7, and 19.2. Is there a statistically significant difference between present interest rates and historical rates? Present a standardized effect size estimate along with your hypothesis test.

8.2 COMPARING TWO POPULATION MEANS BY USING INDEPENDENT SAMPLES: VARIANCES UNKNOWN

LO2

In Chapter 7, we demonstrated methods for testing the difference between two populations when the variances of the populations are known. Suppose that (as is usually the case) the true values of the population variances σ_1^2 and σ_2^2 are not known. We then estimate σ_1^2 and σ_2^2 by using s_1^2 and s_2^2, the variances of the samples randomly selected from the populations being compared. There are two approaches to doing this. The first approach assumes that the population variances σ_1^2 and σ_2^2 are equal. Denoting the common value of these variances as σ^2, it follows that

$$\sigma_{\bar{x}_1 - \bar{x}_2} = \sqrt{\frac{\sigma_1^2}{n_1} + \frac{\sigma_2^2}{n_2}} = \sqrt{\frac{\sigma^2}{n_1} + \frac{\sigma^2}{n_2}} = \sqrt{\sigma^2\left(\frac{1}{n_1} + \frac{1}{n_2}\right)}$$

Because we are assuming that $\sigma_1^2 = \sigma_2^2 = \sigma^2$, we do not need separate estimates of σ_1^2 and σ_2^2. Instead, we combine the results of the two independent random samples to compute a single estimate of σ^2. This estimate is called the *pooled estimate* of σ^2, and it is a weighted average of the two sample variances s_1^2 and s_2^2. Denoting the pooled estimate as s_p^2, it is computed using the formula

$$s_p^2 = \frac{(n_1 - 1)s_1^2 + (n_2 - 1)s_2^2}{n_1 + n_2 - 2}$$

Using s_p^2, the estimate of $\sigma_{\bar{x}_1 - \bar{x}_2}$ is

$$\sqrt{s_p^2\left(\frac{1}{n_1} + \frac{1}{n_2}\right)}$$

and we form the statistic

$$\frac{(\bar{x}_1 - \bar{x}_2) - (\mu_1 - \mu_2)}{\sqrt{s_p^2\left(\frac{1}{n_1} + \frac{1}{n_2}\right)}}$$

It can be shown that, if we have randomly selected independent samples from two normally distributed populations having equal variances, the sampling distribution of this statistic is a t distribution having $(n_1 + n_2 - 2)$ degrees of freedom.

Remember that pooled variance is a weighted average of your variances

The pooled variance is a weighted average of your group variances—meaning that it will be equal to $(\sigma_1^2 + \sigma_2^2)/2$ only when the n sizes are exactly equal. Otherwise, you will need to use the weighted average formula specified above. In any case, we will see the formula for pooled variance coming into play for our conceptual definitions of independent groups ANOVA in Chapter 10.

ROADBLOCK

Example 8.2 Comparing Mean Catalyst Yields

A production supervisor at a major chemical company must determine which of two catalysts, Catalyst XA-100 or Catalyst ZB-200, maximizes the hourly yield of a chemical process. To compare the mean hourly yields obtained by using the two catalysts, the supervisor runs the process using each catalyst for five one-hour periods. The resulting yields (in kilograms per hour) for each catalyst, along with the means and variances of the yields, are given in Table 8.2. Assuming that all other factors affecting yields of the process have been held as constant as possible during the test runs, it seems reasonable to regard the five observed yields for each catalyst as a random sample from the population of all possible hourly yields for the catalyst. Furthermore, since the sample variances $s_1^2 = 386$ and $s_2^2 = 484.2$ do not differ substantially (notice that $s_1 = 19.65$ and $s_2 = 22.00$ differ by even less), it might be reasonable to conclude that the population variances are approximately equal.[1] It follows that the pooled estimate is a point estimate of the common variance σ^2.

$$s_p^2 = \frac{(n_1 - 1)s_1^2 + (n_2 - 1)s_2^2}{n_1 + n_2 - 2}$$

$$= \frac{(5 - 1)(386) + (5 - 1)(484.2)}{5 + 5 - 2} = 435.1$$

We define μ_1 as the mean hourly yield obtained by using Catalyst XA-100, and we define μ_2 as the mean hourly yield obtained by using Catalyst ZB-200. Suppose we want to test a hypothesis about $\mu_1 - \mu_2$. In the following boxed feature, we describe how this can be done. Here we test the null hypothesis $H_0: \mu_1 - \mu_2 = D_0$, where D_0 is a number whose value varies depending on the situation. Often D_0 will be the number 0. In such a case, the null hypothesis $H_0: \mu_1 - \mu_2 = 0$ says there is no difference between the population means μ_1 and μ_2. In this case, each alternative hypothesis in the boxed feature implies that the population means μ_1 and μ_2 differ in a particular way.

TABLE **8.2** Yields of a Chemical Process Obtained Using Two Catalysts

Catalyst XA-100	Catalyst ZB-200
801	752
814	718
784	776
836	742
820	763
$\bar{x}_1 = 811$	$\bar{x}_2 = 750.2$
$s_1^2 = 386$	$s_2^2 = 484.2$

---

[1]We describe how to test the equality of two variances in Section 8.4.

A t Test about the Difference between Two Population Means: Equal Variances

Define the test statistic

$$t = \frac{(\bar{x}_1 - \bar{x}_2) - D_0}{\sqrt{s_p^2\left(\frac{1}{n_1} + \frac{1}{n_2}\right)}}$$

and assume that the sampled populations are normally distributed with equal variances. Then, if

the samples are independent of each other, we can test $H_0: \mu_1 - \mu_2 = D_0$ versus a particular alternative hypothesis at level of significance α by using the appropriate critical value rule, or, equivalently, the corresponding p-value.

Alternative Hypothesis	Critical Value Rule: Reject H_0 if	p-Value (reject H_0 if p-value $< \alpha$)
$H_a: \mu_1 - \mu_2 > D_0$	$t > t_\alpha$	The area under the t distribution curve to the right of t
$H_a: \mu_1 - \mu_2 < D_0$	$t < -t_\alpha$	The area under the t distribution curve to the left of t
$H_a: \mu_1 - \mu_2 \neq D_0$	$\lvert t \rvert > t_{\alpha/2}$—that is, $t > t_{\alpha/2}$ or $t < -t_{\alpha/2}$	Twice the area under the t distribution curve to the right of $\lvert t \rvert$

Here t_α, $t_{\alpha/2}$, and the p-values are based on $n_1 + n_2 - 2$ degrees of freedom.

To compare the mean hourly yields obtained by using Catalysts XA-100 and ZB-200, we will test $H_0: \mu_1 - \mu_2 = 0$ versus $H_a: \mu_1 - \mu_2 \neq 0$ at the .05 level of significance. To perform the hypothesis test, we will use the sample information in Table 8.2 to calculate the value of the **test statistic t.** Then, because $H_a: \mu_1 - \mu_2 \neq 0$ is of the form $H_a: \mu_1 - \mu_2 \neq D_0$, we will **reject $H_0: \mu_1 - \mu_2 = 0$ if the absolute value of t is greater than** $t_{\alpha/2} = t_{.025} = 2.306$. Here the $t_{\alpha/2}$ point is based on $n_1 + n_2 - 2 = 5 + 5 - 2 = 8$ degrees of freedom. Using the data in Table 8.2, the **value of the test statistic** is

$$t = \frac{(\bar{x}_1 - \bar{x}_2) - D_0}{\sqrt{s_p^2\left(\frac{1}{n_1} + \frac{1}{n_2}\right)}} = \frac{(811 - 750.2) - 0}{\sqrt{435.1\left(\frac{1}{5} + \frac{1}{5}\right)}} = 4.6087$$

Because $\lvert t \rvert = 4.6087$ is greater than $t_{.025} = 2.306$, we can reject $H_0: \mu_1 - \mu_2 = 0$ in favour of $H_a: \mu_1 - \mu_2 \neq 0$. We conclude (at an α of .05) that the mean hourly yields obtained by using the two catalysts differ. Furthermore, the point estimate $\bar{x}_1 - \bar{x}_2 = 811 - 750.2 = 60.8$ says we estimate that the mean hourly yield obtained by using Catalyst XA-100 is 60.8 kilograms higher than the mean hourly yield obtained by using catalyst ZB-200.

As we discussed in Section 8.1, it is important to present standardized effect size estimates along with the results of our hypothesis tests, and the t test assessing differences between two independent groups can also be accompanied by a calculation of Hedge's g. For the two-sample test of means, we need to take into account the variance of each population. When the group variances are equal, we can pool the variances, in the same way that we did for the t test that assumes equal samples. For this example, our pooled variance is

$$s_p^2 = \frac{(n_1 - 1)s_1^2 + (n_2 - 1)s_2^2}{n_1 + n_2 - 2} = \frac{(5 - 1)386 + (5 - 1)484.2}{5 + 5 - 2} = 435.1$$

We can now use this pooled variance and the point estimate of population mean differences (i.e., the difference between the sample means) to summarize the difference between catalysts:

$$g = \left\lvert \frac{\bar{x}_1 - \bar{x}_2}{s_p} \right\rvert = \left\lvert \frac{811 - 750.2}{\sqrt{435.1}} \right\rvert = 2.91$$

This suggests that the average hourly yields of the two catalysts are different by 2.91 standard deviations.

FIGURE 8.10 Testing the Equality of Means in the Catalyst Comparison Example in MegaStat

(a) MegaStat output assuming equal variances

XA-100	ZB-200	
811.00	750.20	mean
19.65	22.00	std. dev.
5	5	n
	8	df
	60.800	difference (Group 1 − Group 2)
	435.100	pooled variance
	20.859	pooled std. dev.
	13.192	standard error of difference
	0	hypothesized difference
	4.609	t
	.0017	p-value (two-tailed)

(b) MegaStat output assuming unequal variances

XA-100	ZB-200	
811.00	750.20	mean
19.65	22.00	std. dev.
5	5	n
	7	df
	60.800	difference (Group 1 − Group 2)
	13.192	standard error of difference
	0	hypothesized difference
	4.609	t
	.0025	p-value (two-tailed)

Figure 8.10(a) gives the MegaStat output for using the equal variance t statistic to test H_0 versus H_a. The outputs tell us that $t = 4.6087$ and that the associated p-value is .001736. This very small p-value tells us that we have very strong evidence against H_0: $\mu_1 - \mu_2 = 0$ and in favour of H_a: $\mu_1 - \mu_2 \neq 0$. In other words, we have very strong evidence that the mean hourly yields obtained by using the two catalysts differ. (Note that in Figure 8.10(b) we give the MegaStat output for using an *unequal variances t statistic,* which is discussed in the following pages, to perform the hypothesis test.)

In general, both the "equal variances" and the "unequal variances" procedures outlined in this chapter have been shown to be approximately valid when the sampled populations are only approximately normally distributed (say, if they are mound-shaped). If each of n_1 and n_2 is large (at least 30), *and the n sizes are equal,* both the equal variances procedure and the unequal variances procedure are approximately valid, no matter what probability distributions describe the sampled populations. As the n sizes become progressively more unequal, the Type I error rate of the equal variances procedure is more likely to be inflated. Recent simulation studies have suggested that this inflation of Type I error rate is most likely to occur when the smaller sample size has the larger variance—when the larger sample has the larger variance, the results of a t test conducted using the equal variances procedure are likely to be conservative.[2]

To illustrate the unequal variances procedure,[3] consider the bank customer waiting time situation and recall that $\mu_1 - \mu_2$ is the difference between the mean customer waiting time under the current system and the mean customer waiting time under the new system. Because of cost considerations, the bank manager wants to implement the new system only if it reduces the mean waiting time by more than three minutes. Therefore, the manager will test the

---

[2]"Hazards in choosing between pooled and separate-variances t tests," by D. W. Zimmerman and B. D. Zumbo, *Psicológica, 30,* 2009, pp. 371–390.

[3]There are numerous methods of dealing with unequal variances, but the most commonly employed method is the one outlined in this chapter. It is frequently called *Welch's t test* or the *Welch–Aspin test,* with modified degrees of freedom.

null hypothesis H_0: $\mu_1 - \mu_2 = 3$ versus the alternative hypothesis H_a: $\mu_1 - \mu_2 > 3$. If H_0 can be rejected in favour of H_a at the **.05 level of significance,** the manager will implement the new system. Suppose that a random sample of $n_1 = 100$ waiting times observed under the current system gives a sample mean $\bar{x}_1 = 8.79$ and a sample variance $s_1^2 = 4.8237$. Further, suppose a random sample of $n_2 = 100$ waiting times observed during the trial run of the new system yields a sample mean $\bar{x}_2 = 5.14$ and a sample variance $s_2^2 = 1.7927$. Since each sample is large, we can use the **unequal variances test statistic *t*.** The degrees of freedom for this statistic are

$$df = \frac{(s_1^2/n_1 + s_2^2/n_2)^2}{\dfrac{(s_1^2/n_1)^2}{n_1 - 1} + \dfrac{(s_2^2/n_2)^2}{n_2 - 1}}$$

$$= \frac{[(4.8237/100) + (1.7927/100)]^2}{\dfrac{(4.8237/100)^2}{99} + \dfrac{(1.7927/100)^2}{99}}$$

$$= 163.657$$

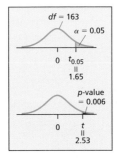

which we will round down to 163. Therefore, because H_a: $\mu_1 - \mu_2 > 3$ is of the form H_a: $\mu_1 - \mu_2 > D_0$, we will **reject H_0: $\mu_1 - \mu_2 = 3$ if the value of the test statistic *t* is greater than** $t_\alpha = t_{.05} = 1.65$ (which is based on 163 degrees of freedom and has been found using a computer program). Using the sample data, the **value of the test statistic** is

$$t = \frac{(\bar{x}_1 - \bar{x}_2) - 3}{\sqrt{\dfrac{s_1^2}{n_1} + \dfrac{s_2^2}{n_2}}} = \frac{(8.79 - 5.14) - 3}{\sqrt{\dfrac{4.8237}{100} + \dfrac{1.7927}{100}}} = \frac{.65}{.25722} = 2.53$$

Because $t = 2.53$ is greater than $t_{.05} = 1.65$, we reject H_0: $\mu_1 - \mu_2 = 3$ in favour of H_a: $\mu_1 - \mu_2 > 3$. We conclude (at an α of .05) that $\mu_1 - \mu_2$ is greater than 3 and, therefore, that the new system reduces the mean customer waiting time by more than 3 minutes. Therefore, the bank manager will implement the new system. Furthermore, the point estimate $\bar{x}_1 - \bar{x}_2 = 3.65$ says that we estimate that the new system reduces mean waiting time by 3.65 minutes.

If we want to present the extent to which the new system reduces mean waiting time as a standardized effect size, then we will need to express the point estimate of the difference between populations in terms of the standard deviation of the distribution of difference scores. When the variances are not substantively different, we can use the pooled standard deviation (i.e., the square root of the pooled variance). When the variances are different, however, this method may not be entirely appropriate. There are numerous ways to accommodate unequal variances in an effect size estimate, but the simplest method was suggested by Cohen—namely, to calculate an average of the variances. This means that the effect size estimate for the difference between the old system and new system in this example, would be calculated as follows:

$$g = \left| \frac{\bar{x}_1 - \bar{x}_2}{\sqrt{\dfrac{s_1^2 + s_2^2}{2}}} \right| = \left| \frac{8.79 - 5.14}{\sqrt{\dfrac{4.8237 + 1.7927}{2}}} \right| = 2.01$$

This suggests that the new system will, on average, result in waiting times that are 2 standard deviations less than the average wait under the old system.

Figure 8.11 gives the MegaStat output resulting from using the unequal variances procedure to test H_0: $\mu_1 - \mu_2 = 3$ versus H_a: $\mu_1 - \mu_2 > 3$. The output tells us that $t = 2.53$ and that the associated *p*-value is .006. The very small *p*-value tells us that we have very strong evidence against H_0: $\mu_1 - \mu_2 = 3$ and in favour of H_a: $\mu_1 - \mu_2 > 3$. That is, we have very strong evidence that $\mu_1 - \mu_2$ is greater than 3 and, therefore, that the new system reduces the mean customer waiting time by more than 3 minutes.

FIGURE **8.11** MegaStat Output of the Unequal Variances Procedure for the Bank Customer Waiting Time Situation

Current	New	
8.79	5.14	mean
2.19629233	1.338917473	std. dev.
100	100	n
	163	df
	3.65000	difference (group 1 − group 2)
	0.25722	standard error of difference
	3	hypothesized difference
	2.527	t
	.0062	p-value (one-tailed, upper)

In general, the degrees of freedom for the unequal variances procedure will always be less than or equal to $n_1 + n_2 - 2$, the degrees of freedom for the equal variances procedure. For example, if we use the unequal variances procedure to analyze the catalyst comparison data in Table 8.2, we can calculate df to be 7.9. This is slightly less than $n_1 + n_2 - 2 = 5 + 5 - 2 = 8$, the degrees of freedom for the equal variances procedure. Figure 8.10(b) gives the MegaStat output of the unequal variances analysis of the catalyst comparison data. Note that the MegaStat unequal variances procedure rounds $df = 7.9$ down to 7 and finds that the test statistic for testing H_0: $\mu_1 - \mu_2 = 0$ versus H_a: $\mu_1 - \mu_2 \neq 0$ is $t = 4.61$ and that the associated p-value is .0025. These results do not differ by much from the results given by the equal variances procedure.

To conclude this section, it is important to point out that if the sample sizes n_1 and n_2 are not large (i.e., they are not at least 30), and if we fear that the sampled populations might be far from normally distributed, we can use a nonparametric method. One nonparametric method for comparing populations when using independent samples is the Wilcoxon rank sum test (sometimes called a *Mann-Whitney U*). This test is discussed in Chapter 13.

ROADBLOCK

We "round off" in a fashion that provides us with the most conservative test
You'll note that we *rounded down* the degrees of freedom when we generated a non-integer degrees of freedom within the unequal variances t test. This is due to the fact that lower degrees of freedom are associated with higher critical values and therefore a more conservative test (i.e., a test with lower Type I error). Although we are always trying to balance both Type I and II errors in our experimental designs, we typically minimize Type I error when rounding values of this sort.

Exercises for Section **8.2**

CONCEPTS

For each of the formulas described below, list all of the assumptions that must be satisfied in order to validly use the formula.

8.15 The t test that is used when variances are assumed to be equal.

8.16 The t test that is used when variances are not assumed to be equal.

8.17 Describe the difference between Hedge's g when used for groups that have equal variances, as compared to when this standardized effect size estimate is used for groups with unequal variances.

METHODS AND APPLICATIONS

Suppose we have taken independent, random samples of sizes $n_1 = 7$ and $n_2 = 7$ from two normally distributed populations having means μ_1 and μ_2, and suppose we obtain $\bar{x}_1 = 240$, $\bar{x}_2 = 210$, $s_1 = 5$, and $s_2 = 6$. Using the equal variances procedure, do Exercises 8.18 and 8.19.

8.18 Use critical values to test the null hypothesis H_0: $\mu_1 - \mu_2 \leq 20$ versus the alternative hypothesis H_a: $\mu_1 - \mu_2 > 20$ by setting α equal to .10, .05, .01, and .001. How much evidence is there that the difference between μ_1 and μ_2 exceeds 20?

8.19 Use critical values to test the null hypothesis H_0: $\mu_1 - \mu_2 = 20$ versus the alternative hypothesis H_a: $\mu_1 - \mu_2 \neq 20$ by setting α equal to .10, .05, .01, and .001. How much evidence is there that the difference between μ_1 and μ_2 is not equal to 20?

8.20 Repeat Exercises 8.18 and 8.19 using the unequal variances procedure. Compare your results to those obtained using the equal variances procedure.

8.21 Suppose that a random sample of 12 stock funds has a mean management expense ratio (MER) of 1.63 percent with a standard deviation of .31 percent, and an independent random sample of 12 municipal bond funds has a mean annual expense of 0.89 percent with a standard deviation of .23 percent. Let μ_1 be the mean annual expense for stock funds, and let μ_2 be the mean annual expense for municipal bond funds. Assuming that stock fund expenses and municipal bond fund expenses are each approximately normally distributed, do parts (a) and (b) using the equal variances procedure. Then repeat (a) and (b) using the unequal variances procedure. Compare your results.

a. Set up the null and alternative hypotheses needed to attempt to establish that the mean annual expense for stock funds is larger than the mean annual expense for municipal bond funds. Test these hypotheses at the .05 level of significance. What do you conclude? Report an appropriate effect size estimate along with your hypothesis test.

b. Set up the null and alternative hypotheses needed to attempt to establish that the mean annual expense for stock funds exceeds the mean annual expense for municipal bond funds by more than .5 percent. Test these hypotheses at the .05 level of significance. What do you conclude?

8.22 In the book *Business Research Methods,* Donald R. Cooper and C. William Emory (1995) discuss a manager who wants to compare the effectiveness of two methods for training new salespeople. The authors describe the situation as follows:

> The company selects 22 sales trainees who are randomly divided into two experimental groups—one receives type *A* and the other type *B* training. The salespeople are then assigned and managed without regard to the training they have received. At the year's end, the manager reviews the performances of salespeople in these groups and finds the following results:

	A Group	B Group
Average Weekly Sales	$\bar{x}_1 = \$1{,}500$	$\bar{x}_2 = \$1{,}300$
Standard Deviation	$s_1 = 225$	$s_2 = 251$

a. Set up the null and alternative hypotheses needed to attempt to establish that type *A* training results in higher mean weekly sales than does type *B* training.

b. Because different sales trainees are assigned to the two experimental groups, it is reasonable to believe that the two samples are independent. Assuming that the normality assumption holds, and using the equal variances procedure, test the hypotheses you set up in part (a) at levels of significance .10, .05, .01, and .001. How much evidence is there that type *A* training produces results that are superior to those of type *B*? Report an appropriate effect size estimate along with your hypothesis test.

8.23 A marketing research firm wants to compare the prices charged by two supermarket chains—Sobeys and Metro. The research firm, using a standardized one-week shopping plan (grocery list) makes identical purchases at 10 of each chain's stores. The stores for each chain are randomly selected, and all purchases are made during a single week.

The shopping expenses obtained at the two chains, along with box plots of the expenses, are as follows:

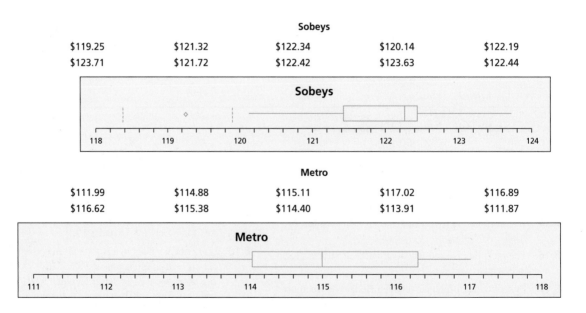

Sobeys				
$119.25	$121.32	$122.34	$120.14	$122.19
$123.71	$121.72	$122.42	$123.63	$122.44

Metro				
$111.99	$114.88	$115.11	$117.02	$116.89
$116.62	$115.38	$114.40	$113.91	$111.87

Because the stores in each sample are different stores in different chains, it is reasonable to assume that the samples are independent, and we assume that weekly expenses at each chain are normally distributed.

a. Letting μ_M be the mean weekly expense for the shopping plan at Sobeys, and letting μ_A be the mean weekly expense for the shopping plan at Metro, Figure 8.12 gives the MegaStat output of the test of $H_0: \mu_M - \mu_A = 0$ (that is, there is no difference between μ_M and μ_A) versus $H_a: \mu_M - \mu_A \neq 0$ (that is, μ_M and μ_A differ). Note that we have employed the equal variances procedure in MegaStat. Use the sample data to show that $\bar{x}_M = 121.92$, $s_M = 1.40$, $\bar{x}_A = 114.81$, $s_A = 1.84$, and $t = 9.73$. Calculate an appropriate effect size estimate to report along with this hypothesis test.

b. Using the t statistic given on the output and critical values, test H_0 versus H_a by setting α equal to .10, .05, .01, and .001. How much evidence is there that the mean weekly expenses at Sobeys and Metro differ?

c. Figure 8.12 gives the p-value for testing $H_0: \mu_M - \mu_A = 0$ versus $H_a: \mu_M - \mu_A \neq 0$. Use the p-value to test H_0 versus H_a by setting α equal to .10, .05, .01, and .001. How much evidence is there that the mean weekly expenses at Sobeys and Metro differ?

d. Set up the null and alternative hypotheses needed to attempt to establish that the mean weekly expense for the shopping plan at Sobeys exceeds the mean weekly expense at Metro by more than $5. Test the hypotheses at the .10, .05, .01, and .001 levels of significance. How much evidence is there that the mean weekly expense at Sobeys exceeds that at Metro by more than $5?

8.24 A large discount chain compares the performance of its credit managers in Alberta and Manitoba by comparing the mean dollar amounts owed by customers with delinquent charge accounts in these two provinces. Here a small mean dollar amount owed is desirable because it indicates that bad credit risks are not being extended large amounts of credit. Two independent, random samples of delinquent accounts are selected from the populations of delinquent accounts in Alberta and Manitoba, respectively. The first sample, which consists of 10 randomly selected delinquent accounts in Alberta, gives a mean dollar amount of $524

with a standard deviation of $68. The second sample, which consists of 20 randomly selected delinquent accounts in Manitoba, gives a mean dollar amount of $473 with a standard deviation of $22.

a. Set up the null and alternative hypotheses needed to test whether there is a difference between the population mean dollar amounts owed by customers with delinquent charge accounts in Alberta and Manitoba.

b. Figure 8.13 gives a MegaStat output that uses the unequal variances procedure to test the equality of mean dollar amounts owed by customers with delinquent charge accounts in Alberta and Manitoba. Assuming that the normality assumption holds, test the hypotheses you set up in part (a) by setting α equal to .10, .05, .01, and .001. How much evidence is there that the mean dollar amounts owed in Alberta and Manitoba differ? Calculate an appropriate effect size estimate to report along with this hypothesis test.

8.25 A loan officer compares the interest rates for 48-month fixed-rate auto loans and 48-month variable-rate auto loans. Two independent, random samples of auto loan rates are selected. A sample of eight 48-month fixed-rate auto loans had the following loan rates:

| 8.29% | 7.75% | 7.50% | 7.99% |
| 7.75% | 7.99% | 9.40% | 8.00% |

while a sample of five 48-month variable-rate auto loans had loan rates as follows:

| 7.59% | 6.75% | 6.99% | 6.50% | 7.00% |

a. Set up the null and alternative hypotheses needed to determine whether the mean rates for 48-month fixed-rate and variable-rate auto loans differ.

b. Figure 8.14 gives the MegaStat output of using the equal variances procedure to test the hypotheses you set up in part (a). Assuming that the normality and equal variances assumptions hold, use the output and critical values to test these hypotheses by setting α equal to .10, .05, .01, and .001. How much evidence is there that the mean rates for 48-month fixed- and variable-rate auto loans differ? Calculate an appropriate effect size estimate to report along with this hypothesis test.

FIGURE **8.12** MegaStat Output of Testing the Equality of Mean Weekly Expenses at Sobeys and Metro Supermarket Chains (for Exercise 8.23)

Sobeys	Metro	
121.9160	114.8070	mean
1.3982	1.8403	std. dev.
10	10	n
	18	df
	7.10900	difference (Sobeys − Metro)
	2.67086	pooled variance
	1.63428	pooled std. dev.
	0.73087	standard error of difference
	0	hypothesized difference
	9.727	t
	1.37E-08	p-value (two-tailed)

FIGURE **8.13** MegaStat Output of Testing the Equality of Mean Dollar Amounts Owed for Alberta and Manitoba (for Exercise 8.24)

Alberta	Manitoba	
524	473	mean
68	22	std. dev.
10	20	n
	9	df
	51.000	difference (Alberta − Manitoba)
	22.059	standard error of difference
	0	hypothesized difference
	2.312	t
	.0461	p-value (two-tailed)

FIGURE **8.14**   MegaStat Output of Testing the Equality of
Mean Loan Rates for Fixed and Variable
48-Month Auto Loans (for Exercise 8.25)

Fixed Rate	Variable Rate	
8.0838	6.9660	mean
0.5810	0.4046	std. dev.
8	5	*n*
	11	*df*
	1.11775	difference (Fixed Rate − Variable Rate)
	0.27437	pooled variance
	0.52381	pooled std. dev.
	0.29862	standard error of difference
	0	hypothesized difference
	3.743	*t*
	.0032	*p*-value (two-tailed)

c. Figure 8.14 gives the *p*-value for testing the
hypotheses you set up in part (a). Use the *p*-value to
test these hypotheses by setting α equal to .10, .05,
.01, and .001. How much evidence is there that the
mean rates for 48-month fixed- and variable-rate
auto loans differ?

d. Use a hypothesis test to establish that the difference
between the mean rates for fixed- and variable-rate
48-month auto loans exceeds .4 percent. Use α equal
to .05.

8.3 PAIRED DIFFERENCE EXPERIMENTS

Example 8.3   Comparing Repair Costs between Garages

LO3

Provincial Casualty, specializing in automobile insurance, wants to compare the repair costs of
moderately damaged cars (repair costs between $700 and $1,400) at two garages. One way to
study these costs would be to take two independent samples (here we arbitrarily assume that
each sample is of size $n = 7$). First we would randomly select seven moderately damaged cars
that have recently been in accidents. Each of these cars would be taken to the first garage
(Garage 1), and repair cost estimates would be obtained. Then we would randomly select seven
different moderately damaged cars, and repair cost estimates for these cars would be obtained
at the second garage (Garage 2). This sampling procedure would give us independent samples
because the cars taken to Garage 1 differ from those taken to Garage 2. However, because the
repair costs for moderately damaged cars can range from $700 to $1,400, there can be substantial differences in damages to moderately damaged cars. These differences might tend to
conceal any real differences between repair costs at the two garages. For example, suppose the
repair cost estimates for the cars taken to Garage 1 are higher than those for the cars taken to
Garage 2. This difference might exist because Garage 1 charges customers more for repair
work than does Garage 2. However, the difference could also arise because the cars taken to
Garage 1 are more severely damaged than the cars taken to Garage 2.

To overcome this difficulty, we can perform a paired difference experiment. Here we could
randomly select one sample of $n = 7$ moderately damaged cars. The cars in this sample would
be taken to both garages and a repair cost estimate for each car would be obtained at each
garage. The advantage of the paired difference experiment is that the repair cost estimates at
the two garages are obtained for the same cars, so any true differences in the repair cost estimates would not be concealed by possible differences in the severity of damages to the cars.

Suppose that when we perform the paired difference experiment, we obtain the repair cost
estimates in Table 8.3. To analyze these data, we calculate the difference between the repair
cost estimates at the two garages for each car. The resulting paired differences are given in the
last column of Table 8.3. The mean of the sample of $n = 7$ paired differences is

$$\bar{d} = \frac{-80 + (-110) + (-120) + \cdots + (-140)}{7} = -80$$

which equals the difference between the sample means of the repair cost estimates at the two garages

$$\bar{x}_1 - \bar{x}_2 = 932.86 - 1{,}012.86 = -80$$

TABLE 8.3   A Sample of $n = 7$ Paired Differences of the Repair Cost Estimates at Garages 1 and 2 📝

Sample of $n = 7$ Damaged Cars	Repair Cost Estimates at Garage 1	Repair Cost Estimates at Garage 2	Sample of $n = 7$ Paired Differences
Car 1	$ 710	$ 790	$d_1 = -80$
Car 2	900	1,010	$d_2 = -110$
Car 3	1,100	1,220	$d_3 = -120$
Car 4	890	880	$d_4 = 10$
Car 5	990	1,040	$d_5 = -50$
Car 6	910	980	$d_6 = -70$
Car 7	1,030	1,170	$d_7 = -140$
	$\bar{x} = \$932.86$	$\bar{x} = \$1,012.86$	$\bar{d} = -80 = \bar{x}_1 - \bar{x}_2$
			$s_d^2 = 2,533.33$
			$s_d = 50.33$

Furthermore, $\bar{d} = -80$ (that is, $-\$80$) is the point estimate of

$$\mu_d = \mu_1 - \mu_2$$

the mean of the population of all possible paired differences of the repair cost estimates (for all possible moderately damaged cars) at Garages 1 and 2—which is equivalent to μ_1, the mean of all possible repair cost estimates at Garage 1, minus μ_2, the mean of all possible repair cost estimates at Garage 2. This says we estimate that the mean of all possible repair cost estimates at Garage 1 is \$80 less than the mean of all possible repair cost estimates at Garage 2.

In addition, the variance and standard deviation of the sample of $n = 7$ paired differences

$$s_d^2 = \frac{\sum_{i=1}^{7}(d_i - \bar{d})^2}{7 - 1} = 2{,}533.33$$

and

$$s_d = \sqrt{2{,}533.33} = 50.33$$

are the point estimates of σ_d^2 and σ_d, the variance and standard deviation of the population of all possible paired differences.

ROADBLOCK

Order matters when subtracting the columns of values to get your average difference score

Remember to follow the same subtraction rule throughout your calculations, when you are deriving an average difference score. Otherwise, your difference score will not accurately reflect the magnitude of the difference between groups and might not reflect the correct direction of the difference. For example, if you were to subtract the scores in Table 8.3 in such a way as to obtain a positive score for each paired difference, you would calculate a group difference of 82.86, rather than -80.

LO4

In general, suppose we want to compare two population means, μ_1 and μ_2. Also suppose that we have obtained two different measurements (for example, repair cost estimates) on the same n units (for example, cars), and suppose we have calculated the n paired differences between these measurements. Let $\bar{d}$ and s_d be the mean and the standard deviation of these n paired differences. If it is reasonable to assume that the paired differences have been randomly selected from a normally distributed (or at least mound-shaped) population of paired differences with mean μ_d and standard deviation σ_d, then the sampling distribution of

$$\frac{\bar{d} - \mu_d}{s_d / \sqrt{n}}$$

is a t distribution having $n - 1$ degrees of freedom.

We can test a hypothesis about μ_d, the mean of a population of paired differences. We show how to test the null hypothesis

$$H_0 : \mu_d = D_0$$

in the following box. Here the value of the constant D_0 depends on the particular problem. Often D_0 equals 0, and the null hypothesis $H_0 : \mu_d = 0$ says that μ_1 and μ_2 do not differ.

Testing a Hypothesis about the Mean, μ_d, of a Population of Paired Differences

Assume that the population of paired differences is normally distributed, and consider testing

$$H_0 : \mu_d = D_0$$

by using the test statistic

$$t = \frac{\bar{d} - D_0}{s_d / \sqrt{n}}$$

We can test $H_0 : \mu_d = D_0$ versus a particular alternative hypothesis at level of significance α by using the appropriate critical value rule, or, equivalently, the corresponding p-value.

Alternative Hypothesis	Critical Value Rule: Reject H_0 if	p-Value (reject H_0 if p-Value $< \alpha$)
$H_a : \mu_d > D_0$	$t > t_\alpha$	The area under the t distribution curve to the right of t
$H_a : \mu_d < D_0$	$t < -t_\alpha$	The area under the t distribution curve to the left of t
$H_a : \mu_d \neq D_0$	$\|t\| > t_{\alpha/2}$—that is, $t > t_{\alpha/2}$ or $t < -t_{\alpha/2}$	Twice the area under the t distribution curve to the right of $\|t\|$

Here t_α, $t_{\alpha/2}$, and the p-values are based on $n - 1$ degrees of freedom.

ROADBLOCK

The paired t test has $df = n - 1$, while the independent groups t test has $df = (n_1 + n_2) - 2$ The paired t test evaluates the mean of the differences between groups, rather than evaluating the differences between the means of the groups. This is a subtle, but important, difference that is reflected in a number of facets of the t test. For one, the paired t test is evaluated as being done on a sample size equal to the *number of pairs*, rather than the number of observations. For another, the mean of these difference scores is evaluated by using the standard deviation of the difference scores, rather than a pooled variance estimate calculated by taking the variability of both groups into account. Finally, because we are evaluating only the pairs within the test, the paired t test has fewer degrees of freedom than an equivalent independent groups t test—with the degrees of freedom of the paired t test calculated to be $n - 1$ and the degrees of freedom for the independent groups t test calculated to be $(n_1 + n_2) - 2$.

Provincial Casualty currently contracts to have moderately damaged cars repaired at Garage 2. However, a local insurance agent suggests that Garage 1 provides less expensive repair service that is of equal quality. Because it has done business with Garage 2 for years, Provincial has decided to give some of its repair business to Garage 1 only if it has very strong evidence that μ_1, the mean repair cost estimate at Garage 1, is smaller than μ_2, the mean repair cost estimate at Garage 2—that is, if $\mu_d = \mu_1 - \mu_2$ is less than zero. Therefore, we will test $H_0 : \mu_d = 0$ or, equivalently, $H_0 : \mu_1 - \mu_2 = 0$, versus $H_a : \mu_d < 0$ or, equivalently, $H_a : \mu_1 - \mu_2 < 0$, at the

.01 level of significance. To perform the hypothesis test, we will use the sample data in Table 8.3 to calculate the value of the **test statistic t.** Because H_a: $\mu_d < 0$ is of the form H_a: $\mu_d < D_0$, we will **reject H_0: $\mu_d = 0$ if the value of t is less than $-t_\alpha = -t_{.01} = -3.143$.** Here the t_α point is based on $n - 1 = 7 - 1 = 6$ degrees of freedom. Using the data in Table 8.3, the **value of the test statistic** is

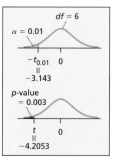

$$t = \frac{\bar{d} - D_0}{s_d/\sqrt{n}} = \frac{-80 - 0}{50.33/\sqrt{7}} = -4.2053$$

Because $t = -4.2053$ is less than $-t_{.01} = -3.143$, we can reject H_0: $\mu_d = 0$ in favour of H_a: $\mu_d < 0$. We conclude (at an α of .01) that μ_1, the mean repair cost estimate at Garage 1, is less than μ_2, the mean repair cost estimate at Garage 2. As a result, Provincial will give some of its repair business to Garage 1. Furthermore, Figure 8.15 gives the MegaStat output of this hypothesis test and shows us that the p-value for the test is .0028. Since this p-value is very small, we have very strong evidence that H_0 should be rejected and that μ_1 is less than μ_2. Had we tested the hypotheses H_0: $\mu_d = 0$ versus H_a: $\mu_d \neq 0$, we would have found a p-value of .0057.

The paired t test looks very similar to the single sample t test that we introduced in Section 8.1. This is because the test is designed to test the difference between the mean of a set of difference scores and our null hypothesized difference between group, and compares this with a standard error that is similarly calculated on a singular set of values. This similarity extends to our calculation of Hedge's g, which now scales our point estimate of the difference between population means (i.e., the average of the paired differences) by the standard deviation of paired differences. For this example, this calculation would look like this:

$$g = \left| \frac{\bar{d}}{s_d} \right| = \left| \frac{-80}{50.33} \right| = 1.59$$

This suggests that the average repair cost at Garage 1 is 1.59 standard deviations lower than the average repair cost at Garage 2.

As explained earlier, an experiment in which we have obtained two different measurements on the same n units is called a *paired difference experiment*. The idea of this type of experiment is to remove the variability due to the variable (for example, the amount of damage to a car) on which the observations are paired. In many situations, a paired difference experiment will provide more information than an independent samples experiment. As another example, suppose that we want to assess which of two different machines produces a higher hourly output. If we randomly select 10 machine operators and randomly assign 5 of these operators to test Machine 1 and the others to test Machine 2, we would be performing an independent samples experiment. This is because different machine operators test Machines 1 and 2. However, any difference in machine outputs could be obscured by differences in the abilities of the machine operators. For instance, if the observed hourly outputs are higher for Machine 1 than for Machine 2, we might not be able to tell whether this is due to (1) the superiority of Machine 1 or (2) the possible higher skill level of the operators who tested Machine 1. Because of this,

FIGURE 8.15 MegaStat Output of Testing H_0: $\mu_d = 0$ versus H_a: $\mu_d < 0$

0.0000	hypothesized value
932.857	mean Garage 1
1012.857	mean Garage 2
−80.000	mean difference (Garage 1 − Garage 2)
50.332	std. dev.
19.024	std. error
7	n
6	df
−4.205	t
.0028	p-value (one-tailed, lower)

it might be better to randomly select five machine operators, thoroughly train each operator to use both machines, and have each operator test both machines. We would then be *pairing on the machine operator*, and this would remove the variability due to the differing abilities of the operators.

The formulas we have given for analyzing a paired difference experiment are based on the *t* distribution, and these formulas assume that the population of all possible paired differences is normally distributed (or at least mound-shaped). If the sample size is large (say, at least 30), the *t*-based interval and tests of this section are approximately valid no matter what the shape of the population of all possible paired differences. If the sample size is small, and if we fear that the population of all paired differences might be far from normally distributed, we can use a nonparametric method. One nonparametric method for comparing two populations when using a paired difference experiment is the Wilcoxon signed ranks test, which is discussed in Chapter 13.

ROADBLOCK

The *p*-value for a two-tailed test is twice as large as the *p*-value for an equivalent one-tailed test

The MegaStat analysis described in Figure 8.15 has a *p*-value of 0.0028 because it was conducted as a one-tailed hypothesis test. Had it been conducted as a two-tailed hypothesis test, the *p*-value would have been twice as large, owing to the fact that there would have been two rejection regions with identical areas under the curve (one in the upper end of the distribution, and one in the lower end of the distribution).

THEORY TO PRACTICE

With the possible exception of a comparison of frequency counts, there really is no quantitative comparison more common than a comparison of means. When you are in school, you compare your grade against the class mean or against your historical best performance in a particular topic. When you shop, you are implicitly comparing prices against your sense of "good value," which is, to some degree, probably based on the average advertised price that you have seen. And finally, in business, we compare performance, using average sales figures, or profit margins, or average percentage returns.

We may compare these averages to historical figures, or we may compare groups, but the point is that you will inevitably encounter situations in which you will be called on to determine whether two mean values are "truly different." This is the crux of the material that has been presented in this chapter to this point. When we assign a *p*-value to a particular mean comparison, we are making a judgment as to the likelihood that our assumption (captured by the null hypothesis statement) is correct. And when we calculate a standardized effect size estimate, we are attempting to reformat the information so that it is on a scale that is intuitively accessible to our intended audience (e.g., standard deviations separating the values in your two groups, or separating your sample mean from a hypothetical mean). Systematicity and rationality (in the form of null hypothesis significance testing) combined with standardized reporting methods (in the form of effect size estimation) is likely to lead to better business decision making, particularly with quantitative questions.

Exercises for Section **8.3**

CONCEPTS

8.26 Explain how a paired difference experiment differs from an independent samples experiment in terms of how the data for these experiments are collected.

8.27 Why is a paired difference experiment sometimes more informative than an independent samples experiment? Give an example of a situation in which a paired difference experiment might be advantageous.

8.28 What assumptions must be satisfied to appropriately carry out a paired difference experiment? When can we carry out a paired difference experiment no matter what the shape of the population of all paired differences might be?

8.29 Suppose a company wants to compare the hourly output of its employees before and after vacations. Explain how you would collect data for a paired difference experiment to make this comparison.

METHODS AND APPLICATIONS

8.30 Suppose a sample of 11 paired differences that has been randomly selected from a normally distributed population of paired differences yields a sample mean of $\bar{d} = 103.5$ and a sample standard deviation of $s_d = 5$.

a. Test the null hypothesis $H_0: \mu_d \leq 100$ versus $H_a: \mu_d > 100$ by setting α equal to .05 and .01. How much evidence is there that $\mu_d = \mu_1 - \mu_2$ exceeds 100?

b. Test the null hypothesis $H_0: \mu_d \geq 110$ versus $H_a: \mu_d < 110$ by setting α equal to .05 and .01. How much evidence is there that $\mu_d = \mu_1 - \mu_2$ is less than 110?

8.31 Suppose a sample of 49 paired differences that have been randomly selected from a normally distributed population of paired differences yields a sample mean of $\bar{d} = 5$ and a sample standard deviation of $s_d = 7$.

a. Test the null hypothesis $H_0: \mu_d = 0$ versus the alternative hypothesis $H_a: \mu_d \neq 0$ by setting α equal to .10, .05, .01, and .001. How much evidence is there that μ_d differs from 0? What does this say about how μ_1 and μ_2 compare? Calculate a standardized effect size estimate to support your conclusions.

b. The p-value for testing $H_0: \mu_d \leq 3$ versus $H_a: \mu_d > 3$ equals .0256. Use the p-value to test these hypotheses with α equal to .10, .05, .01, and .001. How much evidence is there that μ_d exceeds 3? What does this say about the size of the difference between μ_1 and μ_2?

8.32 RateHub.ca provides a summary of mortgage loan interest rates for a variety of different fixed-rate terms available across Canada. You are interested in determining whether there is any systematic difference between 10-year rates and 5-year rates (expressed as annual percentage rate or APR) and, if there is, the size of that difference. Table 8.4 displays mortgage loan rates and the difference between 10-year and 5-year rates for 9 lending institutions. Assuming that the population of paired differences is normally distributed:

a. Set up the null and alternative hypotheses needed to determine whether there is a difference between mean 10-year rates and mean 5-year rates.

TABLE 8.4 Mortgage Loan Interest Rates for Nine Canadian Lending Institutions 🖋

Lending Institution	Annual Percentage Rate		
	10-Year	5-Year	Difference
ING Direct	3.99%	3.09%	.9%
Bank of Montreal	4.49	3.09	1.4
President's Choice Financial	4.29	3.34	.95
Laurentian Bank	6.75	3.79	2.96
Scotiabank	3.99	3.99	0
National Bank of Canada	6.75	3.99	2.76
TD Canada Trust	3.99	5.24	−1.25
Royal Bank of Canada	3.99	5.24	−1.25
CIBC	6.75	5.24	1.51

Source: RateHub.ca, December 31, 2012.

b. Figure 8.16 gives the MegaStat output for testing the hypotheses that you set up in part (a). Use the output and critical values to test these hypotheses by setting α equal to .10, .05, .01, and .001. How much evidence is there that mean mortgage loan rates for 10-year and 5-year terms differ? Present an appropriate effect size estimate along with your hypothesis test.

FIGURE 8.16 MegaStat Paired Difference t Test of the Mortgage Loan Rate Data (for Exercise 8.32)

0.00000	hypothesized value
4.99889	mean 10-year
4.11222	mean 5-year
0.88667	mean difference (10-year − 5-year)
1.51580	std. dev.
0.50527	std. error
9	n
8	df
1.755	t
.1174	p-value (two-tailed)

c. Figure 8.16 gives the p-value for testing the hypotheses that you set up in part (a). Use the p-value to test these hypotheses by setting α equal to .10, .05, .01, and .001. How much evidence is there that mean mortgage loan rates for 10-year and 5-year terms differ?

8.33 In the book *Essentials of Marketing Research*, William R. Dillon, Thomas J. Madden, and Neil H. Firtle (1993) present pre-exposure and post-exposure attitude scores from an advertising study involving 10 respondents. The data for the experiment are given in Table 8.5. Assuming that the differences between pairs of post-exposure and pre-exposure scores are normally distributed:

a. Set up the null and alternative hypotheses needed to attempt to establish that the advertisement increases the mean attitude score (that is, that the mean post-exposure attitude score is higher than the mean pre-exposure attitude score).

TABLE 8.5 Pre-Exposure and Post-Exposure Attitude Scores (for Exercise 8.33) 🖋

Subject	Pre-Exposure Attitudes (A_1)	Post-Exposure Attitudes (A_2)	Attitude Change (d_i)
1	50	53	3
2	25	27	2
3	30	38	8
4	50	55	5
5	60	61	1
6	80	85	5
7	45	45	0
8	30	31	1
9	65	72	7
10	70	78	8

Source: W. R. Dillon, T. J. Madden, and N. H. Firtle, *Essentials of Marketing Research* (Burr Ridge, IL: Richard D. Irwin, 1993), p. 435. Copyright © 1993. Reprinted by permission of McGraw-Hill Companies, Inc.

b. Test the hypotheses you set up in part (a) at the .10, .05, .01, and .001 levels of significance. How much evidence is there that the advertisement increases the mean attitude score? Present an appropriate effect size estimate along with your hypothesis test.

8.34 National Paper Company must purchase a new machine for producing cardboard boxes. The company must choose between two machines. The machines produce boxes of equal quality, so the company will choose the machine that produces (on average) the most boxes. It is known that there are substantial differences in the abilities of the company's machine operators. Therefore National Paper has decided to compare the machines using a paired difference experiment. Suppose that eight randomly selected machine operators produce boxes for one hour using Machine 1 and for one hour using Machine 2, with the following results:

	Machine Operator							
	1	**2**	**3**	**4**	**5**	**6**	**7**	**8**
Machine 1	53	60	58	48	46	54	62	49
Machine 2	50	55	56	44	45	50	57	47

Assuming normality, perform a hypothesis test to determine whether there is a difference between the mean hourly outputs of the two machines. Use $\alpha = .05$. Present an appropriate effect size estimate along with your hypothesis test.

8.35 During 2012, a company implemented a number of policies aimed at reducing the ages of its customers' accounts. To assess the effectiveness of these measures, the company randomly selects 10 customer accounts. The average age of each account is determined for the years 2011 and 2012. These data are given in Table 8.6. Assuming that the population of paired differences between the average ages in 2012 and 2011 is normally distributed:

TABLE 8.6   Average Account Ages in 2011 and 2012 for Ten Randomly Selected Accounts (for Exercise 8.35)

Account	Average Age of Account in 2012 (Days)	Average Age of Account in 2011 (Days)
1	27	35
2	19	24
3	40	47
4	30	28
5	33	41
6	25	33
7	31	35
8	29	51
9	15	18
10	21	28

a. Set up the null and alternative hypotheses needed to establish that the mean average account age has been reduced by the company's new policies.

b. Figure 8.17 gives the MegaStat output needed to test the hypotheses of part (a). Use critical values to test these hypotheses by setting α equal to .10, .05, .01, and .001. How much evidence is there that the mean average account age has been reduced? Present an appropriate effect size estimate along with your hypothesis test.

c. Figure 8.17 gives the *p*-value for testing the hypotheses of part (a). Use the *p*-value to test these hypotheses by setting α equal to .10, .05, .01, and .001. How much evidence is there that account age has been reduced?

FIGURE 8.17   MegaStat Output of a Paired Difference Analysis of the Account Age Data (for Exercise 8.35)

0.000	hypothesized value
27.000	mean 2012
34.000	mean 2011
−7.000	mean difference (2012 − 2011)
6.128	std. dev.
1.938	std. error
10	*n*
9	*df*
−3.612	*t*
.0028	*p*-value (one-tailed, lower)

8.36 Do students reduce study time in courses in which they achieve a higher midterm score? In a *Journal of Economic Education* article (Winter 2005), Gregory Krohn and Catherine O'Connor studied student effort and performance in a class over a semester. In an intermediate macroeconomics course, they found that "students respond to higher midterm scores by reducing the number of hours they subsequently allocate to studying for the course."[4] Suppose that a random sample of $n = 8$ students who performed well on the midterm exam was taken and weekly study times before and after the exam were compared. The resulting data are given in Table 8.7. Assume that the population of all possible paired differences is normally distributed.

TABLE 8.7   Weekly Study Time Data for Students Who Perform Well on the Midterm

Students	1	2	3	4	5	6	7	8
Before	15	14	17	17	19	14	13	16
After	9	9	11	10	19	10	14	10

[4]Source: "Student Effort and Performance over the Semester," by G. A. Krohn and C. M. O'Connor, *Journal of Economic Education,* 36/1, 2005, pp. 3–28.

a. Set up the null and alternative hypotheses to test whether there is a difference in the true mean study time before and after the midterm exam.

b. To the right, we present the MegaStat output for the paired differences test. Use the output and critical values to test the hypotheses at the .10, .05, and .01 levels of significance. Has the true mean study time changed? Present an appropriate effect size estimate along with your hypothesis test.

c. Use the *p*-value to test the hypotheses at the .10, .05, and .01 levels of significance. How much evidence is there against the null hypothesis?

0.000	hypothesized value
15.625	mean Before
11.500	mean After
4.125	mean difference (Before − After)
2.997	std. dev.
1.060	std. error
8	*n*
7	*df*
3.893	*t*
.0060	*p*-value (two-tailed)

8.4 COMPARING TWO POPULATION VARIANCES BY USING INDEPENDENT SAMPLES

We have seen (in Sections 8.2 and 8.3) that we often want to compare two population means. In addition, it is often useful to compare two population variances. For example, in the bank waiting time example, we might compare the variance of the waiting times experienced under the current and new systems. Or, as another example, we might want to compare the variance of the chemical yields obtained when using Catalyst XA-100 with that obtained when using Catalyst ZB-200. Here, the catalyst that produces yields with the smaller variance is giving more consistent (or predictable) results.

If σ_1^2 and σ_2^2 are the population variances that we want to compare, one approach is to test the null hypothesis

$$H_0: \sigma_1^2 = \sigma_2^2$$

We might test H_0 versus an alternative hypothesis of, for instance,

$$H_a: \sigma_1^2 > \sigma_2^2$$

Dividing by σ_2^2, we see that testing these hypotheses is equivalent to testing

$$H_0: \frac{\sigma_1^2}{\sigma_2^2} = 1 \text{ versus } H_a: \frac{\sigma_1^2}{\sigma_2^2} > 1$$

Intuitively, we would reject H_0 in favour of H_a if s_1^2/s_2^2 is significantly larger than 1. Here s_1^2 is the variance of a random sample of n_1 observations from the population with variance σ_1^2, and s_2^2 is the variance of a random sample of n_2 observations from the population with variance σ_2^2. To decide exactly how large s_1^2/s_2^2 must be in order to reject H_0, we need to consider the sampling distribution of s_1^2/s_2^2.[5]

It can be shown that, if the null hypothesis $H_0: \sigma_1^2/\sigma_2^2 = 1$ is true, then the population of all possible values of s_1^2/s_2^2 is described by what is called an **F distribution**. In general, as illustrated in Figure 8.18, the curve of the *F* distribution is skewed to the right. Moreover, the exact shape of this curve depends on two parameters that are called the *numerator degrees of freedom* (denoted df_1) and the *denominator degrees of freedom* (denoted df_2). The values of df_1 and df_2 that describe the **sampling distribution of** s_1^2/s_2^2 are given in the following boxed feature.

LO5

---

[5]Note that we divide by σ_2^2 to form a null hypothesis of the form $H_0: \frac{\sigma_1^2}{\sigma_2^2} = 1$ rather than subtracting σ_2^2 to form a null hypothesis of the form $H_0: \sigma_1^2 - \sigma_2^2 = 0$. This is because the population of all possible values of $s_1^2 - s_2^2$ has no known sampling distribution.

FIGURE 8.18   *F* Distribution Curves and *F* Points

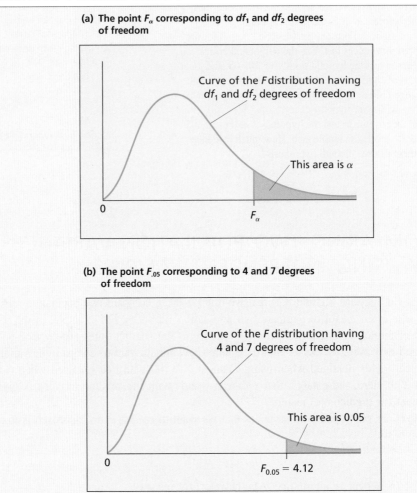

(a) The point F_α corresponding to df_1 and df_2 degrees of freedom

Curve of the *F* distribution having df_1 and df_2 degrees of freedom

This area is α

0

F_α

(b) The point $F_{.05}$ corresponding to 4 and 7 degrees of freedom

Curve of the *F* distribution having 4 and 7 degrees of freedom

This area is 0.05

0

$F_{0.05} = 4.12$

The Sampling Distribution of s_1^2/s_2^2

Suppose we randomly select independent samples from two normally distributed populations having variances σ_1^2 and σ_2^2. Then, if the null hypothesis $H_0: \sigma_1^2/\sigma_2^2 = 1$ is true, the population of all possible values of s_1^2/s_2^2 has an *F* distribution with $df_1 = (n_1 - 1)$ numerator degrees of freedom and with $df_2 = (n_2 - 1)$ denominator degrees of freedom.

LO6

In order to use the *F* distribution, we employ an *F* point, which is denoted F_α. As illustrated in Figure 8.18(a), F_α is the point on the horizontal axis under the curve of the *F* distribution that gives a right-hand tail area equal to α. The value of F_α in a particular situation depends on the size of the right-hand tail area (the size of α) and on the numerator degrees of freedom (df_1) and the denominator degrees of freedom (df_2). Values of F_α are given in an *F* table. Tables A.6, A.7, A.8, and A.9 in Appendix A give values of $F_{.10}$, $F_{.05}$, $F_{.025}$, and $F_{.01}$, respectively. Each table tabulates values of F_α according to the appropriate numerator degrees of freedom (values listed across the top of the table) and the appropriate denominator degrees of freedom (values listed down the left side of the table). A portion of Table A.7, which gives values of $F_{.05}$, is reproduced in this chapter as Table 8.8. For instance, suppose we want to find the *F* point that gives a right-hand tail area of .05 under the curve of the *F* distribution having

TABLE 8.8 A Portion of an F Table: Values of $F_{.05}$

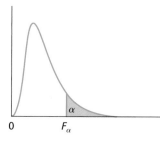

df_2	Numerator Degrees of Freedom, df_1								
	1	2	3	4	5	6	7	8	9
1	161.4	199.5	215.7	224.6	230.2	234.0	236.8	238.9	240.5
2	18.51	19.00	19.16	19.25	19.30	19.33	19.35	19.37	19.38
3	10.13	9.55	9.28	9.12	9.01	8.94	8.89	8.85	8.81
4	7.71	6.94	6.59	6.39	6.26	6.16	6.09	6.04	6.00
5	6.61	5.79	5.41	5.19	5.05	4.95	4.88	4.82	4.77
6	5.99	5.14	4.76	4.53	4.39	4.28	4.21	4.15	4.10
7	5.59	4.71	4.25	4.12	3.97	3.87	3.79	3.73	3.68
8	5.32	4.46	4.07	3.84	3.69	3.58	3.50	3.44	3.39
9	5.12	4.26	3.86	3.63	3.48	3.37	3.29	3.23	3.18
10	4.96	4.10	3.71	3.48	3.33	3.22	3.14	3.07	3.02
11	4.84	3.98	3.59	3.36	3.20	3.09	3.01	2.95	2.90
12	4.75	3.89	3.49	3.26	3.11	3.00	2.91	2.85	2.80
13	4.67	3.81	3.41	3.18	3.03	2.92	2.83	2.77	2.71
14	4.60	3.74	3.34	3.11	2.96	2.85	2.76	2.70	2.65
15	4.54	3.68	3.29	3.06	2.90	2.79	2.71	2.64	2.59
16	4.49	3.63	3.24	3.01	2.85	2.74	2.66	2.59	2.54
17	4.45	3.59	3.20	2.96	2.81	2.70	2.61	2.55	2.49
18	4.41	3.55	3.16	2.93	2.77	2.66	2.58	2.51	2.46
19	4.38	3.52	3.13	2.90	2.74	2.63	2.54	2.48	2.42
20	4.35	3.49	3.10	2.87	2.71	2.60	2.51	2.45	2.39
21	4.32	3.47	3.07	2.84	2.68	2.57	2.49	2.42	2.37
22	4.30	3.44	3.05	2.82	2.66	2.55	2.46	2.40	2.34
23	4.28	3.42	3.03	2.80	2.64	2.53	2.44	2.37	2.32
24	4.26	3.40	3.01	2.78	2.62	2.51	2.42	2.36	2.30
25	4.24	3.39	2.99	2.76	2.60	2.49	2.40	2.34	2.28
26	4.23	3.37	2.98	2.74	2.59	2.47	2.39	2.32	2.27
27	4.21	3.35	2.96	2.73	2.57	2.46	2.37	2.31	2.25
28	4.20	3.34	2.95	2.71	2.56	2.45	2.36	2.29	2.24
29	4.18	3.33	2.93	2.70	2.55	2.43	2.35	2.28	2.22
30	4.17	3.32	2.92	2.69	2.53	2.42	2.33	2.27	2.21
40	4.08	3.23	2.84	2.61	2.45	2.34	2.25	2.18	2.12
60	4.00	3.15	2.76	2.53	2.37	2.25	2.17	2.10	2.04
120	3.92	3.07	2.68	2.45	2.29	2.17	2.09	2.02	1.96
∞	3.84	3.00	2.60	2.37	2.21	2.10	2.01	1.94	1.88

4 numerator and 7 denominator degrees of freedom. To do this, we scan across the top of Table 8.8 until we find the column corresponding to 4 numerator degrees of freedom, and we scan down the left side of the table until we find the row corresponding to 7 denominator degrees of freedom. The table entry in this column and row is the desired F point. We find that the $F_{.05}$ point is 4.12 (see Figure 8.18[b] and Table 8.8).

We now present the procedure for testing the equality of two population variances when the alternative hypothesis is one-tailed.

LO7

Testing the Equality of Population Variances versus a One-Tailed Alternative Hypothesis

Suppose we randomly select independent samples from two normally distributed populations—populations 1 and 2. Let s_1^2 be the variance of the random sample of n_1 observations from population 1, and let s_2^2 be the variance of the random sample of n_2 observations from population 2.

1   In order to test $H_0: \sigma_1^2 = \sigma_2^2$ versus $H_a: \sigma_1^2 > \sigma_2^2$, define the test statistic

$$F = \frac{s_1^2}{s_2^2}$$

and define the corresponding p-value to be the area to the right of F under the curve of the F distribution having $df_1 = n_1 - 1$ numerator degrees of freedom and $df_2 = n_2 - 1$ denominator degrees of freedom. We can reject H_0 at level of significance α if and only if

a $F > F_\alpha$ or, equivalently,

b p-value $< \alpha$.

Here F_α is based on $df_1 = n_1 - 1$ and $df_2 = n_2 - 1$ degrees of freedom.

2   In order to test $H_0: \sigma_1^2 = \sigma_2^2$ versus $H_a: \sigma_1^2 < \sigma_2^2$, define the test statistic

$$F = \frac{s_2^2}{s_1^2}$$

and define the corresponding p-value to be the area to the right of F under the curve of the F distribution having $df_1 = n_2 - 1$ numerator degrees of freedom and $df_2 = n_1 - 1$ denominator degrees of freedom. We can reject H_0 at level of significance α if and only if

a $F > F_\alpha$ or, equivalently,

b p-value, $< \alpha$.

Here F_α is based on $df_1 = n_2 - 1$ and $df_2 = n_1 - 1$ degrees of freedom.

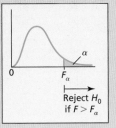

Reject H_0 if $F > F_\alpha$

Example 8.4   Comparing the Variability of Catalyst Yields

Again consider the catalyst comparison situation of Example 8.2, and suppose the production supervisor wants to use the sample data in Table 8.2 to determine whether σ_1^2, the variance of the chemical yields obtained by using Catalyst XA-100, is smaller than σ_2^2, the variance of the chemical yields obtained by using Catalyst ZB-200. To do this, the supervisor will test the null hypothesis

$$H_0: \sigma_1^2 = \sigma_2^2$$

which says the catalysts produce yields having the same amount of variability, versus the alternative hypothesis

$$H_a: \sigma_1^2 < \sigma_2^2 \text{ or, equivalently, } H_a: \sigma_2^2 > \sigma_1^2$$

which says Catalyst XA-100 produces yields that are less variable (that is, more consistent) than the yields produced by Catalyst ZB-200. Recall from Table 8.2 that $n_1 = n_2 = 5$, $s_1^2 = 386$, and $s_2^2 = 484.2$. In order to test H_0 versus H_a, we compute the test statistic

$$F = \frac{s_2^2}{s_1^2} = \frac{484.2}{386} = 1.2544$$

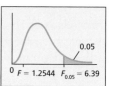

and we compare this value with F_α based on $df_1 = n_2 - 1 = 5 - 1 = 4$ numerator degrees of freedom and $df_2 = n_1 - 1 = 5 - 1 = 4$ denominator degrees of freedom. If we test H_0 versus H_a at the .05 level of significance, then Table 8.8 tells us that when $df_1 = 4$ and $df_2 = 4$, we have $F_{.05} = 6.39$. Because $F = 1.2544$ is not greater than $F_{.05} = 6.39$, we cannot reject H_0 at the .05 level of significance. That is, at the .05 level of significance we cannot conclude that σ_1^2 is less than σ_2^2. This says that there is little evidence that Catalyst XA-100 produces yields that are more consistent than the yields produced by Catalyst ZB-200.

Again considering the catalyst comparison case, suppose we want to test

$$H_0: \sigma_1^2 = \sigma_2^2 \text{ versus } H_a: \sigma_1^2 \neq \sigma_2^2$$

One way to carry out this test is to compute

$$F = \frac{s_1^2}{s_2^2} = \frac{386}{484.2} = .797$$

As illustrated in Figure 8.19, if we set $\alpha = .10$, we compare F with the rejection points $F_{.95}$ and $F_{.05}$ under the curve of the F distribution having $n_1 - 1 = 4$ numerator and $n_2 - 1 = 4$ denominator degrees of freedom. We see that we can easily find the appropriate upper-tail rejection point to be $F_{.05} = 6.39$. To find the lower-tail rejection point, $F_{.95}$, we use the following relationship:

$$F_{(1-\alpha)} \text{ with } df_1 \text{ numerator and } df_2 \text{ denominator degrees of freedom}$$
$$= \frac{1}{F_\alpha \text{ with } df_2 \text{ numerator and } df_1 \text{ denominator degrees of freedom}}$$

This says that for the F curve with 4 numerator and 4 denominator degrees of freedom, $F_{(1-.05)} = F_{.95} = 1/F_{.05} = 1/6.39 = .1565$. Therefore, because $F = .797$ is not greater than $F_{.05} = 6.39$ and since $F = .797$ is not less than $F_{.95} = .1565$, we cannot reject H_0 in favour of H_a at the .10 level of significance.

FIGURE 8.19   Rejection Points for Testing $H_0: \sigma_1^2 - \sigma_2^2$ versus $H_a: \sigma_1^2 \neq \sigma_2^2$ with $\alpha = .10$

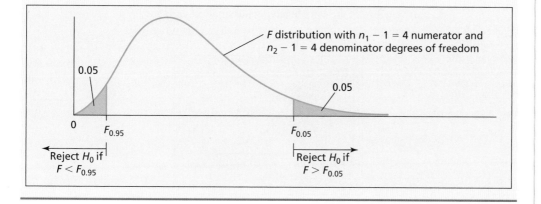

Although we can calculate the lower-tail rejection point for this hypothesis test as just illustrated, it is common practice to compute the test statistic F so that its value is always greater than 1. This means that we will always compare F with the upper-tail rejection point when carrying out the test. This can be done by always calculating F to be the larger of s_1^2 and s_2^2 divided by the smaller of s_1^2 and s_2^2. We obtain the result shown in the following boxed feature.

Testing the Equality of Population Variances (Two-Tailed Alternative)

Suppose we randomly select independent samples from two normally distributed populations and define all notation as in the previous boxed feature "Testing the Equality of Population Variances versus a One-Tailed Alternative Hypothesis". Then, to test $H_0: \sigma_1^2 = \sigma_2^2$ versus $H_a: \sigma_1^2 \neq \sigma_2^2$, define the test statistic

$$F = \frac{\text{Larger of } s_1^2 \text{ and } s_2^2}{\text{Smaller of } s_1^2 \text{ and } s_2^2}$$

and let

$df_1 = \{\text{Size of the sample having the largest variance}\} - 1$

$df_2 = \{\text{Size of the sample having the smallest variance}\} - 1$

Also, define the corresponding p-value to be twice the area to the right of F under the curve of the F distribution having df_1 numerator degrees of freedom

and df_2 denominator degrees of freedom. We can reject H_0 at level of significance α if and only if

1 $F > F_{\alpha/2}$ or, equivalently,

2 p-value $< \alpha$.

Here $F_{\alpha/2}$ is based on df_1 and df_2 degrees of freedom.

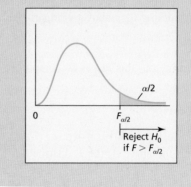

In the catalyst comparison situation, we can reject $H_0: \sigma_1^2 = \sigma_2^2$ in favour of $H_a: \sigma_1^2 \neq \sigma_2^2$ at the .05 level of significance if

$$F = \frac{\text{Larger of } s_1^2 \text{ and } s_2^2}{\text{Smaller of } s_1^2 \text{ and } s_2^2} = \frac{484.2}{386} = 1.2544$$

is greater than $F_{\alpha/2} = F_{.05/2} = F_{.025}$. Here the degrees of freedom are

$$df_1 = \{\text{Size of the sample having the largest variance}\} - 1$$
$$= n_2 - 1 = 5 - 1 = 4$$

and

$$df_2 = \{\text{Size of the sample having the smallest variance}\} - 1$$
$$= n_1 - 1 = 5 - 1 = 4$$

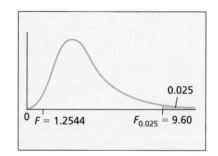

Table A.8 tells us that the appropriate $F_{.025}$ point equals 9.60. Because $F = 1.2544$ is not greater than 9.60, we cannot reject H_0 at the .05 level of significance, and we have little evidence that the consistencies of the yields produced by Catalysts XA-100 and ZB-200 differ.

It has been suggested that the F test of $H_0: \sigma_1^2 = \sigma_2^2$ be used to choose between the equal variances and unequal variances t-based procedures when comparing two means (as described in Section 8.2). Certainly the F test is one approach to making this choice. However, studies have shown that the validity of the F test is very sensitive to violations of the normality assumption—much more sensitive, in fact, than the equal variances procedure is to violations of the equal variances assumption. While opinions vary, some statisticians believe that this is a serious problem and that the F test should never be used to choose between the equal variances and unequal variances procedures. Others feel that performing the test for this purpose is reasonable if the test's limitations are kept in mind. Some statistical software (e.g., SPSS) utilizes a test that is more robust against violations of normality, Levene's test—and in fact this test of homogeneity of variances is often included in the independent t test modules in these programs (i.e., it is run at the same time as the t test). Regardless of whether you choose to use a test of variances prior to conducting your t test, it is critical that you choose the t test (the "equal variances" version or the "unequal variances" version) prior to interpreting your results. To do otherwise (e.g., to run both tests and choose the version that yields the most favourable results) will dramatically inflate your Type I error rate.

As an example for those who believe that using the F test is reasonable, we found in Example 8.4 that we do not reject $H_0: \sigma_1^2 = \sigma_2^2$ at the .05 level of significance in the context of the catalyst comparison situation. This suggests that there is little evidence to suggest that the population variances differ. It follows that it might be reasonable to compare the mean yields of the catalysts by using the equal variances procedures (as we did in our previous treatments of these data).

Exercises for Section **8.4**

CONCEPTS

8.37 Explain what population is described by the sampling distribution of s_1^2/s_2^2.

8.38 Intuitively explain why a value of s_1^2/s_2^2 that is substantially greater than 1 provides evidence that σ_1^2 is not equal to σ_2^2.

METHODS AND APPLICATIONS

8.39 Use Table 8.8 to find the $F_{.05}$ point for each of the following:
  a. $df_1 = 3$ numerator degrees of freedom and $df_2 = 14$ denominator degrees of freedom.
  b. $df_1 = 6$ and $df_2 = 10$.
  c. $df_1 = 2$ and $df_2 = 22$.
  d. $df_1 = 7$ and $df_2 = 5$.

8.40 Use Tables A.6, A.7, A.8, and A.9 to find the following F_α points:
  a. $F_{.10}$ with $df_1 = 4$ numerator degrees of freedom and $df_2 = 7$ denominator degrees of freedom.
  b. $F_{.01}$ with $df_1 = 3$ and $df_2 = 25$.
  c. $F_{.025}$ with $df_1 = 7$ and $df_2 = 17$.
  d. $F_{.05}$ with $df_1 = 9$ and $df_2 = 3$.

8.41 Suppose two independent random samples of sizes $n_1 = 9$ and $n_2 = 7$ that have been taken from two normally distributed populations having variances σ_1^2 and σ_2^2 give sample variances of $s_1^2 = 100$ and $s_2^2 = 20$.
  a. Test $H_0: \sigma_1^2 = \sigma_2^2$ versus $H_a: \sigma_1^2 \neq \sigma_2^2$ with $\alpha = .05$. What do you conclude?
  b. Test $H_0: \sigma_1^2 \leq \sigma_2^2$ versus $H_a: \sigma_1^2 > \sigma_2^2$ with $\alpha = .05$. What do you conclude?

8.42 Suppose two independent random samples of sizes $n_1 = 5$ and $n_2 = 16$ that have been taken from two normally distributed populations having variances σ_1^2 and σ_2^2 give sample standard deviations of $s_1 = 5$ and $s_2 = 9$.
  a. Test $H_0: \sigma_1^2 = \sigma_2^2$ versus $H_a: \sigma_1^2 \neq \sigma_2^2$ with $\alpha = .05$. What do you conclude?
  b. Test $H_0: \sigma_1^2 \geq \sigma_2^2$ versus $H_a: \sigma_1^2 < \sigma_2^2$ with $\alpha = .01$. What do you conclude?

8.43 Consider the situation of Exercise 8.24. Use the sample information to test $H_0: \sigma_1^2 = \sigma_2^2$ versus $H_a: \sigma_1^2 \neq \sigma_2^2$ with $\alpha = .05$. Based on this test, does it make sense to believe that the unequal variances procedure is appropriate? Explain.

8.44 Consider the situation of Exercise 8.25.
  a. Use a critical value to test $H_0: \sigma_1^2 = \sigma_2^2$ versus $H_a: \sigma_1^2 \neq \sigma_2^2$ with $\alpha = .05$. What do you conclude?
  b. Does it make sense to use the equal variances procedure in this situation?

CHAPTER SUMMARY

This chapter expanded on our treatment in Chapter 7 of evaluations of mean differences to the more typical case when population variances are unknown. First, we discussed a method for comparing a mean to a historical or hypothetical mean value. Then, we discussed how to compare two population means by using independent samples. When the populations are normally distributed, or the sample sizes are large, *t*-based inferences are appropriate. The procedure for testing the difference between independent groups differs, depending on the magnitude of the difference between their variances—both equal variances and unequal variances *t*-based procedures exist. We learned that, because it can be difficult

to compare the population variances, many statisticians believe that it is almost always best to use the unequal variances procedure.

Sometimes samples are not independent. We learned that one such case is what is called a *paired difference experiment*. Here we obtain two different measurements on the same sample units and we can compare two population means by using a confidence interval or by conducting a hypothesis test that employs the differences between the pairs of measurements. Finally, we concluded this chapter by discussing how to compare two population variances by using independent samples, and we learned that this comparison is done by using a test based on the *F* distribution.

KEY TERMS

degrees of freedom
F distribution

paired difference experiment
sampling distribution of s_1^2/s_2^2

IMPORTANT FORMULAS AND TESTS

z test about μ

t test about μ

Sampling distribution of $\bar{x}_1 - \bar{x}_2$ (independent random samples)

t test about $\mu_1 - \mu_2$ when $\sigma_1^2 = \sigma_2^2$

t test about $\mu_1 - \mu_2$ when $\sigma_1^2 \neq \sigma_2^2$

Hypothesis test about μ_d

Sampling distribution of s_1^2/s_2^2 (independent random samples)

Hypothesis test about the equality of σ_1^2 and σ_2^2

SUPPLEMENTARY EXERCISES

connect Practise and learn online with *Connect*. Items for which there are online data sets are marked with ✈.

8.45   The cigarette industry requires that models in cigarette ads must appear to be at least 25 years old. A sample of 50 people is randomly selected at a shopping mall. Each person in the sample is shown a "typical cigarette ad" and is asked to estimate the age of the model in the ad.

  a. Let μ be the mean perceived age estimate for all viewers of the ad, and suppose we consider the industry requirement to be met if μ is at least 25. Set up the null and alternative hypotheses needed to attempt to show that the industry requirement is not being met.

  b. Suppose that a random sample of 50 perceived age estimates gives a mean of $\bar{x} = 23.663$ years and a standard deviation of $s = 3.596$ years. Use these sample data and critical values to test the hypotheses of part (a) at the .10, .05, .01, and .001 levels of significance.

  c. How much evidence do we have that the industry requirement is not being met?

  d. Do you think that this result has practical importance? Explain your opinion.

8.46   Consider the cigarette ad situation discussed in Exercise 8.45. Using the sample information given in that exercise, the *p*-value for testing H_0 versus H_a can be calculated to be .0057.

  a. Determine whether H_0 would be rejected at each of $\alpha = .10$, $\alpha = .05$, $\alpha = .01$, and $\alpha = .001$.

  b. Describe how much evidence we have that the industry requirement is not being met.

8.47   In an article in the *Journal of Retailing*, Kumar, Kerwin, and Pereira study factors affecting merger and acquisition activity in retailing. As part of the study, the authors compare the characteristics of "target firms" (firms targeted for acquisition) and "bidder firms" (firms attempting to make acquisitions). Among the variables studied in the comparison were earnings per share, debt-to-equity ratio, growth rate of sales, market share, and extent of diversification.

  a. Let μ be the mean growth rate of sales for all target firms (firms that have been targeted for acquisition in the last five years and that have not bid on other firms), and assume growth rates are approximately normally distributed. Furthermore, suppose a random sample of 25 target firms yields a sample mean sales growth rate of $\bar{x} = 0.16$ with a standard deviation of $s = 0.12$. Use critical values and this sample information to test $H_0: \mu \leq .10$ versus $H_a: \mu > .10$ by setting α equal to .10, .05, .01, and .001. How much evidence is there that the mean growth rate of sales for target firms exceeds .10 (that is, exceeds 10 percent)?

  b. Now let μ be the mean growth rate of sales for all firms that are bidders (firms that have bid to acquire at least one other firm in the last five years), and again assume growth rates are approximately normally distributed. Furthermore, suppose a random sample of 25 bidders yields a sample mean sales growth rate of $\bar{x} = 0.12$ with a standard deviation of $s = 0.09$. Use critical values and this sample information to test $H_0: \mu \leq .10$ versus $H_a: \mu > .10$ by setting α equal to .10, .05, .01, and .001. How much evidence is there that the mean growth rate of sales for bidders exceeds .10 (that is, exceeds 10 percent)?

8.48 Suppose that random samples of 50 returns for each of the following investment classes give the indicated sample mean and sample standard deviation:

Fixed annuities: $\bar{x} = 7.83\%$, $s = .51\%$
Domestic large-cap stocks: $\bar{x} = 13.42\%$, $s = 15.17\%$
Domestic midcap stocks: $\bar{x} = 15.03\%$, $s = 18.44\%$
Domestic small-cap stocks: $\bar{x} = 22.51\%$, $s = 21.75\%$

a. For each investment class, set up the null and alternative hypotheses needed to test whether the current mean return differs from the historical (1970 to 1994) mean return given in Table 8.9.

b. Test each hypothesis you set up in part (a) at the .05 level of significance. What do you conclude? For which investment classes does the current mean return differ from the historical mean?

TABLE 8.9 Mean Return and Standard Deviation for Nine Investment Classes

Investment Class	Mean Return	Standard Deviation
Fixed annuities	8.31%	.54%
Cash equivalents	7.73	.81
Treasury bonds	8.80	5.98
Investment-grade corporate bonds	9.33	7.92
International government bonds	10.95	10.47
Domestic large-cap stocks	11.71	15.30
International equities	14.02	17.16
Domestic midcap stocks	13.64	18.19
Domestic small-cap stocks	14.93	21.82

8.49 How safe are child car seats? *Consumer Reports* (May 2005) tested the safety of child car seats in 50 km/h crashes. They found "slim safety margins" for some child car seats. Suppose that *Consumer Reports* simulated the safety of the market-leading child car seat. The test consisted of placing the maximum claimed weight in the car seat and simulating crashes at higher and higher speeds until a problem occurred. The following data identify the speed (in km/h) at which a problem with the car seat (such as the strap breaking, seat shell cracking, strap adjuster breaking, seat detaching from the base, etc.) first appeared: 51.0, 49.4, 50.4, 48.9, 49.7, 50.1, 52.3, 51.7, 55.4, 49.1, 51.2, 50.2. Let μ denote the true mean speed at which a problem with the car seat first appeared. How much evidence is there that μ exceeded 50 km/h?

8.50 *Fortune* magazine has periodically reported on the rise of fees and expenses charged by stock funds.

a. Suppose that 10 years ago the average annual expense for stock funds was 1.19 percent. Let μ be the current mean annual expense for all stock funds, and assume that stock fund annual expenses are approximately normally distributed. If a random sample of 12 stock funds gives a sample mean annual expense of $\bar{x} = 1.63$ percent with a standard deviation of $s = .31$ percent, use critical values and this sample information to test $H_0: \mu \leq 1.19$ percent versus $H_a: \mu > 1.19$ percent by setting α equal to .10, .05, .01, and .001. How much evidence is there that the current mean annual expense for stock funds exceeds the average of 10 years ago?

b. Do you think that the result in part (a) has practical importance? Explain your opinion.

Exercises 8.51 and 8.52 deal with the following situation:

In an article in the *Journal of Retailing*, Kumar, Kerwin, and Pereira reported on their study of factors affecting merger and acquisition activity in retailing by comparing "target firms" and "bidder firms" with respect to several financial and marketing-related variables. If we consider two of the financial variables included in the study, suppose a random sample of 36 "target firms" gives a mean earnings per share of $1.52 with a standard deviation of $0.92, and that this sample gives a mean debt-to-equity ratio of 1.66 with a standard deviation of 0.82. Furthermore, an independent random sample of 36 "bidder firms" gives a mean earnings per share of $1.20 with a standard deviation of $0.84, and this sample gives a mean debt-to-equity ratio of 1.58 with a standard deviation of 0.81.

8.51 Set up the null and alternative hypotheses needed to test whether the mean earnings per share for all target firms differs from the mean earnings per share for all bidder firms. Test these hypotheses at the .10, .05, .01, and .001 levels of significance. How much evidence is there that these means differ? Explain.

8.52 **a.** Set up the null and alternative hypotheses needed to test whether the mean debt-to-equity ratio for all target firms differs from the mean debt-to-equity ratio for all bidder firms. Test these hypotheses at the .10, .05, .01, and .001 levels of significance. How much evidence is there that these means differ? Explain.

b. Based on the results of this exercise and Exercise 8.51, does a firm's earnings per share or the firm's debt-to-equity ratio seem to have the most influence on whether a firm will be a target or a bidder? Explain.

8.53 A marketing manager wants to compare the mean prices charged for two brands of CD players. The manager conducts a random survey of retail outlets and obtains independent random samples of prices with the following results:

	Onkyo	JVC
Sample mean, $\bar{x}$	$189	$145
Sample standard deviation, s	$ 12	$ 10
Sample size	6	12

Assuming normality and equal variances:

a. Use an appropriate hypothesis test to determine whether the mean prices for the two brands differ. How much evidence is there that the mean prices differ?

b. Use an appropriate hypothesis test to provide evidence supporting the claim that the mean price of the Onkyo CD player is more than $30 higher than the mean price for the JVC CD player. Set α equal to .05.

8.54   Consider the situation in Exercise 8.53. Use the sample information to test $H_0: \sigma_1^2 = \sigma_2^2$ versus $H_a: \sigma_1^2 \neq \sigma_2^2$ with $\alpha = .05$. Based on this test, does it make sense to use the equal variances procedure? Explain.

8.55   **INTERNET EXERCISE**

The Canadian Real Estate Association (CREA) maintains a database of homes for sale in neighbourhoods across Canada. For some local real estate boards, the CREA publishes average home prices, along with the *MLS*®

Home Price Index (HPI) that is intended to assist individuals in determining the extent to which home values are appreciating in their community. Table 8.10 presents a snapshot of prices that were downloaded from the statistics section of the CREA website (crea.ca/statistics).

If we average across Greater Vancouver, Calgary, Regina, Greater Toronto, and Greater Montreal, does it look as though housing prices have increased between November 2007 and November 2012?

TABLE 8.10   Average Home Prices in Communities across Canada

	November 2012	1 Month Previously	3 Months Previously	6 Months Previously	12 Months Previously	36 Months Previously	60 Months Previously
				Benchmark by Time Frame and Property Type: Composite			
Aggregate	$449,600	$450,800	$452,200	$453,900	$434,300	$398,600	$390,800
Lower Mainland	$538,100	$543,000	$548,300	$558,300	$543,000	$500,200	$504,800
Greater Vancouver	$596,900	$603,800	$609,500	$625,100	$607,200	$549,600	$547,000
Fraser Valley	$424,800	$426,000	$430,800	$429,300	$419,400	$403,300	$420,300
Calgary	$382,600	$381,900	$381,700	$376,800	$357,100	$359,600	$398,700
Regina	$307,600	$310,100	$311,700	$306,400	$275,700	$243,100	$200,600
Greater Toronto	$455,800	$457,000	$458,800	$460,900	$435,600	$386,500	$359,400
Greater Montreal	$290,200	$291,200	$291,000	$290,800	$284,900	$255,600	$232,000

Note: Aggregate MLS® HPI series include data for all participating boards and are revised back to January 2005 as additional boards join the MLS®HPI. Some MLS®HPI series may follow a seasonal pattern.

Source: The Canadian Real Estate Association.

CHAPTER **9**
Confidence Intervals

In the previous two chapters, we have tested hypotheses using point estimates of the population mean and the population proportion, and we have also tested the differences between population means and proportions. Although hypothesis testing is a useful tool in decision making and can provide us with evidence to suggest the likelihood that a given sample could have occurred due to chance, it does not provide us with useful descriptive information without the presentation of a meaningful effect size estimate. To this end, we have learned to calculate Cohen's *d* (in situations where the population variance is known) and Hedge's *g* (in situations where the population variance is unknown). Although these statistics provide an important quantification of the effect in terms of the standard deviation of the variable, they do not readily

provide us with meaningful information about the limitations to interpretation for a particular mean, or difference of means.

In this chapter, we learn how to use a confidence interval to estimate a population parameter. A confidence interval for a population parameter is an interval, or range of numbers, constructed around the point estimate so that we are very sure, or confident, that the true value of the population parameter is inside the interval.

By computing such an interval, we estimate—with confidence—the possible values that a population parameter might equal. This, in turn, can help us to assess—with confidence—whether a particular business improvement has been made or is needed.

9.1 CONFIDENCE INTERVALS FOR A POPULATION MEAN WHEN σ IS KNOWN

LO1

As we discussed in Chapter 8, z-based statistics are typically only useful when we know the standard deviation of the population. For situations in which the population standard deviation is unknown, we need to employ a t statistic. For this reason, the z statistic (and confidence interval) are typically used only in the examination of population proportions. As was the case in Chapter 7, however, the z statistic is useful for illustrating basic statistical properties, so for this reason, we will start our discussion of confidence intervals with a review of confidence intervals that are based on the z statistic.

In our earlier discussions of the company that is planning to make a special box of Valentine's Day chocolates, we discussed the company's need to correctly estimate the demand for orders among the major purchasers. If the company estimates incorrectly (in either direction), it will potentially suffer for its error (if the company underestimates demand, it will miss out on sales, and if the company overestimates demand, it will end up with an inventory surplus). Recall that the company opted to test a hypothesis about the potential demand for the new box of candy in determining its production levels—it estimated an increase of 10 percent of sales from previous years. After taking a sample of 100 retail store purchasers, finding a projected order that averaged 326 boxes, and assuming a population standard deviation of 40, the company concluded that its estimate of 330 boxes was a reasonable one.

What if, instead of calculating a hypothesis test, the company had opted to estimate the population value directly, with a particular level of confidence? The company knows that the sample mean will not—unless it is extremely lucky—equal the true value of a population mean. Therefore, the sample mean of 326 boxes does not, by itself, provide the company with any confidence about the true value of the population mean μ. One way to estimate μ with confidence is to calculate a *confidence interval* for this mean.

A **confidence interval** for a population mean is an interval constructed around the sample mean so that we are reasonably sure, or confident, that this interval contains the population mean. Any confidence interval for a population mean is based on what is called a **confidence level.** This confidence level is a percentage (for example, 95 percent or 99 percent) that expresses how confident we are that the confidence interval contains the population mean. To explain the exact meaning of a confidence level, we will begin with the Valentine's Day candy example by finding and interpreting a confidence interval for a population mean that is based on the most commonly used confidence level—the 95 percent level.

Before the company selected the sample of $n = 100$ large retail stores and asked them to estimate the number of boxes of candy that they would purchase for Valentine's Day sales, there were many samples of 100 stores that the company might have obtained. Because different samples generally have different sample means, we consider the probability distribution of the population of all possible sample means that would be obtained from all possible samples of $n = 100$ stores. In Chapter 6 we learned that such a probability distribution is called the *sampling distribution of the sample mean,* and we have studied various properties of sampling distributions. Several of these properties tell us that, if the population from which we will select a sample is normally distributed with mean μ and standard deviation σ, then for any sample size n the sampling distribution of the sample mean is a normal distribution with mean $\mu_{\bar{x}} = \mu$ and standard deviation $\sigma_{\bar{x}} = \sigma/\sqrt{n}$. This allows us to reason as follows:

1   Because the sampling distribution of the sample mean is a normal distribution, we can use the normal distribution to compute probabilities about the sample mean. In particular, recall from Chapter 5 that the area under the standard normal curve between -1.96 and 1.96 is .95. As illustrated in Figure 9.1, this .95 area is the probability that a standard normal random variable z will be between -1.96 and 1.96, or, equivalently, the probability that the sample mean $\bar{x}$ will be within plus or minus $1.96\sigma_{\bar{x}}$ of the population mean μ.

FIGURE 9.1 A Confidence Interval for the Population Mean

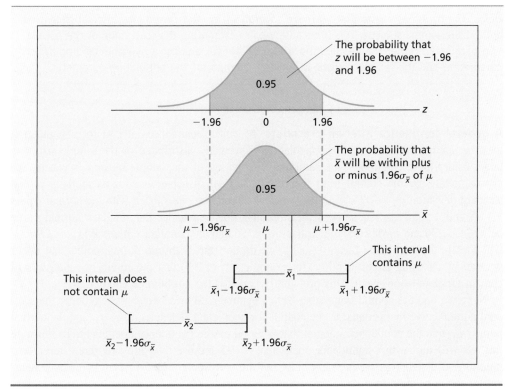

2 Saying

$$\bar{x} \text{ will be within } \pm 1.96\sigma_{\bar{x}} \text{ of } \mu$$

is the same as saying

$$\bar{x} \text{ will be such that the interval } [\bar{x} \pm 1.96\sigma_{\bar{x}}] \text{ contains } \mu$$

To understand this, consider Figure 9.1. This figure shows that, because a particular sample mean—denoted as $\bar{x}_1$—is within plus or minus $1.96\sigma_{\bar{x}}$ of μ, the interval computed using this sample mean—$[\bar{x}_1 \pm 1.96\sigma_{\bar{x}}]$—contains μ. The figure also shows that, because another particular sample mean—denoted as $\bar{x}_2$—is not within plus or minus $1.96\sigma_{\bar{x}}$ of μ, the interval computed using this sample mean—$[\bar{x}_2 \pm 1.96\sigma_{\bar{x}}]$—does not contain μ.

3 In 1, we showed that the probability is .95 that the sample mean $\bar{x}$ will be within plus or minus $1.96\sigma_{\bar{x}}$ of the population mean μ. In 2, we showed that $\bar{x}$ being within plus or minus $1.96\sigma_{\bar{x}}$ of μ is the same as the interval $[\bar{x} \pm 1.96\sigma_{\bar{x}}]$ containing μ. Combining these results, we see that the probability is .95 that the sample mean $\bar{x}$ will be such that the interval

$$[\bar{x} \pm 1.96\sigma_{\bar{x}}] = \left[\bar{x} \pm 1.96\frac{\sigma}{\sqrt{n}}\right]$$

contains the population mean μ. This interval is called a *95 percent confidence interval for the population mean μ*, and the quantity $1.96\sigma_{\bar{x}}$ is called the **margin of error** when estimating μ by $\bar{x}$. Every confidence interval that you will encounter will be structured in this way—an estimate of central tendency (in this case, the mean) and a margin of error that represents the maximum distance that your population value will fall from this estimate of central tendency, given a particular level of confidence.

> **ROADBLOCK**
>
> **The confidence interval is centred around the sample mean**
> Unlike the hypothesis tests that we have covered so far, the confidence interval is centred around the sample statistic. This is because we are estimating the true value of the population parameter, rather than evaluating a sample statistic against a hypothetical population parameter—and the sample statistic is our best estimate of the population parameter.

A general confidence interval procedure To find a confidence interval for a population mean μ, assume that the sampled population is normally distributed or the sample size n is large. Under these conditions, the sampling distribution of the sample mean $\bar{x}$ is exactly (or approximately, by the central limit theorem) a normal distribution with mean $\mu_{\bar{x}} = \mu$ and standard deviation $\sigma_{\bar{x}} = \sigma/\sqrt{n}$. In the previous subsection, we *started* with the normal points -1.96 and 1.96. Then we showed that, because the area under the standard normal curve between -1.96 and 1.96 is .95, the probability is .95 that the confidence interval $[\bar{x} \pm 1.96\sigma_{\bar{x}}]$ will contain the population mean. Usually, we do not start with two normal points, but rather we start by choosing the probability (for example, .95 or .99) that the confidence interval will contain the population mean. This probability is called the **confidence coefficient.**

Next, we find the normal points that have a symmetrical area between them under the standard normal curve that is equal to the confidence coefficient. Then, using $\bar{x}$, $\sigma_{\bar{x}}$, and the normal points, we find the confidence interval that is based on the confidence coefficient. To illustrate this, we will start with a confidence coefficient of .95 and use the following three-step procedure to find the appropriate normal points and the corresponding 95 percent confidence interval for the population mean:

Step 1: As illustrated in Figure 9.2, place a symmetrical area of .95 under the standard normal curve and find the area in the normal curve tails beyond the .95 area. Because the entire area under the standard normal curve is 1, the area in both normal curve tails is $1 - .95 = .05$, and the area in each tail is .025.

Step 2: Find the normal point $z_{.025}$ that gives a right-hand tail area under the standard normal curve equal to .025, and find the normal point $-z_{.025}$ that gives a left-hand tail area under the curve equal to .025. As shown in Figure 9.2, the area under the standard normal curve between $-z_{.025}$ and $z_{.025}$ is .95, and the area under this curve to the left of $z_{.025}$ is .975. Looking up a cumulative area of .975 in Table A.4 in Appendix A at the back of the book or in Table 9.1 (which shows a portion of Table A.4), we find that $z_{.025} = 1.96$.

Step 3: Form the following 95 percent confidence interval for the population mean:

$$[\bar{x} \pm z_{.025}\sigma_{\bar{x}}] = \left[\bar{x} \pm 1.96\frac{\sigma}{\sqrt{n}}\right]$$

If all possible samples were used to calculate this interval, then 95 percent of the resulting intervals would contain the population mean.

In general, we let α denote the probability that a confidence interval for a population mean will *not* contain the population mean. This implies that $1 - \alpha$ is the probability that the confidence interval will contain the population mean. In order to find a confidence interval for a population mean that is based on a confidence coefficient of $1 - \alpha$—that is, a $100(1 - \alpha)$ percent confidence interval for the population mean—we do the following:

Step 1: As illustrated in Figure 9.3, place a symmetrical area of $1 - \alpha$ under the standard normal curve, and find the area in the normal curve tails beyond the $1 - \alpha$ area. Because the entire area under the standard normal curve is 1, the combined areas in the normal curve tails is α, and the area in each tail is $\alpha/2$.

Step 2: Find the normal point $z_{\alpha/2}$ that gives a right-hand tail area under the standard normal curve equal to $\alpha/2$, and find the normal point $-z_{\alpha/2}$ that gives a left-hand tail area under this

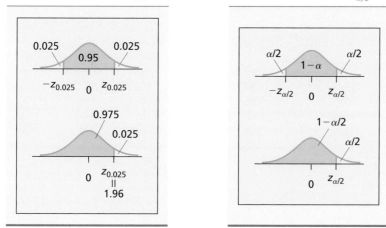

FIGURE **9.2** The Point $z_{.025}$ FIGURE **9.3** The Point $z_{\alpha/2}$

TABLE **9.1** Cumulative Areas under the Standard Normal Curve

z	0.00	0.01	0.02	0.03	0.04	0.05	0.06	0.07	0.08	0.09
1.5	0.9332	0.9345	0.9357	0.9370	0.9382	0.9394	0.9406	0.9418	0.9429	0.9441
1.6	0.9452	0.9463	0.9474	0.9484	0.9495	0.9505	0.9515	0.9525	0.9535	0.9545
1.7	0.9554	0.9564	0.9573	0.9582	0.9591	0.9599	0.9608	0.9616	0.9625	0.9633
1.8	0.9641	0.9649	0.9656	0.9664	0.9671	0.9678	0.9686	0.9693	0.9699	0.9706
1.9	0.9713	0.9719	0.9726	0.9732	0.9738	0.9744	0.9750	0.9756	0.9761	0.9767
2.0	0.9772	0.9778	0.9783	0.9788	0.9793	0.9798	0.9803	0.9808	0.9812	0.9817
2.1	0.9821	0.9826	0.9830	0.9834	0.9838	0.9842	0.9846	0.9850	0.9854	0.9857
2.2	0.9861	0.9864	0.9868	0.9871	0.9875	0.9878	0.9881	0.9884	0.9887	0.9890
2.3	0.9893	0.9896	0.9898	0.9901	0.9904	0.9906	0.9909	0.9911	0.9913	0.9916
2.4	0.9918	0.9920	0.9922	0.9925	0.9927	0.9929	0.9931	0.9932	0.9934	0.9936
2.5	0.9938	0.9940	0.9941	0.9943	0.9945	0.9946	0.9948	0.9949	0.9951	0.9952

curve equal to $\alpha/2$. As shown in Figure 9.3, the area under the standard normal curve between $-z_{\alpha/2}$ and $z_{\alpha/2}$ is $(1 - \alpha)$, and the area under this curve to the left of $z_{\alpha/2}$ is $1 - \alpha/2$. **This implies that we can find $z_{\alpha/2}$ by looking up a cumulative area of $1 - \alpha/2$ in Table A.4.**

Step 3: Form the following $100(1 - \alpha)$ percent confidence interval for the population mean.

$$[\bar{x} \pm z_{\sigma/2}\sigma_{\bar{x}}] = \left[\bar{x} \pm z_{\sigma/2}\frac{\sigma}{\sqrt{n}}\right]$$

If all possible samples were used to calculate this interval, then $100(1 - \alpha)$ percent of the resulting intervals would contain the population mean. Moreover, we call $100(1 - \alpha)$ percent the confidence level associated with the confidence interval.

Table 9.2 summarizes finding the values of $z_{\alpha/2}$ for different values of the confidence level $100(1 - \alpha)$ percent. For example, suppose that we want to find a 99 percent confidence interval for the population mean. Then, as shown in Table 9.2, $100(1 - \alpha)$ percent equals 99 percent, which implies that $1 - \alpha = .99$, $\alpha = .01$, $\alpha/2 = .005$, and $1 - \alpha/2 = .995$. Looking up .995 (see Figure 9.4) in a cumulative normal table, we find that $z_{\alpha/2} = z_{.005} = 2.575$. This normal point is given in Table 9.2. It follows that a 99 percent confidence interval for the population mean is

$$[\bar{x} \pm z_{.005}\sigma_{\bar{x}}] = \left[\bar{x} \pm 2.575\frac{\sigma}{\sqrt{n}}\right]$$

If all possible samples were used to calculate this interval, then 99 percent of the resulting intervals would contain the population mean.

To compare the 95 percent and 99 percent confidence intervals, notice that the margin of error $2.575(\sigma/\sqrt{n})$ used to compute the 99 percent interval is larger than the margin of error

FIGURE 9.4   The Point $z_{.005}$

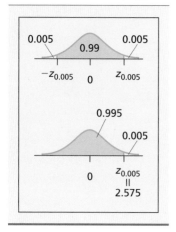

TABLE 9.2   The Normal Point $z_{\alpha/2}$ for Various Levels of Confidence

$100(1 - \alpha)\%$	$1 - \alpha$	α	$\alpha/2$	$1 - \alpha/2$	$z_{\alpha/2}$
90%	.90	.10	.05	.95	$z_{.05} = 1.645$
95%	.95	.05	.025	.975	$z_{.025} = 1.96$
98%	.98	.02	.01	.99	$z_{.01} = 2.33$
99%	.99	.01	.005	.995	$z_{.005} = 2.575$

$1.96(\sigma/\sqrt{n})$ used to compute the 95 percent interval. Therefore, the 99 percent interval is the longer of these intervals. **In general, increasing the confidence level (1) has the advantage of making us more confident that μ is contained in the confidence interval, but (2) has the disadvantage of increasing the margin of error and thus providing a less precise estimate of the true value of μ.** Frequently, 95 percent confidence intervals are used to make conclusions. If conclusions based on stronger evidence are desired, 99 percent intervals are sometimes used.

The following boxed feature summarizes the formula used in calculating a $100(1 - \alpha)$ percent confidence interval for a population mean μ.

A Confidence Interval for a Population Mean μ: σ Known

Suppose that the sampled population is normally distributed with mean μ and standard deviation σ. Then a $100(1 - \alpha)$ percent confidence interval for μ is

$$\left[\bar{x} \pm z_{\alpha/2}\frac{\sigma}{\sqrt{n}} \right] = \left[\bar{x} - z_{\alpha/2}\frac{\sigma}{\sqrt{n}}, \bar{x} + z_{\alpha/2}\frac{\sigma}{\sqrt{n}} \right]$$

Here, $z_{\alpha/2}$ is the normal point that gives a right-hand tail area under the standard normal curve of $\alpha/2$. The normal point $z_{\alpha/2}$ can be found by looking up a cumulative area of $1 - \alpha/2$ in Table A.4. This confidence interval is also approximately valid for non-normal populations if the sample size is large (at least 30).

ROADBLOCK   **Confidence intervals are always two-tailed (at least for our purposes in this book)**
Remember that a confidence interval is just that—an interval that spans the distance between a lower-bound estimate and an upper-bound estimate. This means that it is almost always two-tailed and, for the purposes of this book, it is *always* two-tailed. This means that you will have to remember to "split" your alpha when looking up critical values of z or t for use in your confidence interval.

Example 9.1   Estimating Demand for a Seasonal Box of Chocolates

Part 1: A 95 percent confidence interval: Recall that when the candy company randomly selected the sample of $n = 100$ large retail stores, and asked them to estimate their Valentine's Day purchases, they obtained a sample mean of $\bar{x} = 326$ boxes. We will assume that the distribution of these purchase orders is normally distributed around this mean. To find a 95 percent confidence interval for the population mean number of purchases (μ) of the new box of candy, we assume that the true value of the population standard deviation σ is 40, in a similar fashion to what we did in the hypothesis test for our earlier treatment of these data.

It follows, therefore, that a 95 percent confidence interval for μ is

$$\left[\bar{x} \pm 1.96\frac{\sigma}{\sqrt{n}}\right] = \left[326 \pm 1.96\frac{40}{\sqrt{100}}\right]$$
$$= [326 \pm 7.84]$$
$$= [318.16, 333.84]$$

We are *95 percent confident* that this confidence interval contains μ. That is, we are *95 percent confident* that the mean number of boxes purchased per store will fall between 318.16 and 333.84. Since we cannot sell part-boxes, we would round off both of these values to ensure that the resulting confidence interval contains the decimals specified in our "exact" calculations. So we are 95 percent confident that the mean number of boxes will fall between 318 and 334.

Part 2: The meaning of 95 percent confidence: To explain what we mean by the term *95 percent confident,* note that the margin of error in the 95 percent confidence interval $[\bar{x} \pm 1.96(\sigma/\sqrt{n})]$ is $1.96(\sigma/\sqrt{n})$, which we have calculated to be $1.96(40/\sqrt{100}) = 7.84$. So the 95 percent confidence interval $[\bar{x} \pm 1.96(\sigma/\sqrt{n})]$ can be expressed as $[\bar{x} \pm 7.84]$. This shows that, although the company obtained the sample mean $\bar{x} = 326$ and thus calculated the confidence interval $[326 \pm 7.84] = [318.16, 333.84]$, other sample means that the company could have obtained would have given different confidence intervals.

Figure 9.5 illustrates three possible samples of 100 stores and the means of these samples. Also, this figure assumes that (unknown to anyone) the true value of the population mean μ is 329. Then, as illustrated in Figure 9.5, because the sample mean $\bar{x} = 330$ is within 7.84 of $\mu = 329$, the confidence interval $[330 \pm 7.84] = [322.16, 337.84]$ contains μ. Similarly, because the sample mean $\bar{x} = 324$ is within 7.84 of $\mu = 329$, the confidence interval $[324 \pm 7.84] = [316.16, 331.84]$ contains μ. However, because the sample mean $\bar{x} = 320$ is not within 7.84 of $\mu = 329$, the confidence interval $[320 \pm 7.84] = [312.16, 327.84]$ does not contain μ. Before the company selected the sample, there was a .95 probability that it would obtain a sample mean that gave a confidence interval that contained the population mean μ. This means that 95 percent of all of the confidence intervals that the company could have obtained contain μ, and 5 percent of these confidence intervals do not contain μ.

In reality, of course, we do not know the true value of the population mean (μ). Therefore, we do not know for sure whether the company's confidence interval, [318.16, 333.84], contains μ. However,

FIGURE 9.5 Three 95 Percent Confidence Intervals for μ

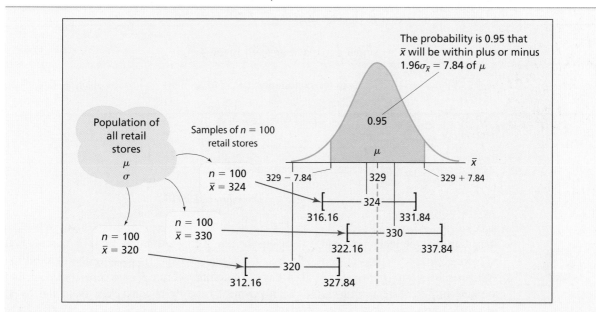

we are 95 percent confident that this confidence interval contains μ. What we mean by this is that we hope that the confidence interval [318.16, 333.84] is one of the 95 percent of all confidence intervals that contain μ and not one of the 5 percent of all confidence intervals that do not contain μ. Here, we say that 95 percent is the confidence level associated with the confidence interval.

Part 3: A practical application: To see a practical application of the candy company's confidence interval, recall that the company intends to increase production by 10 percent if it sees that there is sufficient demand for the new box of candy. The confidence interval calculated, based on the sample data, suggests that the company is 95 percent confident that it will sell between 318 and 334 boxes of candy, on average, per large retail store. This means that the company is estimating that it will have no more than 12 surplus boxes (on average) per store, and that it will fall short of demand by no more than 4 boxes of candy per store. The company can use this information, along with the production costs and profit margins of the candy boxes, to determine whether or not the production increase is fiscally responsible.

This confidence interval is based on the normal distribution and assumes that the true value of the population standard deviation σ is known. Therefore, in the previous example and in the next example, we assume that we know—through theory or history related to the population under consideration—the true value of σ. Of course, in most real-world situations, there would not be a basis for knowing σ. In Section 9.2 we will discuss a confidence interval based on the t distribution that does not assume that σ is known. Furthermore, we will revisit the examples in this section that assume σ is unknown.

Example 9.2   Estimating Mean Payment Time

Recall the management consulting firm that installed a new electronic billing system in a trucking company. The population mean payment time using the trucking company's old billing system was approximately equal to, but no less than, 39 days. To assess whether the population mean payment time, μ, using the new billing system is substantially less than 39 days, the consulting firm will use a sample of $n = 65$ payment times to find a 99 percent confidence interval for μ. The mean of the 65 payment times was $\bar{x} = 18.1077$ days, and we will assume that the true value of the population standard deviation σ for the new billing system is 4.2 days (as discussed in Chapter 7). Then,

Step 1: Draw the top normal curve and areas in Figure 9.4.

Step 2: Find $z_{.005} = 2.575$, as in the bottom normal curve in Figure 9.4 (or as given in Table 9.2).

Step 3: Using the normal point $z_{\alpha/2} = z_{.005} = 2.575$, it follows that a 99 percent confidence interval for μ is

$$\left[\bar{x} \pm z_{.005}\frac{\sigma}{\sqrt{n}}\right] = \left[18.1077 \pm 2.575\frac{4.2}{\sqrt{65}}\right]$$
$$= [18.1077 \pm 1.3414]$$
$$= [16.8, 19.4]$$

Recalling that the mean payment time using the old billing system is 39 days, this interval says that we are 99 percent confident that the mean payment time using the new billing system is between 16.8 days and 19.4 days. Therefore, we are 99 percent confident that the new billing system reduces the mean payment time by at most 22.2 days and by at least 19.6 days.

To compare the 99 percent confidence interval for μ with a 95 percent confidence interval, we note that $z_{.025} = 1.96$ (see Table 9.2), and we compute the 95 percent confidence interval as follows:

$$\left[\bar{x} \pm z_{.025}\frac{\sigma}{\sqrt{n}} \right] = \left[18.1077 \pm 1.96\frac{4.2}{\sqrt{65}} \right]$$

$$= [18.1077 \pm 1.0211]$$

$$= [17.1, 19.1]$$

Although the 99 percent confidence interval is a little longer than the 95 percent confidence interval, the fairly large sample size, $n = 65$, produces intervals that differ only slightly.

THEORY TO PRACTICE

Even though the calculation of the confidence interval appears to be a mathematical concept, and might initially seem foreign to you, it is important to remember that you almost certainly use the concept of confidence intervals in your everyday life—probably without even thinking about it. The specifics of confidence intervals will differ according to the characteristics of the data that you are evaluating (the form of the standard error is going to be determined by the sampling distribution that you are using in your hypothesis test, and the test statistic—z, t, etc.—used to identify confidence level will be based on the hypothesis test that you are supporting with your confidence interval), but the basic form always remains the same: point estimate plus or minus margin of error.

If you were to express a confidence interval in simple English, you might substitute "plus or minus" with "give or take." So it should be clear that, whenever you equivocate your response to a question with "give or take," you are using a confidence interval. For example, if you are asked how long a meeting is going to last, you might say "an hour, give or take fifteen minutes." The point estimate of meeting duration is "one hour" and the margin of error that you are allowing yourself is "fifteen minutes."

More subtly, you are probably using confidence intervals when you say "no more than" or "no less than," as these descriptors are excellent ways to describe the boundaries of a confidence interval. For example, when you are asked how long a meeting will last, you might say "no more than an hour and a quarter" and if you did, you could be describing exactly the same confidence interval listed previously. "An hour, give or take fifteen minutes" translates to a confidence interval that ranges from 45 minutes to an hour and a quarter.

Clearly, confidence intervals are powerful statistical tools that may be harnessed to provide us with easily understood descriptive information and, as we will see later in this chapter, they are useful for identifying whether a given effect is statistically significant. In this way they are, perhaps, more useful than a hypothesis test, when it comes to "testing" the difference between a mean and a hypothetical value or the difference between two means.

Exercises for Section 9.1

CONCEPTS

9.1   Explain why it is important to calculate a confidence interval.

9.2   Explain the meaning of the term "95 percent confidence."

9.3   Under what conditions is the confidence interval $[\bar{x} \pm z_{\alpha/2}(\sigma/\sqrt{n})]$ for μ valid?

9.4   For a fixed sample size, what happens to a confidence interval for μ when we increase the level of confidence?

9.5   For a fixed level of confidence, what happens to a confidence interval for μ when we increase the sample size?

METHODS AND APPLICATIONS

9.6   Suppose that, for a sample of size $n = 100$ measurements, we find that $\bar{x} = 50$. Assuming that σ equals 2, calculate confidence intervals for the population mean μ with the following confidence levels:

   a. 95%   **c.** 97%   **e.** 99.73%
   b. 99%   **d.** 80%   **f.** 92%

9.7 THE TRASH BAG EXAMPLE

Consider the trash bag problem. Suppose that an independent laboratory has tested trash bags and has found that no 30-litre bags that are currently on the market have a mean breaking strength of 25 kilograms or more. On the basis of these results, the producer of the new, improved trash bag feels sure that its 30-litre bag will be the strongest such bag on the market if the new trash bag's mean breaking strength can be shown to be at least 25 kilograms. The mean of a sample of 40 trash bags is found to be $\bar{x} = 25.575$. If we let μ denote the mean of the breaking strengths of all possible trash bags of the new type, and assume that σ equals 1.65:

a. Calculate 95 percent and 99 percent confidence intervals for μ.

b. Using the 95 percent confidence interval, can we be 95 percent confident that μ is at least 25 kilograms? Explain.

c. Using the 99 percent confidence interval, can we be 99 percent confident that μ is at least 25 kilograms? Explain.

d. Based on your answers to parts (b) and (c), how convinced are you that the new 30-litre trash bag is the strongest such bag on the market?

9.8 THE CUSTOMER WAIT TIME EXAMPLE

Recall that a bank manager has developed a new system to reduce the time customers spend waiting to be served by tellers during peak business hours. The mean waiting time during peak business hours under the current system is roughly 9 to 10 minutes. The bank manager hopes that the new system will have a mean waiting time that is less than 6 minutes. The mean of a sample of 100 bank customer waiting times is $\bar{x} = 5.46$. If we let μ denote the mean of all possible bank customer waiting times using the new system and assume that σ equals 2.47:

a. Calculate 95 percent and 99 percent confidence intervals for μ.

b. Using the 95 percent confidence interval, can the bank manager be 95 percent confident that μ is less than 6 minutes? Explain.

c. Using the 99 percent confidence interval, can the bank manager be 99 percent confident that μ is less than 6 minutes? Explain.

d. Based on your answers to parts (b) and (c), how convinced are you that the new mean waiting time is less than 6 minutes?

9.9 THE VIDEO GAME SATISFACTION RATING EXAMPLE

The mean of the sample of 65 customer satisfaction ratings is $\bar{x} = 42.95$. If we let μ denote the mean of all possible customer satisfaction ratings for the XYZ-Box video game system and assume that σ equals 2.64:

a. Calculate 95 percent and 99 percent confidence intervals for μ.

b. Using the 95 percent confidence interval, can we be 95 percent confident that μ is at least 42 (recall that a very satisfied customer gives a rating of at least 42)? Explain.

c. Using the 99 percent confidence interval, can we be 99 percent confident that μ is at least 42? Explain.

d. Based on your answers to parts (b) and (c), how convinced are you that the mean satisfaction rating is at least 42?

9.10 In an article in *Marketing Science,* Silk and Berndt reported on their investigation of the output of advertising agencies. They described ad agency output by finding the shares of dollar billing volume coming from various media categories such as network television, spot television, newspapers, radio, and so forth.

a. Suppose that a random sample of 400 advertising agencies gives an average percentage share of billing volume from network television equal to 7.46 percent, and assume that σ equals 1.42 percent. Calculate a 95 percent confidence interval for the mean percentage share of billing volume from network television for the population of all advertising agencies.

b. Suppose that a random sample of 400 advertising agencies gives an average percentage share of billing volume from spot television commercials equal to 12.44 percent, and assume that σ equals 1.55 percent. Calculate a 95 percent confidence interval for the mean percentage share of billing volume from spot television commercials for the population of all advertising agencies.

c. Compare the confidence intervals in parts (a) and (b). Does it appear that the mean percentage share of billing volume from spot television commercials for advertising agencies is greater than the mean percentage share of billing volume from network television? Explain.

9.11 In an article in *Accounting and Business Research,* Carslaw and Kaplan investigate factors that influence "audit delay." Audit delay, which is defined to be the length of time (in days) from a company's financial year-end to the date of the auditor's report, has been found to affect the market reaction to the report. This is because late reports often seem to be associated with lower returns and early reports often seem to be associated with higher returns.

Carslaw and Kaplan investigated audit delay for two kinds of public companies—owner-controlled and manager-controlled companies. In this case, a company is considered to be owner-controlled if 30 percent or more of the common shares are controlled by a single outside investor (an investor not part of the management group or board of directors). Otherwise, a company is considered manager-controlled. It was felt that the type of control influences audit delay. To quote Carslaw and Kaplan:

> Large external investors, having an acute need for timely information, may be expected to pressure the company and auditor to start and to complete the audit as rapidly as practicable.

a. Suppose that a random sample of 100 public owner-controlled companies is found to give a mean audit delay of $\bar{x} = 82.6$ days, and assume that σ equals 33 days. Calculate a 95 percent confidence interval for the population mean audit delay for all public owner-controlled companies.

b. Suppose that a random sample of 100 public manager-controlled companies is found to give a mean audit delay of $\bar{x} = 93$ days, and assume that σ equals 37 days. Calculate a 95 percent confidence interval for the population mean audit delay for all public manager-controlled companies.

c. Use the confidence intervals you computed in parts (a) and (b) to compare the mean audit delay for all public owner-controlled companies versus that of all public manager-controlled companies. How do the means compare? Explain.

9.12   THE VEHICLE REPLACEMENT EXAMPLE

In an article in the *Journal of Marketing,* Bayus studied the differences between "early replacement buyers" and "late replacement buyers" in making replacement purchases of consumer durable goods. Early replacement buyers are consumers who replace a product during the early part of its lifetime, while late replacement buyers make replacement purchases late in the product's lifetime. In particular, Bayus studied automobile replacement purchases. Consumers who traded in cars with ages of zero to three years and kilometrage of no more than 35,000 kilometres were classified as early replacement buyers. Consumers who traded in cars with ages of seven or more years and kilometrages of more than 73,000 kilometres were classified as late replacement buyers. Bayus compared the two groups of buyers with respect to demographic variables such as income, education, age, and so forth. He also compared the two groups with respect to the amount of search activity in the replacement purchase process. Variables compared included the number of dealers visited, the time spent gathering information, and the time spent visiting dealers.

a. Suppose that a random sample of 800 early replacement buyers yields a mean number of dealers visited of $\bar{x} = 3.3$, and assume that σ equals .71. Calculate a 99 percent confidence interval for the population mean number of dealers visited by early replacement buyers.

b. Suppose that a random sample of 500 late replacement buyers yields a mean number of dealers visited of $\bar{x} = 4.3$, and assume that σ equals .66. Calculate a 99 percent confidence interval for the population mean number of dealers visited by late replacement buyers.

c. Use the confidence intervals you computed in parts (a) and (b) to compare the mean number of dealers visited by early replacement buyers with the mean number of dealers visited by late replacement buyers. How do the means compare? Explain.

9.2 CONFIDENCE INTERVALS FOR A POPULATION MEAN WHEN σ IS UNKNOWN

If we do not know σ (which is usually the case), we can use the sample standard deviation s to help construct a confidence interval for μ. The interval is based on the sampling distribution of

$$t = \frac{\bar{x} - \mu}{s/\sqrt{n}}$$

If the sampled population is normally distributed, then for any sample size n this sampling distribution is what is called a *t* **distribution.**

LO2

Table A.5 in Appendix A gives *t* points for values of *df* from 1 to 100. We can use a computer to find *t* points based on values of *df* greater than 100. Alternatively, because a *t* curve based on more than 100 degrees of freedom is approximately the shape of the standard normal curve, *t* points based on values of *df* greater than 100 can be approximated by their corresponding *z* points. That is, when performing manual calculations, it is reasonable to approximate values of t_α by z_α when *df* is greater than 100.

We now present the formula for a $100(1 - \alpha)$ percent confidence interval for a population mean μ based on the *t* distribution.

A *t*-Based Confidence Interval for a Population Mean μ: σ Unknown

If the sampled population is normally distributed with mean μ, then a $100(1 - \alpha)$ percent confidence interval for μ is

$$\left[\bar{x} \pm t_{\alpha/2} \frac{s}{\sqrt{n}} \right]$$

Here s is the sample standard deviation, $t_{\alpha/2}$ is the *t* point giving a right-hand tail area of $\alpha/2$ under the *t* curve having $n - 1$ degrees of freedom, and n is the sample size. This confidence interval is also approximately valid for non-normal populations if the sample size is large (at least 30).

Before presenting an example, we need to make a few comments. First, even if the sample size is not large, this confidence interval is approximately valid for many populations that are not exactly normally distributed. In particular, this interval is approximately valid for a mound-shaped, or single-peaked, population, even if the population is somewhat skewed to the right or left. Second, this interval employs the point $t_{\alpha/2}$, which gives a right-hand tail area equal to $\alpha/2$ under the t curve having $n-1$ degrees of freedom. Here $\alpha/2$ is determined from the desired confidence level $100(1-\alpha)$ percent.

Example 9.3 Estimating Debt-to-Equity Ratios in a Loan Portfolio

Recall that a measure of a company's financial health is its *debt-to-equity ratio*. This quantity is defined to be the ratio of the company's corporate debt to the company's equity. If this ratio is too high, it is one indication of financial instability. In Chapter 8 (Example 8.1), we presented information about a large bank that decided to initiate a policy limiting the mean debt-to-equity ratio for its portfolio of commercial loans to being less than 1.5. In order to estimate the mean debt-to-equity ratio of its current commercial loan portfolio, the bank randomly selects a sample of 15 of its commercial loan accounts. Audits of these companies result in the following debt-to-equity ratios:

1.31	1.05	1.45	1.21	1.19
1.78	1.37	1.41	1.22	1.11
1.46	1.33	1.29	1.32	1.65

1.0	5
1.1	1 9
1.2	1 2 9
1.3	1 2 3 7
1.4	1 5 6
1.5	
1.6	5
1.7	8

A stem-and-leaf display of these ratios is given in the page margin, and a box plot of the ratios is given below. The stem-and-leaf display looks reasonably mound-shaped, and both the stem-and-leaf display and the box plot look reasonably symmetrical. Furthermore, the sample mean and standard deviation of the ratios can be calculated to be $\bar{x} = 1.3433$ and $s = .1921$.

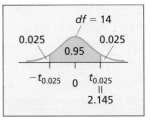

Suppose the bank wants to calculate a 95 percent confidence interval for the loan portfolio's mean debt-to-equity ratio, μ. Because the bank has taken a sample of size $n = 15$, we have $n - 1 = 15 - 1 = 14$ degrees of freedom, and the level of confidence $100(1 - \alpha)\% = 95\%$ implies that $1 - \alpha = .95$ and $\alpha = .05$. Therefore, we use the t point $t_{\alpha/2} = t_{.05/2} = t_{.025}$, which—as illustrated below—is the t point giving a right-hand tail area of .025 under the t curve having 14 degrees of freedom.

Using Table A.5, we find that $t_{.025}$ with 14 degrees of freedom is 2.145. It follows that the 95 percent confidence interval for μ is

$$\left[\bar{x} \pm t_{.025}\frac{s}{\sqrt{n}}\right] = \left[1.3433 \pm 2.145\frac{.1921}{\sqrt{15}}\right]$$

$$= [1.3433 \pm 0.1064]$$

$$= [1.2369, 1.4497]$$

This interval says the bank is 95 percent confident that the mean debt-to-equity ratio for its portfolio of commercial loan accounts is between 1.2369 and 1.4497. Based on this interval, the bank has strong evidence that the portfolio's mean ratio is less than 1.5 (or that the bank is in compliance with its new policy).

Recall that in the two cases discussed in Section 9.1, we calculated z-based confidence intervals for μ by assuming that the population standard deviation σ is known. If σ is actually not known (which would probably be true), we should compute t-based confidence intervals. Furthermore, recall that in each of these cases the sample size is large (at least 30) and that **if the sample size is large, the t-based confidence interval for μ is approximately valid even if the sampled population is not normally distributed.** Therefore, consider the Valentine's Day candy example, wherein the company took a sample of 100 large retail stores and found a mean $\bar{x} = 326$. If the sample standard deviation was 39.1, the 95 percent t-based confidence interval for the population mean number of boxes of candy sold μ of the new box of candy is

$$\left[\bar{x} \pm t_{.025}\frac{s}{\sqrt{n}}\right] = \left[326 \pm 1.984\frac{39.1}{\sqrt{100}}\right] = [318.24, 333.76]$$

where $t_{.025} = 1.984$ is based on $n - 1 = 100 - 1 = 99$ degrees of freedom—see Table A.5. This interval says we are 95 percent confident that the average sales per store will amount to 318 to 334 boxes of candy—a confidence interval that is unchanged from the z-based confidence interval (owing to the large sample size, and sample standard deviation that is a close match to our estimate of the population value).

As another example, the sample of 65 payment times in Example 9.2 has mean $\bar{x} = 18.1077$ and a sample standard deviation $s = 3.9612$. The 99 percent t-based confidence interval for the population mean payment time using the new electronic billing system is illustrated in the margin, and can be calculated to be

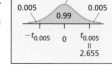

$$\left[\bar{x} \pm t_{.005}\frac{s}{\sqrt{n}}\right] = \left[18.1077 \pm 2.655\frac{3.9612}{\sqrt{65}}\right] = [16.8, 19.4]$$

where $t_{.005} = 2.655$ is based on $n - 1 = 65 - 1 = 64$ degrees of freedom—see Table A.5. Recalling that the mean payment time using the old billing system was 39 days, the interval says that we are 99 percent confident that the mean payment time using the new billing system is between 16.8 days and 19.4 days. Therefore, we are 99 percent confident that the new billing system reduces the mean payment time by at most 22.2 days and by at least 19.6 days.

Example 9.4 Estimating Customer Satisfaction with a New Bottle Design

A company is considering a new bottle design for a popular soft drink, so it takes a random sample of $n = 60$ consumer ratings of this new bottle design. Let μ denote the mean rating of the new bottle design that would be given by all consumers. To assess whether μ exceeds the minimum standard composite score of 25 for a successful bottle design, the company will calculate a 95 percent confidence interval for μ. The mean and the standard deviation of the 60 bottle design ratings are $\bar{x} = 30.35$ and $s = 3.1073$. It follows that a 95 percent confidence interval for μ is

$$\left[\bar{x} \pm t_{.025}\frac{s}{\sqrt{n}}\right] = \left[30.35 \pm 2.001\frac{3.1073}{\sqrt{60}}\right] = [29.5, 31.2]$$

where $t_{.025} = 2.001$ is based on $n - 1 = 60 - 1 = 59$ degrees of freedom—see Table A.5. Since the interval says we are 95 percent confident that the mean rating of the new bottle design is between 29.5 and 31.2, we are 95 percent confident that this mean rating exceeds the minimum standard of 25 by at least 4.5 points and by at most 6.2 points.

FIGURE 9.6 The MegaStat Output for the Debt-to-Equity Ratio Example

Confidence interval - mean	
95%	confidence level
1.3433	mean
0.1921	std. dev.
15	*n*
2.145	*t* (df = 14)
0.1064	margin of error
1.4497	upper confidence limit
1.2369	lower confidence limit

Confidence intervals for μ can be computed using MegaStat. Figure 9.6 gives the MegaStat output of the *t*-based 95 percent confidence interval for the mean debt-to-equity ratio. If we consider the output, we see that $\bar{x} = 1.3433$ (see "mean" in the figure), $s = .1921$ (see "std. dev."), and $t_{.025}(s/\sqrt{n}) = .1064$ [see "margin of error"]. The interval is presented in two separate cells—the "upper confidence limit" (1.4497) and the "lower confidence limit" (1.2369), indicating that the 95 percent confidence interval is $[1.3433 \pm .1064] = [1.2369, 1.4497]$.

To conclude this section, we note that if the sample size *n* is small and the sampled population is not mound-shaped or is highly skewed, then the *t*-based confidence interval for the population mean might not be valid. In this case we can use a nonparametric method—a method that makes no assumption about the shape of the sampled population and is valid for any sample size. In Chapter 13 we discuss nonparametric methods.

Exercises for Section **9.2**

CONCEPTS

9.13 Explain how each of the following changes as *the number of degrees of freedom* describing a *t* curve *increases:*
  a. The standard deviation of the *t* curve.
  b. The points t_α and $t_{\alpha/2}$.

9.14 Discuss when it is appropriate to use the *t*-based confidence interval for μ.   when σ is unknown.

METHODS AND APPLICATIONS

9.15 Using Table A.5, find $t_{.100}$, $t_{.025}$, and $t_{.001}$ based on 11 degrees of freedom. Also, find these *t* points based on 6 degrees of freedom.

9.16 Suppose that for a sample of $n = 11$ measurements, we find that $\bar{x} = 72$ and $s = 5$. Assuming normality, compute confidence intervals for the population mean μ with the following levels of confidence:
  a. 95%   **c.** 80%   **e.** 98%
  b. 99%   **d.** 90%   **f.** 99.8%

9.17 **THE DEBT RATIO EXAMPLE**

The *bad debt ratio* for a financial institution is defined to be the dollar value of loans defaulted divided by the total dollar value of all loans made. Suppose a random sample of seven Manitoba credit unions is selected and that the bad debt ratios (written as percentages) for these banks are 7 percent, 4 percent, 6 percent, 7 percent, 5 percent, 4 percent, and 9 percent. Assuming the bad debt ratios are approximately normally distributed:

a. Calculate the 95 percent confidence interval, and the 99 percent confidence interval for the mean debt-to-equity ratio.

b. Banking officials claim the mean bad debt ratio for all of the banking institutions in the Prairie provinces is 3.5 percent and that the mean bad debt ratio for Manitoba credit unions is higher. Using the 95 percent confidence interval, can we be 95 percent confident that this claim is true? Using the 99 percent confidence interval, can we be 99 percent confident that this claim is true?

9.18 In an article in *Quality Progress,* Blauw and During study how long it takes companies to complete five stages in the adoption of total quality control (TQC). According to Blauw and During, the adoption of TQC can be divided into five stages as follows:
  (1) Knowledge: The organization has heard of TQC.
  (2) Attitude formation: The organization seeks information and compares advantages and disadvantages.
  (3) Decision making: The organization decides to implement TQC.
  (4) Implementation: The organization implements TQC.
  (5) Confirmation: The organization decides to apply TQC as a normal business activity.
Suppose a random sample of five firms that have adopted TQC is selected. Each firm is asked to report how long it took to complete the implementation stage. The firms report the following durations (in years) for

this stage: 2.5, 1.5, 1.25, 3.5, and 1.25. Assuming that the durations are approximately normally distributed, calculate a 95 percent confidence interval for the mean duration of the implementation stage. Based on the 95 percent confidence interval, is there conclusive evidence that the mean duration of the implementation stage exceeds one year? Explain. What is one possible reason for the lack of conclusive evidence?

9.19 THE AIR TRAFFIC CONTROLLER EXAMPLE

Air traffic controllers have the crucial task of ensuring that aircraft don't collide. To do this, they must quickly discern when two planes are about to enter the same air space at the same time. They are aided by video display panels that track the aircraft in their sector and alert the controller when two flight paths are about to converge. The display panel currently in use has a mean "alert time" of 15 seconds. (The alert time is the time elapsing between the instant when two aircraft enter into a collision course and when a controller initiates a call to reroute the planes.) A new display panel has been developed that uses artificial intelligence to project a plane's current flight path into the future. This new panel provides air traffic controllers with an earlier warning that a collision is likely. It is hoped that the mean "alert time," μ, for the new panel is less than 8 seconds. To test the new panel, 15 randomly selected air traffic controllers are trained to use the panel and their alert times for a simulated collision course are recorded. The sample alert times (in seconds) are: 7.2, 7.5, 8.0, 6.8, 7.2, 8.4, 5.3, 7.3, 7.6, 7.1, 9.4, 6.4, 7.9, 6.2, 8.7.

a. Using the fact that $\bar{x} = 7.4$ and $s = 1.026$, find a 95 percent confidence interval for the mean alert time, μ, for the new panel.

b. Can we be 95 percent confident that μ is less than 8 seconds?

9.20 THE WHOLE FOODS EXAMPLE

Whole Foods is an all-natural grocery chain based in the United States that is just starting to enter the Canadian marketplace, with eight stores currently open in Canada. Head office is interested in determining whether the Canadian stores are faring as well as (or better than)

Whole Foods stores in the United States. To do this, the company measures the sales dollars per square metre, in the most recent fiscal year, in a random sample of five of these stores. The data (sales dollars per square metre) are as follows: $79.34, $79.71, $74.42, $82.87, $74.97. Using these data, find a 95 percent confidence interval for the true mean sales dollars per square metre for Canadian Whole Foods supermarkets during the most recent fiscal year. Are we 95 percent confident that this mean is greater than $70, the historical average for Whole Foods stores in the United States?

9.21 THE CHEMICAL CATALYST EXAMPLE

Recall the major chemical company (presented in Example 8.2) that wants to determine whether a new catalyst, Catalyst XA-100, increases the mean hourly yield of a chemical process beyond the current mean hourly yield, which is known to be roughly equal to, but no more than, 750 kilograms per hour. To test the new catalyst, five trial runs using Catalyst XA-100 are made. The resulting yields for the trial runs (in kilograms per hour) are 801, 814, 784, 836, and 820. Assuming that all factors affecting yields of the process have been held as constant as possible during the test runs, it is reasonable to regard the five yields obtained using the new catalyst as a random sample from the population of all possible yields that would be obtained by using the new catalyst. Furthermore, we will assume that this population is approximately normally distributed.

a. Find a 95 percent confidence interval for the mean of all possible yields obtained using Catalyst XA-100.

b. Based on the confidence interval, can we be 95 percent confident that the mean yield using Catalyst XA-100 exceeds 750 kilograms per hour? Explain.

9.22 THE TRASH BAG EXAMPLE

Consider again the trash bag case, in which we are attempting to demonstrate that the new generation of trash bags has a significantly larger breaking strength than the previous generation (i.e., 25 kilograms). The mean and the standard deviation of this sample were $\bar{x} = 25.575$ and $s = 1.6438$. Calculate a t-based 95 percent confidence interval for the mean of all the breaking strengths of all possible trash bags of the new type. Are we 95 percent confident that the mean is at least 25 kilograms?

9.23 THE CUSTOMER WAIT TIME EXAMPLE

The mean and the standard deviation of a sample of 100 bank customer waiting times are $\bar{x} = 5.46$ and $s = 2.475$. Calculate a t-based 95 percent confidence interval for the mean of all possible bank customer waiting times using the new system. Are we 95 percent confident that the mean is less than six minutes?

9.24 THE VIDEO GAME SATISFACTION RATING EXAMPLE

Consider the video game satisfaction example. The mean and the standard deviation of a sample of $n = 65$ customer satisfaction ratings are $\bar{x} = 42.95$ and $s = 2.6424$. Calculate a t-based 95 percent confidence interval for the mean of all possible customer satisfaction ratings for the XYZ-Box video game system. Are we 95 percent confident that the mean is at least 42, the minimal rating given by a very satisfied customer?

9.3 SAMPLE SIZE DETERMINATION

LO3

In Example 9.1 we used a sample of 100 retail stores to construct a 95 percent confidence interval for the average number of candy boxes expected to be sold for Valentine's Day. The size of this sample was not arbitrary—it was planned. To understand this, suppose that before the company selected the random sample of 100 stores, it randomly selected a sample of five stores, and found the following five values for the estimated candy box order:

$$362 \quad 290 \quad 342 \quad 338 \quad 308$$

This sample has mean $\bar{x} = 328$. Assuming that the population of all store estimates is normally distributed and that the population standard deviation σ is known to equal 40, it follows that a 95 percent confidence interval for μ is

$$\left[\bar{x} \pm z_{.025} \frac{\sigma}{\sqrt{n}} \right] = \left[328 \pm 1.96 \frac{40}{\sqrt{5}} \right]$$

$$= [328 \pm 35.06]$$

$$= [292.94, 363.06]$$

Although the sample mean $\bar{x} = 328$ is close to the estimated 10 percent production increase that the company was hoping to target, the 95 percent confidence interval for μ spans a much larger range than the company is comfortable with. In fact, the 95 percent confidence interval for average number of sales per store has a lower-bound estimate that is less than the company's current production levels—which would suggest that the company should not increase production at all. If the company used the confidence interval generated by this small sample, it might not increase its production rate, which might end up being a poor decision, given that the upper limit of the 95 percent confidence interval suggests that the company could accommodate as much as a 20 percent production increase! One reason that this 95 percent interval spans such a large range is that the sample size of 5 is not large enough to make the interval's margin of error

$$z_{.025} \frac{\sigma}{\sqrt{n}} = 1.96 \frac{40}{\sqrt{5}} = 35.06$$

small enough. We can attempt to make the margin of error in the interval smaller by increasing the sample size, so we will now work through a method for finding the size of the sample that will be needed to make the margin of error in a confidence interval for μ as small as we want. To develop a formula for the needed sample size, we will initially assume that we know σ. Then, if the population is normally distributed or the sample size is large, the z-based $100(1 - \alpha)$ percent confidence interval for μ is

$$\left[\bar{x} \pm z_{\alpha/2} \frac{\sigma}{\sqrt{n}} \right]$$

To find the needed sample size, we set $z_{\alpha/2}(\sigma/\sqrt{n})$ equal to the desired margin of error and solve for n. Letting E denote the desired margin of error, we obtain

$$z_{\alpha/2} \frac{\sigma}{\sqrt{n}} = E$$

Multiplying both sides of this equation by $\sqrt{n}$ and dividing both sides by E, we obtain

$$\sqrt{n} = \frac{z_{\alpha/2}\sigma}{E}$$

Squaring both sides of this result gives us the formula for n.

Determining the Sample Size for a Confidence Interval for μ

A sample of size

$$n = \left(\frac{z_{\alpha/2}\sigma}{E}\right)^2$$

makes the margin of error in a 100(1 − α) percent confidence interval for μ equal to E. That is, this

sample size makes us 100(1 − α) percent confident that $\bar{x}$ is within E units of μ. If the calculated value of n is not a whole number, round this value up to the next whole number (so that the margin of error is at least as small as desired).

If we consider the formula for the sample size n, it intuitively follows that the value E is the farthest that the user is willing to allow $\bar{x}$ to be from μ at a given level of confidence, and the normal point $z_{\alpha/2}$ follows directly from the given level of confidence. Furthermore, because the population standard deviation σ is in the numerator of the formula for n, it follows that the more variable that the individual population measurements are, the larger is the sample size needed to estimate μ with a specified accuracy.

To use this formula for n, we must either know σ (which is unlikely) or we must compute an estimate of σ. We first consider the case where we know σ. For example, suppose in the candy company example, we want to find the sample size that is needed to make the margin of error in a 95 percent confidence interval for μ equal to 8. Assuming that σ is known to equal 40, and using $z_{.025} = 1.96$, the appropriate sample size is

$$n = \left(\frac{z_{.025}\sigma}{E}\right)^2 = \left(\frac{1.96(40)}{8}\right)^2 = 96.04$$

Rounding up, we would employ a sample of size 97.

In most real situations, of course, we do not know the true value of σ. If σ is not known, we often estimate σ by using a preliminary sample. In this case we modify the above formula for n by replacing σ by the standard deviation s of the preliminary sample and by replacing $z_{\alpha/2}$ by $t_{\alpha/2}$. So we obtain

$$n = \left(\frac{t_{\alpha/2}s}{E}\right)^2$$

where the number of degrees of freedom for the $t_{\alpha/2}$ point is the size of the preliminary sample minus 1. Intuitively, using $t_{\alpha/2}$ compensates for the fact that the preliminary sample's value of s might underestimate σ.

Example 9.5   Sample Size Requirements for a 95% Confidence Interval

Suppose that in the candy company example, we want to find the sample size that is needed to make the margin of error in a 95 percent confidence interval for μ equal to 8. Assuming we do not know σ, we regard the previously discussed sample of five stores as a preliminary sample. Therefore, we replace σ by the standard deviation of the preliminary sample, which can be calculated to be s = 28.705, and we replace $z_{\alpha/2} = z_{.025} = 1.96$ with $t_{.025} = 2.776$, which is based on n − 1 = 4 degrees of freedom. We find that the appropriate sample size is

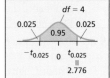

$$n = \left(\frac{t_{.025}s}{E}\right)^2 = \left(\frac{2.776(28.705)}{8}\right)^2 = 99.21$$

Rounding up, we employ a sample of size 100.

When we make the margin of error in our 95 percent confidence interval for μ equal to 8, we can say we are 95 percent confident that the sample mean $\bar{x}$ will be within 8 of μ. To understand this, suppose the true value of μ is 329. Recalling that the mean of the sample of 100 stores that we actually sampled was $\bar{x} = 326$, we see that this sample mean is within 8 of μ

(in fact, it is within 3 boxes of the true mean number of purchases per store). Other samples of 100 stores would give different sample means that would be different distances from μ. When we say that our sample of 100 stores makes us 95 percent confident that $\bar{x}$ is within 8 of μ, we mean that 95 percent of all possible sample means based on 100 stores are within 8 of μ and 5 percent of such sample means are not. Therefore, when we randomly select one sample of size 100 and compute its sample mean to be $\bar{x} = 326$, we can be 95 percent confident that this sample mean is within 8 of μ.

In general, the purpose behind replacing $z_{\alpha/2}$ by $t_{\alpha/2}$ (when we are using a preliminary sample to obtain an estimate of σ) is to be conservative, so that we compute a sample size that is at least as large as needed. Because of this, we often obtain a margin of error that is even smaller than we have requested.

To see that the sample of 100 retail stores has actually produced a 95 percent confidence interval with a margin of error that is as small as we requested, recall that the 100 retail stores have mean $\bar{x} = 326$ and standard deviation $s = 39.1$. Therefore, the t-based 95 percent confidence interval is

$$\left[\bar{x} \pm t_{.025}\frac{s}{\sqrt{n}}\right] = \left[326 \pm 1.984\frac{39.1}{\sqrt{100}}\right] = [318.24, 333.76]$$

where $t_{.025} = 1.984$ is based on $n - 1 = 100 - 1 = 99$ degrees of freedom—see Table A.5. We see that the margin of error in this interval is 7.76, which is smaller than the 8 we asked for. The confidence interval supports the 10 percent production increase that the company has proposed, and does not leave the company exposed to an excessively large inventory surplus, in the event that demand falls short of its prediction.

Finally, sometimes we do not know σ and we do not have a preliminary sample that can be used to estimate σ. In this case, it can be shown that if we can make a reasonable guess of the range of the population being studied, then a conservatively large estimate of σ is this estimated range divided by 4. For example, if the company's marketing department felt that the average order per store should fall within a range no larger than 200 boxes (i.e., 100 boxes above the average order, and 100 boxes below the average order), then a conservatively large estimate of σ is $200/4 = 50$ boxes. When employing such an estimate of σ, it is sufficient to use the z-based sample size formula $n = (z_{\alpha/2}\sigma/E)^2$, because a conservatively large estimate of σ will give us a conservatively large sample size.

Exercises for Section **9.3**

CONCEPTS

9.25 Explain what is meant by the margin of error for a confidence interval. What error are we talking about in the context of an interval for μ?

9.26 Explain exactly what we mean when we say that a sample of size n makes us 99 percent confident that $\bar{x}$ is within E units of μ.

9.27 Why do we often need to take a preliminary sample when determining the size of the sample needed to make the margin of error of a confidence interval equal to E?

METHODS AND APPLICATIONS

9.28 Consider a population having a standard deviation equal to 10. We want to estimate the mean of this population.
   a. How large a random sample is needed to construct a 95 percent confidence interval for the mean of this population with a margin of error equal to 1?

   b. Suppose that we now take a random sample of the size we have determined in part (a). If we obtain a sample mean equal to 295, calculate the 95 percent confidence interval for the population mean. What is the interval's margin of error?

9.29 Referring to part (a) of Exercise 9.11, assume that σ equals 33. How large a random sample of public owner-controlled companies is needed to make us
   a. 95 percent confident that $\bar{x}$, the sample mean audit delay, is within a margin of error of four days of μ, the true mean audit delay?
   b. 99 percent confident that $\bar{x}$ is within a margin of error of four days of μ?

9.30 THE VEHICLE REPLACEMENT EXAMPLE

   Referring to part (b) of Exercise 9.12, assume that σ equals .66. How large a sample of late replacement buyers is needed to make us

a. 99 percent confident that $\bar{x}$, the sample mean number of dealers visited, is within a margin of error of .04 of μ, the true mean number of dealers visited?

b. 99.73 percent confident that $\bar{x}$ is within a margin of error of .05 of μ?

9.31 THE CHEMICAL CATALYST EXAMPLE

Referring to Exercise 9.21, regard the sample of five trial runs for which $s = 19.65$ as a preliminary sample. Determine the number of trial runs of the chemical process needed to make us

a. 95 percent confident that $\bar{x}$, the sample mean hourly yield, is within a margin of error of eight kilograms of the true mean hourly yield μ when Catalyst XA-100 is used.

b. 99 percent confident that $\bar{x}$ is within a margin of error of five kilograms of μ.

9.32 THE WHOLE FOODS EXAMPLE

Referring to Exercise 9.20, regard the sample of 5 stores as a preliminary sample. How large a sample of sales figures is needed to make us 95 percent confident that $\bar{x}$, the sample mean sales dollars per square metre, is within a margin of error of $1.50 of μ, the true mean sales dollars per square metre for all Whole Foods supermarkets in Canada? Given the number of Whole Foods stores that currently exist in Canada, is it still worthwhile estimating the population mean in this way? What else could we do?

9.33 THE AIR TRAFFIC CONTROLLER EXAMPLE

Referring to Exercise 9.19, regard the sample of 15 alert times as a preliminary sample. Determine the sample size needed to make us 95 percent confident that the population mean alert time is within a margin of error of .3 seconds of the sample mean alert time.

9.4 CONFIDENCE INTERVALS FOR A POPULATION PROPORTION

LO4

In Chapter 6, the soft cheese spread producer decided to replace its current spout with the new spout if p, the true proportion of all current purchasers who would stop buying the cheese spread if the new spout was used, is less than .10. Suppose that when 1,000 current purchasers are randomly selected and are asked to try the new spout, 63 say they would stop buying the spread if the new spout was used. The point estimate of the population proportion p is the sample proportion $\hat{p} = 63/1,000 = .063$. This sample proportion says we estimate that 6.3 percent of all current purchasers would stop buying the cheese spread if the new spout was used. Since $\hat{p}$ equals .063, we have some evidence that p is less than .10.

To see if there is strong evidence that p is less than .10, we can calculate a confidence interval for p. As explained in Chapter 6, if the sample size n is large, then the sampling distribution of the sample proportion $\hat{p}$ is approximately a normal distribution with mean $\mu_{\hat{p}} = p$ and standard deviation $\sigma_{\hat{p}} = \sqrt{p(1-p)/n}$. By using the same logic we used in developing confidence intervals for μ, it follows that a $100(1-\alpha)$ percent confidence interval for p is

$$\left[\hat{p} \pm z_{\alpha/2}\sqrt{\frac{p(1-p)}{n}} \right]$$

Estimating $p(1-p)$ by $\hat{p}(1-\hat{p})$, it follows that a $100(1-\alpha)$ percent confidence interval for p can be calculated as summarized in the following boxed feature.

A Large-Sample Confidence Interval for a Population Proportion p

If the sample size n is large, a $100(1-\alpha)$ percent confidence interval for the population proportion p is

$$\left[\hat{p} \pm z_{\alpha/2}\sqrt{\frac{\hat{p}(1-\hat{p})}{n}} \right]$$

Here n should be considered large if both $n\hat{p}$ and $n(1-\hat{p})$ are at least 5.[1]

---

[1] Some statisticians suggest using the more conservative rule that both $n\hat{p}$ and $n(1-\hat{p})$ must be at least 10. Furthermore, because $\hat{p}(1-\hat{p})/(n-1)$ is an unbiased point estimate of $p(1-p)/n$, a more correct $100(1-\alpha)$ percent confidence interval for p is $[\hat{p} \pm z_{\alpha/2}\sqrt{\hat{p}(1-\hat{p})/(n-1)}]$. However, because n is large, there is little difference.

ROADBLOCK	**Tests of proportions (and differences of proportions) remain one of the few domains in which the z test is still in common use**
	The z test of proportions is still in common use, despite the rise in popularity of the t test. The z test is acceptable because it can be shown that $\sqrt{\hat{p}(1 - \hat{p})}$ is an acceptable approximation of the population standard deviation. The z test is useful in practice because this remains one of the few situations in which the population standard deviation is both "known and unknown," owing to the fact that $\sqrt{\hat{p}(1 - \hat{p})}$ is still based on the sample proportion and is therefore easily obtained.

Example 9.6 Sample Size Requirements for a Confidence Interval around a Proportion

Suppose that the cheese spread producer wants to calculate a 99 percent confidence interval for p, the population proportion of purchasers who would stop buying the cheese spread if the new spout was used. To determine whether the sample size $n = 1,000$ is large enough to enable us to use the confidence interval formula just given, recall that the point estimate of p is $\hat{p} = 63/1,000 = .063$. Therefore, because $n\hat{p} = 1,000(.063) = 63$ and $n(1 - \hat{p}) = 1,000(.937) = 937$ are both greater than 5, we can use the confidence interval formula. It follows that the 99 percent confidence interval for p is

$$\left[\hat{p} \pm z_{.005}\sqrt{\frac{\hat{p}(1 - \hat{p})}{n}} \right] = \left[.063 \pm 2.575\sqrt{\frac{(.063)(.937)}{1000}} \right]$$
$$= [.063 \pm .0198]$$
$$= [.0432, .0828]$$

This interval says that we are 99 percent confident that between 4.32 percent and 8.28 percent of all current purchasers would stop buying the cheese spread if the new spout was used. Moreover, because the upper limit of the 99 percent confidence interval is less than .10, we have very strong evidence that the true proportion p of all current purchasers who would stop buying the cheese spread is less than .10. Based on this result, it seems reasonable to use the new spout.

To compare the 99 percent confidence interval for p with a 95 percent confidence interval, we compute the 95 percent confidence interval as follows:

$$\left[\hat{p} \pm z_{.025}\sqrt{\frac{\hat{p}(1 - \hat{p})}{n}} \right] = \left[.063 \pm 1.96\sqrt{\frac{(.063)(.937)}{1000}} \right]$$
$$= [.063 \pm .0151]$$
$$= [.0479, .0781]$$

Although the 99 percent confidence interval is somewhat longer than the 95 percent confidence interval, the fairly large sample size of $n = 1,000$ produces intervals that differ only slightly. This is because the margin of error in the 99 percent confidence interval is .0198, and the margin of error in the 95 percent confidence interval is .0151. Both of these margins of error are reasonably small. Generally, however, quite a large sample is needed to make the margin of error in a confidence interval for p reasonably small. The next two examples demonstrate that a sample size of 200, which most people would consider quite large, does not necessarily give a 95 percent confidence interval for p with a small margin of error.

Example 9.7 Estimating the Prevalence of a Common Drug Side Effect

Antibiotics occasionally cause nausea as a side effect. Scientists working for a major drug company have developed a new antibiotic called Phe-Mycin. The company wants to estimate p, the proportion of all patients who would experience nausea as a side effect when being treated with Phe-Mycin. Suppose that a sample of 200 patients is randomly selected. When these patients are treated with Phe-Mycin, 35 patients experience nausea. The point estimate of the population proportion p is the sample proportion $\hat{p} = 35/200 = .175$. This sample proportion says that we estimate that 17.5 percent of all patients would experience nausea as a side effect of taking Phe-Mycin. Furthermore, because $n\hat{p} = 200(.175) = 35$ and $n(1 - \hat{p}) = 200(.825) = 165$ are both at least 5, we can use the previously given formula to calculate a confidence interval for p. Doing this, we find that a 95 percent confidence interval for p is

$$\left[\hat{p} \pm z_{.025}\sqrt{\frac{\hat{p}(1 - \hat{p})}{n}} \right] = \left[.175 \pm 1.96\sqrt{\frac{(.175)(.825)}{200}} \right]$$
$$= [.175 \pm .053]$$
$$= [.122, .228]$$

This interval says we are 95 percent confident that between 12.2 percent and 22.8 percent of all patients would experience nausea as a side effect of taking Phe-Mycin. Notice that the margin of error (.053) in this interval is rather large. Therefore, this interval is fairly long and it does not provide a very precise estimate of p.

Example 9.8 Ethics in Marketing

As described previously, in their book *Essentials of Marketing Research,* William R. Dillon, Thomas J. Madden, and Neil H. Firtle discuss a survey of marketing professionals, the results of which were originally published by Ishmael P. Akaah and Edward A. Riordan in the *Journal of Marketing Research.* In the study, randomly selected marketing researchers were presented with various scenarios involving ethical issues such as confidentiality, conflict of interest, and social acceptability. The marketing researchers were asked to indicate whether they approved or disapproved of the actions described in each scenario. For instance, one scenario that involved the issue of confidentiality was described as follows:

> **Use of ultraviolet ink** A project director went to the marketing research director's office and requested permission to use an ultraviolet ink to precode a questionnaire for a mail survey. The project director pointed out that although the cover letter promised confidentiality, respondent identification was needed to permit adequate cross-tabulations of the data. The marketing research director gave approval.

Of the 205 marketing researchers who participated in the survey, 117 said they disapproved of the actions taken in the scenario. It follows that a point estimate of p, the proportion of all marketing researchers who disapprove of the actions taken in the scenario, is $\hat{p} = 117/205 = .5707$. Furthermore, because $n\hat{p} = 205(.5707) = 117$ and $n(1 - \hat{p}) = 205(.4293) = 88$ are both at least 5, a 95 percent confidence interval for p is

$$\left[\hat{p} \pm z_{.025}\sqrt{\frac{\hat{p}(1 - \hat{p})}{n}} \right] = \left[.5707 \pm 1.96\sqrt{\frac{(.5707)(.4293)}{205}} \right]$$
$$= [.5707 \pm .0678]$$
$$= [.5029, .6385]$$

This interval says we are 95 percent confident that between 50.29 percent and 63.85 percent of all marketing researchers disapprove of the actions taken in the ultraviolet ink scenario. Notice that since the margin of error (.0678) in this interval is rather large, this interval does not provide a very precise estimate of p.

LO5

To find the size of the sample needed to estimate a population proportion, we consider the theoretically correct interval

$$\left[\hat{p} \pm z_{\alpha/2}\sqrt{\frac{\hat{p}(1-p)}{n}} \right]$$

To obtain the sample size needed to make the margin of error in this interval equal to E, we set

$$z_{\alpha/2}\sqrt{\frac{p(1-p)}{n}} = E$$

and solve for n. When we do this, we get the result shown in the following boxed feature:

Determining the Sample Size for a Confidence Interval for p

A sample of size

$$n = p(1-p)\left(\frac{z_{\alpha/2}}{E}\right)^2$$

makes the margin of error in a $100(1-\alpha)$ percent confidence interval for p equal to E. That is, this sample size makes us $100(1-\alpha)$ percent confident that $\hat{p}$ is within E units of p. If the calculated value of n is not a whole number, round this value up to the next whole number.

Looking at this formula, we see that the larger $p(1-p)$ is, the larger n will be. To make sure n is large enough, consider Figure 9.7, which is a graph of $p(1-p)$ versus p. This figure shows that $p(1-p)$ equals .25 when p equals .5. Furthermore, $p(1-p)$ is never larger than .25. Therefore, if the true value of p could be near .5, we should set $p(1-p)$ equal to .25. This will ensure that n is as large as needed to make the margin of error as small as desired. For example, suppose we want to estimate the proportion p of women enrolled in undergraduate business degrees in Canada. Although sex composition varies between programs in a university or college (and fluctuates from year to year), p could be near .5. Further assume that we want to make the margin of error in a 95 percent confidence interval for p equal to .02. If the sample to be taken is random, it should consist of

$$n = p(1-p)\left(\frac{z_{\alpha/2}}{E}\right)^2 = .25\left(\frac{1.96}{.02}\right)^2 = 2{,}401$$

undergraduate business students.

In reality, a list of "all Canadian undergraduate business students" is not available to survey organizations, so it is not feasible to take a technically correct random sample of these students. For this reason, polling organizations actually employ other, more complicated kinds of samples. For now, we consider the samples taken by survey organizations to be approximately random. Suppose, then, that when the sample of students is actually taken, the proportion $\hat{p}$ of female students turns out to be greater than .52. It follows, because the sample is large enough to make the margin of error in a 95 percent confidence interval for p equal to .02, that the lower limit of such an interval is greater than .50. This says we have strong evidence that a majority of Canadian undergraduate business students are female. For instance, if the sample proportion $\hat{p}$ equals .53, we are 95 percent confident that the proportion of female undergraduate business students is between .51 and .55.

FIGURE **9.7**   The Graph of $p(1 - p)$ versus p

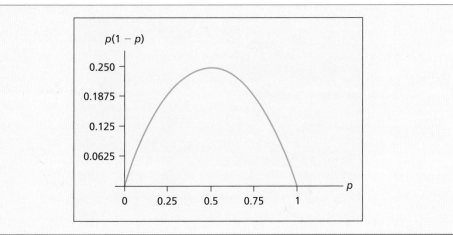

Remember that the *p* that is multiplied by *z* divided by margin of error is the population proportion

It is potentially easy to become confused with the various formulas to which you have been introduced for the z test of proportions. Remember that the proportion used in the determination of the sample size for your confidence interval surrounding a proportion is intended to be the most plausible measure of central tendency in your sampling distribution. This is done to ensure that the standard error proposed for your hypothetical distribution is as accurate as possible. If the proportion is too large, the required *n* size will be spuriously high. If it is too small, the required *n* size will be spuriously low.

Major polling organizations conduct public opinion polls concerning many kinds of issues. While making the margin of error in a 95 percent confidence interval for *p* equal to .02 requires a sample size of 2,401, making the margin of error in such an interval equal to .03 requires a sample size of only

$$n = p(1 - p)\left(\frac{z_{\alpha/2}}{E}\right)^2 = .25\left(\frac{1.96}{.03}\right)^2 = 1,067.1$$

or 1,068 (rounding up). Of course, these calculations assume that the proportion *p* being estimated could be near .5. However, for any value of *p*, increasing the margin of error from .02 to .03 substantially decreases the needed sample size and so saves considerable time and money. For this reason, although a margin of error of .02 is more accurate, the vast majority of public opinion polls use a margin of error of .03 or larger.

When the news media report the results of a public opinion poll, they express the margin of error in a 95 percent confidence interval for *p in percentage points.* For instance, if the margin of error is .03, the media would say the poll's margin of error is 3 percentage points. The media seldom report the level of confidence, but almost all polling results are based on 95 percent confidence. Sometimes the media make a vague reference to the level of confidence. For instance, if the margin of error is 3 percentage points, the media might say that "the sample result will be within 3 percentage points of the population value in 19 out of 20 samples." Here the "19 out of 20 samples" is a reference to the level of confidence, which is $100(19/20) = 100(.95) = 95$ percent.

As an example, suppose a news report says a recent poll found that 34 percent of the public favoured military intervention in an international crisis, and suppose the poll's margin of error was reported to be 3 percentage points. This means the sample taken was large enough to make us 95 percent confident that the sample proportion $\hat{p} = .34$ was within .03 (that is, 3 percentage points) of the true proportion *p* of the entire public that favoured military intervention. That is, we are 95 percent confident that *p* is between .31 and .37.

FIGURE **9.8**   As p Gets Closer to .5, $p(1 - p)$ Increases

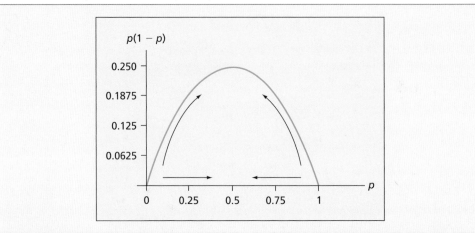

If the population proportion we are estimating is substantially different from .5, setting p equal to .5 will give a sample size that is much larger than is needed. In this case, we should use our intuition or previous sample information—along with Figure 9.8—to determine the largest reasonable value for $p(1 - p)$. Figure 9.8 implies that as p gets closer to .5, $p(1 - p)$ increases. It follows that $p(1 - p)$ is maximized by the reasonable value of p that is closest to .5. Therefore, **when we are estimating a proportion that is substantially different from .5, we use the reasonable value of p that is closest to .5 to calculate the sample size needed to obtain a specified margin of error.**

Example 9.9   Sample Size Requirements for Estimates of Side Effect Prevalence

Again consider estimating the proportion of all patients who would experience nausea as a side effect of taking the new antibiotic Phe-Mycin. Suppose the drug company wants to find the size of the random sample that is needed to obtain a 2 percent margin of error with 95 percent confidence. In Example 9.7 we used a sample of 200 patients to compute a 95 percent confidence interval for p. This interval, which is [.122, .228], makes us very confident that p is between .122 and .228. Because .228 is the reasonable value of p that is closest to .5, the largest reasonable value of $p(1 - p)$ is .228(1 - .228) = .1760, so the drug company should take a sample of

$$n = p(1 - p)\left(\frac{z_{\alpha/2}}{E}\right)^2 = .1760\left(\frac{1.96}{.02}\right)^2 = 1{,}691 \text{ (rounded up)}$$

patients.

Finally, as a last example of choosing p for sample size calculations, suppose that experience indicates that a population proportion p is at least .75. Then, .75 is the reasonable value of p that is closest to .5, and we would use the largest reasonable value of $p(1 - p)$, which is .75(1 - .75) = .1875.

Exercises for Section **9.4**

CONCEPTS

9.34   **a.** What does a population proportion tell us about the population?
  b. Explain the difference between p and $\hat{p}$.
  c. What is meant when a public opinion poll's *margin of error* is 3 percent?

9.35   Suppose we are using the sample size formula in the boxed feature "Determining the Sample Size for a Confidence Interval for p" to find the sample size needed to make the margin of error in a confidence interval for p equal to E. In each of the following situations, explain what value of p would be used in the formula for finding n:

a. We have no idea what value p is—it could be any value between 0 and 1.

b. Past experience tells us that p is no more than .3.

c. Past experience tells us that p is at least .8.

METHODS AND APPLICATIONS

9.36 In each of the following cases, determine whether the sample size n is large enough to use the large-sample formula to compute a confidence interval for p.

a. $\hat{p} = .1, n = 30$ **d.** $\hat{p} = .8, n = 400$
b. $\hat{p} = .1, n = 100$ **e.** $\hat{p} = .9, n = 30$
c. $\hat{p} = .5, n = 50$ **f.** $\hat{p} = .99, n = 200$

9.37 In each of the following cases, compute 95 percent, 98 percent, and 99 percent confidence intervals for the population proportion p.

a. $\hat{p} = .4$ and $n = 100$ **c.** $\hat{p} = .9$ and $n = 100$
b. $\hat{p} = .1$ and $n = 300$ **d.** $\hat{p} = .6$ and $n = 50$

9.38 THE BANK CUSTOMER SATISFACTION EXAMPLE

The Allied Bank of Canada is attempting to improve customer satisfaction and customer loyalty by "listening to the voice of the customer." A key measure of customer satisfaction is the response on a scale from 1 to 10 to the question: "Considering all the business you do with the Allied Bank, what number from 1 to 10 indicates your overall satisfaction with the bank?" Suppose that a random sample of 350 current customers results in 195 customers responding with a 9 or 10, representing "customer delight." Find a 95 percent confidence interval for the true proportion of all current Allied Bank customers who would respond with a 9 or 10. Are we 95 percent confident that this proportion exceeds .48, the historical proportion of customer delight for the Allied Bank of Canada?

9.39 THE MARKETING ETHICS EXAMPLE

Consider the marketing ethics case described in Example 9.8. One of the scenarios presented to the 205 marketing researchers was as follows:

A marketing testing firm to which X Company gives most of its business recently went public. The marketing research director of X Company had been looking for a good investment and proceeded to buy some $20,000 of the X Company's stock. The firm continues as X Company's leading supplier for testing.

Of the 205 marketing researchers who participated in the ethics survey, 111 said that they disapproved of the conflict of interest actions taken in the scenario.

a. Use this sample result to calculate the 95 percent confidence interval for the proportion of all marketing researchers who disapprove of the actions taken in the conflict of interest scenario. Interpret this interval.

b. On the basis of this interval, is there convincing evidence that a majority of all marketing researchers disapprove of the actions taken in the conflict of interest scenario? Explain.

9.40 It has been proposed that a large number of mortgage loans that go into default within the first year of the mortgage were approved on the basis of falsified applications. For instance, loan applicants often exaggerate their income or fail to declare debts. Suppose that a random sample of 1,000 mortgage loans that were defaulted within the first year reveals that 410 of these loans were approved on the basis of falsified applications.

a. Find a point estimate of and a 95 percent confidence interval for p, the proportion of all first-year defaults that are approved on the basis of falsified applications.

b. Based on your interval, what is a reasonable estimate of the minimum percentage of first-year defaults that are approved on the basis of falsified applications?

9.41 The Canadian Press reported on a study for the Media Technology Monitor, in which Canadians were asked about their use of social media. Survey results were based on telephone interviews with 4,001 anglophone Canadians, conducted in the fall of 2012.

a. The Canadian Press report, written by Michael Oliveira, indicated that 1 in 3 Canadians checked their social media feeds every day. Based on this reported value, calculate a 99 percent confidence interval for the proportion of Canadians who say they checked their social media feeds every day.

b. The report also indicated that "almost 7 out of 10" Internet users logged onto social media websites at least once per month. Calculate the margin of error for a 95 percent confidence interval. What is the range of values that you would accept for the approximation made by the Canadian Press reporter?

c. At the end of the article, the author of the Canadian Press report indicated that the "survey results are considered accurate within 1.5 percentage points, 19 times out of 20." To what confidence interval does this allude? Explain how your calculations for part (b) provide evidence for or against this claim.

9.42 As discussed previously, in an article in the *Journal of Advertising*, Weinberger and Spotts compare the use of humour in television ads in the United States and the United Kingdom. They found that a substantially greater percentage of U.K. ads use humour.

a. Suppose that a random sample of 400 television ads in the United Kingdom reveals that 142 of these ads use humour. Find a point estimate of and a 95 percent confidence interval for the proportion of all U.K. television ads that use humour.

b. Suppose a random sample of 500 television ads in the United States reveals that 122 of these ads use humour. Find a point estimate of and a 95 percent confidence interval for the proportion of all U.S. television ads that use humour.

c. Do the confidence intervals you computed in parts (a) and (b) suggest that a greater percentage of U.K. ads use humour? Explain. How might an ad agency use this information?

9.43   THE BANK CUSTOMER SATISFACTION EXAMPLE

Imagine that a sample of 418 telephone interviews were conducted among Canadian business customers concerning their satisfaction with aspects of their banking relationships. Among these interviews, 67 percent of the respondents gave their banks a high rating for overall satisfaction.

   a. Assuming that the sample is randomly selected, calculate a 99 percent confidence interval for the proportion of Canadian business customers who give their banks a high rating for overall satisfaction.

   b. Based on this interval, can we be 99 percent confident that more than 60 percent of Canadian business customers give their banks a high rating for overall satisfaction?

9.44 A survey of 2,221 Canadian MBA students showed that only 20 percent of MBA students expect to stay at their first job five years or more. Assuming that a random sample was employed, find a 95 percent confidence interval for the proportion of all Canadian MBA students who expect to stay at their first job five years or more. Based on this interval, is there strong evidence that less than one-fourth of all Canadian MBA students expect to stay?

9.45 *Consumer Reports* (January 2005) indicated that profit margins on extended warranties were much greater than on the purchase of most products.[2] In this exercise we consider a major electronics retailer that wants to increase the proportion of customers who buy extended warranties on digital cameras. Historically, 20 percent of digital camera customers have purchased the retailer's extended warranty. To increase this percentage, the retailer has decided to offer a new warranty that is less expensive and more comprehensive. Suppose that three months after starting to offer the new warranty, a random sample of 500 customer sales invoices shows that 152 out of 500 digital camera customers purchased the new warranty. Find a 95 percent confidence interval for the proportion of all digital camera customers who purchased the new warranty. Are we 95 percent confident that this proportion exceeds .20?

9.46   THE TELEVISION REPAIR EXAMPLE

The manufacturer of the ColourSmart-5000 television claims 95 percent of its televisions last at least five years without needing a single repair. To test this claim, a consumer group randomly selects 400 consumers who have owned a ColourSmart-5000 television for five years. Of these 400 consumers, 316 say their ColourSmart-5000 television did not need a repair, but 84 say that their ColourSmart-5000 television did need at least one repair.

   a. Find a 99 percent confidence interval for the proportion of all ColourSmart-5000 televisions that have lasted at least five years without needing a single repair.

   b. Does this confidence interval provide strong evidence that the percentage of ColourSmart-5000 televisions that last at least five years without a single repair is less than the 95 percent claimed by the manufacturer? Explain.

9.47 In the book *Cases in Finance,* Nunnally and Plath present a case in which the estimated percentage of uncollectable accounts varies with the age of the account. Here the age of an unpaid account is the number of days elapsed since the invoice date.

Suppose an accountant believes the percentage of accounts that will be uncollectable increases as the ages of the accounts increase. To test this theory, the accountant randomly selects 500 accounts with ages between 31 and 60 days from the accounts receivable ledger dated one year ago. The accountant also randomly selects 500 accounts with ages between 61 and 90 days from the accounts receivable ledger dated one year ago.

   a. If 10 of the 500 accounts with ages between 31 and 60 days were eventually classified as uncollectable, find a point estimate of, and a 95 percent confidence interval for, the proportion of all accounts with ages between 31 and 60 days that will be uncollectable.

   b. If 27 of the 500 accounts with ages between 61 and 90 days were eventually classified as uncollectable, find a point estimate of, and a 95 percent confidence interval for, the proportion of all accounts with ages between 61 and 90 days that will be uncollectable.

   c. Based on these intervals, is there strong evidence that the percentage of accounts aged between 61 and 90 days that will be uncollectable is higher than the percentage of accounts aged between 31 and 60 days that will be uncollectable? Explain.

9.48 Suppose that, in part (b) of Exercise 9.41, we want to find the sample size n needed for us to be 99 percent confident that $\hat{p}$, the sample proportion of respondents who said they logged onto social media websites at least once per month, is within a margin of error of .015 of p, the true proportion. To find an appropriate value for $p(1 - p)$, note that the 95 percent confidence interval for p that you calculated in Exercise 9.41(b) was [.69, .71]. This indicates that the reasonable value for p that is closest to .5 is .69, so the largest reasonable value for $p(1 - p)$ is .69$(1 - .69) = .2139$. Calculate the required sample size n.

9.49   THE TELEVISION REPAIR EXAMPLE

Referring to Exercise 9.46, determine the sample size needed in order to be 99 percent confident that $\hat{p}$, the sample proportion of ColourSmart-5000 televisions that last at least five years without a single repair, is within a margin of error of .03 of p, the true proportion of televisions that last at least five years without a single repair.

9.50 We are interested in exploring the demographic characteristics of consumers who visit a particular clothing store—particularly with regard to the sex of the consumers. Suppose we propose to observe shoppers as they arrive at a few randomly selected stores and aggregate our findings across all of the stores in the chain. Assuming that the sex composition could be evenly split between men and women, determine the sample size needed for us to be 95 percent confident that $\hat{p}$, the sample proportion of female shoppers, is within a margin of error of .01 of p, the true proportion of all female shoppers within this clothing chain.

---

[2]*Consumer Reports,* "Extended Warranties Say Yes, Sometimes," January 1, 2005, page 51.

9.5 CONFIDENCE INTERVALS FOR A DIFFERENCE OF TWO POPULATION MEANS

In Sections 9.1 and 9.2 we noted that single-sample confidence intervals are determined differently when the true value of the population variance is unknown—and not surprisingly, this generalizes to confidence intervals that are calculated around a point estimate of the difference between means. Given that we rarely know the value of the population variances under study, in this section, we will consider only the case where the variance is unknown. This is a pragmatic decision: Outside of sample size estimation, the z distribution is rarely used in practice, given that we typically have ready access to sample descriptives (including the sample variance).

In this section, we will present three different methods for creating confidence intervals around the difference of two population means. The first two methods can be used when the populations are independent, and the second method can be used when the populations are correlated with each other in some way (e.g., the data are the result of a paired experiment).

The first approach to forming a confidence interval around the difference of two population means assumes that the population variances σ_1^2 and σ_2^2 are equal. Denoting the common value of these variances as σ^2, it follows that

LO6

$$\sigma_{\bar{x}_1 - \bar{x}_2} = \sqrt{\frac{\sigma_1^2}{n_1} + \frac{\sigma_2^2}{n_2}} = \sqrt{\frac{\sigma^2}{n_1} + \frac{\sigma^2}{n_2}} = \sqrt{\sigma^2\left(\frac{1}{n_1} + \frac{1}{n_2}\right)}$$

Because we are assuming that $\sigma_1^2 = \sigma_2^2 = \sigma^2$, we do not need separate estimates of σ_1^2 and σ_2^2. Instead, we combine the results of the two independent random samples to compute a single estimate of σ^2. As we discussed in Section 8.2, this estimate is called the *pooled estimate* of σ^2, and it is a weighted average of the two sample variances s_1^2 and s_2^2. Denoting the pooled estimate as s_p^2, it is computed using the formula

$$s_p^2 = \frac{(n_1 - 1)s_1^2 + (n_2 - 1)s_2^2}{n_1 + n_2 - 2}$$

Using s_p^2, the estimate of $\sigma_{\bar{x}_1 - \bar{x}_2}$ is

$$\sqrt{s_p^2\left(\frac{1}{n_1} + \frac{1}{n_2}\right)}$$

and we form the statistic

$$\frac{(\bar{x}_1 - \bar{x}_2) - (\mu_1 - \mu_2)}{\sqrt{s_p^2\left(\frac{1}{n_1} + \frac{1}{n_2}\right)}}$$

Recall that, if we have randomly selected independent samples from two normally distributed populations having equal variances, the sampling distribution of this statistic is a t distribution having $(n_1 + n_2 - 2)$ degrees of freedom. Therefore, we can obtain the confidence interval for $\mu_1 - \mu_2$ that is shown in the following boxed feature.

A *t*-Based Confidence Interval for the Difference between Two Population Means: Equal Variances

Suppose we have randomly selected independent samples from two normally distributed populations having equal variances. Then, a $100(1 - \alpha)$ percent confidence interval for $\mu_1 - \mu_2$ is

$$\left[(\bar{x}_1 - \bar{x}_2) \pm t_{\alpha/2}\sqrt{s_p^2\left(\frac{1}{n_1} + \frac{1}{n_2}\right)}\right] \quad \text{where} \quad s_p^2 = \frac{(n_1 - 1)s_1^2 + (n_2 - 1)s_2^2}{n_1 + n_2 - 2}$$

and $t_{\alpha/2}$ is based on $(n_1 + n_2 - 2)$ degrees of freedom.

Example 9.10   Estimating the True Difference between Two Catalysts

Recall from Example 8.2 that a production supervisor at a major chemical company must determine which of two catalysts, Catalyst XA-100 or Catalyst ZB-200, maximizes the hourly yield of a chemical process. To compare the mean hourly yields obtained by using the two catalysts, the supervisor runs the process using each catalyst for five one-hour periods. The resulting yields (in kilograms per hour) for each catalyst, along with the means and variances, are given in Table 9.3. As discussed in Example 8.2, we assume that all other factors affecting yields of the process have been held as constant as possible during the test runs, and also assume that the five observed yields for each catalyst are a random sample from the population of all possible hourly yields for the catalyst. We can test these sample variances with an F ratio, and demonstrate that they do not differ significantly—and can therefore make the reasonable assumption that the population variances are approximately equal. It follows, therefore, that the pooled estimate

$$
s_p^2 = \frac{(n_1 - 1)s_1^2 + (n_2 - 1)s_2^2}{n_1 + n_2 - 2}
$$

$$
= \frac{(5 - 1)(386) + (5 - 1)(484.2)}{5 + 5 - 2} = 435.1
$$

is a point estimate of the common variance σ^2.

TABLE 9.3   Yields of a Chemical Process Obtained Using Two Catalysts

Catalyst XA-100	Catalyst ZB-200
801	752
814	718
784	776
836	742
820	763
$\bar{x}_1 = 811$	$\bar{x}_2 = 750.2$
$s_1^2 = 386$	$s_2^2 = 484.2$

We define μ_1 as the mean hourly yield obtained by using Catalyst XA-100, and we define μ_2 as the mean hourly yield obtained by using Catalyst ZB-200. If the populations of all possible hourly yields for the catalysts are normally distributed, then a 95 percent confidence interval for $\mu_1 - \mu_2$ is

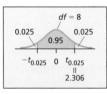

$$
\left[(\bar{x}_1 - \bar{x}_2) \pm t_{.025}\sqrt{s_p^2\left(\frac{1}{n_1} + \frac{1}{n_2}\right)} \right]
$$

$$
= \left[(811 - 750.2) \pm 2.306\sqrt{435.1\left(\frac{1}{5} + \frac{1}{5}\right)} \right]
$$

$$
= [60.8 \pm 30.4217]
$$

$$
= [30.38, 91.22]
$$

Here $t_{.025} = 2.306$ is based on $n_1 + n_2 - 2 = 5 + 5 - 2 = 8$ degrees of freedom. This interval tells us that we are 95 percent confident that the mean hourly yield obtained by using Catalyst XA-100 is between 30.38 and 91.22 kilograms higher than the mean hourly yield obtained by using Catalyst ZB-200.

A *t*-Based Confidence Interval for the Difference between Two Population Means: Unequal Variances

When the sampled populations are normally distributed and the population variances σ_1^2 and σ_2^2 differ, the following can be shown:

1 When the sample sizes n_1 and n_2 are equal, the "equal variances" *t*-based confidence interval and hypothesis test are approximately valid even if the population variances σ_1^2 and σ_2^2 differ substantially. As a rough rule of thumb, if the larger sample variance is not more than three times the smaller sample variance when the sample sizes are equal, we can use the equal variances interval and test.

2 Suppose that the larger sample variance is more than three times the smaller sample variance when the sample sizes are equal or, suppose that both the sample sizes and the sample

variances differ substantially. Then, we can use an approximate procedure that is sometimes called an *unequal variances procedure*. This procedure says that an approximate $100(1 - \alpha)$ percent confidence interval for $\mu_1 - \mu_2$ is

$$\left[(\bar{x}_1 - \bar{x}_2) \pm t_{\alpha/2} \sqrt{\frac{s_1^2}{n_1} + \frac{s_2^2}{n_2}} \right]$$

The degrees of freedom for this distribution are equal to

$$df = \frac{(s_1^2/n_1 + s_2^2/n_2)^2}{\dfrac{(s_1^2/n_1)^2}{n_1 - 1} + \dfrac{(s_2^2/n_2)^2}{n_2 - 1}}$$

Here, if *df* is not a whole number, we can round *df* down to the next smallest whole number.

Example 9.11 Estimating True Differences When Variances are Unequal

To illustrate the unequal variances procedure, recall the bank customer waiting time situation and recall that $\mu_1 - \mu_2$ is the difference between the mean customer waiting time under the current system and the mean customer waiting time under the new system. Because of cost considerations, the bank manager wants to implement the new system only if it reduces the mean waiting time by more than three minutes. In studying this issue, the manager takes a random sample of $n_1 = 100$ waiting times observed under the current system, finding a sample mean $\bar{x}_1 = 8.79$ and a sample variance $s_1^2 = 4.8237$. Further, suppose a random sample of $n_2 = 100$ waiting times observed during the trial run of the new system yields a sample mean $\bar{x}_2 = 5.14$ and a sample variance $s_2^2 = 1.7927$. Since each sample is large, we can use the unequal variances procedure. The degrees of freedom for this distribution are

$$df = \frac{(s_1^2/n_1 + s_2^2/n_2)^2}{\dfrac{(s_1^2/n_1)^2}{n_1 - 1} + \dfrac{(s_2^2/n_2)^2}{n_2 - 1}}$$

$$= \frac{[(4.8237/100) + (1.7927/100)]^2}{\dfrac{(4.8237/100)^2}{99} + \dfrac{(1.7927/100)^2}{99}}$$

$$= 163.657$$

which we will round down to 163.

In evaluating the effectiveness of the new system, the bank manager wants to form the 95 percent confidence interval around the difference between the new system and the old system. Because the variances of the populations are not assumed to be equal, we calculate the confidence interval as follows:

$$\left[(\bar{x}_1 - \bar{x}_2) \pm t_{\alpha/2} \sqrt{\frac{s_1^2}{n_1} + \frac{s_2^2}{n_2}} \right]$$

and determine that the 95 percent confidence interval describing the difference between the old system and the new system is

$$\left[(8.79 - 5.14) \pm 1.96\sqrt{\frac{4.8237}{100} + \frac{1.7927}{100}}\right]$$

$$= [3.65 \pm .5042]$$

$$= [3.1458, 4.1542]$$

LO7

Because the lower-bound estimate of this confidence interval is greater than 3, it suggests that we are 95 percent confident that the new system has improved waiting times by at least three minutes. In other words, we would reject a null hypothesis (in a two-sample test of means) that the difference between the systems is less than or equal to 3. Furthermore, we can now make the additional (and informative) observation that the waiting times under the new system are 95 percent likely to be 3.1458 to 4.1542 minutes faster than under the old system.

A Confidence Interval for the Mean, μ_d, of a Population of Paired Differences

The previous two approaches to generating confidence intervals around differences in population means supposed that the populations were independent. As we discussed in Section 8.3, however, we can design our experiments to utilize paired observations, and this may assist with the control of subject-specific error. In other words, by evaluating our data in pairs, we can control for all of the variability that is shared by members of a pair. When $\bar{d}$ and s_d are designated to be the mean and the standard deviation of n paired differences within a sample, then the sampling distribution of

$$\frac{\bar{d} - \mu_d}{s_d/\sqrt{n}}$$

is a t distribution having $n - 1$ degrees of freedom. This implies that we have the following confidence interval for μ_d:

Let μ_d be the mean of a normally distributed population of paired differences, and let $\bar{d}$ and s_d be the mean and standard deviation of a sample of n paired differences that have been randomly selected from the population. Then, a $100(1 - \alpha)$ percent confidence interval for $\mu_d = \mu_1 - \mu_2$ is

$$\left[\bar{d} \pm t_{\alpha/2}\frac{s_d}{\sqrt{n}}\right]$$

Here $t_{\alpha/2}$ is based on $(n - 1)$ degrees of freedom.

Example 9.12   Estimating the True Difference in Repair Costs

Recall from Example 8.3 that Provincial Casualty wants to compare vehicle repair estimates between two garages, and decides that it would be more valid to control for the amount of damage that is being repaired. They take a random sample of 7 vehicles and obtain repair estimates from two garages on these vehicles, the data for which are presented in Table 8.3. The average difference between garages, calculated on a vehicle-by-vehicle basis is -80 (i.e., Garage 1 produces estimates that are approximately $80 less than Garage 2) and the standard deviation of these difference scores is 50.33. Assuming that the population of paired repair cost differences is normally distributed, a 95 percent confidence interval for $\mu_d = \mu_1 - \mu_2$ is

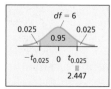

$$\left[\bar{d} \pm t_{.025}\frac{s_d}{\sqrt{n}}\right] = \left[-80 \pm 2.447\frac{50.33}{\sqrt{7}}\right]$$

$$= [-80 \pm 46.54]$$

$$= [-126.54, -33.46]$$

Here $t_{.025} = 2.447$ is based on $n - 1 = 7 - 1 = 6$ degrees of freedom. This interval says that Provincial Casualty can be 95 percent confident that μ_d, the mean of all possible paired differences of the repair cost estimates at Garages 1 and 2, is between −$126.54 and −$33.46. That is, we are 95 percent confident that μ_1, the mean of all possible repair cost estimates at Garage 1, is between $126.54 and $33.46 less than μ_2, the mean of all possible repair cost estimates at Garage 2. Furthermore, because the interval does not contain zero, we can also be 95 percent confident that there is a statistically significant difference between the two garages. Said another way, a two-sample t test would demonstrate a statistically significant difference between groups, with a two-tailed alpha of .05.

Exercises for Section **9.5**

CONCEPTS

9.51 Describe the assumptions that must be satisfied for each of the following:
   a. The confidence interval associated with independent samples with unequal variances.
   b. The confidence interval associated with independent samples with equal variances.
   c. The confidence interval associated with paired samples.

9.52 What happens to the range of a confidence interval as confidence increases (e.g., as one moves from being 90 percent confident to being 95 percent confident)?

METHODS AND APPLICATIONS

9.53 Suppose we have taken independent random samples of sizes $n_1 = 7$ and $n_2 = 7$ from two normally distributed populations having means μ_1 and μ_2, and suppose we obtain $\bar{x}_1 = 240$, $\bar{x}_2 = 210$, $s_1 = 5$, and $s_2 = 6$. Using the equal variances procedure, calculate a 95 percent confidence interval for $\mu_1 - \mu_2$. Can we be 95 percent confident that the population difference is greater than 20? Explain why we can use the equal variances procedure here.

9.54 Repeat Exercise 9.53 using the unequal variances procedure. Compare your results to those obtained using the equal variances procedure.

9.55 Suppose that a random sample of 12 stock funds has a mean management expense ratio (MER) of 1.63 percent with a standard deviation of .31 percent, and an independent random sample of 12 municipal bond funds has a mean MER of 0.89 percent with a standard deviation of .23 percent. Let μ_1 be the mean annual expense for stock funds, and let μ_2 be the mean annual expense for municipal bond funds. Assuming that stock fund expenses and municipal bond fund expenses are each approximately normally distributed:
   a. Use the equal variance procedure to calculate a 95 percent confidence interval for the difference between the MER for stock funds and the MER for bond funds. Can we be 95 percent confident that the MER for stock funds exceeds that for municipal bond funds by more than .5 percent? Explain.
   b. Repeat part (a) using the unequal variance procedure, and compare your results.

9.56 Consider the supermarket research presented in Exercise 8.23, in which a marketing research firm compared prices at Sobeys versus prices at Metro. In a random sample of 10 Sobeys grocery stores, the researchers found that a standardized weekly shopping list generated a sample mean of $121.916, and a sample standard deviation of $1.3982. In an independent random sample of 10 Metro grocery stores, the researchers found that the same standardized weekly shopping list generated a sample mean of $114.807, and a sample standard deviation of $1.8403. Calculate a 90 percent confidence interval for the difference between the two grocery stores, using the equal variance procedure.

9.57 Consider the auto loans described in Exercise 8.25, in which a sample of eight 48-month fixed-rate auto loans had the following loan rates:

   8.29% 7.75% 7.50% 7.99%
   7.75% 7.99% 9.40% 8.00%

and a sample of five 48-month variable-rate auto loans had loan rates as follows:

   7.59% 6.75% 6.99% 6.50% 7.00%

Use the equal variance procedure to calculate a 95 percent confidence interval for the difference between fixed-rate and variable-rate auto loans. Can we be 95 percent confident that the difference between these means is .4 percent or more? Explain.

9.58 Suppose a sample of 11 paired differences that has been randomly selected from a normally distributed population of paired differences yields a sample mean of $\bar{d} = 103.5$ and a sample standard deviation of $s_d = 5$. Calculate 95 percent and 99 percent confidence intervals for $\mu_d = \mu_1 - \mu_2$. Can we be 95 percent confident that the difference between these means exceeds 100? Can we be 99 percent confident?

9.59 Suppose a sample of 49 paired differences that have been randomly selected from a normally distributed population of paired differences yields a sample mean of $\bar{d} = 5$ and a sample standard deviation of $s_d = 7$. Calculate the 95 percent confidence interval for $\mu_d = \mu_1 - \mu_2$. Can we be 95 percent confident that there is a difference between these means?

9.60 Recall Exercise 8.35, which describes a company that has implemented a number of policies aimed at reducing the ages of its customers' accounts. To assess the effectiveness of these measures, the company randomly selected 10 customer accounts. The average age of each account is determined for the years 2011 and 2012. These data are repeated in Table 9.4. Assuming that the population of paired differences between the average ages in 2012 and 2011 is normally distributed, calculate a 95 percent confidence interval for the mean difference in the average account ages between 2011 and 2012.

Estimate the minimum reduction in the mean average account ages between these two years.

TABLE 9.4 Average Account Ages in 2011 and 2012 for 10 Randomly Selected Accounts (for Exercise 9.60)

	1	2	3	4	5	6	7	8	9	10
2012	27	19	40	30	33	25	31	29	15	21
2011	35	24	47	28	41	33	35	51	18	28

9.6 CONFIDENCE INTERVALS FOR A DIFFERENCE OF TWO POPULATION PROPORTIONS

LO8

In this final section, we present the confidence interval that can be created around the difference between two population proportions (p_1 and p_2). As was the case with the confidence interval that can be created around a single population proportion, we are able to use a z table for our estimated range.

If we estimate p_1 by $\hat{p}_1$ and p_2 by $\hat{p}_2$ in the expression for the standard error for the sampling distribution of the difference between these proportions ($\sigma_{\hat{p}_1 - \hat{p}_2}$), then the sampling distribution of $\hat{p}_1 - \hat{p}_2$ implies the $100(1 - \alpha)$ percent confidence interval for $p_1 - p_2$ shown in the following boxed feature.

A Large-Sample Confidence Interval for the Difference between Two Population Proportions

Suppose we randomly select a sample of size n_1 from a population and let $\hat{p}_1$ denote the proportion of elements in this sample that fall into a category of interest. Also suppose we randomly select a sample of size n_2 from another population and let $\hat{p}_2$ denote the proportion of elements in this second sample that fall into the category of interest. Then, if each of the sample sizes n_1 and n_2 is large

($n_1\hat{p}_1$, $n_1(1 - \hat{p}_1)$, $n_2\hat{p}_2$, and $n_2(1 - \hat{p}_2)$ must all be at least 5), and if the random samples are independent of each other, a $100(1 - \alpha)$ percent confidence interval for $p_1 - p_2$ is

$$\left[(\hat{p}_1 - \hat{p}_2) \pm z_{\alpha/2}\sqrt{\frac{\hat{p}_1(1 - \hat{p}_1)}{n_1} + \frac{\hat{p}_2(1 - \hat{p}_2)}{n_2}} \right]$$

Example 9.13 Estimating the True Difference between Two Proportions

Recall the test marketing case conducted in the Vancouver and Toronto metropolitan areas, described in Example 7.9. Equal amounts of money were spent on advertising in the two areas, with different advertising media used in each market. Advertising in the Vancouver area was done entirely on television, while advertising in the Toronto area consisted of a mixture of television, radio, newspaper, and magazine ads. Two months after the advertising campaigns commenced, surveys taken to estimate consumer awareness of the product indicated that 631 of 1,000 randomly selected consumers in the Vancouver area were aware of the product, whereas 798 of 1,000 randomly selected consumers in the Toronto area were aware of the product. It follows that, since the sample proportions of consumers who are aware of the product in the Vancouver and Toronto areas are equal to .631 and .798, respectively, then a point estimate of $p_1 - p_2$ is

$$\hat{p}_1 - \hat{p}_2 = .631 - .798 = -.167$$

This says we estimate that p_1 is .167 less than p_2. That is, we estimate that the percentage of consumers who are aware of the product in the Toronto area is 16.7 percentage points higher than in the Vancouver area. Because $n_1\hat{p}_1 = 1{,}000(.631) = 631$, $n_1(1 - \hat{p}_1) = 1{,}000(1 - .631) = 369$, $n_2\hat{p}_2 = 1{,}000(.798) = 798$, and $n_2(1 - \hat{p}_2) = 1{,}000(1 - .798) = 202$ are all at least 5, both n_1 and n_2 can be considered large. It follows that a 95 percent confidence interval for $p_1 - p_2$ is

$$\left[(\hat{p}_1 - \hat{p}_2) \pm z_{.025}\sqrt{\frac{\hat{p}_1(1 - \hat{p}_1)}{n_1} + \frac{\hat{p}_2(1 - \hat{p}_2)}{n_2}} \right]$$

$$= \left[(.631 - .798) \pm 1.96\sqrt{\frac{(.631)(.369)}{1{,}000} + \frac{(.798)(.202)}{1{,}000}} \right]$$

$$= [-.167 \pm .0389]$$

$$= [-.2059, -.1281]$$

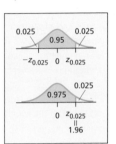

This interval says we are 95 percent confident that p_1, the proportion of all consumers in the Vancouver area who are aware of the product, is between .2059 and .1281 less than p_2, the proportion of all consumers in the Toronto area who are aware of the product. Therefore, we have substantial evidence that advertising the new product by using a mixture of television, radio, newspaper, and magazine ads (as in Toronto) is more effective than spending an equal amount of money on television commercials only.

Exercises for Section **9.6**

CONCEPTS

9.61 Describe the assumptions that must be satisfied when calculating the confidence interval describing the difference between two population proportions.

METHODS AND APPLICATIONS

9.62 Assume that we have selected two independent random samples from populations having proportions p_1 and p_2 and that $\hat{p}_1 = 800/1{,}000 = .8$ and $\hat{p}_2 = 950/1{,}000 = .95$. Calculate a 95 percent confidence interval for $p_1 - p_2$. Interpret this interval. Can we be 95 percent confident that p_1 is less than p_2? Explain.

9.63 Consider again the use of humour in television ads in the United States and in the United Kingdom. Recall that independent random samples of television ads were taken in the two countries. A random sample of 400 television ads in the United Kingdom revealed that 142 use humour, while a random sample of 500 television ads in the United States revealed that 122 use humour. Calculate a 95 percent confidence interval for the difference between the proportion of U.K. ads using humour and the proportion of U.S. ads using humour. Interpret this interval. Can we be 95 percent confident that the proportion of U.K. ads using humour is greater than the proportion of U.S. ads using humour?

9.64 In their book *Essentials of Marketing Research*, William R. Dillon, Thomas J. Madden, and Neil H. Firtle (1993) discuss a research proposal in which a telephone company wants to determine whether the appeal of a new security system varies between homeowners and renters. Independent samples of 140 homeowners and 60 renters are randomly selected. Each respondent views a TV pilot in which a test ad for the new security system is embedded twice. Afterward, each respondent is interviewed to find out whether he or she would purchase the security system. Results show that 25 out of the 140 homeowners definitely would buy the security system, while 9 out of the 60 renters definitely would buy the system. Calculate a 95 percent confidence interval for the difference between the proportions of homeowners and renters who would buy the security system. On the basis of this interval, can we be 95 percent confident that these proportions differ? Explain.

9.65 In their book *Cases in Finance*, Nunnally and Plath (1995) present a case in which the estimated percentage of uncollectable accounts varies with the age of the account. Here the age of an unpaid account is the number of days elapsed since the invoice date. An accountant believes that the percentage of accounts that will be uncollectable increases as the ages of the accounts increase. To test this theory, the accountant randomly selects independent samples of 500 accounts with ages between 31 and 60 days and 500 accounts with ages between 61 and 90 days from the accounts receivable ledger dated one year ago. When the sampled accounts are examined, it is found that 10 of the 500 accounts with ages between 31 and 60 days were eventually classified as uncollectable, while 27 of the 500 accounts with ages between 61 and 90 days were eventually classified as uncollectable. Let p_1 be the proportion of accounts with ages between 31 and 60 days that will be uncollectable and let p_2 be the proportion of accounts with ages between 61 and 90 days that will be uncollectable. Identify a 95 percent confidence interval for $p_1 - p_2$, and estimate the smallest that this difference will be.

CHAPTER SUMMARY

In this chapter, we discussed confidence intervals for population means and proportions, as well as the differences between these parameters. First, we studied how to compute a confidence interval for a population mean. We saw that when the population standard deviation σ is known, we can use the normal distribution to compute a confidence interval for a population mean. When σ is not known, if the population is normally distributed (or at least mound-shaped) or if the sample size n is large, we use the t distribution to compute this interval. We also studied how to find the size of the sample needed if we want to compute a confidence interval for a mean with a prespecified confidence level and with a prespecified margin of error.

Next we saw that we are often interested in estimating the proportion of population elements falling into a category of interest. We showed how to compute a large-sample confidence interval for a population proportion, and we saw how to find the sample size needed to estimate a population proportion with a prespecified confidence level and with a prespecified margin of error.

Finally, we demonstrated methods for extending the calculation of confidence intervals to differences between population means and differences between population proportions, and illustrated the difference between confidence intervals computed for differences between independent samples that have equal variances, independent samples that have unequal variances, and paired sample tests.

KEY TERMS

confidence coefficient
confidence interval

confidence level
margin of error

IMPORTANT FORMULAS

z-based confidence interval for a population mean μ with σ known

t-based confidence interval for a population mean μ with σ unknown

Sample size when estimating μ

Large-sample confidence interval for a population proportion p

Sample size when estimating p

Estimation of a mean and a total for a finite population

Estimation of a proportion and a total for a finite population

SUPPLEMENTARY EXERCISES

connect Practise and learn online with *Connect*. Items for which there are online data sets are marked with ✈.

9.66 In an article in the *Journal of Accounting Research*, Ashton, Willingham, and Elliott studied audit delay (the length of time from a company's fiscal year-end to the date of the auditor's report) for industrial and financial companies. In the study, a random sample of 250 industrial companies yielded a mean audit delay of 68.04 days with a standard deviation of 35.72 days, while a random sample of 238 financial companies yielded a mean audit delay of 56.74 days with a standard deviation of 34.87 days. Use these sample results to do the following:

a. Calculate a 95 percent confidence interval for the mean audit delay for all industrial companies. Note: $t_{.025} = 1.97$ when $df = 249$.

b. Calculate a 95 percent confidence interval for the mean audit delay for all financial companies. Note: $t_{.025} = 1.97$ when $df = 237$.

c. By comparing the 95 percent confidence intervals you calculated in parts (a) and (b), is there strong evidence that the mean audit delay for financial companies is shorter than the mean audit delay for industrial companies? Explain.

9.67 In an article in *Accounting and Business Research*, Beattie and Jones investigate the use and abuse of graphic presentations in the annual reports of United Kingdom firms. The authors found that 65 percent of the sampled companies graph at least one key financial variable, but that 30 percent of the graphics are materially distorted (e.g., non-zero vertical axis, exaggerated trend). Results for Canadian firms have been found to be similar.

a. Suppose that in a random sample of 465 graphics from the annual reports of United Kingdom firms, 142 of the graphics are found to be materially distorted. Find a point estimate of and a 95 percent confidence interval for the proportion of U.K. annual report graphics that are distorted.

b. Based on this interval, can we be 95 percent confident that more than 25 percent of all graphics appearing in the annual reports of U.K. firms are materially distorted? Explain. Does this suggest that auditors should understand proper graphing methods?

c. Determine the sample size needed in order to be 95 percent confident that $\hat{p}$, the sample proportion of U.K. annual report graphics that are distorted, is within a margin of error of .03 of p, the true proportion of U.K. annual report graphics that are distorted.

9.68 THE DISC BRAKE EXAMPLE

National Motors has equipped the ZX-900 with a new disc brake system. We define the stopping distance for a ZX-900 to be the distance (in metres) required to bring the automobile to a complete stop from a speed of 50 km/h under normal driving conditions using this new brake system. In addition, we define μ to be the mean stopping distance of all ZX-900s. One of the ZX-900's major competitors is advertised to achieve a mean stopping distance of 20 metres. National Motors would like to claim in a new advertising campaign that the ZX-900 achieves a shorter mean stopping distance.

Suppose that National Motors randomly selects a sample of $n = 81$ ZX-900s. The company records the stopping distance of each automobile and calculates the mean and standard deviation of the sample of $n = 81$ stopping distances to be 19.27 and 2.34 metres, respectively.

a. Calculate a 95 percent confidence interval for μ. Can National Motors be 95 percent confident that μ is less than 20 metres? Explain.

b. Using the sample of $n = 81$ stopping distances as a preliminary sample, find the sample size necessary to make National Motors 95 percent confident that $\bar{x}$ is within a margin of error of .5 metres of μ.

9.69 In an article in the *Journal of Retailing*, J. G. Blodgett, D. H. Granbois, and R. G. Walters investigated negative word-of-mouth consumer behaviour. In a random sample of 201 consumers, 150 reported that they engaged in negative word-of-mouth behaviour (for instance, they vowed never to patronize a retailer again). In addition, the 150 respondents who engaged in such behaviour, on average, told 4.88 people about their dissatisfying experience (with a standard deviation equal to 6.11).

a. Use these sample results to compute a 95 percent confidence interval for the proportion of all consumers who engage in negative word-of-mouth behaviour. On the basis of this interval, would it be reasonable to claim that more than 70 percent of all consumers engage in such behaviour? Explain.

b. Use the sample results to compute a 95 percent confidence interval for the mean number of people who are told about a dissatisfying experience by consumers who engage in negative word-of-mouth behaviour. On the basis of this interval, would it be reasonable to claim that these dissatisfied consumers tell, on average, at least three people about their bad experience? Explain. Note: $t_{.025} = 1.98$ when $df = 149$.

9.70 A random sample of 50 perceived age estimates for a model in a cigarette advertisement showed that $\bar{x} = 26.22$ years and that $s = 3.7432$ years.

a. Use this sample to calculate a 95 percent confidence interval for the population mean age estimate for all viewers of the ad.

b. Remembering that the cigarette industry requires that models must appear to be at least 25 years old, does the confidence interval make us 95 percent confident that the mean perceived age estimate is at least 25? Is the mean perceived age estimate much more than 25? Explain.

9.71 In an article in the *Journal of Management Information Systems,* Mahmood and Mann investigate how information technology (IT) investment relates to company performance. In particular, Mahmood and Mann obtain sample data concerning IT investment for companies that use information systems effectively. Among the variables studied are the company's IT budget as a percentage of company revenue, percentages of the IT budget spent on staff and training, and number of computers as a percentage of total employees.

a. Suppose a random sample of 15 companies considered to use information systems effectively yields a sample mean IT budget as a percentage of company revenue of $\bar{x} = 2.73$ with a standard deviation of $s = 1.64$. Assuming that IT budget percentages are approximately normally distributed, calculate a 99 percent confidence interval for the mean IT budget as a percentage of company revenue for all firms that use information systems effectively. Does this interval provide evidence that a firm can successfully use information systems with an IT budget that is less than 5 percent of company revenue? Explain.

b. Suppose a random sample of 15 companies considered to use information systems effectively yields a sample mean number of computers as a percentage of total employees of $\bar{x} = 34.76$ with a standard deviation of $s = 25.37$. Assuming approximate normality, calculate a 99 percent confidence interval for the mean number of computers as a percentage of total employees for all firms that use information systems effectively. Why is this interval so wide? What can we do to obtain a narrower (more useful) confidence interval?

9.72 Suppose that random samples of 50 returns for each of the following investment classes give the indicated sample mean and sample standard deviation:

Fixed annuities: $\bar{x} = 7.83\%$, $s = .51\%$
Domestic large-cap stocks: $\bar{x} = 13.42\%$, $s = 15.17\%$
Domestic midcap stocks: $\bar{x} = 15.03\%$, $s = 18.44\%$
Domestic small-cap stocks: $\bar{x} = 22.51\%$, $s = 21.75\%$

For each investment class, compute a 95 percent confidence interval for the population mean return.

9.73 The mean and the standard deviation of a random sample of 35 one-day travel expenses in Montreal are $\bar{x} = \$538$ and $s = \$41$. Find a 95 percent confidence interval for the mean of all one-day travel expenses in Montreal.

9.74 Assume that the insurance survey described in Exercise 7.69 is based on 1,000 randomly selected Canadian households and that 640 of these households spent money for life insurance in 2012. Find a 95 percent confidence interval for the proportion, p, of all Canadian households that spent money for life insurance in 2012.

9.75 How safe are child car seats? *Consumer Reports* (May 2005) tested the safety of child car seats in 50 km/h crashes. They found "slim safety margins" for some child car seats. Suppose that *Consumer Reports* simulates the safety of the market-leading child car seat. The test consists of placing the maximum claimed weight in the car seat and simulating crashes at higher and higher speeds (in km/h) until a problem occurs. The following data identify the speed at which a problem with the car seat (such as the strap breaking, seat shell cracking, strap adjuster breaking, seat detaching from the base, etc.) first appeared: 51.0, 49.4, 50.4, 48.9, 49.7, 50.1, 52.3, 51.7, 55.4, 49.1, 51.2, 50.2. Let μ denote the true mean speed at which a problem with the car seat first appears. Find a 95 percent confidence interval for the true mean speed at which a problem with the car seat first appears. Are we 95 percent confident that this mean is at least 50 km/h?

9.76   INTERNET EXERCISE

Statistics Canada is responsible for collecting, analyzing, and interpreting census data. The data that it provides to the research community are intended to help scientists and policy makers better understand Canada and Canadians and to help direct public and private initiatives aimed at improving the lives of Canadians. Its website contains a wealth of information and is easily mined for interesting, descriptive information about health, economic, and demographic information of interest to Canadians.

In this exercise, we will evaluate some of the preliminary information from the most recent (2011) Canadian census that Statistics Canada has posted on its website. It takes some time for the agency to collect, process, and organize all of the information that is gathered during a census, so at the time of this writing, the available census data was largely limited to sample descriptives that are intended to contextualize the basic survey findings. Even at this early stage, this information is fascinating, however, and has important implications for commerce.

Consider the language characteristics of Canadians who completed the 2011 census. You can easily access this information from the Statistics Canada home page (statcan.gc.ca) by inputting into the search window "Linguistic Characteristics of Canadians." On the resulting page is a list of the highlights of the 2011 census findings, including the fact that more than 200 different "mother tongues" were reported by respondents. A "mother tongue" is defined as the first language learned at home that the individual still understands at the time of the census. Approximately 20 percent of the population reported speaking a language other than English or French (the two official languages of Canada) at home. Despite this linguistic diversity, however, 98 percent of the Canadian population reports being able to carry on a conversation in either of Canada's two official languages.

The 2011 Census was the first Canadian Census to ask three separate language questions[3] of *all* respondents:[4]

1. **Mother Tongue:** *The first language learned at home in childhood and still understood by the individual on May 10, 2011.*

2. **Home Language:** *The language spoken most often or on a regular basis at home by the individual on May 10, 2011.*

3. **Knowledge of Official Languages:** *The ability to conduct a conversation in English only, in French only, in both English and French, or in neither English nor French.*

Because of this change to the method of asking about an individual's mother tongue (as compared with previous surveys), there is some concern that individuals may have changed their reporting on one or more of these questions. Accordingly, Statistics Canada counsels data users to be cautious in their use of this information—particularly in census-to-census comparisons.

With this caution in mind, it is still interesting to look at these variables on both the 2006 and 2011 censuses, particularly in relation to "mother tongue." Approximately 85 percent of Canadians who report having French as their mother tongue live in Quebec. Accordingly, the best way to consider the sample is to split it into two groups—Canadians living in Quebec and Canadians living elsewhere in Canada. Table 9.5 presents 2006 and 2011 data on "mother tongue" for these two groups.

TABLE 9.5   Mother Tongue of Canadians, 2006 and 2011

Language	Year	Quebec	Rest of Canada
English	2006	607,165	17,448,520
		8.17%	73.30%
	2011	647,655	18,489,860
		8.71%	73.07%
French	2006	5,916,840	975,390
		79.57%	4.10%
	2011	6,164,745	1,007,815
		78.87%	4.23%
Other	2006	911,900	5,381,210
		12.26%	22.61%
	2011	1,003,545	5,807,550
		12.84%	22.95%
Total	**2006**	**7,435,905**	**23,805,120**
	2011	**7,815,945**	**25,305,225**

Source: Statistics Canada, *Census of Population*, 2006 and 2011.

There are a few interesting questions that we can ask about the statistics in Table 9.5:

a. Has there been a change between 2006 and 2011 in terms of the number of individuals outside Quebec who list English as their mother tongue?

b. Has there been a change between 2006 and 2011 in terms of the number of individuals in Quebec who list French as their mother tongue?

c. Was there a difference in 2006 between Quebec and the rest of Canada in terms of the number of individuals who report having a mother tongue other than English or French?

d. Was there a difference in 2011 between Quebec and the rest of Canada in terms of the number of individuals who report having a mother tongue other than English or French?

Let's start with the question that has the most subtle difference—the change between 2006 and 2011 in the number of Canadians living outside Quebec who report having English as their mother tongue. In Chapter 7, we demonstrated that hypothesis tests produce infinitesimally small *p*-values when the sample size is very large, so we might find it more useful to answer our question using a confidence interval.

---

[3]These definitions were taken directly from the *Census Dictionary* (input "Census Dictionary" into the search window on the Statistics Canada website).

[4]All of these questions were asked in previous surveys, but they were not asked of *all* respondents.

The confidence interval for a difference of proportions is:

$$(\hat{p}_1 - \hat{p}_2) \pm z_{\alpha/2}\sqrt{\frac{\hat{p}_1(1 - \hat{p}_1)}{n_1} + \frac{\hat{p}_2(1 - \hat{p}_2)}{n_2}}$$

so the 99 percent confidence interval surrounding the difference between 2006 and 2011 on this variable is

$$(.7330 - .7307) \pm 2.575\sqrt{\frac{.7330(1 - .7330)}{17{,}448{,}520} + \frac{.7307(1 - .7307)}{18{,}489{,}860}}$$

$$= .0023 \pm 2.575\sqrt{.00000001121648 + .00000001064246}$$

$$= .0023 \pm 2.575\sqrt{.00000002185894}$$

$$= .0023 \pm .00038070780664$$

$$= [.001919, .002681]$$

In other words, we are 99 percent certain that the difference between years will be between .1919 percent and .2681 percent. This means, of course, that there is a statistically significant difference between survey years because the interval does not contain zero. As we have discussed in numerous other sections of this textbook, however, this difference (although statistically significance) is unlikely to have much practical import.

Use 99 percent confidence intervals to answer parts (b), (c), and (d).

CHAPTER **10**
Experimental Design and Analysis of Variance

LEARNING OBJECTIVES

After reading this chapter, you should be able to

LO1 Define an independent variable (IV) and a dependent variable (DV)

LO2 Summarize the difference between an experiment and an observational study

LO3 Explain how all of the statistics that appear in an ANOVA results table are computed

LO4 Describe how pairwise comparisons are conducted

LO5 Explain the term *randomized block design*

LO6 Compare one-way ANOVA designs with two-way ANOVA designs

CHAPTER OUTLINE

We have learned that sometimes business improvement involves making comparisons. In earlier chapters, we presented several hypothesis testing procedures for comparing two population means. However, business improvement often requires that we compare more than two means. For instance, we might compare the mean sales obtained by using three different advertising campaigns to improve a company's marketing process. Or, we might compare the mean production output obtained by using four different manufacturing process designs to improve productivity.

In this chapter, we consider statistical procedures for comparing two or more means. Each of the methods we discuss is called an **analysis of variance (ANOVA)** procedure.

One advantage of conducting an ANOVA (over multiple comparisons between two conditions) is that the overall Type I (α) error is kept to a fixed level. For example, if there were three groups, comparing the means would require conducting three *t* tests. If each comparison error was treated as an independent test and if the Type I error rate was set to .05 for each *t* test, the overall error for this set of comparisons would be much greater than .05. In the ANOVA procedure, the means are compared in one analysis, keeping the Type I error level to .05. We also present some basic concepts of experimental design, which involves deciding how to collect data in a way that allows us to most effectively compare population means.

10.1 BASIC CONCEPTS OF EXPERIMENTAL DESIGN

LO1

In many statistical studies, researchers are interested in how a **factor** (the *independent variable* or *IV*) influences responses given by participants (the response measured is called the *dependent variable* or *DV*).[1] For example, a marketing company might be interested in the effects of a novel's cover on the likelihood that the novel will be purchased. The variable manipulated (cover appearance) is the independent variable and the self-reported likelihood that the individual would buy the book is the dependent variable. If we cannot control the factor(s) being studied, we say that the data obtained are *observational*. For example, suppose that in order to study how the size of a home relates to the sale price of the home, a real estate agent randomly selects 50 recently sold homes and records the sizes and sale prices of these homes. Because the real estate agent cannot control the sizes of the randomly selected homes, we say that the data are observational.

If we can control the factors being studied, we say that the data are experimental, and the values, or levels, of the factor (or combination of factors) are called *treatment groups* (or simply *groups*). The purpose of most experiments is to compare and estimate the effects of the different treatment groups (IVs) on the **response variable** (DV). For example, suppose that an oil company wants to study how three different gasoline types (*A*, *B*, and *C*) affect the fuel efficiency (L/100 km) obtained by a popular midsized automobile model. Here the response variable is fuel efficiency, and the company will study a single factor—gasoline type. Because the oil company can control which gasoline type is used in the midsized automobile, the data collected are experimental. The levels of the factor "gasoline type" are *A*, *B*, and *C*. This type of experimental design is also described as being a 1×3 design because there is one factor or IV (gasoline type) with three levels. The model's dimensions are given in the notation as one row and three columns, as shown in the following table:

LO2

Gas *A*	Gas *B*	Gas *C*
x_1 litres per 100 km	x_2 litres per 100 km	x_3 litres per 100 km

To collect data in an experiment, the different IV levels are assigned to objects (such as people, cars, animals) that are called **experimental units**. For example, in the fuel efficiency situation, gasoline types *A*, *B*, and *C* will be compared by conducting fuel efficiency tests using a midsized automobile. The automobiles used in the tests are the experimental units.

In general, applying an IV to more than one experimental unit is called **replication**. Furthermore, when the analyst controls the IVs employed and how they are applied to the experimental units, a designed experiment is being carried out. A commonly used, simple experimental design is called the *completely randomized experimental design*.

In a **completely randomized experimental design,** independent random samples of experimental units are assigned to the treatments.

Suppose we assign three experimental units to each of five IV levels (five groups). We can achieve a completely randomized experimental design by assigning experimental units to groups as follows. First, randomly select three experimental units and assign them to the first group. Next, randomly select three *different* experimental units from those remaining and assign them to the second group. That is, select these units from those not assigned to the first group. Third, randomly select three *different* experimental units from those not assigned to either the

---

[1]The independent variable is called "independent" because in an experimental condition, the independent variable is the one that is manipulated by the experimenter and is therefore independent of what the subject (or participant in the study) does. The participant's responses to the conditions set up by the experimenter are then termed as being "dependent" on the condition under which the participant was placed in the experiment.

first or the second group. Assign these experimental units to the third group. Continue this procedure until the required number of experimental units have been assigned to each experimental group.[2]

Once experimental units have been assigned to groups and the experiment has been completed, a value of the response variable is observed for each experimental unit, resulting in a *sample* of values of the response variable for each group. When we employ a completely randomized experimental design, we assume that each sample has been randomly selected from the population of all values of the response variable that could potentially be observed. We also assume that the different samples of response variable values are *independent* of each other. This is usually reasonable because the completely randomized design ensures that each different sample results from *measurements* being taken on *different experimental units*. So we sometimes say that we are conducting an *independent-samples experiment*.

Example 10.1   Training Method Experiment Example

Great White North Cameras wants to increase the efficiency of its packers in terms of the number of camera boxes packed per hour. Clark, a human resources (HR) employee, suggests conducting an independent two-group design comparing passive video training (in which people watch a video about how to improve their efficiency) to interactive training (in which people actually pack boxes while receiving feedback from a trainer). Maggie (another HR employee) suggests adding, for comparison, a third group that receives the basic training already used in the company (which consists of a booklet with photos explaining where the camera parts should be packed in the box and in what order). Clark agrees that this third group provides an excellent group to which to compare the other training methods and to act as a control group. The HR department decides on a completely randomized experimental design with three conditions in which the IV is the training condition (three levels) and the DV is the number of boxes an individual can pack per hour the day after receiving the training.

Fifteen employees are randomly selected from the pool of newly hired employees of Great White North Cameras. Of the fifteen individuals, five are randomly selected for the video training condition, five for the interactive training condition, and five for the standard training condition (the control group). In the following, the notation x_{ij} is used to denote the *j*th number of boxes packed per hour after receiving training type *i*. The data obtained are given in Table 10.1 and represent the average numbers of boxes packed per hour. Examining the box plots shown next to the data, we see some evidence that the interactive training method (*B*) may result in the greatest efficiency in packing camera parts.

TABLE 10.1   The Training Method Data

Video (Group *A*)	Interactive (Group *B*)	Standard (Group *C*)	
$x_{A1} = 34.0$	$x_{B1} = 35.3$	$x_{C1} = 33.3$	
$x_{A2} = 35.0$	$x_{B2} = 36.5$	$x_{C2} = 34.0$	
$x_{A3} = 34.3$	$x_{B3} = 36.4$	$x_{C3} = 34.7$	
$x_{A4} = 35.5$	$x_{B4} = 37.0$	$x_{C4} = 33.0$	
$x_{A5} = 35.8$	$x_{B5} = 37.6$	$x_{C5} = 34.9$	

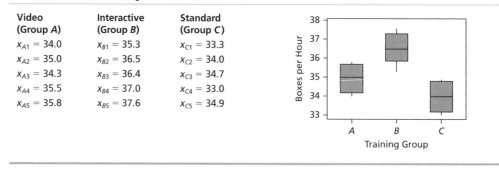

---

[2]This method of sampling is also known as *sampling without replacement*. In experimental designs, it is ideal to have the same number of experimental units (subjects) in each condition. In addition, because the selection of experimental units is random, each unit has an equal probability of being assigned to any of the experimental groups. It also means that different samples will result in different statistics (such as different means, variances).

Example 10.2 The Wine Rating Example

A wine producer wants to evaluate the quality of its new wine across Canada. Using a quasi-experimental design (such that people are not randomly assigned to cities, but the groups are independent as people cannot be in two cities at the same time), the dining facilities of a hotel chain in five major cities are selected for the study (Halifax, Montreal, Toronto, Regina, and Vancouver). On the same day, 15 patrons in each city are asked to taste the wine and rate the overall quality of the wine on a 5-point Likert (interval) scale, with 1 = horrible, 3 = moderately good, and 5 = excellent. The data are presented in Table 10.2 along with a plot of the mean ratings for each location. The plot suggests that there are differences in the assessment of the wine, with patrons in Montreal, Toronto, and Vancouver giving the wine higher ratings than those given by Halifax and Regina patrons.

TABLE **10.2** Wine Rating Data

Halifax	Montreal	Toronto	Regina	Vancouver
1	5	4	3	3
3	4	5	5	4
3	5	4	5	4
2	3	4	2	4
4	5	3	2	4
1	4	3	1	4
1	5	3	1	5
1	3	4	1	5
2	3	4	1	3
3	5	4	3	5
3	4	4	2	3
2	4	5	3	5
2	4	5	2	4
2	5	4	2	4
1	4	5	3	3

Plot: Wine Quality Rating (1 to 5) vs City (Halifax, Montreal, Toronto, Regina, Vancouver)

ROADBLOCK

Use of quasi-experimental designs
Quasi-experimental designs are quite effective in addressing various research questions. It is important to note that the selection of participants in a quasi-experimental study is random within the preselected groups, and it is essential that the participants are independent in that they cannot appear in more than one experimental condition (cell).

Example 10.3 The Shelf Display Example

The Tastee Bakery Company supplies a bakery product to many supermarkets in a metropolitan area. The company wants to study the effect of the shelf display height (the IV) used by the supermarkets for monthly sales (measured in cases of ten units each) of this product. Shelf display height has three levels: bottom (*B*), middle (*M*), and top (*T*). To compare these groups, the bakery uses a completely randomized experimental design. For each shelf height, six supermarkets (the experimental units) of equal sales potential are randomly selected, and each supermarket displays the product using its assigned shelf height for a month.[3] At the end of

---

[3]Note that pure design individuals would state that this model is not a true experiment because the individuals shopping at the supermarkets are *not* randomly assigned to the conditions (in other words, people are not assigned to shop in a certain store). Equating the stores in terms of sales potential is advantageous, but it could be argued that any differences between stores could be due to uncontrollable factors (also called "third factors" or "nuisance variables"), such as unexpected construction near a store decreasing the number of shoppers. True experimentalists would then refer to this design as *quasi-experimental*.

the month, sales of the bakery product (the DV or response variable) at the 18 participating stores are recorded, giving the data in Table 10.3. Here we assume that the set of sales amounts for each display height is a sample randomly selected from the population of all sales amounts that could be obtained (at supermarkets of the given sales potential) at that display height. Examining the box plots that are shown next to the sales data, we seem to have evidence that a middle display height gives the highest bakery product sales (which supports the marketing finding that products at adult eye level are purchased more often than are products at the top or the bottom of a shelf display).

TABLE **10.3**   The Bakery Product Sales Data

Bottom (B)	Middle (M)	Top (T)
58.2	73.0	52.4
53.7	78.1	49.7
55.8	75.4	50.9
55.7	76.2	54.0
52.5	78.4	52.1
58.9	82.1	49.9

Exercises for Section **10.1**

CONCEPTS

10.1 Define the terms *response variable, factor,* and *experimental units*.

10.2 What is a completely randomized experimental design?

METHODS AND APPLICATIONS

10.3 A study compared three different display panels for use by air traffic controllers. Each display panel was tested in a simulated emergency condition; 12 highly trained air traffic controllers took part in the study. Four controllers were randomly assigned to each

display panel. The time (in seconds) needed to stabilize the emergency condition was recorded. The results of the study are given in Table 10.4. For this situation, identify the response variable, factor of interest, and experimental units.

10.4 A consumer preference study compares the effects of three different bottle designs (A, B, and C) on sales of a popular fabric softener. A completely randomized design is employed. Specifically, 15 supermarkets of equal sales potential are selected and 5 of these supermarkets are randomly assigned to each bottle design. The number of bottles sold in 24 hours at each supermarket is recorded. The data obtained are displayed in Table 10.5. For this situation, identify the response variable, factor of interest, and experimental units.

TABLE **10.4**   Display Panel Study Data

A	B	C
21	24	40
27	21	36
24	18	35
26	19	32

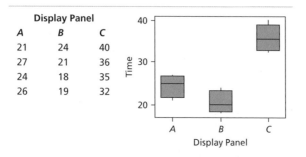

TABLE **10.5**   Bottle Design Study Data

A	B	C
16	33	23
18	31	27
19	37	21
17	29	28
13	34	25

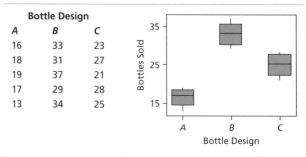

10.2 ONE-WAY ANALYSIS OF VARIANCE

Suppose we want to study the effects of p IV levels $(1, 2, \ldots, p)$ on a response variable. For any particular group, say group i, we define μ_i and σ_i to be the mean and standard deviation of the population of all possible values of the response variable that could potentially be observed for group i. Here we refer to μ_i as the *group mean i*. The goal of **one-way ANOVA** is to estimate and compare the effects of the different IV levels on the response variable. We do this by *estimating and comparing the group means* $\mu_1, \mu_2, \ldots, \mu_p$. Here we assume that a sample has been randomly selected for each of the p groups in a completely randomized experimental design. We let n_i denote the size of the sample that has been randomly selected for group i, and we let x_{ij} denote the jth value of the response variable that is observed. It then follows that the point estimate of μ_i is $\bar{x}_i$, the average of the sample of n_i values of the response variable observed in group i. It further follows that the point estimate of σ_i is s_i, the standard deviation of the sample of n_i values of the response variable observed in group i.

Example 10.4 Training Method Experiment Example

In the training method example, we let μ_A, μ_B, and μ_C denote the means and σ_A, σ_B, and σ_C denote the standard deviations of the populations of all possible numbers of boxes packed per hour using training methods A (video), B (interactive), and C (reading-only or control). To estimate these means and standard deviations, Great White North Cameras has employed a completely randomized experimental design and has obtained the numbers of boxes packed per hour in Table 10.1. The means of these samples—$\bar{x}_A = 34.92$, $\bar{x}_B = 36.56$, and $\bar{x}_C = 33.98$—are the point estimates of μ_A, μ_B, and μ_C. The standard deviations of these samples—$s_A = .7662$, $s_B = .8503$, and $s_C = .8349$—are the point estimates of σ_A, σ_B, and σ_C. Using these point estimates, we will test to see whether there are any statistically significant differences between the means μ_A, μ_B, and μ_C. If such differences exist, we will estimate their magnitudes. This will allow Great White North Cameras to judge whether these differences have practical importance.

The one-way ANOVA formulas allow us to test for significant differences between group means and to estimate differences between group means. The validity of these formulas requires that the assumptions in the following boxed feature hold.

Assumptions for One-Way ANOVA

1 **Constant variance:** The p populations of values of the response variable associated with the IV groups have equal variances.

2 **Normality:** The p populations of values of the response variable within each group all have normal distributions.

3 **Independence:** The samples of experimental units associated with the groups are randomly selected and independent.

The one-way ANOVA results are not very sensitive to violations of the equal-variances assumption. Studies have shown that this is particularly true when the sample sizes are equal (or nearly equal). Therefore, a good way to make sure that unequal variances will not be a problem is to take samples that are the same size. In addition, it is useful to compare the sample standard deviations $s_1, s_2, \ldots, s_p$ to see if they are reasonably equal. As a general rule, *the one-way ANOVA results will be approximately correct if the largest sample standard deviation is no more than twice the smallest sample standard deviation.*[4]

The normality assumption says that each of the p populations is normally distributed. This assumption is not crucial, although the distributions should be examined to ensure that they are reasonably symmetrical and that there are no outliers. If the distributions are fairly mound-shaped (normal), then the ANOVA results can be trusted for sample sizes as small as 4 or 5. As an example, consider the box-packing experiment of Examples 10.1 and 10.4. The box plots in Table 10.1 suggest that the variability of the number of boxes packed per hour in each of the three samples is roughly the same. Furthermore, the sample standard deviations $s_A = .7662$, $s_B = .8503$, and $s_C = .8349$ are reasonably equal (the largest is not even close to twice the smallest). Therefore, it is reasonable to claim that the constant-variance assumption is satisfied. Moreover, because the sample sizes are the same, unequal variances would probably not be a serious problem. Many small independent factors influence packing efficiency, so the distributions of data points for training methods A, B, and C are probably mound-shaped. In addition, the box plots in Table 10.1 indicate that each distribution is roughly symmetrical with no outliers, so the normality assumption probably holds. Finally, because Great White North Cameras has employed a completely randomized design, the independence assumption holds because the packing rates in the different samples were obtained for *different* employees.

Testing for significant differences between group means As a preliminary step in one-way ANOVA, we want to determine whether there are any statistically significant differences between the group means $\mu_1, \mu_2, \ldots, \mu_p$. To do this, we test the null hypothesis

$$H_0: \mu_1 = \mu_2 = \cdots = \mu_p$$

This hypothesis says that all of the means are equal. We test H_0 versus the alternative hypothesis

$$H_a: \text{At least one pair of } \mu_1, \mu_2, \ldots, \mu_p \text{ differ}$$

This alternative says that at least one group has a different mean (compared to the other group means).

To carry out such a test, we compare the between-groups (or between-treatments) variability to the within-group (or within-treatment) variability. For instance, suppose we want to study the effects of three training methods (A, B, and C) on mean packing efficiency, and consider Figure 10.1(a). This figure depicts three independent random samples of numbers of boxes packed per hour obtained using training methods A (video), B (interactive), and C (reading-only or control). Observations obtained from training method A are plotted with blue dots (•), from method B with red dots (•), and from method C with green dots (•). Furthermore, the group means are labelled as "Method A mean," "Method B mean," and "Method C mean." We see that the variability of the means—the between-groups variability—is not large compared to the variability within each sample (the within-group variability). In this case, the differences between the means could quite easily be the result of sampling variation, so we would not have sufficient evidence to reject

$$H_0: \mu_A = \mu_B = \mu_C$$

Figure 10.1(b), depicts a different set of three independent random samples of packing efficiency. Here the variability of the means (the between-groups variability) is large compared to the variability within each group. This would probably provide enough evidence to tell us to reject

$$H_0: \mu_A = \mu_B = \mu_C$$

in favour of

$$H_a: \text{At least one mean is different}$$

---

[4]The variations of the samples can also be compared by constructing a box plot for each sample (as we did for the box-packing data in Table 10.1). Several statistical textbooks also use the sample variances to test the equality of the population variances (see Bowerman and O'Connell [1990] for two of these tests). However, these tests have some drawbacks—in particular, their results are very sensitive to violations of the normality assumption. Because of this, there is controversy over whether these tests should be performed.

FIGURE **10.1**   Comparing Between-Groups Variability and Within-Group Variability

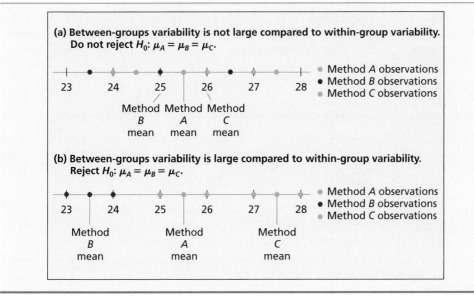

We would conclude that at least one of training methods A, B, and C has a different effect on the mean number of boxes packed per hour.

To numerically compare the between-groups and within-group variability, we define *sums of squares* and *mean squares*. To begin, we define n to be the total number of experimental units employed in the one-way ANOVA, and we define $\bar{x}$ to be the overall mean of all observed values of the response variable. Then we define the sum of squares between groups (*SSB*) as follows:

Between-groups sum of squares: $SSB = \sum_{i=1}^{p} n_i(\bar{x}_i - \bar{x})^2$

To compute the *SSB*, we calculate the difference between each group mean $\bar{x}_i$ and the overall mean $\bar{x}$, we square each of these differences, we multiply each squared difference by the number of observations for that group, and we sum over all groups. The *SSB* measures the variability of the group means. For instance, if all the group means ($\bar{x}_i$ values) were equal, then the *SSB* would be equal to 0. The more the $\bar{x}_i$ values vary, the larger the *SSB* will be. In other words, the *SSB* measures the amount of between-groups variability.

As an example, consider the training method data in Table 10.1. In this experiment, we use a total of

$$n = n_A + n_B + n_C = 5 + 5 + 5 = 15$$

experimental units. Furthermore, the overall mean of the 15 observed numbers of boxes packed per hour is

$$\bar{x} = \frac{34.0 + 35.0 + \cdots + 34.9}{15} = \frac{527.3}{15} = 35.153$$

Then

$$
\begin{aligned}
SSB &= \sum_{i=A,B,C} n_i(\bar{x}_i - \bar{x})^2 \\
&= n_A(\bar{x}_A - \bar{x})^2 + n_B(\bar{x}_B - \bar{x})^2 + n_C(\bar{x}_C - \bar{x})^2 \\
&= 5(34.92 - 35.153)^2 + 5(36.56 - 35.153)^2 + 5(33.98 - 35.153)^2 \\
&= 17.0493
\end{aligned}
$$

Variability within a group is considered to be "noise" or random error. Because of this, within-group variability is the error term in an ANOVA.

Reducing within-group variability
Ideally, within-group variability will be as low as possible. One way to reduce the effects of individual differences in each experimental condition is to have larger sample sizes. An extreme individual (causing a lot of variance) will have less of an influence in a large group than in a small group.

To measure the within-group variability (error), we define the following quantity:

The error sum of squares (*SSE*) is

$$SSE = \sum_{j=1}^{n_1} (x_{1j} - \bar{x}_1)^2 + \sum_{j=1}^{n_2} (x_{2j} - \bar{x}_2)^2 + \cdots + \sum_{j=1}^{n_p} (x_{pj} - \bar{x}_p)^2$$

Here x_{1j} is the *j*th observed value of the response in the first group, x_{2j} is the *j*th observed value of the response in the second group, and so forth. The *SSE* formula says that we compute the *SSE* by calculating the squared difference between each observed value of the response and its corresponding group mean and by summing these squared differences over all of the observations in the experiment.

The *SSE* measures the variability of the observed values of the response variable around their respective group means. For example, if there was no variability within each sample, the *SSE* would be equal to 0. The more the values within the groups vary, the larger the *SSE* will be.

As an example, in the training method study, the group means are $\bar{x}_A = 34.92, \bar{x}_B = 36.56$, and $\bar{x}_C = 33.98$. It follows that

$$SSE = \sum_{j=1}^{n_A} (x_{Aj} - \bar{x}_A)^2 + \sum_{j=1}^{n_B} (x_{Bj} - \bar{x}_B)^2 + \sum_{j=1}^{n_C} (x_{Cj} - \bar{x}_C)^2$$

$$= [(34.0 - 34.92)^2 + (35.0 - 34.92)^2 + (34.3 - 34.92)^2 + (35.5 - 34.92)^2 + (35.8 - 34.92)^2]$$

$$+ [(35.3 - 36.56)^2 + (36.5 - 36.56)^2 + (36.4 - 36.56)^2 + (37.0 - 36.56)^2 + (37.6 - 36.56)^2]$$

$$+ [(33.3 - 33.98)^2 + (34.0 - 33.98)^2 + (34.7 - 33.98)^2 + (33.0 - 33.98)^2 + (34.9 - 33.98)^2]$$

$$= 8.028$$

Finally, we define a sum of squares that measures the total amount of variability in the observed values of the response:

The sum of squares total (*SST*) is

$$SST = SSB + SSE$$

The variability in the observed values of the response must come from one of two sources—the between-groups variability and the within-group variability. It follows that the *SST* equals the sum of the *SSB* and the *SSE*. Therefore, the *SSB and SSE are said to partition the SST*.

In the training method study, we see that

$$SST = SSB + SSE = 17.0493 + 8.028 = 25.0773$$

Using the *SSB* and the *SSE*, we next define two *mean squares*:

The between-groups mean square (*MSB*) is

$$MSB = \frac{SSB}{p - 1}$$

The mean square error (*MSE*) is

$$MSE = \frac{SSE}{n - p}$$

To determine whether there are any statistically significant differences between the group means, we compare the amount of between-groups variability to the amount of within-group variability. This comparison is conducted using the following F test:

An F Test for Differences between Group Means

Suppose that we want to compare p group means $\mu_1, \mu_2, \ldots, \mu_p$ and consider testing

$H_0: \mu_1 = \mu_2 = \cdots = \mu_p$
(All means are equal)

versus

$H_a:$ At least one of $\mu_1, \mu_2, \ldots, \mu_p$ differs
(At least one mean is different)

Define the F statistic

$$F = \frac{MSB}{MSE} = \frac{SSB/(p-1)}{SSE/(n-p)}$$

and its *alpha* value to be the area under the F curve with $p-1$ and $n-p$ degrees of freedom to the right of F. We can reject H_0 in favour of H_a at level of significance α if either of the following equivalent conditions holds:

1   $F > F_\alpha$ 2 p value $< \alpha$

Here the F_α point is based on $p-1$ numerator and $n-p$ denominator degrees of freedom.

A large value of F results when the SSB, which measures the between-groups variability, is large compared to the SSE, which measures the within-group variability. If F is large enough, the implication is that H_0 should be rejected. The rejection point F_α tells us when F is large enough to allow us to reject H_0 at level of significance α. When F is large, the associated p value is small. If this p value is less than α, we can reject H_0 at level of significance α.

Example 10.5 Training Method Experiment Example

From the data presented in Table 10.1, Great White North Cameras wants to determine whether any of the training methods A, B, and C have different effects on the number of boxes packed per hour. That is, they are interested in whether there is a statistically significant difference between μ_A, μ_B, and μ_C. To determine this, we test the null hypothesis

$$H_0: \mu_A = \mu_B = \mu_C$$

which says that training methods A, B, and C have the same effects on mean packing efficiency, versus the alternative

$$H_a: \text{At least one of } \mu_A, \mu_B, \text{ and } \mu_C \text{ is different}$$

which says that at least one of training methods A, B, and C has a different effect on mean packing efficiency.

Since we previously computed the SSB to be 17.0493 and the SSE to be 8.028, and because we are comparing $p = 3$ group means, we have

$$MSB = \frac{SSB}{p-1} = \frac{17.0493}{3-1} = 8.525$$

and

$$MSE = \frac{SSE}{n-p} = \frac{8.028}{15-3} = .669$$

It follows that

$$F = \frac{MSB}{MSE} = \frac{8.525}{.669} = 12.74$$

To test H_0 at the 0.05 level of significance, we use $F_{.05}$ with $p - 1 = 3 - 1 = 2$ numerator and $n - p = 15 - 3 = 12$ denominator degrees of freedom. Table A.7 in Appendix A at the back of this book tells us that this F point equals 3.89, so we have

$$F = 12.74 > F_{.05} = 3.89$$

Therefore, we reject H_0 at the 0.05 level of significance. This says we have strong evidence that at least one of the group means μ_A, μ_B, and μ_C is different. In other words, we conclude that at least one of training methods A, B, and C has a different effect on mean packing efficiency.

Figure 10.2 gives the Excel output of an ANOVA of the training method data. Note that the output gives the value $F = 12.74$ and the related p value, which equals .001 (rounded). Because this p value is less than .05, we reject H_0 at the .05 level of significance.

The results of an ANOVA are often summarized in what is called an **analysis of variance (ANOVA) table** (or just an ANOVA table). This table gives the sums of squares (SSB, SSE, SST), the mean squares (MSB and MSE), and the F statistic and its related p-value for the ANOVA. The table also gives the degrees of freedom associated with each source of variation—between-groups, error, and total. Table 10.6 gives the ANOVA table for the training method experiment. Notice that in the column labelled "Sums of Squares," the SSB and SSE sum to the SST. Also notice that the lower portion of the Excel output in Figure 10.2 gives the ANOVA table of Table 10.6.

FIGURE 10.2　Excel Output of an ANOVA of the Training Method Data in Table 10.1

SUMMARY

Groups	Count	Sum	Average	Variance
Method A	5	174.6	34.92 [11]	0.587
Method B	5	182.8	36.56 [12]	0.723
Method C	5	169.9	33.98 [13]	0.697

ANOVA

Source of Variation	SS	df	MS	F	P-value	F crit
Between Groups	17.0493 [4]	2 [1]	8.5247 [7]	12.7424 [9]	0.0011 [10]	3.8853 [14]
Within Groups	8.0280 [5]	12 [2]	0.6690 [8]			
Total	25.0773 [6]	14 [3]				

[1] $p - 1$　[2] $n - p$　[3] $n - 1$　[4] SSB　[5] SSE　[6] SST　[7] MSB　[8] MSE　[9] F statistic　[10] p value related to F　[11] $\bar{x}_A$　[12] $\bar{x}_B$　[13] $\bar{x}_C$　[14] $F_{0.05}$

LO3

TABLE 10.6　ANOVA Table for Testing H_0: $\mu_A = \mu_B = \mu_C$ in the Training Method Experiment
($p = 3$ Training Methods, $n = 15$ Observations)

Source	Degrees of Freedom	Sums of Squares	Mean Squares	F Statistic	p-Value
Groups	$p - 1 = 3 - 1$ $= 2$	$SSB = 17.0493$	$MSB = \dfrac{SSB}{p-1}$ $= \dfrac{17.0493}{3-1}$ $= 8.525$	$F = \dfrac{MSB}{MSE}$ $= \dfrac{8.525}{.669}$ $= 12.74$	.001
Error	$n - p = 15 - 3$ $= 12$	$SSE = 8.028$	$MSE = \dfrac{SSE}{n-p}$ $= \dfrac{8.028}{15-3}$ $= .669$		
Total	$n - 1 = 15 - 1$ $= 14$	$SST = 25.0773$			

Before we continue, note that if we use the ANOVA F statistic to test the equality of *two* population means, it can be shown that

1   F equals t^2, where t is the equal-variances t statistic used to test the equality of the two population means.

2   The rejection point F_α, which is based on $p - 1 = 2 - 1 = 1$ and $n - p = n_1 + n_2 - 2$ degrees of freedom, equals $t^2_{\alpha/2}$, where $t_{\alpha/2}$ is the rejection point for the equal-variances t test and is based on $n_1 + n_2 - 2$ degrees of freedom.

Hence, the rejection conditions

$$F > F_\alpha \quad \text{and} \quad |t| > t_{\alpha/2}$$

are equivalent. It can also be shown that in this case, the p-value related to F equals the p-value related to t. Therefore, the ANOVA F test of the equality of p group means can be regarded as a generalization of the equal-variances t test of the equality of two group means.

Example 10.6   The Wine Rating Example

Recall the wine rating data in Table 10.2 for the five cities. To test the alternative hypothesis that at least one of the group means differs from the other means (compared to the null hypothesis that all of the means are equal), a one-way ANOVA is conducted on the data. The results from MegaStat are presented in Table 10.7. Looking at the output, the F test results are significant with an alpha of .000000000216. This F value is based on the ratio of the MSB (15.78) to the MSE (.855) and tested against 4 and 70 degrees of freedom. The F test informs us that at least one of the means is different (alternative hypothesis is supported), but the results do not tell us which of the means is different. To address this question, pairwise comparisons are conducted.

TABLE **10.7**   MegaStat Output of the Wine Assessment Data

One-factor ANOVA

Mean	n	Std. Dev	
2.1	15	0.96	Halifax
4.2	15	0.77	Montreal
4.1	15	0.70	Toronto
2.4	15	1.30	Regina
4.0	15	0.76	Vancouver
3.3	75	1.29	Total

ANOVA table

Source	SS	df	MS	F	p-value
Treatment	63.12	4	15.780	18.45	2.16E-10
Error	59.87	70	0.855		
Total	122.99	74			

Pairwise comparisons   If the one-way ANOVA F test says that at least one group mean is different, then we investigate which mean is different and we estimate how large the difference is. We do this by making pairwise comparisons (that is, we compare two group means at a time). One way to make these comparisons is to compute point estimates of and confidence intervals for pairwise differences. For example, in the training method experiment, we would estimate the pairwise differences $\mu_A - \mu_B$, $\mu_A - \mu_C$, and $\mu_B - \mu_C$. Here, for instance, the pairwise difference $\mu_A - \mu_B$ can be interpreted as the change in mean packing efficiency

LO4

achieved by changing from using training method B (interactive training) to using training method A (watching a video). Because these analyses are conducted after the fact, they are referred to as *post hoc analyses*.

There are two approaches to calculating confidence intervals for pairwise differences. The first involves computing the usual, or *individual*, confidence interval for each pairwise difference. Here, if we are computing $100(1 - \alpha)$ percent confidence intervals, we are $100(1 - \alpha)$ percent confident that each individual pairwise difference is contained in its respective interval. That is, the confidence level associated with each (individual) comparison is $100(1 - \alpha)$ percent, and we refer to α as the *comparisonwise error rate*. However, we are less than $100(1 - \alpha)$ percent confident that all of the pairwise differences are simultaneously contained in their respective intervals. A more conservative approach is to compute *simultaneous* confidence intervals. Such intervals make us $100(1 - \alpha)$ percent confident that all of the pairwise differences are simultaneously contained in their respective intervals. That is, when we compute simultaneous intervals, the overall confidence level associated with all of the comparisons being made in the experiment is $100(1 - \alpha)$ percent, and we refer to α as the experimentwise error rate.

Several kinds of simultaneous confidence intervals can be computed. In this book, we present what is called the *Tukey formula* for simultaneous intervals. We do this because *if we are interested in studying all pairwise differences between group means, the Tukey formula yields the most precise (shortest) simultaneous confidence intervals.* In general, a Tukey simultaneous $100(1 - \alpha)$ percent confidence interval is longer than the corresponding individual $100(1 - \alpha)$ percent confidence interval. So, intuitively, we are paying a penalty for simultaneous confidence by obtaining longer intervals. One pragmatic approach to comparing group means is to first determine if we can use the more conservative Tukey intervals to make meaningful pairwise comparisons. If we cannot, then we might see what the individual intervals tell us. In the following boxed feature, we present both individual and Tukey simultaneous confidence intervals for pairwise differences. We also present the formula for a confidence interval for a single group mean, which we might use after we have used pairwise comparisons to determine the "best" group.

Estimation in One-Way ANOVA

1 Consider the pairwise difference $\mu_i - \mu_h$, which can be interpreted to be the change in the mean value of the response variable associated with h versus i. Then a point estimate of the difference $\mu_i - \mu_h$ is $\bar{x}_i - \bar{x}_h$, where $\bar{x}_i$ and $\bar{x}_h$ are the group means associated with i and h.

2 An individual $100(1 - \alpha)$ percent confidence interval for $\mu_i - \mu_h$ is

$$\left[\bar{x}_i - \bar{x}_h \pm t_{\alpha/2} \sqrt{MSE\left(\frac{1}{n_i} + \frac{1}{n_h}\right)} \right]$$

Here the $t_{\alpha/2}$ point is based on $n - p$ degrees of freedom, and MSE is the previously defined error mean square found in the ANOVA table.

3 A Tukey simultaneous $100(1 - \alpha)$ percent confidence interval for $\mu_i - \mu_h$ is

$$\left[\bar{x}_i - \bar{x}_h \pm q_\alpha \sqrt{\frac{MSE}{m}} \right]$$

Here the value q_α is obtained from Table A.10, which is a table of percentage points of the studentized range. In this table, q_α is listed corresponding to values of p and $n - p$. Furthermore, we assume that the sample sizes n_i and n_h are equal to the same value, which we denote as m. If n_i and n_h are not equal, we replace $q_\alpha \sqrt{MSE/m}$ by $(q_\alpha/\sqrt{2}) \sqrt{MSE[(1/n_i) + (1/n_h)]}$.

4 A point estimate of the group mean μ_i is $\bar{x}_i$ and an individual $100(1 - \alpha)$ percent confidence interval for μ_i is

$$\left[\bar{x}_i \pm t_{\alpha/2} \sqrt{\frac{MSE}{n_i}} \right]$$

Here the $t_{\alpha/2}$ point is based on $n - p$ degrees of freedom.

Example 10.7 Training Method Experiment Example

In the training method experiment, we are comparing $p = 3$ group means (μ_A, μ_B, and μ_C). Furthermore, each sample is of size $m = 5$, there are a total of $n = 15$ observed packing times, and the MSE found in Table 10.6 is .669. Because $q_{.05} = 3.77$ is the entry found in Table A.10 corresponding to $p = 3$ and $n - p = 12$, a Tukey simultaneous 95 percent confidence interval for $\mu_B - \mu_A$ is

$$\left[\bar{x}_B - \bar{x}_A \pm q_{.05}\sqrt{\frac{MSE}{m}}\right] = \left[36.56 - 34.92 \pm 3.77\sqrt{\frac{.669}{5}}\right]$$
$$= [1.64 \pm 1.379]$$
$$= [.261, 3.019].$$

Similarly, Tukey simultaneous 95 percent confidence intervals for $\mu_A - \mu_C$ and $\mu_B - \mu_C$ are, respectively,

$$[\bar{x}_A - \bar{x}_C \pm 1.379] \qquad \text{and} \qquad [\bar{x}_B - \bar{x}_C \pm 1.379]$$
$$= [34.92 - 33.98 \pm 1.379] \qquad\qquad = [36.56 - 33.98 \pm 1.379]$$
$$= [-.439, 2.319] \qquad\qquad\qquad = [1.201, 3.959].$$

These intervals make us simultaneously 95 percent confident that

1 Using interactive training (method B) compared to watching a video (method A) increases the mean number of boxes packed per hour by between .261 and 3.019 boxes.

2 Changing the training method from reading instructions only (method C or the control group method) to showing a video (method A) might decrease the mean number of boxes packed by as much as .439 or might increase the mean number of boxes packed by as much as 2.319.

3 Changing the training method from reading instructions only (method C) to interactive training (method B) increases the mean number of boxes packed by between 1.201 and 3.959.

The first and third of these intervals make us 95 percent confident that μ_B is at least .261 boxes greater than μ_A and at least 1.201 boxes greater than μ_C. Therefore, we have strong evidence that training method B yields the highest mean number of boxes packed of the training methods tested. Furthermore, noting that $t_{.025}$ based on $n - p = 12$ degrees of freedom is 2.179, it follows that an individual 95 percent confidence interval for μ_B is

$$\left[\bar{x}_B \pm t_{.025}\sqrt{\frac{MSE}{n_B}}\right] = \left[36.56 \pm 2.179\sqrt{\frac{.669}{5}}\right]$$
$$= [35.763, 37.357].$$

This interval says we can be 95 percent confident that the mean number of boxes packed by using interactive training (method B) is between 35.763 and 37.357 boxes.

We next consider testing $H_0: \mu_i - \mu_h = 0$ versus $H_a: \mu_i - \mu_h \neq 0$. The test statistic t for performing this test is calculated by dividing $\bar{x}_i - \bar{x}_h$ by $\sqrt{MSE[1/n_i + 1/n_h]}$. For example, consider testing $H_0: \mu_B - \mu_A = 0$ versus $H_a: \mu_B - \mu_A \neq 0$. Since $\bar{x}_B - \bar{x}_A = 34.92 - 36.56 = 1.64$ and $\sqrt{MSE[1/n_B + 1/n_A]} = \sqrt{0.669[1/5 + 1/5]} = .5173$, the test statistic t equals $1.64/0.5173 = 3.17$. This test statistic value is given in the table at the left of the following MegaStat output, as is the test statistic value for testing $H_0: \mu_B - \mu_C = 0$ ($t = 4.99$) and the test statistic value for testing $H_0: \mu_A - \mu_C = 0$ ($t = 1.82$):

Tukey simultaneous comparison t-values (d.f. = 12)				p-values for pairwise t-tests			
	Method C	Method A	Method B		Method C	Method A	Method B
	33.98	34.92	36.56		33.98	34.92	36.56
Method C 33.98				Method C 33.98			
Method A 34.92	1.82			Method A 34.92	0.0942		
Method B 36.56	4.99	3.17		Method B 36.56	0.0003	0.0081	

critical values for experimentwise error rate:

0.05	2.67	= Significant at 0.05 level
0.01	3.56	= Significant at 0.01 level
		= Significant at 0.01 level

If we want to use the Tukey simultaneous comparison procedure with an experimentwise error rate of α, we reject H_0: $\mu_i - \mu_h = 0$ in favour of H_a: $\mu_i - \mu_h \neq 0$ if the absolute value of t is greater than the rejection point $q_\alpha / \sqrt{2}$. Table A.10 tells us that $q_{.05}$ is 3.77 and $q_{.01}$ is 5.04. Therefore, the rejection points for experimentwise error rates of .05 and .01 are, respectively, $3.77/\sqrt{2} = 2.67$ and $5.04/\sqrt{2} = 3.56$ (see the MegaStat output). Suppose we set α equal to .05. Then, since the test statistic value for testing H_0: $\mu_B - \mu_A = 0$ ($t = 3.17$) and the test statistic value for testing H_0: $\mu_B - \mu_C = 0$ ($t = 4.99$) are greater than the rejection point 2.67, we reject both null hypotheses. This, along with the fact that $\bar{x}_B = 36.56$ is greater than $\bar{x}_A = 34.92$ and $\bar{x}_C = 33.98$, leads us to conclude that training method B yields the highest mean number of packed boxes of the training methods tested (note that the MegaStat output conveniently arranges the sample means in increasing order). Finally, note that the table at the right of the MegaStat output gives the p-values for individual (rather than simultaneous) pairwise hypothesis tests. For example, the individual p-value for testing H_0: $\mu_B - \mu_C = 0$ is .0003, and the individual p-value for testing H_0: $\mu_B - \mu_A = 0$ is .0081.

Example 10.8 The Wine Rating Example

The F test results of the wine ratings determined that at least one of the means was different. Pairwise comparisons of the means were conducted using MegaStat and the results are listed below:

Post hoc analysis

p-values for pairwise t-tests

		Halifax 2.1	Regina 2.4	Vancouver 4.0	Toronto 4.1	Montreal 4.2
Halifax	2.1					
Regina	2.4	.3270				
Vancouver	4.0	2.38E-07	1.10E-05			
Toronto	4.1	1.07E-07	5.21E-06	.8441		
Montreal	4.2	2.14E-08	1.14E-06	.5556	.6942	

Tukey simultaneous comparison t-values (df = 70)

		Halifax 2.1	Regina 2.4	Vancouver 4.0	Toronto 4.1	Montreal 4.2
Halifax	2.1					
Regina	2.4	0.99				
Vancouver	4.0	5.73	4.74			
Toronto	4.1	5.92	4.94	0.20		
Montreal	4.2	6.32	5.33	0.59	0.39	

The results demonstrate that six of the pairwise comparisons are significant. Recalling that the means were

	Halifax	Montreal	Toronto	Regina	Vancouver
Mean	2.07	4.20	4.07	2.40	4.00

the pairwise results demonstrate that there was no significant difference in the ratings for those people in Halifax and Regina, but that people in Halifax rated the wine significantly lower than people in Montreal, Toronto, and Vancouver. Similarly, people in Regina rated the wine significantly lower than people in Montreal, Toronto, and Vancouver. Ratings between Montreal, Toronto, and Vancouver did not differ significantly.

In general, when we use a completely randomized experimental design, it is important to compare the groups by using experimental units that are essentially the same in relation to the characteristic under study. For example, in the training method experiment, we tested employees of the same type (new employees who have not received training) to compare the different training methods; in the wine rating experiment, we tested people who frequented the same hotel chain; and in the shelf display example, we used grocery stores of the same sales potential for the bakery product to compare the shelf display heights

Sometimes, however, it is not possible to use experimental units that are essentially the same in relation to the characteristic under study. For example, suppose a chain of stores that sells audio and video equipment wants to compare the effects of street, mall, and downtown locations on the sales volume of its stores. The experimental units in this situation are the areas where the stores are located, but these areas do not have the same sales potential because each area is populated by a different number of households. In such a situation, we must explicitly account for the differences in the experimental units. One way to do this is to use regression analysis, which is discussed in Chapters 11 and 12. When we use regression analysis to explicitly account for a variable (such as the number of households in the store's area) that causes differences in the experimental units, we call the variable a *covariate*. Furthermore, we say that we are performing an *analysis of covariance*. Finally, another way to deal with differing experimental units is to employ a *randomized block design*. This experimental design is discussed in Section 10.3.

To conclude this section, we note that if the normality and/or equal-variances assumptions for one-way ANOVA do not hold, we can use a nonparametric approach to compare several populations. One such approach is the Kruskal–Wallis H test, which is discussed in Section 13.4.

Exercises for Section **10.2**

CONCEPTS

10.5   Explain the assumptions that must be satisfied in order to validly use the one-way ANOVA formulas.

10.6   Explain the difference between the between-groups variability and the within-group variability when performing a one-way ANOVA.

10.7   Explain why we conduct pairwise comparisons of group means.

10.8   Explain the difference between individual and simultaneous confidence intervals for a set of several pairwise differences.

METHODS AND APPLICATIONS

10.9   **THE SHELF DISPLAY EXAMPLE**

Consider Example 10.3, and let μ_B, μ_M, and μ_T represent the mean monthly sales when using the bottom, middle, and top shelf display heights, respectively. Figure 10.3 gives the MegaStat output of a one-way ANOVA of the bakery sales study data.

a. Test the null hypothesis that μ_B, μ_M, and μ_T are equal by setting $\alpha = .05$. On the basis of this test, can you conclude that the bottom, middle, and top shelf display heights have different effects on mean monthly sales?

b. Consider the pairwise differences $\mu_M - \mu_B$, $\mu_T - \mu_B$, and $\mu_T - \mu_M$. Which display height maximizes mean sales?

10.10   Consider the display panel situation in Exercise 10.3 and let μ_A, μ_B, and μ_C represent the mean times to stabilize the emergency condition when using display panels A, B, and C, respectively. Figure 10.4 gives the MegaStat output of a one-way ANOVA of the display panel data.

a. Test the null hypothesis that μ_A, μ_B, and μ_C are equal by setting $\alpha = .05$. On the basis of this test, can you conclude that display panels A, B, and C have different effects on the mean time to stabilize the emergency condition?

b. Consider the pairwise differences $\mu_B - \mu_A$, $\mu_C - \mu_A$, and $\mu_C - \mu_B$. Interpret the results by describing the effects of changing from using each display panel to using each of the other panels. Which display panel minimizes the time required to stabilize the emergency condition?

10.11   Consider the bottle design study situation in Exercise 10.4, and let μ_A, μ_B, and μ_C represent mean daily sales using bottle designs A, B, and C, respectively. Figure 10.5 gives the Excel output of a one-way ANOVA of the bottle design study data.

a. Test the null hypothesis that μ_A, μ_B, and μ_C are equal by setting $\alpha = 0.05$. That is, test for statistically significant differences between these group means at the .05 level of significance. Based on this test, can you conclude that bottle designs A, B, and C have different effects on mean daily sales?

b. Consider the pairwise differences $\mu_B - \mu_A$, $\mu_C - \mu_A$, and $\mu_C - \mu_B$. Find a point estimate of and a Tukey simultaneous 95 percent confidence interval for each pairwise difference. Interpret the results in practical terms. Which bottle design maximizes mean daily sales?

c. Find an individual 95 percent confidence interval for each pairwise difference in part (b). Interpret the results in practical terms.

d. Find a 95 percent confidence interval for each of the group means μ_A, μ_B, and μ_C. Interpret these intervals.

FIGURE 10.3   MegaStat Output of a One-Way ANOVA of the Bakery Sales Study Data

One-factor ANOVA

Mean	n	Std. Dev	
55.80	6	2.477	Bottom
77.20	6	3.103	Middle
51.50	6	1.648	Top
61.50	18	11.798	Total

ANOVA table

Source	SS	df	MS	F	p-value
Treatment	2,273.880	2	1,136.9400	184.57	2.74E-11
Error	92.400	15	6.1600		
Total	2,366.280	17			

Post hoc analysis
p-values for pairwise t-tests

		Top 51.50	Bottom 55.80	Middle 77.20
Top	51.50			
Bottom	55.80	.0090		
Middle	77.20	1.52E-11	2.07E-10	

Tukey simultaneous comparison t-values (df = 15)

		Top 51.50	Bottom 55.80	Middle 77.20
Top	51.50			
Bottom	55.80	3.00		
Middle	77.20	17.94	14.93	

FIGURE 10.4   MegaStat Output of a One-Way ANOVA of the Display Panel Study Data

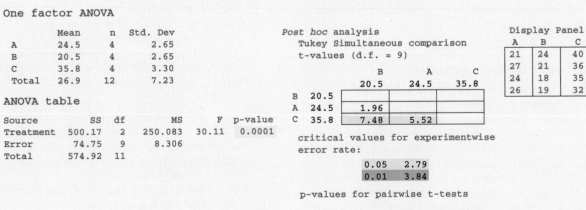

```
One factor ANOVA

        Mean    n   Std. Dev                Post hoc analysis                     Display Panel
A       24.5    4   2.65                        Tukey Simultaneous comparison      A    B    C
B       20.5    4   2.65                        t-values (d.f. = 9)               21   24   40
C       35.8    4   3.30                                B      A      C            27   21   36
Total   26.9    12  7.23                              20.5   24.5   35.8          24   18   35
                                                                                  26   19   32
ANOVA table                                    B   20.5
                                               A   24.5   1.96
Source       SS     df     MS     F    p-value C   35.8   7.48   5.52
Treatment  500.17   2   250.083  30.11 0.0001
Error       74.75   9     8.306             critical values for experimentwise
Total      574.92  11                       error rate:
                                                     0.05   2.79
                                                     0.01   3.84

                                            p-values for pairwise t-tests

                                                        B      A      C
                                                      20.5   24.5   35.8
                                               B   20.5
                                               A   24.5   0.0813
                                               C   35.8  3.76E-05 0.0004
```

FIGURE 10.5 Excel Output of a One-Way ANOVA of the Bottle Design Study Data

SUMMARY							Bottles Sold		
Groups	Count	Sum	Average	Variance				Bottle Design	
							A	B	C
DESIGN A	5	83	16.6	5.3					
DESIGN B	5	164	32.8	9.2			16	33	23
DESIGN C	5	124	24.8	8.2			18	31	27
							19	37	21
ANOVA							17	29	28
Source of Variation	SS	df	MS	F	P-Value	F crit	13	34	25
Between Groups	656.1333	2	328.0667	43.35683	3.23E-06	3.88529			
Within Groups	90.8	12	7.566667						
Total	746.9333	14							

TABLE 10.8 Golf Ball Durability Test Results and a MegaStat Plot of the Results

	Brand				
Alpha	Best	Century	Divot		
281	270	218	364		
220	334	244	302		
274	307	225	325		
242	290	273	337		
251	331	249	355		

10.12 To compare the durability of four different brands of golf balls (Alpha, Best, Century, and Divot), the Canuck Golf Association randomly selects five balls of each brand and places each ball into a machine that exerts the force produced by a 230-m drive. The number of simulated drives needed to crack or chip each ball is recorded. The results are given in Table 10.8. The MegaStat output of a one-way ANOVA of these data is shown in Figure 10.6. Test for statistically significant differences between the group means μ_{Alpha}, μ_{Best}, $\mu_{Century}$, and μ_{Divot}. Set $\alpha = .05$.

10.13 Perform pairwise comparisons of the group means in Exercise 10.12. Which brand(s) are most durable? Find a 95 percent confidence interval for each of the group means.

10.14 THE COMMERCIAL RESPONSE EXAMPLE

Advertising research indicates that when a television program is engrossing, individuals exposed to commercials tend to have difficulty recalling the names of the products advertised. Therefore, in order for companies to make the best use of their advertising dollars, it is important to show their most original and memorable commercials during engrossing programs.

In an article in the *Journal of Advertising Research,* Soldow and Principe studied the effect of program content on the response to commercials. Program content, the factor studied, had three levels: more engrossing programs, less engrossing programs, and no program (that is, commercials only). To compare these groups, Soldow and Principe employed a completely randomized experimental design. For each program content level, 29 people were randomly selected and exposed to commercials in that program content level. Then a brand recall score (measured on a continuous scale) was obtained for each person. The 29 brand recall scores for each program content level are assumed to be a sample randomly selected from the population of all brand recall scores for that program content level. The mean brand recall scores for these three groups were, respectively, $\bar{x}_1 = 1.21$, $\bar{x}_2 = 2.24$, and $\bar{x}_3 = 2.28$. Furthermore, a one-way ANOVA of the data showed that $SSB = 21.40$ and $SSE = 85.56$.

a. Define appropriate group means μ_1, μ_2, and μ_3. Then test for statistically significant differences between these group means. Set $\alpha = .05$.

b. Perform pairwise comparisons of the group means by computing a Tukey simultaneous 95 percent confidence interval for each of the pairwise differences $\mu_1 - \mu_2$, $\mu_1 - \mu_3$, and $\mu_2 - \mu_3$. Which type of program content results in the worst mean brand recall score?

Mean	n	Std. Dev	
253.6	5	24.68	Alpha
306.4	5	27.21	Best
241.8	5	21.67	Century
336.6	5	24.60	Divot
284.6	20	45.63	Total

ANOVA table

Source	SS	df	MS	F	p-value
Treatment	29,860.40	3	9,953.467	16.42	3.85E-05
Error	9,698.40	16	606.150		
Total	39,558.80	19			

Post hoc analysis
p-values for pairwise t-tests

		Century 241.8	Alpha 253.6	Best 306.4	Divot 336.6
Century	241.8				
Alpha	253.6	.4596			
Best	306.4	.0008	.0037		
Divot	336.6	1.57E-05	.0001	.0703	

Tukey simultaneous comparison t-values (df = 16)

		Century 241.8	Alpha 253.6	Best 306.4	Divot 336.6
Century	241.8				
Alpha	253.6	0.76			
Best	306.4	4.15	3.39		
Divot	336.6	6.09	5.33	1.94	

Critical values for experimentwise error rate:

0.05	2.86
0.01	3.67

Comparison of Groups

10.3 THE RANDOMIZED BLOCK DESIGN

LO5

Not all experiments employ a completely randomized design. For instance, suppose that after conducting a completely randomized design, we fail to reject the null hypothesis of equality of group means because the within-groups variability (which is measured by the *SSE*) is large. This could happen because differences between the experimental units are concealing true differences between the groups. We can often remedy this by using what is called a **randomized block design**.

Example 10.9 The Defective Cardboard Box Example

The Universal Paper Company manufactures cardboard boxes. The company wants to investigate the effects of four production methods (methods 1, 2, 3, and 4) on the number of defective boxes produced in an hour. To compare the methods, the company could utilize a completely randomized design. For each of the four production methods, the company would select several (for example, three) machine operators, train each operator to use the production method to which they have been assigned, have each operator produce boxes for one hour, and record the number of defective boxes produced. The three operators using any one production method would be *different* from those using any other production method. That is, the completely randomized design would utilize a total of 12 machine operators. However, the abilities of the machine operators could differ substantially. These differences might tend to conceal any real differences between the production methods.

To overcome this disadvantage, the company will employ a randomized block experimental design, which involves randomly selecting three machine operators and training each operator thoroughly to use all four production methods. Then each operator will produce boxes for one hour using each of the four production methods. The order in which each operator uses the four methods should be random. We record the number of defective boxes produced by each operator using each method. The advantage of the randomized block design is that the defective rates obtained by using the four methods result from using the *same* three operators. So any true differences in the effectiveness of the methods would not be concealed by differences in the operators' abilities.

When Universal Paper uses the randomized block design, it obtains the 12 defective box counts shown in Table 10.9. We let x_{ij} denote the number of defective boxes produced by machine operator j using production method i. For example, $x_{32} = 5$ says that 5 defective boxes were produced by machine operator 2 using production method 3 (see Table 10.9). In addition to the 12 defective box counts, Table 10.9 gives the sample mean of these 12 observations, which is $\bar{x} = 7.5833$, and also gives group means and sample block means. The group means are the average defective box counts obtained when using production methods 1, 2, 3, and 4. Denoting these group means as $\bar{x}_{1\bullet}, \bar{x}_{2\bullet}, \bar{x}_{3\bullet}$, and $\bar{x}_{4\bullet}$, we see from Table 10.9 that $\bar{x}_{1\bullet} = 10.3333, \bar{x}_{2\bullet} = 10.3333, \bar{x}_{3\bullet} = 5.0$, and $\bar{x}_{4\bullet} = 4.6667$. Because $\bar{x}_{3\bullet}$ and $\bar{x}_{4\bullet}$ are less than $\bar{x}_{1\bullet}$ and $\bar{x}_{2\bullet}$, we estimate that the mean number of defective boxes produced per hour by production method 3 or 4 is less than the mean number of defective boxes produced per hour by production method 1 or 2. The sample block means are the average defective box counts obtained by machine operators 1, 2, and 3. Denoting these sample block means as $\bar{x}_{\bullet 1}, \bar{x}_{\bullet 2}$, and $\bar{x}_{\bullet 3}$, we see from Table 10.9 that $\bar{x}_{\bullet 1} = 6.0, \bar{x}_{\bullet 2} = 7.75$, and $\bar{x}_{\bullet 3} = 9.0$. Because $\bar{x}_{\bullet 1}, \bar{x}_{\bullet 2}$, and $\bar{x}_{\bullet 3}$ differ, we have evidence that the abilities of the machine operators differ, so using the machine operators as blocks is reasonable.

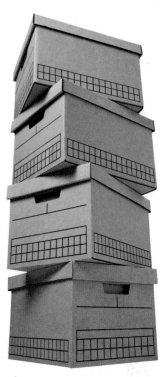

TABLE **10.9** Number of Defective Cardboard Boxes Obtained by Production Methods 1, 2, 3, and 4 and Machine Operators 1, 2, and 3

Group (Production Method)	Block (Machine Operator) 1	2	3	Group Mean
1	9	10	12	10.3333
2	8	11	12	10.3333
3	3	5	7	5.0
4	4	5	5	4.6667
Sample Block Mean	6.0	7.75	9.0	$\bar{x} = 7.5833$

In general, a randomized block design compares p IV levels (for example, production method groups) by using b blocks (for example, machine operators). Each block is used exactly once to measure the effect of each and every treatment. The advantage of the randomized block design over the completely randomized design is that we are comparing the IV levels by using the *same* experimental units. So any true differences in the groups will not be concealed by differences in the experimental units.

In some experiments, a block consists of similar or matched sets of experimental units. For example, suppose we want to compare the performance of business majors, science majors, and fine arts majors on a graduate school admissions test. Here the blocks might be matched sets of students. Each matched set (block) would consist of a business major, a science major, and a fine arts major, selected so that each is in his or her last year, attends the same university, and has the same grade point average. By selecting blocks in this fashion, any true differences between majors would not be concealed by differences between classes, universities, or grade point averages.

To analyze the data obtained in a randomized block design, we define

x_{ij} = Value of the response variable observed when block j uses IV level i

$\bar{x}_{i\bullet}$ = Mean of the b values of the response variable observed in group i

$\bar{x}_{\bullet j}$ = Mean of the p-values of the response variable observed when using block j

$\bar{x}$ = Mean of the total of the bp values of the response variable that we observed in the experiment

The ANOVA procedure for a randomized block design partitions the total sum of squares (*SST*) into three components: the between-groups sum of squares (*SSB*), the block sum of squares (*SSBL*), and the error sum of squares (*SSE*). The formula for this partitioning is

$$SST = SSB + SSBL + SSE$$

The steps for calculating these sums of squares, as well as what is measured by the sums of squares, can be summarized as follows:

Step 1: Calculate the *SSB*, which measures the amount of between-groups variability:

$$SSB = b \sum_{i=1}^{p} (\bar{x}_{i\bullet} - \bar{x})^2$$

Step 2: Calculate the *SSBL*, which measures the amount of variability due to the blocks:

$$SSB = p \sum_{j=1}^{b} (\bar{x}_{\bullet j} - \bar{x})^2$$

Step 3: Calculate the *SST*, which measures the total amount of variability:

$$SST = \sum_{i=1}^{p} \sum_{j=1}^{b} (x_{ij} - \bar{x})^2$$

Step 4: Calculate the *SSE*, which measures the amount of variability due to the error:

$$SSE = SST - SSB - SSBL$$

These sums of squares are shown in Table 10.10, which is the ANOVA table for a randomized block design. This table also gives the degrees of freedom associated with each source of variation—groups, blocks, error, and total—as well as the mean squares and *F* statistics used to test the hypotheses of interest in a randomized block experiment.

TABLE 10.10   ANOVA Table for the Randomized Block Design with *p* Groups and *b* Blocks

Source of Variation	Degrees of Freedom	Sum of Squares	Mean Square	F
Groups	$p - 1$	SSB	$MSB = \dfrac{SSB}{p - 1}$	$F(groups) = \dfrac{MSB}{MSE}$
Blocks	$b - 1$	SSBL	$MSBL = \dfrac{SSBL}{b - 1}$	$F(blocks) = \dfrac{MSBL}{MSE}$
Error	$(p - 1)(b - 1)$	SSE	$MSE = \dfrac{SSE}{(p - 1)(b - 1)}$	
Total	$pb - 1$	SST		

Before discussing these hypotheses, we will illustrate how the entries in the ANOVA table are calculated. The sums of squares in the defective cardboard box example are calculated as follows (note that $p = 4$ production methods and $b = 3$ machine operators):

Step 1: $SSB = 3[(\bar{x}_{1\bullet} - \bar{x})^2 + (\bar{x}_{2\bullet} - \bar{x})^2 + (\bar{x}_{3\bullet} - \bar{x})^2 + (\bar{x}_{4\bullet} - \bar{x})^2]$

$\qquad = 3[(10.3333 - 7.5833)^2 + (10.3333 - 7.5833)^2$
$\qquad\quad + (5.0 - 7.5833)^2 + (4.6667 - 7.5833)^2]$

$\qquad = 90.9167$

Step 2: $SSBL = 4[(\bar{x}_{\bullet 1} - \bar{x})^2 + (\bar{x}_{\bullet 2} - \bar{x})^2 + (\bar{x}_{\bullet 3} - \bar{x})^2]$

$\qquad = 4[(6.0 - 7.5833)^2 + (7.75 - 7.5833)^2 + (9.0 - 7.5833)^2]$

$\qquad = 18.1667$

Step 3: $SST = (9 - 7.5833)^2 + (10 - 7.5833)^2 + (12 - 7.5833)^2$

$\qquad\qquad + (8 - 7.5833)^2 + (11 - 7.5833)^2 + (12 - 7.5833)^2$

$\qquad\qquad + (3 - 7.5833)^2 + (5 - 7.5833)^2 + (7 - 7.5833)^2$

$\qquad\qquad + (4 - 7.5833)^2 + (5 - 7.5833)^2 + (5 - 7.5833)^2$

$\qquad = 112.9167$

Step 4: $SSE = SST - SSB - SSBL$

$\qquad = 112.9167 - 90.9167 - 18.1667$

$\qquad = 3.8333$

Figure 10.7 gives the MegaStat output of a randomized block ANOVA of the defective box data. This figure shows the above-calculated sums of squares, as well as the degrees of freedom (recall that $p = 4$ and $b = 3$), the mean squares, and the F statistics (and associated p-values) used to test the hypotheses of interest.

Of main interest is the test of the null hypothesis H_0 that no differences exist between the IV levels on the mean value of the response variable versus the alternative hypothesis H_a that at least one group differs from the other groups. We can reject H_0 in favour of H_a at level of significance α if

$$F(\text{groups}) = \frac{MSB}{MSE}$$

is greater than the F_α point based on $p - 1$ numerator and $(p - 1)(b - 1)$ denominator degrees of freedom. In the defective cardboard box example, $F_{.05}$ based on $p - 1 = 3$ numerator and $(p - 1)(b - 1) = 6$ denominator degrees of freedom is 4.76 (see Table A.7).

FIGURE 10.7 MegaStat Output of a Randomized Block ANOVA of the Defective Box Data

Randomized blocks ANOVA

Mean	n	Std. Dev	
6.000	4	2.944	Operator1
7.750	4	3.202	Operator2
9.000	4	3.559	Operator3
10.333	3	1.528	Method1
10.333	3	2.082	Method2
5.000	3	2.000	Method3
4.667	3	0.577	Method4
7.583	12	3.204	Total

ANOVA table

Source	SS	df	MS	F	p-value
Treatments	90.92	3	30.306	47.43	0.0001
Blocks	18.17	2	9.083	14.22	0.0053
Error	3.83	6	0.639		
Total	112.92	11			

Post hoc analysis

Tukey simultaneous comparison t-values (d.f. = 6)

		Operator1	Operator2	Operator3
		6.000	7.750	9.000
Operator1	6.000			
Operator2	7.750	3.10		
Operator3	9.000	5.31	2.21	

critical values for experimentwise error rate:

0.05	3.07
0.01	4.48

p-values for pairwise t-tests

		Operator1	Operator2	Operator3
		6.000	7.750	9.000
Operator1	6.000			
Operator2	7.750	0.0212		
Operator3	9.000	0.0018	0.0690	

Because

$$F(\text{groups}) = \frac{MSB}{MSE} = \frac{30.306}{.639} = 47.43$$

is greater than $F_{.05} = 4.76$, we reject H_0 at the .05 level of significance. Therefore, we have strong evidence that at least one production method has a different effect on the mean number of defective boxes produced per hour. Alternatively, we can reject H_0 in favour of H_a at level of significance α if the p-value is less than α. Here the p-value is the area under the curve of the F distribution (with $p - 1$ and $(p - 1)(b - 1)$ degrees of freedom) to the right of F(treatments or groups). The MegaStat output in Figure 10.7 tells us that this p-value is .0001 (that is, less than .01) for the defective box data. Therefore, we have extremely strong evidence that at least one production method has a different effect on the mean number of defective boxes produced per hour.

It is also of interest to test the null hypothesis H_0 that no differences exist between the block effects on the mean value of the response variable versus the alternative hypothesis H_a that at least one block effect is different. We can reject H_0 in favour of H_a at level of significance α if

$$F(\text{blocks}) = \frac{MSBL}{MSE}$$

is greater than the F_α point based on $b - 1$ numerator and $(p - 1)(b - 1)$ denominator degrees of freedom. In the defective cardboard box example, $F_{.05}$ based on $b - 1 = 2$ numerator and $(p - 1)(b - 1) = 6$ denominator degrees of freedom is 5.14 (see Table A.7). Because

$$F(\text{blocks}) = \frac{MSBL}{MSE} = \frac{9.083}{.639} = 14.21$$

is greater than $F_{.05} = 5.14$, we reject H_0 at the .05 level of significance. Therefore, we have strong evidence that at least one machine operator has a different effect on the mean number of defective boxes produced per hour. Alternatively, we can reject H_0 in favour of H_a at level of significance α if the p-value is less than α. Here the p-value is the area under the curve of the F distribution (with $b - 1$ and $(p - 1)(b - 1)$ degrees of freedom) to the right of F(blocks). The MegaStat output tells us that this p-value is .0053 for the defective box data. Therefore, we have very strong evidence that at least one machine operator has a different effect on the mean number of defective boxes produced per hour. This implies that using the machine operators as blocks is reasonable.

If, in a randomized block design, we conclude that at least one group mean differs, we can perform pairwise comparisons to determine how they differ.

Point Estimates and Confidence Intervals in a Randomized Block ANOVA

Consider the difference between groups i and h on the mean value of the response variable.

1   A *point estimate* of this difference is $\bar{x}_{i\bullet} - \bar{x}_{h\bullet}$.

2   An individual $100(1 - \alpha)$ percent confidence interval for this difference is

$$\left[\bar{x}_{i\bullet} - \bar{x}_{h\bullet} \pm t_{\alpha/2}s\sqrt{\frac{2}{b}} \right]$$

Here $t_{\alpha/2}$ is based on $(p - 1)(b - 1)$ degrees of freedom, and s is the square root of the MSE found in the randomized block ANOVA table.

3   A Tukey simultaneous $100(1 - \alpha)$ percent confidence interval for this difference is

$$\left[\bar{x}_{i\bullet} - \bar{x}_{h\bullet} \pm q_\alpha \frac{s}{\sqrt{b}} \right]$$

Here the value q_α is obtained from Table A.10, which is a table of percentage points of the studentized range. In this table, q_α is listed corresponding to values of p and $(p - 1)(b - 1)$.

Example 10.10 The Defective Cardboard Box Example

We previously concluded that we have strong evidence that at least one production method has a different mean number of defective boxes produced per hour. We have also seen that the group means are $\bar{x}_{1\bullet} = 10.3333$, $\bar{x}_{2\bullet} = 10.3333$, $\bar{x}_{3\bullet} = 5.0$, and $\bar{x}_{4\bullet} = 4.6667$. Because $\bar{x}_{4\bullet}$ is the smallest mean, we will use Tukey simultaneous 95 percent confidence intervals to compare the effect of production method 4 to the effects of production methods 1, 2, and 3. To compute these intervals, we first note that $q_{.05} = 4.90$ is the entry in Table A.10 corresponding to $p = 4$ and $(p - 1)(b - 1) = 6$. Also note that the MSE found in the randomized block ANOVA table is .639 (see Figure 10.7), which implies that $s = \sqrt{.639} = .7994$. It follows that a Tukey simultaneous 95 percent confidence interval for the difference between the effects of production methods 4 and 1 on the mean number of defective boxes produced per hour is

$$\left[\bar{x}_{4\bullet} - \bar{x}_{1\bullet} \pm q_{.05} \frac{s}{\sqrt{b}} \right] = \left[4.6667 - 10.3333 \pm 4.90 \left(\frac{.7994}{\sqrt{3}} \right) \right]$$
$$= [-5.6666 \pm 2.2615]$$
$$= [-7.9281, -3.4051].$$

Furthermore, it can be verified that a Tukey simultaneous 95 percent confidence interval for the difference between the effects of production methods 4 and 2 on the mean number of defective boxes produced per hour is also [−7.9281, −3.4051]. Therefore, we can be 95 percent confident that changing from production method 1 or 2 to production method 4 decreases the mean number of defective boxes produced per hour by a machine operator by between 3.4051 and 7.9281 boxes. A Tukey simultaneous 95 percent confidence interval for the difference between the effects of production methods 4 and 3 on the mean number of defective boxes produced per hour is

$$[\bar{x}_{4\bullet} - \bar{x}_{3\bullet} \pm 2.2615] = [4.6667 - 5 \pm 2.2615]$$
$$= [-2.5948, 1.9282].$$

This interval tells us (with 95 percent confidence) that changing from production method 3 to production method 4 might decrease the mean number of defective boxes produced per hour by as many as 2.5948 boxes or might increase this mean by as many as 1.9282 boxes. In other words, because this interval contains 0, we cannot conclude that the effects of production methods 4 and 3 differ.

Exercises for Section 10.3

CONCEPTS

10.15 In your own words, explain why we sometimes use the randomized block design.

10.16 How can we test to determine if the blocks we have chosen are reasonable?

METHODS AND APPLICATIONS

10.17 A marketing organization wants to study the effects of four sales methods on weekly sales of a product. The organization employs a randomized block design in which three salespeople use each sales method. The results obtained are given in Table 10.11. Figure 10.8 gives the Excel output of a randomized block ANOVA of the sales method data.

a. Test the null hypothesis H_0 that no differences exist between the effects of the sales methods (groups) on mean weekly sales. Set $\alpha = .05$. Can you conclude that the different sales methods have different effects on mean weekly sales?

b. Test the null hypothesis H_0 that no differences exist between the effects of the salespeople (blocks) on mean weekly sales. Set $\alpha = .05$. Can you conclude that the different salespeople have different effects on mean weekly sales?

c. Use Tukey simultaneous 95 percent confidence intervals to make pairwise comparisons of the sales method effects on mean weekly sales. Which sales method(s) maximize mean weekly sales?

TABLE 10.11   Results of a Sales Method Experiment Using a Randomized Block Design

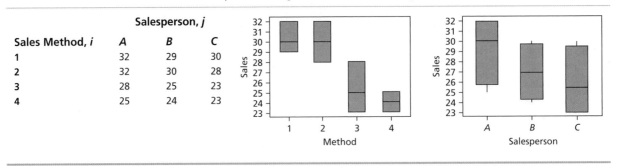

Sales Method, i	Salesperson, j		
	A	B	C
1	32	29	30
2	32	30	28
3	28	25	23
4	25	24	23

FIGURE 10.8   Excel Output of a Randomized Block ANOVA of the Sales Method Data Given in Table 10.11

Anova: Two-Factor Without Replication

SUMMARY	Count	Sum	Average	Variance
Method 1	3	91	30.3333 [12]	2.3333
Method 2	3	90	30 [13]	4
Method 3	3	76	25.3333 [14]	6.3333
Method 4	3	72	24 [15]	1
Salesperson A	4	117	29.25 [16]	11.5833
Salesperson B	4	108	27 [17]	8.6667
Salesperson C	4	104	26 [18]	12.6667

ANOVA

Source of Variation	SS	df	MS	F	P-value	F crit
Rows	93.5833 [1]	3	31.1944 [5]	36.2258 [8]	0.0003 [9]	4.7571
Columns	22.1667 [2]	2	11.0833 [6]	12.8710 [10]	0.0068 [11]	5.1433
Error	5.1667 [3]	6	0.8611 [7]			
Total	120.9167 [4]	11				

[1] SSB   [2] SSBL   [3] SSE   [4] SST   [5] MSB   [6] MSBL   [7] MSE   [8] F(groups)   [9] p value for F(groups)
[10] F(blocks)   [11] p value for F(blocks)   [12] $\bar{x}_1.$ [13] $\bar{x}_2.$ [14] $\bar{x}_3.$ [15] $\bar{x}_4.$ [16] $\bar{x}._1$ [17] $\bar{x}._2$ [18] $\bar{x}._3$

10.18 A consumer preference study involving three different bottle designs (A, B, and C) for the jumbo size of a new liquid laundry detergent was carried out using a randomized block experimental design, with supermarkets as blocks. Specifically, four supermarkets were supplied with all three bottle designs, which were priced the same. Table 10.12 gives the number of bottles of each design sold in a 24-hour period at each supermarket. Using these data, the SSB, SSBL, and SSE can be calculated to be 586.1667, 421.6667, and 1.8333, respectively.

a. Test the null hypothesis H_0 that no differences exist between the effects of the bottle designs on mean daily sales. Set $\alpha = .05$. Can you conclude that the different bottle designs have different effects on mean sales?

b. Test the null hypothesis H_0 that no differences exist between the effects of the supermarkets on mean daily sales. Set $\alpha = .05$. Can you conclude that the different supermarkets have different effects on mean sales?

c. Use Tukey simultaneous 95 percent confidence intervals to make pairwise comparisons of the bottle design effects on mean daily sales. Which bottle design(s) maximize mean sales?

d. Thinking about the research design described above, what possible limitations to the design may affect the results?

TABLE 10.12   Results of a Bottle Design Experiment

Bottle Design, i	Supermarket, j			
	1	2	3	4
A	16	14	1	6
B	33	30	19	23
C	23	21	8	12

TABLE **10.13** Results of a Keyboard Experiment 🖋

Data Entry Specialist	Keyboard Brand		
	A	B	C
1	77	67	63
2	71	62	59
3	74	63	59
4	67	57	54

10.19 To compare three brands of computer keyboards, four data entry specialists were randomly selected. Each specialist used all three keyboards to enter the same kind of text material for ten minutes, and the number of words entered per minute was recorded. The data obtained are given in Table 10.13. Using these data, the *SSB*, *SSBL*, and *SSE* can be calculated to be 392.6667, 143.5833, and 2.6667, respectively.

    a. Test the null hypothesis H_0 that no differences exist between the effects of the keyboard brands on the mean number of words entered per minute. Set $\alpha = .05$.

    b. Test the null hypothesis H_0 that no differences exist between the effects of the data entry specialists on the mean number of words entered per minute. Set $\alpha = .05$.

    c. Use Tukey simultaneous 95 percent confidence intervals to make pairwise comparisons of the keyboard brand effects on the mean number of words entered per minute. Which keyboard brand maximizes the mean number of words entered per minute?

10.20 OECD BROADBAND STATISTICS TO JUNE 2006

    The Organisation for Economic Co-operation and Development (OECD) collected statistics of broadband subscribers in 30 countries around the world. Options of accessing the Internet were DSL, cable, and other. The data, per 100 inhabitants, are presented in Table 10.14.

To test if there is a significant main effect for type of subscription, we can treat the data as a randomized block design, where the IV levels are the three types of subscriptions and the blocks are the 30 countries. Figure 10.9 gives the MegaStat output of a randomized block ANOVA of the broadband statistics.

    a. Test the null hypothesis H_0 that no differences exist between the three subscription types. Do the three subscription types differ?

    b. Make pairwise comparisons of the three subscription types. Which type is the most popular?

10.21 The Coca-Cola Company introduced New Coke in 1985. Within three months of this introduction, negative consumer reaction forced Coca-Cola to reintroduce the original formula of Coke as Coca-Cola Classic. Suppose that two years later, in 1987, a marketing research firm in Vancouver compared the sales of Coca-Cola Classic, New Coke, and Pepsi in public building vending machines. To do this, the marketing research firm randomly selected ten public buildings in Vancouver with both a Coke machine (selling Coke Classic and New Coke) and a Pepsi machine. The data—in number of cans sold over a given period of time—and a MegaStat randomized block ANOVA of the data are given in Figure 10.10.

    a. Test the null hypothesis H_0 that no differences exist between the mean sales of Coca-Cola Classic, New Coke, and Pepsi in Vancouver public building vending machines. Set $\alpha = .05$.

    b. Make pairwise comparisons of the mean sales of Coca-Cola Classic, New Coke, and Pepsi in Vancouver public building vending machines.

    c. By the mid-1990s, the Coca-Cola Company had discontinued making New Coke and had returned to making only its original product. Is there evidence in the 1987 study that this might happen? Explain your answer.

TABLE **10.14** Broadband Subscriber Statistics per 100 Inhabitants for Exercise 10.20

	DSL	Cable	Other	Rank		DSL	Cable	Other	Rank
Denmark	17.4	9	2.8	1	France	16.7	1	0	16
Netherlands	17.2	11.1	0.5	2	Australia	13.9	2.9	0.6	17
Iceland	26.5	0	0.7	3	Germany	14.7	0.3	0.1	18
Korea	13.2	8.8	4.5	4	Spain	10.5	3.1	0.1	19
Switzerland	16.9	9	0.4	5	Italy	12.6	0	0.6	20
Finland	21.7	3.1	0.2	6	Portugal	7.9	5	0	21
Norway	20.4	3.8	0.4	7	New Zealand	10.7	0.5	0.6	22
Sweden	14.4	4.3	4	8	Czech Republic	3.9	2	3.5	23
Canada	10.8	11.5	0.1	9	Ireland	6.8	1	1.4	24
United Kingdom	14.6	4.9	0	10	Hungary	4.8	2.9	0.1	25
Belgium	11.9	7.4	0	11	Poland	3.9	1.3	0.1	26
United States	8	9.8	1.4	12	Turkey	2.9	0	0	27
Japan	11.3	2.7	4.9	13	Slovak Republic	2.2	0.5	0.2	28
Luxembourg	16	1.9	0	14	Mexico	2.1	0.7	0	29
Austria	11.2	6.3	0.2	15	Greece	2.7	0	0	30

Source: OECD Broadband Statistics to June 2006, OECD, 2006.

FIGURE **10.9**   MegaStat Output of a Randomized Block ANOVA of the Internet Data for Exercise 10.20

ANOVA table

Source	SS	df	MS	F	p-value
Treatments	1,828.710 [1]	2	914.3551 [5]	58.13 [8]	1.40E-14 [9]
Blocks	659.182 [2]	29	22.7304 [6]	1.45 [10]	0.1162 [11]
Error	912.350 [3]	58	15.7302 [7]		
Total	3,400.242 [4]	89			

Post hoc analysis

Tukey simultaneous comparison t-values (d.f. = 58)

		OTHER	CABLE	DSL
		0.9133	3.8267	11.5933
OTHER	0.9133			
CABLE	3.8267	2.84		
DSL	11.5933	10.43	7.58	

critical values for experimentwise error rate:

0.05	2.40
0.01	3.04

p-values for pairwise t-tests

		OTHER	CABLE	DSL
		0.9133	3.8267	11.5933
OTHER	0.9133			
CABLE	3.8267	0.0061		
DSL	11.5933	6.39E-15	3.05E-10	

[1] SSB	[2] SSBL	[3] SSE	[4] SST	[5] MSB	[6] MSBL	[7] MSE	[8] F(groups)	[9] p value for F(groups)
[10] F(blocks)	[11] p value for F(blocks)							

FIGURE **10.10**   MegaStat Output of a Randomized Block ANOVA of the Vending Machine Data for Exercise 10.21

Building	1	2	3	4	5	6	7	8	9	10
Coke Classic	45	136	134	41	146	33	71	224	111	87
New Coke	6	114	56	14	39	20	42	156	61	140
Pepsi	24	90	100	43	51	42	68	131	74	107

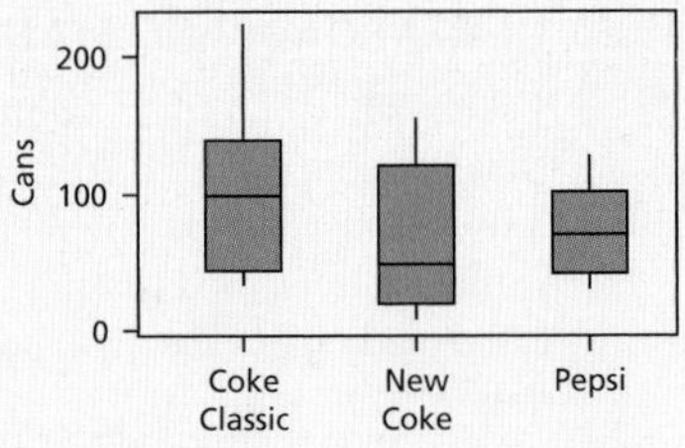

ANOVA table

Source	SS	df	MS	F	p-value
Treatments	7,997.60	2	3,998.800	5.78	0.0115
Blocks	55,573.47	9	6,174.830	8.93	4.97E-05
Error	12,443.73	18	691.319		
Total	76,014.80	29			

Tukey simultaneous comparison t-values (d.f. = 18)

		New Coke	Pepsi	Coke Classic
		64.800	73.000	102.800
New Coke	64.800			
Pepsi	73.000	0.70		
Coke Classic	102.800	3.23	2.53	

critical values for experimentwise error rate:

0.05	2.55
0.01	3.32

p-values for pairwise t-tests

		New Coke	Pepsi	Coke Classic
		64.800	73.000	102.800
New Coke	64.800			
Pepsi	73.000	0.4945		
Coke Classic	102.800	0.0046	0.0208	

10.4 TWO-WAY ANALYSIS OF VARIANCE

LO6   Many response variables are affected by more than one factor. Because of this, we must often conduct experiments in which we study the effects of several factors on the response. In this section, we consider studying the effects of *two* factors on a response variable. To begin, recall that in Example 10.3 we discussed an experiment in which the Tastee Bakery Company investigated the effect of shelf display height on monthly demand for one of its bakery products. This one-factor experiment is actually a simplification of a two-factor experiment carried out by the Tastee Bakery Company. We discuss this two-factor experiment in the following example.

Example 10.11 The Shelf Display Example

The Tastee Bakery Company supplies a bakery product to many supermarkets. The company wants to study the effects of two factors—shelf display height and shelf display width—on monthly demand (measured in cases of ten units each) for this product. The factor "display height" is defined to have three levels: B (bottom), M (middle), and T (top). The factor "display width" is defined to have two levels: R (regular) and W (wide). The IVs in this experiment are display height and display width combinations. This design is also referred to as a 3×2 design because there are three levels of the display height factor (rows) and two levels of the display width factor (columns). The design could also be referred to as a 2×3 design in which the two levels of IV_1 represent the display width factor and the three levels of IV_2 represent the display height factor. This notation depicts what the experimental design looks like in which there are two rows and three columns:

| | **Display Height** | | |
Display Width	Bottom (*B*)	Middle (*M*)	Top (*T*)
Regular (*R*)	RB	RM	RT
Wide (*W*)	WB	WM	WT

Here, for example, the notation RB denotes the condition (cell) of regular width display on the bottom. For each display height and width combination, the company randomly selects a sample of $m = 3$ supermarkets (all supermarkets used in the study have equal sales potential). Each supermarket sells the product for one month using its assigned display height and width combination, and the month's demand for the product is recorded. The six samples obtained in this experiment are given in Table 10.15. We let $x_{ij,k}$ denote the monthly demand obtained at the kth supermarket that used display height i and display width j. For example, $x_{MW,2} = 78.4$

TABLE **10.15**   Six Samples of Monthly Demands for a Bakery Product

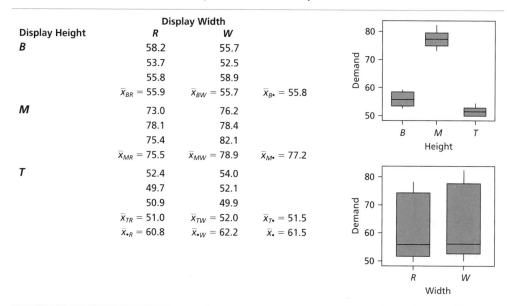

Display Height	Display Width R	W		
B	58.2	55.7		
	53.7	52.5		
	55.8	58.9		
	$\bar{x}_{BR} = 55.9$	$\bar{x}_{BW} = 55.7$	$\bar{x}_{B\bullet} = 55.8$	
M	73.0	76.2		
	78.1	78.4		
	75.4	82.1		
	$\bar{x}_{MR} = 75.5$	$\bar{x}_{MW} = 78.9$	$\bar{x}_{M\bullet} = 77.2$	
T	52.4	54.0		
	49.7	52.1		
	50.9	49.9		
	$\bar{x}_{TR} = 51.0$	$\bar{x}_{TW} = 52.0$	$\bar{x}_{T\bullet} = 51.5$	
	$\bar{x}_{\bullet R} = 60.8$	$\bar{x}_{\bullet W} = 62.2$	$\bar{x}_{\bullet} = 61.5$	

is the monthly demand obtained at the second supermarket that used a middle display height and a wide display width.

In addition to giving the six samples, Table 10.15 gives the sample group mean for each display height and display width combination. For example, $\bar{x}_{BR} = 55.9$ is the mean of the three demands observed at supermarkets using a bottom display height and a regular display width. The table also gives the mean demand for each level of display height (B, M, and T) and for each level of display width (R and W). Specifically,

$\bar{x}_{B\bullet} = 55.8$ = Mean of the six demands observed when using a bottom display height

$\bar{x}_{M\bullet} = 77.2$ = Mean of the six demands observed when using a middle display height

$\bar{x}_{T\bullet} = 51.5$ = Mean of the six demands observed when using a top display height

$\bar{x}_{\bullet R} = 60.8$ = Mean of the nine demands observed when using a regular display width

$\bar{x}_{\bullet W} = 62.2$ = Mean of the nine demands observed when using a wide display width

Finally, Table 10.15 gives $\bar{x} = 61.5$, which is the overall mean of the total of 18 demands observed in the experiment. Because $\bar{x}_{M\bullet} = 77.2$ is considerably larger than $\bar{x}_{B\bullet} = 55.8$ and $\bar{x}_{T\bullet} = 51.5$, we estimate that mean monthly demand is highest when using a middle display height. Since $\bar{x}_{\bullet R} = 60.8$ and $\bar{x}_{\bullet W} = 62.2$ do not differ by very much, we estimate that there is little difference between the effects of a regular display width and a wide display width on mean monthly demand.

Figure 10.11 presents a graphical analysis of the bakery demand data. In this figure, we plot for each display width (R and W) the mean demand associated with changing the display height from bottom (B) to middle (M) to top (T). Note that for both the regular display width (R) and the wide display width (W), the middle display height (M) gives the highest mean monthly demand. Also note that for either a bottom, middle, or top display height, there is little difference between the effects of a regular display width and a wide display width on mean monthly demand. This sort of graphical analysis is useful in determining whether a condition called *interaction* exists.

FIGURE 10.11 Graphical Analysis of the Bakery Demand Data

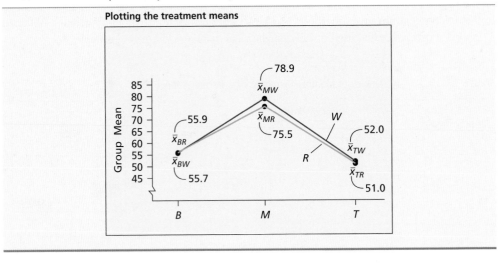

Interaction effects In general, suppose we want to study the effects of two factors on a response variable. We assume that the first factor, which we refer to as *factor 1* (or IV_1), has a levels (levels 1, 2, . . . , a). Further, we assume that the second factor, which we will refer to as *factor 2* (or IV_2), has b levels (levels 1, 2, . . . , b). Here a group (or cell) is considered to be a combination of a level of factor 1 and a level of factor 2. It follows that there is a total of ab cells, and we assume that we will employ a completely randomized experimental design in which we will assign m experimental units to each group. This procedure results in our observing m values of the response variable for each of the ab combinations, and in this situation we say that we are performing a **two-factor factorial experiment**.

The method we will explain for analyzing the results of a two-factor factorial experiment is called **two-way ANOVA**. This method requires that the following assumptions hold.

Assumptions for Two-Way ANOVA

1 **Sample:** We have obtained a random sample corresponding to each IV combination, and the sample sizes in all of the cells are equal.

2 **Independence:** The samples are independent because we have used a completely randomized experimental design.

3 **Normality:** The populations of values of the response variable (DV) associated with the IVs have normal distributions with equal variances.

To understand the various ways in which factor 1 and factor 2 might affect the mean response, consider Figure 10.12. It is possible that only factor 1 significantly affects the mean response (see Figure 10.12[a]). On the other hand, it is possible that only factor 2 significantly affects the mean response (see Figure 10.12[b]). It is also possible that both factors 1 and 2 significantly affect the mean response. If this is so, these factors might affect the mean response independently (see Figure 10.12[c]), or these factors might interact as they affect the mean response (see Figure 10.12[d]). In general, we say that there is **interaction** between

FIGURE **10.12**   Different Possible Treatment Effects in Two-Way ANOVA

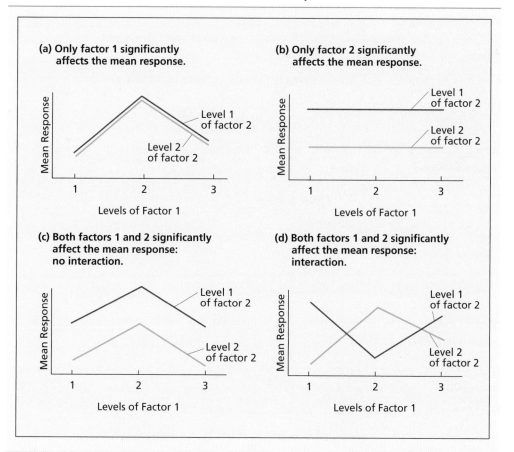

factors 1 and 2 if the relationship between the mean response and one of the factors depends on the level of the other factor. This is clearly true in Figure 10.12(d). Note here that at levels 1 and 3 of factor 1, level 1 of factor 2 gives the highest mean response, whereas at level 2 of factor 1, level 2 of factor 2 gives the highest mean response. On the other hand, the *parallel* line plots in Figure 10.12(a), (b), and (c) indicate a lack of interaction between factors 1 and 2. To graphically check for interaction, we can plot the group means, as we did in Figure 10.11. If we obtain essentially parallel line plots, it might be reasonable to conclude that there is little or no interaction between factors 1 and 2 (this is true in Figure 10.11). On the other hand, if the line plots are not parallel (the two lines intersect), it might be reasonable to conclude that factors 1 and 2 interact.

In addition to graphical analysis, ANOVA is a useful tool for analyzing the data from a two-factor factorial experiment. To explain the ANOVA approach to analyzing such an experiment, we define

$x_{ij,k}$ = kth value of the response variable observed when using level i of factor 1 and level j of factor 2

$\bar{x}_{ij}$ = Mean of the m values observed when using the ith level of factor 1 and the jth level of factor 2

$\bar{x}_{i\bullet}$ = Mean of the bm values observed when using the ith level of factor 1

$\bar{x}_{\bullet j}$ = Mean of the am values observed when using the jth level of factor 2

$\bar{x}$ = Mean of the total of abm values that we have observed in the experiment

The ANOVA procedure for a two-factor factorial experiment partitions the total sum of squares (*SST*) into four components: the factor 1 sum of squares, *SS*(1); the factor 2 sum of squares, *SS*(2); the interaction sum of squares, *SS*(int); and the error sum of squares, *SSE*. The formula for this partitioning is

$$SST = SS(1) + SS(2) + SS(\text{int}) + SSE$$

The steps for calculating these sums of squares, as well as what is measured by the sums of squares, can be summarized as follows:

Step 1: Calculate the *SST*, which measures the total amount of variability:

$$SST = \sum_{i=1}^{a} \sum_{j=1}^{b} \sum_{k=1}^{m} (x_{ij,k} - \bar{x})^2$$

Step 2: Calculate the *SS*(1), which measures the amount of variability due to the different levels of factor 1:

$$SS(1) = bm \sum_{i=1}^{a} (\bar{x}_{i\bullet} - \bar{x})^2$$

Step 3: Calculate the *SS*(2), which measures the amount of variability due to the different levels of factor 2:

$$SS(2) = am \sum_{j=1}^{b} (\bar{x}_{\bullet j} - \bar{x})^2$$

Step 4: Calculate the *SS*(interaction), which measures the amount of variability due to the interaction between factors 1 and 2:

$$SS(\text{int}) = m \sum_{i=1}^{a} \sum_{j=1}^{b} (\bar{x}_{ij} - \bar{x}_{i\bullet} - \bar{x}_{\bullet j} + \bar{x})^2$$

Step 5: Calculate the *SSE*, which measures the amount of variability due to the error:

$$SSE = SST - SS(1) - SS(2) - SS(\text{int})$$

TABLE **10.16**   Two-Way Anova Table

Source of Variation	Degrees of Freedom	Sum of Squares	Mean Square	F
Factor 1	$a - 1$	$SS(1)$	$MS(1) = \dfrac{SS(1)}{a-1}$	$F(1) = \dfrac{MS(1)}{MSE}$
Factor 2	$b - 1$	$SS(2)$	$MS(2) = \dfrac{SS(2)}{b-1}$	$F(2) = \dfrac{MS(2)}{MSE}$
Interaction	$(a - 1)(b - 1)$	$SS(\text{int})$	$MS(\text{int}) = \dfrac{SS(\text{int})}{(a-1)(b-1)}$	$F(\text{int}) = \dfrac{MS(\text{int})}{MSE}$
Error	$ab(m - 1)$	SSE	$MSE = \dfrac{SSE}{ab(m-1)}$	
Total	$abm - 1$	SST		

These sums of squares are shown in Table 10.16, which is called a *two-way ANOVA table*. This table also gives the degrees of freedom associated with each source of variation—factor 1, factor 2, interaction, error, and total—as well as the mean squares and F statistics used to test the hypotheses of interest in a two-factor factorial experiment.

Before discussing these hypotheses, we will illustrate how the entries in the ANOVA table are calculated. The sums of squares in the shelf display example are calculated as follows (note that $a = 3$, $b = 2$, and $m = 3$):

Step 1: $SST = (58.2 - 61.5)^2 + (53.7 - 61.5)^2 + (55.8 - 61.5)^2$
$$+ (55.7 - 61.5)^2 + \cdots + (49.9 - 61.5)^2$$
$$= 2{,}366.28$$

Step 2: $SS(1) = 2 \cdot 3[(\bar{x}_{B\bullet} - \bar{x})^2 + (\bar{x}_{M\bullet} - \bar{x})^2 + (\bar{x}_{T\bullet} - \bar{x})^2]$
$$= 6[(55.8 - 61.5)^2 + (77.2 - 61.5)^2 + (51.5 - 61.5)^2]$$
$$= 6(32.49 + 246.49 + 100)$$
$$= 2{,}273.88$$

Step 3: $SS(2) = 3 \cdot 3[(\bar{x}_{\bullet R} - \bar{x})^2 + (\bar{x}_{\bullet W} - \bar{x})^2]$
$$= 9[(60.8 - 61.5)^2 + (62.2 - 61.5)^2]$$
$$= 9(0.49 + 0.49)$$
$$= 8.82$$

Step 4: $SS(\text{int}) = 3[(\bar{x}_{BR} - \bar{x}_{B\bullet} - \bar{x}_{\bullet R} + \bar{x})^2 + (\bar{x}_{BW} - \bar{x}_{B\bullet} - \bar{x}_{\bullet W} + \bar{x})^2$
$$+ (\bar{x}_{MR} - \bar{x}_{M\bullet} - \bar{x}_{\bullet R} + \bar{x})^2 + (\bar{x}_{MW} - \bar{x}_{M\bullet} - \bar{x}_{\bullet W} + \bar{x})^2$$
$$+ (\bar{x}_{TR} - \bar{x}_{T\bullet} - \bar{x}_{\bullet R} + \bar{x})^2 + (\bar{x}_{TW} - \bar{x}_{T\bullet} - \bar{x}_{\bullet W} + \bar{x})^2]$$
$$= 3[(55.9 - 55.8 - 60.8 + 61.5)^2 + (55.7 - 55.8 - 62.2 + 61.5)^2$$
$$+ (75.5 - 77.2 - 60.8 + 61.5)^2 + (78.9 - 77.2 - 62.2 + 61.5)^2$$
$$+ (51.0 - 51.5 - 60.8 + 61.5)^2 + (52.0 - 51.5 - 62.2 + 61.5)^2]$$
$$= 3(3.36) = 10.08$$

Step 5: $SSE = SST - SS(1) - SS(2) - SS(\text{int})$
$$= 2366.28 - 2273.88 - 8.82 - 10.08$$
$$= 73.50$$

Figure 10.13 gives the MegaStat output of a two-way ANOVA for the shelf display data. This figure shows the above-calculated sums of squares, as well as the degrees of freedom (recall that $a = 3$, $b = 2$, and $m = 3$), mean squares, and F statistics used to test the hypotheses of interest.

FIGURE 10.13   MegaStat Output of a Two-Way ANOVA of the Shelf Display Data

Two-factor ANOVA

Factor 1

Means:

		Bottom	Middle	Top	
	R	55.90	75.50	51.00	60.80
Factor 2	W	55.70	78.90	52.00	62.20
		55.80	77.20	51.50	61.50

ANOVA table

Source	SS	df	MS	F	p-value
Factor 1	2,273.880	2	1,136.9400	185.62	9.42E-10
Factor 2	8.820	1	8.8200	1.44	0.2533
Interaction	10.080	2	5.0400	0.82	0.4625
Error	73.500	12	6.1250		
Total	2,366.280	17			

We first test the null hypothesis H_0 that no interaction exists between factors 1 and 2 versus the alternative hypothesis H_a that interaction does exist. We can reject H_0 in favour of H_a at level of significance α if

$$F(\text{int}) = \frac{MS(\text{int})}{MSE}$$

is greater than the F_α point based on $(a-1)(b-1)$ numerator and $ab(m-1)$ denominator degrees of freedom. In the shelf display example, $F_{.05}$ based on $(a-1)(b-1) = 2$ numerator and $ab(m-1) = 12$ denominator degrees of freedom is 3.89 (see Table A.7). Because

$$F(\text{int}) = \frac{MS(\text{int})}{MSE} = \frac{5.04}{6.12} = .82$$

is less than $F_{.05} = 3.89$, we cannot reject H_0 at the .05 level of significance. We conclude that little or no interaction exists between shelf display height and shelf display width. That is, we conclude that the relationship between mean demand for the bakery product and shelf display height depends little (or not at all) on shelf display width. Further, we conclude that the relationship between mean demand and shelf display width depends little (or not at all) on shelf display height. Notice that these conclusions are suggested by the previously given plot of Figure 10.11.

In general, when we conclude that little or no interaction exists between IV factors 1 and 2, we can separately test the significance of each of factors 1 and 2. We call this *testing the significance of the main effects* (what we do if we conclude that interaction does exist between factors 1 and 2 will be discussed at the end of this section).

To test the significance of factor 1 (the first IV), we test the null hypothesis H_0 that no differences exist between the effects of the different levels of factor 1 on the mean response versus the alternative hypothesis H_a that at least one level of factor 1 has a different effect. We can reject H_0 in favour of H_a at level of significance α if

$$F(1) = \frac{MS(1)}{MSE}$$

is greater than the F_α point based on $a-1$ numerator and $ab(m-1)$ denominator degrees of freedom. In the shelf display example, $F_{0.05}$ based on $a-1 = 2$ numerator and $ab(m-1) = 12$ denominator degrees of freedom is 3.89. Because

$$F(1) = \frac{MS(1)}{MSE} = \frac{1136.94}{6.12} = 185.77$$

is greater than $F_{0.05} = 3.89$, we can reject H_0 at the 0.05 level of significance. Therefore, we have strong evidence that at least one of the bottom, middle, and top display heights has a different effect on mean monthly demand.

To test the significance of factor 2 (the second IV), we test the null hypothesis H_0 that no differences exist between the effects of the different levels of factor 2 on the mean response versus the alternative hypothesis H_a that at least one level of factor 2 has a different effect. We can reject H_0 in favour of H_a at level of significance α if

$$F(2) = \frac{MS(2)}{MSE}$$

is greater than the F_α point based on $b - 1$ numerator and $ab(m - 1)$ denominator degrees of freedom. In the shelf display example, $F_{.05}$ based on $b - 1 = 1$ numerator and $ab(m - 1) = 12$ denominator degrees of freedom is 4.75. Because

$$F(2) = \frac{MS(2)}{MSE} = \frac{8.82}{6.12} = 1.44$$

is less than $F_{.05} = 4.75$, we cannot reject H_0 at the .05 level of significance. Therefore, we do not have strong evidence that the regular display width and the wide display width have different effects on mean monthly demand.

If, in a two-factor factorial experiment, we conclude that at least one level of factor 1 has a different effect or at least one level of factor 2 has a different effect, we can make pairwise comparisons to determine how the effects differ.

THEORY TO PRACTICE

The interaction assessment capability of the two-way ANOVA has been regarded by some researchers as the most important application of the ANOVA statistic. As experiences in life rarely occur in isolation, the interaction of variables on outcomes provides a richer understanding of effects. In particular, it may be found that the combination of variables has a greater impact than the presence of one variable alone. For example, in marketing, it may be found that a coupon and an added gift may increase sales of an item. In human resources, training may be enhanced by the combination of observational and interactive experiences. Combinations can also be increased with the addition of other independent variables, creating possible three-way (or more) interactions.

Point Estimates and Confidence Intervals in Two-Way ANOVA

1   Consider the difference between the effects of levels i and i' of factor 1 on the mean value of the response variable.

   a.   A point estimate of this difference is $\bar{X}_{i\bullet} - \bar{X}_{i'\bullet}$.

   b.   An individual $100(1 - \alpha)$ percent confidence interval for this difference is

$$\left[\bar{X}_{i\bullet} - \bar{X}_{i'\bullet} \pm t_{\alpha/2} \sqrt{MSE\left(\frac{2}{bm}\right)} \right]$$

where the $t_{\alpha/2}$ point is based on $ab(m - 1)$ degrees of freedom, and MSE is the error mean square found in the two-way ANOVA table.

   c.   A Tukey simultaneous $100(1 - \alpha)$ percent confidence interval for this difference (in the set of all possible paired differences

(continued)

between the effects of the different levels of factor 1) is

$$\left[\bar{x}_{i\bullet} - \bar{x}_{i'\bullet} \pm q_\alpha \sqrt{MSE\left(\frac{1}{bm}\right)} \right]$$

where q_α is obtained from Table A.10, which is a table of percentage points of the studentized range. Here q_α is listed corresponding to values of a and $ab(m - 1)$.

2 Consider the difference between the effects of levels j and j' of factor 2 on the mean value of the response variable.

a. A point estimate of this difference is $\bar{X}_{\bullet j} - \bar{X}_{\bullet j'}$.

b. An individual $100(1 - \alpha)$ percent confidence interval for this difference is

$$\left[\bar{x}_{\bullet j} - \bar{x}_{\bullet j'} \pm t_{\alpha/2} \sqrt{MSE\left(\frac{2}{am}\right)} \right]$$

where the $t_{\alpha/2}$ point is based on $ab(m - 1)$ degrees of freedom.

c. A Tukey simultaneous $100(1 - \alpha)$ percent confidence interval for this difference (in the set of all possible paired differences between the effects of the different levels of factor 2) is

$$\left[\bar{x}_{\bullet j} - \bar{x}_{\bullet j'} \pm q_\alpha \sqrt{MSE\left(\frac{1}{am}\right)} \right]$$

where q_α is obtained from Table A.10 and is listed corresponding to values of b and $ab(m - 1)$.

3 Let μ_{ij} denote the mean value of the response variable obtained when using level i of factor 1 and level j of factor 2. A point estimate of μ_{ij} is $\bar{X}_{ij}$, and an individual $100(1 - \alpha)$ percent confidence interval for μ_{ij} is

$$\left[\bar{X}_{ij} \pm t_{\alpha/2} \sqrt{\frac{MSE}{m}} \right]$$

where the $t_{\alpha/2}$ point is based on $ab(m - 1)$ degrees of freedom.

Example 10.12 The Shelf Display Example

We previously concluded that at least two of the bottom, middle, and top display heights have different effects on mean monthly demand. Since $\bar{x}_{M\bullet} = 77.2$ is greater than $\bar{x}_{B\bullet} = 55.8$ and $\bar{x}_{T\bullet} = 51.5$, we will use Tukey simultaneous 95 percent confidence intervals to compare the effect of a middle display height to the effects of the bottom and top display heights. To compute these intervals, we first note that $q_{.05} = 3.77$ is the entry in Table A.10 corresponding to $a = 3$ and $ab(m - 1) = 12$. Also note that the MSE found in the two-way ANOVA table is 6.12 (see Figure 10.13). It follows that a Tukey simultaneous 95 percent confidence interval is

$$\left[\bar{x}_{M\bullet} - \bar{x}_{B\bullet} \pm q_{.05} \sqrt{MSE\left(\frac{1}{bm}\right)} \right] = \left[77.2 - 55.8 \pm 3.77 \sqrt{6.12\left(\frac{1}{2(3)}\right)} \right]$$

$$= [21.4 \pm 3.81]$$

$$= [17.59, 25.21]$$

for the difference between the effects of a middle and a bottom display height on mean monthly demand and

$$[\bar{x}_{M\bullet} - \bar{x}_{T\bullet} \pm 3.81] = [77.2 - 51.5 \pm 3.81]$$

$$= [21.89, 29.51]$$

for the difference between the effects of a middle and a top display height on mean monthly demand.

Together, these intervals make us 95 percent confident that a middle shelf display height is, on average, at least 17.6 cases sold per month better than a bottom shelf display height and at least 21.9 cases sold per month better than a top shelf display height.[5]

---

[5]The 95 percent confidence level applies to all of the calculated confidence intervals simultaneously. If an interval is not included in an interpretation, then we are actually more than 95 percent confident in our statement.

Next, recall that previously conducted F tests suggest that there is little or no interaction between display height and display width and that there is little difference between using a regular display width and a wide display width. However, intuitive and graphical analysis should always be used to supplement the results of hypothesis testing. In this situation, note from Table 10.15 that $\bar{x}_{MR} = 75.5$ and $\bar{x}_{MW} = 78.9$. This implies that we estimate that when we use a middle display height, changing from a regular display width to a wide display width increases mean monthly demand by 3.4 cases (or 34 units). This slight increase can be seen in Figure 10.11 and suggests that it might be best (depending on what supermarkets charge for different display heights and widths) for the bakery to use a wide display width with a middle display height. Since $t_{.025}$ based on $ab(m - 1) = 12$ degrees of freedom is 2.179, an individual 95 percent confidence interval for μ_{MW}, the mean demand obtained when using a middle display height and a wide display width is

$$\left[\bar{x}_{MW} \pm t_{.025}\sqrt{\frac{MSE}{m}}\right] = \left[78.9 \pm 2.179\sqrt{\frac{6.12}{3}}\right]$$
$$= [75.79, 82.01].$$

This interval says that when we use a middle display height and a wide display width, we can be 95 percent confident that mean demand for the bakery product will be between 75.8 and 82.0 cases per month.

If we conclude that an interaction exists between factors 1 and 2, the effects of changing the level of one IV will depend on the level of the other IV. In this case, we cannot separate the analysis of the effects of the levels of the two factors. One simple alternative procedure is to use a one-way ANOVA to compare all of the group means (all instances of μ_{ij}) with the possible purpose of finding the best combination of levels of factors 1 and 2. For example, if there had been interaction in the shelf display example, we could have used one-way ANOVA to compare the six means—μ_{BR}, μ_{BW}, μ_{MR}, μ_{MW}, μ_{TR}, and μ_{TW}—to find the best combination of display height and width. Alternatively, we could study the effects of the different levels of one factor at a specified level of the other factor. This is what we did at the end of the shelf display example, when we noticed that at a middle display height, a wide display width seemed slightly more effective than a regular display width.

Finally, we might want to study the effects of more than two factors on a response variable of interest. The ideas involved in such a study are an extension of those involved in a two-way ANOVA. Although studying more than two factors is beyond the scope of this text, a good reference is Neter, Kutner, Nachtsheim, and Wasserman (1996).

Exercises for Section **10.4**

CONCEPTS

10.22 What is a treatment in the context of a two-factor factorial experiment?

10.23 Explain what we mean when we say that
    a. An interaction exists between factor 1 and factor 2.
    b. No interaction exists between the factors.

METHODS AND APPLICATIONS

10.24 An experiment is conducted to study the effects of two sales approaches—high-pressure (H) and low-pressure (L)—and to study the effects of two sales pitches (1 and 2)

on the weekly sales of a product. The data in Table 10.17 are obtained by using a completely randomized design, and Figure 10.14 gives the Excel output of a two-way ANOVA of the sales experiment data.
    a. Perform graphical analysis to check for interaction between sales pressure and sales pitch.
    b. Test for interaction by setting $\alpha = .05$.
    c. Test for differences in the effects of the levels of sales pressure by setting $\alpha = .05$. That is, test the significance of sales pressure effects with $\alpha = .05$.
    d. Calculate and interpret a 95 percent individual confidence interval for $\mu_{H\cdot} - \mu_{L\cdot}$.

TABLE 10.17 Results of the Sales Approach Experiment 🖎

Sales Pressure	Sales Pitch	
	1	2
H	32	32
	29	30
	30	28
L	28	25
	25	24
	23	23

FIGURE 10.14 Excel Output of a Two-Way ANOVA of the Sales Approach Data

Anova: Two-Factor With Replication

SUMMARY	Pitch 1	Pitch 2	Total
High Pressure			
Count	3	3	6
Sum	91	90	181
Average	30.3333	30	30.1667 [16]
Variance	2.3333	4	2.5667
Low Pressure			
Count	3	3	6
Sum	76	72	148
Average	25.3333	24	24.6667 [17]
Variance	6.3333	1	3.4667
Total			
Count	6	6	
Sum	167	162	
Average	27.8333 [18]	27 [19]	
Variance	10.9667	12.8	

ANOVA

Source of Variation	SS	df	MS	F	P-value	F crit
Pressure	90.75 [1]	1	90.75 [6]	26.5610 [10]	0.0009 [11]	5.3177
Pitch	2.0833 [2]	1	2.0833 [7]	0.6098 [12]	0.4574 [13]	5.3177
Interaction	0.75 [3]	1	0.75 [8]	0.2195 [14]	0.6519 [15]	5.3177
Within	27.3333 [4]	8	3.4167 [9]			
Total	120.917 [5]	11				

[1] $SS(1)$	[2] $SS(2)$	[3] $SS(\text{int})$	[4] SSE	[5] SST
[6] $MS(1)$	[7] $MS(2)$	[8] $MS(\text{int})$	[9] MSE	
[10] $F(1)$	[11] p value for $F(1)$	[12] $F(2)$	[13] p value for $F(2)$	
[14] $F(\text{int})$	[15] p value for $F(\text{int})$	[16] $\bar{x}_{H\bullet}$	[17] $\bar{x}_{L\bullet}$	[18] $\bar{x}_{\bullet1}$	[19] $\bar{x}_{\bullet2}$

TABLE 10.18 Results of a Two-Factor Display Panel Experiment 🖎

Display Panel	Emergency Condition			
	1	2	3	4
A	17	25	31	14
	14	24	34	13
B	15	22	28	9
	12	19	31	10
C	21	29	32	15
	24	28	37	19

e. Test for differences in the effects of the levels of sales pitch by setting $\alpha = .05$. That is, test the significance of sales pitch effects with $\alpha = .05$.

f. Calculate and interpret a 95 percent individual confidence interval for $\mu_{\bullet1} - \mu_{\bullet2}$.

g. Calculate a 95 percent individual confidence interval for mean sales when using high sales pressure and sales pitch 1. Interpret this interval.

10.25 A study compared three display panels used by air traffic controllers. Each display panel was tested for four different simulated emergency conditions. Twenty-four highly trained air traffic controllers were used in the study. Two controllers were randomly assigned to each display panel–emergency condition combination. The time (in seconds) required to stabilize the emergency condition was recorded. The data in Table 10.18 were observed. Figure 10.15 presents the MegaStat output of a two-way ANOVA of the display panel data.

a. Interpret the MegaStat interaction plot in Figure 10.15. Then test for interaction with $\alpha = .05$.

b. Test the significance of display panel effects with $\alpha = .05$.

c. Test the significance of emergency condition effects with $\alpha = .05$.

d. Make pairwise comparisons of display panels A, B, and C.

e. Make pairwise comparisons of emergency conditions 1, 2, 3, and 4.

f. Which display panel minimizes the time required to stabilize an emergency condition? Does your answer depend on the emergency condition? Why?

g. Calculate a 95 percent individual confidence interval for the mean time required to stabilize emergency condition 4 using display panel B.

10.26 A marketing firm studied the effects of two factors on the response to its television advertisements. The first factor is the time of day at which the ad is run, while the second is the position of the ad within the hour. The data in Table 10.19, which were obtained by using a completely randomized experimental design, give the number of calls placed to a toll-free number following a sample broadcast of the advertisement. If we use MegaStat to analyze these data, we obtain the output in Figure 10.16.

FIGURE 10.15 MegaStat Output of a Two-Way ANOVA of the Display Panel Data

Factor 2

Means:

Factor 1		Condition 1	Condition 2	Condition 3	Condition 4	
	Panel A	15.5	24.5	32.5	13.5	21.5
	Panel B	13.5	20.5	29.5	9.5	18.3
	Panel C	22.5	28.5	34.5	17.0	25.6
		17.2	24.5	32.2	13.3	21.8

ANOVA table

Source	SS	df	MS	F	p-value
Display Panel	218.58 [1]	2	109.292 [6]	26.49 [10]	3.96E-05 [11]
Emg Condition	1,247.46 [2]	3	415.819 [7]	100.80 [12]	8.91E-09 [13]
Interaction	16.42 [3]	6	2.736 [8]	0.66 [14]	0.6809 [15]
Error	49.50 [4]	12	4.125 [9]		
Total	1,531.96 [5]	23			

Interaction Plot by Factor 1

Post hoc analysis for Factor 1
Tukey simultaneous comparison t-values (d.f. = 12)

		Panel B 18.3	Panel A 21.5	Panel C 25.6
Panel B	18.3			
Panel A	21.5	3.20		
Panel C	25.6	7.26	4.06	

critical values for experimentwise error rate:

0.05	2.67
0.01	3.56

p-values for pairwise t-tests

		Panel B 18.3	Panel A 21.5	Panel C 25.6
Panel B	18.3			
Panel A	21.5	0.0076		
Panel C	25.6	9.98E-06	0.0016	

Post hoc analysis for Factor 2
Tukey simultaneous comparison t-values (d.f. = 12)

		Condition 4 13.3	Condition 1 17.2	Condition 2 24.5	Condition 3 32.2
Condition 4	13.3				
Condition 1	17.2	3.27			
Condition 2	24.5	9.52	6.25		
Condition 3	32.2	16.06	12.79	6.54	

critical values for experimentwise error rate:

0.05	2.97
0.01	3.89

p-values for pairwise t-tests

		Condition 4 13.3	Condition 1 17.2	Condition 2 24.5	Condition 3 32.2
Condition 4	13.3				
Condition 1	17.2	0.0067			
Condition 2	24.5	6.06E-07	4.23E-05		
Condition 3	32.2	1.77E-09	2.36E-08	2.78E-05	

[1] $SS(1)$	[2] $SS(2)$	[3] $SS(\text{int})$	[4] SSE	[5] SST	[6] $MS(1)$	[7] $MS(2)$	[8] $MS(\text{int})$
[9] MSE	[10] $F(1)$	[11] p value for $F(1)$	[12] $F(2)$	[13] p value for $F(2)$	[14] $F(\text{int})$	[15] p value for $F(\text{int})$	

TABLE 10.19 Results of a Two-Factor Marketing Response Experiment ✐

	Position Of Advertisement			
Time of Day	On the Hour	On the Half-Hour	Early in Program	Late in Program
10:00 morning	42	36	62	51
	37	41	68	47
	41	38	64	48
4:00 afternoon	62	57	88	67
	60	60	85	60
	58	55	81	66
9:00 evening	100	97	127	105
	96	96	120	101
	103	101	126	107

a. Perform graphical analysis to check for interaction between time of day and position of advertisement. Explain your conclusion. Then test for interaction with $\alpha = .05$.

b. Test the significance of time-of-day effects with $\alpha = .05$.

c. Test the significance of position of advertisement effects with $\alpha = .05$.

d. Make pairwise comparisons of the morning, afternoon, and evening times.

e. Make pairwise comparisons of the four advertisement positions.

f. Which time of day and advertisement position maximize consumer response? Compute a 95 percent individual confidence interval for the mean number of calls placed for this time of day–advertisement position combination.

FIGURE **10.16**   MegaStat Output of a Two-Way ANOVA of the Marketing Data

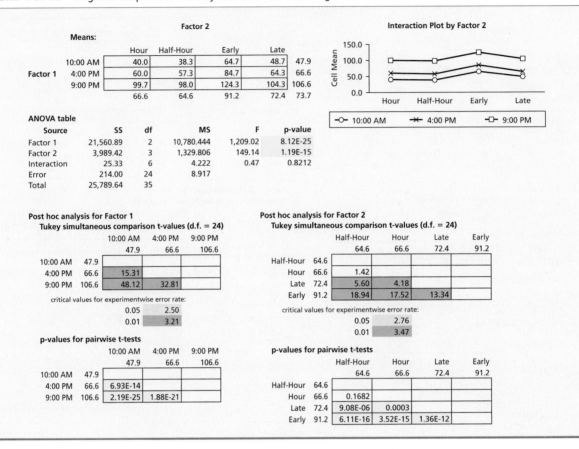

Means:

Factor 1		Hour	Half-Hour	Early	Late	
	10:00 AM	40.0	38.3	64.7	48.7	47.9
	4:00 PM	60.0	57.3	84.7	64.3	66.6
	9:00 PM	99.7	98.0	124.3	104.3	106.6
		66.6	64.6	91.2	72.4	73.7

ANOVA table

Source	SS	df	MS	F	p-value
Factor 1	21,560.89	2	10,780.444	1,209.02	8.12E-25
Factor 2	3,989.42	3	1,329.806	149.14	1.19E-15
Interaction	25.33	6	4.222	0.47	0.8212
Error	214.00	24	8.917		
Total	25,789.64	35			

Post hoc analysis for Factor 1
Tukey simultaneous comparison t-values (d.f. = 24)

		10:00 AM	4:00 PM	9:00 PM
		47.9	66.6	106.6
10:00 AM	47.9			
4:00 PM	66.6	15.31		
9:00 PM	106.6	48.12	32.81	

critical values for experimentwise error rate:

0.05	2.50
0.01	3.21

p-values for pairwise t-tests

		10:00 AM	4:00 PM	9:00 PM
		47.9	66.6	106.6
10:00 AM	47.9			
4:00 PM	66.6	6.93E-14		
9:00 PM	106.6	2.19E-25	1.88E-21	

Post hoc analysis for Factor 2
Tukey simultaneous comparison t-values (d.f. = 24)

		Half-Hour	Hour	Late	Early
		64.6	66.6	72.4	91.2
Half-Hour	64.6				
Hour	66.6	1.42			
Late	72.4	5.60	4.18		
Early	91.2	18.94	17.52	13.34	

critical values for experimentwise error rate:

0.05	2.76
0.01	3.47

p-values for pairwise t-tests

		Half-Hour	Hour	Late	Early
		64.6	66.6	72.4	91.2
Half-Hour	64.6				
Hour	66.6	0.1682			
Late	72.4	9.08E-06	0.0003		
Early	91.2	6.11E-16	3.52E-15	1.36E-12	

TABLE **10.20**   Results of the House Profitability Study

	House Design		
Supervisor	A	B	C
1	10.2	12.2	19.4
	11.1	11.7	18.2
2	9.7	11.6	13.6
	10.8	12.0	12.7

10.27 A small builder of speculative homes builds three basic house designs and employs two supervisors. The builder has used each supervisor to build two houses of each design and has obtained the profits given in Table 10.20 (the profits are given in thousands of dollars). Figure 10.17 presents the MegaStat output of a two-way ANOVA of the house profitability data.

a. Interpret the interaction plot in Figure 10.17. Then test for interaction with $\alpha = .05$. Can you separately test for the significance of house design and supervisor effects? Explain.

b. Which house design–supervisor combination gives the highest profit? When the six house design–supervisor combinations are analyzed using one-way ANOVA, $MSE = .390$. Compute a 95 percent individual confidence interval for mean profit when the best house design–supervisor combination is employed.

10.28 In the article "Humor in American, British, and German ads" (*Industrial Marketing Management, 22,* 1993), McCullough and Taylor study humour in trade magazine advertisements. A sample of 665 advertisements were categorized according to two factors: nationality (American, British, or German) and industry (29 levels, ranging from accounting to travel). A panel of judges ranked the degree of humour in each advertisement on a five-point scale. When the resulting data were analyzed using two-way ANOVA, the *p*-values for testing the significance of nationality, industry, and the interaction between nationality and industry were, respectively, .087, .000, and .046. Discuss why these *p*-values agree with the following conclusions of the authors: "British ads were more likely to be humorous than German or American ads in the graphics industry. German ads were least humorous in the grocery and mining industries, but funnier than American ads in the medical industry and funnier than British ads in the packaging industry."

FIGURE 10.17 MegaStat Output of a Two-Way ANOVA of the House Profitability Data

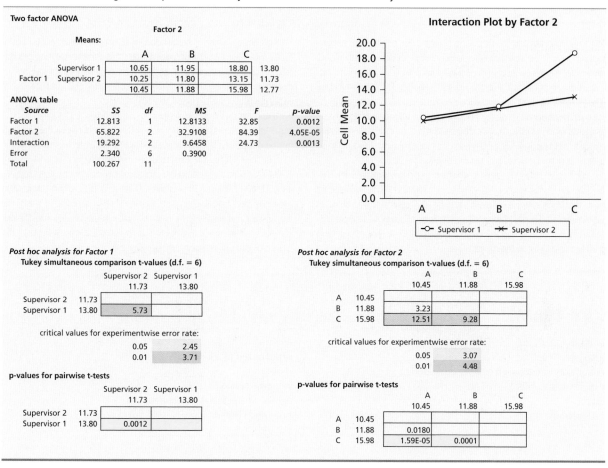

Two factor ANOVA

Factor 2

Means:

		A	B	C	
Factor 1	Supervisor 1	10.65	11.95	18.80	13.80
	Supervisor 2	10.25	11.80	13.15	11.73
		10.45	11.88	15.98	12.77

ANOVA table

Source	SS	df	MS	F	p-value
Factor 1	12.813	1	12.8133	32.85	0.0012
Factor 2	65.822	2	32.9108	84.39	4.05E-05
Interaction	19.292	2	9.6458	24.73	0.0013
Error	2.340	6	0.3900		
Total	100.267	11			

Interaction Plot by Factor 2

Post hoc analysis for Factor 1

Tukey simultaneous comparison t-values (d.f. = 6)

		Supervisor 2 11.73	Supervisor 1 13.80
Supervisor 2	11.73		
Supervisor 1	13.80	5.73	

critical values for experimentwise error rate:

0.05	2.45
0.01	3.71

p-values for pairwise t-tests

		Supervisor 2 11.73	Supervisor 1 13.80
Supervisor 2	11.73		
Supervisor 1	13.80	0.0012	

Post hoc analysis for Factor 2

Tukey simultaneous comparison t-values (d.f. = 6)

		A 10.45	B 11.88	C 15.98
A	10.45			
B	11.88	3.23		
C	15.98	12.51	9.28	

critical values for experimentwise error rate:

0.05	3.07
0.01	4.48

p-values for pairwise t-tests

		A 10.45	B 11.88	C 15.98
A	10.45			
B	11.88	0.0180		
C	15.98	1.59E-05	0.0001	

CHAPTER SUMMARY

We began this chapter by introducing some basic concepts of experimental design. We saw that when we carry out an experiment, we set the values of one or more independent variables (IV) before the values of the response variable (dependent variable, DV) are observed. The purpose of most experiments is to compare and estimate the effects of the various IVs on the DV. We saw that experimental units are assigned to IV groups, and we discussed the completely randomized experimental design. This design assigns independent, random samples of experimental units to the treatments.

We began studying how to analyze experimental data by discussing one-way analysis of variance (ANOVA). Here we studied how one factor (with *p*-levels) affects the response variable. In particular, we learned how to use this methodology to test for differences between group means and to estimate the size of pairwise differences between the means.

Sometimes, even if we randomly select the experimental units, differences between the experimental units conceal differences between the IVs. In such a case, we learned that we can use a randomized block design. Each block (experimental unit or set of experimental units) is used exactly once to measure the effect of each and every IV. Because we are comparing the IVs by using the same experimental units, any true differences between the IVs will not be concealed by differences between the experimental units.

The last technique we studied in this chapter was two-way ANOVA. Here we studied the effects of two factors by carrying out a two-factor factorial experiment. If there is little or no interaction between the two factors, then we are able to separately study the significance of each of the two factors. On the other hand, if substantial interaction exists between the two factors, we study the nature of the differences between the group means.

KEY TERMS

analysis of variance (ANOVA)
analysis of variance (ANOVA) table
completely randomized experimental design
experimental units
factor
interaction

one-way ANOVA
randomized block design
replication
response variable
two-factor factorial experiment
two-way ANOVA

IMPORTANT FORMULAS AND TESTS

One-way ANOVA sums of squares

One-way ANOVA *F* test

One-way ANOVA table

Estimation in one-way ANOVA

Randomized block sums of squares

Randomized block ANOVA table

Estimation in a randomized block experiment

Two-way ANOVA sums of squares

Two-way ANOVA table

Estimation in two-way ANOVA

SUPPLEMENTARY EXERCISES

Practise and learn online with *Connect*. Items for which there are online data sets are marked with 📈.

10.29 A drug company wants to compare the effects of three different drugs (X, Y, and Z) that are being developed to reduce cholesterol levels. Each drug is administered to six patients at the recommended dosage for six months. At the end of this period, the reduction in cholesterol level is recorded for each patient. The results are given in Table 10.21. Analyze these data using one-way ANOVA. Use the MegaStat output in Figure 10.18.

TABLE **10.21**   Reduction of Cholesterol Levels 📈

	Drug	
X	Y	Z
22	40	15
31	35	9
19	47	14
27	41	11
25	39	21
18	33	5

FIGURE 10.18 MegaStat Output of an ANOVA of the Cholesterol Reduction Data

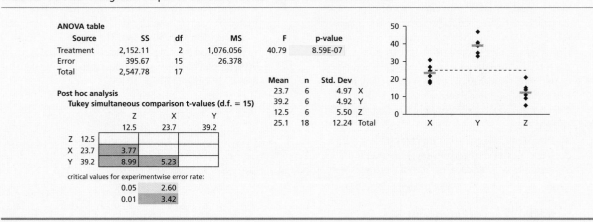

ANOVA table

Source	SS	df	MS	F	p-value
Treatment	2,152.11	2	1,076.056	40.79	8.59E-07
Error	395.67	15	26.378		
Total	2,547.78	17			

Mean	n	Std. Dev	
23.7	6	4.97	X
39.2	6	4.92	Y
12.5	6	5.50	Z
25.1	18	12.24	Total

Post hoc analysis

Tukey simultaneous comparison t-values (d.f. = 15)

		Z	X	Y
		12.5	23.7	39.2
Z	12.5			
X	23.7	3.77		
Y	39.2	8.99	5.23	

critical values for experimentwise error rate:

0.05	2.60
0.01	3.42

10.30 In an article in *Accounting and Finance* (the journal of the Accounting Association of Australia and New Zealand), Church and Schneider reported on a study concerning auditor objectivity. A sample of 45 auditors was randomly divided into three groups: (1) the 15 auditors in group 1 designed an audit program for accounts receivable and evaluated an audit program for accounts payable designed by somebody else, (2) the 15 auditors in group 2 did the reverse, (3) the 15 auditors in group 3 (the control group) evaluated the audit programs for both accounts. All 45 auditors were then instructed to spend an additional 15 hours investigating suspected irregularities in either or both of the audit programs. The mean additional number of hours allocated to the accounts receivable audit program by the auditors in groups 1, 2, and 3 were $\bar{x}_1 = 6.7, \bar{x}_2 = 9.7$, and $\bar{x}_3 = 7.6$. Furthermore, a one-way ANOVA of the data shows that $SSB = 71.51$ and $SSE = 321.3$.

a. Define appropriate group means μ_1, μ_2, and μ_3. Then test for statistically significant differences between these group means. Set $\alpha = .05$. Can you conclude that the different auditor groups have different effects on the mean additional time allocated to investigating the accounts receivable audit program?

b. Perform pairwise comparisons of the group means by computing a Tukey simultaneous 95 percent confidence interval for each of the pairwise differences $\mu_1 - \mu_2, \mu_1 - \mu_3$, and $\mu_2 - \mu_3$. Interpret the results. What do your results imply about the objectivity of auditors? What are the practical implications of this result?

10.31 The loan officers at a large bank can use three different methods for evaluating loan applications. Loan decisions can be based on (1) the applicant's balance sheet (*B*), (2) examination of key financial ratios (*F*), or (3) use of a new decision support system (*D*). To compare these three methods, four of the bank's loan officers are randomly selected. Each officer uses each of the evaluation methods for one month (the methods are used in randomly selected orders). After a year has passed, the percentage of bad loans for each loan officer and evaluation method is determined. The data obtained by using this randomized block design are given in Table 10.22. Analyze the data using a randomized block ANOVA.

TABLE 10.22 Results of a Loan Evaluation Experiment

	Loan Evaluation Method		
Loan Officer	**B**	**F**	**D**
1	8	5	4
2	6	4	3
3	5	2	1
4	4	1	0

10.32 In an article in the *Accounting Review*, Brown and Solomon[6] studied the effects of two factors—confirmation of accounts receivable and verification of sales transactions—on account misstatement risk by auditors. Both factors had two levels—completed or not completed—and a line plot of the treatment mean misstatement risks is shown in Figure 10.19. This line plot makes it appear that an interaction exists between the two factors. In your own words, explain what the interaction means in practical terms.

FIGURE 10.19 Line Plot for Exercise 10.32

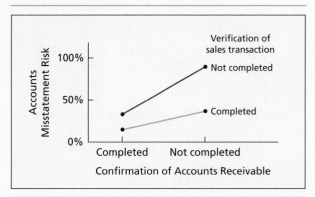

[6]"Configural information processing in auditing: The role of domain-specific knowledge," by C. E. Brown and I. Solomon, *The Accounting Review,* 66/1 (January 1991), p. 105 (Figure 1). Copyright © 1991 American Accounting Association. Used with permission.

10.33 Ergonomics is the science of adjusting the work environment to meet the needs of the employee. An experiment
was conducted at a Canadian university to assess the comfort level of data entry clerks. Two factors were assessed:
size of keys for the entry pad ($B_1 = 1.0$ cm^2; $B_2 = 2.25$ cm^2;
$B_3 = 4.0$ cm^2) and the presence or absence of armrests
on the employee's chair (armrests versus no armrests).
Comfort was measured using a self-report scale
from 1 = Not at all comfortable to 10 = Completely
comfortable.

   a. How many cells are in this experiment?

   b. If a total of 60 employees participated in this
   experiment and an equal number of employees were
   assigned to each condition, how many employees
   were in each condition?

   c. Below is an incomplete MegaStat output for the
   experiment. Using the information provided, compute
   and assess the corresponding significance of the three
   missing F values.

   d. What would you conclude from this experiment?

Two-Factor ANOVA

Means:

Factor 2

		Armrests	No Armrests	
	B1	7.5	6.8	7.2
Factor 1	B2	2.7	6.0	4.4
	B3	2.8	2.8	2.8
		4.3	5.2	4.8

ANOVA table

Source	SS	df	MS	F	p-value
Factor 1	194.43	2	97.217		
Factor 2	11.27	1	11.267		
Interaction	45.63	2	22.817		
Error	147.40	54	2.730		
Total	398.73	59			

10.34 An information systems manager wants to compare the
execution speed (in seconds) for a standard statistical
software package using three different compilers. The
manager tests each compiler using three different computer models and obtains the data shown in Table 10.23.
Analyze the data (using a computer application if you
want). In particular, test for compiler effects and computer
model effects, and also perform pairwise comparisons.

TABLE 10.23   Results of an Execution Speed Experiment
for Three Compilers (Seconds) ✐

	Compiler		
Computer	1	2	3
Model 235	9.9	8.0	7.1
Model 335	12.5	10.6	9.1
Model 435	10.8	9.0	7.8

10.35 A research team at a school of agriculture carried out an
experiment to study the effects of two fertilizer types
(A and B) and four wheat types (M, N, O, and P) on crop
yields (in tonnes per 5-ha plot). The data in Table 10.24
were obtained by using a completely randomized
experimental design. Analyze these data by using the
MegaStat output in Figure 10.20.

TABLE 10.24   Results of a Two-Factor Wheat Yield
Experiment ✐

	Wheat Type			
Fertilizer Type	M	N	O	P
A	19.4	25.0	24.8	23.1
	20.6	24.0	26.0	24.3
	20.0	24.5	25.4	23.7
B	22.6	25.6	27.6	25.4
	21.6	26.8	26.4	24.5
	22.1	26.2	27.0	26.3

10.36 INTERNET EXERCISE

Recently people have been concerned about the fuel
consumption of their vehicles due to rising gasoline prices.
One commonly occurring statement is that larger vehicles
are far less fuel-efficient than are smaller vehicles. Natural
Resources Canada listed the most fuel-efficient vehicles for
2013 on its website at:

   oee.nrcan.gc.ca/cars-light-trucks/buying/most-efficient-
   vehicles/17257

   Group the vehicles into three groups: 1 = two-seater,
subcompact, and compact ($n = 3$); 2 = mid-sized,
full-sized, and station wagon (excluding the diesel model;
$n = 3$); 3 = pickup trucks and special purpose ($n = 2$).

   a. Compute the mean fuel consumption value for each
   group for city driving and for highway driving
   separately.

   b. Conduct a one-way ANOVA on the city driving
   values. What do the results tell you?

   c. Conduct a one-way ANOVA on the highway driving
   values. What do the results tell you?

   d. Based on the findings of the two analyses, what is
   your conclusion regarding the claim that larger
   vehicles are much less fuel-efficient?

FIGURE **10.20**   MegaStat Output of Crop Yields for Exercise 10.35

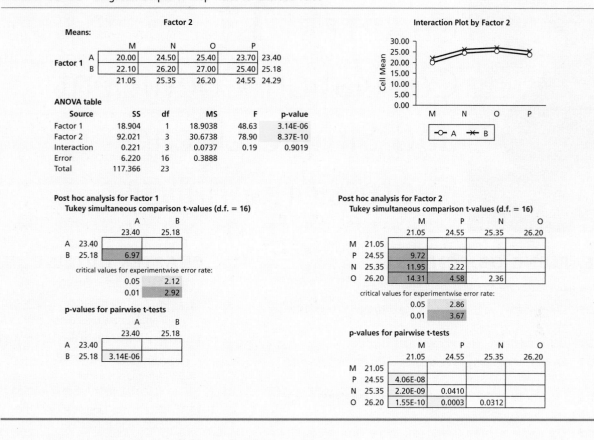

Means:

		Factor 2				
		M	N	O	P	
Factor 1	A	20.00	24.50	25.40	23.70	23.40
	B	22.10	26.20	27.00	25.40	25.18
		21.05	25.35	26.20	24.55	24.29

ANOVA table

Source	SS	df	MS	F	p-value
Factor 1	18.904	1	18.9038	48.63	3.14E-06
Factor 2	92.021	3	30.6738	78.90	8.37E-10
Interaction	0.221	3	0.0737	0.19	0.9019
Error	6.220	16	0.3888		
Total	117.366	23			

Post hoc analysis for Factor 1
Tukey simultaneous comparison t-values (d.f. = 16)

		A	B
		23.40	25.18
A	23.40		
B	25.18	6.97	

critical values for experimentwise error rate:

0.05	2.12
0.01	2.92

p-values for pairwise t-tests

		A	B
		23.40	25.18
A	23.40		
B	25.18	3.14E-06	

Post hoc analysis for Factor 2
Tukey simultaneous comparison t-values (d.f. = 16)

		M	P	N	O
		21.05	24.55	25.35	26.20
M	21.05				
P	24.55	9.72			
N	25.35	11.95	2.22		
O	26.20	14.31	4.58	2.36	

critical values for experimentwise error rate:

0.05	2.86
0.01	3.67

p-values for pairwise t-tests

		M	P	N	O
		21.05	24.55	25.35	26.20
M	21.05				
P	24.55	4.06E-08			
N	25.35	2.20E-09	0.0410		
O	26.20	1.55E-10	0.0003	0.0312	

CHAPTER **11**

Correlation Coefficient and Simple Linear Regression Analysis

LEARNING OBJECTIVES

After reading this chapter, you should be able to

LO1 Describe the two properties of the correlation coefficient statistic

LO2 Calculate the correlation coefficient statistic

LO3 Explain the resulting value of computing r^2 (eta^2) from a correlation

LO4 Define what is meant by *simple linear regression*

LO5 List the assumptions behind linear regression

LO6 Explain the meaning of each term in the linear regression equation

LO7 Define the *F* test in a linear regression

CHAPTER OUTLINE

Managers often make decisions by studying the relationships between variables, and process improvements can often be made by understanding how changes in one or more variables affect the process output. The basic statistic for understanding how two variables are related is the correlation coefficient (*r*), which is also known as the *Pearson-product-moment correlation*, named after its creator Karl Pearson (1857–1936). This useful statistic describes two properties of the linear relationship between variables: the direction (positive or negative) and the strength (from zero, or no relationship, to one, or a perfect relationship). This chapter begins with the correlation coefficient and is then followed by an introduction to simple linear regression analysis (note that *r* was originally chosen as an abbreviation for "regression").

Regression analysis is a statistical technique in which we use observed data to relate a variable of interest, which is called the *dependent* (or *response* or *criterion*) *y* variable, to one or more independent (or *predictor*) *x* variables.

The objective is to build a regression model, or prediction equation, that can be used to describe, predict, and control the dependent variable on the basis of the independent variables. For example, a company might want to examine the relationship between job satisfaction among its employees and the benefits (medical, dental, etc.) that the company offers. After collecting data, the company might use regression analysis to develop an equation to predict job satisfaction on the basis of benefit packages. As another example, a retailer might use regression analysis to describe the relationship between time of day and sales volume to ensure that adequate staff is on duty.

In this chapter, we present the simple linear regression model. Use of this technique is appropriate when we are relating a dependent variable to a single independent variable and when a straight-line model describes the relationship between these two variables.

11.1 CORRELATION COEFFICIENT

As introduced in Chapter 2, a scatter plot can be used to explore the relationship between a dependent variable y and an independent variable x. To construct a scatter plot, a sample of n pairs of values of x and y—(x_1, y_1), (x_2, y_2), . . . , (x_n, y_n)—is collected. Then each value of y is plotted against the corresponding value of x. If the plot points seem to fluctuate around a straight line, we say that there is a *linear relationship* between x and y. For example, suppose that a company's ten sales regions with equal sales potential are randomly selected. The advertising expenditures (in units of $10,000) in these ten sales regions in July of last year (x) are given in the second column of Table 11.1. The sales volumes (y, in units of $10,000) are then recorded for the ten sales regions in the third column of Table 11.1. A scatter plot of sales volume, y, versus advertising expenditure, x, is given in Figure 11.1 and shows a linear relationship between x and y.

A measure of the strength and direction of the linear relationship between x and y is the correlation. To calculate the correlation, we begin with the covariance between the two variables. The sample covariance is calculated by using the sample of n pairs of observed values of x and y. This sample covariance is denoted as s_{xy} and defined as follows:

LO1

$$s_{xy} = \frac{\sum\limits_{i=1}^{n} (x_i - \bar{x})(y_i - \bar{y})}{n - 1}$$

Note: Many statisticians represent the covariance between x and y as cov_{xy}. To use the covariance formula, we first find the mean $\bar{x}$ of the n observed values of x and the mean $\bar{y}$ of the n observed values of y. For each observed (x_i, y_i) combination, we then multiply the deviation of x_i from $\bar{x}$ by the deviation of y_i from $\bar{y}$ to form the product $(x_i - \bar{x})(y_i - \bar{y})$. Finally, we add together the n products $(x_1 - \bar{x})(y_1 - \bar{y})$, $(x_2 - \bar{x})(y_2 - \bar{y})$, . . . , $(x_n - \bar{x})(y_n - \bar{y})$ and divide the resulting sum by $n - 1$. For example, the mean of the ten advertising expenditures in Table 11.1 is $\bar{x} = 9.5$, and the mean of the ten sales volumes in Table 11.1 is $\bar{y} = 108.3$. It follows that the numerator of s_{xy} is the sum of the values of $(x_i - \bar{x})(y_i - \bar{y}) = (x_i - 9.5)(y_i - 108.3)$. Table 11.2 shows that this sum equals 365.50, which implies that the sample covariance is

$$s_{xy} = \frac{\sum (x_i - \bar{x})(y_i - \bar{y})}{n - 1} = \frac{365.50}{9} = 40.61111$$

To interpret the covariance, consider Figure 11.2(a). This figure shows the scatter plot of Figure 11.1 with a vertical blue line drawn at $\bar{x} = 9.5$ and a horizontal red line drawn at

TABLE **11.1** The Sales Volume Data

Sales Region	Advertising Expenditure, x	Sales Volume, y
1	5	89
2	6	87
3	7	98
4	8	110
5	9	103
6	10	114
7	11	116
8	12	110
9	13	126
10	14	130

FIGURE **11.1** A Scatter Plot of Sales Volume versus Advertising Expenditure

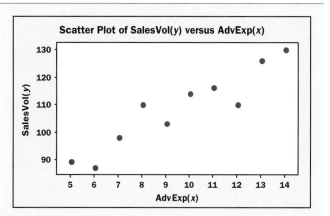

TABLE 11.2   The Calculation of the Numerator of s_{xy}

x_i	y_i	$x_i - 9.5$	$y_i - 108.3$	$(x_i - 9.5)(y_i - 108.3)$
5	89	−4.5	−19.3	86.85
6	87	−3.5	−21.3	74.55
7	98	−2.5	−10.3	25.75
8	110	−1.5	1.7	−2.55
9	103	−0.5	−5.3	2.65
10	114	0.5	5.7	2.85
11	116	1.5	7.7	11.55
12	110	2.5	1.7	4.25
13	126	3.5	17.7	61.95
14	130	4.5	21.7	97.65
Totals 95	1,083	0	0	365.50

FIGURE 11.2   Interpretation of the Sample Covariance

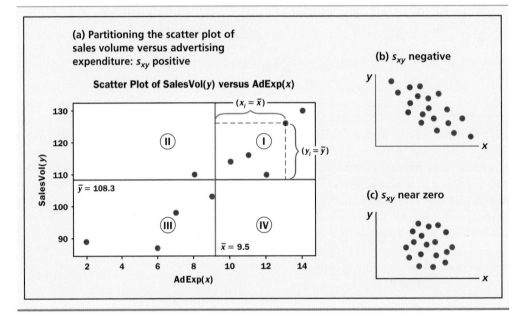

$\bar{y} = 108.3$. The lines divide the scatter plot into four quadrants. Points in quadrant I correspond to x_i greater than $\bar{x}$ and y_i greater than $\bar{y}$ and thus give a value of $(x_i - \bar{x})(y_i - \bar{y})$ greater than 0. Points in quadrant III correspond to x_i less than $\bar{x}$ and y_i less than $\bar{y}$ and thus also give a value of $(x_i - \bar{x})(y_i - \bar{y})$ greater than 0. It follows that if s_{xy} is positive, the points with the greatest influence on $\Sigma(x_i - \bar{x})(y_i - \bar{y})$ and thus on s_{xy} must be in quadrants I and III. Therefore, a positive value of s_{xy} (as in the sales volume example) indicates a positive linear relationship between x and y. That is, as x increases, y increases.

If we further consider Figure 11.2, we see that points in quadrant II correspond to x_i less than $\bar{x}$ and y_i greater than $\bar{y}$. Points in quadrant IV correspond to x_i greater than $\bar{x}$ and y_i less than $\bar{y}$. It follows that if s_{xy} is negative, the points with the greatest influence on $\Sigma(x_i - \bar{x})(y_i - \bar{y})$ and thus on s_{xy} must be in quadrants II and IV. A negative value of s_{xy} indicates a negative linear relationship between x and y. That is, as x increases, y decreases, as shown in Figure 11.2(b). For example, a negative linear relationship might exist between the number of staff working in an office (x) and electricity usage (y) such that the fewer people working results in less electricity used than when more employees are working. Finally, note that if s_{xy} is near zero, the (x_i, y_i) points will be fairly evenly distributed across all four quadrants. This indicates little or no linear relationship between x and y, as shown in Figure 11.2(c).[1]

---

[1]One way to remember the zero correlation is that the scatter plot looks like a circle or a zero.

From the previous discussion, it might seem that a large positive value for the covariance indicates that x and y have a strong positive linear relationship and a large negative value for the covariance indicates that x and y have a strong negative linear relationship. However, one problem with using the covariance as a measure of the strength of the linear relationship between x and y is that the value of the covariance depends on the units in which x and y are measured. A measure of the strength of the linear relationship between x and y that does not depend on the units in which x and y are measured is the correlation coefficient.

The sample covariance s_{xy} is the point estimate of the population covariance, which we denote as σ_{xy}, and the sample correlation coefficient r is the point estimate of the population correlation coefficient, which we denote as ρ. To define σ_{xy} and ρ, let μ_x and σ_x denote the mean and the standard deviation of the population of all possible x values, and let μ_y and σ_y denote the mean and the standard deviation of the population of all possible y values. Then σ_{xy} is the average of all possible values of $(x - \mu_x)(y - \mu_y)$, and ρ equals $\sigma_{xy}/(\sigma_x\sigma_y)$. The **correlation coefficient** is denoted as r and is defined as follows:

$$r = \frac{s_{xy}}{s_x s_y}$$

LO2

Here s_{xy} is the previously defined sample covariance, s_x is the sample standard deviation of the sample of x values, and s_y is the sample standard deviation of the sample of y values. For the sales volume data,

$$s_x = \sqrt{\frac{\sum_{i=1}^{10}(x_i - \bar{x})^2}{9}} = 3.02765 \quad \text{and} \quad s_y = \sqrt{\frac{\sum_{i=1}^{10}(y_i - \bar{y})^2}{9}} = 14.30656$$

Therefore, the sample correlation coefficient is

$$r = \frac{s_{xy}}{s_x s_y} = \frac{40.61111}{(3.02765)(14.30656)} = .93757$$

It can be shown that the sample correlation coefficient r is always between -1 and 1. A value of r near 0 implies little linear relationship between x and y. A value of r close to 1 says that x and y have a strong tendency to relate in a straight-line fashion with a positive slope and, therefore, that x and y are highly related and positively correlated. A value of r close to -1 says that x and y have a strong tendency to relate in a straight-line fashion with a negative slope and, therefore, that x and y are highly related and negatively correlated. Note that if $r = 1$, the (x, y) points fall exactly on a positively sloped straight line, and, if $r = -1$, the (x, y) points fall exactly on a negatively sloped straight line. For example, since $r = .93757$ in the sales volume example, we conclude that advertising expenditure (x) and sales volume (y) have a strong tendency to relate in a straight-line fashion with a positive slope. That is, x and y have a strong positive linear relationship.

To assess the strength of the relationship between two variables, the statistical significance of the obtained correlation value can be assessed. In particular, when there is no relationship between the two variables, then $r = 0$ and the variables are independent of each other. Nonzero correlation values suggest that some relationship between x and y might exist. To test the significance of the correlation, we test the null hypothesis

$$H_0: r = 0$$

against the alternative hypothesis

$$H_a: r \neq 0$$

How large the correlation value has to be to suggest a meaningful relationship between x and y is influenced by the number of pairs of data points, as is reflected in Table 11.3. For example, in the sales volume example, $r = .93757$ was obtained for ten sales regions. Here the $df = n - 2 = 10 - 2 = 8$. Looking at Table 11.3, the critical value for significance is .632 at 5 percent

TABLE **11.3** Critical Values of *r*, Where *df* = *n* − 2 and *n* is the Number of Pairs of Scores

Degrees of Freedom (*df*)	5%	1%	Degrees of Freedom (*df*)	5%	1%
1	0.997	1.000	24	0.388	0.496
2	0.950	0.990	25	0.381	0.487
3	0.878	0.959	26	0.374	0.478
4	0.811	0.917	27	0.367	0.470
5	0.754	0.874	28	0.361	0.463
6	0.707	0.834	29	0.355	0.456
7	0.666	0.798	30	0.349	0.449
8	0.632	0.765	31	0.325	0.418
9	0.602	0.735	32	0.304	0.393
10	0.576	0.708	33	0.288	0.372
11	0.533	0.684	34	0.273	0.354
12	0.532	0.661	35	0.250	0.325
13	0.514	0.641	36	0.232	0.302
14	0.497	0.623	37	0.217	0.283
15	0.482	0.606	38	0.205	0.267
16	0.468	0.590	39	0.195	0.254
17	0.456	0.575	40	0.174	0.228
18	0.444	0.561	41	0.159	0.208
19	0.433	0.549	42	0.138	0.181
20	0.423	0.537	43	0.113	0.148
21	0.413	0.526	44	0.098	0.128
22	0.404	0.515	45	0.088	0.115
23	0.396	0.505	46	0.062	0.081

Source: This table is adapted from Table VII of R. A. Fisher and F. Yates, *Statistical Tables for Biological, Agricultural and Medical Research*, published by Longman Group Ltd., London (previously published by Oliver and Boyd, Edinburgh), and by permission of Pearson Education Limited.

(.05) and .765 at 1 percent (.01). Because .93757 is greater than .765, we can conclude that the likelihood of obtaining the correlation of .93757 is less than .01 and that the relationship between advertising expenditure and sales volume is statistically significant at the .01 level.

Note: Remember when determining the degrees of freedom (*df*) for a correlation that a *df* is lost for each variable (because the mean was calculated), 1 for *x* and 1 for *y*, resulting in a test with *df* = *n* − 2.

ROADBLOCK

Correlation does not equal prediction
A strong positive or strong negative linear relationship between an independent variable *x* and a dependent variable *y* does not necessarily mean that we can accurately *predict y* on the basis of *x*. We discuss predicting *y* on the basis of *x* later in this chapter.

LO3

Another useful statistic derived from the correlation coefficient (*r*) is the **coefficient of determination** or eta squared (η^2 or eta^2) or *r* squared (r^2). Eta^2 is simply the squared correlation value and tells us the amount of variance overlap between the two variables *x* and *y*. For example, if the correlation between number of shares owned in a portfolio and profit made in one year is .24, then eta^2 is .24 × .24 = .0576, or 5.76 percent. From this value, it can be concluded that 5.76 percent of the variance in the number of shares overlaps with the variance in yearly profits.

ROADBLOCK

Overlapping variance is not the same as causality
Although there may be variance overlap between two variables, the overlap does not necessarily mean causality. In the preceding text, the number of shares correlates with yearly profits but does not cause the profit. More about r^2 and variance overlap and predicting *y* from *x* is discussed in Section 11.8.

Exercises for Section **11.1**

CONCEPTS

11.1 Define the term *covariance*. What would the relationship between x and y look like if there was no covariance between these two variables?

11.2 Describe what the scatterplot would look like for each correlation:
a. $r = .02$ **b.** $r = -.85$ **c.** $r = .73$

METHODS AND APPLICATIONS

11.3 Chemical BFYR is used in the production of a cosmetic product, and chemists feel that the amount of chemical BFYR might be related to the viscosity of the cosmetic product. To verify and quantify this relationship, 24 batches of the product are produced. The amount (x) of chemical BFYR (in grams) is varied from batch to batch, and the viscosity (y) obtained for each batch is measured. For the 24 batches, the following is found:

$$\sum_{i=1}^{24} (x_i - \bar{x})(y_i - \bar{y}) = 10.2281$$

$$s_x = .7053 \quad \text{and} \quad s_y = .6515$$

Using this information, calculate the sample covariance s_{xy} and the sample correlation coefficient r. Interpret r. What can you say about the strength of the linear relationship between x and y? (Hint: Refer to Table 11.3.)

11.4 Statistics Canada (statcan.gc.ca) collects data on the social behaviour of Canadians. One activity for which data are collected deals with donations to charities. Average donations (in dollars) are reported by Statistics Canada by age groups of Canadians for the year 2010, and the values are provided below for adults aged 15 and over.

Age Group	Average Donation ($)
15–24 years	143
25–34 years	305
35–44 years	431
45–54 years	477
55–64 years	626
65–74 years	592
75 years and over	725

Source: Martin Turcotte, "Charitable Giving by Canadians," *Canadian Social Trends*, Statistics Canada, Catalogue No. 11-008-X., April 16, 2012.

For these data, compute the correlation value and interpret r (use a single number to represent each age group, such as 1, 2, 3, etc.). Also compute r^2 (eta^2). Based on the r^2 (eta^2) value, what percentage of variance overlap is found between age and average donation amount?

11.2 TESTING THE SIGNIFICANCE OF THE POPULATION CORRELATION COEFFICIENT

The sample correlation coefficient (r) measures the linear relationship between the observed values of x and the observed values of y that make up the sample. A similar coefficient of linear correlation can be defined for the population of *all possible combinations of observed values of x and y*. We call this coefficient the *population correlation coefficient* and denote it by the symbol ρ (rho). We use r as the point estimate of ρ. In addition, we can carry out a hypothesis test. Here we test the null hypothesis H_0: $\rho = 0$, which says there is no linear relationship between x and y, against the alternative hypothesis H_a: $\rho \neq 0$, which says there is a (nonzero) positive or negative linear relationship between x and y. This test uses the test statistic

$$t = \frac{r\sqrt{n-2}}{\sqrt{1-r^2}}$$

and is based on the assumption that the population of all possible observed combinations of values of x and y has a bivariate normal probability distribution (see Wonnacott and Wonnacott

[1981] for a discussion of this distribution). If the bivariate normal distribution assumption for the test concerning ρ is badly violated, we can use a nonparametric approach to correlation. One such approach is Spearman's rank correlation coefficient. This approach is discussed in Section 13.5.

Exercises for Section **11.2**

CONCEPTS

11.5 Explain what is meant by the *population correlation coefficient* ρ.

11.6 Explain how to test H_0: $\rho = 0$ versus H_a: $\rho \neq 0$. What do you conclude if you reject H_0: $\rho = 0$?

METHODS AND APPLICATIONS

11.7 In a study conducted by the human resources department of a large organization, the correlation between job satisfaction (x) and attendance (y) was found to be .23 based on surveys completed by 200 employees. Assuming that the bivariate normal

probability distribution assumption holds, test H_0: $\rho = 0$ versus H_a: $\rho \neq 0$ by setting α equal to .001. What do you conclude about how x and y are related?

11.8 In a smaller organization, the human resources department tried to replicate the findings of the larger organization described in Exercise 11.7. Based on surveys completed by ten employees, the correlation between job satisfaction (x) and attendance (y) was again found to be .23. As in the previous exercise, test H_0: $\rho = 0$ versus H_a: $\rho \neq 0$. What can you conclude about the relationship between x and y based on this smaller sample of employees?

11.3 THE SIMPLE LINEAR REGRESSION MODEL

The simple linear regression model assumes that the relationship between the *dependent variable, y*, and the *independent variable, x*, can be approximated by a straight line. We can tentatively decide whether there is an approximate straight-line relationship between y and x by making a scatter diagram, or scatter plot, of y versus x. First, data concerning the two variables are observed in pairs. To construct the scatter plot, each value of y is plotted against its corresponding value of x. If the y values tend to increase or decrease in a straight-line fashion as the x values increase, and if there is a scattering of the (x, y) points around the straight line, then it is reasonable to describe the relationship between y and x by using the simple linear regression model.

We suppose that we have gathered n observations—each observation consists of an observed value of x and its corresponding value of y. Then we have the following:

The Simple Linear Regression Model

The **simple linear (or straight-line) regression model** is $y = \mu_{y|x} + \varepsilon = \beta_0 + \beta_1 x + \varepsilon$.

1. $\mu_{y|x} = \beta_0 + \beta_1 x$ is the mean value of the dependent variable y when the value of the independent variable is x.

2. β_0 is the **y intercept**. β_0 is the mean value of y when x equals zero.

3. β_1 is the **slope**. β_1 is the change (amount of increase or decrease) in the mean value of y

associated with a one-unit increase in x. If β_1 is positive, the mean value of y increases as x increases. If β_1 is negative, the mean value of y decreases as x increases.

4. ε is an error term that describes the effects on y of all factors other than the value of the independent variable x.

LO4   This model is illustrated in Figure 11.3 (note that x_0 in this figure denotes a specific value of the independent variable x). The y intercept β_0 and the slope β_1 are called *regression parameters*. Because we do not know the true values of these parameters, we must

FIGURE 11.3 The Simple Linear Regression Model (Here the Slope β_1 Is Positive)

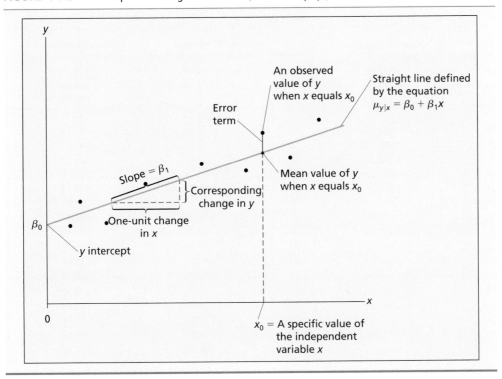

use the sample data to estimate them. We will see how this is done in Section 11.5. In later sections, we will show how to use these estimates to predict y, where $\hat{y}$ is the predicted value of y.

Example 11.1 The QHIC Example

Quality Home Improvement Centre (QHIC) operates five stores in a large metropolitan area. The marketing department at QHIC wants to study the relationship between x, home value (in thousands of dollars), and y, yearly expenditure on home upkeep (in dollars). A random sample of 40 homeowners is taken and asked to estimate their expenditures during the previous year on the types of home-upkeep products and services offered by QHIC. Public city records are used to obtain the previous year's assessed values of the homeowners' homes. The resulting x and y values are given in Table 11.4(a). Because the 40 observations are for the same year (for different homes), these are **cross-sectional data** (data observed at a single point in time as opposed to time series data, which are longitudinal).

The Excel scatter plot of y versus x is given in Table 11.4(b). We see that the observed values of y tend to increase in a straight-line (or slightly curved) fashion as x increases. Assuming that $\mu_{y|x}$ and x have a straight-line relationship, it is reasonable to relate y to x by using the simple linear regression model with positive slope ($\beta_1 > 0$)

$$y = \beta_0 + \beta_1 x + \varepsilon$$

The slope β_1 is the change (increase) in mean dollar yearly upkeep expenditure associated with each $1,000 increase in home value. In later examples, the marketing department at QHIC will use predictions given by this simple linear regression model to help determine which homes should be sent advertising brochures promoting QHIC's products and services.

TABLE **11.4**   The QHIC Upkeep Expenditure Data

(a) The data

Home	Value of Home, x (Thousands of Dollars)	Upkeep Expenditure, y (Dollars)	Home	Value of Home, x (Thousands of Dollars)	Upkeep Expenditure, y (Dollars)
1	237.00	1,412.08	21	153.04	849.14
2	153.08	797.20	22	232.18	1,313.84
3	184.86	872.48	23	125.44	602.06
4	222.06	1,003.42	24	169.82	642.14
5	160.68	852.90	25	177.28	1,038.80
6	99.68	288.48	26	162.82	697.00
7	229.04	1,288.46	27	120.44	324.34
8	101.78	423.08	28	191.10	965.10
9	257.86	1,351.74	29	158.78	920.14
10	96.28	378.04	30	178.50	950.90
11	171.00	918.08	31	272.20	1,670.32
12	231.02	1,627.24	32	48.90	125.40
13	228.32	1,204.76	33	104.56	479.78
14	205.90	857.04	34	286.18	2,010.64
15	185.72	775.00	35	83.72	368.36
16	168.78	869.26	36	86.20	425.60
17	247.06	1,396.00	37	133.58	626.90
18	155.54	711.50	38	212.86	1,316.94
19	224.20	1,475.18	39	122.02	390.16
20	202.04	1,413.32	40	198.02	1,090.84

(b) Excel Plot of upkeep expenditure versus value of home

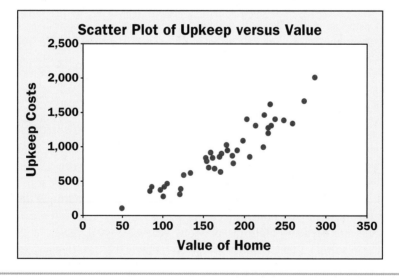

We have interpreted the slope β_1 of the simple linear regression model to be the change in the mean value of y associated with a one-unit increase in x. We sometimes refer to this change as *the effect of the independent variable x on the dependent variable y*. However, we cannot prove that a *change in an independent variable causes a change in the dependent variable*. Rather, regression can be used only to establish that the two variables relate and that the independent variable contributes information for predicting the dependent variable. For instance, regression analysis might be used to establish that as liquor sales have increased over the years, university professors' salaries have also increased. However, this does not prove that increases in liquor sales cause increases in university professors' salaries. Rather, both variables are influenced by a third variable—long-run growth in the economy.

Exercises for Section **11.3**

CONCEPTS

11.9 When does the scatter plot of the values of a dependent variable y versus the values of an independent variable x suggest that the simple linear regression model

$$y = \mu_{y|x} + \varepsilon$$
$$= \beta_0 + \beta_1 x + \varepsilon$$

might appropriately relate y to x?

11.10 In the simple linear regression model, what are y, $\mu_{y|x}$, and ε?

11.11 In the simple linear regression model, define the slope β_1 and the y intercept β_0.

11.12 What is the difference between time series data and cross-sectional data?

METHODS AND APPLICATIONS

11.13 THE SERVICE TIME EXAMPLE

Accu-Copiers sells and services the Accu-500 copying machine. As part of its standard service contract, the company agrees to perform routine service on this copier. To obtain information about the time it takes to perform routine service, Accu-Copiers has collected data for 11 service calls. The data are as shown in Figure 11.4.

Using the Excel scatter plot of y versus x, discuss why the simple linear regression model might appropriately relate y to x.

11.14 THE SERVICE TIME EXAMPLE

Consider the simple linear regression model describing the service time data in Exercise 11.13.
  a. Interpret $\mu_{y|x = 4} = \beta_0 + \beta_1(4)$.
  b. Interpret $\mu_{y|x = 6} = \beta_0 + \beta_1(6)$.
  c. Interpret the slope parameter β_1.
  d. Interpret the y intercept β_0. Does this interpretation make practical sense?
  e. The error term ε describes the effects of many factors on service time. What are these factors? Give two specific examples.

11.15 THE FRESH DETERGENT EXAMPLE

Enterprise Industries produces Fresh, a brand of liquid laundry detergent. To study the relationship between

price and demand for the large bottle of Fresh, the company has gathered data concerning demand for Fresh over the previous 30 sales periods (each sales period is four weeks). Here, for each sales period,

y = Demand for the large bottle of Fresh (in hundreds of thousands of bottles) in the sales period

x = Difference between the average industry price (in dollars) of competitors' similar detergents and the price (in dollars) of Fresh as offered by Enterprise Industries in the sales period

The data is listed below along with an Excel scatter plot of y versus x. Using this information, discuss why the simple linear regression model might appropriately relate y to x.

Fresh Detergent Demand Data

Sales Period	y	x	Sales Period	y	x
1	7.38	−0.05	16	8.87	0.30
2	8.51	0.25	17	9.26	0.50
3	9.52	0.60	18	9.00	0.50
4	7.50	0	19	8.75	0.40
5	9.33	0.25	20	7.95	−0.05
6	8.28	0.20	21	7.65	−0.05
7	8.75	0.15	22	7.27	−0.10
8	7.87	0.05	23	8.00	0.20
9	7.10	−0.15	24	8.50	0.10
10	8.00	0.15	25	8.75	0.50
11	7.89	0.20	26	9.21	0.60
12	8.15	0.10	27	8.27	−0.05
13	9.10	0.40	28	7.67	0
14	8.86	0.45	29	7.93	0.05
15	8.90	0.35	30	9.26	0.55

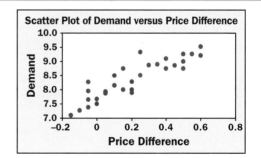

FIGURE 11.4 Routine Copier Service Times for Exercise 11.13

Service Call	Number of Copiers Serviced, x	Number of Minutes Required, y
1	4	109
2	2	58
3	5	138
4	7	189
5	1	37
6	3	82
7	4	103
8	5	134
9	2	68
10	4	112
11	6	154

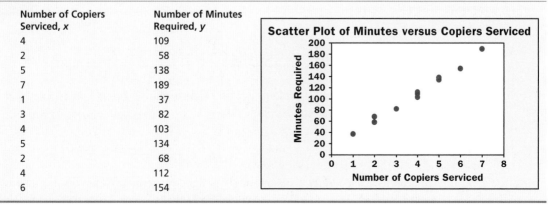

TABLE 11.5   Data for Exercises 11.17 and 11.19

| (a) Direct Labour Cost Data | | (b) Dog Biscuit Sales | |
Direct Labour Cost, y ($100s)	Batch Size, x	Number of Bags Sold, y	Number of Coupons Issued, x
71	5	180	23
663	62	98	11
381	35	173	20
138	12	137	17
861	83	141	15
145	14	166	21
493	46	194	24
548	52	128	13
251	23	164	19
1024	100	173	25
435	41		
772	75		

11.16 THE FRESH DETERGENT EXAMPLE

Consider the simple linear regression model relating demand, y, to the price difference, x, and the Fresh demand data in Exercise 11.15.

a. Interpret $\mu_{y|x = .10} = \beta_0 + \beta_1(.10)$.

b. Interpret $\mu_{y|x = -.05} = \beta_0 + \beta_1(-.05)$.

c. Interpret the slope parameter β_1.

d. Interpret the y intercept β_0. Does this interpretation make practical sense?

e. What factors are represented by the error term in this model? Give two specific examples.

11.17 THE DIRECT LABOUR COST EXAMPLE

An accountant wants to predict direct labour cost (y) on the basis of the batch size (x) of a product produced in a job shop. Data for 12 production runs are given in Table 11.5(a).

a. Construct a scatter plot of y versus x.

b. Discuss whether the scatter plot suggests that a simple linear regression model might appropriately relate y to x.

11.18 THE DIRECT LABOUR COST EXAMPLE

Consider the simple linear regression model describing the direct labour cost data in Exercise 11.17.

a. Interpret $\mu_{y|x = 60} = \beta_0 + \beta_1(60)$.

b. Interpret $\mu_{y|x = 30} = \beta_0 + \beta_1(30)$.

c. Interpret the slope parameter β_1.

d. Interpret the y intercept β_0. Does this interpretation make practical sense?

e. What factors are represented by the error term in this model? Give two specific examples of these factors.

11.19 DOG BISCUIT SALES

A manufacturer of dog biscuits is interested in improving sales by providing "cents-off" coupons to customers. Ten supermarkets are used in the data collection (all of equal sales potential). The number of coupons issued (x) on the store shelf where the dog biscuits are located is varied and monthly sales of the number of bags of dog biscuits sold (y) are compiled. The data are listed in Table 11.5(b).

a. Construct a scatter plot of y versus x.

b. Discuss whether the scatter plot suggests that a simple linear regression model might appropriately relate y to x.

11.20 DOG BISCUIT SALES

Consider the simple linear regression model describing the data in Exercise 11.19.

a. Interpret $\mu_{y|x = 20} = \beta_0 + \beta_1(20)$.

b. Interpret $\mu_{y|x = 18} = \beta_0 + \beta_1(18)$.

c. Interpret the slope parameter β_1.

d. Interpret the y intercept β_0. Does this interpretation make practical sense?

e. What factors are represented by the error term in this model? Give two specific examples.

11.4 MODEL ASSUMPTIONS

Model assumptions To perform hypothesis tests and set up various types of intervals when using the simple linear regression model

$$y = \mu_{y|x} + \varepsilon$$
$$= \beta_0 + \beta_1 x + \varepsilon$$

we need to make certain assumptions about the error term ε. At any given value of x, there is a population of error term values that could potentially occur. These error term values describe the different potential effects on y of all factors other than the value of x. Therefore, these error term values explain the variation in the y values that could be observed when the independent variable is x. Our statement of the simple linear regression model assumes that $\mu_{y|x}$, the mean of the population of all y values that could be observed when the independent variable is x, is $\beta_0 + \beta_1 x$. This model also implies that $\varepsilon = y - (\beta_0 + \beta_1 x)$, so this is equivalent to assuming that the mean of the corresponding population of potential error term values is 0. We make four regression assumptions about the simple linear regression model. These assumptions can be stated in terms of potential y values or, equivalently, in terms of potential error term values. Following tradition, we begin by stating in the following boxed feature these assumptions in terms of potential error term values.

LO5

The Regression Assumptions

1 **Error mean assumption:** At any given value of x, the population of potential error term values has a *mean equal to 0*.

2 **Constant-variance assumption:** At any given value of x, the population of potential error term values has a variance that does not depend on the value of x. That is, the different populations of potential error term values corresponding to different values of x have *equal variances*. We denote the *constant variance as* σ^2.

3 **Normality assumption:** At any given value of x, the population of potential error term values has a *normal distribution*.

4 **Independence assumption:** Any one value of the error term, ε, is *statistically independent* of any other value of ε. That is, the value of the error term ε corresponding to an observed value of y is statistically independent of the value of the error term corresponding to any other observed value of y.

Taken together, the first three assumptions say that at any given value of x, the population of potential error term values is *normally distributed* with *mean zero* and a *variance σ^2 that does not depend on the value of* x. Because the potential error term values cause the variation in the potential y values, these assumptions imply that the population of all y values that could be observed when the independent variable is x is *normally distributed* with *mean $\beta_0 + \beta_1 x$* and *a variance σ^2 that does not depend on* x. These three assumptions are illustrated in Figure 11.5 (based on the data in Table 11.6). Specifically, this figure depicts the populations of y values corresponding to two x values: 32.5 and 45.9. Note that these populations are shown to be normally distributed with different means (each of which is on the line of means) and with the same variance (or spread).

FIGURE **11.5** An Illustration of the Model Assumptions

TABLE **11.6** Data

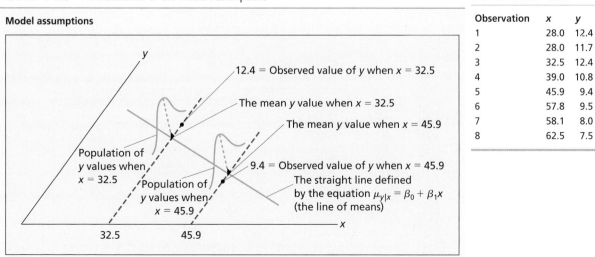

Model assumptions

12.4 = Observed value of y when $x = 32.5$

The mean y value when $x = 32.5$

The mean y value when $x = 45.9$

Population of y values when $x = 32.5$

Population of y values when $x = 45.9$

9.4 = Observed value of y when $x = 45.9$

The straight line defined by the equation $\mu_{y|x} = \beta_0 + \beta_1 x$ (the line of means)

Observation	x	y
1	28.0	12.4
2	28.0	11.7
3	32.5	12.4
4	39.0	10.8
5	45.9	9.4
6	57.8	9.5
7	58.1	8.0
8	62.5	7.5

The independence assumption is most likely to be violated when time series data are being utilized in a regression study. This assumption says that there is no pattern of positive error terms being followed (in time) by other positive error terms, and there is no pattern of positive error terms being followed by negative error terms. That is, there is no pattern of higher than average *y* values being followed by other higher than average *y* values.

It is important to point out that the regression assumptions very seldom, if ever, hold exactly in any practical regression problem. However, it has been found that regression results are not extremely sensitive to mild departures from these assumptions. In practice, only pronounced departures from these assumptions require attention. For the examples in this chapter, we will suppose that the assumptions are valid.

When we predict an individual value of the dependent variable, we predict the error term to be 0. To see why we do this, note that the regression assumptions state that at any given value of the independent variable, the population of all error term values that can potentially occur is normally distributed with a mean equal to 0. Because we also assume that successive error terms are statistically independent, each error term has a 50 percent chance of being positive and a 50 percent chance of being negative. Therefore, it is reasonable to predict any particular error term value to be 0.

11.5 THE LEAST SQUARES ESTIMATES, AND POINT ESTIMATION AND PREDICTION

The true values of the *y* intercept (β_0) and slope (β_1) in the simple linear regression model are unknown. Therefore, it is necessary to use observed data to compute estimates of these regression parameters.

Consider the data and scatter plot of *y* versus *x* in Table 11.6 and Figure 11.6. The figure suggests that the simple linear regression model appropriately relates *y* to *x*. We now want to use the data in Table 11.6 to estimate the intercept β_0 and the slope β_1 of the line of means. To do this, it might be reasonable to estimate the line of means by "fitting" the "best" straight line to the plotted data in Figure 11.6. But how do we fit the best straight line? One approach would be to simply "eyeball" a line through the points. Then we could read the *y* intercept and slope off the visually fitted line and use these values as the estimates of β_0 and β_1. For example, Figure 11.7 shows a line that has been visually fitted to the plot of the data. We see that this line intersects the *y* axis at *y* = 15. Therefore, the *y* intercept of the line is 15. In addition, the figure shows that the slope of the line is

$$\frac{\text{Change in } y}{\text{Change in } x} = \frac{12.8 - 13.8}{20 - 10} = \frac{-1}{10} = -.1$$

Therefore, based on the visually fitted line, we estimate that β_0 is 15 and β_1 is $-.1$.

FIGURE 11.6   Excel Output of a Scatter Plot of *y* versus *x*

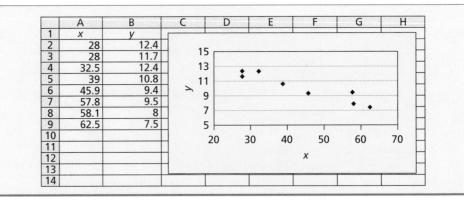

FIGURE **11.7** Visually Fitting a Line

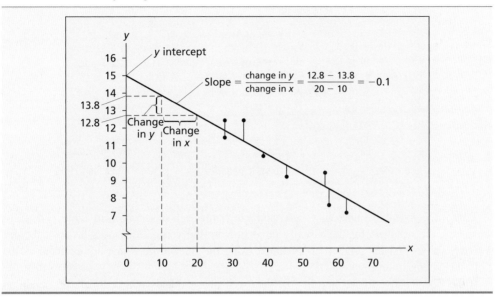

To evaluate how "good" our point estimates of β_0 and β_1 are, consider using the visually fitted line to predict y. Denoting such a prediction as $\hat{y}$, a reasonable prediction of y when x is a certain value is simply the point on the visually fitted line corresponding to x. For instance, when x is 28,

$$\hat{y} = 15 - .1x = 15 - .1(28) = 12.2$$

as shown in Figure 11.8. We can evaluate how well the visually determined line fits the points on the scatter plot by comparing each observed value of y to the corresponding predicted value of y given by the fitted line. We do this by computing the **residual**, $y - \hat{y}$. For instance, looking at the first observation in Table 11.6, we observe $y = 12.4$ and $x = 28.0$. Since the predicted y value when x equals 28 is $\hat{y} = 12.2$, the residual $y - \hat{y}$ equals $12.4 - 12.2 = .2$.

FIGURE **11.8** Using the Visually Fitted Line to Predict y When $x = 28$

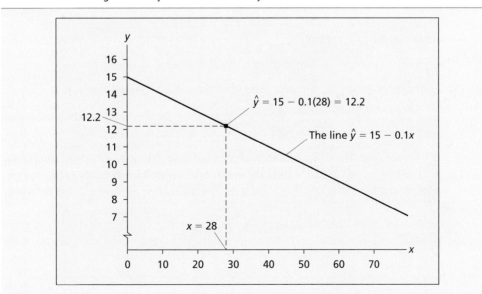

TABLE 11.7   Calculation of the *SSE* for a Line Visually Fitted to the Sample Data

y	x	$\hat{y} = 15 - 0.1x$	$y - \hat{y}$
12.4	28.0	$15 - 0.1(28.0) = 12.2$	$12.4 - 12.2 = 0.2$
11.7	28.0	$15 - 0.1(28.0) = 12.2$	$11.7 - 12.2 = -0.5$
12.4	32.5	$15 - 0.1(32.5) = 11.75$	$12.4 - 11.75 = 0.65$
10.8	39.0	$15 - 0.1(39.0) = 11.1$	$10.8 - 11.1 = -0.3$
9.4	45.9	$15 - 0.1(45.9) = 10.41$	$9.4 - 10.41 = -1.01$
9.5	57.8	$15 - 0.1(57.8) = 9.22$	$9.5 - 9.22 = 0.28$
8.0	58.1	$15 - 0.1(58.1) = 9.19$	$8.0 - 9.19 = -1.19$
7.5	62.5	$15 - 0.1(62.5) = 8.75$	$7.5 - 8.75 = -1.25$

$$SSE = \sum (y - \hat{y})^2 = (0.2)^2 + (-0.5)^2 + (0.65)^2 + \cdots + (-1.25)^2 = 4.8796$$

Table 11.7 gives the values of y, x, $\hat{y}$, and $y - \hat{y}$ for each observation in Table 11.6. Geometrically, the residuals for the visually fitted line are the vertical distances between the observed y values and the predictions obtained using the fitted line, which are depicted as the eight line segments in Figure 11.7.

If the visually determined line fits the data well, the residuals will be small. To obtain an overall measure of the quality of the fit, we compute the sum of squared residuals or sum of squared errors, denoted *SSE*. This quantity is obtained by squaring each of the residuals (so that all values are positive) and adding the results. Table 11.7 demonstrates this calculation and shows that $SSE = 4.8796$ when we use the visually fitted line to calculate predictions. Note: Computing the *SSE* is very similar to computing variance.

Clearly, the line shown in Figure 11.7 is not the only line that could be fitted to the observed data. Different people would obtain somewhat different visually fitted lines. However, it can be shown that there is exactly one line that gives the smallest possible *SSE*, the least squares regression line, and its equation is the least squares prediction equation.

To show how to find the least squares line, we first write the general form of a straight-line prediction equation. Letting $\hat{y}$ denote the predicted value of y when the value of the independent variable is x, we write this equation as

$$\hat{y} = b_0 + b_1 x$$

LO6

Here b_0 is *the y intercept* and b_1 is *the slope* of the line. Now suppose we have collected n observations (x_1, y_1), (x_2, y_2), . . . , (x_n, y_n), and consider a particular observation (x_i, y_i). The predicted value of y_i is

$$\hat{y}_i = b_0 + b_1 x_i$$

and the residual for this observation is

$$e_i = y_i - \hat{y}_i = y_i - (b_0 + b_1 x_i)$$

Then the least squares line is the line that *minimizes the sum of squared residuals*

$$SSE = \sum_{i=1}^{n} (y_i + (b_0 + b_1 x_i))^2$$

To find this line, we find the values of the y intercept b_0 and the slope b_1 that minimize the *SSE*. These values of b_0 and b_1 are called the **least squares point estimates** of β_0 and β_1. Using calculus, it can be shown that these estimates are calculated as shown in the following feature box.[2]

Using the data in Table 11.6, we illustrate in the next section how to calculate these point estimates and how to use them to estimate mean values and predict individual values of the

---

[2]In order to simplify notation, we will often drop the limits on summations. That is, instead of using the summation $\sum_{i=1}^{n}$, we will simply write $\sum$.

The Least Squares Point Estimates

For the simple linear regression model:

1   The least squares point estimate of the slope β_1 is $b_1 = \dfrac{SS_{xy}}{SS_{xx}}$, where

$$SS_{xy} = \sum (x_i - \bar{x})(y_i - \bar{y}) = \sum x_i y_i - \frac{\left(\sum x_i\right)\left(\sum y_i\right)}{n}$$

and

$$SS_{xx} = \sum (x_i - \bar{x})^2 = \sum x_i^2 - \frac{\left(\sum x_i\right)^2}{n}$$

2   The least squares point estimate of the y intercept β_0 is $b_0 = \bar{y} - b_1\bar{x}$, where

$$\bar{y} = \frac{\sum y_i}{n} \quad \text{and} \quad \bar{x} = \frac{\sum x_i}{n}$$

Here n is the number of observations (an observation is an observed value of x and its corresponding value of y).

dependent variable. Note that the quantities SS_{xy} and SS_{xx} used to calculate the least squares point estimates are also used throughout this chapter to perform other important calculations.

Part 1: Calculating the least squares point estimates To compute the least squares point estimates of the regression parameters β_0 and β_1, we first calculate the following preliminary summations, as shown in the following table.

y_i	x_i	x_i^2	$x_i y_i$
12.4	28.0	$(28.0)^2 = 784$	$(28.0)(12.4) = 347.2$
11.7	28.0	$(28.0)^2 = 784$	$(28.0)(11.7) = 327.6$
12.4	32.5	$(32.5)^2 = 1,056.25$	$(32.5)(12.4) = 403$
10.8	39.0	$(39.0)^2 = 1,521$	$(39.0)(10.8) = 421.2$
9.4	45.9	$(45.9)^2 = 2,106.81$	$(45.9)(9.4) = 431.46$
9.5	57.8	$(57.8)^2 = 3,340.84$	$(57.8)(9.5) = 549.1$
8.0	58.1	$(58.1)^2 = 3,375.61$	$(58.1)(8.0) = 464.8$
7.5	62.5	$(62.5)^2 = 3,906.25$	$(62.5)(7.5) = 468.75$
$\sum y_i = 81.7$	$\sum x_i = 351.8$	$\sum x_i^2 = 16,874.76$	$\sum x_i y_i = 3,413.11$

Using these summations, we calculate SS_{xy} and SS_{xx} as follows:

$$SS_{xy} = \sum x_i y_i - \frac{\left(\sum x_i\right)\left(\sum y_i\right)}{n}$$

$$= 3,413.11 - \frac{(351.8)(81.7)}{8} = -179.6475$$

$$SS_{xx} = \sum x_i^2 - \frac{\left(\sum x_i\right)^2}{n}$$

$$= 16,874.76 - \frac{(351.8)^2}{8} = 1,404.355$$

It follows that the least squares point estimate of the slope β_1 is

$$b_1 = \frac{SS_{xy}}{SS_{xx}} = \frac{-179.6475}{1,404.355} = -.1279$$

Furthermore, because

$$\bar{y} = \frac{\sum y_i}{8} = \frac{81.7}{8} = 10.2125 \quad \text{and} \quad \bar{x} = \frac{\sum x_i}{8} = \frac{351.8}{8} = 43.975$$

the least squares point estimate of the y intercept β_0 is

$$b_0 = \bar{y} - b_1\bar{x} = 10.2125 - (-.1279)(43.975) = 15.84$$

TABLE 11.8   Calculation of the *SSE* Obtained by Using the Least Squares Point Estimates

y_i	x_i	$\hat{y} = 15.84 - 0.1279x_i$	$y_i - \hat{y}$ = residual
12.4	28.0	$15.84 - 0.1279(28.0) = 12.2588$	$12.4 - 12.2588 = .1412$
11.7	28.0	$15.84 - 0.1279(28.0) = 12.2588$	$11.7 - 12.2588 = -.5588$
12.4	32.5	$15.84 - 0.1279(32.5) = 11.68325$	$12.4 - 11.68325 = .71675$
10.8	39.0	$15.84 - 0.1279(39.0) = 10.8519$	$10.8 - 10.8519 = -.0519$
9.4	45.9	$15.84 - 0.1279(45.9) = 9.96939$	$9.4 - 9.96939 = -.56939$
9.5	57.8	$15.84 - 0.1279(57.8) = 8.44738$	$9.5 - 8.44738 = 1.05262$
8.0	58.1	$15.84 - 0.1279(58.1) = 8.40901$	$8.0 - 8.40901 = -.40901$
7.5	62.5	$15.84 - 0.1279(62.5) = 7.84625$	$7.5 - 7.84625 = -.34625$

$$SSE = \sum (y_i - \hat{y}_i)^2 = 0.1412^2 + (-0.5588)^2 + \cdots + (-0.346\,25)^2 = 2.568$$

Because $b_1 = -.1279$, we estimate that y decreases (b_1 is negative) by .1279 when x increases by 1. Because $b_0 = 15.84$, we estimate that y is 15.84 when x is 0.

Table 11.8 gives predictions of y for each observation obtained by using the least squares line (or prediction equation)

$$\hat{y} = b_0 + b_1x = 15.84 - .1279x$$

The table also gives each of the residuals and the sum of squared residuals ($SSE = 2.568$) obtained by using this prediction equation. Notice that the SSE here, which was obtained using the least squares point estimates, is smaller than the SSE of Table 11.7, which was obtained using the visually fitted line $\hat{y} = 15 - .1x$. In general, the SSE obtained by using the least squares point estimates is smaller than the value of the SSE that would be obtained by using any other estimates of β_0 and β_1. Figure 11.9 illustrates the eight observed y values (the dots in the figure) and the eight predicted y values (the squares in the figure) given by the least squares line. The distances between the observed and predicted values are the residuals. Therefore, when we say that the least squares point estimates minimize the SSE, we are saying that these estimates position the least squares line so as to minimize the sum of the squared distances between the observed and predicted y values. In this sense, the least squares line is

FIGURE 11.9   The Least Squares Line for the Sample Data

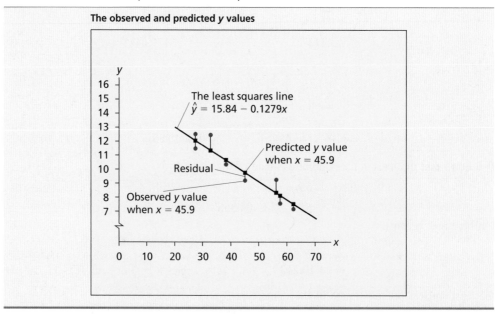

the best straight line that can be fitted to the eight observed y values. In general, we will rely on Excel and MegaStat to compute the least squares estimates (and to perform many other regression calculations).

Part 2: Estimating a mean y value and predicting an individual y value We define the **experimental region** to be the range of the observed values of x. For the data in Table 11.6, the experimental region consists of the range of x values from 28 to 62.5. The simple linear regression model relates y to x for values of x that are in the experimental region. For such values of x, the least squares line is the estimate of the line of means.

We now consider finding a point estimate of

$$\mu_{y|x} = \beta_0 + \beta_1 x$$

which is the mean of all of the y values that could be observed for x. Because the least squares line is the estimate of the line of means, the point estimate of $\mu_{y|x}$ is the point on the least squares line that corresponds to the average x value:

$$\hat{y} = b_0 + b_1 x$$
$$= 15.84 - .1279x$$

This point estimate is intuitively logical because it is obtained by replacing the unknown parameters β_0 and β_1 in the expression for $\mu_{y|x}$ by their least squares estimates b_0 and b_1.

The quantity $\hat{y}$ is also the point prediction of the individual value

$$y = \beta_0 + \beta_1 x + \varepsilon$$

which is the y value corresponding to the average value of x. To understand why $\hat{y}$ is the point prediction of y, note that y is the sum of the mean $\beta_0 + \beta_1 x$ and the error term ε. We have already seen that $\hat{y} = b_0 + b_1 x$ is the point estimate of $\beta_0 + \beta_1 x$, and we will now explain why *we should use a value of 0 for the error term ε*. Recall that we are using the average value of all of the instances of y for a given value of x to estimate a single value of $\hat{y}$, so, logically, it makes sense to use the average value of all of the errors to estimate a single error. This allows us to use the average value of the errors, or 0, in place of the error term when using $\hat{y}$ as the point estimate of a single value of y.

Now suppose a forecasted average x value is 40. Because 40 is in the experimental region,

$$\hat{y} = 15.84 - .1279(40)$$
$$= 10.72$$

and $\hat{y}$ is (1) the point estimate of y when the average x value is 40 and (2) the point prediction of an individual y value when the average x value is 40. This says that (1) we estimate that the average of all y values that could be observed when x is 40 equals 10.72, and (2) we predict that y in a single observation when $x = 40$ will be 10.72. Note that Figure 11.10 illustrates $\hat{y} = 10.72$ as a square on the least squares line.

To conclude, Figure 11.11 illustrates the potential danger of using the least squares line to predict outside the experimental region. In the figure, we extrapolate the least squares line beyond the experimental region to obtain a prediction for $x = -10$. As shown in Figure 11.6, for values of x in the experimental region, the observed values of y tend to decrease in a straight-line fashion as the values of x increase. However, for x values lower than 28, the relationship between y and x might become curved. If it does, extrapolating the straight-line prediction equation to obtain a prediction for $x = -10$ might badly underestimate y (see Figure 11.11).

The previous situation illustrates that when we are using a least squares regression line, we should not estimate a mean value or predict an individual value unless the corresponding value of x is in the experimental region—the range of the observed values of x. If the value $x = 0$ is not in the experimental region, then it would not be appropriate to interpret the y intercept b_0 as the estimate of the mean value of y when x equals 0. For example, Figure 11.11 illustrates

FIGURE **11.10**   Point Estimation and Point Prediction

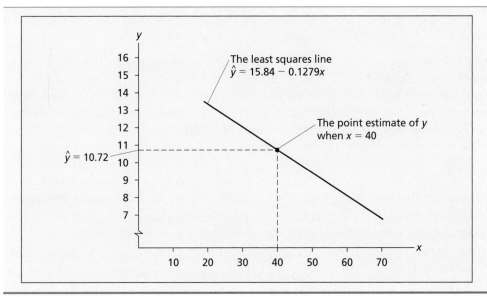

FIGURE **11.11**   The Danger of Extrapolation Outside the Experimental Region

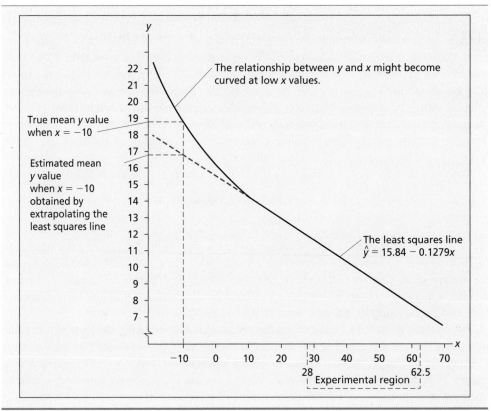

that $x = 0$ is not in the experimental region. Therefore, it would not be appropriate to use $b_0 = 15.84$ as the point estimate of y when $x = 0$. Because it is not meaningful to interpret the y intercept in many regression situations, we often omit such interpretations.

A general procedure for estimating a mean value and predicting an individual value is provided in the following boxed feature.

Point Estimation and Point Prediction in Simple Linear Regression

Let b_0 and b_1 be the least squares point estimates of the y intercept β_0 and the slope β_1 in the simple linear regression model, and suppose that x_0, a specified value of the independent variable x, is inside the experimental region. Then

$$\hat{y} = b_0 + b_1x_0$$

1 is the point estimate of the mean value of the dependent variable when the value of the independent variable is x_0.

2 is the point prediction of an individual value of the dependent variable when the value of the independent variable is x_0. Here we predict the error term to be 0.

Example 11.2 The QHIC Example

Consider the simple linear regression model relating yearly home-upkeep expenditure, y, to home value, x. Using the data in Table 11.4, we can calculate the least squares point estimates of the y intercept β_0 and the slope β_1 to be $b_0 = -348.3921$ and $b_1 = 7.2583$. Because $b_1 = 7.2583$, we estimate that mean yearly upkeep expenditure increases by \$7.26 for each additional \$1,000 increase in home value. Consider a home worth \$220,000 and note that $x_0 = 220$ is in the range of observed values of x: 48.9 to 286.18 (see Table 11.4). It follows that

$$\begin{aligned}
\hat{y} &= b_0 + b_1x_0 \\
&= -348.3921 + 7.2583(220) \\
&= 1248.43 \ (\text{or } \$1,248.43)
\end{aligned}$$

is the point estimate of the mean yearly upkeep expenditure for all homes worth \$220,000 and the point prediction of a yearly upkeep expenditure for an individual home worth \$220,000.

The marketing department at QHIC wants to determine which homes should be sent advertising brochures promoting QHIC's products and services. The prediction equation $\hat{y} = b_0 + b_1x$ implies that the home value x corresponding to a predicted upkeep expenditure of $\hat{y}$ is

$$x = \frac{\hat{y} - b_0}{b_1} = \frac{\hat{y} - (-348.3921)}{7.2583} = \frac{\hat{y} + 348.3921}{7.2583}$$

For instance, if we set predicted upkeep expenditure $\hat{y}$ equal to \$500, we have

$$x = \frac{\hat{y} + 348.3921}{7.2583} = \frac{500 + 348.3921}{7.2583} = 116.886 \ (\$116,886)$$

Therefore, if QHIC wants to send an advertising brochure to any home with a predicted upkeep expenditure of at least \$500, QHIC should send this brochure to any home with a value of at least \$116,886.

The mean square error and the standard error To present statistical inference formulas in later sections, we need to be able to compute point estimates of the variance (σ^2) and standard deviation (σ) of the error term populations. The point estimate of σ^2 is the mean square error and the point estimate of σ is the standard error. In the following boxed feature we show how to compute these estimates.

The Mean Square Error and the Standard Error

If the regression assumptions are satisfied and the SSE is the sum of squared residuals:

1 The point estimate of σ^2 is the mean square error

$$s^2 = \frac{SSE}{n-2}$$

2 The point estimate of σ is the standard error

$$s = \sqrt{\frac{SSE}{n-2}}$$

To understand these point estimates, recall that σ^2 is the variance of the population of y values (for a given value of x) around the mean value $\mu_{y|x}$. Because $\hat{y}$ is the point estimate of this mean, we use

$$SSE = \sum (y_i - \hat{y}_i)^2$$

to help construct a point estimate of σ^2. We divide the SSE by $n - 2$ because doing so makes the resulting s^2 an unbiased point estimate of σ^2. Here we call $n - 2$ the number of degrees of freedom associated with the SSE.

Consider the data from Table 11.6. The calculated sum of squared residuals for these data is $SSE = 2.568$. It follows, because we have $n = 8$ observations, that the point estimate of σ^2 is the mean square error

$$s^2 = \frac{SSE}{n - 2} = \frac{2.568}{8 - 2} = .428$$

and the point estimate of σ is the standard error

$$s = \sqrt{s^2} = \sqrt{.428} = .6542$$

As another example, the standard error for the simple linear regression model describing the QHIC data is $s = 146.8970$. To conclude this section, note that in Section 11.11 we present a shortcut formula for calculating the SSE.

Exercises for Sections **11.4** and **11.5**

CONCEPTS

11.21 What four assumptions are made about the simple linear regression model?

11.22 What is estimated by the mean square error, and what is estimated by the standard error?

11.23 What does the SSE measure?

11.24 What is the least squares regression line, and what are the least squares point estimates?

11.25 How can you obtain a point estimate of the mean value of the dependent variable and a point prediction of an individual value of the dependent variable?

11.26 Why is it dangerous to extrapolate outside the experimental region?

METHODS AND APPLICATIONS

11.27 THE SERVICE TIME EXAMPLE

When a least squares line is fit to the 11 observations in the service time data, we obtain $SSE = 191.7017$. Calculate s^2 and s.

11.28 THE FRESH DETERGENT EXAMPLE

When a least squares line is fit to the 30 observations in the Fresh detergent data, we obtain $SSE = 2.806$. Calculate s^2 and s.

11.29 THE DIRECT LABOUR COST EXAMPLE

When a least squares line is fit to the 12 observations in the labour cost data, we obtain $SSE = 746.7624$. Calculate s^2 and s.

11.30 DOG BISCUIT SALES

When a least squares line is fit to the 10 observations in the biscuit sales data, we obtain $SSE = 888.96$. Calculate s^2 and s.

11.31 Ten sales regions of equal sales potential for a company were randomly selected. The advertising expenditures (in units of $10,000) in these ten sales regions were purposely set during July of last year at, respectively, 5, 6, 7, 8, 9, 10, 11, 12, 13, and 14. The sales volumes (in units of $10,000) were then recorded for the ten sales regions and found to be, respectively, 89, 87, 98, 110, 103, 114, 116, 110, 126, and 130. Assuming that the simple linear regression model is appropriate, it can be shown that $b_0 = 66.2121$, $b_1 = 4.4303$, and $SSE = 222.8242$. Calculate s^2 and s.

FIGURE 11.12   Flight Simulator Test Results for Exercise 11.32

(a) Flight simulator test results

Age	Errors	Age	Errors
19	7	20	8
19	8	23	5
21	6	19	3
24	5	26	2
20	6	19	7
19	7	19	8
19	8	18	7
19	6	19	6
22	3	20	9
19	9	22	9
19	9	18	8
19	8	21	9
19	6	19	6
19	4		

(b) Scatter plot of flight simulator test results

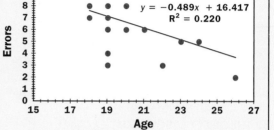

(c) MegaStat regression analysis of flight simulator test results

Regression Analysis

r^2 0.220   n 27
r −0.469   k 1
Std. Error 1.786   Dep. Var. Errors

ANOVA table

Source	SS	df	MS	F	p-value
Regression	22.5106	1	22.5106	7.05	0.0136
Residual	79.7857	25	3.1914		
Total	102.2963	26			

Regression output   **confidence interval**

variables	coefficients	std. error	t (df=25)	p-value	95% lower	95% upper	std. coeff.
Intercept	16.4169	3.7012	4.436	0.0002	8.7941	24.0396	0.000
Age	−0.4894	0.1843	−2.656	0.0136	−0.8688	−0.1099	−0.469

11.32 A Canadian youth training program tested 27 undergraduate students to examine the relationship between age and errors made on a flight simulator test. The average age of the participants was 20 years and the ages ranged from 18 to 26 years. The number of errors made was found for each individual. The data are presented in Figure 11.12(a). In Figure 11.12(b) and (c) are the scatter plot of the resulting data and the regression results from MegaStat. From the results given

a. Explain the relationship between age and errors.
b. Compute s^2 and s.
c. Find the values of b_0 and b_1.

11.33 THE SERVICE TIME EXAMPLE

The following output is obtained when Excel is used to fit a least squares line to the service time data given in Exercise 11.13.

a. Find the least squares point estimates b_0 and b_1 on the computer output and report their values. Interpret b_0 and b_1. Does the interpretation of b_0 make practical sense?

b. Use the least squares line to compute a point estimate of the mean time to service four copiers and a point prediction of the time to service four copiers during a single call.

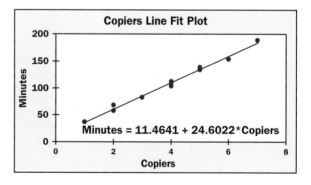

11.34 THE FRESH DETERGENT EXAMPLE

For the Fresh detergent demand data given in Exercise 11.15, the regression equation is found to be

$$\text{Demand} = 7.814 + 2.665(\text{PriceDif})$$

a. Use the least squares line to compute a point estimate of the mean demand in all sales periods when the price difference is .10 and a point prediction of the actual demand in an individual sales period when the price difference is .10.

b. If Enterprise Industries wants to maintain a price difference that corresponds to a predicted demand of 850,000 bottles (that is, $\hat{y} = 8.5$), what should this price difference be?

11.35 THE DIRECT LABOUR COST EXAMPLE

The following output is obtained when Excel is used to fit a least squares line to the direct labour cost data given in Exercise 11.17.

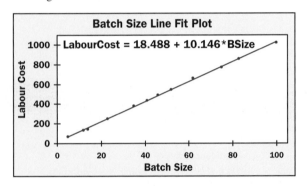

Batch Size Line Fit Plot

LabourCost = 18.488 + 10.146*BSize

a. By using the formulas illustrated in this section and the data of Exercise 11.17, verify that $b_0 = 18.488$ and $b_1 = 10.146$, as shown on the Excel output.

b. Interpret b_0 and b_1. Does the interpretation of b_0 make practical sense?

c. Write the least squares prediction equation using x and y notation.

d. Use the least squares line to obtain a point estimate of the mean direct labour cost for all batches of size 60 and a point prediction of the direct labour cost for an individual batch of size 60.

11.36 DOG BISCUIT SALES

The least squares line for the coupons issued versus dog biscuit sales data from Exercise 11.19 was found to be

$$\text{Sales} = 47.8 + 5.72(\text{Coupons})$$

a. By using the data in Exercise 11.19, verify that $b_0 = 47.8$ and $b_1 = 5.72$.

b. Interpret b_0 and b_1. Does the interpretation of b_0 make practical sense?

c. Write the least squares prediction equation using x and y notation.

d. Use the least squares line to obtain a point estimate of the monthly sales when 20 coupons are issued.

11.6 TESTING THE SIGNIFICANCE OF THE SLOPE AND y INTERCEPT

Testing the significance of the slope A simple linear regression model is not likely to be useful unless there is a *significant relationship between y and x*. In order to judge the significance of the relationship between y and x, we test the null hypothesis

$$H_0: \beta_1 = 0$$

which states that there is no change in the mean value of y associated with a change in x, versus the alternative hypothesis

$$H_a: \beta_1 \neq 0$$

which states that there is a (positive or negative) change in the mean value of y associated with a change in x. It would be reasonable to conclude that x is significantly related to y if we can be quite certain that we should reject H_0 in favour of H_a.

To test these hypotheses, recall that we compute the least squares point estimate b_1 of the true slope β_1 by using a sample of n observed values of the dependent variable y. Different samples of n observed y values would yield different values of the least squares point estimate b_1.

It can be shown that if the regression assumptions hold, the population of all possible values of b_1 is normally distributed with a mean of β_1 and a standard deviation of

$$\sigma_{b_1} = \frac{\sigma}{\sqrt{SS_{xx}}}$$

The standard error s is the point estimate of σ, so it follows that a point estimate of σ_{b_1} is

$$s_{b_1} = \frac{s}{\sqrt{SS_{xx}}}$$

which is the standard error of the estimate b_1. Furthermore, if the regression assumptions hold, then the population of all values of

$$\frac{b_1 - \beta_1}{s_{b_1}}$$

has a t distribution with $n - 2$ degrees of freedom. It follows that if the null hypothesis $H_0: \beta_1 = 0$ is true, the population of all possible values of the test statistic

$$t = \frac{b_1}{s_{b_1}}$$

has a t distribution with $n - 2$ degrees of freedom. Therefore, we can test the significance of the regression relationship as shown in the following boxed feature.

Testing the Significance of the Regression Relationship: Testing the Significance of the Slope

Define the test statistic

$$t = \frac{b_1}{s_{b_1}} \quad \text{where} \quad s_{b_1} = \frac{s}{\sqrt{SS_{xx}}}$$

and suppose that the regression assumptions hold. Then we can test $H_0: \beta_1 = 0$ versus a particular alter- native hypothesis at significance level α (setting the probability of a Type I error equal to α) by using the appropriate rejection point rule or, equivalently, the corresponding p-value.

Alternative Hypothesis	Rejection Point Condition: Reject H_0 if	p-Value (Reject H_0 if p-Value $< \alpha$)
$H_a: \beta_1 \neq 0$	$\lvert t \rvert > t_{\alpha/2}$	Twice the area under the t curve to the right of $\lvert t \rvert$
$H_a: \beta_1 > 0$	$t > t_{\alpha}$	The area under the t curve to the right of t
$H_a: \beta_1 < 0$	$t < -t_{\alpha}$	The area under the t curve to the left of t

Here, $t_{\alpha/2}$, t_{α}, and all p-values are based on $n - 2$ degrees of freedom. *If we can reject $H_0: \beta_1 = 0$ at a given value of α, then we conclude that the slope* (or, equivalently, the regression relationship) is sig- nificant at the α level.

Typically we use the two-sided alternative $H_a: \beta_1 \neq 0$ for this test of significance, although sometimes a one-sided alternative is appropriate if we have an *a priori* hypothesis (for example, if the test is to assess whether the slope β_1 is negative, resulting in the one-sided alternative $H_a: \beta_1 < 0$). Most computer applications (such as Excel) present results for testing a two-sided alternative hypothesis. For these reasons, we will emphasize the two-sided test.

Alpha and regression significance

If we can decide that the slope is significant at a certain value of α, then we have concluded that x is significantly related to y by using a test that allows a α-value probability (.05, .01, etc.) of concluding that x is significantly related to y when it is not. The smaller the signifi- cance level α at which H_0 can be rejected, the stronger is the evidence that the regression relationship is significant.

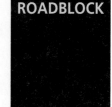
ROADBLOCK

In addition to testing the significance of the slope, it is often useful to calculate a confidence interval for β_1. We show how this is done in the following boxed feature.

A Confidence Interval for the Slope

If the regression assumptions hold, a $100(1 - \alpha)$ percent confidence interval for the true slope β_1 is

$[b_1 \pm t_{\alpha/2}s_{b_1}]$. Here $t_{\alpha/2}$ is based on $n - 2$ degrees of freedom.

Example 11.3   The QHIC Example

Figure 11.13 presents the MegaStat output of a simple linear regression analysis of the QHIC data. We summarize some important quantities from the output as follows: $b_0 = -348.3921$ [1], $b_1 = 7.2583$ [2], $s = 146.897$ [8], $s_{b_1} = .4156$ [4], and $t = b_1/s_{b_1} = 17.466$ [6]. Because the p-value related to $t = 17.466$ is less than .001 (see the MegaStat output), we can reject $H_0: \beta_1 = 0$ in favour of $H_a: \beta_1 \neq 0$ at the .001 level of significance. It follows that we have extremely strong evidence that the regression relationship is significant. The MegaStat output also tells us that a 95 percent confidence interval for the true slope β is [6.4170, 8.0995]. This interval says we are 95 percent confident that mean yearly upkeep expenditure increases by between \$6.42 and \$8.10 for each additional \$1,000 increase in home value.

FIGURE **11.13**   MegaStat Output of a Simple Linear Regression Analysis of the QHIC Data

Regression Analysis		r^2 0.889 [9]			n 40		
		r 0.943			k 1		
		Std. Error 146.897 [8]			Dep. Var. Upkeep		

ANOVA table

Source	SS	df	MS	F [13]	p-value [14]
Regression	6,582,759.6972 [10]	1	6,582,759.6972	305.06	9.49E-20
Residual	819,995.5427 [11]	38	21,578.8301		
Total	7,402,755.2399 [12]	39			

Regression output

variables	coefficients	std. error	t (df=38)	p-value [7]	confidence interval 95% lower	95% upper
Intercept	−348.3921 [1]	76.1410 [3]	−4.576 [5]	4.95E-05	−502.5314	−194.2527
Value	7.2583 [2]	0.4156 [4]	17.466 [6]	9.49E-20	6.4170 [19]	8.0995 [19]

Predicted values for: Upkeep

Value	Predicted [15]	95% Confidence Interval [16] lower	upper	95% Prediction Interval [17] lower	upper	Leverage [18]
220	1,248.42597	1,187.78944	1,309.06251	944.92879	1,551.92315	0.042

[1] b_0 = point estimate of the y intercept   [2] b_1 = point estimate of the slope   [3] s_{b_0} = standard error of the estimate b_0 [4] s_{b_1} = standard error of the estimate b_1 [5] t for testing significance of the y intercept   [6] t for testing significance of the slope   [7] p values for t statistics   [8] s = standard error   [9] r^2 (eta²)   [10] Explained variation   [11] SSE = unexplained variation   [12] Total variation   [13] F(model) statistic   [14] p value for F(model)   [15] $\hat{y}$ = point prediction when $x = 220$ [16] 95% confidence interval when $x = 220$ [17] 95% prediction interval when $x = 220$ [18] Distance value   [19] 95% confidence interval for the slope β_1

Testing the significance of the y intercept We can also test the significance of the y intercept β_0. We do this by testing the null hypothesis $H_0: \beta_0 = 0$ versus the alternative hypothesis $H_a: \beta_0 \neq 0$. To carry out the hypothesis test, we use the test statistic

$$t = \frac{b_0}{s_{b_0}} \quad \text{where} \quad s_{b_0} = s\sqrt{\frac{1}{n} + \frac{\bar{x}^2}{SS_{xx}}}$$

Here the rejection point and p-value conditions for rejecting H_0 are the same as those given previously for testing the significance of the slope, except that t is calculated as b_0/s_{b_0}. For example, in Figure 11.13, $b_0 = -348.3921$ [1], $s_{b_0} = 76.1410$ [3], $t = -4.576$ [5], and p-value = .000.

Because $t = |{-4.576}| > t_{.025} = 2.447$ and *p*-value $< .05$, we can reject $H_0: \beta_0 = 0$ in favour of $H_a: \beta_0 \neq 0$ at the .05 level of significance. In fact, because *p*-value $< .001$, we can also reject H_0 at the .001 level of significance. This provides extremely strong evidence that the *y* intercept β_0 does not equal 0 and thus is significant.

In general, if we fail to conclude that the intercept is significant at a level of significance of .05, it might be reasonable to drop the *y* intercept from the model. However, remember that β_0 equals the mean value of *y* when *x* equals 0. If, logically speaking, the mean value of *y* would not equal 0 when *x* equals 0, then it is common practice to include the *y* intercept whether or not $H_0: \beta_0 = 0$ is rejected.

Exercises for Section **11.6**

CONCEPTS

11.37 What can you conclude if you can reject $H_0: \beta_1 = 0$ in favour of $H_a: \beta_1 \neq 0$ by setting
  a. α equal to .05?
  b. α equal to .01?

11.38 Give an example of a practical application of the confidence interval for β_1.

METHODS AND APPLICATIONS

In Exercises 11.39 through 11.42, we refer to MegaStat and Excel output of simple linear regression analyses of the data sets related to four examples introduced in the exercises for Section 11.3. Using the appropriate output for each example:
  a. Find the least squares point estimates b_0 and b_1 of β_0 and β_1 on the output and report their values.
  b. Find the *SSE* on the output and report its value.
  c. Find s_{b_1} and the *t* statistic for testing the significance of the slope on the output and report their values. Show how *t* was calculated by using b_1 and s_{b_1} from the output.
  d. Using the *t* statistic and an appropriate rejection point, test $H_0: \beta_1 = 0$ versus $H_a: \beta_1 \neq 0$ by setting α equal

to .05. Is the slope (regression relationship) significant at the .05 level?
  e. Using the *t* statistic and an appropriate rejection point, test $H_0: \beta_1 = 0$ versus $H_a: \beta_1 \neq 0$ by setting α equal to .01. Is the slope (regression relationship) significant at the .01 level?
  f. Find the *p*-value for testing $H_0: \beta_1 = 0$ versus $H_a: \beta_1 \neq 0$ on the output and report its value. Using the *p*-value, determine whether we can reject H_0 by setting α equal to .10, .05, .01, and .001. How much evidence is there that the slope (regression relationship) is significant?
  g. Calculate the 95 percent confidence interval for β_1 using numbers on the output. Interpret the interval.
  h. Find s_{b_0} and the *t* statistic for testing the significance of the *y* intercept on the output and report their values. Show how *t* was calculated by using b_0 and s_{b_0} from the output.
  i. Find the *p*-value for testing $H_0: \beta_0 = 0$ versus $H_a: \beta_1 \neq 0$. Using the *p*-value, determine whether you can reject H_0 by setting α equal to .10, .05, .01, and .001. What do you conclude?

11.39 THE SERVICE TIME EXAMPLE

The MegaStat output of a simple linear regression analysis of the data set for this example is given in Figure 11.14.

FIGURE 11.14 MegaStat Output of a Simple Linear Regression Analysis of the Service Time Data

Regression Analysis	r^2 0.990		n 11			
	r 0.995		k 1			
	Std. Error 4.615		Dep. Var. Minutes (y)			

ANOVA table

Source	SS	df	MS	F	p-value	
Regression	19,918.8438	1	19,918.8438	935.15	2.09E-10	
Residual	191.7017	9	21.3002			
Total	20,110.5455	10				

Regression output

variables	coefficients	std. error	t (df=9)	p-value	confidence interval 95% lower	95% upper
Intercept	11.4641	3.4390	3.334	0.0087	3.6845	19.2437
Copiers (x)	24.6022	0.8045	30.580	2.09E-10	22.7823	26.4221

Predicted values for: Minutes (y)

Copiers (x)	Predicted	95% Confidence Intervals lower	upper	95% Prediction Intervals lower	upper	Leverage
1	36.066	29.907	42.226	23.944	48.188	0.348
2	60.669	55.980	65.357	49.224	72.113	0.202
3	85.271	81.715	88.827	74.241	96.300	0.116
4	109.873	106.721	113.025	98.967	120.779	0.091
5	134.475	130.753	138.197	123.391	145.559	0.127
6	159.077	154.139	164.016	147.528	170.627	0.224
7	183.680	177.233	190.126	171.410	195.950	0.381

FIGURE 11.15 Excel Output of a Simple Linear Regression Analysis of the Fresh Detergent Demand Data

SUMMARY OUTPUT

Regression Statistics

Multiple R	0.889671764
R Square	0.791515848
Adjusted R Square	0.784069986
Standard Error	0.316560873
Observations	30

ANOVA

	df	SS	MS	F	Significance F
Regression	1	10.65268464	10.65268	106.3028	4.88134E-11
Residual	28	2.805902023	0.100211		
Total	29	13.45858667			

	Coefficients	Standard Error	t Stat	P-value	Lower 95%	Upper 95%	Lower 95.0%	Upper 95.0%
Intercept	7.814087575	0.079884322	97.81754	4.85E-37	7.650451776	7.9777234	7.65045178	7.97772337
PriceDif	2.665214492	0.258499595	10.31032	4.88E-11	2.135701482	3.1947275	2.13570148	3.1947275

FIGURE 11.16 Excel and MegaStat Output of a Simple Linear Regression Analysis of the Direct Labour Cost Data

(a) The Excel Output

Regression Statistics

Multiple R	0.9996
R Square	0.9993
Adjusted R Square	0.9992
Standard Error	8.6415
Observations	12

ANOVA	df	SS	MS	F	Significance F
Regression	1	1,024,592.9043	1,024,592.9043	13,720.4677	5.04E-17
Residual	10	746.7624	74.6762		
Total	11	1,025,339.6667			

	Coefficients	Standard Error	t Stat	P-value	Lower 95%	Upper 95%
Intercept	18.4875	4.6766	3.9532	0.0027	8.0674	28.9076
BatchSize (x)	10.1463	0.0866	117.1344	5.04E-17	9.9533	10.3393

(b) Prediction Using MegaStat

Predicted values for: LabourCost (y)

BatchSize (x)	Predicted	95% Confidence Interval		95% Prediction Interval		Leverage
		lower	upper	lower	upper	
60	627.263	621.054	633.472	607.032	647.494	0.104

11.40 THE FRESH DETERGENT EXAMPLE

The Excel output of a simple linear regression analysis of the data set is given in Figure 11.15.

11.41 THE DIRECT LABOUR COST EXAMPLE

The Excel and MegaStat outputs of a simple linear regression analysis of the data set are given in Figure 11.16.

11.42 DOG BISCUIT SALES

The Excel output of a simple linear regression analysis of the data set is given in Figure 11.17.

11.43 Find and interpret a 95 percent confidence interval for the slope β_1 of the simple linear regression model describing the Canadian youth training program data in Exercise 11.32.

FIGURE 11.17   Excel Output of a Simple Linear Regression Analysis of the Dog Biscuit Sales Data

SUMMARY OUTPUT

Regression Statistics

Multiple R	0.938803701
R Square	0.881352389
Adjusted R Square	0.866521438
Standard Error	10.54131963
Observations	10

ANOVA

	df	SS	MS	F	Significance F
Regression	1	6603.444643	6603.444643	59.42655806	5.6967E-05
Residual	8	888.9553571	111.1194196		
Total	9	7492.4			

	Coefficients	Standard Error	t Stat	P-value	Lower 95%	Upper 95%	Lower 95.0%	Upper 95.0%
Intercept	47.80357143	14.35004134	3.331249737	0.010365121	14.71229536	80.89484749	14.71229536	80.89484749
Coupons Issued	5.723214286	0.742420095	7.708862306	5.6967E-05	4.011189369	7.435239202	4.011189369	7.435239202

11.7 CONFIDENCE AND PREDICTION INTERVALS

The point on the least squares line corresponding to a particular value x_0 of the independent variable x is

$$\hat{y} = b_0 + b_1 x_0$$

Unless we are very lucky, $\hat{y}$ will not exactly equal either the mean value of y when x equals x_0 or a particular individual value of y when x equals x_0. Therefore, we need to place bounds on how far $\hat{y}$ might be from these values. We can do this by calculating a *confidence interval for the mean value of y* and a *prediction interval for an individual value of y.*

Both of these intervals employ a quantity called the *distance value*, which for simple linear regression is calculated as shown in the following boxed feature.

The Distance Value for Simple Linear Regression

In simple linear regression, the **distance value** for a particular value x_0 of x is

$$\text{Distance value} = \frac{1}{n} + \frac{(x_0 - \bar{x})^2}{SS_{xx}}$$

This quantity is a measure of the distance between the value x_0 of x and $\bar{x}$, the average of the observed values of x. Notice from the above formula that the farther x_0 is from $\bar{x}$, which can be regarded as the centre of the experimental region, the larger is the distance value.

We now consider establishing a confidence interval for the mean value of y when x equals a particular value x_0 (labelled as $\mu_{y|x_0}$). Because each possible sample of n values of the dependent variable gives values of b_0 and b_1 that differ from the values given by other samples, different samples give different values of the point estimate

$$\hat{y} = b_0 + b_1 x_0$$

It can be shown that if the regression assumptions hold, the population of all possible values of $\hat{y}$ is normally distributed with mean $\mu_{y|x_0}$ and standard deviation

$$\sigma_{\hat{y}} = \sigma \sqrt{\text{Distance value}}$$

The point estimate of $\sigma_{\hat{y}}$ is

$$s_{\hat{y}} = s \sqrt{\text{Distance value}}$$

which is called the *standard error of the estimate $\hat{y}$.* Using this standard error, we form a confidence interval as shown in the following boxed feature.

A Confidence Interval for a Mean Value of y

If the regression assumptions hold, a $100(1 - \alpha)$ per-cent confidence interval for the mean value of y when the value of the independent variable is x_0 is

$$[\hat{y} \pm t_{\alpha/2}s\sqrt{\text{Distance value}}]$$

Here $t_{\alpha/2}$ is based on $n - 2$ degrees of freedom.

Data

Observation	x	y
1	28.0	12.4
2	28.0	11.7
3	32.5	12.4
4	39.0	10.8
5	45.9	9.4
6	57.8	9.5
7	58.1	8.0
8	62.5	7.5

For the data from Table 11.6 (reproduced in the margin), suppose we want to compute a 95 percent confidence interval for the y value when $x_0 = 40$. Previously, we calculated the point estimate of this mean to be

$$\hat{y} = b_0 + b_1 x_0$$
$$= 15.84 - .1279(40)$$
$$= 10.72$$

The mean of x is 43.98, the SS_{xx} is 1,404.355, and there are eight cases, so we can compute

$$\text{Distance value} = \frac{1}{n} + \frac{(x_0 - \bar{x})^2}{SS_{xx}}$$
$$= \frac{1}{8} + \frac{(40 - 43.98)^2}{1,404.355}$$
$$= .1363$$

For this data, $s = .6542$ and because $t_{\alpha/2} = t_{.025}$ based on $n - 2 = 8 - 2 = 6$ degrees of freedom equals 2.447, it follows that the desired 95 percent confidence interval is

$$[\hat{y} \pm t_{\alpha/2}s\sqrt{\text{Distance value}}] = [10.72 \pm 2.447(.6542)\sqrt{.1363}]$$
$$= [10.72 \pm .59]$$
$$= [10.13, 11.31]$$

This interval says we are 95 percent confident that the y value that would be observed in all observations where $x = 40$ is between 10.13 and 11.31.

We develop an interval for an individual value of y when x equals a particular value x_0 by considering the prediction error $y - \hat{y}$. After calculating the point prediction based on a sample, we could observe any one of an infinite number of different individual values of y (because of different possible error terms). Therefore, an infinite number of different prediction errors could be observed. If the regression assumptions hold, it can be shown that the population of all possible prediction errors is normally distributed with mean of 0 and standard deviation

$$\sigma_{(y-\hat{y})} = \sigma\sqrt{1 + \text{Distance value}}$$

The point estimate of $\sigma_{(y-\hat{y})}$ is

$$s_{(y-\hat{y})} = s\sqrt{1 + \text{Distance value}}$$

called the *standard error of the prediction error.* Using this quantity, we obtain a prediction interval as shown in the following boxed feature.

A Prediction Interval for an Individual Value of y

If the regression assumptions hold, a $100(1 - \alpha)$ per-cent prediction interval for an individual value of y when the value of the independent variable is x_0 is

$$[\hat{y} \pm t_{\alpha/2}s\sqrt{1 + \text{Distance value}}]$$

Here $t_{\alpha/2}$ is based on $n - 2$ degrees of freedom.

Prediction versus confidence intervals

The prediction interval is useful if it is important to predict an individual value of the dependent variable (a certain y value). A confidence interval is useful if it is important to estimate the mean value, such as when observations are affected by a very large number of values of the dependent variable when the independent variable equals a particular value (we illustrate this in Example 11.4).

Example 11.4 The QHIC Example

Consider a home worth $220,000. We have seen that the predicted yearly upkeep expenditure for such a home is

$$\hat{y} = b_0 + b_1 x_0$$
$$= -348.3921 + 7.2583(220)$$
$$= 1248.43 \text{ (or } \$1,248.43)$$

This predicted value is given at the bottom of the MegaStat output in Figure 11.13, which we repeat here:

Predicted values for: Upkeep

Value	Predicted	95% Confidence Interval		95% Prediction Interval		Leverage
		lower	upper	lower	upper	
220	1,248.42597	1,187.78944	1,309.06251	944.92879	1,551.92315	0.042

In addition to giving $\hat{y} = 1,248.43$, the MegaStat output also tells us that the distance value, which is given under the heading "Leverage" on the output, equals .042. Therefore, because s equals 146.897 (see Figure 11.13), it follows that a 95 percent prediction interval for the yearly upkeep expenditure of an individual home worth $220,000 is calculated as follows:

$$\left[\hat{y} \pm t_{.025} s \sqrt{1 + \text{Distance value}} \right]$$
$$= \left[1,248.43 \pm 2.024(146.897)\sqrt{1.042} \right]$$
$$= \left[944.93, 1,551.93 \right]$$

Here $t_{.025}$ is based on $n - 2 = 40 - 2 = 38$ degrees of freedom. Note that this interval is given on the MegaStat output.

Because there are many homes worth roughly $220,000 in the metropolitan area, QHIC is more interested in the mean upkeep expenditure for all such homes than in the individual upkeep expenditure for one such home. The MegaStat output tells us that a 95 percent confidence interval for this mean upkeep expenditure is [1,187.79, 1,309.06]. This interval says that QHIC is 95 percent confident that the mean upkeep expenditure for all homes worth $220,000 is at least $1,187.79 and no more than $1,309.06.

THEORY TO PRACTICE

So far we have seen that the simple linear regression equation is a powerful statistical tool. For example, a human resources researcher may want to know how well a structured selection interview predicts job performance. A marketing researcher may want to know the relationship between "green" (environmental) attitudes and the purchase of eco-friendly products. A finance researcher may want to examine the relationship between age of investors and degree of risk investors are willing to take in their investments.

As will be covered in the next chapter, the regression statistic becomes even more informative when additional predictors are added into the equation, resulting in multiple regression models.

Exercises for Section **11.7**

CONCEPTS

11.44 What does the distance value measure?

11.45 What is the difference between a confidence interval and a prediction interval?

11.46 Discuss how the distance value affects the length of a confidence interval and a prediction interval.

METHODS AND APPLICATIONS

11.47 THE SERVICE TIME EXAMPLE

The partial MegaStat regression output in Figure 11.18 for the service time data relates to predicting service times for 1, 2, 3, 4, 5, 6, and 7 copiers.

a. Report (as shown on the computer output) a point estimate of and a 95 percent confidence interval for the mean time to service four copiers.

b. Report (as shown on the computer output) a point prediction of and a 95 percent prediction interval for the time to service four copiers during a single call.

c. For this example, $n = 11$, $b_0 = 11.4641$, $b_1 = 24.6022$, and $s = 4.615$. Using this information and a distance value from the MegaStat output, manually calculate (within rounding) the confidence interval of part (a) and the prediction interval of part (b).

d. Examine the service time data and note that there was at least one call during which Accu-Copiers serviced each of the 7 copiers. The 95 percent confidence intervals for the mean service times on these calls might be used to schedule future service calls. To understand this, note that a person making service calls will (in, say, a year or more) make a very large number of service calls. Some of the person's individual service times will be below, and some will be above, the corresponding mean service times. However, since the very large number of individual service times will average out to the mean service times, it seems fair to both the efficiency of the company and the person making service calls to schedule service calls by using estimates of the mean service times. Therefore, suppose you want to schedule a call to service five copiers. Examine the MegaStat output and note that a 95 percent confidence interval for the mean time to service five copiers is [130.753, 138.197]. Since the mean time might be 138.197 minutes, it would seem

fair to allow 138 minutes to make the service call. Now suppose you want to schedule a call to service four copiers. Determine how many minutes to allow for the service call.

11.48 THE FRESH DETERGENT EXAMPLE

The partial MegaStat regression output in Figure 11.19(a) for the Fresh detergent data relates to predicting demand for future sales periods in which the price difference will be .10 and .25.

a. Report (as shown on the computer output) a point estimate of and a 95 percent confidence interval for the mean demand for Fresh in all sales periods when the price difference is .10.

b. Report (as shown on the computer output) a point prediction of and a 95 percent prediction interval for the actual demand for Fresh in an individual sales period when the price difference is .10.

c. Remembering that $s = .316561$ and that the distance value equals $(s_{\hat{y}}/s)^2$, use $s_{\hat{y}}$ from the computer output to manually calculate the distance value when $x = .10$.

d. For this example, $n = 30$, $b_0 = 7.81409$, $b_1 = 2.6652$, and $s = .316561$. Using this information and your result from part (c), find 99 percent confidence and prediction intervals for mean and individual demands when $x = .10$.

e. Repeat parts (a), (b), (c), and (d) when $x = .25$.

FIGURE 11.18   Partial MegaStat Regression Output for Exercise 11.47

Predicted values for: Minutes (y)

Copiers (x)	Predicted	95% Confidence Intervals		95% Prediction Intervals		Leverage
		lower	upper	lower	upper	
1	36.066	29.907	42.226	23.944	48.188	0.348
2	60.669	55.980	65.357	49.224	72.113	0.202
3	85.271	81.715	88.827	74.241	96.300	0.116
4	109.873	106.721	113.025	98.967	120.779	0.091
5	134.475	130.753	138.197	123.391	145.559	0.127
6	159.077	154.139	164.016	147.528	170.627	0.224
7	183.680	177.233	190.126	171.410	195.950	0.381

FIGURE **11.19**   MegaStat Output for Exercises 11.48, 11.49, and 11.50

(a) Fresh detergent data for Exercise 11.48

Predicted values for: Demand

PriceDif	Predicted	95% Confidence Intervals		95% Prediction Intervals		Leverage
		lower	upper	lower	upper	
0.10	8.08061	7.94788	8.21334	7.41872	8.74250	0.042
0.25	8.48039	8.36042	8.60036	7.82094	9.13984	0.034

(b) Labour cost data for Exercise 11.49

Predicted values for: LabourCost (y)

BatchSize (x)	Predicted	95% Confidence Interval		95% Prediction Interval		Leverage
		lower	upper	lower	upper	
60	627.263	621.054	633.472	607.032	647.494	0.104

(c) Dog biscuit sales data for Exercise 11.50

Predicted values for: Sales

Coupons Issued	Predicted	95% Confidence Interval		95% Prediction Interval		Leverage
		lower	upper	lower	upper	
20	162.268	154.311	170.225	136.690	187.845	0.107

11.49 THE DIRECT LABOUR COST EXAMPLE

The partial MegaStat regression output in Figure 11.19(b) for the direct labour cost data relates to predicting direct labour cost when the batch size is 60.

a. Report (as shown on the MegaStat output) a point estimate of and a 95 percent confidence interval for the mean direct labour cost of all batches of size 60.

b. Report (as shown on the MegaStat output) a point prediction of and a 95 percent prediction interval for the actual direct labour cost of an individual batch of size 60.

c. For this example, $n = 12$, $b_0 = 18.4875$, $b_1 = 10.1463$, and $s = 8.6415$. Use this information and the distance value from the MegaStat output to compute 99 percent confidence and prediction intervals for the mean and individual labour costs when $x = 60$.

11.50 DOG BISCUIT SALES

The partial MegaStat regression output in Figure 11.19(c) for the dog biscuit sales data relates to predicting the average number of bags sold in a month when 20 coupons are issued at a supermarket.

a. Report (as shown on the MegaStat output) a point estimate of and a 95 percent confidence interval for the mean monthly sales for all supermarkets with 20 coupons issued.

b. Report (as shown on the MegaStat output) a 95 percent prediction interval for the mean monthly sales of an individual supermarket with 20 coupons issued.

11.51 Using the sales volume data introduced in Exercise 11.31 and reproduced below, find a point prediction of and a 95 percent prediction interval for sales volume when advertising expenditure is 11 (that is, $110,000).

	(in units of $10,000)	
Region	Advertising Expenditure	Sales Volume
1	5	89
2	6	87
3	7	98
4	8	110
5	9	103
6	10	114
7	11	116
8	12	110
9	13	126
10	14	130

11.8 COEFFICIENTS OF DETERMINATION AND CORRELATION

The coefficient of determination   The coefficient of determination (r^2 or eta^2) was introduced in Section 11.1 and is a measure of the usefulness of a simple linear regression model. Suppose we have observed n values of the dependent variable y. However, we choose to predict y without using a predictor (independent) variable x. In such a case, the only reasonable prediction of a specific value of y, say y_i, is $\bar{y}$, which is simply the average of the n observed values $y_1, y_2, \ldots, y_n$. Here the error of prediction in predicting y_i is $y_i - \bar{y}$ and represents the prediction errors obtained when we do not use the information provided by the independent variable x.

If we decide to use the predictor variable x and observe the values $x_1, x_2, \ldots, x_n$ corresponding to the observed values of y, then the prediction of y_i is

$$\hat{y}_i = b_0 + b_1 x_i$$

and the prediction error is $y_i - \hat{y}_i$. Using the predictor variable x decreases the prediction error in predicting y_i from $(y_i - \bar{y})$ to $(y_i - \hat{y}_i)$, or by an amount equal to

$$(y_i - \bar{y}) - (y_i - \hat{y}_i) = \hat{y}_i - \bar{y}$$

It can be shown that in general

$$\sum (y_i - \bar{y})^2 - \sum (y_i - \hat{y}_i)^2 = \sum (\hat{y}_i - \bar{y})^2$$

The sum of squared prediction errors obtained when we do not employ the predictor variable x, $\sum (y_i - \bar{y})^2$, is called the *total variation*. This quantity measures the total amount of variation exhibited by the observed values of y. The sum of squared prediction errors obtained when we use the predictor variable x, $\sum (y_i - \hat{y}_i)^2$, is called the *unexplained variation* (this is another name for the *SSE*). This quantity measures the amount of variation in the values of y that is not explained by the predictor variable. The quantity $\sum (\hat{y}_i - \bar{y})^2$ is called the *explained variation*. Using these definitions and the above equation involving these summations, we see that

$$\text{Total variation} - \text{Unexplained variation} = \text{Explained variation}$$

ROADBLOCK

Total variance explained
Total variation is simply the variance value of y.

It follows that the explained variation is the reduction in the sum of squared prediction errors that has been accomplished by using the predictor variable x to predict y. It also follows that

$$\text{Total variation} = \text{Explained variation} + \text{Unexplained variation}$$

This equation implies that the explained variation represents the amount of the total variation in the observed values of y that is explained by the predictor variable x (and the simple linear regression model).

We now define the coefficient of determination to be

$$\text{eta}^2 = r^2 = \frac{\text{Explained variation}}{\text{Total variation}}$$

That is, r^2 (or eta^2) is the proportion of the total variation in the n observed values of y that is explained by the simple linear regression model. Neither the explained variation nor the total variation can be negative (both quantities are sums of squares). Therefore, r^2 is greater than or equal to 0. Because the explained variation must be less than or equal to the total variation, r^2 cannot be greater than 1. The nearer r^2 is to 1, the larger is the proportion of the total variation that is explained by the model, and the greater is the utility of the model in predicting y. If the value of r^2 is closer to 0, then the independent variable in the model (x) does not provide accurate predictions of y. In such a case, a different predictor variable must be found in order to accurately predict y. It is also possible that no regression model employing a single predictor variable will accurately predict y. In this case, the model must be improved by including more than one independent variable. We will see how to do this in Chapter 12.

In the following boxed feature, we summarize the results of this section:

The Coefficient of Determination, r^2 (eta²)

For the simple linear regression model:

1   **Total variation** = $\sum (y_i - \bar{y})^2$

2   **Explained variation** = $\sum (\hat{y}_i - \bar{y})^2$

3   **Unexplained variation** = $\sum (y_i - \hat{y}_i)^2$

4   **Total variation** = **Explained variation** + **Unexplained variation**

5   The **coefficient of determination is**
$$r^2 = \frac{\text{Explained variation}}{\text{Total variation}}$$

6   r^2 is the proportion of the total variation in the *n* observed values of the dependent variable that is explained by the simple linear regression model.

Example 11.5 The QHIC Example

In the QHIC data, it can be shown that total variation = 7,402,755.2399, explained variation = 6,582,759.6972, *SSE* = unexplained variation = 819,995.5427, and

$$r^2 = \frac{\text{Explained variation}}{\text{Total variation}} = \frac{6,582,759.6972}{7,402,755.2399} = .889$$

This value of r^2 (eta²) says that the simple linear regression model that employs home value as a predictor variable explains 88.9 percent of the total variation in the 40 observed home-upkeep expenditures.

In Section 11.11, we present some shortcut formulas for calculating the total, explained, and unexplained variations.

Exercises for Section **11.8**

CONCEPTS

11.52 Discuss the meanings of the total variation, the unexplained variation, and the explained variation.

11.53 What does the coefficient of determination measure?

METHODS AND APPLICATIONS

In Exercises 11.54 through 11.57, we give the total variation, the unexplained variation (*SSE*), and the least squares point estimate (b_1) that are obtained when simple linear regression is used to analyze the data set related to each of four previously discussed examples. Using the information given in each exercise, find the explained variation, the coefficient of determination (r^2 or eta²), and the correlation coefficient (*r*). Interpret r^2 (eta²).

11.54 THE SERVICE TIME EXAMPLE

Total variation = 20,110.5455, *SSE* = 191.7017, b_1 = 24.6022.

11.55 THE FRESH DETERGENT EXAMPLE

Total variation = 13.459, *SSE* = 2.806, b_1 = 2.6652.

11.56 THE DIRECT LABOUR COST EXAMPLE

Total variation = 1,025,339.6667, *SSE* = 746.7624, b_1 = 10.1463.

11.57 DOG BISCUIT SALES

Total variation = 7,492.4, *SSE* = 888.96, b_1 = 5.72.

11.9 AN *F* TEST FOR THE MODEL

In this section, we discuss an *F* test that can be used to test the significance of the regression relationship between *x* and *y* (sometimes referred to as *testing the significance of the simple linear regression model*). For simple linear regression, this test is another way to test the null hypothesis H_0: $\beta_1 = 0$ (the relationship between *x* and *y* is not significant) versus H_a: $\beta_0 \neq 0$ (the relationship between *x* and *y* is significant). If we can reject H_0 at level of significance α, we often say that *the simple linear regression model is significant at level of significance* α.

LO7

An *F* Test for the Simple Linear Regression Model

Suppose that the regression assumptions hold, and define the overall *F* statistic to be

$$F(\text{model}) = \frac{\text{Explained variation}}{\text{Unexplained variation}/(n-2)}$$

Also define the *p*-value related to *F*(model) to be the area under the curve of the *F* distribution (with 1 numerator and $n-2$ denominator degrees of freedom) to the right of *F*(model)—see Figure 11.20(b).

We can reject H_0: $\beta_1 = 0$ in favour of H_a: $\beta_1 \neq 0$ at level of significance α if either of the following equivalent conditions holds:

1 $F(\text{model}) > F_\alpha$

2 *p*-value $< \alpha$

Here the point F_α is based on 1 numerator and $n-2$ denominator degrees of freedom.

FIGURE **11.20**   An *F* Test for the Simple Linear Regression Model

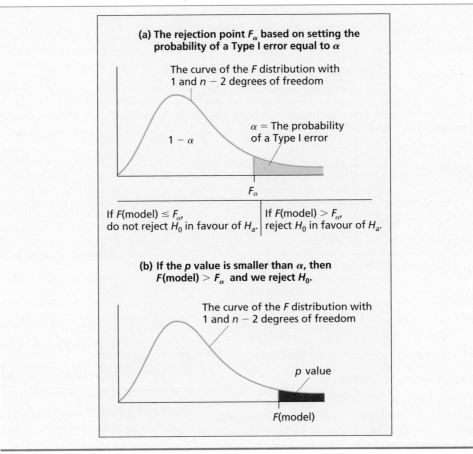

The first condition in the *F* test for the simple linear regression model says we should reject H_0: $\beta_1 = 0$ (and conclude that the relationship between *x* and *y* is significant) when *F*(model) is larger than the *F*-value at the corresponding alpha value. A large overall *F* statistic will be obtained when the explained variation is large compared to the unexplained variation. This occurs if *x* is significantly related to *y*, which implies that the slope β_1 is not equal to 0. Figure 11.20(a) illustrates that we reject H_0 when *F*(model) is greater than F_α. As can be seen in Figure 11.20(b), when *F*(model) is large, the related *p*-value is small. When the *p*-value is small enough, we reject H_0. Figure 11.20(b) illustrates that the second condition in the box (*p*-value $< \alpha$) is an equivalent way to carry out this test.

For example, a partial Excel output of a simple linear regression analysis relating y to x is given below:

ANOVA	df	SS	MS	F	Significance F
Regression	1	22.9808	22.9808	53.6949	0.0003
Residual	6	2.5679	0.4280		
Total	7	25.5488			

Looking at this output, we see that the explained variation is 22.9808 and the unexplained variation is 2.5679. It follows that

$$F(\text{model}) = \frac{\text{Explained variation}}{\text{Unexplained variation}/n - 2}$$

$$= \frac{22.9808}{2.5679/(8 - 2)} = \frac{22.9808}{.4280}$$

$$= 53.69$$

The p-value related to $F(\text{model})$ is the area to the right of 53.69 under the curve of the F distribution with 1 numerator and 6 denominator degrees of freedom. This p-value is given on the Excel output (labelled "Significance F") and is less than .001. If we want to test the significance of the regression relationship with level of significance $\alpha = .05$, we use the rejection point $F_{.05}$ based on 1 numerator and 6 denominator degrees of freedom. Using Table A.7, we find that $F_{.05} = 5.99$. Because $F(\text{model}) = 53.69 > F_{.05} = 5.99$, we can reject H_0: $\beta_1 = 0$ in favour of H_a: $\beta_1 \neq 0$ at level of significance .05. Alternatively, because the p-value is smaller than .05, .01, and .001, we can reject H_0 at level of significance .05, .01, or .001. Therefore, we have extremely strong evidence that H_0: $\beta_1 = 0$ should be rejected and that the regression relationship (the simple linear model) between x and y is significant.

As another example, consider the following partial MegaStat output for the QHIC data:

ANOVA table					
Source	SS	df	MS	F	p-value
Regression	6,582,759.6972	1	6,582,759.6972	305.06	9.49E-20
Residual	819,995.5427	38	21,578.8301		
Total	7,402,755.2399	39			

This output tells us that the simple linear regression model, $F(\text{model})$ is 305.06 and the related p-value is less than .001. Because the p-value is less than .001, we have extremely strong evidence that the regression relationship is significant.

Testing the significance of the regression relationship between y and x by using the overall F statistic and its related p-value is equivalent to doing this test by using the t statistic $(t = b_1/s_{b1})$ and its related p-value. Specifically, it can be shown that $t^2 = F(\text{model})$ and that $(t_{\alpha/2})^2$ based on $n - 2$ degrees of freedom equals F_α based on 1 numerator and $n - 2$ denominator degrees of freedom. It follows that the rejection point conditions

$$|t| > t_{\alpha/2} \quad \text{and} \quad F(\text{model}) > F_\alpha$$

are equivalent. Furthermore, the p-values related to t and $F(\text{model})$ can be shown to be equal, but this situation applies only when there is one predictor, x. When there are multiple predictors (a multiple regression situation), the F test is not equivalent to a t test. This is further explained in Chapter 12.

Exercises for Section **11.9**

CONCEPTS

11.58 What are the null and alternative hypotheses for the F test in simple linear regression?

11.59 The F test in simple linear regression is equivalent to what other test?

METHODS AND APPLICATIONS

In Figure 11.21, we give MegaStat and Excel outputs of simple linear regression analyses of the data sets related to four previously discussed examples. Use the appropriate computer output to do the following for Exercises 11.60 through 11.63:

a. Use the explained variation and the unexplained variation as given on the computer output to calculate the F(model) statistic.

b. Use the F(model) statistic and the appropriate rejection point to test $H_0: \beta_1 = 0$ versus $H_a: \beta_1 \neq 0$ by setting α equal to .05. What do you conclude about the regression relationship between y and x?

c. Use the F(model) statistic and the appropriate rejection point to test $H_0: \beta_1 = 0$ versus $H_a: \beta_1 \neq 0$ by setting α equal to .01. What do you conclude about the regression relationship between y and x?

d. Find the p-value related to F(model) on the computer output and report its value. Using the p-value, test the significance of the regression model at the .10, .05, .01, and .001 levels of significance. What do you conclude?

e. Show that the F(model) statistic is (within rounding) the square of the t statistic for testing $H_0: \beta_1 = 0$ versus $H_a: \beta_1 \neq 0$. Also show that the $F_{.05}$ rejection point is the square of the $t_{.025}$ rejection point.

Note that in the lower right-hand corner of each output we give (in parentheses) the number of observations, n, used to perform the regression analysis and the t statistic for testing $H_0: \beta_1 = 0$ versus $H_a: \beta_1 \neq 0$.

11.60 THE SERVICE TIME EXAMPLE

The MegaStat output for this example is given in Figure 11.21(a).

11.61 THE FRESH DETERGENT EXAMPLE

The Excel output for this example is given in Figure 11.21(b).

11.62 THE DIRECT LABOUR COST EXAMPLE

The Excel output for this example is given in Figure 11.21(c).

11.63 DOG BISCUIT SALES

The Excel output for this example is given in Figure 11.21(d).

FIGURE 11.21   MegaStat and Excel Outputs for Exercises 11.60 through 11.63

(a) MegaStat output for Exercise 11.60 (Service Time Data)

ANOVA table

Source	SS	df	MS	F	p-value
Regression	19,918.8438	1	19,918.8438	935.15	2.09E-10
Residual	191.7017	9	21.3002		
Total	20,110.5455	10		(n = 11; t = 30.580)	

(b) Excel output for Exercise 11.61 (Fresh Detergent Data)

ANOVA

	df	SS	MS	F	Significance F
Regression	1	10.65268	10.65268	106.3028	4.88134E-11
Residual	28	2.805902	0.100211		
Total	29	13.45859		(n = 30; t = 10.31)	

(c) Excel output for Exercise 11.62 (Direct Labour Cost Data)

ANOVA	df	SS	MS	F	Significance F
Regression	1	1,024,592.9043	1,024,592.9043	13,720.4677	5.04E-17
Residual	10	746.7624	74.6762		
Total	11	1,025,339.6667		(n = 12; t = 117.1344)	

(d) Excel output for Exercise 11.63 (Dog Biscuit Sales Data)

ANOVA

	df	SS	MS	F	Significance F
Regression	1	6603.444643	6603.444643	59.42655806	5.6967E-05
Residual	8	888.9553571	111.1194196		
Total	9	7492.4		(n = 10, t = 7.71)	

11.10 RESIDUAL ANALYSIS

In this section, we explain how to check the validity of the regression assumptions. The required checks are carried out by analyzing the regression residuals. The residuals are defined as follows:

For any particular observed value of y, the corresponding residual is

$$e = y - \hat{y} = (\text{Observed value of } y - \text{Predicted value of } y)$$

where the predicted value of y is calculated using the least squares prediction equation

$$\hat{y} = b_0 + b_1 x$$

The linear regression model $y = \beta_0 + \beta_1 x + \varepsilon$ implies that the error term ε is given by the equation $\varepsilon = y - (\beta_0 + \beta_1 x)$. Because $\hat{y}$ is the point estimate of $\beta_0 + \beta_1 x$, we see that the residual $e = y - \hat{y}$ is the point estimate of the error term ε. If the regression assumptions are valid, then for any given value of the independent variable, the population of potential error term values will be normally distributed with mean 0 and variance σ^2 (see the regression assumptions in Section 11.4). Furthermore, the different error terms will be statistically independent. Because the residuals provide point estimates of the error terms, we have the following:

If the regression assumptions hold, the residuals should look like they have been randomly and independently selected from normally distributed populations with mean 0 and variance σ^2.

In any applied regression problem, the regression assumptions will not hold exactly, but mild departures from the regression assumptions do not seriously hinder our ability to use a regression model to make statistical inferences. Therefore, we are looking for pronounced, rather than subtle, departures from the regression assumptions. Because of this, we will require that the residuals only approximately fit the description just given.

Residual plots One useful way to analyze residuals is to plot them versus various criteria. The resulting plots are called *residual plots*. To construct a **residual plot**, we compute the residual for each observed y value. The calculated residuals are then plotted versus some criterion. To validate the regression assumptions, we make residual plots against (1) values of the independent variable x; (2) values of $\hat{y}$, the predicted value of the dependent variable; and (3) the time order in which the data have been observed (if the regression data are time series data).

We next look at an example of constructing residual plots. Then we explain how to use these plots to check the regression assumptions.

Example 11.6 The QHIC Example

Figure 11.22 gives the QHIC upkeep expenditure data and an Excel scatter plot of the data. If we use a simple linear regression model to describe the QHIC data, we find that the least squares point estimates of β_0 and β_1 are $b_0 = -348.3921$ and $b_1 = 7.2583$. The MegaStat output in Figure 11.23(a) presents the predicted home-upkeep expenditures and residuals that are given by the simple linear regression model. Here each residual is computed as

$$e = y - \hat{y} = y - (b_0 + b_1 x) = y - (-348.3921 + 7.2583x)$$

For instance, for the first observation (Home 1) listed in Figure 11.22, when $y = 1412.08$ and $x = 237.00$ the residual is

$$e = 1,412.08 - (-348.3921 + 7.2583(237))$$
$$= 1,412.08 - 1,371.825 = 40.255$$

The MegaStat output in Figure 11.23(b) and (c) gives plots of the residuals for the QHIC linear regression model for each observation and against values of $\hat{y}$. To understand how these plots are constructed, recall that for the first observation (Home 1), $y = 1,412.08$,

FIGURE **11.22**   The QHIC Upkeep Expenditure Data and an Excel Scatter Plot of the Data

Home	Value of Home, x (Thousands of Dollars)	Upkeep Expenditure, y (Dollars)	Home	Value of Home, x (Thousands of Dollars)	Upkeep Expenditure, y (Dollars)
1	237.00	1,412.08	21	153.04	849.14
2	153.08	797.20	22	232.18	1,313.84
3	184.86	872.48	23	125.44	602.06
4	222.06	1,003.42	24	169.82	642.14
5	160.68	852.90	25	177.28	1,038.80
6	99.68	288.48	26	162.82	697.00
7	229.04	1,288.46	27	120.44	324.34
8	101.78	423.08	28	191.10	965.10
9	257.86	1,351.74	29	158.78	920.14
10	96.28	378.04	30	178.50	950.90
11	171.00	918.08	31	272.20	1,670.32
12	231.02	1,627.24	32	48.90	125.40
13	228.32	1,204.76	33	104.56	479.78
14	205.90	857.04	34	286.18	2,010.64
15	185.72	775.00	35	83.72	368.36
16	168.78	869.26	36	86.20	425.60
17	247.06	1,396.00	37	133.58	626.90
18	155.54	711.50	38	212.86	1,316.94
19	224.20	1,475.18	39	122.02	390.16
20	202.04	1,413.32	40	198.02	1,090.84

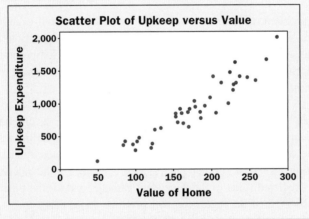

$x = 237.00$, $\hat{y} = 1{,}371.816$, and the residual is $1412.08 - 1371.816 = 40.264$, so the first point on the plot in Figure 11.23(b) is (237.00, 40.264). The point plotted in Figure 11.23(c) corresponding to the first observation has a horizontal axis coordinate of the $\hat{y}$ value 1,371.816 and a vertical axis coordinate of the residual 40.264. Finally, note that the QHIC data are cross-sectional data, not time series data, so we cannot make a residual plot versus time.

The constant-variance assumption To check the validity of the constant-variance assumption, we examine plots of the residuals against values of x, $\hat{y}$, and time (if the regression data are time series data). When we look at these plots, the residuals fluctuate around 0, and tell us about the validity of the constant-variance assumption. A residual plot that fans out [as in Figure 11.24(a)] suggests that the error terms are becoming more spread out as the horizontal plot value increases and that the constant-variance assumption is violated. Here we would say that an increasing error variance exists. A residual plot that funnels in [as in Figure 11.24(b)] suggests that the spread of the error terms is decreasing as the horizontal plot value increases and that again the constant-variance assumption is violated. In this case, we would say that a decreasing error variance exists. A residual plot with a horizontal band appearance [as in Figure 11.24(c)] suggests that the spread of the error terms around 0 is not changing much as the horizontal plot value increases. Such a plot tells us that the constant-variance assumption (approximately) holds.

FIGURE 11.23 MegaStat and Excel Output of the Residuals and Residual Plots for the QHIC Simple Linear Regression Model

(a) MegaStat output of the residuals

Observation	Upkeep	Predicted	Residual	Observation	Upkeep	Predicted	Residual
1	1,412.080	1,371.816	40.264	21	849.140	762.413	86.727
2	797.200	762.703	34.497	22	1,313.840	1,336.832	−22.992
3	872.480	993.371	−120.891	23	602.060	562.085	39.975
4	1,003.420	1,263.378	−259.958	24	642.140	884.206	−242.066
5	852.900	817.866	35.034	25	1,038.800	938.353	100.447
6	288.480	375.112	−86.632	26	697.000	833.398	−136.398
7	1,288.460	1,314.041	−25.581	27	324.340	525.793	−201.453
8	423.080	390.354	32.726	28	965.100	1,038.662	−73.562
9	1,351.740	1,523.224	−171.484	29	920.140	804.075	116.065
10	378.040	350.434	27.606	30	950.900	947.208	3.692
11	918.080	892.771	25.309	31	1,670.320	1,627.307	43.013
12	1,627.240	1,328.412	298.828	32	125.400	6.537	118.863
13	1,204.760	1,308.815	−104.055	33	479.780	410.532	69.248
14	857.040	1,146.084	−289.044	34	2,010.640	1,728.778	281.862
15	775.000	999.613	−224.613	35	368.360	259.270	109.090
16	869.260	876.658	−7.398	36	425.600	277.270	148.330
17	1,396.000	1,444.835	−48.835	37	626.900	621.167	5.733
18	711.500	780.558	−69.058	38	1,316.940	1,196.602	120.338
19	1,475.180	1,278.911	196.269	39	390.160	537.261	−147.101
20	1,413.320	1,118.068	295.252	40	1,090.840	1,088.889	1.951

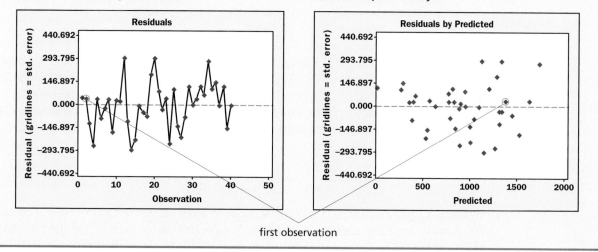

(b) Plot of residuals by observation

(c) Residual plot versus $\hat{y}$

first observation

As an example, consider the QHIC example and the residual plot in Figure 11.23(c). This plot tells us that the residuals appear to fan out as $\hat{y}$ (predicted y) increases. Also note that the scatter plot of y versus x in Figure 11.22 shows the increasing error variance—the y values appear to fan out as x increases. In fact, one might ask why we need to consider residual plots when we can simply look at scatter plots of y versus x. One answer is that, in general, because of possible differences in scaling between residual plots and scatter plots of y versus x, one of these types of plots might be more informative in a particular situation. Therefore, we should always consider both types of plots.

When the constant-variance assumption is violated, we cannot use the formulas in this chapter to make statistical inferences. Later in this section, we discuss how we can make statistical inferences when a nonconstant error variance exists.

The assumption of correct functional form If the functional form of a regression model is incorrect, the residual plots constructed by using the model often display a pattern suggesting the form of a more appropriate model. For instance, if we use a simple linear regression model when the true relationship between y and x is curved, the residual plot will have a curved appearance. Later in this section, we discuss one way to model curved relationships.

FIGURE **11.24**   Residual Plots and the Constant-Variance Assumption

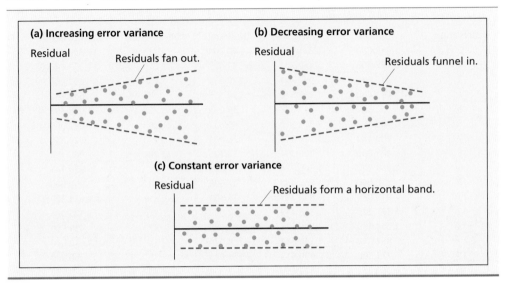

The normality assumption   If the normality assumption holds, a histogram and/or a stem-and-leaf display of the residuals should look reasonably bell-shaped and symmetric about 0. Figure 11.25(a) gives the MegaStat output of a histogram of the residuals from the simple linear regression model describing the QHIC data. The histogram looks fairly bell-shaped and symmetric about 0. However, the tails look somewhat long and heavy or thick, indicating a possible violation of the normality assumption.

Another way to check the normality assumption is to construct a **normal plot** of the residuals. To make a normal plot, we first arrange the residuals in order from smallest to largest. Letting the ordered residuals be denoted as $e_{(1)}$, $e_{(2)}$, . . . , $e_{(n)}$, we denote the ith residual in the ordered listing as $e_{(i)}$. We plot $e_{(i)}$ on the vertical axis against a point called $z_{(i)}$ on the horizontal axis. Here $z_{(i)}$ is defined to be the point on the horizontal axis under the standard normal curve so that the area under this curve to the left of $z_{(i)}$ is $(3i - 1)/(3n + 1)$. For example, recall in the QHIC example that $n = 40$ residuals are given in Figure 11.23(a). It follows that when $i = 1$,

$$\frac{3i - 1}{3n + 1} = \frac{3(1) - 1}{3(40) + 1} = \frac{2}{121} = .0165$$

Therefore, $z_{(1)}$ is the normal point with an area of .0165 under the standard normal curve to its left. This implies that the area under the standard normal curve between $z_{(1)}$ and 0 is $.5 - .0165 = .4835$. So, as illustrated in Figure 11.25(b), $z_{(1)}$ equals -2.13. Because the smallest residual in Figure 11.23(a) is -289.044, the first point plotted is $e_{(1)} = -289.044$ on the vertical scale versus $z_{(1)} = -2.13$ on the horizontal scale. When $i = 2$, it can be verified that $(3i - 1)/(3n + 1)$ equals .0413, so $z_{(2)} = -1.74$. Therefore, because the second-smallest residual in Figure 11.23(a) is -259.958, the second point plotted is $e_{(2)} = -259.958$ on the vertical scale versus $z_{(2)} = -1.74$ on the horizontal scale. This process is continued until the entire normal plot is constructed. The MegaStat output of this plot is given in Figure 11.25(c).

If the normality assumption holds, the expected value of the ith ordered residual $e_{(i)}$ is proportional to $z_{(i)}$. Therefore, a plot of the $e_{(i)}$ values on the vertical scale versus the $z_{(i)}$ values on the horizontal scale [see Figure 11.25(c)] should have a straight-line appearance. That is, if the normality assumption holds, then the normal plot should have a straight-line appearance. A normal plot that does not look like a straight line (admittedly a subjective decision) indicates that the normality assumption is violated. Because the normal plot in Figure 11.25 has some curvature (particularly in the upper right portion), there is a possible violation of the normality assumption.

One further way of assessing the normality of the residual values is by using the chi-square test (see Chapter 14). For the QHIC residuals in Figure 11.25, the mean is 0 and the standard

FIGURE **11.25** Histogram and Normal Plots of the Residuals from the Simple Linear Regression Model Describing the QHIC Data

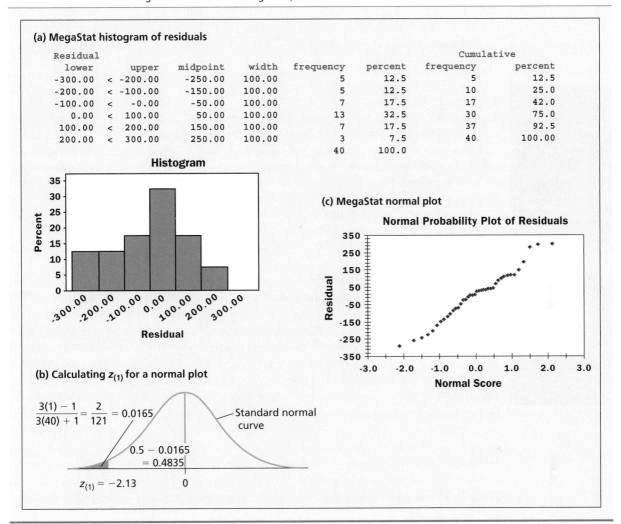

(a) MegaStat histogram of residuals

Residual lower		upper	midpoint	width	frequency	percent	Cumulative frequency	percent
-300.00	<	-200.00	-250.00	100.00	5	12.5	5	12.5
-200.00	<	-100.00	-150.00	100.00	5	12.5	10	25.0
-100.00	<	-0.00	-50.00	100.00	7	17.5	17	42.0
0.00	<	100.00	50.00	100.00	13	32.5	30	75.0
100.00	<	200.00	150.00	100.00	7	17.5	37	92.5
200.00	<	300.00	250.00	100.00	3	7.5	40	100.00
					40	100.0		

Histogram

(c) MegaStat normal plot

Normal Probability Plot of Residuals

(b) Calculating $z_{(1)}$ for a normal plot

$$\frac{3(1) - 1}{3(40) + 1} = \frac{2}{121} = 0.0165$$

Standard normal curve

$0.5 - 0.0165 = 0.4835$

$z_{(1)} = -2.13$

deviation is 145.00. Examining each interval in the histogram in Figure 11.25, the probability (in terms of z scores) is determined. For the first interval, the probability of a score less than -200 is calculated by computing the z for the -200 point, or $(-200 - 0)/145 = -1.38$. The probability of a score with a z less than -1.38 is .0838 (using the z table). The probability value is then multiplied by the sample size (40) to generate an expected frequency value. For interval one, the expected frequency value is .0838(40) = 3.352. The observed frequency is then subtracted from the expected frequency and this difference is squared and then divided by the expected frequency. For the first interval, the result would be $(5 - 3.352)^2/3.352 = .8102$. This computation and the values for the other five intervals are listed below:

Obs Freq	P(z)	p	Expected Frequency (E = np)	(Obs-Exp)²	/Exp
5	p1 = p(score<-200)	0.0838	3.352	2.715904	0.810234
5	p2 = p(-200<score<-100)	0.1613	6.452	2.108304	0.326768
7	p3 = p(-100<score<0)	0.2549	10.196	10.214416	1.001806
13	p4 = p(0<score<100)	0.2549	10.196	7.862416	0.771128
7	p5 = p(100<score<200)	0.1613	6.452	0.300304	0.046544
3	p6 = p(200<score)	0.0838	3.352	0.123904	0.036964
				Sum=	2.993444

The sum, 2.9934, is the obtained chi-squared value. This value is tested against a chi-squared critical value at k(number of intervals) $-1-2$ degrees of freedom. For the QHIC residuals, the degrees of freedom are $6-1-2=3$. At $\alpha < .05$ with 3 df, the chi-square critical value is 7.81473 (see Table A.18 in Appendix A at the back of this book). The obtained chi-square is less than the critical chi-square (2.99 < 7.81), so we do not reject the assumption of normality at alpha less than .05.

ROADBLOCK   **Violations of assumptions**

It is important to realize that violations of the constant-variance and correct functional form assumptions can often cause a histogram and/or a stem-and-leaf display of the residuals to look non-normal and can cause the normal plot to have a curved appearance. Because of this, it is usually a good idea to use residual plots to check for non-constant variance and incorrect functional form before making any final conclusions about the normality assumption (for example, with using the chi-square statistic).

Later in this section, we discuss a procedure that sometimes remedies simultaneous violations of the constant-variance, correct functional form, and normality assumptions.

The independence assumption The independence assumption is most likely to be violated when the regression data are **time series data** (data that have been collected in a time sequence; see also Chapter 16, Time Series Forecasting). For such data, the time-ordered errors can be autocorrelated. Errors occurring over time have **positive autocorrelation** if a positive error in time period i tends to produce, or be followed by, another positive error in time period $i + k$ (some later time period) and if a negative error in time period i tends to produce, or be followed by, another negative error in time period $i + k$. In other words, positive autocorrelation exists when positive errors tend to be followed over time by positive errors and when negative errors tend to be followed over time by negative errors. Positive autocorrelation is depicted in Figure 11.26(a), which illustrates a *positive autocorrelation producing a cyclical error pattern over time*. An example of the pattern seen in Figure 11.26(a) could be sales of lawn mowers across months. The simple linear regression model implies that a positive error produces a greater than average value of y and a negative error produces a smaller than average value of y. It follows that positive autocorrelation means that greater than average values of y tend to be followed by greater than average values of y, and smaller than average values of y tend to be followed by smaller than average values of y.

In contrast to positive autocorrelation, errors occurring over time have **negative autocorrelation** if a positive error in time period i tends to produce, or be followed by, a negative error in time period $i + k$ and if a negative error in time period i tends to produce, or be followed by, a positive error in time period $i + k$. In other words, negative autocorrelation exists when positive errors tend to be followed over time by negative errors and negative errors tend to be followed over time

FIGURE 11.26   Positive and Negative Autocorrelation

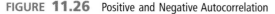

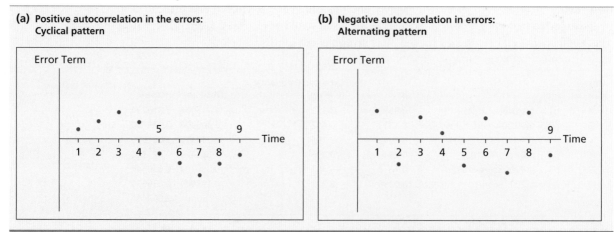

by positive errors. An example of negative autocorrelation is depicted in Figure 11.26(b), which illustrates that *negative autocorrelation can produce an alternating pattern over time*. It follows that negative autocorrelation means that greater than average values of y tend to be followed by smaller than average values of y and smaller than average values of y tend to be followed by greater than average values of y. An example of negative autocorrelation might be provided by a retailer's weekly stock orders. Here a larger than average stock order one week might result in an oversupply and hence a smaller than average order the next week.

The independence assumption states that the time-ordered error terms display no positive or negative autocorrelation. This says that *the errors occur in a random pattern over time*, implying that the errors (and their corresponding y values) are statistically independent.

Because the residuals are point estimates of the errors, a residual plot versus time is used to check the independence assumption. If a residual plot versus the data's time sequence has a cyclical appearance, the errors are positively autocorrelated and the independence assumption is violated. If a plot of the time-ordered residuals has an alternating pattern, the errors are negatively autocorrelated, and again the independence assumption is violated. However, if a plot of the time-ordered residuals displays a random pattern, the errors have little or no autocorrelation. In such a case, it is reasonable to conclude that the independence assumption holds.

Example 11.7 Bookstore Sales

Figure 11.27(a) presents data concerning weekly sales at Folio Bookstore (Sales), Folio's weekly advertising expenditure (Adver), and the weekly advertising expenditure of Folio's main competitor (Compadv). Here the sales values are expressed in thousands of dollars, and the advertising expenditure values are expressed in hundreds of dollars. Figure 11.27(a) also gives the residuals that are obtained when MegaStat is used to perform a simple linear regression analysis relating Folio's sales to Folio's advertising expenditure. These residuals are plotted versus time in Figure 11.27(b) and appear to have a cyclical pattern. This tells us that the errors for the model are positively autocorrelated and the independence assumption is violated. Furthermore, there tend to be positive residuals when the competitor's advertising expenditure is lower (in weeks 1 through 8 and weeks 12 through 16) and negative residuals when the competitor's advertising expenditure is higher (in weeks 9 through 11). Therefore, the competitor's advertising expenditure seems to be causing the positive autocorrelation.

To conclude this example, note that the simple linear regression model relating Folio's sales to Folio's advertising expenditure has a standard error, s, of 5.038. The MegaStat residual plot in Figure 11.27(b) includes grid lines that are placed one and two standard errors above and below the residual mean of 0. All MegaStat residual plots use such grid lines to help better diagnose potential violations of the regression assumptions.

When the independence assumption is violated, various remedies can be employed. One approach is to identify which independent variable (for example, competitors' advertising expenditure) is causing the errors to be autocorrelated. We can then remove this independent variable from the error term and insert it directly into the regression model, forming a multiple regression model. (Multiple regression models are discussed in Chapter 12.)

The Durbin–Watson test One type of positive or negative autocorrelation is called *first-order autocorrelation*. It says that ε_t, the error in time period t, is related to ε_{t-1}, the error in time period $t - 1$. To check for first-order autocorrelation, we can use the Durbin–Watson statistic

$$d = \frac{\sum_{t=2}^{n} (e_t - e_{t-1})^2}{\sum_{t=1}^{n} e_t^2}$$

where $e_1, e_2, \ldots, e_n$ are the time-ordered residuals.

FIGURE 11.27   Folio Bookstore Sales and Advertising Data, and Residual Analysis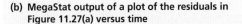

(a) The data and the MegaStat output of the residuals from a simple linear regression relating Folio's sales to Folio's advertising expenditure

Observation	Adver	Compadv	Sales	Predicted	Residual
1	18	10	22	18.7	3.3
2	20	10	27	23.0	4.0
3	20	15	23	23.0	−0.0
4	25	15	31	33.9	−2.9
5	28	15	45	40.4	4.6
6	29	20	47	42.6	4.4
7	29	20	45	42.6	2.4
8	28	25	42	40.4	1.6
9	30	35	37	44.7	−7.7
10	31	35	39	46.9	−7.9
11	34	35	45	53.4	−8.4
12	35	30	52	55.6	−3.6
13	36	30	57	57.8	−0.8
14	38	25	62	62.1	−0.1
15	41	20	73	68.6	4.4
16	45	20	84	77.3	6.7

Durbin-Watson = 0.65

(b) MegaStat output of a plot of the residuals in Figure 11.27(a) versus time

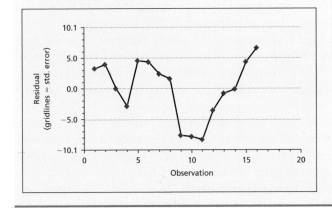

Small values of d lead us to conclude that there is positive autocorrelation. This is because, if d is small, the differences $(e_t - e_{t-1})$ are small. This indicates that the adjacent residuals e_t and e_{t-1} are of the same magnitude, suggesting that the adjacent error terms ε_t and ε_{t-1} are positively correlated. Consider testing the null hypothesis H_0 that the errors are not autocorrelated versus the alternative hypothesis H_a that the errors are positively autocorrelated. Durbin and Watson have shown that there are lower and upper points (denoted $d_{L,\alpha}$ and $d_{U,\alpha}$, respectively) such that if α is the probability of a Type I error, we have the following:

1   If $d < d_{L,\alpha}$, we reject H_0.

2   If $d > d_{U,\alpha}$, we do not reject H_0.

3   If $d_{L,\alpha} \leq d \leq d_{U,\alpha}$, the test is inconclusive.

So that the Durbin–Watson test can be done easily, tables containing the points $d_{L,\alpha}$ and $d_{U,\alpha}$ have been constructed. These tables give the appropriate $d_{L,\alpha}$ and $d_{U,\alpha}$ points for various values of α; k, the number of independent variables used by the regression model; and n, the number of observations. Tables A.12, A.13, and A.14 give these points for $\alpha = .05$, $\alpha = .025$, and $\alpha = .01$. A portion of Table A.12 is given in Table 11.9. Note that when we are considering a simple linear regression model, which uses *one* independent variable, we look up the points $d_{L,\alpha}$ and $d_{U,\alpha}$ under

TABLE **11.9** Critical Values for the Durbin–Watson d Statistic ($\alpha = .05$)

	k = 1		k = 2		k = 3		k = 4	
n	$d_{L,0.05}$	$d_{U,0.05}$	$d_{L,0.05}$	$d_{U,0.05}$	$d_{L,0.05}$	$d_{U,0.05}$	$d_{L,0.05}$	$d_{U,0.05}$
15	1.08	1.36	0.95	1.54	0.82	1.75	0.69	1.97
16	1.10	1.37	0.98	1.54	0.86	1.73	0.74	1.93
17	1.13	1.38	1.02	1.54	0.90	1.71	0.78	1.90
18	1.16	1.39	1.05	1.53	0.93	1.69	0.82	1.87
19	1.18	1.40	1.08	1.53	0.97	1.68	0.86	1.85
20	1.20	1.41	1.10	1.54	1.00	1.68	0.90	1.83

the heading "$k = 1$." Other values of k are used when we study multiple regression models in Chapter 12. Using the residuals in Figure 11.27(a), we can calculate the Durbin–Watson statistic for the simple linear regression model relating Folio's sales to Folio's advertising expenditure to be

$$d = \frac{\sum\limits_{t=2}^{16} (e_t - e_{t-1})^2}{\sum\limits_{t=1}^{16} e_t^2}$$

$$= \frac{(4.0 - 3.3)^2 + (.0 - 4.0)^2 + \cdots + (6.7 - 4.4)^2}{3.3^2 + 4.0^2 + \cdots + 6.7^2}$$

$$= .65$$

A MegaStat output of the Durbin–Watson statistic is given at the bottom of Figure 11.27(a). To test for positive autocorrelation, we note that there are $n = 16$ observations and the regression model uses $k = 1$ independent variable. Therefore, if we set $\alpha = .05$, Table 11.9 tells us that $d_{L,.05} = 1.10$ and $d_{U,.05} = 1.37$. Because $d = .65$ is less than $d_{L,.05} = 1.10$, we reject the null hypothesis of no autocorrelation and conclude (at an α of .05) that there is positive (first-order) autocorrelation.

It can be shown that the Durbin–Watson statistic d is always between 0 and 4. Large values of d (and hence small values of $4 - d$) lead us to conclude that there is negative autocorrelation because if d is large, this indicates that the differences ($e_t - e_{t-1}$) are large. This says that the adjacent errors ε_t and ε_{t-1} are negatively autocorrelated. Consider testing the null hypothesis H_0 that the errors are not autocorrelated versus the alternative hypothesis H_a that the errors are negatively autocorrelated. Durbin and Watson have shown that based on setting the probability of a Type I error equal to α, the points $d_{L,\alpha}$ and $d_{U,\alpha}$ are such that we have the following:

1 If $4 - d < d_{L,\alpha}$, we reject H_0.

2 If $4 - d > d_{U,\alpha}$, we do not reject H_0.

3 If $d_{L,\alpha} \leq 4 - d \leq d_{U,\alpha}$, the test is inconclusive.

As an example, for the Folio sales simple linear regression model, we see that

$$4 - d = 4 - .65 = 3.35 > d_{U,.05} = 1.37$$

Therefore, on the basis of setting α equal to .05, we do not reject the null hypothesis of no autocorrelation and conclude that there is no evidence of negative (first-order) autocorrelation.

We can also use the Durbin–Watson statistic to test for positive or negative autocorrelation. Specifically, consider testing the null hypothesis H_0 that the errors are not autocorrelated versus the alternative hypothesis H_a that the error terms are positively or negatively autocorrelated. Durbin and Watson have shown that based on setting the probability of a Type I error equal to α, we have the following:

1 If $d < d_{L,\alpha/2}$ or $4 - d < d_{L,\alpha/2}$, we reject H_0.

2 If $d > d_{U,\alpha/2}$ and $4 - d > d_{U,\alpha/2}$, we do not reject H_0.

3 If $d_{L,\alpha/2} \leq d \leq d_{U,\alpha/2}$ or $d_{L,\alpha/2} \leq 4 - d \leq d_{U,\alpha/2}$, the test is inconclusive.

For example, consider testing for positive or negative autocorrelation in the Folio sales model. If we set α equal to .05, then $\alpha/2 = .025$, and we need to find the points $d_{L,.025}$ and $d_{U,.025}$ when $n = 16$ and $k = 1$. Looking up these points in Table A.13, we find that $d_{L,.025} = .98$ and $d_{U,.025} = 1.24$. Because $d = .65$ is less than $d_{L,.025} = .98$, we reject the null hypothesis of no autocorrelation and conclude (at an α of .05) that there is first-order autocorrelation.

ROADBLOCK

Positive autocorrelation and time series

Positive autocorrelation is more common in time series data than is negative autocorrelation, so the Durbin–Watson test for positive autocorrelation is used most often. Also note that each Durbin–Watson test assumes that the population of all possible residuals at any time t has a normal distribution.

Transforming the dependent variable: A possible remedy for violations of the constant-variance, correct functional form, and normality assumptions In general, if a data or residual plot indicates that the error variance of a regression model increases as an independent variable or the predicted value of the dependent variable increases, then we can sometimes remedy the situation by transforming the dependent variable. One transformation that works well is to take each y value to a fractional power. As an example, we might use a transformation in which we take the square root (or one-half power) of each y value. Letting y^* denote the value obtained when the transformation is applied to y, we write the square root transformation as

$$y^* = \sqrt{y} = y^{.5}$$

Another commonly used transformation is the quartic root transformation. Here we take each y value to the one-fourth power. That is,

$$y^* = y^{.25}$$

In addition, we sometimes use the logarithmic transformation

$$y^* = \ln y$$

which takes the natural logarithm of each y value. In general, when we take a fractional power (including the natural logarithm) of the dependent variable, the transformation tends to not only equalize the error variance but also straighten out certain types of nonlinear data plots. Specifically, if a data plot indicates that the dependent variable is increasing at an increasing rate (as in Figure 11.22), then a fractional power transformation tends to straighten out the data plot. A fractional power transformation can also help to remedy a violation of the normality assumption. Because we cannot know which fractional power to use before we actually take the transformation, we recommend taking all of the square root, quartic root, and natural logarithm transformations and seeing which one best equalizes the error variance and (possibly) straightens out a nonlinear data plot.

Example 11.8 The QHIC Example

Consider the QHIC upkeep expenditures and the curved data plot in Figure 11.22. In Figures 11.28, 11.29, and 11.30, we show the plots that result when we take the square root, quartic root, and natural logarithmic transformations of the upkeep expenditures and plot the transformed values versus the home values. The square root transformation seems to best equalize the error variance and straighten out the plot. Note that the natural logarithm transformation seems to overtransform the data—the error variance tends to decrease as the home value increases and the data plot seems to bend down. The plot of the quartic roots indicates that the quartic root transformation also seems to overtransform the data (but not by as much as the logarithmic transformation). In general, as the fractional power gets smaller, the transformation gets stronger. Different fractional powers are best in different situations.

FIGURE 11.28 MegaStat Plot of the Square Roots of the Upkeep Expenditures versus the Home Values

FIGURE 11.29 MegaStat Plot of the Quartic Roots of the Upkeep Expenditures versus the Home Values

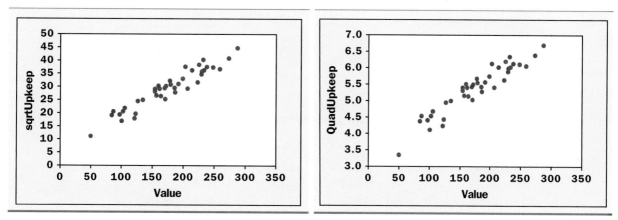

FIGURE 11.30 MegaStat Plot of the Natural Logarithms of the Upkeep Expenditures versus the Home Values

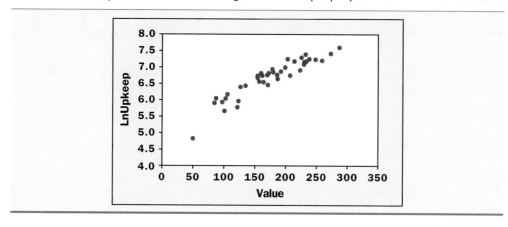

Because the plot in Figure 11.28 of the square roots of the upkeep expenditures versus the home values has a straight-line appearance, we consider the model

$$y^* = \beta_0 + \beta_1 x + \varepsilon$$

where

$$y^* = y^{.5}$$

The MegaStat output of a regression analysis using this transformed model is given in Figure 11.31, and the MegaStat output of an analysis of the model's residuals is given in Figure 11.32. Note that the residual plot versus x for the transformed model in Figure 11.32 has a horizontal band appearance. Therefore, we conclude that the constant-variance and correct functional form assumptions approximately hold for the transformed model and therefore we can use this model to make statistical inferences. Consider a home worth \$220,000. Using the least squares point estimates on the MegaStat output in Figure 11.31, it follows that a point prediction of y^* for such a home is

$$\hat{y}^* = 7.2007 + .1270(220)$$
$$= 35.141$$

This point prediction is given (within rounding) at the bottom of the output, as is the 95 percent prediction interval for y^*, which is [30.348, 39.954]. It follows that a point prediction of the upkeep expenditure for a home worth \$220,000 is $(35.141)^2 = \$1,234.89$ and that a 95 percent prediction interval for this upkeep expenditure is $[(30.348)^2, (39.954)^2] = [\$921.00, \$1,596.32]$.

FIGURE 11.31   MegaStat Output of a Regression Analysis of the Upkeep Expenditure Data by Using the Model $y^* = \beta_0 + \beta_1 x + \varepsilon$, where $y^* = y^5$

Regression Analysis

r^2	0.908	n	40	
r	0.953	k	1	
Std. Error	2.325	Dep. Var.	sqrtUpkeep	

ANOVA table

Source	SS	df	MS	F	p-value
Regression	2,016.8421	1	2,016.8421	373.17	3.01E-21
Residual	205.3764	38	5.4046		
Total	2,222.2185	39			

Regression output

variables	coefficients	std. error	t (df=38)	p-value	confidence interval 95% lower	95% upper
Intercept	7.2007	1.2050	5.976	6.15E-07	4.7613	9.6401
Value	0.1270	0.0066	19.318	3.01E-21	0.1137	0.1404

Predicted values for: sqrtUpkeep

Value	Predicted	95% Confidence Interval lower	upper	95% Prediction Interval lower	upper	Leverage
220	35.1510672	34.1914370	36.1106974	30.3479388	39.9541956	0.042

Suppose that QHIC wants to send an advertising brochure to any home that has a predicted upkeep expenditure of at least $500. Solving the prediction equation $\hat{y}^* = b_0 + b_1 x$ for x, and noting that a predicted upkeep expenditure of $500 corresponds to a $\hat{y}^*$ of $\sqrt{500} = 22.36068$, we obtain

$$x = \frac{\hat{y}^* - b_0}{b_1} = \frac{22.36068 - 7.2007}{.1270} = 119.3699 \ (\text{or } \$119{,}370)$$

It follows that QHIC should send the advertising brochure to any home that has a value of at least $119,370.

Recall that because there are many homes of a particular value in the metropolitan area, QHIC is interested in estimating the mean upkeep expenditure corresponding to this value. Consider all homes worth, for example, $220,000. The output in Figure 11.31 tells us that a point estimate of the mean of the square roots of the upkeep expenditures for all such homes is 35.151 and that a 95 percent confidence interval for this mean is [34.191, 36.111]. Unfortunately, the

FIGURE 11.32   MegaStat Output of Residual Analysis for the Upkeep Expenditure Model $y^* = \beta_0 + \beta_1 x + \varepsilon$, where $y^* = y^5$

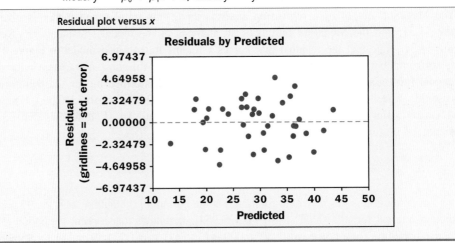

mean of the square root is not the square root of the mean. Therefore, we cannot transform the results for the mean of the square roots back into a result for the mean of the original upkeep expenditures. This is a major drawback to transforming the dependent variable and one reason why many statisticians avoid doing this unless the regression assumptions are badly violated. In Chapter 12, we discuss other remedies for violations of the regression assumptions that do not have some of the drawbacks of transforming the dependent variable. Some of these remedies involve transforming the independent variable.

Exercises for Section **11.10**

CONCEPTS

11.64 In a regression analysis, what variables should the residuals be plotted against? What types of patterns in residual plots indicate violations of the regression assumptions?

11.65 In regression analysis, how do you check the normality assumption?

11.66 What is one possible remedy for violations of the constant-variance, correct functional form, and normality assumptions?

METHODS AND APPLICATIONS

11.67 THE FRESH DETERGENT EXAMPLE

Figure 11.33 gives the MegaStat output of residual diagnostics that are obtained when the simple linear regression model is fit to the Fresh detergent demand data. Interpret the diagnostics and determine if they indicate any violations of the regression assumptions.

FIGURE 11.33   MegaStat Residual Diagnostics for Exercise 11.67

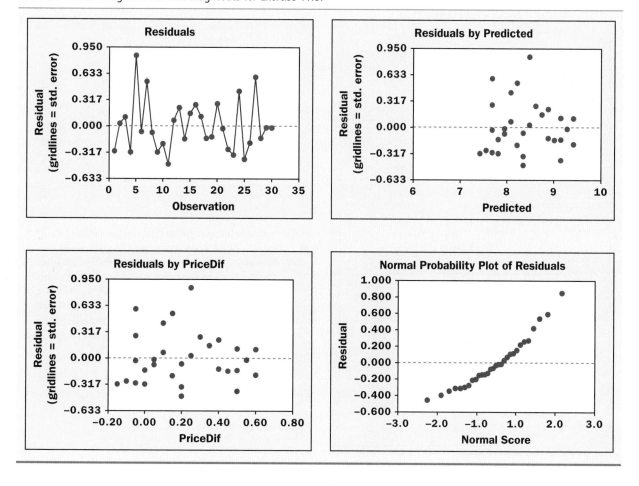

11.68 THE SERVICE TIME EXAMPLE

The MegaStat output of the residuals given by the service time model is given in Figure 11.34 and the MegaStat output of residual plots versus x and $\hat{y}$ is given in Figure 11.35(a) and (b). Do the plots indicate any violations of the regression assumptions?

FIGURE 11.34   MegaStat Output of the Residuals for the Service Time Model

Observation	Minutes	Predicted	Residual
1	109.0	109.9	−0.9
2	58.0	60.7	−2.7
3	138.0	134.5	3.5
4	189.0	183.7	5.3
5	37.0	36.1	0.9
6	82.0	85.3	−3.3
7	103.0	109.9	−6.9
8	134.0	134.5	−0.5
9	68.0	60.7	7.3
10	112.0	109.9	2.1
11	154.0	159.1	−5.1

FIGURE 11.35   MegaStat Residual Plots for the Service Time Model

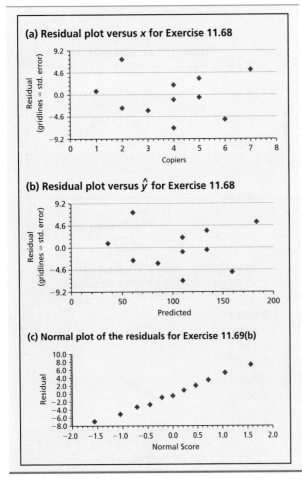

(a) Residual plot versus x for Exercise 11.68

(b) Residual plot versus $\hat{y}$ for Exercise 11.68

(c) Normal plot of the residuals for Exercise 11.69(b)

11.69 THE SERVICE TIME EXAMPLE

Figure 11.34 gives the MegaStat output of the residuals from the simple linear regression model describing the service time data.

a. In this exercise, we construct a normal plot of the residuals from the simple linear regression model. To construct this plot, we must first arrange the residuals in order from smallest to largest. These ordered residuals are given in Table 11.10. Denoting the ith ordered residual as $e_{(i)}$ ($i = 1, 2, \ldots, 11$), we next compute for each value of i the point $z_{(i)}$. These computations are summarized in Table 11.10. Show how $z_{(4)} = -.46$ and $z_{(10)} = 1.05$ were obtained.

b. The ordered residuals (the instances of $e_{(i)}$) are plotted against the instances of $z_{(i)}$ on the MegaStat output of Figure 11.35(c). Does this figure indicate a violation of the normality assumption?

c. Analyze the residual values in Figure 11.34 using the chi-square statistic to test the assumption of normality. At an alpha of .05, what would you conclude?

TABLE 11.10   Ordered Residuals and Normal Plot Calculations

i	Ordered Residual, $e_{(i)}$	$\dfrac{3i-1}{3n+1}$	$z_{(i)}$
1	−6.9	0.0588	−1.565
2	−5.1	0.1470	−1.05
3	−3.3	0.2353	−0.72
4	−2.7	0.3235	−0.46
5	−0.9	0.4118	−0.22
6	−0.5	0.5000	0
7	0.9	0.5882	0.22
8	2.1	0.6765	0.46
9	3.5	0.7647	0.72
10	5.3	0.8529	1.05
11	7.3	0.9412	1.565

11.70 A simple linear regression model is employed to analyze the 24 monthly observations given in Table 11.11. Residuals are computed and are plotted versus time. The resulting residual plot is shown in Figure 11.36. Discuss why the residual plot suggests the existence of positive autocorrelation. The Durbin–Watson statistic d can be calculated to be .473. Test for positive (first-order) autocorrelation at $\alpha = .05$, and test for negative (first-order) autocorrelation at $\alpha = .05$.

TABLE 11.11 Sales and Advertising Data for Exercise 11.70

Month	Monthly Total Sales, y	Advertising Expenditures, x	Month	Monthly Total Sales, y	Advertising Expenditures, x
1	202.66	116.44	13	260.51	129.85
2	232.91	119.58	14	266.34	122.65
3	272.07	125.74	15	281.24	121.64
4	290.97	124.55	16	286.19	127.24
5	299.09	122.35	17	271.97	132.35
6	296.95	120.44	18	265.01	130.86
7	279.49	123.24	19	274.44	122.90
8	255.75	127.55	20	291.81	117.15
9	242.78	121.19	21	290.91	109.47
10	255.34	118.00	22	264.95	114.34
11	271.58	121.81	23	228.40	123.72
12	268.27	126.54	24	209.33	130.33

Source: "Sales and advertising data," by S. Makridakis, S. C. Wheelwright, and V. E. McGee, *Forecasting: Methods and Applications* (Copyright © 1983 John Wiley & Sons, Inc.). Reprinted by permission of John Wiley & Sons, Inc.

FIGURE 11.36 Residual Plot for Exercise 11.70

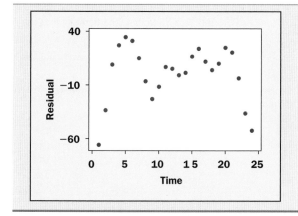

FIGURE 11.37 The Data and Data Plots for Exercise 11.71

(a) Western Steakhouse openings for the last 15 years

Year, t	Steakhouse Openings, y	Year, t	Steakhouse Openings, y
1	11	9	82
2	14	10	99
3	16	11	119
4	22	12	156
5	28	13	257
6	36	14	284
7	46	15	403
8	67		

(b) Time series plot of y versus t

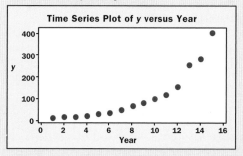

(c) Time series plot of natural logarithm of y versus t

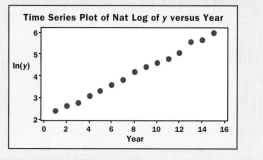

11.71 USING A NATURAL LOGARITHM TRANSFORMATION

Western Steakhouse, a fast-food chain, opened 15 years ago. Each year since then, the number of steakhouses in operation, y, has been recorded. An analyst for the firm wants to use these data to predict the number of steakhouses that will be in operation next year. The data are given in Figure 11.37(a) and a plot of the data is given in Figure 11.37(b). Examining the data plot, we see that the number of steakhouse openings has increased over time at an increasing rate and with increasing variation. A plot of the natural logarithms of the steakhouse values versus time [see Figure 11.37(c)] has a straight-line appearance with constant variation. Therefore, we consider the model

$$\ln y_t = \beta_0 + \beta_1 t + \varepsilon_t$$

If we use MegaStat, we find that the least squares point estimates of β_0 and β_1 are $b_0 = 2.0701$ and $b_1 = .2569$. We also find that a point prediction of and a 95 percent prediction interval for the natural logarithm of the number of steakhouses in operation next year (year 16) are 6.1802 and [5.9945, 6.3659]. See the MegaStat output in Figure 11.38.

FIGURE 11.38   MegaStat Output of a Regression Analysis of the Steakhouse Data Using the Model $y^* = \beta_0 + \beta_1 x + \varepsilon$, where $y^* = \ln y$

Regression Analysis

r^2	0.996	n	15
r	0.998	k	1
Std. Error	0.076	Dep. Var.	ln(y)

ANOVA table

Source	SS	df	MS	F	p-value
Regression	18.4765	1	18.4765	3239.97	5.60E-17
Residual	0.0741	13	0.0057		
Total	18.5506	14			

Regression output

variables	coefficients	std. error	t (df=13)	p-value	confidence interval 95% lower	95% upper
Intercept	2.0701	0.0410	50.451	2.67E-16	1.9815	2.1588
Year	0.2569	0.0045	56.921	5.60E-17	0.2471	0.2666

Predicted values for: ln(y)

Year	Predicted	95% Confidence Interval lower	upper	95% Prediction Interval lower	upper	Leverage
16	6.180206	6.091562	6.268851	5.994536	6.365877	0.295

a. Use the least squares point estimates to verify the point prediction.

b. By exponentiating the point prediction and prediction interval—that is, by calculating $e^{6.1802}$ and $[e^{5.9945}, e^{6.3659}]$—find a point prediction of and a 95 percent prediction interval for the number of steakhouses in operation next year.

c. The Durbin–Watson statistic is found to be 1.88. Test for positive autocorrelation at the .05 level of significance.

d. The model $\ln y_t = \beta_0 + \beta_1 t + \varepsilon_t$ is called a growth curve model because it implies that

$$y_t = e^{(\beta_0 + \beta_1 t + \varepsilon_t)} = (e^{\beta_0})(e^{\beta_1 t})(e^{\varepsilon_t}) = \alpha_0 \alpha_1^t \eta_t$$

where $\alpha_0 = e^{\beta_0}$, $\alpha_1 = e^{\beta_1}$, and $\eta_t = e^{\varepsilon_t}$. Here $\alpha_1 = e^{\beta_1}$ is called the *growth rate of the y values*. Noting that the least squares point estimate of β_1 is $b_1 = .2569$, estimate the growth rate α_1. Also interpret this growth rate by using the fact that $y_t = \alpha_0 \alpha_1^t \eta_t = (\alpha_0 \alpha_1^{t-1})\alpha_1 \eta_t \approx (y_{t-1})\alpha_1 \eta_t$. This says that y_t is expected to be approximately α_1 times y_{t-1}.

11.72 THE UNEQUAL-VARIANCES SERVICE TIME EXAMPLE

Figure 11.39(a) presents data concerning the time, y, required to perform service and the number of microcomputers serviced, x, for 15 service calls. Figure 11.39(b) gives a plot of y versus x, and Figure 11.39(c) gives the Excel output of a plot of the residuals versus x for a simple linear regression model. What regression assumption appears to be violated?

FIGURE 11.39   The Data, Data Plot, and Residual Plot for Exercise 11.72

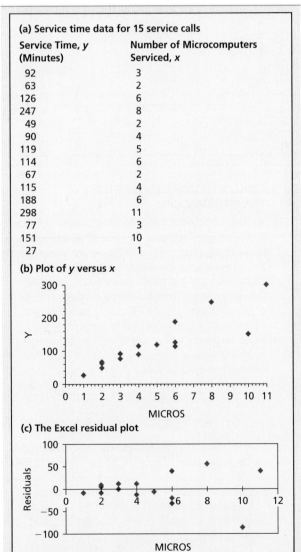

(a) Service time data for 15 service calls

Service Time, y (Minutes)	Number of Microcomputers Serviced, x
92	3
63	2
126	6
247	8
49	2
90	4
119	5
114	6
67	2
115	4
188	6
298	11
77	3
151	10
27	1

(b) Plot of y versus x

(c) The Excel residual plot

FIGURE 11.40 MegaStat Output of a Regression Analysis of the Service Time Data Using the Model $y/x = \beta_0 + \beta_1(1/x) + \varepsilon/x$

Regression Analysis

	r^2	0.095	n	15
	r	0.308	k	1
	Std. Error	5.158	Dep. Var.	Y/X

ANOVA table

Source	SS	df	MS	F	p-value
Regression	36.2685	1	36.2685	1.36	0.2640
Residual	345.8857	13	26.6066		
Total	382.1542	14			

Regression output

					confidence interval	
variables	coefficients	std. error	t (df = 13)	p-value	95% lower	95% upper
Intercept	24.0406	2.2461	10.703	8.13E-08	19.1883	28.8929
1/X	6.7642	5.7936	1.168	0.2640	−5.7521	19.2804

Predicted values for: Y/X

		95% Confidence Intervals		95% Prediction Intervals		
1/X	Predicted	lower	upper	lower	upper	Leverage
0.1429	25.0069	21.4335	28.5803	13.3044	36.7094	0.103

11.73 THE UNEQUAL-VARIANCES SERVICE TIME EXAMPLE

Consider the simple linear regression model describing the service time data in Figure 11.39(a). Figure 11.39(c) shows that the residual plot versus x for this model fans out, indicating that the error term ε tends to become larger in magnitude as x increases. To remedy this violation of the constant-variance assumption, we divide all terms in the simple linear regression model by x. This gives the transformed model

$$\frac{y}{x} = \beta_0\left(\frac{1}{x}\right) + \beta_1 + \frac{\varepsilon}{x}$$

or, equivalently,

$$\frac{y}{x} = \beta_0 + \beta_1\left(\frac{1}{x}\right) + \frac{\varepsilon}{x}$$

Figure 11.40 and Figure 11.41 give a regression output and a residual plot versus x, respectively, for this model.

a. Does the residual plot indicate that the constant-variance assumption holds for the transformed model?

b. Consider a future service call during which seven microcomputers will be serviced. Let μ_0 represent the mean service time for all service calls during which seven microcomputers will be serviced, and let y_0 represent the actual service time for an individual service call during which seven microcomputers will be serviced. The bottom of the MegaStat output in Figure 11.40 tells us that

$$\frac{\hat{y}}{7} = 24.0406 + 6.7642\left(\frac{1}{7}\right) = 25.0069$$

is a point estimate of $\mu_0/7$ and a point prediction of $y_0/7$. Multiply this result by 7 to obtain $\hat{y}$. Multiply the ends of the confidence interval and prediction interval shown on the MegaStat output by 7. This will give a 95 percent confidence interval for μ_0 and a 95 percent prediction interval for y_0. If the number of minutes you will allow for the future service call is the upper limit of the 95 percent confidence interval for μ_0, how many minutes will you allow?

FIGURE 11.41 MegaStat Residual Plot for Exercise 11.73

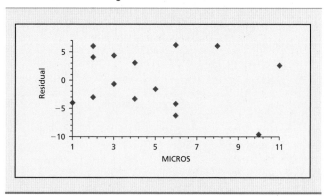

11.11 SOME SHORTCUT FORMULAS

Calculating the sum of squared residuals A shortcut formula for the sum of squared residuals is

$$SSE = SS_{yy} - \frac{SS_{xy}^2}{SS_{xx}}$$

where

$$SS_{yy} = \sum (y_i - \bar{y})^2 = \sum y_i^2 - \frac{\left(\sum y_i\right)^2}{n}$$

For example, consider the data in Table 11.12. If we square each of the eight observed y values and add up the resulting squared values, we find that $\sum y_i^2 = 859.91$. Also, for these data, it has been found that $\sum y_i = 81.7$, $SS_{xy} = -179.6475$, and $SS_{xx} = 1{,}404.355$. It follows that

$$SS_{yy} = \sum y_i^2 - \frac{\left(\sum y_i\right)^2}{n}$$

$$= 859.91 - \frac{81.7^2}{8} = 25.549$$

and

$$SSE = SS_{yy} - \frac{SS_{xy}^2}{SS_{xx}} = 25.549 - \frac{(-179.6475)^2}{1{,}404.355}$$

$$= 25.549 - 22.981 = 2.568.$$

Finally, note that SS_{xy}^2/SS_{xx} equals $b_1 SS_{xx}$. However, we recommend using the first of these expressions, because doing so usually gives less round-off error.

TABLE **11.12**   Data

Observation	x	y
1	28.0	12.4
2	28.0	11.7
3	32.5	12.4
4	39.0	10.8
5	45.9	9.4
6	57.8	9.5
7	58.1	8.0
8	62.5	7.5

Calculating the total, explained, and unexplained variations The unexplained variation is the SSE and the quantity SS_{yy} is the total variation, and the expression SS_{xy}^2/SS_{xx} equals the explained variation.

CHAPTER SUMMARY

In this chapter, we discussed the correlation coefficient (r) and simple linear regression analysis, which relates a dependent variable to a single independent (predictor) variable. We began by considering the simple linear regression model, which employs two parameters: the slope and the y intercept.

We next discussed how to compute the least squares point estimates of these parameters and how to use these estimates to calculate a point estimate of the mean value of the dependent variable and a point prediction of an individual value of the dependent variable. Then, after considering the assumptions behind the simple linear regression model, we discussed testing the significance of the regression relationship (slope), calculating a confidence interval for the mean value of the dependent variable, and calculating a prediction interval for an individual value of the dependent variable.

We then explained several measures of the utility of the simple linear regression model. These include the coefficient of determination and an F test for the simple linear model. We concluded this chapter by discussing using residual analysis to detect violations of the regression assumptions. We learned that we can sometimes remedy violations of these assumptions by transforming the dependent variable.

KEY TERMS

coefficient of determination
correlation coefficient (r)
cross-sectional data
distance value
experimental region
least squares point estimates
negative autocorrelation
normal plot

positive autocorrelation
residual
residual plot
simple linear (or straight-line) regression model
slope (of the simple linear regression model)
time series data
y intercept (of the simple linear regression model)

IMPORTANT FORMULAS AND TESTS

Correlation coefficient

Testing the significance of the population correlation coefficient

Simple linear regression model

Mean square error

Standard error

Least squares point estimates of β_0 and β_1

Least squares line (prediction equation)

The predicted value of y_i

Sum of squared residuals

The residual

Point estimate of a mean value of y

Point prediction of an individual value of y

Sampling distribution of b_1

Standard error of the estimate b_1

Testing the significance of the slope

Confidence interval for the slope

Testing the significance of the y intercept

Distance value

Sampling distribution of $\hat{y}$

Standard error of $\hat{y}$

Confidence interval for a mean value of y

Prediction interval for an individual value of y

Unexplained variation

Explained variation

Total variation

Coefficient of determination

An F test for the simple linear regression model

Durbin–Watson test

SUPPLEMENTARY EXERCISES

connect Practise and learn online with *Connect*. Items for which there are online data sets are marked with ✎.

11.74 Consider the following data concerning the demand (y) and price (x) of a consumer product.

Demand, y	252	244	241	234	230	223
Price, x	$2.00	$2.20	$2.40	$2.60	$2.80	$3.00

a. Plot y versus x. Does it seem reasonable to use the simple linear regression model to relate y to x?

b. Calculate the least squares point estimates of the parameters in the simple linear regression model.

c. Write the least squares prediction equation. Graph this equation on the plot of y versus x.

FIGURE 11.42   Excel Output for Exercise 11.75

SUMMARY OUTPUT

Regression Statistics
Multiple R	0.991786163
R Square	0.983639793
Adjusted R Square	0.981594768
Standard Error	5.336268132
Observations	10

ANOVA

	df	SS	MS	F	Significance F
Regression	1	13696.59394	13696.59394	480.9913802	1.97186E-08
Residual	8	227.8060606	28.47575758		
Total	9	13924.4			

	Coefficients	Standard Error	t Stat	P-value	Lower 95%	Upper 95%	Lower 95.0%	Upper 95.0%
Intercept	74.72727273	1.903729846	39.25308671	1.95043E-10	70.33726099	79.11728446	70.33726099	79.11728446
WidthDiff	-6.442424242	0.293751893	-21.93151568	1.97186E-08	-7.11981776	-5.765030725	-7.11981776	-5.765030725

d. Test the significance of the regression relationship between y and x.

e. Find a point prediction of and a 95 percent prediction interval for the demand corresponding to each of the prices $2.10, $2.75, and $3.10.

11.75 In an article in *Public Roads* (1983), Bissell, Pilkington, Mason, and Woods studied bridge safety (measured in accident rates per 100 million vehicles) and the difference between the width of the bridge and the width of the roadway approach (road plus shoulder):[3]

WidthDiff.	−6	−4	−2	0	2	4	6	8	10	12
Accident	120	103	87	72	58	44	31	20	12	7

The Excel output of a simple linear regression analysis relating accident to width difference is as in Figure 11.42. Use the Excel output to do the following:

a. Identify and interpret the least squares point estimate of the slope of the simple linear regression model.

b. Identify and interpret the p-value for testing $H_0: \beta_1 = 0$ versus $H_a: \beta_1 \neq 0$.

c. Compute and interpret r^2 (eta^2).

11.76 An organizational behaviour researcher wants to predict job satisfaction with perceived control over the work environment under the hypothesis that those employees who feel that they have greater control over their work will be more satisfied with their jobs. Employees ($n = 25$) completed a self-report survey asking about job satisfaction, measured on a 1 (not at all satisfied) to 10 (completely satisfied) scale, and perceived control, measured on a 1 (no control, told what to do) to 10 (have complete control) scale. The data are reported in Table 11.13.

a. Calculate the correlation between the control and satisfaction variables.

b. Use the simple linear regression model and a computer to compute the model. What is the F value of the resulting model?

c. Based on the regression analysis, how much of the variance in job satisfaction can be predicted by perceived control?

d. What conclusions can you draw from the study?

e. Figure 11.43 is the MegaStat normal probability of the plot of residuals. What can you conclude from this plot?

f. Using MegaStat, generate a list of the residuals. Using the chi-square statistic and the histogram of the residuals provided in Figure 11.44, what can you conclude about the assumption of normality for the residuals?

TABLE 11.13   Perceived Control and Job Satisfaction Data for 25 Employees

Employee	Control	Satisfaction
1	8	10
2	2	5
3	9	6
4	4	7
5	8	8
6	1	5
7	4	4
8	3	1
9	1	2
10	10	9
11	5	5
12	6	7
13	4	3
14	5	2
15	7	10
16	3	1
17	8	9
18	6	5
19	4	6
20	5	7
21	5	8
22	1	3
23	8	6
24	2	4
25	3	5

[3]Source: "Roadway cross section and alignment," by H. H. Bissell, G. B. Pilkington II, J. M. Mason, and D. L. Woods, *Public Roads*, 46 (March 1983), pp. 132–141.

FIGURE 11.43   MegaStat Normal Probability Plot of the Residuals for Exercise 11.76(e)

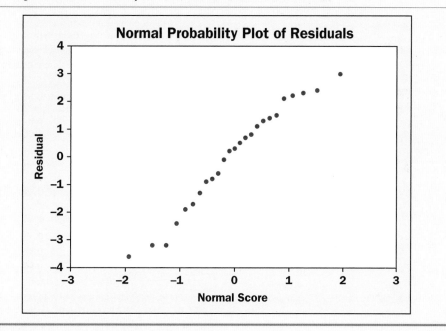

FIGURE 11.44   Histogram of the Residuals for Exercise 11.76(f)

Resids lower		upper	midpoint	width	frequency	percent
−4.00	<	−3.00	−3.50	1.00	3	12.0
−3.00	<	−2.00	−2.50	1.00	1	4.0
−2.00	<	−1.00	−1.50	1.00	3	12.0
−1.00	<	−0.00	−0.50	1.00	4	16.0
0.00	<	1.00	0.50	1.00	5	20.0
1.00	<	2.00	1.50	1.00	4	16.0
2.00	<	3.00	2.50	1.00	5	20.0
					25	100.0

11.77 Table 11.14 presents the public and publicly guaranteed external debt for 27 countries according to the World Bank for the second quarter of 2009. Also in Table 11.14 are the 2010 population statistics from the United Nations.

   a. Enter the data into Excel and calculate the correlation between debt and population. What is the value? How would you interpret the correlation?

   b. Analyze the data using regression analysis predicting debt (y) with population (x). How does the multiple R compare to the correlation found in part (a)?

   c. Calculate the residuals. Which country had the least residual value? Which country had the greatest residual value?

11.78 In analyzing the stock market, we sometimes use the model $y = \beta_0 + \beta_1 x + \varepsilon$ to relate y, the rate of return on a particular stock, to x, the rate of return on the overall stock market. When using this model, we can interpret β_1 to be the percentage point change in the mean (or expected) rate of return on the particular stock that is associated with an increase of one percentage point in the rate of return on the overall stock market.

If regression analysis can be used to conclude (at a high level of confidence) that β_1 is greater than 1 (for example, if the 95 percent confidence interval for β_1 is [1.1826, 1.4723]), this indicates that the mean rate of return on the particular stock changes more quickly than the rate of return on the overall stock market. Such a stock is called an *aggressive stock* because gains for such a stock tend to be greater than overall market gains (which occur when the market is bullish). However, losses for such a stock tend to be greater than overall market losses (which occur when the market is bearish). Aggressive stocks should be purchased if you expect the market to rise and avoided if you expect the market to fall.

If regression analysis can be used to conclude (at a high level of confidence) that β_1 is less than 1 (for example, if the 95 percent confidence interval for β_1 is [.4729, .7861]), this indicates that the mean rate of return on the particular stock changes more slowly than the rate of return on the overall stock market. Such a stock is called a *defensive stock*. Losses for such a stock tend to be less

TABLE **11.14**   Public and Publicly Guaranteed External
Debt (US$ millions) and Population for
27 Countries

Country	2009Q2	2010 Population
Albania	2,622	3,169
Algeria	3,187	35,423
Bahamas, The	473	346
Bolivia	2,569	10,031
Burkina Faso	1,771	16,287
Cambodia	2,749	15,053
Cameroon	2,002	19,958
China	67,621	1,354,146
Dominica	208	71
Ethiopia	4,365	84,976
Georgia	2,980	4,219
Ghana	4,704	24,333
Guatemala	4,784	14,377
Honduras	2,457	7,616
Kenya	7,038	40,863
Lebanon	21,103	4,255
Madagascar	2,174	20,146
Nepal	3,577	29,853
Nigeria	3,719	158,259
Pakistan	42,264	184,753
Panama	8,907	3,508
Rwanda	704	10,277
Sri Lanka	15,437	20,410
Tajikistan	1,473	7,075
Tonga	103	104
Uganda	2,046	33,796
Yemen	5,920	24,256

Debt data are in millions.
Population data are in thousands.

Source: This table has been adapted from The World Bank Table
C1- Public and Publicly-Guaranted [sic] External Debt Position (US$ millions),
ddp-ext.worldbank.org/ext/ddpreports/ViewSharedReport?REPORT_
ID=10836&REQUEST_TYPE=VIEW; and United Nations Statistics Division
Social Indicators: Indicators on Population, unstats.un.org/unsd/
demographic/products/socind/population.htm

than overall market losses, whereas gains for such a stock tend to be less than overall market gains. Defensive stocks should be held if you expect the market to fall and sold if you expect the market to rise.

If the least squares point estimate b_1 of β_1 is nearly equal to 1, and if the 95 percent confidence interval for β_1 contains 1, this might indicate that the mean rate of return on the particular stock changes at roughly the same rate as the rate of return on the overall stock market. Such a stock is called a *neutral stock*.

In a 1984 article in *Financial Analysts Journal*, Levy considers how a stock's value of β_1 depends on the length of time for which the rate of return is calculated. Levy

calculated estimated values of β_1 for return length times varying from 1 to 30 months for each of 38 aggressive stocks, 38 defensive stocks, and 68 neutral stocks. Each estimated value was based on data from 1946 to 1975. In the following table, we present the average estimate of β_1 for each stock type for different return length times:

	Average Estimate of β_1		
Return Length Time	Aggressive Stocks	Defensive Stocks	Neutral Stocks
1	1.37	0.50	0.98
3	1.42	0.44	0.95
6	1.53	0.41	0.94
9	1.69	0.39	1.00
12	1.83	0.40	0.98
15	1.67	0.38	1.00
18	1.78	0.39	1.02
24	1.86	0.35	1.14
30	1.83	0.33	1.22

Source: Reprinted by permission from "Measuring risk and performance over alternative investment horizons," by H. Levy, *Financial Analysts Journal* (March–April 1984), pp. 61–68. Copyright © 1984, CFA Institute. Reproduced and modified from *Financial Analysts Journal* with permission of CFA Institute.

Let y = average estimate of β_1 and x = return length time, and consider relating y to x for each stock type by using the simple linear regression model

$$y = \beta_0^* + \beta_1^* x + \varepsilon$$

Here β_0^* and β_1^* are regression parameters relating y to x. We use the asterisks to indicate that these regression parameters are different from β_0 and β_1. Calculate a 95 percent confidence interval for β_1^* for each stock type. Carefully interpret each interval.

11.79   INTERNET EXERCISE

Organizations that depend on volunteers can gain information about the age, income, and other personal characteristics of people and the average number of hours that these people volunteer from the statistics reported by Statistics Canada. Find the most recent data reported on the Statistics Canada website (statcan.gc.ca) and enter into Excel the age groups (assign a number to the age intervals, starting with 1 for the youngest) in the first column. In the second column, enter the corresponding average number of volunteer hours. Compute the correlation between age and average hours. What does this value tell you? Compute r^2 (eta^2) from the correlation. What can you conclude from this value? Also run a linear regression analysis with average hours as the dependent (y) variable and age as the independent (x) variable. What does the result of the regression analysis tell you? If you were asked by volunteer organizations which age groups to target to look for volunteers, which group would you suggest?

CHAPTER **12**
Multiple Regression

LEARNING OBJECTIVES

After reading this chapter, you should be able to

LO1 Describe the experimental region in a multiple regression

LO2 List the assumptions for the multiple regression model

LO3 Explain what is meant by the *least squares point estimate of a model parameter*

LO4 Define the multiple coefficient of determination

LO5 Compute an *F* test from the results output

LO6 Distinguish between a confidence interval and a prediction interval for *y*

CHAPTER OUTLINE

Part 1 Basic Multiple Regression

12.1 The Multiple Regression Model

12.2 Model Assumptions and the Standard Error

12.3 Multicollinearity

12.4 The Least Squares Estimates, and Point Estimation and Prediction

12.5 R^2 and Adjusted R^2

12.6 The Overall *F* Test

12.7 Testing the Significance of an Independent Variable

12.8 Confidence and Prediction Intervals

Part 2 Using Squared and Interaction Terms (Optional)

12.9 The Quadratic Regression Model

12.10 Interaction

Part 3 Dummy Variables and Advanced Statistical Inferences (Optional)

12.11 Using Dummy Variables to Model Qualitative Independent Variables

12.12 The Partial *F* Test: Testing the Significance of a Portion of a Regression Model

Important Note:

Part 1 of this chapter covers basic multiple regression analysis and is the only prerequisite for Optional Parts 2 and 3. Parts 2 and 3 cover more advanced regression topics and can be read independently of each other. They can be read in any order without loss of continuity.

Often we can more accurately describe, predict, and control a dependent variable by using a regression model that uses more than one independent variable, such as when deciding on whom to hire for a position. In this situation, multiple pieces of information are preferable to a single question and answer. For example, a job candidate's past employment experience might be a good indicator of future work behaviour. If an interviewer can also add information such as a work sample or personality–job fit measures, then the hiring decision will be sounder. Such a model is called a **multiple regression model**, which is the subject of this chapter.

PART 1
Basic Multiple
Regression

12.1 THE MULTIPLE REGRESSION MODEL

Regression models that use more than one independent variable are called *multiple regression models.*

Part 1: The data and a regression model In Chapter 11, we used a single predictor variable x to predict y. We now consider predicting y using an additional variable, x_2.

Consider the data in Table 12.1. Figure 12.1 presents a scatter plot of y versus x_1. This plot shows that y tends to decrease in a straight-line fashion as x_1 increases. This suggests that if we want to predict y on the basis of x_1 only, the simple linear regression model

$$y = \beta_0 + \beta_1 x_1 + \varepsilon$$

relates y to x_1. Figure 12.2 presents a scatter plot of y versus x_2. This plot shows that y tends to increase in a straight-line fashion as x_2 increases. This suggests that if we want to predict y on the basis of x_2 only, the simple linear regression model

$$y = \beta_0 + \beta_1 x_2 + \varepsilon$$

relates y to x_2. If we want to predict y on the basis of both x_1 and x_2, it seems reasonable to combine these models to form the model

$$y = \beta_0 + \beta_1 x_1 + \beta_2 x_2 + \varepsilon$$

to relate y to x_1 and x_2. Here we have arbitrarily placed the $\beta_1 x_1$ term first and the $\beta_2 x_2$ term second, and we have renumbered β_1 and β_2 to be consistent with the subscripts on x_1 and x_2. This regression model says that

1 β_0, β_1, and β_2 are regression parameters relating the mean value of y to x_1 and x_2.

2 ε is an error term that describes the effects on y of all factors other than x_1 and x_2.

TABLE 12.1
Sample Data

x_1	x_2	y
28.0	18	12.4
28.0	14	11.7
32.5	24	12.4
39.0	22	10.8
45.9	8	9.4
57.8	16	9.5
58.1	1	8.0
62.5	0	7.5

When predicting y with x_1 and x_2, ideally the correlations between y and x_1 and between y and x_2 will both be high (in either the positive or negative direction), resulting in greater prediction of y. A concern in multiple regression models is when the relationship between x_1 and x_2 is high. In a perfect world, the correlation between x_1 and x_2 would be zero so that when both were entered into a multiple regression equation, each would predict a unique proportion of the variance in y. Typically the correlation between x_1 and x_2 is not zero, resulting in some overlap between x_1 and x_2. If the correlation between x_1 and x_2 is too high, then there is evidence of multicollinearity and a substantial part of either x_1 or x_2 is redundant. Therefore, before a multiple regression analysis is conducted, the correlations between y, x_1, and x_2 should be examined.

FIGURE 12.1 Plot of y versus x_1

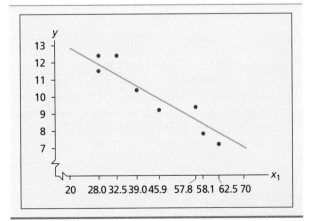

FIGURE 12.2 Plot of y versus x_2

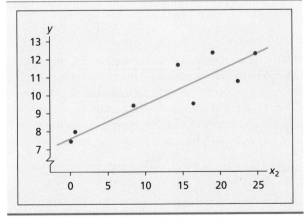

Part 2: Interpreting the regression parameters β_0, β_1, and β_2 The exact interpretations of the parameters β_0, β_1, and β_2 are quite simple. First suppose that $x_1 = 0$ and $x_2 = 0$. Then

$$\beta_0 + \beta_1 x_1 + \beta_2 x_2 = \beta_0 + \beta_1(0) + \beta_2(0) = \beta_0$$

So β_0 is the mean y value when $x_1 = 0$ and $x_2 = 0$. The parameter β_0 is called the *intercept* in the regression model. You might wonder whether β_0 has any practical interpretation, since it might be unlikely for x_1 and x_2 to equal zero. Indeed, sometimes the parameter β_0 and other parameters in a regression analysis do not have practical interpretations because the situations related to the interpretations are not likely to occur in practice. In fact, sometimes each parameter does not, by itself, have much practical importance. Rather, the parameters relate the mean of the dependent variable to the independent variables in an overall sense.

We next interpret β_1 and β_2 individually. To examine the interpretation of β_1, consider two observations. Suppose that for x_1, the value is c, and for x_2, the value is d. The mean y value is then

$$\beta_0 + \beta_1(c) + \beta_2(d)$$

For the second observation, suppose that the x_1 value is $c + 1$ and the x_2 value is d. The mean y value is

$$\beta_0 + \beta_1(c + 1) + \beta_2(d)$$

It is easy to see that the difference between these mean y values is β_1 because the two observations differ only in that x_1 is one greater in the second observation than in the first. In the following, we can interpret the parameter β_1 as the mean change in y associated with a one-point increase in x_1 (note that x_2 did not change in value).

The interpretation of β_2 can be established similarly. We can interpret β_2 as the change in mean y values that is associated with a one-unit increase in x_2 when x_1 does not change.

Part 3: A geometric interpretation of the regression model To interpret a multiple regression model geometrically, we begin by defining the experimental region to be the range of the combinations of the observed values of x_1 and x_2. From the data in Table 12.1, it is reasonable to depict the experimental region as the shaded region in Figure 12.3. Here the combinations of x_1 and x_2 values are the ordered pairs in the figure.

LO1

We next write the mean value of y when IV_1 (independent variable one) is x_1 and IV_2 is x_2 as $\mu_{y|x_1, x_2}$ (mu of y given x_1 and x_2) and consider the equation

$$\mu_{y|x_1, x_2} = \beta_0 + \beta_1 x_1 + \beta_2 x_2$$

which relates mean y values to x_1 and x_2. Because this is a linear equation with two variables, geometrically this equation is the equation of a plane in three-dimensional space. We sometimes refer

FIGURE 12.3 The Experimental Region

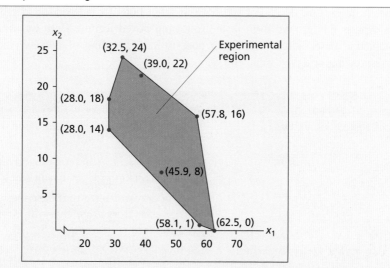

FIGURE **12.4**   A Geometrical Interpretation of the Regression Model Relating y to x_1 and x_2

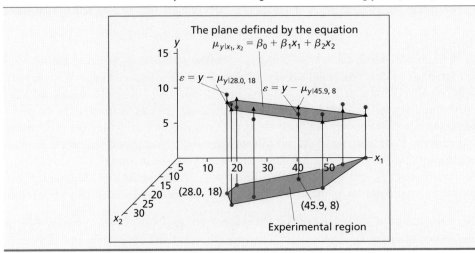

to this plane as the *plane of means*, and we illustrate the portion of this plane corresponding to the (x_1, x_2) combinations in the experimental region in Figure 12.4. As illustrated in this figure, the model

$$y = \mu_{y|x_1, x_2} + \varepsilon$$
$$= \beta_0 + \beta_1 x_1 + \beta_2 x_2 + \varepsilon$$

says that the error terms cause the observed y values (the red dots in the upper portion of the figure) to deviate from the mean y values (the triangles in the figure), which lie exactly on the plane of means

$$\mu_{y|x_1, x_2} = \beta_0 + \beta_1 x_1 + \beta_2 x_2$$

For example, consider the first row of data in Table 12.1 ($y = 12.4$, $x_1 = 28.0$, $x_2 = 18$). Figure 12.4 shows that the error term for this observation is positive, causing y to be higher than $\mu_{y|28.0, 18}$ (mean y value when $x_1 = 28.0$ and $x_2 = 18$). Here factors other than x_1 and x_2 have resulted in a positive error term. As another example, the error term for row 5 in Table 12.1 ($y = 9.4$, $x_1 = 45.9$, $x_2 = 8$) is negative, so y is lower than $\mu_{y|45.9, 8}$ (mean y value when $x_1 = 45.9$ and $x_2 = 8$). Here factors other than x_1 and x_2 have resulted in a negative error term.

The regression model presented in Figure 12.4 expresses the dependent variable as a function of two independent variables. In general, we can use a multiple regression model to express a dependent variable as a function of any number of independent variables. For example, hiring decisions could be based on four independent variables, such as education, past work experience, personality, and a current work sample. The general form of a multiple regression model expresses the dependent variable y as a function of k independent variables $x_1, x_2, \ldots, x_k$. We express this general form in the following boxed feature. Here we assume that we have obtained n observations, with each observation consisting of an observed value of y and corresponding observed values of $x_1, x_2, \ldots, x_k$.

The Multiple Regression Model

The multiple regression model relating y to $x_1, x_2, \ldots, x_k$ is

$$y = \mu_{y|x_1, x_2, \ldots, x_k} + \varepsilon$$
$$= \beta_0 + \beta_1 x_1 + \beta_2 x_2 + \cdots + \beta_k x_k + \varepsilon$$

Here

1 $\mu_{y|x_1, x_2, \ldots, x_k} = \beta_0 + \beta_1 x_1 + \beta_2 x_2 + \cdots + \beta_k x_k$ is the mean value of the dependent variable y when

the values of the independent variables are $x_1, x_2, \ldots, x_k$.

2 $\beta_0, \beta_1, \beta_2, \ldots, \beta_k$ are (unknown) regression parameters relating the mean value of y to $x_1, x_2, \ldots, x_k$.

3 ε is an error term that describes the effects on y of all factors other than the values of the independent variables $x_1, x_2, \ldots, x_k$.

Example 12.1 Predicting Sales Performance

Suppose the sales manager of a company wants to evaluate the performance of the company's sales representatives. Each sales representative is solely responsible for one sales territory, and the manager decides that it is reasonable to measure the performance, y, of a sales representative by using the yearly sales of the company's product in the representative's sales territory. The manager wants to investigate how sales performance, y, depends on five independent variables:

x_1 = Number of months the representative has been employed by the company,

x_2 = Sales of the company's product and competing products in the sales territory (market potential),

x_3 = Dollar advertising expenditure in the territory,

x_4 = Weighted average of the company's market share in the territory for the previous four years,

x_5 = Change in the company's market share in the territory over the previous four years.

In Table 12.2, we present values of y and x_1 through x_5 for 25 randomly selected sales representatives. To understand the values of y and x_2 in the table, note that sales of the company's product or any competing product are measured in hundreds of units of the product sold. Therefore, for example, the first sales figure of 3,669.88 in Table 12.2 means that the first randomly selected sales representative sold 366,988 units of the company's product during the year.

TABLE **12.2** Sales Territory Performance Study Data

	Sales, y	Time with Company, x_1	Market Potential, x_2	Advertising, x_3	Market Share, x_4	Market Share Change, x_5
	3,669.88	43.10	74,065.11	4,582.88	2.51	0.34
	3,473.95	108.13	58,117.30	5,539.78	5.51	0.15
	2,295.10	13.82	21,118.49	2,950.38	10.91	−0.72
	4,675.56	186.18	68,521.27	2,243.07	8.27	0.17
	6,125.96	161.79	57,805.11	7,747.08	9.15	0.50
	2,134.94	8.94	37,806.94	402.44	5.51	0.15
	5,031.66	365.04	50,935.26	3,140.62	8.54	0.55
	3,367.45	220.32	35,602.08	2,086.16	7.07	−0.49
	6,519.45	127.64	46,176.77	8,846.25	12.54	1.24
	4,876.37	105.69	42,053.24	5,673.11	8.85	0.31
	2,468.27	57.72	36,829.71	2,761.76	5.38	0.37
	2,533.31	23.58	33,612.67	1,991.85	5.43	−0.65
	2,408.11	13.82	21,412.79	1,971.52	8.48	0.64
	2,337.38	13.82	20,416.87	1,737.38	7.80	1.01
	4,586.95	86.99	36,272.00	10,694.20	10.34	0.11
	2,729.24	165.85	23,093.26	8,618.61	5.15	0.04
	3,289.40	116.26	26,878.59	7,747.89	6.64	0.68
	2,800.78	42.28	39,571.96	4,565.81	5.45	0.66
	3,264.20	52.84	51,866.15	6,022.70	6.31	−0.10
	3,453.62	165.04	58,749.82	3,721.10	6.35	−0.03
	1,741.45	10.57	23,990.82	860.97	7.37	−1.63
	2,035.75	13.82	25,694.86	3,571.51	8.39	−0.43
	1,578.00	8.13	23,736.35	2,845.50	5.15	0.04
	4,167.44	58.54	34,314.29	5,060.11	12.88	0.22
	2,799.97	21.14	22,809.53	3,552.00	9.14	−0.74

Source: This data set is from a research study published in "An analytical approach for evaluation of sales territory performance," by David W. Cravens, Robert B. Woodruff, and Joseph C. Stamper, *Journal of Marketing,* January 1972, 31–37. We have updated the situation in our case study to be more modern.

Plots of y versus x_1 through x_5 are given beside Table 12.2. Because each plot has an approximate straight-line appearance, it is reasonable to relate y to x_1 through x_5 by using the regression model

$$y = \beta_0 + \beta_1 x_1 + \beta_2 x_2 + \beta_3 x_3 + \beta_4 x_4 + \beta_5 x_5 + \varepsilon$$

Here, $\mu_{y|x_1, x_2, \ldots, x_5} = \beta_0 + \beta_1 x_1 + \beta_2 x_2 + \beta_3 x_3 + \beta_4 x_4 + \beta_5 x_5$ is the mean sales in all sales territories, where the values of the five independent variables are x_1, x_2, x_3, x_4, and x_5. Furthermore, for example, the parameter β_3 equals the increase in mean sales that is associated with a \$1 increase in advertising expenditure (x_3) when the other four independent variables do not change. The main objective of the regression analysis is to help the sales manager evaluate sales performance by comparing actual performance to predicted performance.

Exercises for Section **12.1**

CONCEPTS

For Exercises 12.1 through 12.5, consider the multiple regression model

$$y = \mu_{y|x_1, x_2, \ldots, x_k} + \varepsilon$$
$$= \beta_0 + \beta_1 x_1 + \beta_2 x_2 + \cdots + \beta_k x_k + \varepsilon$$

12.1 What is y? What are $x_1, x_2, \ldots, x_k$?

12.2 Interpret $\mu_{y|x_1, x_2, \ldots, x_k}$

12.3 What are $\beta_0, \beta_1, \beta_2, \ldots, \beta_k$?

12.4 What does the error term ε describe?

12.5 In your own words, interpret β_0, β_1, and β_2.

METHODS AND APPLICATIONS

12.6 THE WORK ATTENDANCE EXAMPLE

A human resources manager conducts a small study to examine factors that might predict employee attendance. For ten employees, the manager collects the following information:

y = Attendance (in percentage of days worked)

x_1 = Job satisfaction (from an opinion survey with 1 = not satisfied to 10 = very satisfied)

x_2 = Commuting distance (in kilometres)

The data and data plots are provided in Table 12.3. Using these data, the manager plans to test the following model:

$$y = \mu_{y|x_1, x_2} + \varepsilon$$
$$= \beta_0 + \beta_1 x_1 + \beta_2 x_2 + \varepsilon$$

a. Discuss why the data plots given under Table 12.3 indicate that this model might be reasonable.

b. Interpret

$$\mu_{y|x_1 = 2, x_2 = 9} = \beta_0 + \beta_1(2) + \beta_2(9)$$

c. Interpret β_0, β_1, and β_2.

d. What factors are represented by the error term in this model? Give a specific example of these factors.

TABLE **12.3** Work Attendance Data

Attendance (y)	Job Satisfaction (x_1)	Commuting Distance (x_2)
66	3	12
100	8	5
78	5	9
95	9	7
82	7	11
97	7	6
87	6	13
71	4	8
73	6	6
81	7	3

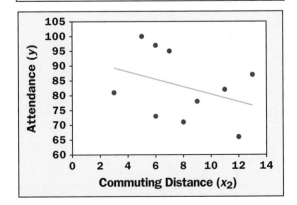

12.7 THE FRESH DETERGENT EXAMPLE

Enterprise Industries produces Fresh, a brand of liquid laundry detergent. To more effectively manage its inventory and make revenue projections, the company would like to better predict demand for Fresh. To develop a prediction model, the company has gathered data concerning demand for Fresh over the previous 30 sales periods (each sales period is defined to be a four-week period). The demand data are presented in Table 12.4. Here, for each sales period,

y = Demand for the large bottle of Fresh (in hundreds of thousands of bottles) in the sales period

x_1 = Price (in dollars) of Fresh as offered by Enterprise Industries in the sales period

x_2 = Average industry price (in dollars) of competitors' similar detergents in the sales period

x_3 = Enterprise Industries' advertising expenditure (in hundreds of thousands of dollars) to promote Fresh in the sales period

$x_4 = x_2 - x_1$ = "Price difference" in the sales period

Consider relating y to x_1, x_2, and x_3 by using the model

$$y = \beta_0 + \beta_1 x_1 + \beta_2 x_2 + \beta_3 x_3 + \varepsilon$$

a. Discuss why the data plots given under Table 12.4 indicate that this model might be reasonable.

b. Interpret

$\mu_{y|x_1 = 3.70,\, x_2 = 3.90,\, x_3 = 6.50}$
$= \beta_0 + \beta_1(3.70) + \beta_2(3.90) + \beta_3(6.50)$

c. Interpret β_0, β_1, β_2, β_3, and ε in the model.

d. Discuss why the data plots given under Table 12.4 indicate that it might be reasonable to use the alternative model

$$y = \beta_0 + \beta_1 x_4 + \beta_2 x_3 + \varepsilon$$

12.8 THE HOSPITAL LABOUR NEEDS EXAMPLE

Table 12.5 presents data concerning the need for labour in 16 hospitals. Here

y = Monthly labour hours required

x_1 = Monthly X-ray exposures

x_2 = Monthly occupied bed days (a hospital has one occupied bed day if one bed is occupied for an entire day)

x_3 = Average length of patients' stay (in days)

The main objective of the regression analysis is to evaluate the performance of hospitals in terms of how many labour hours are used relative to how many labour hours are needed. Sixteen efficiently run hospitals are selected and a regression model based on efficiently run hospitals is created to evaluate the efficiency of other hospitals. Consider relating y to x_1, x_2, and x_3 by using the model

$$y = \beta_0 + \beta_1 x_1 + \beta_2 x_2 + \beta_3 x_3 + \varepsilon$$

Discuss why the data plots given beside Table 12.5 indicate that this model might be reasonable. Interpret β_0, β_1, β_2, β_3, and ε in this model.

TABLE **12.4** Historical Data Concerning Demand for Fresh Detergent

Sales Period	Price for Fresh, x_1	Average Industry Price, x_2	Price Difference, $x_4 = x_2 - x_1$	Advertising Expenditure for Fresh, x_3	Demand for Fresh, y	Sales Period	Price for Fresh, x_1	Average Industry Price, x_2	Price Difference, $x_4 = x_2 - x_1$	Advertising Expenditure for Fresh, x_3	Demand for Fresh, y
1	3.85	3.80	−0.05	5.50	7.38	16	3.80	4.10	0.30	6.80	8.87
2	3.75	4.00	0.25	6.75	8.51	17	3.70	4.20	0.50	7.10	9.26
3	3.70	4.30	0.60	7.25	9.52	18	3.80	4.30	0.50	7.00	9.00
4	3.70	3.70	0	5.50	7.50	19	3.70	4.10	0.40	6.80	8.75
5	3.60	3.85	0.25	7.00	9.33	20	3.80	3.75	−0.05	6.50	7.95
6	3.60	3.80	0.20	6.50	8.28	21	3.80	3.75	−0.05	6.25	7.65
7	3.60	3.75	0.15	6.75	8.75	22	3.75	3.65	−0.10	6.00	7.27
8	3.80	3.85	0.05	5.25	7.87	23	3.70	3.90	0.20	6.50	8.00
9	3.80	3.65	−0.15	5.25	7.10	24	3.55	3.65	0.10	7.00	8.50
10	3.85	4.00	0.15	6.00	8.00	25	3.60	4.10	0.50	6.80	8.75
11	3.90	4.10	0.20	6.50	7.89	26	3.65	4.25	0.60	6.80	9.21
12	3.90	4.00	0.10	6.25	8.15	27	3.70	3.65	−0.05	6.50	8.27
13	3.70	4.10	0.40	7.00	9.10	28	3.75	3.75	0	5.75	7.67
14	3.75	4.20	0.45	6.90	8.86	29	3.80	3.85	0.05	5.80	7.93
15	3.75	4.10	0.35	6.80	8.90	30	3.70	4.25	0.55	6.80	9.26

TABLE 12.5   Hospital Labour Needs Data ✎

Hospital	Monthly X-Ray Exposures, x_1	Monthly Occupied Bed Days, x_2	Average Length of Stay, x_3	Monthly Labour Hours Required, y
1	2,463	472.92	4.45	566.52
2	2,048	1,339.75	6.92	696.82
3	3,940	620.25	4.28	1,033.15
4	6,505	568.33	3.90	1,603.62
5	5,723	1,497.60	5.50	1,611.37
6	11,520	1,365.83	4.60	1,613.27
7	5,779	1,687.00	5.62	1,854.17
8	5,969	1,639.92	5.15	2,160.55
9	8,461	2,872.33	6.18	2,305.58
10	20,106	3,655.08	6.15	3,503.93
11	13,313	2,912.00	5.88	3,571.89
12	10,771	3,921.00	4.88	3,741.40
13	15,543	3,865.67	5.50	4,026.52
14	34,703	12,446.33	10.78	11,732.17
15	39,204	14,098.40	7.05	15,414.94
16	86,533	15,524.00	6.35	18,854.45

Source: *Procedures and Analysis for Staffing Standards Development Regression Analysis Handbook* (San Diego, CA: Navy Manpower and Material Analysis Center, 1979).

12.2 MODEL ASSUMPTIONS AND THE STANDARD ERROR

Model assumptions To perform hypothesis tests and set up various types of intervals when using the multiple regression model

$$y = \beta_0 + \beta_1 x_1 + \beta_2 x_2 + \cdots + \beta_k x_k + \varepsilon$$

we need to make certain assumptions about the error term ε. At any given combination of values of $x_1, x_2, \ldots, x_k$, there is a population of error term values that could potentially occur. These error term values describe the different potential effects on y of all factors other than the combination of values of $x_1, x_2, \ldots, x_k$. Therefore, these error term values explain the variation in the y values that could be observed at the combination of values of $x_1, x_2, \ldots, x_k$. As shown in the following boxed feature, we make four assumptions about the potential error term values.

Assumptions for the Multiple Regression Model

1   **Mean error value assumption:** At any given combination of values of $x_1, x_2, \ldots, x_k$, the population of potential error term values has a mean equal to 0.

2   **Constant-variance assumption:** At any given combination of values of $x_1, x_2, \ldots, x_k$, the population of potential error term values has a variance that does not depend on the combination of values of $x_1, x_2, \ldots, x_k$. That is, the different populations of potential error term values corresponding to different combinations of values of $x_1, x_2, \ldots, x_k$ have equal variances. We denote the constant variance as σ^2.

3   **Normality assumption:** At any given combination of values of $x_1, x_2, \ldots, x_k$, the population of potential error term values has a *normal distribution*.

4   **Independence assumption:** Any one value of the error term ε is *statistically independent* of any other value of ε. That is, the value of the error term ε corresponding to an observed value of y is statistically independent of the error term corresponding to any other observed value of y.

Taken together, the first three assumptions say that at any given combination of values of $x_1, x_2, \ldots, x_k$, the population of potential error term values is normally distributed with mean 0 and a variance σ^2 that does not depend on the combination of values of $x_1, x_2, \ldots, x_k$. Because the potential error term values cause the variation in the potential y values, the first three assumptions imply that at any given combination of values of $x_1, x_2, \ldots, x_k$, the population of y values that could be observed is normally distributed with mean $\beta_0 + \beta_1 x_1 + \beta_2 x_2 + \ldots + \beta_k x_k$ and a variance σ^2 that does not depend on the combination of values of $x_1, x_2, \ldots, x_k$. Furthermore, the independence assumption says that when time series data are utilized in a regression study, there are no patterns in the error term values. As in simple linear regression, only pronounced departures from the assumptions must be remedied.

The mean square error and the standard error To present statistical inference formulas in later sections, we need to be able to compute point estimates of σ^2 and σ (the constant variance and standard deviation of the different error term populations). We show how to do this in the following boxed feature.

The Mean Square Error and the Standard Error

Suppose that the multiple regression model

$$y = \beta_0 + \beta_1 x_1 + \beta_2 x_2 + \cdots + \beta_k x_k + \varepsilon$$

utilizes k independent variables and thus has $(k + 1)$ parameters $\beta_0, \beta_1, \beta_2, \ldots, \beta_k$. Then, if the regression assumptions are satisfied and if the SSE is the sum of squared residuals for the model:

1. A point estimate of σ^2 is the *mean square error*

$$s^2 = \frac{SSE}{n - (k + 1)}$$

2. A point estimate of σ is the *standard error*

$$s = \sqrt{\frac{SSE}{n - (k + 1)}}$$

To explain these point estimates, recall that σ^2 is the variance of the population of y values (for given values of $x_1, x_2, \ldots, x_k$) around the mean value $\mu_{y|x_1, x_2, \ldots, x_k}$. Because $\hat{y}$ is the point estimate of this mean, we use $SSE = \sum (y_i - \hat{y}_i)^2$ to help construct a point estimate of σ^2. We divide the SSE by $n - (k + 1)$ because doing so makes the resulting s^2 an unbiased point estimate of σ^2. We call $n - (k + 1)$ the *number of degrees of freedom* associated with the SSE.

We will see in Section 12.8 that if a particular regression model gives a small standard error, then the model will give short prediction intervals and thus accurate predictions of individual y values. For example, for Table 12.1 the SSE for the model

$$y = \beta_0 + \beta_1 x_1 + \beta_2 x_2 + \varepsilon$$

is .674. This model utilizes $k = 2$ independent variables and thus has $k + 1 = 3$ parameters $(\beta_0, \beta_1, \text{ and } \beta_2)$, so a point estimate of σ^2 is the mean square error

$$s^2 = \frac{SSE}{n - (k + 1)} = \frac{.674}{8 - 3} = \frac{.674}{5} = .1348$$

and a point estimate of σ is the standard error $s = \sqrt{.1348} = .3671$.

As another example, the SSE for the sales territory performance model

$$y = \beta_0 + \beta_1 x_1 + \beta_2 x_2 + \beta_3 x_3 + \beta_4 x_4 + \beta_5 x_5 + \varepsilon$$

is 3,516,890.0266. This model utilizes $k = 5$ independent variables and so has $k + 1 = 6$ parameters. A point estimate of σ^2 is the mean square error

$$s^2 = \frac{SSE}{n - (k + 1)} = \frac{3,516,890.0266}{25 - 6} = 185,099.4751$$

and a point estimate of σ is the standard error $s = \sqrt{185,099.4751} = 430.2319$. Note that these values of the SSE, s^2, and s are given on the MegaStat output in Figure 12.9.

ROADBLOCK

Regression and ANOVA share a number of common features
As we begin to explore the methods for identifying the statistical significance of the prediction equation in a multiple regression equation, you will note a number of similarities between ANOVA and multiple regression. Our discussion of the mean square error in this section underscores the parallels between these two concepts (even in terminology)—and this error term will be used to evaluate the overall predictive power of the independent variables. ANOVA can be thought of as a method of conducting a regression analysis with categorical independent variables, so multiple regression and factorial ANOVA (i.e., ANOVA with more than one independent variable) are different sides of the same coin. You would conduct a multiple regression when your independent variables are continuous, and you would conduct a factorial ANOVA when your independent variables are categorical.

12.3 MULTICOLLINEARITY

Consider the sales territory performance data presented in Table 12.2. These data consist of values of the dependent variable y (SALES) and of the independent variables x_1 (TIME), x_2 (MKTPOTEN), x_3 (ADVER), x_4 (MKTSHARE), and x_5 (CHANGE). The complete sales territory performance data analyzed by Cravens, Woodruff, and Stamper (1972) consist of the data presented in Table 12.2 and data concerning three additional independent variables. These three independent variables are defined as follows:

x_6 = Number of accounts handled by the representative (we will sometimes denote this variable as ACCTS)

x_7 = Average workload per account, measured by using a weighting based on the sizes of the orders by the accounts and other workload-related criteria (we will sometimes denote this variable as WKLOAD)

x_8 = Aggregate rating on eight dimensions of the representative's performance, made by a sales manager and expressed on a 1–7 scale (we will sometimes denote this variable as RATING)

Table 12.6 gives the observed values of x_6, x_7, and x_8, and Figure 12.5 presents the MegaStat output of a correlation matrix for the sales territory performance data. Examining the first column of this matrix, we see that the simple correlation coefficient between SALES and WKLOAD is $-.117$ and that the p-value for testing the significance of the relationship between

TABLE 12.6

Values of ACCTS, WKLOAD, and RATING

Accounts, x_6	Work-load, x_7	Rating, x_8
74.86	15.05	4.9
107.32	19.97	5.1
96.75	17.34	2.9
195.12	13.40	3.4
180.44	17.64	4.6
104.88	16.22	4.5
256.10	18.80	4.6
126.83	19.86	2.3
203.25	17.42	4.9
119.51	21.41	2.8
116.26	16.32	3.1
142.28	14.51	4.2
89.43	19.35	4.3
84.55	20.02	4.2
119.51	15.26	5.5
80.49	15.87	3.6
136.58	7.81	3.4
78.86	16.00	4.2
136.58	17.44	3.6
138.21	17.98	3.1
75.61	20.99	1.6
102.44	21.66	3.4
76.42	21.46	2.7
136.58	24.78	2.8
88.62	24.96	3.9

FIGURE 12.5   A Correlation Matrix for the Sales Territory Performance Data

	Sales	Time	MktPoten	Adver	MktShare	Change	Accts	WkLoad
Time	0.623 0.001							
MktPoten	0.598 0.002	0.454 0.023			Cell Contents: Pearson correlation P-Value			
Adver	0.596 0.002	0.249 0.230	0.174 0.405					
MktShare	0.484 0.014	0.106 0.613	−0.211 0.312	0.264 0.201				
Change	0.489 0.013	0.251 0.225	0.268 0.195	0.377 0.064	0.085 0.685			
Accts	0.754 0.000	0.758 0.000	0.479 0.016	0.200 0.338	0.403 0.046	0.327 0.110		
WkLoad	−0.117 0.577	−0.179 0.391	−0.259 0.212	−0.272 0.188	0.349 0.087	−0.288 0.163	−0.199 0.341	
Rating	0.402 0.046	0.101 0.631	0.359 0.078	0.411 0.041	−0.024 0.911	0.549 0.004	0.229 0.272	−0.277 0.180

SALES and WKLOAD is .577. This indicates that there is little or no relationship between SALES and WKLOAD. However, the simple correlation coefficients between SALES and the other seven independent variables range from .402 to .754, with associated *p*-values ranging from .046 to .000. This indicates the existence of potentially useful relationships between SALES and these seven independent variables.

While simple correlation coefficients (and scatter plots) give us a preliminary understanding of the data, they cannot be relied on alone to tell us which independent variables are significantly related to the dependent variable. One reason for this is a condition called *multicollinearity*. Multicollinearity is said to exist among the independent variables in a regression situation if these independent variables are related to or dependent on each other. One way to investigate multicollinearity is to examine the correlation matrix. To understand this, note that all of the simple correlation coefficients located in the first column of this matrix measure the simple correlations between the independent variables. For example, the simple correlation coefficient between ACCTS and TIME is .758, which says that the ACCTS values increase as the TIME values increase. Such a relationship makes sense because it is logical that the longer a sales representative has been with the company, the more accounts the representative handles. Statisticians often regard multicollinearity in a data set to be severe if at least one simple correlation coefficient between the independent variables is at least .9. Since the largest such simple correlation coefficient in Figure 12.5 is .758, this is not true for the sales territory performance data. Note, however, that even moderate multicollinearity can be a potential problem. This will be demonstrated later using the sales territory performance data.

Another way to measure multicollinearity is to use variance inflation factors. Consider a regression model relating a dependent variable *y* to a set of independent variables $x_1, \ldots, x_{j-1}$, $x_j, x_{j+1}, \ldots, x_k$. The variance inflation factor for the independent variable x_j in this set is denoted VIF_j and is defined by the equation

$$VIF_j = \frac{1}{1 - R_j^2}$$

where R_j^2 is the multiple coefficient of determination for the regression model that relates x_j to all the other independent variables $x_1, \ldots, x_{j-1}, x_{j+1}, \ldots, x_k$ in the set. For example, Figure 12.6 gives the MegaStat output of the *t* statistics, *p*-values, and variance inflation factors for the sales territory performance model that relates *y* to all eight independent variables. The largest variance inflation factor is $VIF_6 = 5.639$. To calculate VIF_6, MegaStat first calculates the multiple coefficient of determination for the regression model that relates x_6 to $x_1, x_2, x_3, x_4, x_5, x_7$, and x_8 to be $R_6^2 = .822673$. It then follows that

$$VIF_6 = \frac{1}{1 - R_6^2} = \frac{1}{1 - .822673} = 5.639$$

FIGURE 12.6 MegaStat Output of the *t* Statistics, *p*-Values, and Variance Inflation Factors for the Sales Territory Performance Model $y = \beta_0 + \beta_1 x_1 + \beta_2 x_2 + \beta_3 x_3 + \beta_4 x_4 + \beta_5 x_5 + \beta_6 x_6 + \beta_7 x_7 + \beta_8 x_8 + \varepsilon$

Regression output					confidence interval		
variables	coefficients	std. error	t (df = 16)	p-value	95% lower	95% upper	VIF
Intercept	−1,507.8137	778.6349	−1.936	0.0707	−3158.4457	142.8182	
Time	2.0096	1.9307	1.041	0.3134	−2.0832	6.1024	3.343
MktPoten	0.0372	0.0082	4.536	0.0003	0.0198	0.0546	1.978
Adver	0.1510	0.0471	3.205	0.0055	0.0511	0.2509	1.910
MktShare	199.0235	67.0279	2.969	0.0090	56.9307	341.1164	3.236
Change	290.8551	186.7820	1.557	0.1390	−105.1049	686.8152	1.602
Accts	5.5510	4.7755	1.162	0.2621	−4.5728	15.6747	5.639
WkLoad	19.7939	33.6767	0.588	0.5649	−51.5975	91.1853	1.818
Rating	8.1893	128.5056	0.064	0.9500	−264.2304	280.6090	1.809
							2.667 mean VIF

In general, if $R_j^2 = 0$, which says that x_j is not related to the other independent variables, then the variance inflation factor VIF_j equals 1. On the other hand, if $R_j^2 > 0$, which says that x_j is related to the other independent variables, then $(1 - R_j^2)$ is less than 1, making VIF_j greater than 1. Both the largest variance inflation factor among the independent variables and the mean $\overline{VIF}$ of the variance inflation factors for the independent variables indicate the severity of multicollinearity. Generally, the multicollinearity between independent variables is considered severe if

1   The largest variance inflation factor is greater than 10 (which means that the largest R_j^2 is greater than .9).

2   The mean $\overline{VIF}$ of the variance inflation factors is substantially greater than 1.

The largest variance inflation factor in Figure 12.6 is not greater than 10, and the average of the variance inflation factors, which is 2.667, would probably not be considered substantially greater than 1. Therefore, we would probably not consider the multicollinearity among the eight independent variables to be severe.

The picket fence display

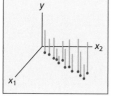

The reason that VIF_j is called the variance inflation factor is that it can be shown that, when VIF_j is greater than 1, the standard deviation σ_{b_j} of the population of all possible values of the least squares point estimate b_j is likely to be inflated beyond its value when $R_j^2 = 0$. If σ_{b_j} is greatly inflated, two slightly different samples of values of the dependent variable can yield two substantially different values of b_j. To intuitively understand why strong multicollinearity can significantly affect the least squares point estimates, consider the so-called picket fence display in the page margin. This figure depicts two independent variables (x_1 and x_2) exhibiting strong multicollinearity (note that as x_1 increases, x_2 increases). The heights of the pickets on the fence represent the y observations. If we assume that the model

$$y = \beta_0 + \beta_1 x_1 + \beta_2 x_2 + \varepsilon$$

adequately describes these data, then calculating the least squares point estimates amounts to fitting a plane to the points on the top of the picket fence. Clearly, this plane would be quite unstable. That is, a slightly different height of one of the pickets (a slightly different y value) could cause the slant of the fitted plane (and the least squares point estimates that determine this slant) to radically change. It follows that, when strong multicollinearity exists, sampling variation can result in least squares point estimates that differ substantially from the true values of the regression parameters. In fact, some of the least squares point estimates may have a sign (positive or negative) that differs from the sign of the true value of the parameter (we will see an example of this in the exercises). Therefore, when strong multicollinearity exists, it is dangerous to individually interpret the least squares point estimates.

The most important problem caused by multicollinearity is that, even when multicollinearity is not severe, it can hinder our ability to use the t statistics and related p-values to assess the importance of the independent variables. Recall that we can reject $H_0: \beta_j = 0$ in favour of $H_a: \beta_j \neq 0$ at level of significance α if and only if the absolute value of the corresponding t statistic is greater than $t_{\alpha/2}$ based on $n - (k + 1)$ degrees of freedom or, equivalently, if and only if the related p-value is less than α. So the larger (in absolute value) the t statistic is and the smaller the p-value is, the stronger is the evidence that we should reject $H_0: \beta_j = 0$ and the stronger is the evidence that the independent variable x_j is significant. When multicollinearity exists, the sizes of the t statistic and of the related p-value measure the additional importance of the independent variable x_j over the combined importance of the other independent variables in the regression model.

Since two or more correlated independent variables contribute redundant information, multicollinearity often causes the t statistics obtained by relating a dependent variable to a set of correlated independent variables to be smaller (in absolute value) than the t statistics that would be obtained if separate regression analyses were run, where each separate regression analysis relates the dependent variable to a smaller set (for example, only one) of the correlated independent variables. So multicollinearity can cause some of the correlated independent variables to appear less important—in terms of having small absolute t statistics and large p-values—than they really are.

Another way to understand this is to note that since multicollinearity inflates σ_{b_j}, it inflates the point estimate s_{bj} of σ_{b_j}. Since $t = b_j/s_{bj}$, an inflated value of s_{bj} can (depending on the size of b_j) cause t to be small (and the related p-value to be large). This would suggest that x_j is not significant even though x_j might really be important.

12.4 THE LEAST SQUARES ESTIMATES, AND POINT ESTIMATION AND PREDICTION

The regression parameters $\beta_0, \beta_1, \beta_2, \ldots, \beta_k$ in the multiple regression model are unknown, so they must be estimated from data (observations of $y, x_1, x_2, \ldots, x_k$). To see how we might do this, let $b_0, b_1, b_2, \ldots, b_k$ denote point estimates of the unknown parameters. Then a point prediction of an observed value of the dependent variable

$$y = \beta_0 + \beta_1 x_1 + \beta_2 x_2 + \cdots + \beta_k x_k + \varepsilon$$

is

$$\hat{y} = b_0 + b_1 x_1 + b_2 x_2 + \cdots + b_k x_k$$

LO3

which is called the *least squares prediction equation*. It is obtained by replacing β_0, β_1, and β_2 by their estimates b_0, b_1, and b_2. You will notice that the error term is not present in this equation. One of the assumptions in the regression model is that the expected value of the error term is 0 (more regression assumptions were discussed in Section 12.2). Next, let y_i and $\hat{y}_i$ denote the observed and predicted values of the dependent variable for the ith observation, and define the residual for the ith observation to be $e_i = y_i - \hat{y}_i$. We then consider the sum of squared residuals

$$SSE = \sum_{i=1}^{n} (y_i - \hat{y}_i)^2$$

If any particular values of $b_0, b_1, b_2, \ldots, b_k$ are good point estimates, they will make (for $i = 1, 2, \ldots, n$) the predicted value $\hat{y}_i$ fairly close to the observed value y_i and thus will make the SSE fairly small. We define the least squares point estimates to be the values of $b_0, b_1, b_2, \ldots, b_k$ that minimize the SSE.

It can be shown that a formula exists for computing the least squares point estimates of the parameters in the multiple regression model. This formula is written using a branch of mathematics called *matrix algebra* and is presented in Appendix F on *Connect*. In practice, the least squares point estimates can easily be computed using many standard statistical computer packages. In our discussion of multiple regression here, we will rely on Excel and MegaStat to compute the needed estimates.

Example 12.2   Predicting Outcomes Using Least Squares Point Estimates

Part 1: The least squares point estimates Consider the model of the data in Table 12.1 (reproduced in the margin):

$$y = \beta_0 + \beta_1 x_1 + \beta_2 x_2 + \varepsilon$$

The Excel output in Figure 12.7 tells us that if we use the data to calculate the least squares point estimates of the parameters β_0, β_1, and β_2, we obtain $b_0 = 13.1087$, $b_1 = -.0900$, and $b_2 = .0825$.

The point estimate $b_1 = -.0900$ of β_1 says we estimate that y decreases (b_1 is negative) by .0900 when x_1 increases by one and x_2 does not change. The point estimate $b_2 = .0825$ of β_2 says we estimate that y increases (b_2 is positive) by .0825 when there is a one-unit increase in x_2 and x_1 does not change.

Sample Data

x_1	x_2	y
28.0	18	12.4
28.0	14	11.7
32.5	24	12.4
39.0	22	10.8
45.9	8	9.4
57.8	16	9.5
58.1	1	8.0
62.5	0	7.5

FIGURE 12.7   Excel Output of a Regression Analysis of the Data in
Table 12.1 Using the Model $y = \beta_0 + \beta_1 x_1 + \beta_2 x_2 + \varepsilon$

Regression Statistics

Multiple R	0.9867
R Square	0.9736 [8]
Adjusted R Square	0.9631 [9]
Standard Error	0.3671 [7]
Observations	8

ANOVA

	df	SS	MS	F	Significance F
Regression	2	24.8750 [10]	12.4375	92.3031 [13]	0.0001 [14]
Residual	5	0.6737 [11]	0.1347		
Total	7	25.5488 [12]			

	Coefficients	Standard Error [4]	t Stat [5]	P-value [6]	Lower 95% [15]	Upper 95% [15]
Intercept	13.1087 [1]	0.8557	15.3193	2.15E-05	10.9091	15.3084
X1	−0.0900 [2]	0.0141	−6.3942	0.0014	−0.1262	−0.0538
X2	0.0825 [3]	0.0220	3.7493	0.0133	0.0259	0.1391

[1] b_0 [2] b_1 [3] b_2 [4] s_{b_j} = standard error of the estimate b_j [5] t statistics   [6] p-values for t statistics   [7] s = standard error
[8] R^2 [9] Adjusted R^2 [10] Explained variation   [11] SSE = unexplained variation   [12] Total variation   [13] F(model) statistic
[14] p-value for F(model)   [15] 95% confidence interval for β_j

The equation

$$\hat{y} = b_0 + b_1 x_1 + b_2 x_2$$
$$= 13.1087 - .0900 x_1 + .0825 x_2$$

is the least squares prediction equation. We can use this equation to compute a prediction for any observed value of y. For instance, a point prediction of $y_1 = 12.4$ (when $x_1 = 28.0$ and $x_2 = 18$) is

$$\hat{y}_1 = 13.1087 - .0900(28.0) + .0825(18)$$
$$= 12.0737$$

This results in a residual equal to

$$e_1 = y_1 - \hat{y}_1 = 12.4 - 12.0737 = .3263$$

Table 12.7 gives the point prediction obtained using the least squares prediction equation and the residual for each of the eight observed y values. In addition, this table tells us that the sum of squared residuals (SSE) equals .674. Some of the numbers in Table 12.7 have been rounded.

The least squares prediction equation is the equation of a plane that is sometimes called the *least squares plane*. Figure 12.8 illustrates a portion of this plane—the portion that corresponds to the (x_1, x_2) combinations in the experimental region. Figure 12.8 also shows the residuals for each observation (here $n = 8$). These residuals are depicted as line segments drawn between the observed y values (the dots scattered around the least squares plane) and the predicted y values (the squares on the least squares plane). Because the least squares point estimates minimize the sum of squared residuals, we can interpret them as positioning the planar prediction equation in three-dimensional space so as to minimize the sum of squared distances between the observed and predicted y values. In this sense, we can say that the plane defined by the least squares point estimates is the best plane that can be positioned between the observed y values.

Part 2: Estimating means and predicting individual values For combinations of values of x_1 and x_2 that are in the experimental region, the least squares plane is the estimate of

TABLE 12.7 The Point Predictions and Residuals Using the Least Squares Point Estimates $b_0 = 13.1$, $b_1 = -.0900$, and $b_2 = .0825$

x_1	x_2	y	$\hat{y} = b_0 + b_1x_1 + b_2x_2$ $= 13.1 - 0.0900x_1 + 0.0825x_2$	Residual, $e = y - \hat{y}$
28.0	18	12.4	12.0733	0.3267
28.0	14	11.7	11.7433	-0.0433
32.5	24	12.4	12.1632	0.2368
39.0	22	10.8	11.4131	-0.6131
45.9	8	9.4	9.6371	-0.2371
57.8	16	9.5	9.2259	0.2741
58.1	1	8.0	7.9614	0.0386
62.5	0	7.5	7.4829	0.0171

$$SSE = (0.3267)^2 + (-0.0433)^2 + \cdots + (0.0171)^2 = 0.674$$

FIGURE 12.8 A Geometrical Interpretation of the Prediction Equation Relating $\hat{y}$ to x_1 and x_2

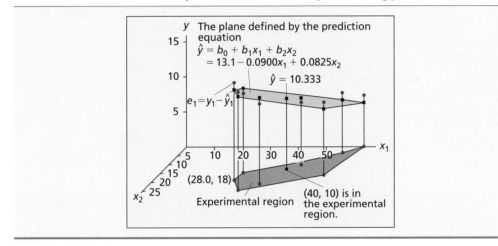

the plane of means. This implies that the point on the least squares plane corresponding to x_1 and x_2,

$$\hat{y} = b_0 + b_1x_1 + b_2x_2$$
$$= 13.1087 - .0900x_1 + .0825x_2$$

is the point estimate of $\mu_{y|x_1, x_2}$, the mean of all y values that could be observed at x_1 and x_2. In addition, because we predict the error term to be 0, $\hat{y}$ is also the point prediction of $y = \mu_{yx_1, x_2} + \varepsilon$.

Generalizing the previous example, we obtain the following:

Point Estimation and Point Prediction in Multiple Regression

Let b_0, b_1, b_2, . . . , b_k be the least squares point estimates of the parameters β_0, β_1, β_2, . . . , β_k in the multiple regression model, and suppose that x_{01}, x_{02}, . . . , x_{0k} are specified values of the independent variables x_1, x_2, . . . , x_k. If the combination of specified values is inside the experimental region, then

$$\hat{y} = b_0 + b_1x_{01} + b_2x_{02} + \cdots + b_kx_{0k}$$

is the point estimate of the mean value of the dependent variable when the values of the independent variables are x_{01}, x_{02}, . . . , x_{0k}. In addition, $\hat{y}$ is the point prediction of an individual value of the dependent variable when the values of the independent variables are x_{01}, x_{02}, . . . , x_{0k}. Again, you will notice that the error term is not included in the estimated multiple regression model because the expected value of the error term is 0.

Example 12.3 Predicting Sales Performance Using Least Squares Estimates

Figure 12.9 presents the MegaStat output of a regression analysis of the data in Table 12.2 using the model

$$y = \beta_0 + \beta_1 x_1 + \beta_2 x_2 + \beta_3 x_3 + \beta_4 x_4 + \beta_5 x_5 + \varepsilon$$

On this output, x_1, x_2, x_3, x_4, and x_5 are denoted as Time, MktPoten, Adver, MktShare, and Change, respectively. The MegaStat output tells us that the least squares point estimates of the model parameters are $b_0 = -1,113.7879$, $b_1 = 3.6121$, $b_2 = .0421$, $b_3 = .1289$, $b_4 = 256.9555$, and $b_5 = 324.5334$. These estimates give the least squares prediction equation

$$\hat{y} = -1,113.7879 + 3.6121x_1 + .0421x_2 + .1289x_3 + 256.9555x_4 + 324.5334x_5$$

Recalling that the sales values in Table 12.2 are measured in hundreds of units of the product sold, the point estimate $b_3 = .1289$ says we estimate that mean sales increase by .1289 hundreds of units—that is, by 12.89 units—for each dollar increase in advertising expenditure when the other four independent variables do not change. If the company sells each unit for $1.10, this implies that we estimate that mean sales revenue increases by ($1.10)(12.89) = $14.18 for each dollar increase in advertising expenditure when the other four independent variables do not change. The other β values in the model can be interpreted similarly.

Consider a sales representative for whom Time = 85.42, MktPoten = 35,182.73, Adver = 7,281.65, MktShare = 9.64, and Change = .28. The point prediction of the sales corresponding to this combination of values of the independent variables is

$$\hat{y} = -1,113.7879 + 3.6121(85.42) + .0421(35,182.73)$$
$$+ .1289(7,281.65) + 256.9555(9.64) + 324.5334(.28)$$
$$= 4,181.74^* \text{ (or 418,174 units)}$$

---

*This value actually works out to be 4,182.47 when rounding to the decimal points shown. It is given as 4,181.74 for illustrative purposes (i.e., so that this value corresponds to the MegaStat output shown in Figure 12.9). We have also followed this practice throughout the remainder of the chapter (i.e., setting calculation examples to be equal to the MegaStat output).

FIGURE **12.9** MegaStat Output of the Sales Territory Performance Data Using the Model $y = \beta_0 + \beta_1 x_1 + \beta_2 x_2 + \beta_3 x_3 + \beta_4 x_4 + \beta_5 x_5 + \varepsilon$

Regression Analysis	R^2 0.915	6				= significant at 0.05 level
	Adjusted R^2 0.893	7	n 25			= significant at 0.01 level
	R 0.957		k 5			
	Std. Error 430.232	8	Dep. Var. **Sales**			

ANOVA table

Source	SS	df	MS	F	p-value
Regression	37,862,658.9002 1	5	7,572,531.7800	40.91 4	1.59E-09 5
Residual	3,516,890.0266 2	19	185,099.4751		
Total	41,379,548.9269 3	24			

Regression output

variables	coefficients 9	std. error 10	t(df=19) 11	p-value 12	confidence interval 17 95% lower	95% upper
Intercept	−1,113.7879	419.8869	−2.653	0.0157	−1,992.6213	−234.9545
Time	3.6121	1.1817	3.057	0.0065	1.1388	6.0854
MktPoten	0.0421	0.0067	6.253	5.27E-06	0.0280	0.0562
Adver	0.1289	0.0370	3.479	0.0025	0.0513	0.2064
MktShare	256.9555	39.1361	6.566	2.76E-06	175.0428	338.8683
Change	324.5334	157.2831	2.063	0.0530	−4.6638	653.7307

Predicted values for: Sales

Predicted 13	95% Confidence Interval 14 lower	upper	95% Prediction Interval 15 lower	upper	Leverage 16
4,181.74333	3,884.90651	4,478.58015	3,233.59431	5,129.89235	0.109

1 Explained variation	2 SSE = unexplained variation	3 Total variation	4 F(model)	5 p value for F(model)
6 R^2	7 Adjusted R^2	8 s = standard error	9 b_j = least squares estimate of β_j	10 s_{b_j} = standard error of the estimate b_j
11 t statistics for testing significance of independent variables		12 p values for t statistics	13 $\hat{y}$ = point prediction	
14 95% confidence interval	15 95% prediction interval	16 Distance value	17 95% confidence interval for β_j	

which is given on the MegaStat output. The actual sales for the sales representative were 3,087.52. This sales figure is 1,094.22 less than the point prediction $\hat{y} = 4,181.74$. Later, when we study prediction intervals (see Section 12.8), we will be able to determine whether there is strong evidence that this sales figure is unusually low.

12.5 R^2 AND ADJUSTED R^2

The multiple coefficient of determination, R^2 In this section, we discuss several ways to assess the utility of a multiple regression model. We first discuss a quantity called the *multiple coefficient of determination*, which is denoted R^2. The formulas for R^2 and other related quantities are given in the following boxed feature.

LO4

The Multiple Coefficient of Determination, R^2

For the multiple regression model:

1   Total variation $= \sum (y_i - \bar{y})^2$.

2   Explained variation $= \sum (\hat{y}_i - \bar{y})^2$.

3   Unexplained variation $= \sum (y_i - \hat{y}_i)^2$.

4   Total variation = Explained variation
                        + Unexplained variation

5   The multiple coefficient of determination is

$$R^2 = \frac{\text{Explained variation}}{\text{Total variation}}$$

6   R^2 is the proportion of the total variation in the n observed values of the dependent variable that is explained by the overall regression model.

7   Multiple correlation coefficient $= R = \sqrt{R^2}$

For example, consider the model

$$y = \beta_0 + \beta_1 x_1 + \beta_2 x_2 + \varepsilon$$

and the following Excel output from the data in Table 12.1.

SUMMARY OUTPUT	Data:	x1	x2	y
		28	18	12.4
		28	14	11.7
Regression Statistics		32.5	24	12.4
Multiple R	0.986727	39	22	10.8
R Square	0.97363	45.9	8	9.4
Adjusted R Square	0.963081	57.8	16	9.5
Standard Error	0.367078	58.1	1	8
Observations	8	62.5	0	7.5

ANOVA

	df	SS	MS	F	Significance F
Regression	2	24.87502	12.43751	92.30309	0.000112926
Residual	5	0.673732	0.134746		
Total	7	25.54875			

	Coefficients	Standard Error	t Stat	P-value	Lower 95%	Upper 95%	Lower 95.0%	Upper 95.0%
Intercept	13.10874	0.855698	15.31935	2.15E-05	10.90909894	15.308375	10.9090989	15.3083755
x1	−0.090014	0.014077	−6.394229	0.001386	−0.12620082	−0.0538269	−0.1262008	−0.0538269
x2	0.082495	0.022003	3.749337	0.013303	0.025935717	0.1390542	0.02593572	0.13905423

This Excel output tells us that the total variation (SS Total), explained variation (SS Regression), and unexplained variation (SS Residual) for the model are, respectively, 25.54875, 24.87502, and .673732. The output also tells us that the multiple coefficient of determination is

$$R^2 = \frac{\text{Explained variation}}{\text{Total variation}} = \frac{24.87502}{25.54875} = .97363$$

The multiple correlation coefficient is $R = \sqrt{.97363} = .986727$. The rounded value of $R^2 = .974$ says that the two-independent-variable model explains 97.4 percent of the total variation in the eight observed y values.

As another example, consider the sales territory performance model

$$y = \beta_0 + \beta_1 x_1 + \beta_2 x_2 + \beta_3 x_3 + \beta_4 x_4 + \beta_5 x_5 + \varepsilon$$

and the following MegaStat output:

Regression Analysis

	R^2	0.915		
	Adjusted R^2	0.893	n	25
	R	0.957	k	5
	Std. Error	430.232	Dep. Var.	Sales

ANOVA table

Source	SS	df	MS	F	p-value
Regression	37,862,658.9002	5	7,572,531.7800	40.91	1.59E-09
Residual	3,516,890.0266	19	185,099.4751		
Total	41,379,548.9269	24			

This output tells us that the total, explained, and unexplained variations for the model are, respectively, 41,379,548.9269, 37,862,658.9002, and 3,516,890.0266. The MegaStat output also tells us that R^2 equals .915.

ROADBLOCK

The concept of R^2 is one of the more important concepts in multiple regression
R^2 represents the percentage of variability within the dependent variable that is accounted for by the combination of independent variables used in your equation. It is, therefore, one of the major descriptive statistics for a multiple regression calculation. As we will discuss in subsequent sections of this chapter, the primary goal of a multiple regression calculation is to predict, and R^2 gives us a sense of how successful we are at this task.

Adjusted R^2 Even if the independent variables in a regression model are unrelated to the dependent variable, they will make R^2 somewhat greater than 0. To avoid overestimating the importance of the independent variables, many analysts recommend calculating an *adjusted* multiple coefficient of determination, as shown in the following boxed feature.

Adjusted R^2

The adjusted multiple coefficient of determination (adjusted R^2) is

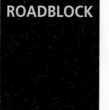

$$\bar{R}^2 = \left(R^2 - \frac{k}{n-1}\right)\left(\frac{n-1}{n-(k+1)}\right)$$

where R^2 is the multiple coefficient of determination, n is the number of observations, and k is the number of independent variables in the model under consideration.

Note that subtracting $k/(n-1)$ from R^2 helps avoid overestimating the importance of the k independent variables. Furthermore, multiplying $[R^2 - (k/(n-1))]$ by $(n-1)/(n-(k+1))$ makes $\bar{R}^2$ equal to 1 when R^2 equals 1.

As an example, consider the model of Table 12.1:

$$y = \beta_0 + \beta_1 x_1 + \beta_2 x_2 + \varepsilon$$

From the Excel output on the previous page, $R^2 = .97363$. So it follows that

$$\bar{R}^2 = \left(R^2 - \frac{k}{n-1}\right)\left(\frac{n-1}{n-(k+1)}\right)$$

$$= \left(.97363 - \frac{2}{8-1}\right)\left(\frac{8-1}{8-(2+1)}\right)$$

$$= .96309$$

which is also given in the Excel output. Similarly, in addition to telling us that $R^2 = .915$ for the five-independent-variable sales territory performance model, the MegaStat output tells us that $R = .893$ for this model.

If R^2 is less than $k/(n-1)$ (which can happen), then R will be negative. In this case, statistical software systems set R equal to 0. Historically, R^2 and R have been popular measures of model utility—possibly because they are unitless and between 0 and 1. In general, we want R^2 and R to be near 1. However, sometimes even if a regression model has an R^2 and an R that are near 1, the model may still not be able to predict accurately. As we proceed through this chapter, we will discuss assessing a model's ability to predict accurately, as well as using R^2 and R to help choose a regression model.

ROADBLOCK

R^2_{adj} is a demonstration of the extent to which R^2 is sensitive to the *n* size of your sample
At various points in the preceding chapters, we have identified aspects of inferential statistics that are impacted by your sample size. The adjustment to R^2 is another illustration of this relationship. If you look at the formula that is used to adjust R^2, it is sensitive to two factors in your design: (1) the number of participants in your sample and (2) the number of independent variables in the equation.

Intuitively enough, larger samples can accommodate a greater number of predictors—and conversely, studies with smaller samples should avoid specifying too many predictor variables. Regardless, reporting the adjusted R^2 provides a better picture of the amount of variance accounted for by the independent variables.

12.6 THE OVERALL *F* TEST

LO5

Another way to assess the utility of a regression model is to test the significance of the regression relationship between y and $x_1, x_2, \ldots, x_k$. For the multiple regression model, we test the null hypothesis $H_0: \beta_1 = \beta_2 = \cdots = \beta_k = 0$, which says that *none of the independent variables x_1, $x_2, \ldots, x_k$ is significantly related to y (the regression relationship is not significant)*, versus the alternative hypothesis H_a: at least one of $\beta_1, \beta_2, \ldots, \beta_k$ does not equal 0, which says that *at least one of the independent variables is significantly related to y (the regression relationship is significant)*. If we can reject H_0 at level of significance α, we say that *the multiple regression model is significant at level of significance α*. We carry out the test as described in the following boxed feature.

An *F* Test for the Multiple Regression Model

Suppose that the regression assumptions hold and that the multiple regression model has $(k + 1)$ parameters, and consider testing

$$H_0: \beta_1 = \beta_2 = \cdots = \beta_k = 0$$

versus

H_a: At least one of $\beta_1, \beta_2, \ldots, \beta_k$ does not equal 0

We define the overall *F* statistic to be

$$F(\text{model}) = \frac{\text{Explained variation}/k}{\text{Unexplained variation}/[n-(k+1)]}$$

The *p*-value related to *F*(model) is the area under the curve of the *F* distribution (with k and $[n-(k+1)]$ degrees of freedom) to the right of *F*(model). We can reject H_0 in favour of H_a at level of significance α if either of the following equivalent conditions holds:

1 $F(\text{model}) > F_\alpha$

2 *p*-value $< \alpha$

Here the point F_α is based on k numerator and $n - (k + 1)$ denominator degrees of freedom.

Condition 1 is intuitively reasonable because a large value of $F(\text{model})$ would be caused by an explained variation that is large relative to the unexplained variation. This would occur if at least one independent variable in the regression model significantly affected y, which would imply that H_0 is false and H_a is true. For example, consider the model

$$y = \beta_0 + \beta_1 x_1 + \beta_2 x_2 + \varepsilon$$

from the sample data in Table 12.1 and the following Excel output:

ANOVA	df	SS	MS	F	Significance F
Regression	2	24.8750	12.4375	92.3031	0.0001
Residual	5	0.6737	0.1347		
Total	7	25.5488			

This output tells us that the explained and unexplained variations for this model are, respectively, 24.8750 and .6737. It follows, since there are $k = 2$ independent variables, that

$$F(\text{model}) = \frac{\text{Explained variation}/k}{\text{Unexplained variation}/[n - (k + 1)]}$$

$$= \frac{24.8750/2}{.6737/[8 - (2 + 1)]} = \frac{12.4375}{.1347}$$

$$= 92.3031$$

The p-value related to $F(\text{model})$ is the area to the right of 92.30 under the curve of the F distribution with $k = 2$ numerator and $n - (k + 1) = 8 - 3 = 5$ denominator degrees of freedom. The Excel output says this p-value is less than .001.

If we want to test the significance of the regression model at level of significance $\alpha = .05$, we use the rejection point $F_{.05}$ based on 2 numerator and 5 denominator degrees of freedom. Using Table A.7, we find that $F_{.05} = 5.79$. Because $F(\text{model}) = 92.30 > F_{.05} = 5.79$, we can reject H_0 in favour of H_a at level of significance .05. Alternatively, the p-value is smaller than .001, so we can reject H_0 at level of significance .001, and we have extremely strong evidence that the model is significant and that at least one of the independent variables x_1 and x_2 in the model is significantly related to y.

Similarly, consider the following MegaStat output based on the sales territory performance example:

ANOVA table

Source	SS	df	MS	F	p-value
Regression	37,862,658.9002	5	7,572,531.7800	40.91	1.59E-09
Residual	3,516,890.0266	19	185,099.4751		
Total	41,379,548.9269	24			

This output tells us that $F(\text{model}) = 40.91$ and that the p-value related to $F(\text{model})$ is less than .001, suggesting that we have extremely strong evidence that at least one of the five independent variables in this model is significantly related to sales territory performance.

If the overall F test tells us that at least one independent variable in a regression model is significant, we next attempt to decide which independent variables are significant. In the next section, we discuss one way to do this.

Exercises for Sections **12.2**, **12.3**, **12.4**, **12.5**, and **12.6**

CONCEPTS

12.9 What is estimated by the mean square error? The standard error?

12.10 In the multiple regression model, what sum of squared deviations do the least squares point estimates minimize?

12.11 When using the multiple regression model, how do you obtain a point estimate of the mean value of the dependent variable and a point prediction of an individual value of the dependent variable?

12.12 a. What do R^2 and $\overline{R}^2$ measure?
b. How do R^2 and $\overline{R}^2$ differ?

12.13 What is the purpose of the overall F test?

METHODS AND APPLICATIONS

In Exercises 12.14 through 12.16, we give MegaStat and Excel outputs of regression analyses of the data sets related to three examples introduced in Section 12.1. The outputs are shown in Figure 12.10. In each exercise, we give the regression model and the number of observations, n, used to perform the regression analysis under consideration. Using the appropriate model, sample size n, and output:

a. Report the SSE as shown on the output. Calculate s^2 from the SSE and other numbers.

b. Report the total variation and the explained variation as shown on the output.

c. Report R^2 and $\overline{R}^2$ as shown on the output. Interpret R^2 and $\overline{R}^2$. Show how $\overline{R}^2$ has been calculated from R^2 and other numbers.

d. Calculate the F(model) statistic by using the explained variation, the unexplained variation, and other relevant quantities. Find F(model) on the output to check your answer.

e. Use the F(model) statistic and the appropriate rejection point to test the significance of the linear regression model under consideration by setting α equal to .05.

f. Use the F(model) statistic and the appropriate rejection point to test the significance of the linear regression model under consideration by setting α equal to .01.

g. Find the p-value related to F(model) on the output. Using the p-value, test the significance of the linear regression model by setting $\alpha = .10, .05, .01$, and $.001$. What do you conclude?

12.14 THE WORK ATTENDANCE EXAMPLE

Model: $y = \beta_0 + \beta_1 x_1 + \beta_2 x_2 + \varepsilon$

Sample size: $n = 10$

12.15 THE FRESH DETERGENT EXAMPLE

Model: $y = \beta_0 + \beta_1 x_1 + \beta_2 x_2 + \beta_3 x_3 + \varepsilon$

Sample size: $n = 30$

12.16 THE HOSPITAL LABOUR NEEDS EXAMPLE

Model: $y = \beta_0 + \beta_1 x_1 + \beta_2 x_2 + \beta_3 x_3 + \varepsilon$

Sample size: $n = 16$

FIGURE 12.10 Output for Exercises 12.14, 12.15, and 12.16

(a) MegaStat output for Exercise 12.14

Regression Analysis

R^2	0.732		
Adjusted R^2	0.655	n	10
R	0.855	k	2
Std. Error	6.802	Dep. Var.	Attendance (y)

ANOVA table

Source	SS	df	MS	F	p-value
Regression	884.0887	2	442.0443	9.55	0.0100
Residual	323.9113	7	46.2730		
Total	1,208.0000	9			

(b) MegaStat output for Exercise 12.15

Regression Analysis

R^2	0.894		
Adjusted R^2	0.881	n	30
R	0.945	k	3
Std. Error	0.235	Dep. Var.	Demand (y)

ANOVA table

Source	SS	df	MS	F	p-value
Regression	12.0268	3	4.0089	72.80	8.88E-13
Residual	1.4318	26	0.0551		
Total	13.4586	29			

(c) Excel output for Exercise 12.16

Regression Statistics

Multiple R	0.9981
R Square	0.9961
Adjusted R Square	0.9952
Standard Error	387.1598
Observations	16

ANOVA

	df	SS	MS	F	Significance F
Regression	3	462,327,889.4	154,109,296.5	1,028.1309	9.92E-15
Residual	12	1,798,712.2	149,892.7		
Total	15	464,126,601.6			

12.17 THE WORK ATTENDANCE EXAMPLE

Figure 12.11 gives the Excel output of a regression analysis of the work attendance study data in Table 12.3 using the model

$$y = \beta_0 + \beta_1 x_1 + \beta_2 x_2 + \varepsilon.$$

On the Excel output, find the values of b_0, b_1, and b_2 (the least squares point estimates of β_0, β_1, and β_2). Report and interpret b_0, b_1, and b_2.

12.18 THE FRESH DETERGENT EXAMPLE

Figure 12.12 gives the MegaStat output of a regression analysis of the Fresh detergent demand data in Table 12.4 using the model

$$y = \beta_0 + \beta_1 x_1 + \beta_2 x_2 + \beta_3 x_3 + \varepsilon$$

a. Find (on the output) and report the values of b_0, b_1, b_2, and b_3, the least squares point estimates of β_0, β_1, β_2, and β_3. Interpret b_0, b_1, b_2, and b_3.

b. Consider the demand for Fresh detergent in a future sales period when Enterprise Industries' price for Fresh will be $x_1 = 3.70$, the average price of competitors' similar detergents will be $x_2 = 3.90$, and Enterprise Industries' advertising expenditure

FIGURE **12.11**   Excel Output of a Regression Analysis of the Work Attendance Data Using the Model $y = \beta_0 + \beta_1 x_1 + \beta_2 x_2 + \varepsilon$

SUMMARY OUTPUT

Regression Statistics

Multiple R	0.85548904
R Square	0.73186149
Adjusted R Square	0.65525049
Standard Error	6.80242938
Observations	10

ANOVA

	df	SS	MS	F	Significance F
Regression	2	884.0886821	442.0443	9.552955	0.00998291
Residual	7	323.9113179	46.27305		
Total	9	1208			

	Coefficients	Standard Error	t Stat	P-value	Lower 95%	Upper 95%
Intercept	44.6631219	13.50112214	3.308104	0.012975	12.73806393	76.5881799
Job Satis (x1)	5.74060008	1.437002571	3.994843	0.005224	2.342631377	9.13856878
Commute Dist (x2)	0.3431447	0.806379492	0.425537	0.683222	−1.563638436	2.24992784

FIGURE **12.12**   MegaStat Output of a Regression Analysis of the Fresh Detergent Demand Data Using the Model $y = \beta_0 + \beta_1 x_1 + \beta_2 x_2 + \beta_3 x_3 + \varepsilon$

Regression Analysis

	R^2 0.894		
	Adjusted R^2 0.881	n 30	
R 0.945	k 3		
	Std. Error 0.235	Dep. Var. **Demand (y)**	

ANOVA table

Source	SS	df	MS	F	p-value
Regression	12.0268	3	4.0089	72.80	8.88E-13
Residual	1.4318	26	0.0551		
Total	13.4586	29			

Regression output

variables	coefficients	std. error	t (df = 26)	p-value	confidence interval 95% lower	95% upper
Intercept	7.5891	2.4450	3.104	0.0046	2.5633	12.6149
Price (x1)	−2.3577	0.6379	−3.696	0.0010	−3.6690	−1.0464
IndPrice (x2)	1.6122	0.2954	5.459	1.01E-05	1.0051	2.2193
AdvExp (x3)	0.5012	0.1259	3.981	0.0005	0.2424	0.7599

Predicted values for: Demand (y)

Price (x1)	IndPrice (x2)	AdvExp (x3)	Predicted	95% Confidence Interval lower	upper	95% Prediction Interval lower	upper	Leverage
3.7	3.9	6.5	8.4107	8.3143	8.5070	7.9188	8.9025	0.040

FIGURE 12.13 Excel and MegaStat Output of a Regression Analysis of the Hospital Labour Needs Data Using the Model $y = \beta_0 + \beta_1 x_1 + \beta_2 x_2 + \beta_3 x_3 + \varepsilon$

(a) The Excel output

Regression Statistics

Multiple R	0.9981
R Square	0.9961
Adjusted R Square	0.9952
Standard Error	387.1598
Observations	16

ANOVA

	df	SS	MS	F	Significance F
Regression	3	462,327,889.4	154,109,296.5	1,028.1309	9.92E-15
Residual	12	1,798,712.2	149,892.7		
Total	15	464,126,601.6			

	Coefficients	Standard Error	t Stat	P-value	Lower 95%	Upper 95%
Intercept	1,946.8020	504.1819	3.8613	0.0023	848.2840	3,045.3201
XRay (x1)	0.0386	0.0130	2.9579	0.0120	0.0102	0.0670
BedDays (x2)	1.0394	0.0676	15.3857	2.91E-09	0.8922	1.1866
LengthStay (x3)	−413.7578	98.5983	−4.1964	0.0012	−628.5850	−198.9306

(b) Prediction using MegaStat

Predicted values for: LabourHours

XRay (x1)	BedDays (x2)	LengthStay (x3)	Predicted	95% Confidence Interval lower	95% Confidence Interval upper	95% Prediction Interval lower	95% Prediction Interval upper	Leverage
56,194	14,077.88	6.89	15,896.2473	15,378.0313	16,414.4632	14,906.2361	16,886.2584	0.3774

for Fresh will be $x_3 = 6.50$. The point prediction of this demand is given at the bottom of the MegaStat output. Report this point prediction and show how it was calculated.

12.19 THE HOSPITAL LABOUR NEEDS EXAMPLE

Figure 12.13 gives the Excel and MegaStat output of a regression analysis of the hospital labour needs data in Table 12.5 using the model

$$y = \beta_0 + \beta_1 x_1 + \beta_2 x_2 + \beta_3 x_3 + \varepsilon$$

Note that the variables x_1, x_2, and x_3 are denoted as XRay, BedDays, and LengthStay on the output.

a. Find on the output and interpret b_0, b_1, b_2, and b_3, the least squares point estimates of β_0, β_1, β_2, and β_3.

b. Consider a hospital for which XRay = 56,194, BedDays = 14,077.88, and LengthStay = 6.89. A point prediction of the labour hours corresponding to this combination of values of the independent variables is given in the MegaStat output. Report this point prediction and show how it was calculated.

c. If the actual number of labour hours used by the hospital was $y = 17,207.31$, how does this y value compare with the point prediction?

12.7 TESTING THE SIGNIFICANCE OF AN INDEPENDENT VARIABLE

Consider the multiple regression model

$$y = \beta_0 + \beta_1 x_1 + \beta_2 x_2 + \cdots + \beta_k x_k + \varepsilon$$

To gain information about which of the independent variables significantly affect y, we can test the significance of a single independent variable. We arbitrarily refer to this variable as x_j and assume that it is multiplied by the parameter β_j. For example, if $j = 1$, we are testing the significance of x_1, which is multiplied by β_1; if $j = 2$, we are testing the significance of x_2, which is multiplied by β_2. To test the significance of x_j, we test the null hypothesis $H_0: \beta_j = 0$.

We usually test H_0 versus the alternative hypothesis H_a: $\beta_j \neq 0$. *It is reasonable to conclude that x_j is significantly related to y in the regression model under consideration if H_0 can be rejected in favour of H_a at a small level of significance.* Here the phrase "in the regression model under consideration" is very important because whether x_j is significantly related to y in a particular regression model can depend on what other independent variables are included in the model.

Testing the significance of x_j in a multiple regression model is similar to testing the significance of the slope in the simple linear regression model (recall we test H_0: $\beta_1 = 0$ in simple regression). If the regression assumptions hold, the population of all possible values of the least squares point estimate b_j is normally distributed with mean β_j and standard deviation σ_{b_j}. The point estimate of σ_{b_j} is called the *standard error of the estimate b_j* and is denoted s_{b_j}. The formula for s_{b_j} involves matrix algebra and is discussed in Appendix F on *Connect*. In our discussion here, we will rely on MegaStat and Excel to compute s_{b_j}. If the regression assumptions hold, the population of all possible values of

$$\frac{b_j + \beta_j}{s_{b_j}}$$

has a t distribution with $n - (k + 1)$ degrees of freedom. It follows that if the null hypothesis H_0: $\beta_j = 0$ is true, the population of all possible values of the test statistic

$$t = \frac{b_j}{s_{b_j}}$$

has a t distribution with $n - (k + 1)$ degrees of freedom. Therefore, we can test the significance of x_j as shown in the following boxed feature.

Testing the Significance of the Independent Variable x_j

Define the test statistic

$$t = \frac{b_j}{s_{b_j}}$$

and suppose that the regression assumptions hold.

Then we can test H_0: $\beta_j = 0$ versus a particular alternative hypothesis at significance level α by using the appropriate rejection point rule or, equivalently, the corresponding p-value.

Alternative Hypothesis	Rejection Point Rule: Reject H_0 If	p-Value (Reject H_0 If p-Value $< \alpha$)
H_a: $\beta_j \neq 0$	$|t| > t_{\alpha/2}$	Twice the area under the t curve to the right of $|t|$
H_a: $\beta_j > 0$	$t > t_\alpha$	The area under the t curve to the right of t
H_a: $\beta_j < 0$	$t < -t_\alpha$	The area under the t curve to the left of t

Here $t_{\alpha/2}$, t_α, and all p-values are based on $n - (k + 1)$ degrees of freedom.

As in testing H_0: $\beta_1 = 0$ in simple linear regression, we usually use the two-sided alternative hypothesis H_a: $\beta_j \neq 0$ unless we have theoretical reasons to believe that β_j has a particular (plus or minus) sign (referred to as a *one-tailed prediction*). Moreover, MegaStat and Excel present the results for the two-sided test.

It is customary to test the significance of every independent variable in a regression model. Generally speaking, we have the following:

1 If we can reject H_0: $\beta_j = 0$ at the .05 level of significance, we have strong evidence that the independent variable x_j is significantly related to y in the regression model.

2 If we can reject H_0: $\beta_j = 0$ at the .01 level of significance, we have very strong evidence that x_j is significantly related to y in the regression model.

3 The smaller the significance level α at which H_0 can be rejected, the stronger is the evidence that x_j is significantly related to y in the regression model.

Example 12.4   Evaluating the Significance of Sales Performance Predictors

Consider the sales territory performance model

$$y = \beta_0 + \beta_1 x_1 + \beta_2 x_2 + \beta_3 x_3 + \beta_4 x_4 + \beta_5 x_5 + \varepsilon$$

Because the MegaStat output in Figure 12.14 tells us that the p-values associated with Time, MktPoten, Adver, and MktShare are all less than .01, we have very strong evidence that these variables are significantly related to y and therefore are important in this model. The p-value associated with Change is .0530, suggesting weaker evidence that this variable is important.

FIGURE 12.14   MegaStat Output of t Statistics and p-Values for the Sales Territory Performance Model

Regression output					confidence interval	
variables	coefficients	std. error	t (df=19)	p-value	95% lower	95% upper
Intercept	−1,113.7879	419.8869	−2.653	0.0157	−1,992.6213	−234.9545
Time	3.6121	1.1817	3.057	0.0065	1.1388	6.0854
MktPoten	0.0421	0.0067	6.253	5.27E-06	0.0280	0.0562
Adver	0.1289	0.0370	3.479	0.0025	0.0513	0.2064
MktShare	256.9555	39.1361	6.566	2.76E-06	175.0428	338.8683
Change	324.5334	157.2831	2.063	0.0530	−4.6638	653.7307

The following boxed feature demonstrates how to calculate a confidence interval for a regression parameter. In Section 12.8, confidence and prediction intervals are discussed.

A Confidence Interval for the Regression Parameter β_j

If the regression assumptions hold, a $100(1 - \alpha)$ percent confidence interval for B_j is

$$[b_j \pm t_{\alpha/2} s_{b_j}]$$

Here $t_\alpha/2$ is based on $n - (k + 1)$ degrees of freedom.

Determining whether to exclude variables from an equation The notion of p-values and significance tests for individual predictors in a regression equation introduces the notion of selecting particular variables for inclusion in a regression equation. The two methods most frequently used for this type of decision making are *stepwise regression* and *backward elimination*. Both methods have a similar goal—to achieve greater parsimony in the use of predictors within the regression equation—but they take slightly different approaches. Both methods require that you determine an alpha for including a variable and an alpha for excluding a variable that is already in the analysis—and both methods use an iterative approach to identify the independent variables that are to be part of the final prediction equation.

Stepwise regression involves adding the "best" predictors from among the independent variables of interest, one at a time, until no statistically significant predictors remain. Backward elimination essentially involves performing this procedure in reverse—all predictors are added to the prediction equation and then removed one at a time, starting with the "worst" predictor. This process continues until the equation includes only statistically significant predictors. Stepwise regression and backward elimination are described in greater detail in Appendix K.

THEORY TO PRACTICE

It should be apparent from the content of this chapter that multiple regression is a potentially useful tool for predicting continuous variables in the workplace. For example, if you are looking for factors that predict sales figures or market demand, multiple regression allows you to identify the magnitude of individual factors (controlling for other predictors in the equation), as well as the overall predictive power of the equation.

Furthermore, multiple regression techniques like stepwise regression and backward elimination allow us to create a prediction equation with the fewest number of predictors. In this way, we can not only estimate an outcome measure (such as the total sales volume in a department) with a series of independent variables, but we can identify which variables are "most important" to the prediction of the outcome. Although we have introduced the concept of stepwise regression and backward elimination, it is also possible to rationally select predictors based on the ease with which they can be measured or the cost of their administration. In this way, we can come up with the best possible prediction equation that takes into account the resources that we have available for the assessment.

Exercises for Section **12.7**

CONCEPTS

12.20 What do you conclude about x_j if you can reject $H_0: \beta_j = 0$ in favour of $H_a: \beta_j \neq 0$ by setting
   a. α equal to .05?
   b. α equal to .01?

12.21 Give an example of a practical application of the confidence interval for β_j.

METHODS AND APPLICATIONS

In Exercises 12.22 through 12.24, we refer to MegaStat and Excel outputs of regression analyses of the data sets related to three examples introduced in Section 12.1. The outputs are given

in Figure 12.15. Using the appropriate output, do the following for *each parameter* β_j in the model under consideration:

   a. Find b_j, s_{b_j}, and the t statistic for testing $H_0: \beta_j = 0$ on the output, and report their values. Show how t was calculated by using b_j and s_{b_j}.

   b. Using the t statistic and appropriate rejection points, test $H_0: \beta_j = 0$ versus $H_a: \beta_j \neq 0$ by setting α equal to .05. Which independent variables are significantly related to y in the model with $\alpha = .05$?

   c. Using the t statistic and appropriate rejection points, test $H_0: \beta_j = 0$ versus $H_a: \beta_j \neq 0$ by setting α equal to .01. Which independent variables are significantly related to y in the model with $\alpha = .01$?

FIGURE 12.15   *t* Statistics and *p*-Values for Three Examples

(a) MegaStat output for the work attendance examples (sample size: $n = 10$)

Regression output

variables	coefficients	std. error	t (df=7)	p-value	confidence interval 95% lower	95% upper
Intercept	44.6631	13.5011	3.308	0.0130	12.7381	76.5882
Job Satis (x1)	5.7406	1.4370	3.995	0.0052	2.3426	9.1386
Commute Dist (x2)	0.3431	0.8064	0.426	0.6832	−1.5636	2.2499

(b) MegaStat output for the Fresh detergent example (sample size: $n = 30$)

Regression output

variables	coefficients	std. error	t (df=26)	p-value	confidence interval 95% lower	95% upper
Intercept	7.5891	2.4450	3.104	0.0046	2.5633	12.6149
Price (x1)	−2.3577	0.6379	−3.696	0.0010	−3.6690	−1.0464
IndPrice (x2)	1.6122	0.2954	5.459	1.01E-05	1.0051	2.2193
AdvExp (x3)	0.5012	0.1259	3.981	0.0005	0.2424	0.7599

(c) Excel output for the hospital labour needs example (sample size: $n = 16$)

	Coefficients	Standard Error	t Stat	P-value	Lower 95%	Upper 95%
Intercept	1,946.8020	504.1819	3.8613	0.0023	848.2840	3,045.3201
XRay (x1)	0.0386	0.0130	2.9579	0.0120	0.0102	0.0670
BedDays (x2)	1.0394	0.0676	15.3857	2.91E-09	0.8922	1.1866
LengthStay (x3)	−413.7578	98.5983	−4.1964	0.0012	−628.5850	−198.9306

d. Find the *p*-value for testing H_0: $\beta_j = 0$ versus H_a: $\beta_j \neq 0$ on the output. Using the *p*-value, determine whether you can reject H_0 by setting α equal to .10, .05, .01, and .001. What do you conclude about the significance of the independent variables in the model?

e. Calculate the 95 percent confidence interval for β_j. Discuss one practical application of this interval.

f. Calculate the 99 percent confidence interval for β_j. Discuss one practical application of this interval.

12.22 THE WORK ATTENDANCE EXAMPLE

Use the MegaStat output in Figure 12.15(a) to do parts (a) through (f) for each of β_0, β_1, and β_2.

12.23 THE FRESH DETERGENT EXAMPLE

Use the MegaStat output in Figure 12.15(b) to do parts (a) through (f) for each of β_0, β_1, β_2, and β_3.

12.24 THE HOSPITAL LABOUR NEEDS EXAMPLE

Use the Excel output in Figure 12.15(c) to do parts (a) through (f) for each of β_0, β_1, β_2, and β_3.

12.8 CONFIDENCE AND PREDICTION INTERVALS

In this section, we show how to use the multiple regression model to find a confidence interval for a mean value of *y* and a prediction interval for an individual value of *y*. We first present an example of these intervals, and then we discuss the logic behind and formulas used to compute the intervals.

Example 12.5 Establishing the Limits of Prediction

Consider a sales representative for whom Time = 85.42, MktPoten = 35,182.73, Adver = 7,281.65, MktShare = 9.64, and Change = .28. We saw in Example 12.3 that the point prediction of the sales corresponding to this combination of values of the independent variables is

$$\hat{y} = -1,113.7879 + 3.6121(85.42) + .0421(35,182.73)$$
$$+ .1289(7,281.65) + 256.9555(9.64) + 324.5334(.28)$$
$$= 4,181.74 \text{ (or } 418,174 \text{ units)}$$

This point prediction is given at the bottom of the MegaStat output in Figure 12.9, which we repeat here:

Predicted values for: Sales

	95% Confidence Interval		95% Prediction Interval		
Predicted	lower	upper	lower	upper	Leverage
4,181.74333	3,884.90651	4,478.58015	3,233.59431	5,129.89235	0.109

In addition to giving $\hat{y} = 4,181.74$, the MegaStat output tells us that a 95 percent prediction interval for *y* is [3,233.59, 5,129.89]. Furthermore, the actual sales *y* for the representative were 3,087.52. This actual sales figure is less than the point prediction $\hat{y} = 4,181.74$ and is less than the lower bound of the 95 percent prediction interval for *y*, [3,233.59, 5,129.89]. Therefore, we conclude that there is strong evidence that the actual performance of the representative is less than the predicted performance.

In general,

$$\hat{y} = b_0 + b_1 x_{01} + \cdots + b_k x_{0k}$$

is the *point estimate of the mean value of y* when the values of the independent variables are $x_{01}, x_{02}, \ldots, x_{0k}$. Calling this mean value $\mu_{y|x_{01}, x_{02}, \ldots, x_{0k}}$, if the regression assumptions hold, the population of all possible values of $\hat{y}$ is normally distributed with mean $\mu_{y|x_{01}, x_{02}, \ldots, x_{0k}}$ and standard deviation

$$\sigma_{\hat{y}} = \sigma \sqrt{\text{Distance value}}$$

The formula for the distance value involves matrix algebra and is given in Appendix F on *Connect*. We will soon see how to use the MegaStat output to find the distance value. It can be shown that the farther the values $x_{01}, x_{02}, \ldots, x_{0k}$ are from the centre of the experimental region, the larger is the distance value. We regard the centre of the experimental region to be the point $(\bar{x}_1, \bar{x}_2, \ldots, \bar{x}_k)$, where $\bar{x}_1$ is the average of the observed x_1 values, $\bar{x}_2$ is the average of the observed x_2 values, and so forth. Because s is the point estimate of σ, the point estimate of $\sigma_{\hat{y}}$ is

$$s_{\hat{y}} = s\sqrt{\text{Distance value}}$$

L06

which is called the **standard error of the estimate $\hat{y}$**. Using this standard error, we can form a confidence interval, as shown in the following boxed feature.

A Confidence Interval for a Mean Value of y

If the regression assumptions hold, a $100(1 - \alpha)$ percent confidence interval for the mean value of y when the values of the independent variables are $x_{01}, x_{02}, \ldots, x_{0k}$ is

$$\left[\hat{y} \pm t_{\alpha/2}s\sqrt{\text{Distance value}}\right]$$

Here $t_{\alpha/2}$ is based on $n - (k + 1)$ degrees of freedom.

To develop an interval for an individual value of y, we consider the prediction error $y - \hat{y}$. If the regression assumptions hold, the population of all possible prediction errors is normally distributed with mean 0 and standard deviation

$$\sigma_{(y-\hat{y})} = \sigma\sqrt{1 + \text{Distance value}}$$

The point estimate of $\sigma_{(y-\hat{y})}$ is

$$s_{(y-\hat{y})} = s\sqrt{1 + \text{Distance value}}$$

which is called the *standard error of the prediction error*. Using this standard error, we can form a prediction interval, as shown in the following boxed feature.

A Prediction Interval for an Individual Value of y

If the regression assumptions hold, a $100(1 - \alpha)$ percent prediction interval for an individual value of y when the values of the independent variables are $x_{01}, x_{02}, \ldots, x_{0k}$ is

$$\left[\hat{y} \pm t_{\alpha/2}s\sqrt{1 + \text{Distance value}}\right]$$

Here $t_{\alpha/2}$ is based on $n - (k + 1)$ degrees of freedom.

Recall that the farther the values $x_{01}, x_{02}, \ldots, x_{0k}$ are from the centre of the experimental region, the larger is the distance value. It follows that the farther the values $x_{01}, x_{02}, \ldots, x_{0k}$ are from the centre of the experimental region, the longer (less precise) are the confidence intervals and prediction intervals provided by a regression model.

For example, the MegaStat output in Example 12.5 tells us that $\hat{y} = 4{,}181.74$. This output also tells us that the distance value, which is given under the heading "Leverage" on the output, equals .109. Therefore, since s for the five-variable sales territory performance model equals 430.232, it follows that the 95 percent prediction interval given on the MegaStat output of Example 12.5 was calculated as follows:

$$\left[\hat{y} \pm t_{.025}s\sqrt{1 + \text{Distance value}}\right]$$
$$= \left[4{,}181.74 \pm 2.093(430.232)\sqrt{1 + .109}\right]$$
$$= \left[3{,}233.59, 5{,}129.89\right]$$

Here $t_{.025} = 2.093$ is based on $n - (k + 1) = 25 - 6 = 19$ degrees of freedom.

Exercises for Section **12.8**

CONCEPTS

12.25 What does the distance value measure?

12.26 How is the distance value obtained from a MegaStat output?

METHODS AND APPLICATIONS

12.27 THE WORK ATTENDANCE EXAMPLE

The MegaStat output in Figure 12.16(a) relates to predictions based on two different employee cases.

a. Report (as shown on the output) the predicted attendance and the 95 percent prediction interval for an employee who is very satisfied with the job and lives close to work. (Hint: Recall that satisfaction ranged from 1 = Not satisfied to 10 = Very satisfied.)

b. Report (as shown in the output) the predicted attendance and the 95 percent prediction interval for an employee who is dissatisfied with the job and who lives 8 km from work.

c. Comparing the results of the two predictions, which has the larger distance value?

12.28 THE FRESH DETERGENT EXAMPLE

Consider the demand for Fresh detergent in a future sales period when Enterprise Industries' price for Fresh will be $x_1 = 3.70$, the average price of competitors' similar detergents will be $x_2 = 3.90$, and Enterprise Industries' advertising expenditure for Fresh will be $x_3 = 6.50$. A 95 percent prediction interval for this demand is given in the MegaStat output in Figure 12.16(b).

a. Find and report the 95 percent prediction interval on the output. If Enterprise Industries plans to have in inventory the number of bottles implied by the upper limit of this interval, it can be very confident that it will have enough bottles to meet demand for Fresh in the future sales period. How many bottles is this? If we multiply the number of bottles implied by the lower limit of the prediction interval by the price of

Fresh ($3.70), we can be very confident that the resulting dollar amount will be the minimal revenue from Fresh in the future sales period. What is this dollar amount?

b. Calculate a 99 percent prediction interval for the demand for Fresh in the future sales period. The standard error is .235, and $n = 30$.

c. Recall that the data plots given at the bottom of Table 12.4 suggest that the model $y = \beta_0 + \beta_1 x_4 + \beta_2 x_3 + \varepsilon$ might appropriately relate demand for Fresh (y) to the price difference ($x_4 = x_2 - x_1$) and advertising expenditure (x_3). The 95 percent prediction interval given by this model for the demand for Fresh in the future sales period is [7.89034, 8.88523]. Is this interval shorter or longer than the interval in part (a)? What does this imply about which model might best predict y?

12.29 THE HOSPITAL LABOUR NEEDS EXAMPLE

Consider a hospital for which XRay = 56,194, BedDays = 14,077.88, and LengthStay = 6.89. A 95 percent prediction interval for the labour hours corresponding to this combination of values of the independent variables is given in the MegaStat output in Figure 12.16(c). Find and report the prediction interval on the output. Then use this interval to determine if the actual number of labour hours used by the hospital ($y = 17,207.31$) is unusually low or high.

FIGURE 12.16   MegaStat Outputs for Exercises 12.27, 12.28, and 12.29

(a) Output for Exercise 12.27

Predicted values for: Attendance (y)

Job Satis (x1)	Commute Dist (x2)	Predicted	95% Confidence Intervals lower	95% Confidence Intervals upper	95% Prediction Intervals lower	95% Prediction Intervals upper	Leverage
8	2	91.274	80.085	102.463	71.680	110.868	0.484
2	8	58.889	43.739	74.040	36.792	80.987	0.887

(b) Output for Exercise 12.28

Predicted	95% Confidence Interval lower	95% Confidence Interval upper	95% Prediction Interval lower	95% Prediction Interval upper	Leverage
8.4107	8.3143	8.5070	7.9188	8.9025	0.040

(c) Output for Exercise 12.29

Predicted	95% Confidence Interval lower	95% Confidence Interval upper	95% Prediction Interval lower	95% Prediction Interval upper	Leverage
15,896.2473	15,378.0313	16,414.4632	14,906.2361	16,886.2584	0.3774

PART 2
**Using Squared
and Interaction
Terms
(Optional)**

12.9 THE QUADRATIC REGRESSION MODEL

One useful form of the multiple regression model is what we call the *quadratic regression model*. Assuming that we have obtained *n* observations—each consisting of an observed value of *y* and a corresponding value of *x*—the model is as shown in the following boxed feature.

The Quadratic Regression Model

The quadratic regression model relating *y* to *x* is

$$y = \beta_0 + \beta_1 x + \beta_2 x^2 + \varepsilon$$

where

1   $\beta_0 + \beta_1 x + \beta_2 x^2$ is $\mu_{y|x}$ (the mean value of the dependent variable *y* when the value of the independent variable is *x*).

2   β_0, β_1, and β_2 are (unknown) regression parameters relating the mean value of *y* to *x*.

3   ε is an error term that describes the effects on *y* of all factors other than *x* and x^2.

The quadratic equation $\mu_{y|x} = \beta_0 + \beta_1 x + \beta_2 x^2$ that relates $\mu_{y|x}$ to *x* is the equation of a parabola. Two parabolas are shown in Figure 12.17(a) and (b) and help to interpret the parameters β_0, β_1, and β_2. Here β_0 is the *y* intercept of the parabola (the value of $\mu_{y|x}$ when $x = 0$). Furthermore, β_1 is the shift parameter of the parabola: The value of β_1 shifts the parabola to the left or right. Specifically, increasing the value of β_1 shifts the parabola to

FIGURE 12.17   The Mean Value of the Dependent Variable Changing in a Quadratic Fashion as *x* Increases
($\mu_{y|x} = \beta_0 + \beta_1 x + \beta_2 x^2$)

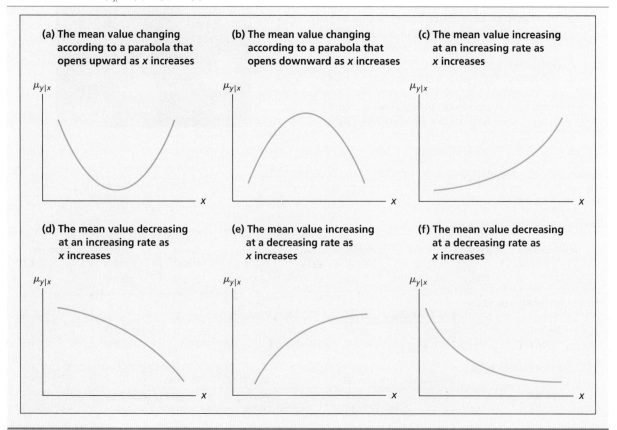

(a) The mean value changing according to a parabola that opens upward as *x* increases

(b) The mean value changing according to a parabola that opens downward as *x* increases

(c) The mean value increasing at an increasing rate as *x* increases

(d) The mean value decreasing at an increasing rate as *x* increases

(e) The mean value increasing at a decreasing rate as *x* increases

(f) The mean value decreasing at a decreasing rate as *x* increases

the left. Lastly, β_2 is the rate of curvature of the parabola. If β_2 is greater than 0, the parabola opens upward [see Figure 12.17(a)]. If β_2 is less than 0, the parabola opens downward [see Figure 12.17(b)]. If a scatter plot of y versus x shows points scattered around a parabola, or a part of a parabola [some typical parts are shown in Figure 12.17(c), (d), (e), and (f)], then the quadratic regression model might appropriately relate y to x.

Example 12.6 Stress and Work Motivation

Stress is typically a difficult psychological variable to measure. Although the word *stress* usually has negative connotations, some stress may actually be motivating in the workplace. Stress researchers have suggested that too little stress and too much stress result in lower work performance, but a moderate amount of stress is motivating and improves work performance (so the pattern/correlation would be nonlinear in nature). To test this hypothesis, a human resources (HR) department administers a stress questionnaire to 15 employees in which people rate their stress level on a 0 (no stress) to 4 (high stress) scale. Work performance is measured as the average number of projects completed by the employee per year, averaged over the previous five years (in order to improve the reliability of the measure). Table 12.8(a) gives the results of the test. Here the dependent variable y is productivity (in projects per year) and the independent variable x is the self-reported stress level.

Table 12.8(b) gives a scatter plot of y versus x. Because the scatter plot has the appearance of a quadratic curve (that is, part of a parabola), it seems reasonable to relate y to x by using the quadratic model

$$y = \beta_0 + \beta_1 x + \beta_2 x^2 + \varepsilon$$

Figure 12.18 gives the MegaStat output of a regression analysis of the data using this quadratic model. Here the squared term x^2 is denoted as x2 on the output. The output tells us that the least squares point estimates of the model parameters are $b_0 = 25.7152$, $b_1 = 4.9762$, and $b_2 = -1.0190$. These estimates give us the least squares prediction equation

$$\hat{y} = 25.7152 + 4.9762x + 1.0190x^2$$

TABLE **12.8** The Stress and Work Motivation Study Data, and a Scatter Plot of the Data

(a) The data

Self-Reported Stress Level, x	Productivity, y (Projects per Year)
0	25.8
0	26.1
0	25.4
1	29.6
1	29.2
1	29.8
2	32.0
2	31.4
2	31.7
3	31.7
3	31.5
3	31.2
4	29.4
4	29.0
4	29.5

(b) Scatter plot of y versus x

This is the equation of the best quadratic curve that can be fitted to the data plotted in Table 12.8(b). The output also tells us that the p-values related to x and x^2 are less than .001. This implies that we have extremely strong evidence that each of these model components is significant. The fact that x^2 seems significant confirms the graphical evidence that there is a quadratic relationship between y and x. Once we have such confirmation, we usually retain the linear term x in the model no matter what the size of its p-value. The reason is that geometrical considerations indicate that it is best to use both x and x^2 to model a quadratic relationship.

FIGURE 12.18   MegaStat Output of a Regression Analysis of the Stress and Motivation Data Using the Quadratic Model

Regression Analysis

R²	0.986		
Adjusted R²	0.983	n	15
R	0.993	k	2
Std. Error	0.286	Dep. Var.	Productivity, y (projects per year)

ANOVA table

Source	SS	df	MS	F	p-value
Regression	67.9152	2	33.9576	414.92	8.39E-12
Residual	0.9821	12	0.0818		
Total	68.8973	14			

Regression output

variables	coefficients	std. error	t (df=12)	p-value	confidence interval 95% lower	95% upper
Intercept	25.7152	0.1554	165.431	1.60E-21	25.3766	26.0539
Stress Level, x	4.9762	0.1841	27.025	4.05E-12	4.5750	5.3774
x2	−1.0190	0.0441	−23.085	2.60E-11	−1.1152	−0.9229

Predicted values for: Productivity, y (projects per year)

Stress Level, x	x2	Predicted	95% Confidence Interval lower	upper	95% Prediction Interval lower	upper	Leverage
2.44	5.936	31.8081	31.5648	32.0514	31.1390	32.4772	0.152

The HR department wants to find the value of x that results in the highest productivity score. Using calculus, it can be shown that the value $x = 2.44$ maximizes predicted productivity, suggesting that, in theory, productivity will be highest for an individual worker who scores between 2 and 3 on the stress scale. This will result in a predicted productivity score equal to

$$\hat{y} = 25.7152 + 4.9762(2.44) - 1.01905(2.44)^2$$
$$= 31.7901 \text{ average projects completed per year}$$

Note that $\hat{y} = 31.8081$ is given at the bottom of the output in Figure 12.18. In addition, the output tells us that a 95 percent confidence interval for the mean productivity score that would be obtained by all of the employees is [31.5648, 32.0514]. The output also tells us that a 95 percent prediction interval for the average number of projects completed by an individual employee is [31.1390, 32.4772].

We now consider a model that employs both a linear and a quadratic term for one independent variable and also employs another linear term for a second independent variable.

Example 12.7   Fresh Detergent

Enterprise Industries produces Fresh, a brand of liquid laundry detergent. To more effectively manage its inventory and make revenue projections, the company would like to better predict demand for Fresh. To develop a prediction model, the company has gathered data concerning demand for Fresh over the previous 30 sales periods (each sales period is defined to be a four-week period). The demand data are presented in Table 12.9. Here, for each sales period,

y = Demand for the large bottle of Fresh (in hundreds of thousands of bottles) in the sales period

x_1 = Price (in dollars) of Fresh as offered by Enterprise Industries in the sales period

x_2 = Average industry price (in dollars) of competitors' similar detergents in the sales period

x_3 = Enterprise Industries' advertising expenditure (in hundreds of thousands of dollars) to promote Fresh in the sales period

$x_4 = x_2 - x_1$ = Price difference in the sales period

To begin our analysis, suppose that Enterprise Industries believes on theoretical grounds that the single independent variable x_4 adequately describes the effects of x_1 and x_2 on y. That is, perhaps demand for Fresh depends more on how the price for Fresh compares to competitors' prices than it does on the absolute levels of the prices for Fresh and other competing detergents. This makes sense since most consumers must buy a certain amount of detergent no matter what the price is (we will examine the validity of using x_4 to predict y more fully in Exercise 12.33). For now, we will build a prediction model utilizing x_3 and x_4.

TABLE 12.9   Historical Data, Including Price Differences, Concerning Demand for Fresh Detergent

Sales Period	Price for Fresh, x_1 (Dollars)	Average Industry Price, x_2 (Dollars)	Price Difference, $x_4 = x_2 - x_1$ (Dollars)	Advertising Expenditure for Fresh, x_3 (Hundreds of Thousands of Dollars)	Demand for Fresh, y (Hundreds of Thousands of Bottles)
1	3.85	3.80	−0.05	5.50	7.38
2	3.75	4.00	0.25	6.75	8.51
3	3.70	4.30	0.60	7.25	9.52
4	3.70	3.70	0	5.50	7.50
5	3.60	3.85	0.25	7.00	9.33
6	3.60	3.80	0.20	6.50	8.28
7	3.60	3.75	0.15	6.75	8.75
8	3.80	3.85	0.05	5.25	7.87
9	3.80	3.65	−0.15	5.25	7.10
10	3.85	4.00	0.15	6.00	8.00
11	3.90	4.10	0.20	6.50	7.89
12	3.90	4.00	0.10	6.25	8.15
13	3.70	4.10	0.40	7.00	9.10
14	3.75	4.20	0.45	6.90	8.86
15	3.75	4.10	0.35	6.80	8.90
16	3.80	4.10	0.30	6.80	8.87
17	3.70	4.20	0.50	7.10	9.26
18	3.80	4.30	0.50	7.00	9.00
19	3.70	4.10	0.40	6.80	8.75
20	3.80	3.75	−0.05	6.50	7.95
21	3.80	3.75	−0.05	6.25	7.65
22	3.75	3.65	−0.10	6.00	7.27
23	3.70	3.90	0.20	6.50	8.00
24	3.55	3.65	0.10	7.00	8.50
25	3.60	4.10	0.50	6.80	8.75
26	3.65	4.25	0.60	6.80	9.21
27	3.70	3.65	−0.05	6.50	8.27
28	3.75	3.75	0	5.75	7.67
29	3.80	3.85	0.05	5.80	7.93
30	3.70	4.25	0.55	6.80	9.26

FIGURE **12.19** Scatter Plots of the Fresh Demand Data

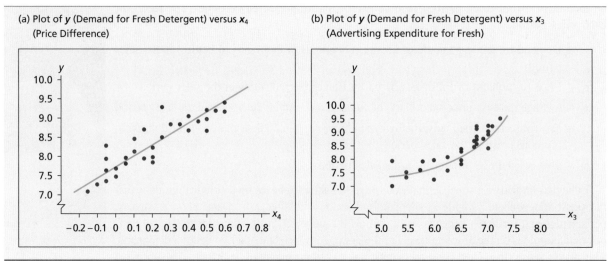

Figure 12.19 presents scatter plots of y versus x_4 and y versus x_3. The plot in Figure 12.19(a) indicates that y tends to increase in a straight-line fashion as x_4 increases. This suggests that the simple linear model

$$y = \beta_0 + \beta_1 x_4 + \varepsilon$$

might appropriately relate y to x_4. The plot in Figure 12.19(b) indicates that y tends to increase in a curved fashion as x_3 increases. Since this curve appears to have the shape of Figure 12.17(c), this suggests that the quadratic model

$$y = \beta_0 + \beta_1 x_3 + \beta_2 x_3^2 + \varepsilon$$

might appropriately relate y to x_3.

To construct a prediction model based on both x_3 and x_4, it seems reasonable to combine these two models to form the regression model

$$y = \beta_0 + \beta_1 x_4 + \beta_2 x_3 + \beta_3 x_3^2 + \varepsilon$$

Here we have arbitrarily ordered the x_4, x_3, and x_3^2 terms in the combined model, and we have renumbered the subscripts on the instances of β appropriately. In the combined model,

$$\beta_0 + \beta_1 x_4 + \beta_2 x_3 + \beta_3 x_3^2$$

is the mean demand for Fresh when the price difference is x_4 and the advertising expenditure is x_3. The error term describes the effects on demand of all factors other than x_4 and x_3.

Figure 12.20(a) presents the Excel output of a regression analysis of the Fresh demand data using the combined model. The output tells us that the least squares point estimates of the model parameters are $b_0 = 17.3244$, $b_1 = 1.3070$, $b_2 = -3.6956$, and $b_3 = .3486$. The output also tells us that the p-values related to x_4, x_3, and x_3^2 are .0002, .0564, and .0293. Therefore, we have strong evidence that each of the model components x_4 and x_3^2 is significant. Furthermore, although the p-value related to x_3 is slightly greater than .05, we retain x_3 in the model because x_3^2 is significant.

To predict demand in a future sales period, Enterprise Industries must determine future values of x_3 and $x_4 = x_2 - x_1$. The company can set x_1 (its price for Fresh) and x_3 (its advertising expenditure) and feels that by examining the prices of competitors' similar products immediately prior to a future period, it can very accurately predict x_2 (the average industry price for competitors' similar detergents). Furthermore, the company can react to any change in a competitor's price to maintain any desired price difference $x_4 = x_2 - x_1$. This is an advantage of predicting on the basis of x_4 rather than on the basis of x_1 and x_2 (which the company cannot control). Therefore, suppose that the company will maintain a price difference of $.20 ($x_{04} = .20$) and will spend $650,000 on advertising ($x_{03} = 6.50$) in a future sales period. This combination of price difference and

FIGURE 12.20   Excel and MegaStat Output of a Regression Analysis of the Fresh Demand Data in Table 12.9 Using the Model $y = \beta_0 + \beta_1 x_4 + \beta_2 x_3 + \beta_3 x_3^2 + \varepsilon$

(a) The Excel output

Regression Statistics

Multiple R	0.9515
R Square	0.9054
Adjusted R Square	0.8945
Standard Error	0.2213
Observations	30

ANOVA	df	SS	MS	F	Significance F
Regression	3	12.1853	4.0618	82.9409	1.94E-13
Residual	26	1.2733	0.0490		
Total	29	13.4586			

	Coefficients	Standard Error	t Stat	P-value	Lower 95%	Upper 95%
Intercept	17.3244	5.6415	3.0709	0.0050	5.7282	28.9206
PriceDif (x4)	1.3070	0.3036	4.3048	0.0002	0.6829	1.9311
AdvExp (x3)	−3.6956	1.8503	−1.9973	0.0564	−7.4989	0.1077
x3Sq	0.3486	0.1512	2.3060	0.0293	0.0379	0.6594

(b) Prediction using MegaStat
Predicted values for: Y

	95% Confidence Interval		95% Prediction Interval		
Predicted	lower	upper	lower	upper	Leverage
8.29330	8.17378	8.41281	7.82298	8.76362	0.06

advertising expenditure is in the experimental region defined by the data in Table 12.9. A point prediction of demand in the future sales period is

$$\hat{y} = 17.3244 + 1.3070 x_{04} - 3.6956 x_{03} + .3486 x_{03}^2$$
$$= 17.3244 + 1.3070(.20) - 3.6956(6.50) + .3486(6.50)^2$$
$$= 8.29330 \text{ (or } 829{,}330 \text{ bottles).}$$

This quantity, in addition to being the point prediction of demand in a single sales period when the price difference is \$.20 and the advertising expenditure is \$650,000, is also the point estimate of the mean of all possible demands when $x_4 = .20$ and $x_3 = 6.50$. Note that $\hat{y} = 8.29330$ is given in the MegaStat output in Figure 12.20(b). The output also gives a 95 percent confidence interval for mean demand when x_4 equals .20 and x_3 equals 6.50, which is [8.17378, 8.41281], and a 95 percent prediction interval for an individual demand when x_4 equals .20 and x_3 equals 6.50, which is [7.82298, 8.76362]. This latter interval says we are 95 percent confident that the actual demand in the future sales period will be between 782,298 bottles and 876,362 bottles.

The upper limit of this interval can be used for inventory control. It says that if Enterprise Industries plans to have 876,362 bottles on hand to meet demand in the future sales period, then the company can be very confident that it will have enough bottles. The lower limit of the interval can be used to better understand Enterprise Industries' cash flow situation. It says the company can be very confident that it will sell at least 782,298 bottles in the future sales period. Therefore, for example, if the average competitor's price is \$3.90 and Enterprise Industries' price is \$3.70, the company can be very confident that its minimum revenue from the large bottle of Fresh in the future period will be at least 782,298 × \$3.70 = \$2,894,502.60.

One cautionary note about the quadratic regression model is that the bend (or bends) in the scatter plot of x and y should reflect an overall pattern and not simply be due to the influence of a few extreme cases, or outliers. An outlier is an observation that is well separated from the rest of the data. An observation that would cause some important aspect of the regression analysis (for example, the least squares point estimates or the standard error s) to substantially change if it was removed from the data set is called an **influential observation**. An observation might be an outlier with respect to its y value and/or its x values, but an outlier might or might not be influential.

FIGURE **12.21**   Data Plot Illustrating Outlying and Influential Observations

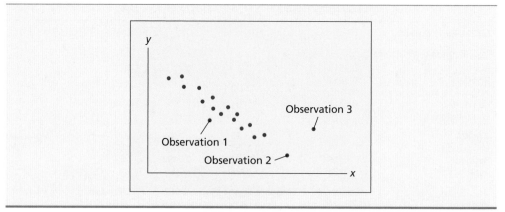

FIGURE **12.21**   Data Plot Illustrating Outlying and Influential Observations

We illustrate these ideas by considering Figure 12.21, which is a hypothetical plot of the values of a dependent variable y against an independent variable x. Observation 1 in this figure is outlying with respect to its y value. However, it is not outlying with respect to its x value, because its x value is near the middle of the other x values. Moreover, observation 1 might not be influential because there are several observations with similar x values and nonoutlying y values, which will keep the least squares point estimates from being excessively influenced by observation 1. Observation 2 in Figure 12.21 is outlying with respect to its x value, but since its y value is consistent with the regression relationship displayed by the nonoutlying observations, it is probably not influential. Observation 3, however, is probably influential, because it is outlying with respect to its x value and because its y value is not consistent with the regression relationship displayed by the other observations. Observation 3 might also give the impression that there is a curved relationship between x and y.

What should we do about outlying and influential observations? We recommend first dealing with outliers with respect to their y values because they affect the overall fit of the model. Often when we decide what to do with such outliers, other problems become much less important or disappear. In general, we should first check to see if the y value in question was recorded correctly. If it was recorded incorrectly, it should be corrected and the regression should be rerun. If it cannot be corrected, we should consider discarding the corresponding observation and rerunning the regression.

Exercises for Section **12.9**

CONCEPTS

12.30 When does a scatter plot suggest the use of the quadratic regression model?

12.31 In the quadratic regression model, what are y, $\beta_0 + \beta_1 x + \beta_2 x^2$, and ε?

METHODS AND APPLICATIONS

12.32 A line manager of a distribution company is interested in investigating the relationship between the length of a shift and the productivity of the employees. Employees at this company are required to package products to be sent to retailers. The manager collects the average number of shipments completed during each hour of an eight-hour shift (the lunch hour is not counted) and reports the data in Table 12.10.

a. Based on the scatter plot of the data given in Table 12.10, describe the relationship between the length of a shift and the productivity of the employees.

b. The manager decides that to test the regression equation, the time variable should be squared (becoming x^2). The manager does this transformation and tests the model

$$y = \beta_0 + \beta_1 x_1 + \beta_2 x_1^2 + \varepsilon$$

The Excel output of the regression analysis is presented in Figure 12.22. Do the p-values for the independent variables in this model indicate that these independent variables are significant? Explain your answer.

TABLE **12.10**   Productivity by Time of Shift

Productivity (y)	Time (x_1)
22	1
25	2
13	3
12	4
11	5
18	6
27	7
26	8

Productivity by Time

FIGURE **12.22**   Excel Output of a Regression Analysis of the Work Productivity Data Using the Model $y = \beta_0 + \beta_1 x_1 + \beta_2 x_1^2 + \varepsilon$

SUMMARY OUTPUT

Regression Statistics

Multiple R	0.82433
R Square	0.67952
Adjusted R Square	0.551328
Standard Error	4.439541
Observations	8

ANOVA	df	SS	MS	F	Significance F
Regression	2	208.952381	104.4762	5.300797	0.058143683
Residual	5	98.54761905	19.70952		
Total	7	307.5			

	Coefficients	Standard Error	t Stat	P-value	Lower 95%	Upper 95%	Lower 95.0%	Upper 95.0%
Intercept	32.53571	6.193801762	5.252947	0.003318	16.614066	48.457363	16.614066	48.4573626
Time (x1)	−9.02381	3.157860114	−2.857571	0.035507	−17.1413341	−0.9062849	−17.1413341	−0.90628494
TimeSQ (x2)	1.071429	0.34251802	3.128094	0.026013	0.190959409	1.9518977	0.19095941	1.95189773

12.33 THE FRESH DETERGENT EXAMPLE

Consider the demand for Fresh detergent in a future sales period when Enterprise Industries' price for Fresh will be $x_1 = 3.70$, the average price of competitors' similar detergents will be $x_2 = 3.90$, the price difference $x_4 = x_2 − x_1$ will be .20, and Enterprise Industries' advertising expenditure for Fresh will be $x_3 = 6.50$. You saw in Example 12.7 that the 95 percent prediction interval for this demand given by the model

$$y = \beta_0 + \beta_1 x_4 + \beta_2 x_3 + \beta_3 x_3^2 + \varepsilon$$

is [7.82298, 8.76362]. The 95 percent prediction interval for this demand given by the model

$$y = \beta_0 + \beta_1 x_1 + \beta_2 x_2 + \beta_3 x_3 + \beta_4 x_3^2 + \varepsilon$$

is [7.84139, 8.79357]. Which interval is shorter? Based on this, which model seems better?

12.34 Pop-Canada is trying to decide on the right combination of two independent variables— x_1, caramel colour (0, 1, or 2 units), and x_2, maple syrup flavouring (0, 1, 2, or 3 units)—to improve the taste of its beverages. Taste tests were carried out using focus groups across Canada. The combinations of x_1 and x_2

used in the experiment, along with the corresponding values of y, are given in Table 12.11.

a. Discuss why the data plots given beside Table 12.11 indicate that the model

$$y = \beta_0 + \beta_1 x_1 + \beta_2 x_1^2 + \beta_3 x_2 + \beta_4 x_2^2 + \varepsilon$$

might appropriately relate y to x_1 and x_2.

b. If we use MegaStat to analyze the data in Table 12.11 by using the model in part (a), we obtain the output in Figure 12.23. Noting from Table 12.11 that the combination of one unit of caramel colour and two units of maple syrup seems to maximize rated taste, assume that Pop-Canada will use this combination to make its beverage. The estimation and prediction results at the bottom of the MegaStat output are for the combination $x_1 = 1$ and $x_2 = 2$.

TABLE **12.11**   Pop-Canada's Focus Group Results

Rated Taste, y	Caramel Colour, x_1	Maple Syrup, x_2	
27.4	0	0	
28.0	0	0	
28.6	0	0	
29.6	1	0	
30.6	1	0	
28.6	2	0	
29.8	2	0	
32.0	0	1	
33.0	0	1	
33.3	1	1	
34.5	1	1	
32.3	0	2	
33.5	0	2	
34.4	1	2	
35.0	1	2	
35.6	1	2	
33.3	2	2	
34.0	2	2	
34.7	2	2	
33.4	1	3	
32.0	2	3	
33.0	2	3	

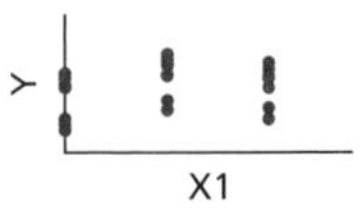

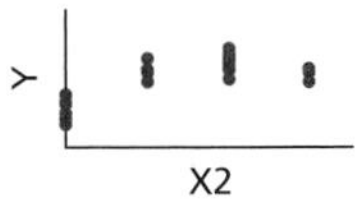

(1) Use the computer output to find and report a point estimate of and a 95 percent confidence interval for the mean rated taste obtained by all samples of the beverage when it is made using one unit of caramel colour and two units of maple syrup.

(2) Use the computer output to find and report a point prediction of and a 95 percent prediction interval for the rated taste that would be obtained by an individual sample of the beverage when it is made using one unit of caramel colour and two units of maple syrup.

FIGURE **12.23**   MegaStat Output of a Regression Analysis of the Pop-Canada Data Using the Model $y = \beta_0 + \beta_1 x_1 + \beta_2 x_1^2 + \beta_3 x_2 + \beta_4 x_2^2 + \varepsilon$

Regression Analysis

R^2	0.947		
Adjusted R^2	0.935	n	22
R	0.973	k	4
Std. Error	0.631	Dep. Var.	Y

ANOVA table

Source	SS	df	MS	F	p-value
Regression	120.7137	4	30.1784	75.90	1.30E-10
Residual	6.7590	17	0.3976		
Total	127.4727	21			

Regression output

variables	coefficients	std. error	t (df = 17)	p-value	confidence interval 95% lower	95% upper
Intercept	28.1589	0.2902	97.040	9.01E-25	27.5467	28.7711
X1	3.3133	0.5896	5.619	3.07E-05	2.0693	4.5573
X1SQ	−1.4111	0.2816	−5.012	0.0001	−2.0051	−0.8170
X2	5.2752	0.4129	12.776	3.83E-10	4.4041	6.1463
X2SQ	−1.3964	0.1509	−9.257	4.74E-08	−1.7146	−1.0781

Predicted values for: Y

Predicted	95% Confidence Interval lower	upper	95% Prediction Interval lower	upper	Leverage
35.0261	34.4997	35.5525	33.5954	36.4568	0.157

12.10 INTERACTION

Multiple regression models often contain interaction variables. We form an interaction variable by multiplying two independent variables together. For instance, if a regression model includes the independent variables x_1 and x_2, then we can form the interaction variable x_1x_2. It is appropriate to employ an interaction variable if the relationship between the mean value of the dependent variable y and one of the independent variables is dependent on (i.e., is different depending on) the value of the other independent variable. We explain the concept of interaction in the following example.

Example 12.8 Froid Frozen Foods

Part 1: The data and data plots   Froid Frozen Foods has designed an experiment to study the effects of two types of advertising expenditures on sales of one of its lines of frozen foods. Twenty-five sales regions of equal sales potential were selected. Different combinations of $x_1 =$ Radio expenditures (measured in units of $1,000) and $x_2 =$ Print expenditures (measured in units of $1,000) were specified and randomly assigned to the sales regions. Table 12.12 shows the expenditure combinations along with the associated values of sales volume, measured in units of $10,000 and denoted y, for the sales regions during August of last year.

To help decide whether an interaction exists between x_1 and x_2, we can plot the data in Table 12.12. To do this, we first plot y versus x_1. In constructing this plot, we make the plot character for each point the corresponding value of x_2 ($x_2 = 1, 2, 3, 4, 5$). The resulting plot (shown in Figure 12.24) is called a *plot of y versus x_1 for the different "levels" of x_2.* Looking at this plot, we see that the straight line relating y to x_1 when $x_2 = 5$ appears to have a smaller slope than does the line relating y to x_1 when $x_2 = 1$. That is, the rate of increase of the line corresponding to $x_2 = 5$ is less steep than the rate of increase of the line corresponding to $x_2 = 1$. Examining the entire data plot, we see that Figure 12.24 might suggest that the larger x_2 is, the smaller is the slope of the straight line relating y to x_1.

In Figure 12.25 on the next page, we plot y versus x_2 for the different levels of x_1 ($x_1 = 1, 2, 3, 4, 5$). Here the plot character for each point is the corresponding value of x_1. We see that the straight line relating y to x_2 when $x_1 = 5$ appears to have a smaller slope than does the straight line relating y to x_2 when $x_1 = 1$. Looking at the entire data plot, we see that Figure 12.25 might suggest that the larger x_1 is, the smaller is the slope of the straight line relating y to x_2.

TABLE **12.12**   Froid Frozen Foods Sales Volume Data

Sales Region	Radio Expenditures, x_1	Print Expenditures, x_2	Sales Volume, y	Sales Region	Radio Expenditures, x_1	Print Expenditures, x_2	Sales Volume, y
1	1	1	3.27	14	3	4	17.99
2	1	2	8.38	15	3	5	19.85
3	1	3	11.28	16	4	1	9.46
4	1	4	14.50	17	4	2	12.61
5	1	5	19.63	18	4	3	15.50
6	2	1	5.84	19	4	4	17.68
7	2	2	10.01	20	4	5	21.02
8	2	3	12.46	21	5	1	12.23
9	2	4	16.67	22	5	2	13.58
10	2	5	19.83	23	5	3	16.77
11	3	1	8.51	24	5	4	20.56
12	3	2	10.14	25	5	5	21.05
13	3	3	14.75				

In summary of this part of Example 12.8, Figures 12.24 and 12.25 seem to imply that the more money is spent on one type of advertising, the smaller is the slope of the straight line relating sales volume to the amount spent on the other type of advertising. This says that there is an interaction between x_1 and x_2 because

1   The relationship between y and x_1 (the slope of the line relating y to x_1) is different for different values of x_2.

2   The relationship between y and x_2 (the slope of the line relating y to x_2) is different for different values of x_1.

An interaction between x_1 and x_2 makes sense because as Froid Frozen Foods spends more money on one type of advertising, increases in spending on the other type of advertising might become less effective.

FIGURE **12.24**   Plot of y versus x_1 (Plot Character Is the Corresponding Value of x_2):
The Larger x_2 Is, the Smaller Is the Slope of the Straight Line Relating y to x_1

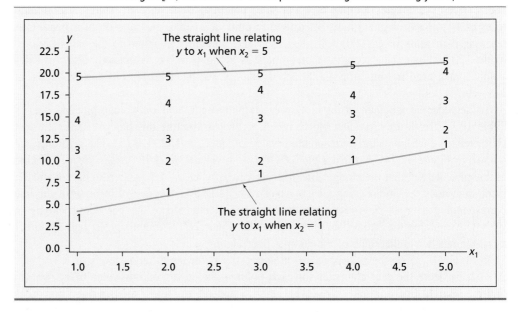

FIGURE **12.25**   Plot of y versus x_2 (Plot Character Is the Corresponding Value of x_1):
The Larger x_1 Is, the Smaller Is the Slope of the Straight Line Relating y to x_2

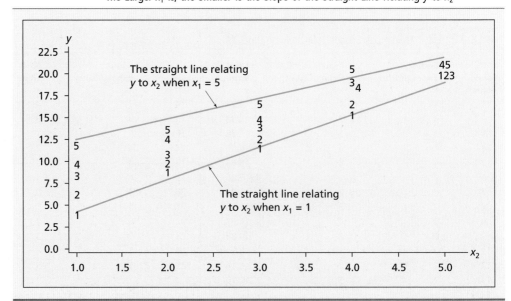

Part 2: Modelling the interaction between x_1 and x_2 The regression model

$$y = \beta_0 + \beta_1 x_1 + \beta_2 x_2 + \varepsilon$$

cannot describe the interaction between x_1 and x_2 because this model says that mean sales volume equals

$$\beta_0 + \beta_1 x_1 + \beta_2 x_2 = (\beta_0 + \beta_1 x_1) + \beta_2 x_2$$

This implies that for any particular value of x_1, the slope of the straight line relating the mean value of y to x_2 will always be β_2. That is, no matter what the value of x_1 is, the slope of the line relating mean y to x_2 is always the same. This rules out the possibility of describing the relationships illustrated in Figure 12.25 by using the above model. The model also says that mean sales volume equals

$$\beta_0 + \beta_1 x_1 + \beta_2 x_2 = (\beta_0 + \beta_2 x_2) + \beta_1 x_1$$

This implies that no matter what the value of x_2 is, the slope of the line relating mean y to x_1 is always the same (here the slope equals β_1). This rules out the possibility of describing the relationships illustrated in Figure 12.24 by using the above model. In short, we say that the above model assumes *no interaction* between x_1 and x_2.

To model the interaction between x_1 and x_2, we can use the cross-product term or interaction term $x_1 x_2$. Therefore, we consider the model

$$y = \beta_0 + \beta_1 x_1 + \beta_2 x_2 + \beta_3 x_1 x_2 + \varepsilon$$

This model says that mean sales volume equals

$$\beta_0 + \beta_1 x_1 + \beta_2 x_2 + \beta_3 x_1 x_2$$

which can be rewritten as $(\beta_0 + \beta_1 x_1) + (\beta_2 + \beta_3 x_1)x_2$. *This implies that the slope of the line relating mean y to x_2, which is $\beta_2 + \beta_3 x_1$, will be different for different values of x_1.* This allows the interaction model to describe relationships such as those illustrated in Figure 12.25. Furthermore, for this model the mean sales volume

$$\beta_0 + \beta_1 x_1 + \beta_2 x_2 + \beta_3 x_1 x_2$$

can also be rewritten as $(\beta_0 + \beta_2 x_2) + (\beta_1 + \beta_3 x_2)x_1$. *This implies that the slope of the line relating mean y to x_1, which is $\beta_1 + \beta_3 x_2$, will be different for different values of x_2.* This allows the interaction model to describe relationships such as those illustrated in Figure 12.24. In short, we say that the model using the term $x_1 x_2$ assumes that *an interaction exists* between x_1 and x_2.

Part 3: Statistical inference Figure 12.26 gives the MegaStat output of a regression analysis of the data in Table 12.12 by using the model

$$y = \beta_0 + \beta_1 x_1 + \beta_2 x_2 + \beta_3 x_1 x_2 + \varepsilon$$

Because all of the p-values related to the intercept and the independent variables are less than .01, we have very strong evidence that each of β_0, x_1, x_2, and $x_1 x_2$ is significant in the above model. In particular, the very small p-value related to $x_1 x_2$ confirms that an interaction exists between x_1 and x_2, as was originally suggested by the plots in Figures 12.24 and 12.25. (If there was little or no interaction between x_1 and x_2, the term $x_1 x_2$ would be nonsignificant since it would not help us to model the data.)

Next, suppose that Froid Frozen Foods will spend \$2,000 on radio advertising ($x_1 = 2$) and \$5,000 on print advertising ($x_2 = 5$) in a future month in a particular sales region. If there are

FIGURE **12.26**   MegaStat Output of a Regression Analysis of the Sales Volume Data in Table 12.12 by Using
the Model $y = \beta_0 + \beta_1 x_1 + \beta_2 x_2 + \beta_3 x_1 x_2 + \varepsilon$

Regression Analysis

R^2	0.986			
Adjusted R^2	0.984	n	25	
R	0.993	k	3	
Std. Error	0.626	Dep. Var.	**y**	

ANOVA table

Source	SS	df	MS	F	p-value
Regression	590.4057	3	196.8019	502.67	1.05E-19
Residual	8.2218	21	0.3915		
Total	598.6275	24			

Regression output

variables	coefficients	std. error	t (df=21)	p-value	confidence interval 95% lower	95% upper
Intercept	−2.3497	0.6883	−3.414	0.0026	−3.7811	−0.9183
x1	2.3611	0.2075	11.377	1.93E-10	1.9295	2.7927
x2	4.1831	0.2075	20.157	3.21E-15	3.7515	4.6147
x1x2	−0.3489	0.0626	−5.576	1.56E-05	−0.4790	−0.2188

Predicted values for: y

x1	x2	x1x2	Predicted	95% Confidence Interval lower	upper	95% Prediction Interval lower	upper	Leverage
2	5	10	19.79900	19.24693	20.35107	18.38550	21.21250	0.180

no trend, seasonal, or other time-related influences affecting monthly sales volume, then it is reasonable to believe that the regression relationship between y and x_1 and x_2 that we have developed probably applies to the future month and particular sales region. It follows that

$$\hat{y} = -2.3497 + 2.3611(2) + 4.1831(5) - .3489(2)(5)$$
$$= 19.799 \text{ (or } \$197,990)$$

is a point estimate of mean sales volume when \$2,000 is spent on radio advertising and \$5,000 is spent on print advertising. In addition, $\hat{y}$ is a point prediction of the individual sales volume that will be observed in the future month in the particular sales region. In addition, the output in Figure 12.26 tells us that the 95 percent confidence interval for mean sales volume is [19.24693, 20.35107] and the 95 percent prediction interval for an individual sales volume is [18.38550, 21.21250]. This prediction interval says we are 95 percent confident that the individual sales volume in the future month in the particular sales region will be between \$183,855 and \$212,125. In Exercise 12.37, we will continue this example.

It is easy to construct data plots to check for interaction in the Froid Frozen Foods example because the company has carried out a designed experiment. In many regression problems, however, we do not carry out a designed experiment, and the data are unstructured. In such a case, it may not be possible to construct the data plots needed to detect an interaction between independent variables. For example, if we consider the Fresh demand data in Table 12.9, we might suspect that there is an interaction between x_3 (advertising expenditure) and x_4 (the price difference). That is, we might suspect that the relationship between mean demand for Fresh and advertising expenditure is different for different levels of the price difference. For instance, increases in advertising expenditures might be more effective at some price differences than at others. To detect such an interaction, we can use t statistics and p-values related to potential interaction terms. We illustrate this in Example 12.9.

Example 12.9 Interactions among Variables in the Fresh Detergent Example

Part 1: An interaction model and statistical inference In Example 12.7, we considered the Fresh demand model

$$y = \beta_0 + \beta_1 x_4 + \beta_2 x_3 + \beta_3 x_3^2 + \varepsilon$$

We might logically suspect that there is an interaction between x_4 (price difference) and x_3 (advertising expenditure), so we include the interaction term $x_4 x_3$ in this model as follows:

$$y = \beta_0 + \beta_1 x_4 + \beta_2 x_3 + \beta_3 x_3^2 + \beta_4 x_4 x_3 + \varepsilon$$

Figure 12.27(a) presents the Excel output obtained by using this model to perform a regression analysis of the Fresh demand data. This output shows that each of the p-values for testing the independent variables is less than .05. Therefore, we have strong evidence that each of x_4, x_3, x_3^2, and $x_4 x_3$ is significant. In particular, since the p-value related to $x_4 x_3$ is .0361, we have strong evidence that the interaction variable $x_4 x_3$ is important.

Suppose again that Enterprise Industries wants to predict demand for Fresh in a future sales period when the price difference will be \$.20 ($x_4 = .20$) and the advertising expenditure for Fresh will be \$650,000 ($x_3 = 6.50$). Using the least squares point estimates in Figure 12.27, the needed point prediction is

$$\hat{y} = 29.1133 + 11.1342(.20) - 7.6080(6.50) + .6712(6.50)^2 - 1.4777(.20)(6.50)$$
$$= 8.32533 \text{ (or } 832,533 \text{ bottles)}$$

This point prediction is given (within rounding) in the MegaStat output in Figure 12.27(b), which also tells us that the 95 percent confidence interval for mean demand when x_4 equals .20 and x_3 equals 6.50 is [8.21121, 8.44329] and the 95 percent prediction interval for an individual demand when x_4 equals .20 and x_3 equals 6.50 is [7.88673, 8.76777]. Notice that this prediction interval is shorter than the 95 percent prediction interval—[7.82298, 8.76362]—obtained using the model that omits the interaction term $x_4 x_3$ and predicts y on the basis of x_4, x_3, and x_3^2. This is another indication that it is useful to include the interaction variable $x_4 x_3$ in the model.

FIGURE 12.27 Excel and MegaStat Output of a Regression Analysis of the Fresh Demand Data by Using the Interaction Model $y = \beta_0 + \beta_1 x_4 + \beta_2 x_3 + \beta_3 x_3^2 + \beta_4 x_4 x_3 + \varepsilon$

(a) The Excel output

Regression Statistics	
Multiple R	0.9596
R Square	0.9209
Adjusted R Square	0.9083
Standard Error	0.2063
Observations	30

ANOVA	df	SS	MS	F		Significance F
Regression	4	12.3942	3.0985	72.7771		2.11E-13
Residual	25	1.0644	0.0426			
Total	29	13.4586				

	Coefficients	Standard Error	t Stat	P-value	Lower 95%	Upper 95%
Intercept	29.1133	7.4832	3.8905	0.0007	13.7013	44.5252
PriceDif (x4)	11.1342	4.4459	2.5044	0.0192	1.9778	20.2906
AdvExp (x3)	−7.6080	2.4691	−3.0813	0.0050	−12.6932	−2.5228
x3sq	0.6712	0.2027	3.3115	0.0028	0.2538	1.0887
x4x3	−1.4777	0.6672	−2.2149	0.0361	−2.8518	−0.1037

(b) Prediction using MegaStat

Predicted values for: Y

	95% Confidence Interval		95% Prediction Interval		
Predicted	lower	upper	lower	upper	Leverage
8.32725	8.21121	8.44329	7.88673	8.76777	0.075

Part 2: The nature of the interaction between x_3 and x_4 To understand the exact nature of the interaction between x_3 and x_4, consider the prediction equation

$$\hat{y} = 29.1133 + 11.1342x_4 - 7.6080x_3 + .6712x_3^2 - 1.4777x_4x_3$$

obtained by using the Fresh demand interaction model. If we set x_4 equal to .10 and place this value of x_4 into the prediction equation, we obtain

$$\begin{aligned} \hat{y} &= 29.1133 + 11.1342x_4 - 7.6080x_3 + .6712x_3^2 - 1.4777x_4x_3 \\ &= 29.1133 + 11.1342(.10) - 7.6080x_3 + .6712x_3^2 - 1.4777(.10)x_3 \\ &= 30.2267 - 7.7558x_3 + .6712x_3^2 \end{aligned}$$

This quadratic equation shows us how predicted demand changes as advertising expenditure x_3 increases when the price difference is .10. Next we set x_4 equal to .30. If we place this value of x_4 into the Fresh prediction equation, we obtain

$$\begin{aligned} \hat{y} &= 29.1133 + 11.1342x_4 - 7.6080x_3 + .6712x_3^2 - 1.4777x_4x_3 \\ &= 29.1133 + 11.1342(.30) - 7.6080x_3 + .6712x_3^2 - 1.4777(.30)x_3 \\ &= 32.4535 - 8.0513x_3 + .6712x_3^2 \end{aligned}$$

This quadratic equation shows us how predicted demand changes as advertising expenditure x_3 increases when the price difference is .30.

In Figure 12.28(a) and (b), we calculate three points (predicted demands) on each of these quadratic curves. Figure 12.28(c) shows graphs of the two quadratic curves with the predicted demands plotted on these graphs. Comparing these graphs, we see that predicted demand is higher when x_4 equals .30 than when x_4 equals .10. This makes sense—predicted demand should be higher when Enterprise Industries has a larger price advantage. Furthermore, for each curve we see that predicted demand increases at an increasing rate as x_3 increases. However, the rate of increase in predicted demand is slower when x_4 equals .30 than when x_4 equals .10—this is the effect of the interaction between x_3 and x_4.

This type of interaction is logical because when the price difference is large (the price for Fresh is low relative to the average industry price), the mean demand for Fresh will be high (assuming the quality of Fresh is comparable to competing brands). So, with mean demand already high because many consumers are buying Fresh on the basis of price, there might be little opportunity for increased advertising expenditure to increase mean demand. However, when the price difference is smaller, there might be more potential consumers who are not buying Fresh who can be convinced to do so by increased advertising. So, when the price difference is smaller, increased advertising expenditure is more effective than it is when the price difference is larger.

FIGURE 12.28   Interaction between x_4 and x_3 in the Fresh Detergent

(a) Calculating values of predicted demand when x_4 equals 0.10

x_3	$\hat{y} = 30.2267 - 7.7558x_3 + 0.6712x_3^2$
6.0	$\hat{y} = 30.2267 - 7.7558(6.0) + 0.6712(6.0)^2 = 7.86$
6.4	$\hat{y} = 30.2267 - 7.7558(6.4) + 0.6712(6.4)^2 = 8.08$
6.8	$\hat{y} = 30.2267 - 7.7558(6.8) + 0.6712(6.8)^2 = 8.52$

(b) Calculating values of predicted demand when x_4 equals 0.30

x_3	$\hat{y} = 32.4535 - 8.0513x_3 + 0.6712x_3^2$
6.0	$\hat{y} = 32.4535 - 8.0513(6.0) + 0.6712(6.0)^2 = 8.31$
6.4	$\hat{y} = 32.4535 - 8.0513(6.4) + 0.6712(6.4)^2 = 8.42$
6.8	$\hat{y} = 32.4535 - 8.0513(6.8) + 0.6712(6.8)^2 = 8.74$

(c) Illustrating the interaction

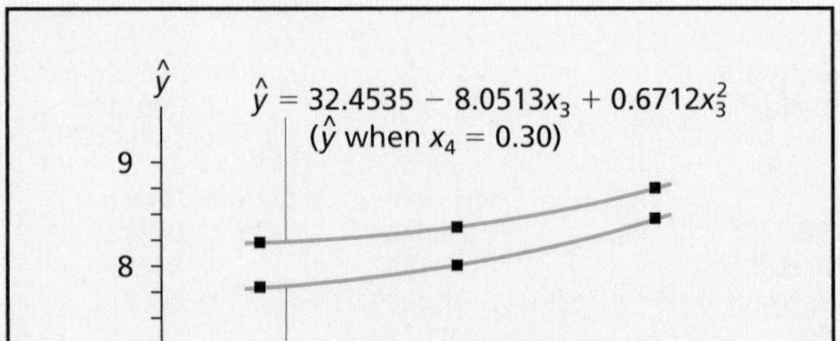

It should be noted that this type of interaction between x_4 and x_3 was estimated from the observed Fresh demand data in Table 12.9. This is because we obtained the least squares point estimates using these data. We can only hypothesize the reasons behind the interaction and should point out that this type of interaction can be assumed to exist only for values of x_4 and x_3 inside the experimental region. Examination of the Fresh demand data shows that Fresh was being sold at either a price advantage (when the price of Fresh is lower than the average industry price) or a slight price disadvantage (when the price of Fresh is slightly higher than the average industry price). However, if Fresh was sometimes sold at a large price disadvantage, the type of interaction that exists between x_4 and x_3 might be different. In such a case, increases in advertising expenditure might be very ineffective because most consumers will not want to buy a product with a much higher price.

A final comment is in order. If a *p*-value indicates that an interaction term (say, x_1x_2) is significant, then it is usual practice to retain the corresponding linear terms (x_1 and x_2) in the model no matter what the size of their *p*-values. The reason is that doing so can be shown to give a model that will better describe the interaction between x_1 and x_2.

Exercises for Section **12.10**

CONCEPTS

12.35 If a regression model utilizes the independent variables x_1 and x_2, how do we form an interaction variable involving x_1 and x_2?

12.36 What is meant when we say that *interaction exists between two independent variables*?

METHODS AND APPLICATIONS

12.37 Consider the Froid Frozen Foods sales volume model
$$y = \beta_0 + \beta_1 x_1 + \beta_2 x_2 + \beta_3 x_1 x_2 + \varepsilon$$

a. You saw in Example 12.8 that $\beta_1 + \beta_3 x_2$ is the slope of the line relating the mean y to x_1 at a given value of x_2. This slope is the increase in mean sales volume (in units of $10,000) obtained by increasing radio advertising by $1,000 when print advertising is x_2 thousand dollars. Using $b_1 = 2.3611$ and $b_3 = -.3489$ from the MegaStat output in Figure 12.26, a point estimate of the slope $\beta_1 + \beta_3 x_2$ is $2.3611 - .3489x_2$. Calculate this point estimate for each of the values 1, 2, 3, 4, and 5 of x_2. Interpret the five point estimates.

b. You saw in Example 12.8 that $\beta_2 + \beta_3 x_1$ is the slope of the line relating mean y to x_2 at a given value of x_1. This slope is the increase in mean sales volume (in units of $10,000) obtained by increasing print advertising by $1,000 when radio advertising is x_1 thousand dollars. Using $b_2 = 4.1831$ and $b_3 = -.3489$ from the MegaStat output in Figure 12.26, a point estimate of the slope $\beta_2 + \beta_3 x_1$ is $4.1831 - .3489x_1$. Calculate this point estimate for each of the values 1, 2, 3, 4, and 5 of x_1. Interpret the five point estimates.

c. By comparing the five point estimates calculated in part (b) with the five point estimates calculated in part (a), discuss why it is reasonable to conclude that increasing print advertising expenditures is more effective than increasing radio advertising expenditures.

12.38 Managers who are transferred to a different country sometimes experience stress in the new environment, a state referred to as *culture shock*. To try to alleviate this state, a study is conducted on 30 managers. Before their departure, managers are given books (maximum ten) and videos (maximum five) detailing the culture that they will be working in. The number of books read and the number of videos watched are recorded. After six months in the new environment, managers self-report their level of culture shock on a 10-point scale, where 1 = Feeling perfectly comfortable with the new environment and 10 = Experiencing great distress (lower scores reflect less culture shock). The data for this study are reported in Table 12.13.

a. Figure 12.29(a) presents the Excel output of the regression analysis predicting culture shock with books read (x_1) and videos watched (x_2). Based on the result, do books and videos significantly reduce culture shock? Write the resulting regression equation.

b. To investigate the possible interaction effects of books (x_1) and videos (x_2), a further analysis was conducted examining the joint effect of both (x_1x_2). The results of this analysis are presented in Figure 12.29(b). By combining books and videos, how well is culture shock predicted? Write the resulting regression equation.

c. Compare and contrast the results from the two analyses. Which is a stronger predictor of culture shock? Based on these findings, what would you suggest would be the best method to reduce culture shock for managers transferred to other countries?

TABLE **12.13**   Self-Reported Culture Shock and Prior Number of Books Read and Videos Watched

Culture Shock (y)	Books (x_1)	Videos (x_2)	Culture Shock (y)	Books (x_1)	Videos (x_2)
8	1	1	8	2	1
2	10	4	7	2	3
3	9	5	1	10	4
4	8	4	2	9	5
5	6	1	9	0	1
6	1	2	5	3	2
1	9	5	3	2	3
9	0	1	9	1	0
2	9	5	1	9	5
5	4	1	8	1	3
3	8	3	7	1	2
4	5	4	2	9	5
6	2	2	10	1	1
7	1	2	3	7	5
2	10	5	2	10	4

FIGURE **12.29**   Excel Output of a Regression Analysis of the Culture Shock Data

(a) Excel output of the regression analysis

SUMMARY OUTPUT

Regression Statistics

Multiple R	0.930435
R Square	0.865709
Adjusted R Square	0.855761
Standard Error	1.076052
Observations	30

ANOVA

	df	SS	MS	F	Significance F
Regression	2	201.537	100.7685	87.02788	1.69E-12
Residual	27	31.26297	1.157888		
Total	29	232.8			

	Coefficients	Standard Error	t Stat	p-value	Lower 95%	Upper 95%	Lower 95.0%	Upper 95.0%
Intercept	8.843314	0.414223	21.34916	1.93E-18	7.993399	9.693229	7.993399	9.693229
Books (x1)	−0.478789	0.093215	−5.136386	2.11E-05	−0.670051	−0.287528	−0.670051	−0.287528
Videos (x2)	−0.555967	0.215487	−2.580047	0.015639	−0.998109	−0.113824	−0.998119	−0.113824

(b) Excel analysis of joint effect

SUMMARY OUTPUT

Regression Statistics

Multiple R	0.94186076
R Square	0.88710169
Adjusted R Square	0.87407496
Standard Error	1.00542235
Observations	30

ANOVA

	df	SS	MS	F	Significance F
Regression	3	206.5172735	68.83909	68.09858	1.92E-12
Residual	26	26.28272647	1.010874		
Total	29	232.8			

	Coefficients	Standard Error	t Stat	p-value	Lower 95%	Upper 95%	Lower 95.0%	Upper 95.0%
Intercept	9.9909913	0.645871131	15.46902	1.25E-14	8.663383	11.318599	8.6633833	11.3185993
Books (x1)	−0.8315653	0.181236103	−4.588298	9.97E-05	−1.204102	−0.459029	−1.2041017	−0.45902893
Videos (x2)	−1.0985413	0.316690341	−3.468818	0.001836	−1.749508	−0.447575	−1.749508	−0.44757451
x1x2	0.11203898	0.050476874	2.21961	0.035376	0.008282	0.2157957	0.0082822	0.21579575

12.11 USING DUMMY VARIABLES TO MODEL QUALITATIVE INDEPENDENT VARIABLES

PART 3 Dummy Variables and Advanced Statistical Inferences (Optional)

While the levels (or values) of a quantitative independent variable are numerical, the levels of a qualitative independent variable are defined by describing them. For instance, the type of sales technique used by a door-to-door salesperson is a qualitative independent variable. Here we might define three different levels—high pressure, medium pressure, and low pressure.

We can model the effects of the different levels of a qualitative independent variable by using what we call **dummy variables** (also called **indicator variables**). Such variables are usually defined so that they take on two values—either 0 or 1. To see how we use dummy variables, we begin with an example.

Example 12.10 Electronics World

Part 1: The data and data plots Suppose that Electronics World, a chain of stores that sells audio and video equipment, has gathered the data in Table 12.14. These data concern store sales volume in July of last year (y, measured in thousands of dollars), the number of households in the store's area (x, measured in thousands), and the location of the store (on a suburban street or in a suburban shopping mall—a qualitative independent variable). Figure 12.30 gives a data plot of y versus x. Stores with a street location are plotted as solid dots, while stores with a mall location are plotted as asterisks. Notice that the line relating y to x for mall locations has a higher y intercept than does the line relating y to x for street locations.

Part 2: A dummy variable model To model the effects of the street and shopping mall locations, we define a dummy variable denoted D_M as follows:

$$D_M = \begin{cases} 1 & \text{If a store is in a mall location} \\ 0 & \text{Otherwise} \end{cases}$$

TABLE 12.14 The Electronics World Sales Volume Data

Store	Number of Households, x	Location	Sales Volume, y
1	161	Street	157.27
2	99	Street	93.28
3	135	Street	136.81
4	120	Street	123.79
5	164	Street	153.51
6	221	Mall	241.74
7	179	Mall	201.54
8	204	Mall	206.71
9	214	Mall	229.78
10	101	Mall	135.22

FIGURE 12.30 Plot of the Sales Volume Data and a Geometrical Interpretation of the Model $y = \beta_0 + \beta_1 x + \beta_2 D_M + \varepsilon$

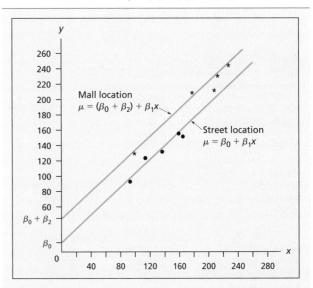

Using this dummy variable, we consider the regression model

$$y = \beta_0 + \beta_1 x + \beta_2 D_M + \varepsilon$$

This model and the definition of D_M imply the following:

1   For a street location, mean sales volume equals

$$\beta_0 + \beta_1 x + \beta_2 D_M = \beta_0 + \beta_1 x + \beta_2(0)$$
$$= \beta_0 + \beta_1 x$$

2   For a mall location, mean sales volume equals

$$\beta_0 + \beta_1 x + \beta_2 D_M = \beta_0 + \beta_1 x + \beta_2(1)$$
$$= (\beta_0 + \beta_2) + \beta_1 x$$

So the dummy variable allows us to model the situation illustrated in Figure 12.30. Here the lines relating mean sales volume to x for street and mall locations have different y intercepts—β_0 and $(\beta_0 + \beta_2)$—and the same slope, β_1. Note that β_2 is the difference between the mean monthly sales volume for stores in mall locations and the mean monthly sales volume for stores in street locations, when all of these stores have the same number of households in their areas. That is, we can say that β_2 represents the effect on mean sales of a mall location compared to a street location. The Excel output in Figure 12.31 tells us that the least squares point estimate of β_2 is $b_2 = 29.2157$. This says that for any given number of households in a store's area, we estimate that the mean monthly sales volume in a mall location is \$29,215.70 greater than the mean monthly sales volume in a street location.

Part 3: A dummy variable model for comparing three locations In addition to the data concerning street and mall locations in Table 12.14, Electronics World has also collected data concerning downtown locations. The complete data set is given in Table 12.15 and plotted in Figure 12.32. Here stores with a downtown location are plotted as open circles. A model describing these data is

$$y = \beta_0 + \beta_1 x + \beta_2 D_M + \beta_3 D_D + \varepsilon$$

The dummy variable D_M is as previously defined and the dummy variable D_D is defined as follows:

$$D_D = \begin{cases} 1 & \text{If a store is in a downtown location} \\ 0 & \text{Otherwise} \end{cases}$$

FIGURE 12.31   Excel Output of a Regression Analysis of the Sales Volume Data Using the Model $y = \beta_0 + \beta_1 x + \beta_2 D_M + \varepsilon$

Regression Statistics						
Multiple R	0.9913					
R Square	0.9827					
Adjusted R Square	0.9778					
Standard Error	7.3288					
Observations	10					
ANOVA	df	SS	MS	F	Significance F	
Regression	2	21,411.7977	10,705.8989	199.3216	6.75E-07	
Residual	7	375.9817	53.7117			
Total	9	21,787.7795				
	Coefficients	Standard Error	t Stat	p-value	Lower 95%	Upper 95%
Intercept	17.3598	9.4470	1.8376	0.1087	−4.9788	39.6985
Households (x)	0.8510	0.0652	13.0439	3.63E-06	0.6968	1.0053
DummyMall	29.2157	5.5940	5.2227	0.0012	15.9881	42.4434

TABLE 12.15 The Complete Electronics World Sales Volume Data

Store	Number of Households, x	Location	Sales Volume, y
1	161	Street	157.27
2	99	Street	93.28
3	135	Street	136.81
4	120	Street	123.79
5	164	Street	153.51
6	221	Mall	241.74
7	179	Mall	201.54
8	204	Mall	206.71
9	214	Mall	229.78
10	101	Mall	135.22
11	231	Downtown	224.71
12	206	Downtown	195.29
13	248	Downtown	242.16
14	107	Downtown	115.21
15	205	Downtown	197.82

FIGURE 12.32 Plot of the Complete Electronics World Sales Volume Data and a Geometrical Interpretation of the Model

$$y = \beta_0 + \beta_1 x + \beta_2 D_M + \beta_3 D_D + \varepsilon$$

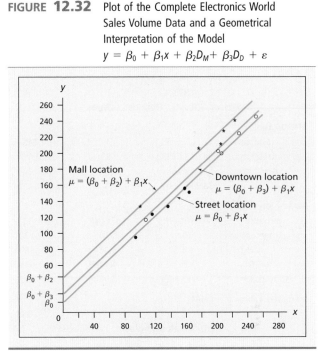

Then we have the following:

1 For a street location, mean sales volume equals

$$\beta_0 + \beta_1 x + \beta_2 D_M + \beta_3 D_D = \beta_0 + \beta_1 x + \beta_2(0) + \beta_3(0)$$
$$= \beta_0 + \beta_1 x$$

2 For a mall location, mean sales volume equals

$$\beta_0 + \beta_1 x + \beta_2 D_M + \beta_3 D_D = \beta_0 + \beta_1 x + \beta_2(1) + \beta_3(0)$$
$$= (\beta_0 + \beta_2) + \beta_1 x$$

3 For a downtown location, mean sales volume equals

$$\beta_0 + \beta_1 x + \beta_2 D_M + \beta_3 D_D = \beta_0 + \beta_1 x + \beta_2(0) + \beta_3(1)$$
$$= (\beta_0 + \beta_3) + \beta_1 x$$

The dummy variables allow us to model the situation illustrated in Figure 12.32. Here the lines relating mean sales volume to x for street, mall, and downtown locations have different y intercepts—β_0, $(\beta_0 + \beta_2)$, and $(\beta_0 + \beta_3)$—and the same slope, β_1. Note that β_2 represents the effect on mean sales of a mall location compared to a street location, and β_3 represents the effect on mean sales of a downtown location compared to a street location. Furthermore, the difference between β_2 and β_3, $\beta_2 - \beta_3$, represents the effect on mean sales of a mall location compared to a downtown location.

Part 4: Comparing the three locations Figure 12.33 gives the MegaStat output of a regression analysis of the sales volume data using the dummy variable model. The output tells us that the least squares point estimate of β_2 is $b_2 = 28.3738$. This says that for any given number of households in a store's area, we estimate that the mean monthly sales volume in a mall location is $28,373.80 greater than the mean monthly sales volume in a street location. Furthermore, the output tells us that a 95 percent confidence interval for β_2 is [18.5545, 38.1930], so we are 95 percent confident that for any given number of households in a store's area, the mean monthly sales volume in a mall location is between $18,554.50 and $38,193.00 greater than the mean monthly sales volume in a street location. The output also shows that

FIGURE 12.33   MegaStat Output of a Regression Analysis of the Sales Volume Data Using the Model
$$y = \beta_0 + \beta_1 x + \beta_2 D_M + \beta_3 D_D + \varepsilon$$

Regression Analysis

R^2	0.987		
Adjusted R^2	0.983	n	15
R	0.993	k	3
Std. Error	6.349	Dep. Var.	**Sales**

ANOVA table

Source	SS	df	MS	F	p-value
Regression	33,268.6953	3	11,089.5651	275.07	1.27E-10
Residual	443.4650	11	40.3150		
Total	33,712.1603	14			

Regression output

variables	coefficients	std. error	t (df=11)	p-value	confidence interval 95% lower	95% upper
Intercept	14.9777	6.1884	2.420	0.0340	1.3570	28.5984
DM	28.3738	4.4613	6.360	0.0001	18.5545	38.1930
DD	6.8638	4.7705	1.439	0.1780	−3.6360	17.3635
Households	0.8686	0.0405	21.452	2.52E-10	0.7795	0.9577

Predicted values for: Sales

DM	DD	Households	Predicted	95% Confidence Interval lower	upper	95% Prediction Interval lower	upper	Leverage
1	0	200	217.06913	210.65476	223.48351	201.69240	232.44586	0.211

the t statistic for testing $H_0: \beta_2 = 0$ versus $H_a: \beta_2 \neq 0$ equals 6.360 and that the related p-value is .001. So we have very strong evidence that there is a difference between the mean monthly sales volumes in mall and street locations.

We next note that the output in Figure 12.33 shows that the least squares point estimate of β_3 is $b_3 = 6.8638$. Therefore, we estimate that for any given number of households in a store's area, the mean monthly sales volume in a downtown location is $6,863.80 greater than the mean monthly sales volume in a street location. Furthermore, the output shows that a 95 percent confidence interval for β_3 is $[−3.6360, 17.3635]$. This says we are 95 percent confident that for any given number of households in a store's area, the mean monthly sales volume in a downtown location is between $3,636.00 less than and $17,363.50 greater than the mean monthly sales volume in a street location. The output also shows that the t statistic and p-value for testing $H_0: \beta_3 = 0$ versus $H_a: \beta_3 \neq 0$ are, respectively, 1.439 and .1780. So we do not have strong evidence that there is a difference between the mean monthly sales volumes in downtown and street locations.

Finally, note that since $b_2 = 28.3738$ and $b_3 = 6.8638$, the point estimate of $\beta_2 − \beta_3$ is $b_2 − b_3 = 28.3738 − 6.8638 = 21.51$. Therefore, we estimate that the mean monthly sales volume in a mall location is $21,510 higher than the mean monthly sales volume in a downtown location. Near the end of this section, we will show how to compare the mall and downtown locations by using a confidence interval and a hypothesis test. We will find that there is very strong evidence that the mean monthly sales volume in a mall location is higher than the mean monthly sales volume in a downtown location. In summary, the mall location seems to give a higher mean monthly sales volume than either the street or the downtown location.

Part 5: Predicting future sales volume   Suppose that Electronics World wants to predict the sales volume in a future month for an individual store that has 200,000 households in its area and is located in a shopping mall. The point prediction of this sales volume is (since $D_M = 1$ and $D_D = 0$ when a store is in a shopping mall)

$$\hat{y} = b_0 + b_1(200) + b_2(1) + b_3(0)$$
$$= 14.9777 + .8686(200) + 28.3738(1)$$
$$= 217.07$$

This point prediction is given at the bottom of the output in Figure 12.33(a). The corresponding 95 percent prediction interval, which is [201.69, 232.45], says we are 95 percent confident that the sales volume in a future sales period for an individual mall store that has 200,000 households in its area will be between $201,690 and $232,450.

Part 6: Interaction models Consider the Electronics World data for street and mall locations given in Table 12.14 and the model

$$y = \beta_0 + \beta_1 x + \beta_2 D_M + \beta_3 x D_M + \varepsilon$$

This model uses the cross-product, or interaction, term $x D_M$ and implies the following:

1 For a street location, mean sales volume equals (since $D_M = 0$)

$$\beta_0 + \beta_1 x + \beta_2(0) + \beta_3 x(0) = \beta_0 + \beta_1 x$$

2 For a mall location, mean sales volume equals (since $D_M = 1$)

$$\beta_0 + \beta_1 x + \beta_2(1) + \beta_3 x(1) = (\beta_0 + \beta_2) + (\beta_1 + \beta_3)x$$

As illustrated in Figure 12.34, if we use this model, the straight lines relating mean sales volume to x for street and mall locations have *different y intercepts* and *different slopes*. Therefore, we say that this model assumes an *interaction* between x and store location. Such a model is appropriate if the relationship between mean sales volume and x depends on (that is, is different for) the street and mall store locations. In general, an interaction exists between two independent variables if the relationship between (for example, the slope of the line relating) the mean value of the dependent variable and one of the independent variables depends on the value (or level) of the other independent variable.

Figure 12.35 gives the MegaStat output of a regression analysis of the sales volume data using the interaction model. Here D_M and $x D_M$ are labelled as DM and XDM, respectively, on the output. The output tells us that the p-value related to the significance of $x D_M$ is .5886. This large p-value tells us that the interaction term is not important. It follows that the no-interaction model seems best.

Next consider the Electronics World data for street, mall, and downtown locations given in Table 12.15. In modelling these data, if we believe that an interaction exists between

FIGURE 12.34 Geometrical Interpretation of the Sales Volume Model
$$y = \beta_0 + \beta_1 x + \beta_2 D_M + \beta_3 x D_M + \varepsilon$$

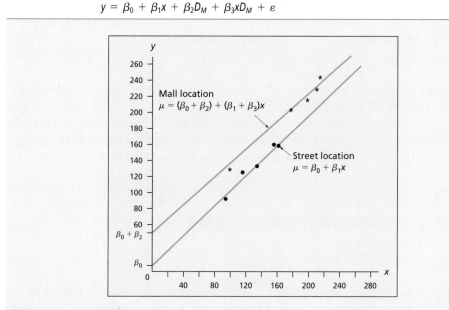

FIGURE **12.35**   MegaStat Output Using the Interaction Model $y = \beta_0 + \beta_1 x + \beta_2 D_M + \beta_3 x D_M + \varepsilon$

Regression Analysis

	R^2	0.984			
	Adjusted R^2	0.975		n	10
	R	0.992		k	3
	Std. Error	7.709		Dep. Var.	**Sales**

ANOVA table

Source	SS	df	MS	F	p-value
Regression	21,431.1861	3	7,143.7287	120.20	9.53E-06
Residual	356.5933	6	59.4322		
Total	21,787.7795	9			

Regression output					confidence interval	
variables	coefficients	std. error	t (df = 6)	p-value	95% lower	95% upper
Intercept	7.9004	19.3142	0.409	0.6967	−39.3598	55.1607
X	0.9207	0.1399	6.579	0.0006	0.5783	1.2631
DM	42.7297	24.3812	1.753	0.1302	−16.9290	102.3885
XDM	−0.0917	0.1606	−0.571	0.5886	−0.4846	0.3012

the number of households in a store's area and store location, we might consider using the model

$$y = \beta_0 + \beta_1 x + \beta_2 D_M + \beta_3 D_D + \beta_4 x D_M + \beta_5 x D_D + \varepsilon$$

Similar to Figure 12.34, this model implies that the straight lines relating mean sales volume to x for the street, mall, and downtown locations have *different y intercepts* and *different slopes*. If we perform a regression analysis of the sales volume data using this interaction model, we find that the p-values related to the significance of $x D_M$ and $x D_D$ are large: $-.5334$ and $.8132$, respectively. Because these interaction terms are not significant, it seems best to use the no-interaction model.

In general, if we want to model the effect of a qualitative independent variable with a levels, we use $a - 1$ dummy variables. The parameter multiplied by a particular dummy variable expresses the effect of the level represented by that dummy variable with respect to the effect of the level that is not represented by a dummy variable. For example, if we want to compare the effects on sales, y, of four different types of advertising campaigns—television (T), radio (R), magazine (M), and mailed coupons (C)—we might use the model

$$y = \beta_0 + \beta_1 D_T + \beta_2 D_R + \beta_3 D_M + \varepsilon$$

This model does not use a dummy variable to represent the mailed coupon advertising campaign. The parameter β_1 is the difference between mean sales when a television advertising campaign is used and mean sales when a mailed coupon advertising campaign is used. The interpretations of β_2 and β_3 follow similarly. As another example, if we want to employ a confidence interval and a hypothesis test to compare the mall and downtown locations in the Electronics World example, we can use the model

$$y = \beta_0 + \beta_1 x + \beta_2 D_S + \beta_3 D_M + \varepsilon$$

Here the dummy variable D_M is as previously defined, and

$$D_S = \begin{cases} 1 & \text{If a store is in a street location} \\ 0 & \text{Otherwise} \end{cases}$$

Because this model does not use a dummy variable to represent the downtown location, the parameter β_2 expresses the effect on mean sales of a street location compared to a downtown location, and the parameter β_3 expresses the effect on mean sales of a mall location compared to a downtown location.

The Excel output of the least squares point estimates of the parameters of this model is as shown in the following table:

	Coefficients	Standard Error	t Stat	P-value	Lower 95%	Upper 95%
Intercept	21.8415	8.5585	2.5520	0.0269	3.0044	40.6785
Households (x)	0.8686	0.0405	21.4520	2.52E-10	0.7795	0.9577
DummyStreet	−6.8638	4.7705	−1.4388	0.1780	−17.3635	3.6360
DummyMall	21.5100	4.0651	5.2914	0.0003	12.5628	30.4572

Because the least squares point estimate of β_3 is $b_3 = 21.51$, we estimate that for any given number of households in a store's area, the mean monthly sales volume in a mall location is $21,510 higher than the mean monthly sales volume in a downtown location. The Excel output tells us that a 95 percent confidence interval for β_3 is [12.5628, 30.4572]. Therefore, we are 95 percent confident that for any given number of households in a store's area, the mean monthly sales volume in a mall location is between $12,562.80 and $30,457.20 greater than the mean monthly sales volume in a downtown location. The output also shows that the t statistic and p-value for testing $H_0: \beta_3 = 0$ versus $H_a: \beta_3 \neq 0$ in this model are, respectively, 5.2914 and .0003. So we have extremely strong evidence that there is a difference between the mean monthly sales volumes in mall and downtown locations.

In some situations, dummy variables represent the effects of unusual events or occurrences that may have an important effect on the dependent variable. For instance, suppose we want to build a regression model relating quarterly sales of automobiles (y) to automobile prices (x_1), fuel prices (x_2), and personal income (x_3). If an autoworkers' strike occurred in a particular quarter that had a major effect on automobile sales, then we might define a dummy variable D_S to be equal to 1 if an autoworkers' strike occurs and 0 otherwise. The least squares point estimate of the regression parameter multiplied by D_S would estimate the effect of the strike on mean auto sales. Finally, dummy variables can be used to model the impact of regularly occurring *seasonal* influences on time series data—for example, the effect of the hot summer months on soft drink sales. This is discussed in Chapter 16.

Exercises for Section **12.11**

CONCEPTS

12.39 What is a qualitative independent variable?

12.40 How are dummy variables used to model the effects of a qualitative independent variable?

12.41 What does the parameter multiplied by a dummy variable express?

METHODS AND APPLICATIONS

12.42 Neter, Kutner, Nachtsheim, and Wasserman (1996) relate the speed, y, with which a particular insurance innovation is adopted to the size of the insurance firm, x, and the type of firm. The dependent variable y is measured by the number of months elapsed between the time the first firm adopted the innovation and the time the firm being considered adopted the innovation. The size of the firm, x, is measured by the total assets of the firm, and the type of firm—a qualitative independent variable—is either a mutual company or a stock company. The data in Table 12.16 are observed.

a. Discuss why the data plot below indicates that the model
$$y = \beta_0 + \beta_1 x + \beta_2 D_S + \varepsilon$$
might appropriately describe the observed data. Here D_S equals 1 if the firm is a stock company and 0 if the firm is a mutual company.

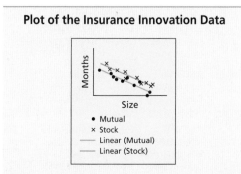

Plot of the Insurance Innovation Data

TABLE **12.16**   The Insurance Innovation Data 📈

Firm	Number of Months Elapsed, y	Size of Firm (Millions of Dollars), x	Type of Firm	Firm	Number of Months Elapsed, y	Size of Firm (Millions of Dollars), x	Type of Firm
1	17	151	Mutual	11	28	164	Stock
2	26	92	Mutual	12	15	272	Stock
3	21	175	Mutual	13	11	295	Stock
4	30	31	Mutual	14	38	68	Stock
5	22	104	Mutual	15	31	85	Stock
6	0	277	Mutual	16	21	224	Stock
7	12	210	Mutual	17	20	166	Stock
8	19	120	Mutual	18	13	305	Stock
9	4	290	Mutual	19	30	124	Stock
10	16	238	Mutual	20	14	246	Stock

b. The model in part (a) implies that the mean adoption time of an insurance innovation by mutual companies with asset size x equals

$$\beta_0 + \beta_1 x + \beta_2(0) = \beta_0 + \beta_1 x$$

and that the mean adoption time by stock companies with asset size x equals

$$\beta_0 + \beta_1 x + \beta_2(1) = \beta_0 + \beta_1 x + \beta_2$$

The difference between these two means equals the model parameter β_2. In your own words, interpret β_2. Does this interpretation make practical sense?

c. Figure 12.36 presents the Excel output of a regression analysis of the insurance innovation data using the model of part (a). Using the output, test $H_0: \beta_2 = 0$ versus $H_a: \beta_2 \neq 0$ by setting $\alpha = .05$ and .01. Interpret the result of this test. Does this interpretation make practical sense? Also use the computer output to find, report, and interpret a 95 percent confidence interval for β_2.

d. If we add the interaction term xD_S to the model of part (a), we find that the p-value related to this term is .9821. What does this imply?

12.43 THE SHELF DISPLAY EXAMPLE

📈 The Tastee Bakery Company supplies a bakery product to many supermarkets in a metropolitan area. The company wants to study the effect of the height of the shelf display used by the supermarkets on monthly sales, y (measured in

cases of ten units each), for this product. Shelf display height has three levels—bottom (B), middle (M), and top (T). For each shelf display height, six supermarkets of equal sales potential will be randomly selected, and each supermarket will display the product using its assigned shelf height for a month. At the end of the month, sales of the bakery product at the 18 participating stores will be recorded. When the experiment is carried out, the data in Table 12.17 are obtained. Here we assume that the set of sales amounts for each display height is a sample that has been randomly selected from the population of all sales amounts that could be obtained (at supermarkets of the given sales potential) when using that display height. To compare the population mean sales amounts μ_B, μ_M, and μ_T that would be obtained by using the bottom, middle, and top display heights, we use the following dummy variable regression model:

$$y = \beta_B + \beta_M D_M + \beta_T D_T + \varepsilon$$

Here D_M equals 1 if a middle display height is used and 0 otherwise; D_T equals 1 if a top display height is used and 0 otherwise. Figure 12.37 presents the MegaStat output of a regression analysis of the bakery sales study data using this model.[1]

---

[1]In general, the regression approach of this exercise produces the same comparisons of several population means that are produced by one-way analysis of variance (see Section 10.2). In Appendix G on *Connect*, we discuss the regression approach to two-way analysis of variance (see Section 10.4).

FIGURE **12.36**   Excel Output of a Regression Analysis of the Insurance Innovation Data Using the Model $y = \beta_0 + \beta_1 x + \beta_2 D_S + \varepsilon$

Regression Statistics	
Multiple R	0.9461
R Square	0.8951
Adjusted R Square	0.8827
Standard Error	3.2211
Observations	20

ANOVA	df	SS	MS	F	Significance F
Regression	2	1,504.4133	752.2067	72.4971	4.77E-09
Residual	17	176.3867	10.3757		
Total	19	1,680.8			

	Coefficients	Standard Error	t Stat	P-value	Lower 95%	Upper 95%
Intercept	33.8741	1.8139	18.6751	9.15E-13	30.0472	37.7010
Size of Firm (x)	−0.1017	0.0089	−11.4430	2.07E-09	−0.1205	−0.0830
DummyStock	8.0555	1.4591	5.5208	3.74E-05	4.9770	11.1339

TABLE 12.17 Bakery Sales Study Data (Sales in Cases) 📏

Bottom, B	Middle, M	Top, T
	Shelf Display Height	
58.2	73.0	52.4
53.7	78.1	49.7
55.8	75.4	50.9
55.7	76.2	54.0
52.5	78.4	52.1
58.9	82.1	49.9

a. By using the definitions of the dummy variables, show that

$$\mu_B = \beta_B, \ \mu_M = \beta_B + \beta_M, \text{ and } \mu_T = \beta_B + \beta_T$$

b. Use the overall F statistic to test $H_0: \beta_M = \beta_T = 0$ or, equivalently, $H_0: \mu_B = \mu_M = \mu_T$. Interpret the result of this test. Does this interpretation make practical sense?

c. Show that your results in part (a) imply that

$$\mu_M - \mu_B = \beta_M, \ \mu_T - \mu_B = \beta_T$$
$$\text{and } \mu_M - \mu_T = \beta_M - \beta_T$$

Then use the least squares point estimates of the model parameters to find a point estimate of each of the three differences in means. Also find a 95 percent confidence interval for and test the significance of each of the first two differences in means. Interpret your results.

d. Find a point estimate of mean sales when using a middle display height, a 95 percent confidence interval for mean sales when using a middle display height, and a 95 percent prediction interval for sales at an individual supermarket that employs a middle display height (see the bottom of the output in Figure 12.37).

e. Consider the alternative model

$$y = \beta_T + \beta_B D_B + \beta_M D_M + \varepsilon$$

Here D_B equals 1 if a bottom display height is used and 0 otherwise. The output of the least squares point estimates of the parameters of this model is as shown in the following table:

	Coefficients	Standard Error	t Stat	P-value
Intercept	51.5	1.013246	50.82677	3.3E-18
Middle	25.7	1.432946	17.93508	1.52E-11
Bottom	4.3	1.432946	3.000812	0.008958

Because β_M expresses the effect of the middle display height with respect to the effect of the top display height, β_M equals $\mu_M - \mu_T$. Use the output to calculate a 95 percent confidence interval for and test the significance of $\mu_M - \mu_T$. Interpret your results.

12.44 THE FRESH DETERGENT EXAMPLE

Recall from Exercise 12.7 that Enterprise Industries has observed the historical data in Table 12.4 concerning y (demand for Fresh liquid laundry detergent), x_1 (the price of Fresh), x_2 (the average industry price of competitors' similar detergents), and x_3 (Enterprise Industries' advertising expenditure for Fresh). To ultimately increase the demand for Fresh, Enterprise Industries' marketing department is comparing the effectiveness of three different advertising campaigns. These campaigns are denoted as campaigns A, B, and C. Campaign A consists entirely of television commercials, campaign B consists of a balanced mixture of television and radio commercials, and campaign C consists of a balanced mixture of television, radio, newspaper, and magazine advertisements. To conduct the study, Enterprise Industries has randomly selected one advertising campaign to be used in each of the 30 sales periods in Table 12.4. Although each of campaigns A, B, and C should be used in 10 of the 30 sales periods, Enterprise Industries has made previous

FIGURE 12.37 MegaStat Output of a Dummy Variable Regression Analysis of the Bakery Sales Data in Table 12.17

Regression Analysis

R²	0.961			
Adjusted R²	0.956		n	18
R	0.980		k	2
Std. Error	2.482		Dep. Var.	**Sales (y)**

ANOVA table

Source	SS	df	MS	F	p-value
Regression	2,273.8800	2	1,136.9400	184.57	2.74E-11
Residual	92.4000	15	6.1600		
Total	2,366.2800	17			

Regression output

					confidence interval	
variables	coefficients	std. error	t (df = 15)	p-value	95% lower	95% upper
Intercept	55.8000	1.0132	55.071	9.96E-19	53.6403	57.9597
Middle	21.4000	1.4329	14.934	2.07E-10	18.3457	24.4543
Top	−4.3000	1.4329	−3.001	0.0090	−7.3543	−1.2457

Predicted values for: Sales (y)

			95% Confidence Interval		95% Prediction Interval		
Middle	Top	Predicted	lower	upper	lower	upper	Leverage
1	0	77.2000	75.0403	79.3597	71.4860	82.9140	0.167

commitments to the advertising media involved in the study. As a result, campaigns A, B, and C were randomly assigned to, respectively, 9, 11, and 10 sales periods. Furthermore, advertising was done in only the first three weeks of each sales period, so that the carry-over effect of the campaign used in a sales period to the next sales period would be minimized. Table 12.18 lists the campaigns used in the sales periods.

To compare the effectiveness of advertising campaigns A, B, and C, we define two dummy variables. Specifically, we define the dummy variable D_B to equal 1 if campaign B is used in a sales period and 0 otherwise. Furthermore, we define the dummy variable D_C to equal 1 if campaign C is used in a sales period and 0 otherwise. Figure 12.38 presents the MegaStat output of a regression analysis of the Fresh demand data by using the model

$$y = \beta_0 + \beta_1 x_1 + \beta_2 x_2 + \beta_3 x_3 + \beta_4 D_B + \beta_5 D_C + \varepsilon$$

a. In this model, the parameter β_4 represents the effect on mean demand of advertising campaign B compared to advertising campaign A, and the parameter β_5 represents the effect on mean demand of advertising campaign C compared to advertising campaign A. Use the regression output to find and report a point estimate of each of the above effects and to test the significance of each of the above effects. Also find and report a 95 percent confidence interval for each of the above effects. Interpret your results.

b. The prediction results at the bottom of the MegaStat output correspond to a future period when the price of Fresh will be $x_1 = 3.70$, the competitors' average price of similar detergents will be $x_2 = 3.90$, the advertising expenditure for Fresh will be $x_3 = 6.50$, and advertising campaign C will be used. Show how $\hat{y} = 8.61621$ is calculated. Then find, report, and interpret a 95 percent confidence interval for mean

TABLE 12.18   Advertising Campaigns Used by Enterprise Industries

Sales Period	Advertising Campaign	Sales Period	Advertising Campaign
1	B	16	B
2	B	17	B
3	B	18	A
4	A	19	B
5	C	20	B
6	A	21	C
7	C	22	A
8	C	23	A
9	B	24	A
10	C	25	A
11	A	26	B
12	C	27	C
13	C	28	B
14	A	29	C
15	B	30	C

demand and a 95 percent prediction interval for an individual demand when $x_1 = 3.70$, $x_2 = 3.90$, $x_3 = 6.50$, and campaign C is used.

c. Consider the alternative model

$$y = \beta_0 + \beta_1 x_1 + \beta_2 x_2 + \beta_3 x_3$$
$$+ \beta_4 D_A + \beta_5 D_C + \varepsilon$$

Here D_A equals 1 if advertising campaign A is used and 0 otherwise. Describe the effect represented by the regression parameter β_5.

d. The MegaStat output of the least squares point estimates of the parameters of the model in part (c) is as shown in Figure 12.39. Use the MegaStat output to test the significance of the effect represented by β_5 and find a 95 percent confidence interval for β_5. Interpret your results.

FIGURE 12.38   MegaStat Output of a Dummy Variable Regression Model Analysis of the Fresh Demand Data

Regression Analysis

R²	0.960					
Adjusted R²	0.951		n	30		
R	0.980		k	5		
Std. Error	0.150		Dep. Var.	**Demand**		

ANOVA table

Source	SS	df	MS	F	p-value	
Regression	12.9166	5	2.5833	114.39	6.24E-16	
Residual	0.5420	24	0.0226			
Total	13.4586	29				

Regression output

					confidence interval	
variables	coefficients	std. error	t (df = 24)	p-value	95% lower	95% upper
Intercept	8.7154	1.5849	5.499	1.18E-05	5.4443	11.9866
X1	−2.7680	0.4144	−6.679	6.58E-07	−3.6234	−1.9127
X2	1.6667	0.1913	8.711	6.77E-09	1.2718	2.0616
X3	0.4927	0.0806	6.110	2.60E-06	0.3263	0.6592
DB	0.2695	0.0695	3.880	0.0007	0.1262	0.4128
DC	0.4396	0.0703	6.250	1.85E-06	0.2944	0.5847

Predicted values for: Demand

	95% Confidence Interval		95% Prediction Interval			
Predicted	lower	upper	lower	upper	Leverage	
8.61621	8.51380	8.71862	8.28958	8.94285	0.109	

FIGURE 12.39 MegaStat Output for Exercise 12.44(d)

Regression output variables	coefficients	std. error	t (df = 23)	p-value	confidence interval 95% lower	95% upper
Intercept	8.9849	1.5971	5.626	8.61E-06	5.6888	12.2811
X1	−2.7680	0.4144	−6.679	6.58E-07	−3.6234	−1.9127
X2	1.6667	0.1913	8.711	6.77E-09	1.2718	2.0616
X3	0.4927	0.0806	6.110	2.60E-06	0.3263	0.6592
DA	−0.2695	0.0695	−3.880	0.0007	−0.4128	−0.1262
DC	0.1701	0.0669	2.543	0.0179	0.0320	0.3081

FIGURE 12.40 MegaStat Output of a Regression Analysis of the Fresh Demand Data Using the Model
$$y = \beta_0 + \beta_1 x_1 + \beta_2 x_2 + \beta_3 x_3 + \beta_4 D_B + \beta_5 D_C + \beta_6 x_3 D_B + \beta_7 x_3 D_C + \varepsilon$$

Regression output variables	coefficients	std. error	t (df = 22)	p-value	confidence interval 95% lower	95% upper
Intercept	8.7619	1.7071	5.133	3.82E-05	5.2216	12.3021
X1	−2.7895	0.4339	−6.428	1.81E-06	−3.6894	−1.8895
X2	1.6365	0.2062	7.938	6.72E-08	1.2089	2.0641
X3	0.5160	0.1288	4.007	0.0006	0.2489	0.7831
DB	0.2539	0.8722	0.291	0.7737	−1.5550	2.0628
DC	0.8435	0.9739	0.866	0.3958	−1.1762	2.8631
X3DB	0.0030	0.1334	0.023	0.9822	−0.2736	0.2797
X3DC	−0.0629	0.1502	−0.419	0.6794	−0.3744	0.2486

Predicted values for: Demand						R^2 0.960
	95% Confidence Interval		95% Prediction Interval			Adjusted R^2 0.948
Predicted	lower	upper	lower	upper	Leverage	R 0.980
8.61178	8.50372	8.71984	8.27089	8.95266	0.112	Std. Error 0.156

12.45 THE FRESH DETERGENT EXAMPLE

Figure 12.40 presents the MegaStat output of a regression analysis of the Fresh demand data using the model

$$y = \beta_0 + \beta_1 x_1 + \beta_2 x_2 + \beta_3 x_3 + \beta_4 D_B + \beta_5 D_C + \beta_6 x_3 D_B + \beta_7 x_3 D_C + \varepsilon$$

where the dummy variables D_B and D_C are defined as in Exercise 12.44.

a. This model assumes that there is an interaction between advertising expenditure, x_3, and type of advertising campaign. What do the *p*-values related to the significance of the cross-product terms $x_3 D_B$ and $x_3 D_C$ say about the need for these interaction

terms and about whether there is an interaction between x_3 and the type of advertising campaign?

b. The prediction results at the bottom of Figure 12.40 are for a future sales period in which $x_1 = 3.70$, $x_2 = 3.90$, $x_3 = 6.50$, and advertising campaign *C* will be used. Use the output to find and report a point prediction of and a 95 percent prediction interval for Fresh demand in such a sales period. Is the 95 percent prediction interval given by this model shorter or longer than the 95 percent prediction interval given by the model that utilizes D_B and D_C in Exercise 12.44? What are the implications of this comparison?

12.12 THE PARTIAL *F* TEST: TESTING THE SIGNIFICANCE OF A PORTION OF A REGRESSION MODEL

We now present a partial *F* test that allows us to test the significance of a set of independent variables in a regression model. That is, we can use this *F* test to test the significance of a *portion* of a regression model. For example, in the Electronics World situation, we used the dummy variable model

$$y = \beta_0 + \beta_1 x + \beta_2 D_M + \beta_3 D_D + \varepsilon$$

It might be useful to test the significance of the dummy variables D_M (mall location) and D_D (downtown location). We can do this by testing the null hypothesis

$$H_0: \beta_2 = \beta_3 = 0$$

which says that neither dummy variable significantly affects y, versus the alternative hypothesis

$$H_a: \text{at least one of } \beta_2 \text{ and } \beta_3 \text{ does not equal } 0$$

which says that at least one of the dummy variables significantly affects y. Because β_2 and β_3 represent the effects of the mall and downtown locations with respect to the street location, the null hypothesis says that the effects of the mall, downtown, and street locations on mean sales volume do not differ (nonsignificant dummy variables). The alternative hypothesis says that at least two locations have different effects on mean sales volume (at least one significant dummy variable).

In general, consider the regression model

$$y = \beta_0 + \beta_1 x_1 + \cdots + \beta_g x_g + \beta_{g+1} x_{g+1} + \cdots + \beta_k x_k + \varepsilon$$

Suppose we want to test the null hypothesis

$$H_0: \beta_{g+1} = \beta_{g+2} = \cdots = \beta_k = 0$$

which says that none of the independent variables $x_{g+1}, x_{g+2}, \ldots, x_k$ affects y, versus the alternative hypothesis

$$H_a: \text{At least one of } \beta_{g+1}, \beta_{g+2}, \ldots, \beta_k \text{ does not equal } 0$$

which says that at least one of the independent variables $x_{g+1}, x_{g+2}, \ldots, x_k$ affects y. If we can reject H_0 in favour of H_a by specifying a *small* probability of a Type I error, then it is reasonable to conclude that at least one of $x_{g+1}, x_{g+2}, \ldots, x_k$ *significantly* affects y. In this case, we use t statistics and other techniques to determine which of $x_{g+1}, x_{g+2}, \ldots, x_k$ significantly affect y. To test H_0 versus H_a, consider the following two models:

Complete model: $y = \beta_0 + \beta_1 x_1 + \cdots + \beta_g x_g + \beta_{g+1} x_{g+1} + \cdots + \beta_k x_k + \varepsilon$
Reduced model: $y = \beta_0 + \beta_1 x_1 + \cdots + \beta_g x_g + \varepsilon$

Here the complete model is assumed to have k independent variables, the reduced model is the complete model under the assumption that H_0 is true, and $(k - g)$ denotes the number of regression parameters we have set equal to 0 in the statement of H_0.

To carry out this test, we calculate SSE_C, the unexplained variation for the complete model, and SSE_R, the unexplained variation for the reduced model. The appropriate test statistic is based on the difference

$$SSE_R - SSE_C$$

which is called the *drop in the unexplained variation attributable to the independent variables* $x_{g+1}, x_{g+2}, \ldots, x_k$. In the following boxed feature, we give the formula for the test statistic and show how to carry out the test.

The Partial F Test: An F Test for a Portion of a Regression Model

Suppose that the regression assumptions hold and consider testing

$$H_0: \beta_{g+1} = \beta_{g+2} = \cdots = \beta_k = 0$$

versus

H_a: At least one of $\beta_{g+1} = \beta_{g+2} \ldots, \beta_k$ does not equal 0

We define the partial F statistic to be

$$F = \frac{(SSE_R - SSE_C)/(k - g)}{SSE_C/[n - (k + 1)]}$$

Also, we define the p-value related to F to be the area under the curve of the F distribution (with $k - g$ and $n - (k + 1)$ degrees of freedom) to the right of F. Then we can reject H_0 in favour of H_a at level of significance α if either of the following equivalent conditions holds:

1   $F > F_\alpha$

2   p-value $< \alpha$

Here the point F_α is based on $k - g$ numerator and $n - (k + 1)$ denominator degrees of freedom.

It can be shown that the "extra" independent variables $x_{g+1}, x_{g+2}, \ldots, x_k$ will always explain some of the variation in the observed y values and, therefore, will always make SSE_C somewhat smaller than SSE_R. Condition 1 says that we should reject H_0 if

$$F = \frac{(SSE_R - SSE_C)/(k - g)}{SSE_C/[n - (k + 1)]}$$

is large. This is reasonable because a large value of F would result from a large value of $(SSE_R - SSE_C)$, which would be obtained if at least one of the independent variables $x_{g+1}, x_{g+2}, \ldots, x_k$ makes SSE_C substantially smaller than SSE_R. This would suggest that H_0 is false and H_a is true.

Before looking at an example, we should point out that testing the significance of a single independent variable by using a partial F test is equivalent to carrying out this test by using the previously discussed t test (see Section 12.7).[2]

Example 12.11   The Effect of Store Location on Sales Volume

In Example 12.10, we used the dummy variable model

$$y = \beta_0 + \beta_1 x + \beta_2 D_M + \beta_3 D_D + \varepsilon$$

to make pairwise comparisons of the street, mall, and downtown store locations by carrying out a t test for each of the parameters β_2, β_3, and $\beta_2 - \beta_3$. There is a theoretical problem with this because although we can set the probability of a Type I error equal to .05 for each individual test, it is possible that the probability of falsely rejecting H_0 in *at least one* of these tests is greater than .05 (note that the Type I error is additive). Because of this problem, some people feel that before making pairwise comparisons we should test for overall differences between the effects of the locations by testing the null hypothesis

$$H_0\colon \beta_2 = \beta_3 = 0$$

which says that the street, mall, and downtown locations have the same effects on mean sales volume (no differences between locations), versus the alternative hypothesis

$$H_a\colon \text{At least one of } \beta_2 \text{ and } \beta_3 \text{ does not equal } 0$$

which says that at least two locations have different effects on mean sales volume.

To carry out this test, we consider the following:

Complete model: $y = \beta_0 + \beta_1 x + \beta_2 D_M + \beta_3 D_D + \varepsilon$

For this complete model (which has $k = 3$ independent variables), we obtain an unexplained variation equal to $SSE_C = 443.4650$. The reduced model is the complete model when H_0 is true. Therefore, we obtain

Reduced model: $y = \beta_0 + \beta_1 x + \varepsilon$

For this model, the unexplained variation is $SSE_R = 2{,}467.8067$. Noting that two parameters (β_2 and β_3) are set equal to 0 in the statement of H_0, we have $k - g = 2$. Therefore, the needed partial F statistic is

$$\begin{aligned} F &= \frac{(SSE_R - SSE_C)/(k - g)}{SSE_C/[n - (k + 1)]} \\ &= \frac{(2{,}467.8067 - 443.4650)/2}{443.4650/(15 - 4)} \\ &= 25.1066 \end{aligned}$$

---

[2]When we test $H_0\colon \beta_j = 0$ versus $H_a\colon \beta_j \neq 0$ using a partial F test,

$$F = t^2 \quad \text{and} \quad F_\alpha = (t_{\alpha/2})^2$$

Here $t_{\alpha/2}$ is based on $n - (k + 1)$ degrees of freedom, and F_α is based on 1 numerator and $n - (k + 1)$ denominator degrees of freedom. Hence, the rejection conditions

$$|t| > t_{\alpha/2} \quad \text{and} \quad F > F_\alpha$$

are equivalent. In this case the p-value related to t equals the p-value related to F.

We compare F to $F_{.01} = 7.21$, which is based on $k - g = 2$ numerator and $n - (k + 1) = 15 - 4 = 11$ denominator degrees of freedom. Since

$$F = 25.1066 > 7.21,$$

we can reject H_0 at the .01 level of significance, and we have very strong statistical evidence that at least two locations have different effects on mean sales volume. Having reached this conclusion, it makes sense to compare the effects of specific pairs of locations. We have already done this in Example 12.10. It should also be noted that even if H_0 was not rejected, pairwise comparisons could still be made in order to test specific *a priori* hypotheses.

Exercises for Section **12.12**

CONCEPTS

12.46 When we perform a partial F test, what are the complete and reduced models?

12.47 When we perform a partial F test, what is $(k - g)$? What is $n - (k + 1)$?

METHODS AND APPLICATIONS

THE FRESH DETERGENT EXAMPLE 🖋

In Exercises 12.48 through 12.50, you will perform partial F tests by using the following three Fresh detergent models:

Model 1: $y = \beta_0 + \beta_1 x_1 + \beta_2 x_2 + \beta_3 x_3 + \varepsilon$

Model 2: $y = \beta_0 + \beta_1 x_1 + \beta_2 x_2 + \beta_3 x_3 + \beta_4 D_B + \beta_5 D_C + \varepsilon$

Model 3: $y = \beta_0 + \beta_1 x_1 + \beta_2 x_2 + \beta_3 x_3 + \beta_4 D_B + \beta_5 D_C + \beta_6 x_3 D_B + \beta_7 x_3 D_C + \varepsilon$

The values of the *SSE* for models 1, 2, and 3 are, respectively, 1.4318, .5420, and .5347.

12.48 In Model 2, test H_0: $\beta_4 = \beta_5 = 0$ by setting α equal to .05 and .01. Interpret your results.

12.49 In Model 3, test H_0: $\beta_4 = \beta_5 = \beta_6 = \beta_7 = 0$ by setting α equal to .05 and .01. Interpret your results.

12.50 In Model 3, test H_0: $\beta_6 = \beta_7 = 0$ by setting α equal to .05 and .01. Interpret your results.

THEORY TO PRACTICE

Another practical application of multiple regression theory is in the prediction of wages in the workplace. Wages tend to be predicted by years of service, level of education, and (depending on the nature of the workplace) job performance. Years of service might demonstrate a nonlinear predictive function, as wages might plateau or "top out" after an employee has been with the organization for a while. Level of education is similarly interesting in its prediction of salary: It might demonstrate a nonlinear relationship with salary (i.e., there might be a demonstrated "diminished level of return" on education, if it is possible to be "overqualified" in the organization), or it might demonstrate no relationship at all with salary—even if educational qualifications are a selection criterion for the job!

Consider tenured professors, all of whom are generally required to have a PhD. Because there is very little variability in the educational qualifications in the professorate, "level of education" will show little to no relationship with salary. Finally, consider the importance of demonstrating that there is no relationship between salary and certain demographic variables, for example, gender. If it can be determined that an organization has a regression coefficient for "gender" that is significantly different from zero, the organization will need to take steps to establish pay equity.

Clearly, multiple regression calculations can be used to ensure that the prediction of important workplace variables takes into account the relationship among numerous variables in their prediction of the outcome(s) of interest—and might also be used to facilitate important business decisions.

CHAPTER SUMMARY

In this chapter, we have discussed multiple regression analysis. We began by considering the multiple regression model. We next discussed the least squares point estimates of the model parameters, the assumptions behind the model, and some ways to judge overall model utility—the standard error, the multiple coefficient of determination, the adjusted multiple coefficient of determination, and the overall F test. Then we considered testing the significance of a single independent variable in a multiple regression model, calculating a confidence interval for the mean value of the dependent variable, and calculating a prediction interval for an individual value of the dependent variable.

We continued this chapter by discussing the use of squared terms to model quadratic relationships, using cross-product terms to model interaction, and using dummy variables to model qualitative independent variables. We concluded this chapter by examining how to use the partial F test to evaluate a portion of a regression model.

KEY TERMS

dummy variable (indicator variable)
influential observation

multiple regression model
standard error of the estimate

IMPORTANT FORMULAS AND TESTS

Multiple regression model

Point prediction of an individual value of y

Mean square error

Standard error

Least squares point estimates

Point estimate of a mean value of y

Total variation

Explained variation

Unexplained variation

Multiple coefficient of determination

Multiple correlation coefficient

Adjusted multiple coefficient of determination

An F test for the linear regression model

Testing the significance of an independent variable

Confidence interval for β_j

Sampling distribution of $\hat{y}$ (and the distance value)

Confidence interval for a mean value of y

Prediction interval for an individual value of y

Quadratic regression model

Partial F test

SUPPLEMENTARY EXERCISES

connect Practise and learn online with *Connect*. Items for which there are online data sets are marked with .

12.51 In a September 1982 article in *Business Economics*, Allmon related y = Crest toothpaste sales in a given year (in thousands of dollars) to x_1 = Crest advertising budget in the year (in thousands of dollars), x_2 = Ratio of Crest's advertising budget to Colgate's advertising budget in the year, and x_3 = U.S. personal disposable income in the year (in billions of dollars). The data analyzed are given in Table 12.19. When we perform a regression analysis of these data using the model

$$y = \beta_0 + \beta_1 x_1 + \beta_2 x_2 + \beta_3 x_3 + \varepsilon$$

we find that the least squares point estimates of the model parameters and their associated p-values (given in parentheses) are $b_0 = 30{,}626$ (.156), $b_1 = 3.893$ (.094), $b_2 = -29{,}607$ (.245), and $b_3 = 86.52$ (< .001). Suppose it was estimated at the end of 1979 that in 1980 the advertising budget for Crest would be 28,000, the ratio of Crest's advertising budget to Colgate's advertising budget would be 1.56, and the U.S. personal disposable income would be 1,821.7. Using the model, we would obtain a point prediction of about 251,057, thus giving the 95 percent prediction interval [221,986, 280,128] for Crest sales in 1980. Show how the point prediction was calculated.

12.52 The trend in home-building in recent years has been to emphasize open spaces and great rooms, rather than smaller living rooms and family rooms. A builder of speculative homes (Oxford Homes) in London, Ontario, had been building such homes, but these homes had been taking many months to sell and selling for substantially less than the asking price. To determine what types of homes would attract members of the community, the builder contacted a statistician. The statistician went to a local real estate agency and obtained the data in Table 12.20. This table presents the sales price y, total floor area x_1, number of rooms x_2, number of bedrooms x_3, and age x_4 for each of 63 single-family residences recently sold in the community. When we perform a regression analysis of these data using the model

$$y = \beta_0 + \beta_1 x_1 + \beta_2 x_2 + \beta_3 x_3 + \beta_4 x_4 + \varepsilon$$

we find that the least squares point estimates of the model parameters and their associated p-values (given in parentheses) are $b_0 = 10.3676$ (.3710), $b_1 = .0500$ (< .001), $b_2 = 6.3218$ (.0152), $b_3 = -11.1032$ (.0635), and $b_4 = -.4319$ (.0002). Discuss why the estimates $b_2 = 6.3218$ and $b_3 = -11.1032$ suggest that it might be more profitable when building a house with a specified floor area (1) to

TABLE 12.19 Crest Toothpaste Sales Data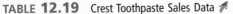

Year	Crest Sales, y	Crest Budget, x_1	Ratio, x_2	U.S. Personal Disposable Income, x_3
1967	105,000	16,300	1.25	547.9
1968	105,000	15,800	1.34	593.4
1969	121,600	16,000	1.22	638.9
1970	113,750	14,200	1.00	695.3
1971	113,750	15,000	1.15	751.8
1972	128,925	14,000	1.13	810.3
1973	142,500	15,400	1.05	914.5
1974	126,000	18,250	1.27	998.3
1975	162,000	17,300	1.07	1,096.1
1976	191,625	23,000	1.17	1,194.4
1977	189,000	19,300	1.07	1,311.5
1978	210,000	23,056	1.54	1,462.9
1979	224,250	26,000	1.59	1,641.7

Source: "Advertising and sales relationships for toothpaste: Another look," by C. I. Allmon, *Business Economics* (September 1982), pp. 17, 58. Reprinted by permission. Copyright © 1982 National Association for Business Economics.

TABLE 12.20 Measurements Taken on 63 Single-Family Residences

Residence	Sales Price, y (× $1,000)	Floor area x_1	Rooms, x_2	Bedrooms, x_3	Age, x_4	Residence	Sales Price, y (× $1,000)	Floor area x_1	Rooms, x_2	Bedrooms, x_3	Age, x_4
1	53.5	1,008	5	2	35	33	63.0	1,053	5	2	24
2	49.0	1,290	6	3	36	34	60.0	1,728	6	3	26
3	50.5	860	8	2	36	35	34.0	416	3	1	42
4	49.9	912	5	3	41	36	52.0	1,040	5	2	9
5	52.0	1,204	6	3	40	37	75.0	1,496	6	3	30
6	55.0	1,204	5	3	10	38	93.0	1,936	8	4	39
7	80.5	1,764	8	4	64	39	60.0	1,904	7	4	32
8	86.0	1,600	7	3	19	40	73.0	1,080	5	2	24
9	69.0	1,255	5	3	16	41	71.0	1,768	8	4	74
10	149.0	3,600	10	5	17	42	83.0	1,503	6	3	14
11	46.0	864	5	3	37	43	90.0	1,736	7	3	16
12	38.0	720	4	2	41	44	83.0	1,695	6	3	12
13	49.5	1,008	6	3	35	45	115.0	2,186	8	4	12
14	105.0	1,950	8	3	52	46	50.0	888	5	2	34
15	152.5	2,086	7	3	12	47	55.2	1,120	6	3	29
16	85.0	2,011	9	4	76	48	61.0	1,400	5	3	33
17	60.0	1,465	6	3	102	49	147.0	2,165	7	3	2
18	58.5	1,232	5	2	69	50	210.0	2,353	8	4	15
19	101.0	1,736	7	3	67	51	60.0	1,536	6	3	36
20	79.4	1,296	6	3	11	52	100.0	1,972	8	3	37
21	125.0	1,996	7	3	9	53	44.5	1,120	5	3	27
22	87.9	1,874	5	2	14	54	55.0	1,664	7	3	79
23	80.0	1,580	5	3	11	55	53.4	925	5	3	20
24	94.0	1,920	5	3	14	56	65.0	1,288	5	3	2
25	74.0	1,430	9	3	16	57	73.0	1,400	5	3	2
26	69.0	1,486	6	3	27	58	40.0	1,376	6	3	103
27	63.0	1,008	5	2	35	59	141.0	2,038	12	4	62
28	67.5	1,282	5	3	20	60	68.0	1,572	6	3	29
29	35.0	1,134	5	2	74	61	139.0	1,545	6	3	9
30	142.5	2,400	9	4	15	62	140.0	1,993	6	3	4
31	92.2	1,701	5	3	15	63	55.0	1,130	5	2	21
32	56.0	1,020	6	3	16						

include both a smaller living room and a family room rather than a larger great room and (2) to not increase the number of bedrooms (at the cost of another type of room) that would normally be included in a house with the specified floor area.

Note: Based on the statistical results, the builder realized that there are many families with children in London and that the parents in such families would rather have one living area for the children (the family room) and a separate living area for themselves (the living room). The builder started modifying the open-space homes accordingly and greatly increased profits.

12.53 Interest in eBook readers has been growing in Canada. Typical prices for these readers range from $140 to $270. A researcher decided to examine how age, gender, and price influence interest in purchasing an eBook reader and surveyed 29 adults who did not own an eBook reader. Of these 29 adults, 15 were men and 14 were women. Each individual was given the same advertisement for an eBook reader, each with a randomly set price (x_2), falling between $140 and $270. Individuals provided their age (x_1) and were asked to report how interested (y) they were in an eBook reader (from 1 = Not at all interested to 10 = Very interested). The data are reported in Table 12.21.

a. Using a computer, perform the multiple regression analysis for all participants and summarize the results.

b. Perform the multiple regression analyses separately for men (M) and women (F). How do the results differ between men and women?

12.54 RESTAURANT SATISFACTION DATA

The owner of a restaurant wants to investigate customer satisfaction. Over the course of an evening, customers are asked to complete a satisfaction card with scores ranging from 1 (not at all satisfied) to 5 (extremely satisfied). The average satisfaction ratings are compiled for each table of guests ($n = 25$ tables). Also measured is the average price of the meal per person (x_1) and

the average number of items ordered per person (x_2). The data are presented in Table 12.22, along with the scatter plots. The results of the regression analysis are presented in Figure 12.41.

TABLE 12.22 Restaurant Data

Table Number	Average Satisfaction (y)	Average Bill (x_1)	Average Item (x_2)
1	2	33.21	1.1
2	2	55.01	1.35
3	2	22.75	1.2
4	3	47.31	1.1
5	2	37.12	1.18
6	4	9.18	1.25
7	3	20.06	1.25
8	3	49.63	1.57
9	2	46.87	1.4
10	2	24.16	1.45
11	3	26.15	1.48
12	4	33.03	1.9
13	3	33.49	1.85
14	5	19.12	1.8
15	5	18.65	1.58
16	2	64.28	1.5
17	2	48.64	0.93
18	4	17.13	1.6
19	2	62.79	1.4
20	2	54.65	1.3
21	3	59.98	1.62
22	2	41.18	1.13
23	2	34.44	1.28
24	3	41.89	1.45
25	3	31.36	1.21

TABLE 12.21 Data for Exercise 12.53

Interest (y)	Age (x_1)	Price (x_2)	Gender
8	18	140	M
7	48	181	M
5	65	225	M
9	22	170	M
1	59	220	M
6	48	252	M
5	63	199	M
7	29	177	M
8	31	140	M
10	24	153	M
9	19	144	M
8	30	160	M
6	33	200	M
7	25	188	M
9	67	155	F
2	19	265	F
3	20	250	F
6	80	184	F
5	40	233	F
4	32	256	F
8	66	162	F
9	70	156	F
10	69	139	F
1	21	260	F
3	26	257	F
2	31	233	F
8	59	155	F
7	64	188	F
6	48	173	F

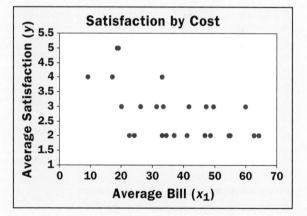

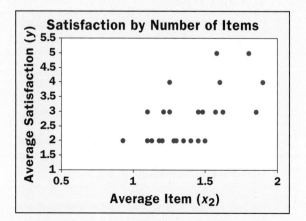

FIGURE **12.41**   Restaurant Satisfaction Data

Regression Statistics

Multiple R	0.772805226
R Square	0.597227917
Adjusted R Square	0.560612273
Standard Error	0.634643272
Observations	25

ANOVA	df	SS	MS	F	Significance F
Regression	2	13.13901417	6.569507	16.310731	4.53E-05
Residual	22	8.860985826	0.402772		
Total	24	22			

	Coefficients	Standard Error	t Stat	P-value	Lower 95%	Upper 95%	Lower 95.0%	Upper 95.0%
Intercept	1.144082814	0.841244082	1.359989	0.18760824	−0.600553	2.888718	−0.600553	2.888718
Avg Bill (x1)	−0.031821898	0.008386506	−3.794417	0.00099447	−0.049214	−0.014429	−0.049214	−0.014429
Avg Item (x2)	2.037227195	0.529363909	3.848444	0.00087221	0.939392	3.135062	0.939392	3.135062

FIGURE **12.42**   Testing an Interaction in the Restaurant Data

Regression Statistics

Multiple R	0.793082
R Square	0.62898
Adjusted R Square	0.575977
Standard Error	0.623449
Observations	25

ANOVA	df	SS	MS	F	Significance F
Regression	3	13.83754992	4.61251664	11.86688	9.26483E-05
Residual	21	8.16245008	0.388688099		
Total	24	22			

	Coefficients	Standard Error	t Stat	P-value	Lower 95%	Upper 95%	Lower 95.0%	Upper 95.0%
Intercept	−1.941907	2.445820453	−0.793969428	0.436094	−7.028269623	3.144456	−7.02827	3.144456
Avg Bill (x1)	0.054431	0.064865471	0.839143126	0.41084	−0.08046374	0.189327	−0.080464	0.189327
Avg Item (x2)	4.183635	1.683434061	2.485179192	0.021454	0.682741912	7.684529	0.682742	7.684529
x1x2	−0.060513	0.045138978	−1.340582963	0.194379	−0.154384204	0.033359	−0.154384	0.033359

a. Describe the relationship between satisfaction and average price.

b. Describe the relationship between satisfaction and number of items.

c. Are price and number of items significant predictors of satisfaction?

d. Write the resulting regression equation.

12.55 TESTING AN INTERACTION IN THE RESTAURANT DATA

As a follow-up to the regression analysis in Exercise 12.54, the restaurant owner wanted to see if the interaction of average cost (x_1) and average number of items ordered (x_2) added to the regression equation. So the x_1x_2 variable was computed and was added to the analysis. The results are presented in Figure 12.42.

a. Does the interaction term add to the prediction of sales?

b. How do the results of Figures 12.41 and 12.42 differ?

12.56 DEMONSTRATING THE EFFECTS OF AN OUTLIER IN THE SALES TERRITORY DATA

In Example 12.1 at the beginning of this chapter, a sales manager was investigating sales based on a variety of predictors. In this exercise, suppose that the manager is inter-

ested in predicting sales (y) based only on number of months with the company (x_1) and advertising expenditures (x_3). The regression results of the original sample with the two predictors are given in Figure 12.43(a). One additional salesperson has been added to the data set compiled by the manager in Table 12.2. This employee is considered to be of exceptional ability. She has been with the company for only five months, has spent only $250.00 on advertising, and yet has had $6,978.85 in sales. When this employee is added to the regression analysis, the new results are calculated and the regression results are presented in Figure 12.43(b).

a. How does adding this exceptional employee to the analysis change the results?

b. How do the results of Figure 12.43(a) and 12.43(b) differ?

c. Write the resulting regression equations.

d. If the manager asked your opinion, what would you suggest regarding the inclusion of the exceptional employee into the regression analysis?

FIGURE 12.43 Regression Results for Exercise 12.56

(a) Regression results of original sales territory data

Regression Statistics

Multiple R	0.771585
R Square	0.5953435
Adjusted R Square	0.5585565
Standard Error	872.41841
Observations	25

ANOVA	df	SS	MS	F	Significance F
Regression	2	24635043.52	12317522	16.18355	4.76379E-05
Residual	22	16744505.4	761113.9		
Total	24	41379548.93			

	Coefficients	Standard Error	t Stat	P-value	Lower 95%	Upper 95%	Lower 95.0%	Upper 95.0%
Intercept	1703.672	355.1447204	4.797121	8.62E-05	967.1461647	2440.198	967.14616	2440.1989
Time with Company, x1	7.651244	2.118531925	3.611578	0.001548	3.257673016	12.04482	3.257673	12.0448151
Advertising, x3	0.22957	0.068380534	3.357242	0.002847	0.087757269	0.371383	0.0877573	0.37138267

(b) Regression results of sales territory data with new employee included

Regression Statistics

Multiple R	0.506732
R Square	0.256778
Adjusted R Square	0.192149
Standard Error	1319.386
Observations	26

ANOVA	df	SS	MS	F	Significance F
Regression	2	13832798	6916399	3.973159	0.032950855
Residual	23	40037955	1740781		
Total	25	53870752			

	Coefficients	Standard Error	t Stat	P-value	Lower 95%	Upper 95%	Lower 95.0%	Upper 95.0%
Intercept	2416.529	500.4962	4.828266	7.14E-05	1381.174916	3451.883	1381.175	3451.883
Time with Company, x1	6.335721	3.183677	1.990064	0.0586	−0.250207207	12.92165	−0.25021	12.92165
Advertising, x3	0.133716	0.100039	1.336636	0.194414	−0.073230523	0.340662	−0.07323	0.340662

12.57 THE FRESH DETERGENT EXAMPLE

Recall from Exercise 12.44 that Enterprise Industries has advertised Fresh liquid laundry detergent by using three different advertising campaigns—advertising campaign A (television commercials), advertising campaign B (a balanced mixture of television and radio commercials), and advertising campaign C (a balanced mixture of television, radio, newspaper, and magazine advertisements). To compare the effectiveness of these advertising campaigns, consider the model

$$y = \beta_0 + \beta_1 x_4 + \beta_2 x_3 + \beta_3 x_3^2 + \beta_4 x_4 x_3 + \beta_5 D_B + \beta_6 D_C + \varepsilon$$

Here, y is demand for Fresh, x_4 is the price difference, x_3 is Enterprise Industries' advertising expenditure for Fresh, D_B equals 1 if advertising campaign B is used in a sales period and 0 otherwise, and D_C equals 1 if advertising campaign C is used in a sales period and 0 otherwise. If we use this model to perform a regression analysis of the data in Table 12.23, we obtain the partial MegaStat output in Figure 12.44(a).

a. In the model given at the beginning of this exercise, the parameter β_5 represents the effect on mean demand of advertising campaign B compared to

advertising campaign A, and the parameter β_6 represents the effect on mean demand of advertising campaign C compared to advertising campaign A. Use the regression output to find a point estimate of and test the significance of each of the above effects. Also find a 95 percent confidence interval for each of the above effects. Interpret your results.

b. Consider the alternative model
$$y = \beta_0 + \beta_1 x_4 + \beta_2 x_3 + \beta_3 x_3^2 + \beta_4 x_4 x_3 + \beta_5 D_A + \beta_6 D_C + \varepsilon$$

Here D_A equals 1 if advertising campaign A is used and 0 otherwise. The MegaStat output of the least squares point estimates of the parameters of this model is as in Figure 12.44(b). Noting that β_6 represents the effect on mean demand of advertising campaign C compared to advertising campaign B, find a point estimate of and a 95 percent confidence interval for this effect. Also test the significance of this effect. Interpret your results.

c. Consider the alternative model
$$y = \beta_0 + \beta_1 x_4 + \beta_2 x_3 + \beta_3 x_3^2 + \beta_4 x_4 x_3 + \beta_5 D_B + \beta_6 D_C + \beta_7 x_3 D_B + \beta_8 x_3 D_C + \varepsilon$$

The MegaStat output of the least squares point estimates of the parameters of this model is as in Figure 12.44(c).

TABLE **12.23**   Fresh Advertising Data ✈

Price x_1	IndPrice x_2	PriceDif x_4	AdvExp x_3	Demand y	AdCamp	DA	DB	DC
3.85	3.80	−0.05	5.50	7.38	B	0	1	0
3.75	4.00	0.25	6.75	8.51	B	0	1	0
3.70	4.30	0.60	7.25	9.52	B	0	1	0
3.70	3.70	0.00	5.50	7.50	A	1	0	0
3.60	3.85	0.25	7.00	9.33	C	0	0	1
3.60	3.80	0.20	6.50	8.28	A	1	0	0
3.60	3.75	0.15	6.75	8.75	C	0	0	1
3.80	3.85	0.05	5.25	7.87	C	0	0	1
3.80	3.65	−0.15	5.25	7.10	B	0	1	0
3.85	4.00	0.15	6.00	8.00	C	0	0	1
3.90	4.10	0.20	6.50	7.89	A	1	0	0
3.90	4.00	0.10	6.25	8.15	C	0	0	1
3.70	4.10	0.40	7.00	9.10	C	0	0	1
3.75	4.20	0.45	6.90	8.86	A	1	0	0
3.75	4.10	0.35	6.80	8.90	B	0	1	0
3.80	4.10	0.30	6.80	8.87	B	0	1	0
3.70	4.20	0.50	7.10	9.26	B	0	1	0
3.80	4.30	0.50	7.00	9.00	A	1	0	0
3.70	4.10	0.40	6.80	8.75	B	0	1	0
3.80	3.75	−0.05	6.50	7.95	B	0	1	0
3.80	3.75	−0.05	6.25	7.65	C	0	0	1
3.75	3.65	−0.10	6.00	7.27	A	1	0	0
3.70	3.90	0.20	6.50	8.00	A	1	0	0
3.55	3.65	0.10	7.00	8.50	A	1	0	0
3.60	4.10	0.50	6.80	8.75	A	1	0	0
3.65	4.25	0.60	6.80	9.21	B	0	1	0
3.70	3.65	−0.05	6.50	8.27	C	0	0	1
3.75	3.75	0.00	5.75	7.67	B	0	1	0
3.80	3.85	0.05	5.80	7.93	C	0	0	1
3.70	4.25	0.55	6.80	9.26	C	0	0	1

Let $\mu_{[d,a,A]}$, $\mu_{[d,a,B]}$, and $\mu_{[d,a,C]}$ denote the mean demands for Fresh when the price difference is d; the advertising expenditure is a; and we use advertising campaigns A, B, and C, respectively. The model of this part implies that

$$\mu_{[d,a,A]} = \beta_0 + \beta_1 d + \beta_2 a + \beta_3 a^2 + \beta_4 da$$
$$+ \beta_5(0) + \beta_6(0) + \beta_7 a(0) + \beta_8 a(0)$$

$$\mu_{[d,a,B]} = \beta_0 + \beta_1 d + \beta_2 a + \beta_3 a^2 + \beta_4 da$$
$$+ \beta_5(1) + \beta_6(0) + \beta_7 a(1) + \beta_8 a(0)$$

$$\mu_{[d,a,C]} = \beta_0 + \beta_1 d + \beta_2 a + \beta_3 a^2 + \beta_4 da$$
$$+ \beta_5(0) + \beta_6(1) + \beta_7 a(0) + \beta_8 a(1)$$

Using these equations, verify that $\mu_{[d,a,C]} - \mu_{[d,a,A]}$ equals $\beta_6 + \beta_8 a$. Then, using the least squares point estimates, show that a point estimate of $\mu_{[d,a,C]} - \mu_{[d,a,A]}$ equals .3266 when $a = 6.2$ and .4080 when $a = 6.6$. Also verify that $\mu_{[d,a,C]} - \mu_{[d,a,B]}$ equals $\beta_6 - \beta_5 + \beta_8 a - \beta_7 a$. Using the least squares point estimates, show that a point estimate of $\mu_{[d,a,C]} - \mu_{[d,a,B]}$ equals .14266 when $a = 6.2$ and .18118 when $a = 6.6$. Discuss why these results imply that the larger advertising expenditure a is, the larger

is the improvement in mean sales obtained by using advertising campaign C rather than advertising campaign A or B.

d. The prediction results given at the bottom of the MegaStat outputs in Figure 12.44(a) and (c) correspond to a future period when the price difference will be $x_4 = .20$, the advertising expenditure will be $x_3 = 6.50$, and campaign C will be used. Which model—the first model or the third model of this exercise—gives the shortest 95 percent prediction interval for Fresh demand? Using all of the results in this exercise, discuss why there might be a small amount of interaction between advertising expenditure and advertising campaign.

12.58 INTERNET EXERCISE

Statistics Canada (statcan.gc.ca) is conducting an ongoing study of Canadian Internet use, with the most recently available results being presented in the *Canadian Internet Use Survey* (CIUS). In the 2010 study description (released in 2011), read the section dealing with data accuracy and explain how multiple regression techniques could be used to help detect possible outliers.

FIGURE 12.44   MegaStat Output for Exercise 12.57

(a) Partial MegaStat output for Exercise 12.57

Regression output

variables	coefficients	std. error	t (df = 23)	p-value	confidence interval 95% lower	95% upper
Intercept	25.6127	4.7938	5.343	2.00E-05	15.6960	35.5294
X4	9.0587	3.0317	2.988	0.0066	2.7871	15.3302
X3	−6.5377	1.5814	−4.134	0.0004	−9.8090	−3.2664
X3SQ	0.5844	0.1299	4.500	0.0002	0.3158	0.8531
X43	−1.1565	0.4557	−2.538	0.0184	−2.0992	−0.2137
DB	0.2137	0.0622	3.438	0.0022	0.0851	0.3423
DC	0.3818	0.0613	6.233	2.33E-06	0.2551	0.5085

Predicted values for: Y

	95% Confidence Interval		95% Prediction Interval			
Predicted	lower	upper	lower	upper	Leverage	
8.50068	8.40370	8.59765	8.21322	8.78813	0.128	

R^2 0.971
Adjusted R^2 0.963
R 0.985
Std. Error 0.131

(b) MegaStat output of least squares point estimates for Exercise 12.57(b)

Regression output

variables	coefficients	std. error	t (df = 23)	p-value	confidence interval 95% lower	95% upper
Intercept	25.8264	4.7946	5.387	1.80E-05	15.9081	35.7447
X4	9.0587	3.0317	2.988	0.0066	2.7871	15.3302
X3	−6.5377	1.5814	−4.134	0.0004	−9.8090	−3.2664
X3SQ	0.5844	0.1299	4.500	0.0002	0.3158	0.8531
X43	−1.1565	0.4557	−2.538	0.0184	−2.0992	−0.2137
DA	−0.2137	0.0622	−3.438	0.0022	−0.3423	−0.0851
DC	0.1681	0.0637	2.638	0.0147	0.0363	0.2999

(c) MegaStat output of least squares point estimates for Exercise 12.57(c)

Regression output

variables	coefficients	std. error	t (df = 21)	p-value	confidence interval 95% lower	95% upper	
Intercept	28.6873	5.1285	5.594	1.50E-05	18.0221	39.3526	R^2 0.974
X4	10.8253	3.2988	3.282	0.0036	3.9651	17.6855	Adjusted R^2 0.964
X3	−7.4115	1.6617	−4.460	0.0002	−10.8671	−3.9558	R 0.987
X3SQ	0.6458	0.1346	4.798	0.0001	0.3659	0.9257	Std. Error 0.129
X43	−1.4156	0.4929	−2.872	0.0091	−2.4406	−0.3907	
DB	−0.4807	0.7309	−0.658	0.5179	−2.0007	1.0393	n 30
DC	−0.9351	0.8357	−1.119	0.2758	−2.6731	0.8029	k 8
X3DB	0.1072	0.1117	0.960	0.3480	−0.1251	0.3395	Dep. Var. Y
X3DC	0.2035	0.1288	1.580	0.1291	−0.0644	0.4714	

Predicted values for: Y

	95% Confidence Interval		95% Prediction Interval			
Predicted	lower	upper	lower	upper	Leverage	
8.51183	8.41229	8.61136	8.22486	8.79879	0.137	

CHAPTER **13**
Nonparametric Methods

LO1 Parametric statistics, such as the t test, correlation, multiple regression, and analysis of variance, require that the data being analyzed be of the interval or ratio level of measurement. All of these procedures also assume that the sampled populations are normally distributed (or mound-shaped and not highly skewed to the right [positively] or left [negatively]). When the level of measurement is qualitative (nominal or ordinal) and/or when the assumptions of the population's distribution are not satisfied, then nonparametric methods can be used. Specifically, we consider four nonparametric tests that can be used in place of the t and F tests. These four nonparametric tests are: the sign test; the Wilcoxon rank sum test; the Wilcoxon signed ranks test; and the Kruskal–Wallis H test. These tests require no assumptions about the shapes of the sampled populations. In addition, these nonparametric tests are usually better than the t and F tests at correctly finding statistically significant differences in the presence of outliers and extreme skewness. We also consider a fifth nonparametric

test, Spearman's rank order correlation coefficient, which can be used in place of Pearson's product moment correlation.

Each **nonparametric test** discussed in this chapter theoretically assumes that each sampled population under consideration is described by a continuous probability distribution. However, in most situations, each nonparametric technique is slightly statistically conservative if the sampled population is described by a discrete probability distribution. This means, for example, that a nonparametric hypothesis test has a slightly smaller chance of falsely rejecting the null hypothesis than the specified α-value seems to indicate if the sampled population is described by a discrete probability distribution. Furthermore, because each nonparametric technique is based essentially on ranking the observed sample values, and not on the exact sizes of the sample values, it can be used to analyze any type of data that can be ranked. This includes ordinal data and quantitative data.

ROADBLOCK
Parametrics versus nonparametrics and normality
t and F tests are more powerful (better at correctly finding statistically significant differences) than nonparametric tests when the sampled populations are normally distributed.

13.1 THE SIGN TEST: A HYPOTHESIS TEST ABOUT THE MEDIAN

LO2

If a population is highly skewed to the right or left (positively or negatively skewed), then the population median might be a better measure of central tendency than the population mean. Furthermore, if the sample size is small and the population is highly skewed or clearly not mound-shaped, then the *t* test for the population might not be valid. For these reasons, when we have taken a small sample and if it is possible that the sampled population might be far from being normally distributed, it is sometimes useful to use a hypothesis test about the population median. This test, called the **sign test**, is valid for any sample size and population shape. To illustrate the sign test, consider Example 13.1.

Example 13.1 Digital Music Player Lifetime

A leading digital music player is advertised to have a median lifetime (or time to failure) of 6,000 hours of continuous play. The developer of a new digital music player wants to show that the median lifetime of the new player exceeds 6,000 hours of continuous play, so the developer randomly selects 20 new players and tests them in continuous play until each fails. Figure 13.1(a) presents the 20 lifetimes obtained (expressed in hours and arranged in increasing order), and Figure 13.1(b) shows a stem-and-leaf display of these lifetimes. The stem-and-leaf display and the three low lifetimes of 5, 947, and 2,142 suggest that the population of all lifetimes might be highly skewed to the left (i.e., negatively skewed). In addition, the sample size is small. Therefore, it might be reasonable to use the sign test.

To show that the population median lifetime, M_d, of the new digital music player exceeds 6,000 (hours), recall that this median divides the population of ordered lifetimes into two equal parts. It follows that if more than half of the individual population lifetimes exceed 6,000, the population median, M_d, exceeds 6,000. Let p denote the proportion of the individual population lifetimes that exceed 6,000. Then we can reject $H_0: M_d = 6,000$ in favour of $H_a: M_d > 6,000$ if we can reject $H_0: p = .5$ in favour of $H_a: p > .5$. Let x denote the total number of lifetimes that exceed 6,000 in a random sample of 20 lifetimes. If $H_0: p = .5$ is true, then x is a binomial random variable where $n = 20$ and $p = .5$. This says that if $H_0: p = .5$ is true, then we would expect $\mu_x = np = 20(.5) = 10$ of the 20 lifetimes to exceed 6,000. Considering the 20 lifetimes

---

FIGURE 13.1 The Digital Music Player Lifetime Data and Associated Statistical Analyses

(a) The digital music player lifetime data

5	947	2,142	4,867	5,840	6,085	6,238	6,411	6,507	6,687
6,827	6,985	7,082	7,176	7,285	7,410	7,563	7,668	7,724	7,846

(c) MegaStat output of the sign test of $H_0: M_d = 6,000$ versus $H_a: M_d > 6,000$

Sign Test

6,000	hypothesized value	5 below	binomial
6,757	median Lifetime	0 equal	0.0207 p-value (one-tailed, upper)
20	n	15 above	

(b) A stem-and-leaf display

```
0   005
0   947
1
1
2   142
2
3
3
4
4   867
5
5   840
6   085 238 411
6   507 687 827 985
7   082 176 285 410
7   563 668 724 846
```

Binomial Probabilities
(*n* equal to 20)

$n = 20$	p
	0.50
0.0000	20
0.0000	19
0.0002	18
0.0011	17
0.0046	16
0.0148	15
0.0370	14
0.0739	13
0.1201	12
0.1602	11
0.1762	10
0.1602	9
0.1201	8
0.0739	7
0.0370	6
0.0148	5
0.0046	4
0.0011	3
0.0002	2
0.50	$x\!\uparrow$

Source: Computed by D. K. Hildebrand. Found in D. K. Hildebrand and L. Ott, *Statistical Thinking for Managers*, 3rd ed. (Boston, MA: PWS-KENT Publishing Company, 1991).

we have actually observed, we note that 15 of these 20 lifetimes exceed 6,000. The *p* value for testing H_0: $p = .5$ versus H_a: $p > .5$ is the probability, computed assuming that H_0: $p = .5$ is true, of observing a sample result that is as large as or larger than the sample result we have actually observed. The *p*-value is calculated as follows:

$$p\text{-Value} = P(x \geq 15) = \sum_{x=15}^{20} \frac{20}{x!(20-x)!}(.5)^x(.5)^{20-x}$$

Using the binomial distribution table in Table A.1 in Appendix A at the back of the book (a section of it has been reproduced in the margin), we find that

$$p\text{-Value} = P(x \geq 15)$$
$$= P(x = 15) + P(x = 16) + P(x = 17) + P(x = 18) + P(x = 19) + P(x = 20)$$
$$= .0148 + .0046 + .0011 + .0002 + .0000 + .0000$$
$$= .0207$$

This says that if H_0: $p = .5$ is true, then the probability that at least 15 out of 20 lifetimes would exceed 6,000 is only .0207. Therefore, we have strong evidence against H_0: $p = .5$ and in favour of H_a: $p > .5$. That is, we have strong evidence that H_0: $M_d = 6,000$ is false and H_a: $M_d > 6,000$ is true. This implies that it is reasonable to conclude that the median lifetime of the new digital music player exceeds the advertised median lifetime of the market's leading digital music player. Figure 13.1(c) presents the MegaStat output of the sign test of H_0: $M_d = 6,000$ versus H_a: $M_d > 6,000$. In addition, the output tells us that a point estimate of the population median lifetime is the sample median of 6,757 hours.

We summarize how to carry out the sign test in the following boxed feature.

The Sign Test for a Population Median

Suppose we randomly select a sample of size *n* from a population, and suppose we want to test the null hypothesis H_0: $M_d = M_0$ versus one of H_a: $M_d < M_0$, H_a: $M_d > M_0$, and H_a: $M_d \neq M_0$, where M_d denotes the population median. Define the test statistic *S* as follows:

1 If the alternative is H_a: $M_d < M_0$, then $S =$ Number of sample measurements less than M_0

2 If the alternative is H_a: $M_d > M_0$, then $S =$ Number of sample measurements greater than M_0

3 If the alternative is H_a: $M_d \neq M_0$, then $S =$ Larger of S_1 and S_2, where S_1 is the number of sample measurements less than M_0 and S_2 is the number of sample measurements greater than M_0

Furthermore, define *x* to be a binomial variable with parameters *n* and $p = .5$. Then we can test H_0: $M_d = M_0$ versus a particular alternative hypothesis at level of significance α by using the appropriate *p*-value.

Alternative Hypothesis	**p-Value (Reject H_0 If p-Value $< \alpha$)**
H_a: $M_d < M_0$	The probability that *x* is greater than or equal to *S*
H_a: $M_d > M_0$	The probability that *x* is greater than or equal to *S*
H_a: $M_d \neq M_0$	Twice the probability that *x* is greater than or equal to *S*

Here we can use Table A.1 to find the *p*-value.

Note that when we take a large sample, we can use the normal approximation to the binomial distribution to implement the sign test. Here, when the null hypothesis H_0: $M_d = M_0$ (or H_0: $p = .5$) is true, the binomial variable *x* is approximately normally distributed with mean $np = n(.5) = .5n$ and standard deviation $\sqrt{np(1-p)} = \sqrt{n(.5)(1-.5)} = .5\sqrt{n}$. The test is based on the test statistic

$$z = \frac{S - .5 - .5n}{.5\sqrt{n}}$$

where S is as defined in the previous box and where we subtract .5 from S as a correction for continuity. This motivates the test shown in the following boxed feature.

The Large-Sample Sign Test for a Population Median

Suppose we have taken a large sample (for this test, $n \geq 10$). Define S as in the previous boxed feature and define the test statistic

$$z = \frac{S - .5 - .5n}{.5\sqrt{n}}$$

We can test $H_0: M_d = M_0$ versus a particular alternative hypothesis at level of significance α by using the appropriate rejection point rule or, equivalently, the corresponding p-value.

Alternative Hypothesis	Rejection Point Rule: Reject H_0 If	p-Value (Reject H_0 If p-Value < α)
$H_a: M_d > M_0$	$z > z_\alpha$	The area under the standard normal curve to the right of z
$H_a: M_d < M_0$	$z > z_\alpha$	The area under the standard normal curve to the right of z
$H_a: M_d \neq M_0$	$z > z_{\alpha/2}$	Twice the area under the standard normal curve to the right of z

---

Example 13.2 Large-Sample Sign Test for Digital Music Player Lifetime

Consider Example 13.1. Because the sample size $n = 20$ is greater than 10, we can use the large-sample sign test to test $H_0: M_d = 6,000$ versus $H_a: M_d > 6,000$. Because $S = 15$ is the number of digital music player lifetimes that exceed $M_0 = 6,000$, the test statistic z is

$$z = \frac{S - .5 - .5n}{.5\sqrt{n}} = \frac{15 - .5 - .5(20)}{.5\sqrt{20}} = 2.01$$

The p-value for the test is the area under the standard normal curve to the right of $z = 2.01$, which is $.5 - .4778 = .0222$. Because this p-value is less than .05, we have strong evidence that $H_a: M_d > 6,000$ is true. Also note that the large-sample, approximate p-value of .0222 given by the normal distribution is fairly close to the exact p-value of .0207 given by the binomial distribution [see Figure 13.1(c)].

To conclude this section, consider the DVD recorder rating example discussed in Chapter 2. In this example, the manufacturer of a DVD recorder randomly selected a sample of 20 purchasers who had owned the recorder for one year. Each purchaser in the sample was asked to rank his or her satisfaction with the recorder along the following 10-point scale:

1	2	3	4	5	6	7	8	9	10
Not satisfied				Fairly satisfied				Extremely satisfied	

The stem-and-leaf display below gives the 20 ratings obtained:

```
 1  0
 2
 3  0
 4
 5  00
 6
 7  0
 8  000000
 9  00000
10  0000
```

Let M_d denote the median rating that would be given by all purchasers who have owned the DVD recorder for one year. Below is the MegaStat output of the sign test of $H_0: M_d = 7.5$ versus $H_a: M_d > 7.5$.

Sign Test

7.5	hypothesized value
8	median Ratings
5	below
0	equal
15	above
20	n
	binomial
0.0207	p-value (one-tailed, upper)

Because the p-value of .0207 is less than .05, we have strong evidence that the population median rating exceeds 7.5. Furthermore, note that the sign test has reached this conclusion by showing that *more than 50 percent* of all DVD recorder ratings exceed 7.5. It follows, since a rating exceeding 7.5 is the same as a rating being at least 8 (because of the discrete nature of the ratings), that we have strong evidence that the population median rating is at least 8.

Exercises for Section **13.1**

CONCEPTS

13.1 What is a nonparametric test? Why would such a test be particularly useful when we must take a small sample?

13.2 When we perform the sign test, we use the sample data to compute a p-value. What probability distribution is used to compute the p-value? Explain.

METHODS AND APPLICATIONS

13.3 Consider the following sample of five chemical yields:

801   814   784   836   820

a. Use this sample to test $H_0: M_d = 800$ versus $H_a: M_d \neq 800$ by setting $\alpha = .01$.
b. Use this sample to test $H_0: M_d = 750$ versus $H_a: M_d > 750$ by setting $\alpha = .05$.

13.4 Consider the following sample of seven bad-debt ratios:

7%   4%   6%   7%   5%   4%   9%

Use this sample and the MegaStat output in Figure 13.2 to test the null hypothesis that the median bad-debt ratio equals 3.5 percent versus the alternative hypothesis that the median bad-debt ratio exceeds 3.5 percent by setting α equal to .05.

13.5 A local newspaper randomly selects 20 patrons of the Springwood Restaurant on a given Saturday night and has each patron rate the quality of her or his meal as 5 (excellent), 4 (good), 3 (average), 2 (poor), or 1 (unsatisfactory). When the results are summarized, it is found that there are sixteen ratings of 5, three ratings of 4, and one rating of 3. Let M_d denote the population median rating that would be given by all possible patrons of the restaurant on that Saturday night.
a. Test $H_0: M_d = 4.5$ versus $H_a: M_d > 4.5$ by setting $\alpha = .05$.
b. Does the conclusion that you reached in part (a) imply that you have very strong evidence that the median rating that would be given by all possible patrons is 5?

13.6 Suppose that a particular type of plant has a median growing height of 20 cm in a specified time period when the best plant food currently on the market is used as directed. The developer of a new plant food wants to show that it increases the median growing height. If a stem-and-leaf display indicates that the population of all growing heights using the new plant food is markedly nonnormal, it would be appropriate to use the

FIGURE 13.2   MegaStat Output for Exercise 13.4

Sign Test

3.5	hypothesized value
6	median
0	below
0	equal
7	above
7	n
	binomial
0.0078	p-value (one-tailed, upper)

TABLE **13.1**   Results of a Taste Test of Coke versus Pepsi

Customer	Preference (Coke or Pepsi)	Value (Sign)
1	Coke	+1
2	Pepsi	−1
3	Pepsi	−1
4	Coke	+1
5	Coke	+1
6	Pepsi	−1
7	Coke	+1
8	Coke	+1
9	Pepsi	−1

Sign Test			
	0 hypothesized value	4 below	binomial
9 n	1 median Value (sign)	0 equal	1.0000 p-value (two-tailed)
		5 above	

sign test to test $H_0: M_d = 20$ versus $H_a: M_d > 20$. Here M_d denotes the population median growing height when the new plant food is used. Suppose that 13 out of 15 sample plants grown using the new plant food reach a height of more than 20 cm. Test $H_0: M_d = 20$ versus $H_a: M_d > 20$ by using the large-sample sign test.

13.7   A common application of the sign test deals with analyzing consumer preferences. For instance, suppose that a blind taste test is administered to nine randomly selected convenience store customers. Each participant is asked to express a preference for either Coke or Pepsi after tasting unidentified samples of each soft drink. The sample results are expressed by recording +1 for each consumer who prefers Coke and −1 for each consumer who prefers Pepsi. Note that sometimes, rather than recording either +1 or −1, we simply record the sign + or −, hence the name "sign test." If a consumer is unable to rank the two brands, 0 is recorded, and these observations are eliminated from the analysis.

The null hypothesis in this application says that there is no difference in preferences for Coke and Pepsi. If this null hypothesis is true, then the number of +1 values in the population of all preferences should equal the number of −1 values, which implies that the median preference is $M_d = 0$ (and that the proportion p of +1 values equals .5). The alternative hypothesis says that there is a significant difference in preferences (or that there is a significant difference in the number of +1 values and −1 values in the population of all preferences). This implies that the median preference does not equal 0 (and that the proportion p of +1 values does not equal .5).

a. Table 13.1 gives the results of the taste test administered to the nine randomly selected consumers. If we consider testing $H_0: M_d = 0$ versus $H_a: M_d \neq 0$, where M_d is the median of the (+1 and −1) preference rankings, determine the values of S_1, S_2, and S for the sign test needed to test H_0 versus H_a. Identify the value of S in the MegaStat output.

b. Use the value of S to find the p-value for testing $H_0: M_d = 0$ versus $H_a: M_d \neq 0$. Then use the p-value to test H_0 versus H_a by setting α equal to .10, .05, .01, and .001. How much evidence is there of a difference in the preferences for Coke and Pepsi? What do you conclude?

13.2 THE WILCOXON RANK SUM TEST

LO3

We can use t tests to compare two population means in an independent-samples experiment. If the sampled populations are far from normally distributed and the sample sizes are small, the t test is not valid and a nonparametric method should be used to compare the populations.

We have seen that the mean of a population measures the central tendency, or location, of the probability distribution describing the population, and if a t test provides strong evidence that μ_1 is greater than μ_2, we might conclude that the probability distribution of population 1 is *shifted to the right* of the probability distribution of population 2. The nonparametric test for comparing the locations of two populations is not (necessarily) a test about the difference between population means. Rather, it is a more general test to detect whether the probability distribution of population 1 is shifted to the right (or left) of the probability distribution of population 2.[1] Furthermore, *the nonparametric test is valid for any shapes that might describe the sampled populations.*

---

[1]To be precise, we say that the probability distribution of population 1 is shifted to the right (or left) of the probability distribution of population 2 if there is more than a 50 percent chance that a randomly selected observation from population 1 will be greater than (or less than) a randomly selected observation from population 2.

In this section, we present the **Wilcoxon rank sum test** (also called the **Mann–Whitney test**), which is used to compare the locations of two populations when *independent samples* are selected. To perform this test, we first combine all of the observations in both samples into a single set, and we rank these observations from smallest to largest, with the smallest observation receiving rank 1, the next smallest observation receiving rank 2, and so forth. The sum of the ranks of the observations in each sample is then calculated. If the probability distributions of the two populations are identical, we would expect the sum of the ranks for sample 1 to roughly equal the sum of the ranks for sample 2. However, if, for example, the sum of the ranks for sample 1 is substantially larger than the sum of the ranks for sample 2, this would suggest that the probability distribution of population 1 is shifted to the right of the probability distribution of population 2. We explain how to carry out the Wilcoxon rank sum test in the following boxed feature.

The Wilcoxon Rank Sum Test

Let D_1 and D_2 denote the probability distributions of populations 1 and 2, and assume that we randomly select independent samples of sizes n_1 and n_2 from populations 1 and 2. Rank the $n_1 + n_2$ observations in the two samples from the smallest (rank 1) to the largest (rank $n_1 + n_2$). Here, if two or more observations are equal, we assign to each tied observation a rank equal to the average of the consecutive ranks that would otherwise be assigned to the tied observations. Let T_1 denote the sum of the ranks of the observations in sample 1, and let T_2 denote the sum of the ranks of the observations in sample 2. Furthermore, define the test statistic T to be T_1 if $n_1 \leq n_2$ and T_2 if $n_1 > n_2$. Then, we can test

H_0: D_1 and D_2 are identical probability
       distributions

versus

A particular alternative hypothesis at level of significance α by using the appropriate rejection point rule

Alternative Hypothesis	Rejection Point Rule: Reject H_0 If
H_a: D_1 is shifted to the right of D_2	$T \geq T_U$ if $n_1 \leq n_2$ $T \leq T_L$ if $n_1 > n_2$
H_a: D_1 is shifted to the left of D_2	$T \leq T_L$ if $n_1 \leq n_2$ $T \geq T_U$ if $n_1 > n_2$
H_a: D_1 is shifted to the right or left of D_2	$T \leq T_L$ or $T \geq T_U$

The first two alternative hypotheses above are one-sided, while the third alternative hypothesis is two-sided. Values of the rejection points T_U and T_L are given in Table A.15 for values of n_1 and n_2 from 3 to 10.

Table 13.2 repeats a portion of Table A.15. This table gives the rejection point (T_U or T_L) for testing a one-sided alternative hypothesis at level of significance $\alpha = .05$ and the rejection points (T_U and T_L) for testing a two-sided alternative hypothesis at level of significance $\alpha = .10$. The rejection points are tabulated according to n_1 and n_2, the sizes of the samples taken from populations 1 and 2, respectively. For instance, as shown in Table 13.2, if we have taken a sample of size $n_1 = 10$ from population 1 and a sample of size $n_2 = 7$ from population 2, then for a one-sided test with $\alpha = .05$, we use $T_U = 80$ or $T_L = 46$. Similarly, if $n_1 = 10$ and $n_2 = 7$, we use $T_U = 80$ and $T_L = 46$ for a two-sided test with $\alpha = .10$.

TABLE 13.2 A Portion of the Wilcoxon Rank Sum Table Rejection Points for $\alpha = .05$ (One-Sided); $\alpha = .10$ (Two-Sided)

n_1	3		4		5		6		7		8		9		10	
n_2	T_L	T_U	T_L	T_U	T_L	T_U	T_L	T_U	T_L	T_U	T_L	T_U	T_L	T_U	T_L	T_U
3	6	15	7	17	7	20	8	22	9	24	9	27	10	29	11	31
4	7	17	12	24	13	27	14	30	15	33	16	36	17	39	18	42
5	7	20	13	27	19	36	20	40	22	43	24	46	25	50	26	54
6	8	22	14	30	20	40	28	50	30	54	32	58	33	63	35	67
7	9	24	15	33	22	43	30	54	39	66	41	71	43	76	46	80
8	9	27	16	36	24	46	32	58	41	71	52	84	54	90	57	95
9	10	29	17	39	25	50	33	63	43	76	54	90	66	105	69	111
10	11	31	18	42	26	54	35	67	46	80	57	95	69	111	83	127

$\alpha = .05$ one-sided; $\alpha = .10$ two-sided

Example 13.3   Train Speeds

The Railway Association of Canada (see railcan.ca) reports that passenger trains travel at an average speed of 160 km/h and freight trains at 105 km/h. One complaint that many city commuters have about the train system is that the flow of traffic is interrupted by trains passing through the city on level crossings. Wait times were assessed in a city for those waiting at passenger rail crossovers (ten measures taken) versus freight crossovers (seven measures taken). The resulting wait times (in seconds) are given in Figure 13.3. The box plots indicate that the population of all possible wait times for the two populations of train types (passenger and freight) might be skewed to the right. A Wilcoxon rank sum test will be conducted on the data.

Because passenger trains travel 55 km/h faster than freight trains in Canada, it was predicted that wait times would be shorter for passenger train crossings than for freight train crossings. Therefore, the null hypothesis is

H_0: Crossing wait times will be the same for passenger and freight trains

versus the alternative hypothesis of

H_a: Wait times will be shorter for passenger trains than for freight trains

To perform the test, rank the $n_1 + n_2 = 10 + 7 = 17$ wait times in the two samples as shown in Figure 13.3(a). Note that two wait times of 145 seconds are tied as the sixth and seventh wait times, so these values are each assigned the average rank of 6.5. The sum of the ranks in wait times is $T_1 = 72.5$ for the passenger trains and $T_2 = 80.5$ for the freight trains. Because $n_1 = 10$ is greater than $n_2 = 7$, the summary box states that the test statistic is $T_2 = 80.5$ and that H_0 can be rejected in favour of H_a at the .05 significance level if T is greater than or equal to T_U. Because $T_2 = 80.5$ is greater than $T_U = 80$ (see Table 13.2), we can conclude at the .05 level of significance that the passenger wait times are shifted to the left and are therefore "systematically less than" the wait times for freight trains. This might result because passenger trains travel faster than freight trains. Of course it might also result from freight trains being longer than passenger trains, but that is a topic for another study!

FIGURE 13.3   Analysis of Passenger and Freight Train Level Crossing Times

(a) Wait times (in seconds)

Passenger Time	Rank	Freight Time	Rank
48	1	109	4
97	2	145	6.5
103	3	196	10
117	5	273	13
145	6.5	289	14
151	8	417	16
179	9	505	17
220	11		$T_2 = 80.5$
257	12		
294	15		
	$T_1 = 72.5$		

Box Plots of Passenger and Freight Times

(b) MegaStat output of the Wilcoxon rank sum test for the wait times

Wilcoxon – Mann/Whitney Test

n	sum of ranks	
10	72.5	Passenger
7	80.5	Freight
17	153	total
	0.0485	p-value (one-tailed, lower)

Figure 13.3(b) presents the MegaStat output of the Wilcoxon rank sum test for the wait times. In general, MegaStat gives T_1, the sum of the ranks of the observations in sample 1, and T_2, the sum of the ranks for sample 2. In this example, n_1 is greater than n_2 so the correct test statistic is T_2.

In addition, MegaStat gives the p-value related to the hypothesis test, which is .0485.

As another example, suppose that on a given Saturday night a local newspaper randomly selects 20 patrons from each of two restaurants and has each patron rate the quality of his or her meal as 5 (excellent), 4 (good), 3 (average), 2 (poor), or 1 (unsatisfactory). The following results are obtained:

Rating	Restaurant 1 Patrons	Restaurant 2 Patrons	Total Patrons	Ranks Involved	Average Rank	Restaurant 1 Rank Sum	Restaurant 2 Rank Sum
5	15	5	20	21–40	30.5	(15)(30.5) = 457.5	(5)(30.5) = 152.5
4	4	11	15	6–20	13	(4)(13) = 52	(11)(13) = 143
3	1	2	3	3, 4, 5	4	(1)(4) = 4	(2)(4) = 8
2	0	1	1	2	2	(0)(2) = 0	(1)(2) = 2
1	0	1	1	1	1	(0)(1) = 0	(1)(1) = 1
						$T_1 = 513.5$	$T_2 = 306.5$

Suppose that we want to test

H_0: Probability distributions of all possible Saturday night meal ratings
    for restaurants 1 and 2 are identical

versus

H_a: Probability distribution of all possible Saturday night meal ratings for
    restaurant 1 is shifted to the right or left of the probability distribution of all
    possible Saturday night meal ratings for restaurant 2

Because there are only five numerical ordinal ratings, there are many ties. The above table shows how we determine the sum of the ranks for each sample. Because $n_1 = 20$ and $n_2 = 20$, we cannot obtain rejection points by using Table A.15 (which gives rejection points for sample sizes up to $n_1 = 10$ and $n_2 = 10$). However, we can use a large-sample, normal approximation, which is valid if both n_1 and n_2 are at least 10. The normal approximation involves making two modifications. First, we replace the test statistic T in the previously given summary box by a standardized value of the test statistic. This standardized value, denoted z, is calculated by subtracting the mean $\mu_T = n_i(n_1 + n_2 + 1)/2$ from the test statistic T and then dividing the resulting difference by the standard deviation $\sigma_T = \sqrt{n_1 n_2(n_1 + n_2 + 1)/12}$. Here n_i in the expression for μ_T equals n_1 if the test statistic T is T_1 and n_2 if T is T_2. Second, when testing a one-sided alternative hypothesis, we replace the rejection points T_U and T_L by the normal points z_α and $-z_\alpha$. When testing a two-sided alternative hypothesis, we replace T_U and T_L by $z_{\alpha/2}$ and $-z_{\alpha/2}$. For the current example, $n_1 = n_2$, so the test statistic T is $T_1 = 513.5$. Furthermore,

$$\mu_T = \frac{n_1(n_1 + n_2 + 1)}{2} = \frac{20(20 + 20 + 1)}{2} = 410$$

$$\sigma_T = \sqrt{\frac{n_1 n_2(n_1 + n_2 + 1)}{12}} = \sqrt{\frac{20(20)(41)}{12}} = 36.968455$$

and

$$z = \frac{T - \mu_T}{\sigma_T} = \frac{513.5 - 410}{36.968455} = 2.7997$$

Because we are testing a "shifted right or left" (that is, a two-sided) alternative hypothesis, we reject the null hypothesis if $T \leq T_L$ or $T \geq T_U$. Stated in terms of standardized values, we reject the null hypothesis if $z < -z_{\alpha/2}$ or $z > z_{\alpha/2}$ (here we use strict inequalities to be consistent with other normal distribution rejection point conditions). If we set $\alpha = .01$, we use the rejection points $-z_{.005} = -2.575$ and $z_{.005} = 2.575$. Because $z = 2.7997$ is greater than $z_{.005} = 2.575$, we reject the null hypothesis at the .01 level of significance. Therefore, we have very strong evidence that there is a systematic difference between the Saturday night meal ratings at restaurants 1 and 2. Looking at the original data, we would estimate that Saturday night meal ratings are higher at restaurant 1.

We will conclude this section with a final comment. When there are ties, an adjusted formula for σ_T takes the ties into account. If (as in the restaurant example) we ignore the formula, the results that we obtain are statistically conservative. Therefore, if we rejected the null hypothesis by using the unadjusted formula, we would reject the null hypothesis by using the adjusted formula.

Exercises for Section **13.2**

CONCEPTS

13.8 Explain the circumstances under which the Wilcoxon rank sum test should be used.

13.9 Identify the parametric test corresponding to the Wilcoxon rank sum test. What assumption is needed for the validity of this parametric test (and not needed for the Wilcoxon rank sum test)?

METHODS AND APPLICATIONS

13.10 A loan officer at a bank wants to compare the mortgage rates charged at banks with the mortgage rates of brokers. Two independent random samples of bank mortgage rates and broker mortgage rates are obtained, with the results as shown in Figure 13.4(a).

Because both samples are small, the bank officer is uncertain about the shape of the distributions of bank and broker mortgage rates. Therefore, the Wilcoxon rank sum test will be used to compare the two types of mortgage rates.

   a. Let D_1 be the distribution of bank mortgage rates and D_2 be the distribution of broker mortgage rates. Carry out the Wilcoxon rank sum test to determine whether D_1 and D_2 are identical versus the alternative that D_1 is shifted to the right or left of D_2. Use $\alpha = .05$.

   b. Carry out the Wilcoxon rank sum test to determine whether D_1 is shifted to the right of D_2. Use $\alpha = .025$. What do you conclude?

13.11 A company collected employee absenteeism data (in hours per year) at two of its manufacturing plants. The data were obtained by randomly selecting one sample from all of the employees at the first plant and another, independent, sample from all of the employees at the second plant. For each randomly selected employee, absenteeism records were used to determine the exact number of hours the employee had been absent during

the past year. The results in Figure 13.4(b) were obtained.

Use a Wilcoxon rank sum test and the MegaStat output in Figure 13.4(c) to determine whether absenteeism is different at the two plants. Use $\alpha = .05$.

13.12 Kevin travels frequently to Winnipeg, Manitoba, from London, Ontario. He uses either ExecuAir or EconoAir. He realizes that flight delays are inevitable but would prefer to give his business to the airline with the best on-time arrival record. The number of minutes that his flight arrived late for the last seven trips is given below. Negative numbers mean that the flight was early.

> ExecuAir: 2, −1, 4, −5, 3, 7, −2
> EconoAir: −3, 6, 8, 9, 10 −7, 5

Is there evidence to suggest that ExecuAir is superior to EconoAir in terms of its on-time arrival record? Use the Wilcoxon rank sum test and test at $\alpha = .05$.

13.13 Moore (2000) reports on a study by Boo (1997), who asked the following question of 303 randomly selected people at fairs:

> How often do you think people become sick because of food they consume prepared at outdoor fairs and festivals?

The possible responses were 5 (always), 4 (often), 3 (more often than not), 2 (once in a while), and 1 (very rarely). The data in Figure 13.4(d) were obtained.

The computer output at the right of the data presents the results of a Wilcoxon rank sum test that attempts to determine if men and women systematically differ in their responses. Here the normal approximation has been used to calculate the p value of .0009. What do you conclude?

FIGURE 13.4   Data and Output for Exercises 13.10, 13.11, and 13.13

(a) Mortgage rates for Exercise 13.10

Bank Rates:	11.25	10.50	11.50	11.00	10.00	9.75	11.50	10.25
Broker Rates:	9.25	10.25	8.75	11.00	9.50	9.00	9.10	8.50

(b) Absenteeism results for Exercise 13.11

Plant 1:	10	131	53	37	59	29	45	26	39	36
Plant 2:	21	46	33	31	49	33	39	19	12	35

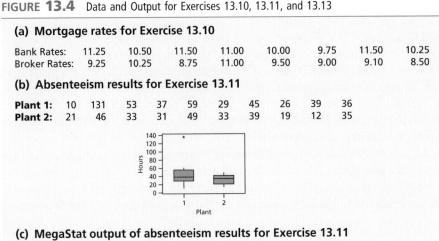

(c) MegaStat output of absenteeism results for Exercise 13.11

Wilcoxon - Mann/Whitney Test

n	sum of ranks	
10	120.5	Plant 1
10	89.5	Plant 2
20	210	total

105.00	expected value
13.22	standard deviation
1.13	z, corrected for ties
0.2565	p-value (two-tailed)

(d) Illness data for Exercise 13.13

Response	Females	Males	Total		Sex	N	Sum of Scores
5	2	1	3		Female	196	31996.5
4	23	5	28		Male	107	14059.5
3	50	22	72				
2	108	57	165		$T = 14059.5$	$z = -3.33353$	
1	13	22	35		**Test significant at 0.0009**		

Source: "Consumers' perceptions and concerns about safety and healthfulness of food served at fairs and festivals," by H. C. Boo, M.S. thesis, Purdue University, 1997.

13.3 THE WILCOXON SIGNED RANKS TEST

We can use a *t* test to compare two population means in a paired-differences situation such as an experiment. If the sample size is small and the population of paired differences is far from normally distributed, the *t* test is not valid and we should use a nonparametric test. In this section, we present the **Wilcoxon signed ranks test**, which is a nonparametric test for comparing two populations when a paired-differences experiment has been carried out.

The Wilcoxon Signed Ranks Test

Let D_1 and D_2 denote the probability distributions of populations 1 and 2, and assume that we have randomly selected n matched pairs of observations from populations 1 and 2. Calculate the paired differences of the n matched pairs by subtracting each paired population 2 observation from the corresponding population 1 observation, and rank the absolute values of the n paired differences from the smallest (rank 1) to the largest (rank n). Here paired differences equal to 0 are eliminated, and the number n of paired differences is reduced accordingly. Furthermore, if two or more absolute paired differences are equal, we assign to each tied absolute paired difference a rank equal to the average of the consecutive ranks that would otherwise be assigned to the tied absolute paired differences. Let

T^- = Sum of the ranks associated with the negative paired differences

and

T^+ = Sum of the ranks associated with the positive paired differences

We can test

H_0: D_1 and D_2 are identical probability distributions

versus

A particular alternative hypothesis at level of significance α by using the appropriate test statistic and the corresponding rejection point rule

Alternative Hypothesis	Test Statistic	Rejection Point Rule: Reject H_0 if
H_a: D_1 is shifted to the right of D_2	T^-	$T^- \leq T_0$
H_a: D_1 is shifted to the left of D_2	T^+	$T^+ \leq T_0$
H_a: D_1 is shifted to the right or left of D_2	T = the smaller of T^- and T^+	$T \leq T_0$

The first two alternative hypotheses above are one-sided, while the third alternative hypothesis is two-sided. Values of the rejection point T_0 are given in Table A.16 for values of n from 5 to 50.

Table 13.3 repeats a portion of Table A.16. This table gives the rejection point T_0 for testing one-sided and two-sided alternative hypotheses at several different values of α. The rejection points are tabulated according to n, the number of paired differences. For instance, Table 13.3 shows that if we are analyzing ten paired differences, the rejection point for testing a one-sided alternative hypothesis at the .01 level of significance is equal to $T_0 = 5$. This table also shows that we would use the rejection point $T_0 = 5$ to test a two-sided alternative hypothesis at level of significance $\alpha = .02$.

TABLE 13.3   A Portion of the Wilcoxon Signed Ranks Table

One-Sided	Two-Sided	$n = 5$	$n = 6$	$n = 7$	$n = 8$	$n = 9$	$n = 10$
$\alpha = 0.05$	$\alpha = 0.10$	1	2	4	6	8	11
$\alpha = 0.025$	$\alpha = 0.05$		1	2	4	6	8
$\alpha = 0.01$	$\alpha = 0.02$			0	2	3	5
$\alpha = 0.005$	$\alpha = 0.01$				0	2	3
		$n = 11$	$n = 12$	$n = 13$	$n = 14$	$n = 15$	$n = 16$
$\alpha = 0.05$	$\alpha = 0.10$	14	17	21	26	30	36
$\alpha = 0.025$	$\alpha = 0.05$	11	14	17	21	25	30
$\alpha = 0.01$	$\alpha = 0.02$	7	10	13	16	20	24
$\alpha = 0.005$	$\alpha = 0.01$	5	7	10	13	16	19

Example 13.4   The Repair Cost Comparison Example

Consider the automobile repair cost data given in Figure 13.5(a). If we think that the population of all possible paired differences of repair cost estimates at garages 1 and 2 might be far from normally distributed, we can perform the Wilcoxon signed ranks test. Here we test

H_0: Probability distributions of the populations of all possible repair cost estimates at garages 1 and 2 are identical

versus

H_a: Probability distribution of repair cost estimates at garage 1 is shifted to the left of the probability distribution of repair cost estimates at garage 2

To perform this test, we find the absolute value of each paired difference and we assign ranks to the absolute differences [see Figure 13.5(a)]. Because of the form of the alternative hypothesis, we use the test statistic

T^+ = Sum of the ranks associated with the positive paired differences

FIGURE 13.5   Analysis of Repair Cost Estimates at Two Garages

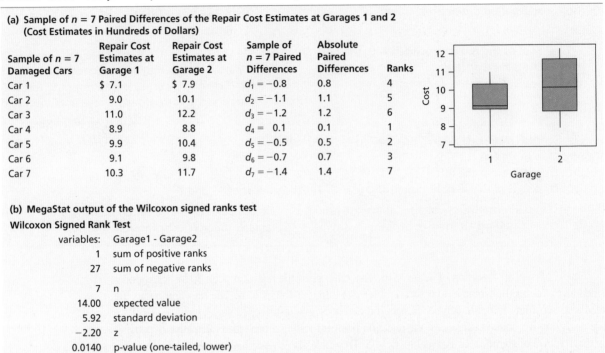

(a) Sample of $n = 7$ Paired Differences of the Repair Cost Estimates at Garages 1 and 2 (Cost Estimates in Hundreds of Dollars)

Sample of $n = 7$ Damaged Cars	Repair Cost Estimates at Garage 1	Repair Cost Estimates at Garage 2	Sample of $n = 7$ Paired Differences	Absolute Paired Differences	Ranks
Car 1	$ 7.1	$ 7.9	$d_1 = -0.8$	0.8	4
Car 2	9.0	10.1	$d_2 = -1.1$	1.1	5
Car 3	11.0	12.2	$d_3 = -1.2$	1.2	6
Car 4	8.9	8.8	$d_4 = 0.1$	0.1	1
Car 5	9.9	10.4	$d_5 = -0.5$	0.5	2
Car 6	9.1	9.8	$d_6 = -0.7$	0.7	3
Car 7	10.3	11.7	$d_7 = -1.4$	1.4	7

(b) MegaStat output of the Wilcoxon signed ranks test

Wilcoxon Signed Rank Test

variables:	Garage1 - Garage2
1	sum of positive ranks
27	sum of negative ranks
7	n
14.00	expected value
5.92	standard deviation
−2.20	z
0.0140	p-value (one-tailed, lower)

Because .1 is the only positive paired difference, and because the rank associated with this difference equals 1, we find that $T^+ = 1$ [see Figure 13.5(b)]. The alternative hypothesis is one-sided and we are analyzing $n = 7$ paired differences. Table 13.3 tells us that we can test H_0 versus H_a at the .05, .025, and .01 levels of significance by setting the rejection point T_0 equal to 4, 2, and 0, respectively. The rejection point condition is $T^+ \le T_0$. It follows that since $T^+ = 1$ is less than or equal to 4 and 2 but not less than or equal to 0, we can reject H_0 in favour of H_a at the .05 and .025 levels of significance, but not at the .01 level of significance. Therefore, we have strong evidence that the probability distribution of repair cost estimates at garage 1 is shifted to the left of the probability distribution of repair cost estimates at garage 2. That is, the repair cost estimates at garage 1 seem to be systematically lower than the repair cost estimates at garage 2.

Notice that in Example 13.4 the nonparametric Wilcoxon signed ranks test would not allow us to reject H_0 in favour of H_a at the .01 level of significance. On the other hand, a parametric paired-differences t test would allow us to reject H_0: $\mu_1 - \mu_2 = 0$ in favour of H_a: $\mu_1 - \mu_2 < 0$ at the .01 level of significance when the mean of garage 1 (9.329) is compared with the mean of garage 2 (10.129), as shown in the MegaStat output in Figure 13.6.

ROADBLOCK   **Sample size shapes and hypothesis testing**

In general, *a parametric test is often more powerful* than the analogous nonparametric test. That is, the parametric test often allows us to reject H_0 at smaller values of α. Therefore, if the assumptions for the parametric test are satisfied—for example, if, when we are using small samples, the sampled populations are approximately normally distributed—it is preferable to use the parametric test. *The advantage of nonparametric tests is that they can be used without assuming that the sampled populations have the shapes of any particular probability distributions,* which can be important when the sampled populations are approximately normally distributed.

FIGURE **13.6**   MegaStat Output of a Paired-Differences
Test for the Repair Cost Estimates

Hypothesis Test: Paired Observations

0.0000	hypothesized value
9.3286	mean Garage1
10.1286	mean Garage2
−0.8000	mean difference (Garage1 - Garage2)
0.5033	std. dev.
0.1902	std. error
7	n
6	df
−4.21	t
0.0057	p-value (two-tailed)

Finally, if the sample size n is at least 25, we can use a large-sample approximation of the Wilcoxon signed ranks test. This is done by making two modifications. First, replace the test statistic (T^- or T^+) by a standardized value of the test statistic. This standardized value is calculated by subtracting the mean $n(n + 1)/4$ from the test statistic (T^- or T^+) and then dividing the resulting difference by the standard deviation $\sqrt{n(n + 1)(2n + 1)/24}$. Second, when testing a one-sided alternative hypothesis, replace the rejection point T_0 by the normal point $-z_\alpha$. When testing a two-sided alternative hypothesis, we replace T_0 by $-z_{\alpha/2}$.

Exercises for Section **13.3**

CONCEPTS

13.14 Explain the circumstances under which to use the Wilcoxon signed ranks test.

13.15 Identify the parametric test corresponding to the Wilcoxon signed ranks test. What assumption is needed for the validity of the parametric test (but not for the Wilcoxon signed ranks test)?

METHODS AND APPLICATIONS

13.16 A consumer advocacy group is concerned about the ability of tax preparation firms to correctly prepare complex returns. To test the performance of tax preparers in two different tax preparation firms—Speedy Tax and Discount Tax—the group designed a tax case for a family with a gross annual income of $150,000 involving several thorny tax issues. In a "tax-off" competition, the advocacy group randomly selected independent samples of ten preparers from each firm and asked each preparer to compute the tax liability for the test case. The preparers' returns were collected and the group computed the difference between each preparer's computed tax and the actual tax that should have been computed. The data in Table 13.4 consist of the resulting two sets of tax computation errors, one for preparers from Speedy Tax and the other for preparers from Discount Tax. Fully interpret the MegaStat output in Table 13.4 of a Wilcoxon signed ranks test analysis of these data.

13.17 Table 13.5 lists the number of permanent residents in Canada by source country for the years 2010 and 2011 as published by Citizenship and Immigration Canada. Enter the data into Excel and conduct the Wilcoxon test (using MegaStat). Based on the output, would you suggest that there has been a significant change in the pattern of immigration from the ten countries listed? Explain your answer.

13.18 A human resources director wants to assess the benefits of sending a company's managers to an innovative management course. Twelve of the company's managers are randomly selected to attend the course, and a psychologist interviews each participating manager before and after taking the course. Based on these interviews, the psychologist rates the manager's leadership ability on a 1-to-100 scale. The pretest and posttest leadership scores for each of the 12 managers are given in Table 13.6.

a. Let D_1 be the distribution of leadership scores before taking the course and D_2 be the distribution of leadership scores after taking the course. Carry out the Wilcoxon signed ranks test to test whether D_1 and D_2 are identical (that is, the course has no effect on leadership scores) versus the alternative that D_2 is shifted to the right or left of D_1 (that is, the course affects leadership scores). Use $\alpha = .05$.

b. Carry out the Wilcoxon signed ranks test to determine whether D_2 is shifted to the right of D_1. Use $\alpha = .05$. What do you conclude?

TABLE **13.4**   Tax Computation Errors and MegaStat Output for Exercise 13.7

Speedy Tax Errors	Discount Tax Errors	Difference
857	156	701
920	200	720
1,090	202	888
1,594	390	1,204
1,820	526	1,294
1,943	749	1,194
1,987	911	1,076
2,008	920	1,088
2,083	2,145	−62
2,439	2,602	−163

Wilcoxon Signed Rank Test

variables:	Speedy − Discount
52	sum of positive ranks
3	sum of negative ranks
10	n
27.50	expected value
9.81	standard deviation
2.50	z
0.0125	p-value (two-tailed)

No.	Label	Data	Rank
1		701	3
2		720	4
3		888	5
4		1204	9
5		1294	10
6		1194	8
7		1076	6
8		1088	7
9		−62	1
10		−163	2

13.19 In a study examining the difference in attitudes between preexposure and postexposure to an advertisement, ten people were tested. The data obtained and the related MegaStat output are shown in Table 13.7. Use the Wilcoxon signed ranks test and the MegaStat output to determine whether the distributions of preexposure and postexposure attitude scores are different. Use $\alpha = .05$.

TABLE **13.5**   Permanent Residents in Canada by Top Ten Source Countries (Number of People) 🖋

Source country	2010	2011
Philippines	36,580	34,991
China, People's Republic of	30,195	28,696
India	30,252	24,965
United States	9,245	8,829
Iran	6,815	6,840
United Kingdom	9,499	6,550
Haiti	4,552	6,208
Pakistan	4,986	6,073
France	6,934	5,867
United Arab Emirates	6,796	5,223

Source: Citizenship and Immigration Canada, *Facts and figures 2011—Immigration overview: Permanent and temporary residents,* "Permanent Residents."

TABLE **13.6**   Pretest and Posttest Leadership Scores 🖋

Manager	Pretest Score	Posttest Score	Difference
1	35	54	−19
2	27	43	−16
3	51	53	−2
4	38	50	−12
5	32	42	−10
6	44	58	−14
7	33	35	−2
8	26	39	−13
9	40	47	−7
10	50	48	2
11	36	41	−5
12	31	37	−6

TABLE **13.7** Preexposure and Postexposure Attitude Scores for an Advertising Study

Subject	Preexposure Attitudes (A_1)	Postexposure Attitudes (A_2)	Attitude Change (d_i)	Wilcoxon Signed Rank Test
				variables: Pre. Attitudes(A1) - Post. Attitudes(A2)
1	50	53	3	0 sum of positive ranks
2	25	27	2	45 sum of negative ranks
3	30	38	8	
4	50	55	5	
5	60	61	1	
6	80	85	5	9 n
7	45	45	0	22.50 expected value
8	30	31	1	7.89 standard deviation
9	65	72	7	−2.85 z, corrected for ties
10	70	78	8	0.0043 p-value (two-tailed)

Source: *Essentials of Marketing Research*, by W. R. Dillon, T. J. Madden, and N. H. Firtle (Burr Ridge, IL: Richard D. Irwin, 1993), p. 435. Copyright © 1993. Reprinted by permission of McGraw-Hill Companies, Inc.

13.4 COMPARING SEVERAL POPULATIONS USING THE KRUSKAL–WALLIS *H* TEST

LO4
LO5

If we fear that the normality and/or equal-variances assumptions for one-way ANOVA do not hold, we can use a nonparametric approach to compare several populations. One such approach is the **Kruskal–Wallis *H* test**, which compares the locations of three or more populations by using independent random samples and a completely randomized experimental design.

In general, suppose we want to use the Kruskal–Wallis *H* test to compare the locations of *p* populations by using *p* independent samples of observations randomly selected from these populations. We first rank all of the observations in the *p* samples from smallest to largest. If n_i denotes the number of observations in the *i*th sample, we are ranking a total of $n = (n_1 + n_2 + \cdots + n_p)$ observations. Furthermore, we assign tied observations the average of the consecutive ranks that would otherwise be assigned to the tied observations. Next we calculate the sum of the ranks of the observations in each sample. Letting T_i denote the rank sum for the *i*th sample, we obtain the rank sums $T_1, T_2, \ldots, T_p$. For example, suppose that a company wants to decrease the culture shock experienced by managers who work on a project in a foreign country for a year. Three types of enculturation training methods are assessed using the experimental method, and learning of the new culture is tested using a standard test. Training type *A* uses information about the new culture only (books, videotapes, etc.). Training type *B* is interactive and includes behavioural modelling with an instructor from the new culture. Training type *C* is the control group, which receives no information or behavioural modelling. Fifteen managers in total are tested, with five being randomly assigned to each of the three training types.

The resulting data are presented in Table 13.8 in which higher scores represent greater learning about the new culture on the standard test (rank values are given in brackets). If we sum the ranks in each sample, we find that $T_1 = 37.5$, $T_2 = 63$, and $T_3 = 19.5$. Note that although the box plots in Table 13.8 do not indicate any serious violations of the normality or equal-variances assumptions, the samples are quite small so we cannot be sure that these assumptions approximately hold. Therefore, it is reasonable to compare training types *A*, *B*, and *C* by using the Kruskal–Wallis *H* test.

TABLE **13.8**   The Training Type Results and Rank Sums

Training Type A	Training Type B	Training Type C
34.0 (3.5)	35.3 (9)	33.3 (2)
35.0 (8)	36.5 (13)	34.0 (3.5)
34.3 (5)	36.4 (12)	34.7 (6)
35.5 (10)	37.0 (14)	33.0 (1)
35.8 (11)	37.6 (15)	34.9 (7)
$T_1 = 37.5$	$T_2 = 63$	$T_3 = 19.5$

The Kruskal–Wallis H Test

Consider testing the null hypothesis H_0 that the p populations under consideration are identical versus the alternative hypothesis H_a that at least two populations differ in location (that is, are shifted either to the left or to the right of one another). We can reject H_0 in favour of H_a at level of significance α if the Kruskal–Wallis H statistic

$$H = \frac{12}{n(n+1)} \sum_{i=1}^{p} \frac{T_i^2}{n_i} - 3(n+1)$$

is greater than the χ_α^2 point based on $p-1$ degrees of freedom.

ROADBLOCK   **Sample size requirements for the Kruskal–Wallis H statistic**
For the Kruskal–Wallis H statistic test to be valid, there should be five or more observations in each sample. Furthermore, the number of ties should be small relative to the total number of observations. Values of χ_α^2 are given in Table A.18.

A Chi-Square Table: Value of χ_α^2

df	$\chi_{0.10}^2$	$\chi_{0.05}^2$
1	2.70554	3.84146
2	4.60517	5.99147
3	6.25139	7.81473
4	7.77944	9.48773
5	9.23635	11.0705
6	10.6446	12.5916
7	12.0170	14.0671
8	13.3616	15.5073
9	14.6837	16.9190
10	15.9871	18.3070

In the training type example, $\chi_{.05}^2$ based on $p - 1 = 2$ degrees of freedom is 5.99147 (see the section of the table in the margin). Furthermore, in this example, $n = n_1 + n_2 + n_3 = 15$, so the Kruskal–Wallis H statistic is

$$H = \frac{12}{15(15+1)}\left[\frac{37.5^2}{5} + \frac{63^2}{5} + \frac{19.5^2}{5}\right] - 3(15+1)$$

$$= \frac{1}{20}\left[\frac{1,406.25}{5} + \frac{3,969}{5} + \frac{380.25}{5}\right] - 48 = 9.555$$

Because $H = 9.555 > \chi_{.05}^2 = 5.99147$, we can reject H_0 at the .05 level of significance, so we have strong evidence that at least two of the three populations of test scores differ in location. Figure 13.7 presents the MegaStat output of the Kruskal–Wallis H test in this training type example.

To conclude this section, note that if the Kruskal–Wallis H test leads to the conclusion that the p populations differ in location, there are various procedures for comparing pairs of populations. A simple procedure is to use the Wilcoxon rank sum test to compare pairs of populations. For example, if we use this test to make separate, *two-sided* comparisons of (1) training types A and B, (2) training types A and C, and (3) training types B and C, and if we set α equal to .05 for each comparison, we find that the test scores given by training type B differ systematically from the scores given by training types A and C. Examining the scores in Table 13.8, we would estimate that training type B results in the highest test scores. One problem, however, with using the Wilcoxon rank sum test to make pairwise comparisons is that it is difficult to know how to set α for each comparison. Therefore, some practitioners prefer to make *simultaneous* pairwise comparisons (such as given by the Tukey simultaneous confidence intervals discussed in Chapter 10). Gibbons (1985) discusses a nonparametric approach for making simultaneous pairwise comparisons.

FIGURE 13.7 MegaStat Output of the Kruskal–Wallis *H* Test in the Training Method Experiment

Kruskal–Wallis Test

Median	n	Avg. Rank	
35.00	5	7.50	Type A
36.50	5	12.60	Type B
34.00	5	3.90	Type C
35.00	15		Total

9.572	H (corrected for ties)
2	d.f.
0.0083	p-value

multiple comparison values for avg. ranks
6.77 (0.05)   8.30 (0.01)

No.	Label	Data	Rank		No.	Label	Data	Rank
1	Type A	34	3.5		9	Type B	37	14
2	Type A	35	8		10	Type B	38	15
3	Type A	34	5		11	Type C	33	2
4	Type A	36	10		12	Type C	34	3.5
5	Type A	36	11		13	Type C	35	6
6	Type B	35	9		14	Type C	33	1
7	Type B	37	13		15	Type C	35	7
8	Type B	36	12					

Exercises for Section **13.4**

CONCEPTS

13.20 Explain the circumstances under which to use the Kruskal–Wallis *H* test.

13.21 Identify the parametric test corresponding to the Kruskal–Wallis *H* test.

13.22 What assumptions are needed for the validity of the parametric test identified in Exercise 13.21 that are not needed for the Kruskal–Wallis *H* test?

METHODS AND APPLICATIONS

In each of Exercises 13.23 through 13.26, use the given independent samples to perform the Kruskal–Wallis *H* test of the null hypothesis H_0 that the corresponding populations are identical versus the alternative hypothesis H_a that at least two populations differ in location. Note that we previously analyzed each of these data sets using the one-way ANOVA *F* test in Chapter 10.

13.23 Use the Kruskal–Wallis *H* test to compare display panels *A*, *B*, and *C* using the data in Table 13.9. Use $\alpha = .05$.

13.24 Use the Kruskal–Wallis *H* test to compare bottle designs *A*, *B*, and *C* using the data in Table 13.10. Use $\alpha = .01$.

13.25 Use the Kruskal–Wallis *H* test and the MegaStat output in Figure 13.8 to compare the bottom (*B*), middle (*M*), and top (*T*) display heights using the data in Table 13.11. Use $\alpha = .05$. Then repeat the analysis if the first sales value for the middle display height is found to be incorrect and must be removed from the data set.

TABLE 13.9 Display Panel Study Data (Time, in Seconds, Required to Stabilize Air Traffic Emergency Condition)

	Display Panel	
A	*B*	*C*
21	24	40
27	21	36
24	18	35
26	19	32
25	20	37

TABLE 13.10 Bottle Design Study Data (Sales during a 24-Hour Period)

	Bottle Design	
A	*B*	*C*
16	33	23
18	31	27
19	37	21
17	29	28
13	34	25

FIGURE **13.8**   MegaStat Output of the Kruskal–Wallis *H* Test for the Bakery Sales Data

Kruskal-Wallis Test

Median	n	Avg. Rank	
55.75	6	9.17	Bottom
77.15	6	15.50	Middle
51.50	6	3.83	Top
55.75	18		Total

14.363	H	
2	d.f.	
0.0008	p-value	

multiple comparison values for avg. ranks

7.38 (0.05)			9.05 (0.01)

No.	Label	Data	Rank
1	Bottom	58	11
2	Bottom	54	7
3	Bottom	56	10
4	Bottom	56	9
5	Bottom	53	6
6	Bottom	59	12
7	Middle	73	13
8	Middle	78	16
9	Middle	75	14
10	Middle	76	15
11	Middle	78	17
12	Middle	82	18
13	Top	52	5
14	Top	50	1
15	Top	51	3
16	Top	54	8
17	Top	52	4
18	Top	50	2

13.26 Use the Kruskal–Wallis *H* test to compare golf ball brands Alpha, Best, Century, and Divot using the data in Table 13.12. Use $\alpha = .01$ and the MegaStat output to the right in Table 13.12.

13.27 A statistics professor at a local university believes that the amount of time that students spend studying depends on the term the student is studying in. Fall, winter, and spring terms were considered. Students were randomly selected during three different times of year during a one-year period and asked to estimate the number of hours spent studying per week. Here are the students' estimates:

> **Fall:** 5, 2, 6, 9, 4, 7, 5, 3
> **Winter:** 9, 7, 12, 11, 8, 10, 6, 11, 5, 9
> **Spring:** 6, 9, 5, 8, 8, 5, 3, 4, 7

Conduct a Kruskal–Wallis test at the $\alpha = .05$ level of significance. Based on the results of the hypothesis test, is there evidence to suggest that the average study times are not all the same, that is, that the amount of time studying differs throughout the school year?

TABLE **13.11**   Bakery Sales Study Data (Sales in Cases)

	Shelf Display Height	
Bottom (*B*)	Middle (*M*)	Top (*T*)
58.2	73.0	52.4
53.7	78.1	49.7
55.8	75.4	50.9
55.7	76.2	54.0
52.5	78.4	52.1
58.9	82.1	49.9

TABLE **13.12**   Golf Ball Durability Test Results

	Brand				Kruskal–Wallis Test					
Alpha	Best	Century	Divot	Median	n	Avg. Rank		13.834	H
281	270	218	364	251.00	5	6.80	Alpha	3	d.f.
220	334	244	302	307.00	5	13.40	Best	0.0031	p-value
274	307	225	325	244.00	5	4.80	Century		
242	290	273	337	337.00	5	17.00	Divot		
251	331	249	355	277.50	20		Total		

13.5 SPEARMAN'S RANK CORRELATION COEFFICIENT

In Chapter 11, we showed how to test the significance of a population correlation coefficient. This test is based on the assumption that the population of all possible combinations of values of *x* and *y* has a bivariate normal probability distribution. If we fear that this assumption is violated, we can use a nonparametric approach. One such approach is **Spearman's rank correlation coefficient,**[2] which is denoted r_s.

---

[2]Charles Spearman was the advisor of Karl Pearson, who developed the correlation coefficient described in Chapter 11.

TABLE 13.13 Electronics World Sales Volume Data and Ranks for 15 Stores

Store	Number of Households, x	Sales Volume, y	x Rank	y Rank	Difference, d	d²
1	161	157.27	6	7	−1	1
2	99	93.28	1	1	0	0
3	135	136.81	5	5	0	0
4	120	123.79	4	3	1	1
5	164	153.51	7	6	1	1
6	221	241.74	13	14	−1	1
7	179	201.54	8	10	−2	4
8	204	206.71	9	11	−2	4
9	214	229.78	12	13	−1	1
10	101	135.22	2	4	−2	4
11	231	224.71	14	12	2	4
12	206	195.29	11	8	3	9
13	248	242.16	15	15	0	0
14	107	115.21	3	2	1	1
15	205	197.82	10	9	1	1

$$\sum d^2 = 32$$

To illustrate, suppose that Electronics World, a chain of stores that sells audio and video equipment, has gathered the data in Table 13.13. The company wants to study the relationship between store sales volume in July of last year (y, measured in thousands of dollars) and the number of households in the store's area (x, measured in thousands). Spearman's rank correlation coefficient is found by first ranking the values of x and y separately (ties are treated by averaging the tied ranks), and then by using the equation for the correlation coefficient (r), we replace the x and y values by their ranks. If there are no ties in the ranks, this formula can be calculated by the simple equation

$$r_s = 1 - \frac{6\sum d_i^2}{n(n^2 - 1)}$$

where d_i is the difference between the x rank and the y rank for the ith observation (if there are few ties in the ranks, this formula is approximately valid). To deal with a tie, sum the tied ranks and divide the sum by the number of ties to create an "average" rank value to assign to the tied cases. For example, Table 13.13 gives the ranks of x and y, the difference between the ranks, and the squared difference for each of the $n = 15$ stores in the Electronics World example. Because the sum of the squared differences is 32, we calculate r_s to be

$$r_s = 1 - \frac{6(32)}{15(225 - 1)} = .9429$$

Equivalently, if we have MegaStat analyze the data, we obtain the following output:

LO6

Spearman Coefficient of Rank Correlation

	X	Y
X	1.000	
Y	0.943	1.000

15 sample size

± 0.514 critical value 0.05 (two-tail)
± 0.641 critical value 0.01 (two-tail)

X	Y		X	Y
6	7		12	13
1	1		2	4
5	5		14	12
4	3		11	8
7	6		15	15
13	14		3	2
8	10		10	9
9	11			

LO7

This large positive value of r_s says that there is a strong positive rank correlation between the numbers of households and sales volumes in the sample.

In general, let ρ_s denote the population rank correlation coefficient—the rank correlation coefficient for the population of all possible (x, y) values. We can test the significance of ρ_s by using Spearman's rank correlation test, as described in the following boxed feature.

Spearman's Rank Correlation Test

Let r_s denote Spearman's rank correlation coefficient. Then we can test $H_0: \rho_s = 0$ versus a particular alternative hypothesis at level of significance α by using the appropriate rejection point rule.

Alternative Hypothesis

$H_a: \rho_s > 0$
$H_a: \rho_s < 0$
$H_a: \rho_s \neq 0$

Rejection Point Rule:
Reject H_0 If

$r_s > r_\alpha$
$r_s < -r_\alpha$
$|r_s| > r_{\alpha/2}$

Table A.17 gives values of the rejection points r_α, $-r_\alpha$, and $r_{\alpha/2}$ for values of n from 5 to 30. Note that for this test to be valid, the number of ties encountered in ranking the observations should be small relative to the number of observations.

A portion of Table A.17 is reproduced here as Table 13.14. To illustrate using this table, suppose in the Electronics World example that we want to test $H_0: \rho_s = 0$ versus $H_a: \rho_s > 0$ by setting $\alpha = .05$. Because there are $n = 15$ stores, Table 13.14 tells us that we use the rejection point $r_{.05} = .441$. Because $r_s = .9429$ is greater than this rejection point, we can reject $H_0: \rho_s = 0$ in favour of $H_a: \rho_s > 0$ at $\alpha = .05$. Therefore, we have strong evidence that in July of last year, the sales volume of an Electronics World store was positively correlated with the number of households in the store's area.

To illustrate testing a two-sided alternative hypothesis, consider Table 13.15. This table presents the rankings of $n = 12$ midsized cars given by two automobile magazines. Here, each magazine has ranked the cars from 1 (best) to 12 (worst) on the basis of overall ride. Because the two magazines sometimes have differing views, we cannot theorize about whether their rankings would be positively or negatively correlated. Therefore, we will test $H_0: \rho_s = 0$ versus $H_a: \rho_s \neq 0$. The boxed feature "Spearman's Rank Correlation Test" tells us that to perform

TABLE **13.14** Critical Values for Spearman's Rank Correlation Coefficient

n	$\alpha = 0.05$	$\alpha = 0.025$	$\alpha = 0.01$	$\alpha = 0.005$
10	0.564	0.648	0.745	0.794
11	0.523	0.623	0.736	0.818
12	0.497	0.591	0.703	0.780
13	0.475	0.566	0.673	0.745
14	0.457	0.545	0.646	0.716
15	0.441	0.525	0.623	0.689
16	0.425	0.507	0.601	0.666
17	0.412	0.490	0.582	0.645
18	0.399	0.476	0.564	0.625
19	0.388	0.462	0.549	0.608
20	0.377	0.450	0.534	0.591

TABLE **13.15** Rankings of 12 Midsize Cars by Two Automobile Magazines

Car	Magazine 1 Ranking	Magazine 2 Ranking
1	5	7
2	1	1
3	4	5
4	7	4
5	6	6
6	8	10
7	9	8
8	12	11
9	2	3
10	3	2
11	10	12
12	11	9

this test at level of significance α, we use the rejection point $r_{\alpha/2}$. To look up $r_{\alpha/2}$ in Table A.17 (or Table 13.14), we replace the symbol α by the symbol $\alpha/2$. For example, consider setting $\alpha = .05$. Then, since $\alpha/2 = .025$, we look in Table 13.14 for the value .025. Because there are $n = 12$ cars, we find that $r_{.025} = .591$. Spearman's rank correlation coefficient for the car-ranking data can be calculated to be .8951. Because $r_s = .8951$ is greater than $r_{.025} = .591$, we reject H_0 at the .05 level of significance. Therefore, we conclude that the midsized car ride rankings given by the two magazines are correlated. Furthermore, because $r_s = .8951$, we estimate that these rankings are positively correlated.

To conclude this section, we make two comments. First, the car-ranking example illustrates that Spearman's rank correlation coefficient and test can be used when the raw measurements of the x and/or y variables are themselves ranks. Ranks are measurements of an ordinal variable, and Spearman's nonparametric approach applies to ordinal variables. Second, it can be shown that if the sample size n is at least 10, then we can carry out an approximation to Spearman's rank correlation test by replacing r_s by the t statistic

$$t = \frac{r_s \sqrt{n-2}}{\sqrt{1 - r_s^2}}$$

and by replacing the rejection points r_α, $-r_\alpha$, and $r_{\alpha/2}$ by the t points t_α, $-t_\alpha$, and $t_{\alpha/2}$ (with $n-2$ degrees of freedom). Table A.17 gives r_α points for sample sizes up to $n = 30$. However, if the sample size exceeds 30, we can use the z points z_α, $-z_\alpha$, and $z_{\alpha/2}$ in place of the corresponding t points.

THEORY TO PRACTICE

Understanding how two variables are related is of great interest in many areas. A human resources researcher might want to examine the relationship between job satisfaction and shifts (day, swing, and evening) in a manufacturing plant. Answering this question should be done using the Spearman rank correlation. Other variables that are best suited for the Spearman rank correlation include variables such as movie revenues, stock preferences, and product selection.

Exercises for Section **13.5**

CONCEPTS

13.28 Explain the circumstances under which to use Spearman's rank correlation coefficient.

13.29 Write the formula that is used to compute Spearman's rank correlation coefficient in each case.
   a. There are no (or few) ties in the ranks of the x and y values.
   b. There are many ties in the ranks of the x and y values.

METHODS AND APPLICATIONS

13.30 A sales manager ranks ten people at the end of their training on the basis of their sales potential. A year later, the number of units sold by each person is determined. The data and MegaStat output in

Table 13.16(a) are obtained. Note that the manager's ranking of 1 is "best."
   a. Find r_s in the MegaStat output and use Table 13.14 to find the critical value for testing $H_0: \rho_s = 0$ versus $H_a: \rho_s \neq 0$ at the .05 level of significance. Do you reject H_0?
   b. The MegaStat output gives approximate critical values for $\alpha = .05$ and $\alpha = .01$. Do these approximate critical values, which are based on the t distribution, differ by much from the exact critical values in Table 13.14 (recall that $n = 10$)?

13.31 Use the MegaStat output in Table 13.16(b) to find r_s, and then test $H_0: \rho_s = 0$ versus $H_a: \rho_s > 0$ for the service time data in Table 13.16(b).

TABLE 13.16   Data and MegaStat Output for Exercises 13.30 and 13.31

(a) Training data and MegaStat output for Exercise 13.30

Person	1	2	3	4	5	6	7	8	9	10
Manager's Ranking, x	7	4	2	6	1	10	3	5	9	8
Units Sold, y	770	630	820	580	720	440	690	810	560	470

	MgrRank, x	UnitSold, y
MgrRank, x	1.000	
UnitSold, y	−0.721	1.000

±0.632 critical value 0.05 (two-tail)
±0.765 critical value 0.01 (two-tail)

10 sample size

(b) Service time data and MegaStat output for Exercise 13.31

Copiers Serviced, x	4	2	5	7	1	3	4	5	2	4	6
Minutes Required, y	109	58	138	189	37	82	103	134	68	112	154

Spearman Coefficient of Rank Correlation

	Copiers, x	Minutes, y
Copiers, x	1.000	
Minutes, y	0.986	1.000

11 sample size

± 0.602 critical value 0.05 (two-tail)
± 0.735 critical value 0.01 (two-tail)

Copiers, x	Minutes, y
6	6
2.5	2
8.5	9
11	11
1	1
4	4
6	5
8.5	8
2.5	3
6	7
10	10

CHAPTER SUMMARY

The validity of many of the inference procedures presented in this book requires that various assumptions be met, such as the normality assumption. In this chapter, we have learned that when the needed assumptions are not met, we must use a nonparametric method. Such a method does not require any assumptions about the shape(s) of the distribution(s) of the sampled population(s).

We first studied the sign test, which is a hypothesis test about a population median. This test is useful when we have taken a sample from a population that might not be normally distributed. We next studied two nonparametric tests for comparing the locations of two populations. The first such test, the Wilcoxon rank sum test, is appropriate when an independent-samples experiment has been carried out. The second, the Wilcoxon signed ranks test, is appropriate when

a paired-differences experiment has been carried out. Both of these tests can be used without assuming that the sampled populations have the shapes of any particular probability distributions.

We then discussed the Kruskal–Wallis H test, which is a nonparametric test for comparing the locations of several populations by using independent samples. This test, which employs the chi-square distribution, can be used when the normality and/or equal-variances assumptions for one-way ANOVA do not hold.

Finally, we presented a nonparametric approach for testing the significance of a population correlation coefficient. Here we saw how to compute Spearman's rank correlation coefficient, and we discussed how to use this quantity to test the significance of the population correlation coefficient.

KEY TERMS

Kruskal–Wallis H test
nonparametric test
sign test
Spearman's rank correlation coefficient

Wilcoxon rank sum test (also called the **Mann–Whitney test**)
Wilcoxon signed ranks test

IMPORTANT FORMULAS AND TESTS

Sign test for a population median

Large-sample sign test

Wilcoxon rank sum test

Wilcoxon rank sum test (large-sample approximation)

Wilcoxon signed ranks test

Wilcoxon signed ranks test (large-sample approximation)

Kruskal–Wallis H test

Kruskal–Wallis H statistic

Spearman's rank correlation coefficient

Spearman's rank correlation test

SUPPLEMENTARY EXERCISES

connect Practise and learn online with *Connect*. Items for which there are online data sets are marked with ✎.

13.32 A marketing research firm wants to compare the prices charged by two supermarket chains—Miller's and Albert's. The research firm, using a standardized one-week shopping list, makes identical purchases at ten of each chain's stores. The stores for each chain are randomly selected, and all purchases are made during a single week.

The shopping expenses obtained at the two chains are given below.

Miller's

$119.25	$121.32	$122.34	$120.14	$122.19
$123.71	$121.72	$122.42	$123.63	$122.44

Albert's

$111.99	$114.88	$115.11	$117.02	$116.89
$116.62	$115.38	$114.40	$113.91	$111.87

Because the sample sizes are small, there might be reason to doubt that the populations of expenses at the two chains are normally distributed. Therefore, use a Wilcoxon rank sum test to determine whether expenses at Miller's and Albert's differ. Use $\alpha = .05$.

13.33 A drug company wants to compare the effects of three different drugs (X, Y, and Z) that are being developed to reduce cholesterol levels. Each drug is administered to six patients at the recommended dosage for six months. At the end of this period, the reduction in cholesterol level is recorded for each patient. The results are given in Table 13.17. Assuming that the three samples are independent, use a nonparametric test to see whether the effects of the three drugs differ. Use $\alpha = .05$.

TABLE 13.17 Reduction of Cholesterol Levels Using Three Drugs ✎

	Drug	
X	**Y**	**Z**
22	40	15
31	35	9
19	47	14
27	41	11
25	39	21
18	33	5

13.34 Table 13.18 lists the monthly receipts for restaurants, caterers, and taverns by province for October 2012 in millions of dollars. Also listed in Table 13.18 is the population of each province in 2012, in thousands. Enter the data into Excel and compute both the Pearson correlation coefficient (from Chapter 11) and the Spearman rank correlation coefficient. How do the two values differ? Which statistic do you feel is most appropriate and why?

13.35 During 2012, a company implemented a number of policies aimed at reducing the ages (in days) of its customers' accounts. In order to assess the effectiveness of these measures, the company randomly selects ten customer accounts. The average age of each account is determined for each of the years 2012 and 2013. These data are given in Table 13.19. Use a nonparametric technique to attempt to show that average account ages have decreased. Use $\alpha = .05$.

13.36 The following data represent the total number of people employed and the total revenue (in thousands of dollars) for a film and video distribution company for the years 2008 to 2013. Compute the Spearman rank correlation coefficient for these two variables. What does the resulting value tell you about the relationship between the number of employees and total revenue?

Year	Number of Employees	Total Revenue ($1,000s)
2008/09	3,592	$2,813,116
2009/10	3,900	3,036,646
2010/11	4,033	3,278,386
2011/12	3,972	3,437,629
2012/13	4,152	359,617

TABLE 13.18   Monthly Receipts for Restaurants, Caterers, and Taverns for October 2012 and Population Values by Province for 2012

Province	Receipts ($1,000,000s)	Population (1,000s)
Newfoundland and Labrador	62,974	512.7
Prince Edward Island	16,232	146.1
Nova Scotia	111,190	948.7
New Brunswick	82,111	756
Quebec	860,414	8054.8
Ontario	1,675,320	13505.9
Manitoba	129,854	1267
Saskatchewan	139,946	1080
Alberta	648,909	3873.7
British Columbia	664,784	4622.6

Source: Statistics Canada, *Summary Tables*, "Monthly receipts for food services and drinking places, by province and territory" and "Population by year, by province and territory."

13.37 A loan officer wants to compare the interest rates being charged for 48-month fixed-rate auto loans and 48-month variable-rate auto loans. Two independent, random samples of auto loan rates are selected. A sample of eight 48-month fixed-rate auto loans had the following loan rates:

10.29%	9.75%	9.50%	9.99%	9.75%
9.99%	11.40%	10.00%		

A sample of five 48-month variable-rate auto loans had loan rates as follows:

9.59%	8.75%	8.99%	8.50%	9.00%

Perform a nonparametric test to determine whether loan rates for 48-month fixed-rate auto loans differ from loan rates for 48-month variable-rate auto loans. Use $\alpha = .05$. Explain your conclusion.

13.38 A large bank wants to limit the median debt-to-equity ratio for its portfolio of commercial loans to 1.5. The bank randomly selects 15 of its commercial loan accounts. Audits result in the following debt-to-equity ratios:

1.31	1.05	1.45	1.21	1.19
1.78	1.37	1.41	1.22	1.11
1.46	1.33	1.29	1.32	1.65

Can it be concluded that the median debt-to-equity ratio is less than 1.5 at the .05 level of significance? Explain.

13.39 INTERNET EXERCISE

Go to the website of The Data and Story Library and click on "Data subjects," then click on "Sports," and then on "Helium football datafile." Carry out the Wilcoxon signed ranks test to determine whether the distributions of the distances for air-filled and helium-filled footballs are different. Use $\alpha = .05$.

TABLE 13.19   Average Account Ages in 2012 and 2013 for Ten Randomly Selected Accounts

Account	Average Age of Account in 2012 (Days)	Average Age of Account in 2013 (Days)
1	35	27
2	24	19
3	47	40
4	28	30
5	41	33
6	33	25
7	35	31
8	51	29
9	18	15
10	28	21

CHAPTER **14**
Chi-Square Tests

LEARNING OBJECTIVES

After reading this chapter, you should be able to

LO1 Describe the type of data used in a chi-square goodness of fit test

LO2 Conduct a chi-square goodness of fit test

LO3 Compute the degrees of freedom of the chi-square test statistic

LO4 Explain the significance of the chi-square test statistic

LO5 Define the purpose of a control variable in a chi-square goodness of fit test

LO6 Describe how a chi-square goodness of fit test can be used to test the assumption that the sample was drawn from a normal population

LO7 Explain how graphs can be used to demonstrate the relationship between variables

CHAPTER OUTLINE

14.1 Chi-Square Goodness of Fit Tests

14.2 A Chi-Square Test for Independence

In this chapter, we present two useful hypothesis tests based on the chi-square distribution. First, we consider the chi-square goodness of fit test. This test evaluates whether data falling into several categories do so with a hypothesized set of probabilities. Second, we discuss the chi-square test for independence. Here data are classified on two dimensions and are summarized in a contingency table. The test for independence then evaluates whether the cross-classified (or cross-tabulated) variables are independent of each other. If we conclude that the variables are not independent, we have established that the variables in question are related and we must then investigate the nature of the relationship.

14.1 CHI-SQUARE GOODNESS OF FIT TESTS

LO1

Multinomial probabilities Sometimes we collect count data in order to study how the counts are distributed among several categories or cells. As an example, we might study consumer preferences for four different brands of a product. To do this, we select a random sample of consumers, and we ask each survey participant to indicate a brand preference. Note that in this situation, the participant in the study is asked which one of the four brands she or he prefers (as opposed to rating how much the participant likes each brand). Also note that in this situation, there are no ties. Even if an individual prefers two brands equally, that person chooses only one of the options. Also, if the individual does not like any of the brands, he or she is still required to pick one. We then count the number of consumers who prefer each of the four brands. In this example, we have four categories (brands) and we study the distribution of the counts in each category in order to see which brands are preferred.

We often use categorical data[1] to carry out a statistical inference. For instance, suppose that a major wholesaler in London, Ontario, carries four different brands of microwave ovens. Historically, consumer behaviour in London has resulted in the market shares shown in Table 14.1. The wholesaler plans to begin doing business in a new territory—Edmonton, Alberta. To study whether its policies for stocking the four brands of ovens in London can also be used in Edmonton, the wholesaler compares consumer preferences for the four ovens in Edmonton with the historical market shares observed in London. A random sample of 400 consumers in Edmonton gives the preferences shown in Table 14.2.

To compare consumer preferences in London and Edmonton, we must consider a **multinomial experiment**, which is similar to the binomial experiment. However, a binomial experiment concerns count data that can be classified into two categories, while a multinomial experiment concerns count data that are classified into three or more categories. Specifically, the assumptions for the multinomial experiment are as shown in the following boxed feature.

The Multinomial Experiment

1   We perform an experiment in which we carry out n identical trials and in which there are k possible outcomes on each trial.

2   The probabilities of the k outcomes are denoted $p_1, p_2, \ldots, p_k$, where $p_1 + p_2 + \cdots + p_k = 1$. These probabilities stay the same from trial to trial.

3   The trials in the experiment are independent.

4   The results of the experiment are observed frequencies (counts) of the number of trials that result in each of the k possible outcomes. The frequencies are denoted $f_1, f_2, \ldots, f_k$. That is, f_1 is the number of trials resulting in the first possible outcome, f_2 is the number of trials resulting in the second possible outcome, and so forth.

Notice that the definition of a multinomial experiment is similar to that of a binomial experiment. In fact, a binomial experiment is simply a multinomial experiment in which k equals 2 (there are two possible outcomes in each trial).

TABLE **14.1** Market Shares for Four Microwave Oven Brands in London, Ontario

Brand	Market Share (%)
1	20%
2	35
3	30
4	15

TABLE **14.2** Brand Preferences for Four Microwave Ovens Expressed by 400 people in Edmonton, Alberta

Brand	Observed Frequency (Number of Consumers Sampled Who Prefer the Brand)
1	102
2	121
3	120
4	57

[1]Note that categorical data are the same as nominal data (as described in the four levels of measurement in Chapter 1).

In general, the probabilities $p_1, p_2, \ldots, p_k$ are unknown, and we estimate their values. Or, we compare estimates of these probabilities with a set of specified values. Now, back to the microwave oven example.

Example 14.1 The Microwave Oven Preference Example

Suppose the microwave oven wholesaler wants to compare consumer preferences in Edmonton with the historical market shares in London. If the consumer preferences in Edmonton are substantially different, the wholesaler will consider changing its policies for stocking the ovens. Here:

p_1 = Proportion of Edmonton consumers who prefer Brand 1

p_2 = Proportion of Edmonton consumers who prefer Brand 2

p_3 = Proportion of Edmonton consumers who prefer Brand 3

p_4 = Proportion of Edmonton consumers who prefer Brand 4

Remembering that the historical market shares for Brands 1, 2, 3, and 4 in London were 20 percent, 35 percent, 30 percent, and 15 percent, we test the null hypothesis

$$H_0: p_1 = .20 \quad p_2 = .35 \quad p_3 = .30 \quad p_4 = .15$$

which says that consumer preferences in Edmonton are consistent with the historical market shares in London. We test H_0 versus

H_a: Null hypothesis is not supported (at least one of the percentages is different)

To test H_0, we must compare the observed frequencies given in Table 14.2 with the expected frequencies for the brands calculated on the assumption that H_0 is true using the percentages in Table 14.1. For instance, if H_0 is true, we would expect $400(.20) = 80$ of the 400 Edmonton consumers surveyed to prefer Brand 1. Denoting this expected frequency for Brand 1 as E_1, the expected frequencies for Brands 2, 3, and 4 when H_0 is true are $E_2 = 400(.35) = 140$, $E_3 = 400(.30) = 120$, and $E_4 = 400(.15) = 60$. Recalling that Table 14.2 gives the observed frequency for each brand, we have $f_1 = 102, f_2 = 121, f_3 = 120,$ and $f_4 = 57$. We now compare the observed and expected frequencies by computing a chi-square statistic (the chi-square obtained) as follows:

LO2

$$\chi^2 = \sum_{i=1}^{k=4} \frac{(f_i - E_i)^2}{E_i}$$

$$= \frac{(102 - 80)^2}{80} + \frac{(121 - 140)^2}{140} + \frac{(120 - 120)^2}{120} + \frac{(57 - 60)^2}{60}$$

$$= \frac{484}{80} + \frac{361}{140} + \frac{0}{120} + \frac{9}{60} = 8.7786.$$

The more the observed frequencies differ from the expected frequencies, the larger χ^2 will be and the more doubt will be cast on the null hypothesis. If the chi-square statistic is large enough (beyond a rejection point), then we reject H_0.

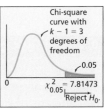

Chi-square curve with $k - 1 = 3$ degrees of freedom
0.05
$\chi^2_{0.05} = 7.81473$
Reject H_0.

ROADBLOCK

Number of expected observations in cells
The recommended expected cell frequency for a chi-square statistic is suggested to be at least 5 observations.

To find an appropriate rejection point, it can be shown that when the null hypothesis is true, the sampling distribution of the χ^2 statistic is approximately a χ^2 distribution with $k - 1$

LO3

degrees of freedom. If we want to test H_0 at the .05 level of significance, we reject H_0 if and only if

$$\chi^2_{\text{Obtained}} > \chi^2_{.05}$$

Table A.18 provides the chi-square values for various rejection levels. In the microwave example, there are four brand conditions, which results in $k - 1 = 4 - 1 = 3$ degrees of freedom. Table A.18 tells us that the $\chi^2_{.05}$ point corresponding to 3 degrees of freedom equals 7.81473. Therefore,

$$\chi^2_{\text{Obtained}} = 8.7786 > \chi^2_{.05} = 7.81473$$

and we reject H_0 at the .05 level of significance and conclude that consumer preferences in Edmonton for the four brands of ovens are not consistent with the historical market shares in London. Based on this conclusion, the wholesaler should consider changing its stocking policies for microwave ovens when it enters the Edmonton market.

To study how to change its policies, the wholesaler might compute a 95 percent confidence interval for, say, the proportion of consumers in Edmonton who prefer Brand 2. Computing this confidence interval involves the expression used for computing a population proportion:

$$\left[\hat{p} \pm z_{\alpha/2}\sqrt{\frac{\hat{p}(1 - \hat{p})}{n}} \right]$$

For example, for Brand 2, $\hat{p}_2 = 121/400 = .3025$ so the 95 percent confidence interval is

$$\left[\hat{p}_2 \pm z_{.025}\sqrt{\frac{\hat{p}_2(1 - \hat{p}_2)}{n}} \right] = \left[.3025 \pm 1.96\sqrt{\frac{.3025(1 - .3025)}{400}} \right]$$
$$= [.2575, .3475]$$

Note: Remember to divide the alpha value in half; if there is a 95 percent confidence interval, then there will be $.05/2 = .025$ in each tail.

This entire interval is below .35, suggesting that (1) the market share for Brand 2 ovens in Edmonton will be smaller than the 35 percent market share that this brand commands in London, and (2) fewer Brand 2 ovens (on a percentage basis) should be stocked in Edmonton than they have been in London. For Brand 1, the interval is found to be [.2123, .2977], which is greater than the historic .20, suggesting market shares may be larger for Brand 1 in Edmonton. The confidence interval for Brand 3 is [.2551, .3449], which contains the historic .30, suggesting the same level of interest. For Brand 4, the interval is [.1082, .1768], which contains the historic .15, suggesting, as is the case for Brand 3, the same level of interest in Edmonton as in London.

In the following boxed feature, we give a general chi-square **goodness of fit test for multinomial probabilities**.

A Goodness of Fit Test for Multinomial Probabilities

Consider a multinomial experiment in which each of n randomly selected items (observations) is classified into one of k groups. We let

f_i = Number of items classified into group i (that is, the ith observed frequency)

$E_i = np_i$

= Expected number of items (observations) that would be classified into group i if p_i is the probability of a randomly selected item being classified into group i (that is, the ith expected frequency)

If we want to test

H_0: Values of the multinomial probabilities are $p_1, p_2, \ldots, p_k$ (that is, the probability of a randomly selected item being classified into group 1 is p_1, the probability of a randomly selected item being classified into group 2 is p_2, and so forth)

versus

H_a: At least one of the multinomial probabilities is not equal to the value stated in H_0

(continued)

we define the *chi-square goodness of fit statistic* to be

$$\chi^2 = \sum_{i=1}^{k} \frac{(f_i - E_i)^2}{E_i}$$

Also, we define the *p*-value related to χ^2 to be the area under the curve of the chi-square distribution with $k - 1$ degrees of freedom to the right of χ^2.

Then we can reject H_0 in favour of H_a at a level of significance α if

$$\chi^2 > \chi_\alpha^2$$

Here the χ_α^2 point is based on $k - 1$ degrees of freedom.

This test is based on the fact that when H_0 is true, the sampling distribution of χ^2 is approximately a chi-square distribution with $k - 1$ degrees of freedom if the sample size n is large. *It is generally agreed that n should be considered large if all of the "expected cell frequencies" (E_i values) are at least 5.* Furthermore, research implies that this condition on the E_i values can be somewhat relaxed. For example, Moore and McCabe (1993) indicate that *it is reasonable to use the chi-square approximation if the number of groups (k) exceeds 4, the average of the E_i values is at least 5, and the smallest E_i value is at least 1.* In Example 14.1, all of the E_i values are much larger than 5. Therefore, the chi-square test is valid.

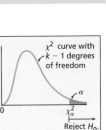

Using control variables A control variable is an additional factor added to the model to examine if the pattern of the data changes or stays the same when this additional factor is considered. For example, in the microwave oven case, say the researcher examined the sex of the people tested in Edmonton. If an equal number of men and women were tested, then there were 200 of each (the total sample was 400). Suppose the observed brand preferences were found to be as follows:

LO5

Brand	Men	Women
1	41	61
2	68	53
3	58	62
4	33	24
Total	200	200

Then separate chi-square analyses could be conducted for the men and women. To compute the expected frequency values, it should be remembered that the total number within each sex is now 200. So the expected frequency is now .20(200) = 40 for Brand 1, .35(200) = 70 for Brand 2, .30(200) = 60 for Brand 3, and 30 for Brand 4. Calculating the chi-square values with these data results in $\chi^2 = .4488$ for men and $\chi^2 = 16.4202$ for women. As stated above, for 3 degrees of freedom at $\alpha = .05$, $\chi^2_{critical} = 7.81473$, which is greater than the obtained value for men but less than the obtained value for women. From these results we can conclude that the pattern of brand preferences differs for women in Edmonton but not for men in Edmonton.

Test for homogeneity A special version of the chi-square goodness of fit test for multinomial probabilities is called a **test for homogeneity**. This involves testing the null hypothesis that all of the multinomial probabilities are equal. For instance, in the microwave oven situation, we would test

$$H_0: p_1 = p_2 = p_3 = p_4 = .25$$

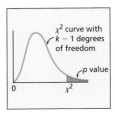

which would say that no single brand of microwave oven is preferred over any of the other brands (equal preferences). If this null hypothesis is rejected in favour of

$$H_a: \text{At least one of } p_1, p_2, p_3 \text{ and } p_4 \text{ exceeds } .25$$

we would conclude that there is a preference for one or more of the brands. Here each of the expected cell frequencies equals $.25(400) = 100$. Remembering that the observed cell frequencies are $f_1 = 102$, $f_2 = 121$, $f_3 = 120$, and $f_4 = 57$, the chi-square statistic for homogeneity is

$$\chi^2 = \sum_{i=1}^{4} \frac{(f_i - E_i)^2}{E_i}$$

$$= \frac{(102 - 100)^2}{100} + \frac{(121 - 100)^2}{100} + \frac{(120 - 100)^2}{100} + \frac{(57 - 100)^2}{100}$$

$$= .04 + 4.41 + 4 + 18.49 = 26.94$$

Because $\chi^2 = 26.94$ is greater than $\chi_{.05}^2 = 7.81473$ (see the section of Table A.18 in the margin with $k - 1 = 4 - 1 = 3$ degrees of freedom), we reject H_0 at level of significance .05. We conclude that preferences for the four brands are not equal and that at least one brand is preferred to the others.

LO6

Normal distributions We have seen that many statistical methods are based on the assumption that a random sample has been selected from a normally distributed population. We can check the validity of the normality assumption by using frequency distributions, stem-and-leaf displays, histograms, and normal plots. Another approach is to use a chi-square goodness of fit test to check the normality assumption (as was first introduced in Chapter 11, Correlation Coefficient and Simple Linear Regression Analysis, Section 11.10 for testing the normality assumption for regression residuals).

Consider the sample of 49 test scores given in Table 14.3. The stem-and-leaf display of these scores (in Figure 14.1) is fairly symmetrical and bell-shaped. This suggests that the sample of test scores has been randomly selected from a normally distributed population. In this example, we use a chi-square **goodness of fit test to check the normality of the scores**.

TABLE 14.3   A Sample of 49 Test Scores

30.8	30.9	32.0	32.3	32.6
31.7	30.4	31.4	32.7	31.4
30.1	32.5	30.8	31.2	31.8
31.6	30.3	32.8	30.6	31.9
32.1	31.3	32.0	31.7	32.8
33.3	32.1	31.5	31.4	31.5
31.3	32.5	32.4	32.2	31.6
31.0	31.8	31.0	31.5	30.6
32.0	30.4	29.8	31.7	32.2
32.4	30.5	31.1	30.6	

FIGURE 14.1   MegaStat Output of a Stem-and-Leaf Display of the 49 Test Scores

Stem and Leaf plot for Scores

stem unit = 1
leaf unit = 0.1

Frequency	Stem	Leaf
1	29	8
4	30	1344
7	30	5666889
9	31	001233444
11	31	55566777889
10	32	0001122344
6	32	556788
1	33	3
49		

To perform this test, we first divide the number line into intervals (or categories). One way to do this is to use the class boundaries typical of a histogram. Table 14.4 gives these intervals and also gives observed frequencies (counts of the number of scores in each interval). The chi-square test is done by comparing these observed frequencies with the expected frequencies in the rightmost column of Table 14.4. To explain how the expected frequencies are calculated, we first use the sample mean $\bar{x} = 31.55$ and the sample standard deviation $s = .8$ of the 49 scores as point estimates of the population mean μ and population standard deviation σ. Then, for example, consider p_1,

TABLE 14.4 Observed and Expected Cell Frequencies for a Chi-Square Goodness of Fit Test for Testing the Normality of the 49 Test Scores in Table 14.3 ✎

Interval	Observed Frequency (f_i)	p_i If the Population of Scores Is Normally Distributed	Expected Frequency, $E_i = np_i = 49p_i$
Less than 30.35	3	$p_1 = P(\text{score} < 30.35) = 0.0668$	$E_1 = 49(0.0668) = 3.2732$
[30.35, 30.95]	9	$p_2 = P(30.35 < \text{score} < 30.95) = 0.1598$	$E_2 = 49(0.1598) = 7.8302$
[30.95, 31.55]	12	$p_3 = P(30.95 < \text{score} < 31.55) = 0.2734$	$E_3 = 49(0.2734) = 13.3966$
[31.55, 32.15]	13	$p_4 = P(31.55 < \text{score} < 32.15) = 0.2734$	$E_4 = 49(0.2734) = 13.3966$
[32.15, 32.75]	9	$p_5 = P(32.15 < \text{score} < 32.75) = 0.1598$	$E_5 = 49(0.1598) = 7.8302$
Greater than 32.75	3	$p_6 = P(\text{score} > 32.75) = 0.0668$	$E_6 = 49(0.0668) = 3.2732$

the probability that a randomly selected score will be in the first interval (less than 30.35) in Table 14.4 if the population of all scores is normally distributed. We estimate p_1 to be

$$p_1 = P(\text{score} < 30.35) = P\left(z < \frac{30.35 - 31.55}{.8}\right)$$
$$= P(z < -1.5) = .5 - .4332 = .0668$$

Note: Use the z table here to obtain the probability below a z of -1.5.

If the scores are normally distributed, we would expect that 6.68 percent of the 49 observations would fall in that interval. Therefore, it follows that $E_1 = 49p_1 = 49(.0668) = 3.2732$ is the expected frequency for the first interval under the normality assumption. Next, if we consider p_2, the probability that a randomly selected score will be in the second interval in Table 14.4 if the population of all scores is normally distributed, we estimate p_2 to be

$$p_2 = P(30.35 < \text{score} < 30.95) = P\left(\frac{30.35 - 31.55}{.8} < z < \frac{30.95 - 31.55}{.8}\right)$$
$$= P(-1.5 < z < -.75) = .4332 - .2734 = .1598$$

It follows that $E_2 = 49p_2 = 49(0.1598) = 7.8302$ is the expected frequency for the second interval under the normality assumption. The other expected frequencies are computed similarly. Note that for both the first and last intervals, the expected value is less than 5. If this situation occurs, the researcher either can continue with the chi-square calculation, noting that the expected value for two of the cells is less than 5, or can combine categories, which is discussed after the calculation of the chi-square with the smaller expected frequency values.

In general, p_i is the probability that a randomly selected score will be in interval i if the population of all possible scores is normally distributed with mean 31.55 and standard deviation .8, and E_i is the expected number of the 49 scores that would be in interval i if the population of all possible scores has this normal distribution.

It seems reasonable to reject the null hypothesis

H_0: Population of all scores is normally distributed

in favour of the alternative hypothesis

H_a: Population of all scores is not normally distributed

if the observed frequencies in Table 14.4 differ substantially from the corresponding expected frequencies. We compare the observed frequencies with the expected frequencies under the normality assumption by computing the chi-square statistic

$$\chi^2 = \sum_{i=1}^{6} \frac{(f_i - E_i)^2}{E_i}$$
$$= \frac{(3 - 3.2732)^2}{3.2732} + \frac{(9 - 7.8302)^2}{7.8302} + \frac{(12 - 13.3966)^2}{13.3966}$$
$$+ \frac{(13 - 13.3966)^2}{13.3966} + \frac{(9 - 7.8302)^2}{7.8302} + \frac{(3 - 3.2732)^2}{3.2732}$$
$$= .55247$$

Because we have estimated $m = 2$ parameters (μ and σ) in computing the expected frequencies (E_i values) for a normal distribution, the sampling distribution of χ^2 is approximately a chi-square distribution with $k - 1 - m = 6 - 1 - 2 = 3$ degrees of freedom. Therefore, we can reject H_0 at level of significance α if

$$\chi^2 > \chi_\alpha^2$$

where the χ_α^2 point is based on $k - 1 - m = 6 - 1 - 2 = 3$ degrees of freedom. If we want to test H_0 at the .05 level of significance, Table A.18 tells us that $\chi_{.05}^2 = 7.81473$. Therefore, because

$$\chi^2 = .55247 < \chi_{.05}^2 = 7.81473$$

we cannot reject H_0 at the .05 level of significance, and we cannot reject the hypothesis that the population of all scores is normally distributed. Therefore, it is probably reasonable to assume that the population of all test scores is approximately normally distributed and that inferences based on this assumption are valid.

Note, as mentioned above, some of the expected cell frequencies in Table 14.4 are not at least 5, but the number of classes (groups) is 6 and the average of the expected cell frequencies is at least 5. Therefore, it may be reasonable to consider the result of this chi-square test valid. If we choose to base the chi-square test on the more restrictive assumption that all of the expected cell frequencies are at least 5, we can combine adjacent cell frequencies as follows:

Original f_i Values	Original p_i Values	Original E_i Values	Combined E_i Values	Combined p_i Values	Combined f_i Values
3	0.0668	3.2732 ⎫			
9	0.1598	7.8302 ⎭	11.1034	0.2266	12
12	0.2734	13.3966	13.3966	0.2734	12
13	0.2734	13.3966	13.3966	0.2734	13
9	0.1598	7.8302 ⎫			
3	0.0668	3.2732 ⎭	11.1034	0.2266	12

When we use these combined cell frequencies, the chi-square approximation is based on $k - 1 - m = 4 - 1 - 2 = 1$ degree of freedom. We find that our calculated chi-square is $\chi^2 = .30214$. The critical chi-square for .05 level of significance at 1 degree of freedom is 3.84146, which is greater than our obtained chi-square value. Therefore, we cannot reject the hypothesis of normality at the .05 level of significance.

In the test score example, we based the intervals used in the chi-square goodness of fit test on the class boundaries typical of a histogram. Another way to establish intervals for such a test is to compute the sample mean $\bar{x}$ and the sample standard deviation s and to use intervals based on the empirical rule as follows:

Interval 1: Less than $\bar{x} - 2s$

Interval 2: $\bar{x} - 2s$ to less than $\bar{x} - s$

Interval 3: $\bar{x} - s$ to less than $\bar{x}$

Interval 4: $\bar{x}$ to less than $\bar{x} + s$

Interval 5: $\bar{x} + s$ to less than $\bar{x} + 2s$

Interval 6: Greater than $\bar{x} + 2s$

However, care must be taken to ensure that each of the expected frequencies is large enough (using the previously discussed criteria).

No matter how the intervals are established, we use $\bar{x}$ as an estimate of the population mean μ and s as an estimate of the population standard deviation σ when we calculate the expected frequencies (E_i values). Because we are estimating $m = 2$ population parameters, the rejection point χ_α^2 is based on $k - 1 - m = k - 1 - 2 = k - 3$ degrees of freedom, where k is the number of intervals used.

In the following boxed feature, we summarize how to carry out this chi-square test.

A Goodness of Fit Test for a Normal Distribution

1 We will test the following null and alternative hypotheses:

H_0: Population has a normal distribution

H_a: Population does not have a normal *distribution*

2 Select a random sample of size n and compute the sample mean $\bar{x}$ and sample standard deviation s.

3 Define k intervals for the test. Two ways to do this are to use the classes of a histogram of the data or to use intervals based on the empirical rule.

4 Record the observed frequency (f_i) for each interval.

5 Calculate the expected frequency (E_i) for each interval under the normality assumption. Do this by computing the probability that a normal variable

with mean $\bar{x}$ and standard deviation s is within the interval and by multiplying this probability by n. Make sure that each expected frequency is large enough. If necessary, combine intervals to make the expected frequencies large enough.

6 Calculate the chi-square statistic

$$\chi^2 = \sum_{i=1}^{k} \frac{(f_i - E_i)^2}{E_i}$$

and define the p-value for the test to be the area under the curve of the chi-square distribution with $k - 3$ degrees of freedom to the right of χ^2.

7 Reject H_0 in favour of H_a at level of significance α if $\chi^2 > \chi^2_\alpha$.

Here, the χ^2_α point is based on $k - 3$ degrees of freedom.

While chi-square goodness of fit tests are often used to verify that it is reasonable to assume that a random sample has been selected from a normally distributed population, such tests can also check other distribution forms. For instance, we might verify that it is reasonable to assume that a random sample has been selected from a Poisson distribution. In general, *the number of degrees of freedom for the chi-square goodness of fit test will equal $k - 1 - m$*, where k is the number of intervals or categories employed in the test and m is the number of population parameters that must be estimated to calculate the needed expected frequencies.

Exercises for Section **14.1**

CONCEPTS

14.1 Describe the characteristics that define a multinomial experiment.

14.2 Give the conditions that the expected cell frequencies must meet in order to validly carry out a chi-square goodness of fit test.

14.3 Explain the purpose of a goodness of fit test.

14.4 When performing a chi-square goodness of fit test, why does a large value of the chi-square statistic provide evidence that H_0 should be rejected?

14.5 Define a control variable and describe what might happen to the analysis when a control variable is introduced.

14.6 State two ways to obtain intervals for a goodness of fit test of normality.

METHODS AND APPLICATIONS

14.7 The proportions of yearly sales across a province in Canada for five popular fruits (apples, oranges, bananas, peaches, and grapefruit, in terms of units sold to each person per year) were found to be 36 percent, 26 percent, 21 percent, 9 percent, and 8 percent, respectively. Suppose that a new survey of 1,000 shoppers in a city in that province was conducted and the following purchase frequencies were found:

Apples	Oranges	Bananas	Peaches	Grapefruit
391	202	275	53	79

a. Show that it is appropriate to carry out a chi-square test using these data.

b. Test to determine whether the city market shares differ from those of the province. Use $\alpha = .05$.

14.8 Last rating period, the percentages of viewers watching several channels in a certain time period in a major TV market were as follows:

Station 1 (News)	Station 2 (News)	Station 3 (Sitcom)	Station 4 (News)	Others
15%	19%	22%	16%	28%

Suppose that in the current rating period, a survey of 2,000 viewers gives the following frequencies:

Station 1 (News)	Station 2 (News)	Station 3 (Sitcom)	Station 4 (News)	Others
182	536	354	151	777

a. Show that it is appropriate to carry out a chi-square test using these data.
b. Test to determine whether the viewing shares in the current rating period differ from those in the last rating period at the .10 level of significance. What do you conclude?

14.9 In the *Journal of Marketing Research* article identified in Table 14.5, Gupta studied the extent to which the purchase behaviour of scanner panels is representative of overall brand preferences. A scanner panel is a sample of households whose purchase data are recorded when a magnetic identification card is presented at a store checkout. Table 14.5 gives peanut butter purchase data collected by the ACNielsen Company using a panel of 2,500 households in Sioux Falls, South Dakota. The data were collected over 102 weeks. The table also gives the market shares obtained by recording all peanut butter purchases at the same stores during the same period.
a. Show that it is appropriate to carry out a chi-square test.
b. Test to determine whether the purchase behaviour of the panel of 2,500 households is consistent with the purchase behaviour of the population of all peanut butter purchasers. Assume here that purchase decisions by panel members are reasonably independent, and set $\alpha = .05$.

14.10 A warehouse manager wants to investigate the productivity of her employees. It is expected that an employee will complete 100 orders in one day. Five employees are assessed and the following data are collected:

Employee	Orders Completed
A	120
B	88
C	93
D	117
E	97

a. Calculate the chi-square value.
b. What are the degrees of freedom?
c. Based on the results, are employees performing as expected?

14.11 Using the data from Exercise 14.10, sex of the employee was included as a control variable. If employees A and D represent female employees, how does the chi-square value change? What would you conclude about the female employees' performance?

14.12 Using the data from Exercise 14.10, age of the employee was included as a control variable. If employees B, C, and E represent older employees, how does the chi-square value change? What would you conclude about the older employees' performance?

14.13 The purchase frequencies for six different brands of digital cameras are observed at an electronics store over one month:

Brand	Purchase Frequency
A	131
B	273
C	119
D	301
E	176
F	200

a. Carry out a test of homogeneity for these data with $\alpha = .025$.
b. Interpret the results of your test.

TABLE 14.5 Peanut Butter Purchase Data

Brand	Size	Number of Purchases by Household Panel	Market Shares	Goodness of Fit Test obs	expected	O − E	(O − E)²/E	% of chisq
Jif	18 oz.	3,165	20.10%	3,165	3,842.115	−677.115	119.331	13.56
Jif	28	1,892	10.10	1,892	1,930.615	−38.615	0.772	0.09
Jif	40	726	5.42	726	1,036.033	−310.033	92.777	10.54
Peter Pan	10	4,079	16.01	4,079	3,060.312	1,018.689	339.092	38.51
Skippy	18	6,206	28.65	6,206	5,476.448	729.552	97.188	11.04
Skippy	28	1,627	12.38	1,627	2,366.437	−739.437	231.051	26.24
Skippy	40	1,420	7.32	1,420	1,399.218	20.782	0.309	0.03
Total		19,115		19,115	19,111.180	3.823	880.521	100.00

880.52 chisquare   6 df   6.11E-187   *p*-value

Source: Reprinted with permission from *The Journal of Marketing Research*, published by the American Marketing Association. "Do household scanner data provide representative inferences from brand choices? A comparison with store data," by S. Gupta et al., *The Journal of Marketing Research*, 33, November 1996, p. 393 (Table 6).

FIGURE 14.2 Excel Output for Exercise 14.14

pi	Ei	fi	(f-E)^2/E	
0.87	435	479	4.4506	
0.08	40	10	22.5000	
0.03	15	8	3.2667	
0.01	5	2	1.8000	
0.01	5	1	3.2000	
		Chi-Square	35.21724	p-value 0.0000001096

14.14 A wholesaler recently developed a computerized sales invoicing system. Prior to implementing this system, a manual system was used. The distribution of the number of errors per invoice for the manual system is as follows:

Errors per Invoice	0	1	2	3	More Than 3
Percentage of Invoices	87%	8%	3%	1%	1%

After implementation of the computerized system, a random sample of 500 invoices gives the following error distribution:

Errors per Invoice	0	1	2	3	More Than 3
Number of Invoices	479	10	8	2	1

a. Show that it is appropriate to carry out a chi-square test using these data.

b. Use the Excel output in Figure 14.2 to determine whether the error percentages for the computerized system differ from those for the manual system at the .05 level of significance. What do you conclude?

14.15 Consider the sample of 65 payment times given in Table 14.6. Use these data to carry out a chi-square goodness of fit test to test whether the population of all payment times is normally distributed by doing the following:

a. It can be shown that $\bar{x} = 18.1077$ and $s = 3.9612$ for the payment time data. Use these values to compute the following intervals:

(1) Less than $\bar{x} - 2s$.
(2) $\bar{x} - 2s$ to less than $\bar{x} - s$.
(3) $\bar{x} - s$ to less than $\bar{x}$.
(4) $\bar{x}$ to less than $\bar{x} + s$.
(5) $\bar{x} + s$ to less than $\bar{x} + 2s$.
(6) Greater than $\bar{x} + 2s$.

b. Assuming that the population of all payment times is normally distributed, find the probability that a randomly selected payment time will be contained in each of the intervals in part (a). Use these probabilities to compute the expected frequency under the normality assumption for each interval.

c. Verify that the average of the expected frequencies is at least 5 and that the smallest expected frequency is at least 1. What does this tell you?

d. Formulate the null and alternative hypotheses for the chi-square test of normality.

e. For each interval in part (a), find the observed frequency. Then calculate the chi-square statistic needed for the chi-square test of normality.

f. Use the chi-square statistic to test normality at the .05 level of significance. What do you conclude?

14.16 Consider the sample of 60 bottle design ratings given in Table 14.7. Use these data to carry out a chi-square goodness of fit test to determine whether the population of all bottle design ratings is normally distributed. Use $\alpha = .05$, and note that $\bar{x} = 30.35$ and $s = 3.1073$ for the 60 bottle design ratings.

TABLE 14.6 A Sample of Payment Times (in Days) for 65 Randomly Selected Invoices

22	29	16	15	18	17	12	13	17	16	15
19	17	10	21	15	14	17	18	12	20	14
16	15	16	20	22	14	25	19	23	15	19
18	23	22	16	16	19	13	18	24	24	26
13	18	17	15	24	15	17	14	18	17	21
16	21	25	19	20	27	16	17	16	21	

TABLE 14.7 A Sample of Bottle Design Ratings (Composite Scores for a Systematic Sample of 60 Shoppers)

34	33	33	29	26	33	28	25	32	33
32	25	27	33	22	27	32	33	32	29
24	30	20	34	31	32	30	35	33	31
32	28	30	31	31	33	29	27	34	31
31	28	33	31	32	28	26	29	32	34
32	30	34	32	30	30	32	31	29	33

14.2 A CHI-SQUARE TEST FOR INDEPENDENCE

One way to study the relationship between two variables is to classify multinomial count data on two scales (or dimensions) by setting up a contingency table.

Example 14.2 The Client Satisfaction Example

A financial institution sells three kinds of investment products—a stock fund, a bond fund, and a tax-deferred annuity. The company is examining whether customer satisfaction depends on the type of investment product purchased. To do this, 100 clients are randomly selected from the population of clients who have purchased shares in exactly one of the funds. The company records the fund type purchased by these clients and asks each sampled client to rate his or her level of satisfaction with the fund as high, medium, or low. Table 14.8 gives the survey results.

We can look at the data in Table 14.8 in an organized way by constructing a **contingency table** (also called a **two-way cross-classification table**). Such a table classifies the data on two

TABLE 14.8 Results of a Customer Satisfaction Survey Given to 100 Randomly Selected Clients Who Invest in One of Three Fund Types—a Stock Fund, a Bond Fund, or a Tax-Deferred Annuity

Client	Fund Type	Level of Satisfaction	Client	Fund Type	Level of Satisfaction	Client	Fund Type	Level of Satisfaction
1	BOND	HIGH	35	STOCK	HIGH	69	BOND	MED
2	STOCK	HIGH	36	BOND	MED	70	TAXDEF	MED
3	TAXDEF	MED	37	TAXDEF	MED	71	TAXDEF	MED
4	TAXDEF	MED	38	TAXDEF	LOW	72	BOND	HIGH
5	STOCK	LOW	39	STOCK	HIGH	73	TAXDEF	MED
6	STOCK	HIGH	40	TAXDEF	MED	74	TAXDEF	LOW
7	STOCK	HIGH	41	BOND	HIGH	75	STOCK	HIGH
8	BOND	MED	42	BOND	HIGH	76	BOND	HIGH
9	TAXDEF	LOW	43	BOND	LOW	77	TAXDEF	LOW
10	TAXDEF	LOW	44	TAXDEF	LOW	78	BOND	MED
11	STOCK	MED	45	STOCK	HIGH	79	STOCK	HIGH
12	BOND	LOW	46	BOND	HIGH	80	STOCK	HIGH
13	STOCK	HIGH	47	BOND	MED	81	BOND	MED
14	TAXDEF	MED	48	STOCK	HIGH	82	TAXDEF	MED
15	TAXDEF	MED	49	TAXDEF	MED	83	BOND	HIGH
16	TAXDEF	LOW	50	TAXDEF	MED	84	STOCK	MED
17	STOCK	HIGH	51	STOCK	HIGH	85	STOCK	HIGH
18	BOND	HIGH	52	TAXDEF	MED	86	BOND	MED
19	BOND	MED	53	STOCK	HIGH	87	TAXDEF	MED
20	TAXDEF	MED	54	TAXDEF	MED	88	TAXDEF	LOW
21	TAXDEF	MED	55	STOCK	LOW	89	STOCK	HIGH
22	BOND	HIGH	56	BOND	HIGH	90	TAXDEF	MED
23	TAXDEF	MED	57	STOCK	HIGH	91	BOND	HIGH
24	TAXDEF	LOW	58	BOND	MED	92	TAXDEF	HIGH
25	STOCK	HIGH	59	TAXDEF	LOW	93	TAXDEF	LOW
26	BOND	HIGH	60	TAXDEF	LOW	94	TAXDEF	LOW
27	TAXDEF	LOW	61	STOCK	MED	95	STOCK	HIGH
28	BOND	MED	62	BOND	LOW	96	BOND	HIGH
29	STOCK	HIGH	63	STOCK	HIGH	97	BOND	MED
30	STOCK	HIGH	64	TAXDEF	MED	98	STOCK	HIGH
31	BOND	MED	65	TAXDEF	MED	99	TAXDEF	MED
32	TAXDEF	MED	66	TAXDEF	LOW	100	TAXDEF	MED
33	BOND	HIGH	67	STOCK	HIGH			
34	STOCK	MED	68	BOND	HIGH			

FIGURE **14.3** MegaStat Output of a Contingency Table of Fund Type versus
Level of Client Satisfaction (See the Survey Results in Table 14.8) ✐

Cross-tabulation

			Satisfaction Rating			
			HIGH	MED	LOW	Total
F	**BOND**	Observed	15	12	3	30
u		% of row	50.0%	40.0%	10.0%	100.0%
n		% of column	37.5%	30.0%	15.0%	30.0%
d		% of total	15.0%	12.0%	3.0%	30.0%
	STOCK	Observed	24	4	2	30
T		% of row	80.0%	13.3%	6.7%	100.0%
y		% of column	60.0%	10.0%	10.0%	30.0%
p		% of total	24.0%	4.0%	2.0%	30.0%
e	**TAXDEF**	Observed	1	24	15	40
		% of row	2.5%	60.0%	37.5%	100.0%
		% of column	2.5%	60.0%	75.0%	40.0%
		% of total	1.0%	24.0%	15.0%	40.0%
	Total	Observed	40	40	20	100
		% of row	40.0%	40.0%	20.0%	100.0%
		% of column	100.0%	100.0%	100.0%	100.0%
		% of total	40.0%	40.0%	20.0%	100.0%

46.44^a chi-square
4 df
$2.00E\text{-}09^b$ p-value

[a]Chi-square statistic
[b]p-value for chi-square

dimensions—type of fund and degree of client satisfaction. Figure 14.3 gives the MegaStat output of a contingency table of fund type versus level of satisfaction. This table consists of a row for each fund type and a column for each level of satisfaction. Together, the rows and columns form a "cell" for each fund type–satisfaction level combination. That is, there is a cell for each contingency in relation to fund type and satisfaction level. A cell frequency for each cell, which is the red number at the top of the cell, is reported. This is a count (observed frequency) of the number of surveyed clients with the cell's fund type–satisfaction level combination. For instance, 15 of the surveyed clients invest in the bond fund and report high satisfaction, while 24 of the surveyed clients invest in the tax-deferred annuity and report medium satisfaction. In addition to the cell frequencies, the output also gives the following:

Row totals (at the far right of the table): These are counts of the numbers of clients who invest in each fund type. These row totals tell us that

1 30 clients invest in the bond fund.
2 30 clients invest in the stock fund.
3 40 clients invest in the tax-deferred annuity.

Column totals (at the bottom of the table): These are counts of the numbers of clients who report high, medium, and low satisfaction. These column totals tell us that

1 40 clients report high satisfaction.
2 40 clients report medium satisfaction.
3 20 clients report low satisfaction.

Overall total (the bottom right entry in the table): This tells us that a total of 100 clients were surveyed.

Besides the row and column totals, the output lists row and total percentages (directly below the row and column totals). For example, 30.0 percent of the surveyed clients invest in the bond fund, and 20.0 percent of the surveyed clients report low satisfaction. In addition to a cell frequency, the output gives a row percentage, a column percentage, and a cell percentage for each cell (these are below the cell frequency in each cell). For instance, looking at the bond fund–high satisfaction cell, we see that the 15 clients in this cell make up 50.0 percent of the 30 clients who invest in the bond fund, and they make up 37.5 percent of the 40 clients who report high satisfaction. In addition, these 15 clients make up 15.0 percent of the 100 clients surveyed.

Looking at the contingency table, it appears that the level of client satisfaction may be related to the fund type. We see that higher satisfaction ratings seem to be reported by stock and bond fund investors, while holders of tax-deferred annuities report lower satisfaction ratings. To carry out a formal statistical test, we can test the null hypothesis

H_0: Fund type and level of client satisfaction are independent

versus

H_a: Fund type and level of client satisfaction are dependent.

To perform this test, we compare the counts (or observed cell frequencies) in the contingency table with the counts that would appear in the contingency table if we assumed that fund type and level of satisfaction were independent. Because these latter counts are computed by assuming independence, we call them the expected cell frequencies under the independence assumption.

ROADBLOCK

Cell numbers and sample sizes
When the independence assumption is being tested, the number of cells typically increases. To meet the conservative criteria of expected cells sizes of at least five, more observations will be required.

To illustrate how to calculate these expected cell frequencies, consider the cell corresponding to the bond fund and high client satisfaction. We first use the data in the contingency table to compute an estimate of the probability that a randomly selected client invests in the bond fund. Denoting this probability as p_B, we estimate p_B by dividing the row total for the bond fund by the total number of clients surveyed. That is, denoting the row total for the bond fund as r_B and letting n denote the total number of clients surveyed, the estimate of p_B is $r_B/n = 30/100 = .3$. Next we compute an estimate of the probability that a randomly selected client will report high satisfaction. Denoting this probability as p_H, we estimate p_H by dividing the column total for high satisfaction by the total number of clients surveyed. That is, denoting the column total for high satisfaction as c_H, the estimate of p_H is $c_H/n = 40/100 = .4$.

Next, assuming that investing in the bond fund and reporting high satisfaction are independent, we compute an estimate of the probability that a randomly selected client invests in the bond fund and reports high satisfaction. Denoting this probability as p_{BH}, we can compute its estimate. If two events A and B are statistically independent, then the probability of A and B equals $P(A)P(B)$. It follows that if we assume that investing in the bond fund and reporting high satisfaction are independent, we can compute an estimate of p_{BH} by multiplying the estimate of p_B by the estimate of p_H. That is, the estimate of p_{BH} is $(r_B/n)(c_H/n) = (.3)(.4) = .12$. Finally, we compute an estimate of the expected cell frequency under the independence assumption. Denoting the expected cell frequency as E_{BH}, the estimate of E_{BH} is

$$\hat{E}_{BH} = n\left(\frac{r_B}{n}\right)\left(\frac{c_H}{n}\right) = 100(.3)(.4) = 12$$

Noting that the expression for $\hat{E}_{BH}$ can be written as

$$\hat{E}_{BH} = n\left(\frac{r_B}{n}\right)\left(\frac{c_H}{n}\right) = \frac{r_B c_H}{n}$$

we can generalize to obtain a formula for the estimated expected cell frequency for any cell in the contingency table. Letting $\hat{E}_{ij}$ denote the estimated expected cell frequency corresponding to row i and column j in the contingency table, we see that

$$\hat{E}_{ij} = \frac{r_i c_j}{n}$$

where r_i is the row total for row i and c_j is the column total for column j. For example, for the fund type–satisfaction level contingency table, we obtain for the stock–low satisfaction cell:

$$\hat{E}_{SL} = \frac{r_S c_L}{n} = \frac{30(20)}{100} = \frac{600}{100} = 6$$

and for the tax-deferred–medium level of satisfaction cell:

$$\hat{E}_{TM} = \frac{r_T c_M}{n} = \frac{40(40)}{100} = \frac{1,600}{100} = 16$$

Intuitively, these estimated expected cell frequencies tell us what the contingency table looks like if fund type and level of client satisfaction are independent.

To test the null hypothesis of independence, we will compute a chi-square statistic that compares the observed cell frequencies with the estimated expected cell frequencies calculated assuming independence. Letting f_{ij} denote the observed cell frequency for cell ij, we compute

$$\chi^2 = \sum_{\text{all cells}} \frac{(f_{ij} - \hat{E}_{ij})^2}{\hat{E}_{ij}}$$

$$= \frac{(f_{BH} - \hat{E}_{BH})^2}{\hat{E}_{BH}} + \frac{(f_{BM} - \hat{E}_{BM})^2}{\hat{E}_{BM}} + \cdots + \frac{(f_{TL} - \hat{E}_{TL})^2}{\hat{E}_{TL}}$$

$$= \frac{(15 - 12)^2}{12} + \frac{(12 - 12)^2}{12} + \frac{(3 - 6)^2}{6} + \frac{(24 - 12)^2}{12} + \frac{(4 - 12)^2}{12}$$

$$+ \frac{(2 - 6)^2}{6} + \frac{(1 - 16)^2}{16} + \frac{(24 - 16)^2}{16} + \frac{(15 - 8)^2}{8}$$

$$= 46.4375$$

If the value of the chi-square statistic is large, this indicates that the observed cell frequencies differ substantially from the expected cell frequencies calculated by assuming independence. Therefore, the larger the value of chi-square, the more doubt is cast on the null hypothesis of independence.

To find an appropriate rejection point, we let r denote the number of rows in the contingency table and c denote the number of columns. Then, when the null hypothesis of independence is true, the sampling distribution of χ^2 is approximately a χ^2 distribution with $(r - 1)(c - 1) = (3 - 1)(3 - 1) = 4$ degrees of freedom. If we test H_0 at the .05 level of significance, we reject H_0 if and only if

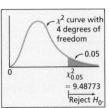

$$\chi^2 > \chi^2_{.05}$$

Table A.18 tells us that the $\chi^2_{.05}$ point corresponding to $(r - 1)(c - 1) = 4$ degrees of freedom equals 9.48773, so

$$\chi^2 = 46.4375 > \chi^2_{.05} = 9.48773$$

and we reject H_0 at the .05 level of significance. We conclude that fund type and level of client satisfaction are not independent.

In the following boxed feature, we summarize how to carry out a **chi-square test for independence**.

A Chi-Square Test for Independence

Suppose that each of n randomly selected elements is classified on two dimensions, and suppose that the result of the two-way classification is a contingency table with r rows and c columns. Let

f_{ij} = Cell frequency corresponding to row i and column j of the contingency table (that is, the number of elements classified in row i and column j)

r_i = Row total for row i in the contingency table

c_j = Column total for column j in the contingency table

$$\hat{E}_{ij} = \frac{r_i c_j}{n}$$

= Estimated expected number of elements that would be classified in row i and column j of the contingency table if the two classifications are statistically independent

If we want to test

H_0: Two classifications are statistically independent

versus

H_a: Two classifications are statistically dependent

we define the test statistic

$$\chi^2 = \sum_{\text{All cells}} \frac{(f_{ij} - \hat{E}_{ij})^2}{\hat{E}_{ij}}$$

Also, we define the p-value related to χ^2 to be the area under the curve of the chi-square distribution with $(r-1)(c-1)$ degrees of freedom to the right of χ^2.

Then we can reject H_0 in favour of H_a at level of significance α if

$$\chi^2 > \chi_\alpha^2$$

Here the χ_α^2 point is based on $(r-1)(c-1)$ degrees of freedom.

This test is based on the fact that when the null hypothesis of independence is true, the sampling distribution of χ^2 is approximately a chi-square distribution with $(r-1)(c-1)$ degrees of freedom if the sample size n is large. *It is generally agreed that n should be considered large if all of the estimated expected cell frequencies ($\hat{E}_{ij}$ values) are at least 5.* Moore and McCabe (1993) indicate that *it is reasonable to use the chi-square approximation if the number of cells (rc) exceeds 4, the average of the $\hat{E}_{ij}$ values is at least 5, and the smallest $\hat{E}_{ij}$ value is at least 1.*

Again consider the MegaStat output in Figure 14.3, which gives the contingency table of fund type versus level of client satisfaction. The chi-square statistic ($= 46.438$) for testing the null hypothesis of independence, as well as the related p-value, are listed. We see that this p-value is less than .001. It follows that we can reject

H_0: Fund type and level of client satisfaction are independent

at the .05 level of significance because the p-value is less than .05.

To study the nature of the dependency between the classifications in a contingency table, it is often useful to plot the row and/or column percentages. As an example, Figure 14.4 gives

FIGURE 14.4 Plots of Row Percentages versus Investment Type for the Contingency Table in Figure 14.3

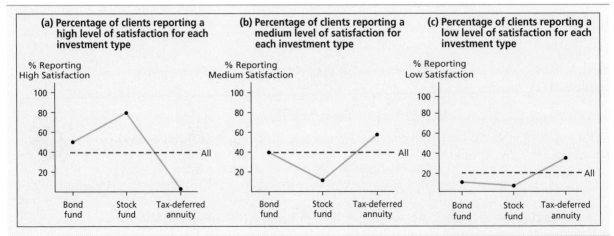

plots of the row percentages in the contingency table of Figure 14.3. For instance, the column in this contingency table corresponding to a high level of satisfaction tells us that 40.0 percent of the surveyed clients report a high level of satisfaction. If fund type and level of satisfaction really were independent, then we would expect roughly 40 percent of the clients in each of the three categories—bond fund participants, stock fund participants, and tax-deferred annuity holders—to report a high level of satisfaction. That is, we would expect the row percentages in the high satisfaction column to be roughly 40 percent in each row. However, Figure 14.4(a) gives a plot of the percentages of clients reporting a high level of satisfaction for each invest-ment type (that is, the figure plots the three row percentages in the high satisfaction column).

We see that these percentages vary considerably. Noting that the dashed line in the figure is the 40 percent reporting a high level of satisfaction for the overall group, we see that the percentage of stock fund participants reporting high satisfaction is 80 percent. This is far above the 40 percent we would expect if independence existed. On the other hand, the percentage of tax-deferred annuity holders reporting high satisfaction is only 2.5 percent—way below the expected 40 percent if independence existed. In a similar fashion, Figure 14.4(b) and (c) plot the row percentages for the medium and low satisfaction columns in the contingency table. These plots indicate that stock fund participants report medium and low levels of satisfaction less frequently than the overall group of clients, and that tax-deferred annuity participants report medium and low levels of satisfaction more frequently than the overall group of clients. Note that the chi-square test for independence can be used to test the equality of several population proportions.

LO7

Exercises for Section **14.2**

CONCEPTS

14.17 What is the purpose of summarizing data in a two-way contingency table?

14.18 When performing a chi-square test for independence, how are the cell frequencies under the independence assumption calculated? Why are these frequencies calculated?

METHODS AND APPLICATIONS

14.19 A marketing research firm wants to study the relationship between wine consumption and whether a person likes to watch professional tennis on television. One hundred randomly selected people are asked whether they drink wine and whether they watch tennis. The following results are obtained:

	Watch Tennis	Do Not Watch Tennis	Totals
Drink Wine	16	24	40
Do Not Drink Wine	4	56	60
Totals	20	80	100

  a. For each row and column total, calculate the corresponding row or column percentage.
  b. For each cell, calculate the corresponding cell, row, and column percentages.
  c. Test the hypothesis that whether people drink wine is independent of whether people watch tennis. Set $\alpha = .05$.
  d. Given the results of the chi-square test, does it make sense to advertise wine during a televised tennis match (assuming that the ratings for the tennis match are high enough)? Explain.

14.20 A random sample of Canadian university undergraduate students was given a questionnaire designed to find out whether they would consider seeking a graduate degree. Male and female students were questioned and their responses were as follows:

Pursue a Graduate Degree	Male	Female	Total
Yes	79	121	200
No	86	114	200
Total	165	235	400

At $\alpha = .05$, test the hypothesis that the decision to pursue a graduate degree is independent of sex for these university students.

14.21 The *Labour Force Survey* conducted by Statistics Canada provides employment figures for men and women. Table 14.9 provides the 2009 values (in thousands) reported for men and women who were employed full-time and part-time separately.

  a. Test the hypothesis that the relationship between sex and employment status is independent by computing the chi-square value.
  b. Looking at the percentage values in Table 14.9, what conclusions can you draw for men versus women in terms of patterns of employment?

TABLE **14.9**   Employment by Sex Statistics for Canadians in 2009 ✐

		Men	Women	Total
Full-time	Count	7,726	5,902	13,628
	Expected Count	7,095.5	6,532.5	
	Percent within employ	56.7	43.3	
	Percent within sex	88.1	73.1	
	Percent of Total	45.9	35	
Part-time	Count	1,046	2,174	3,220
	Expected Count	1,676.5	1,543.5	
	Percent within employ	32.5	67.5	
	Percent within sex	11.9	26.9	
	Percent of Total	6.2	12.9	
Total	Count	8,772	8,076	16,848

Source: Adapted from Statistics Canada (statcan.gc.ca), *Summary Tables*, "Labour force characteristics by sex and age group," Table 282–0002.

TABLE **14.10**   A Contingency Table Relating Delivery Time and Computer-Assisted Ordering ✐

Computer-Assisted Ordering	Delivery Time			Row Total
	Below Industry Average	Equal to Industry Average	Above Industry Average	
No	4	12	8	24
Yes	10	4	2	16
Column Total	14	16	10	40

14.22 In the book *Essentials of Marketing Research*, Dillon, Madden, and Firtle discuss the relationship between delivery time and computer-assisted ordering. A sample of 40 firms shows that 16 use computer-assisted ordering, while 24 do not. Furthermore, past data are used to categorize each firm's delivery times as below the industry average, equal to the industry average, or above the industry average. The results obtained are given in Table 14.10.
  a. Test the hypothesis that delivery time performance is independent of whether computer-assisted ordering is used. What do you conclude by setting $\alpha = .05$?
  b. Verify that a chi-square test is appropriate.
  c. Is there a difference in delivery-time performance between firms using computer-assisted ordering and those not using computer-assisted ordering?
  d. Carry out graphical analysis to investigate the relationship between delivery-time performance and computer-assisted ordering. Describe the relationship.

14.23 A television station wants to study the relationship between viewership of its 11 P.M. news program and viewer age (18 years or less, 19 to 35, 36 to 54, 55 or older). A sample of 250 television viewers in each age group is randomly selected, and the number who watch the station's 11 P.M. news is found for each sample. The results are given in Table 14.11.
  a. Let p_1, p_2, p_3, and p_4 be the proportions of all viewers in each age group who watch the station's 11 P.M. news. If these proportions are equal, then whether a viewer watches the station's 11 P.M. news is independent of the viewer's age group. Therefore, we can test the null hypothesis H_0 that p_1, p_2, p_3, and p_4 are equal by carrying out a chi-square test for independence. Perform this test by setting $\alpha = .05$.
  b. Compute a 95 percent confidence interval for the difference between p_1 and p_4.

TABLE **14.11**   A Summary of the Results of a TV Viewership Study ✐

Watch 11 P.M. News?	Age Group				Total
	18 or Less	19 to 35	36 to 54	55 or Older	
Yes	37	48	56	73	214
No	213	202	194	177	786
Total	250	250	250	250	1,000

CHAPTER SUMMARY

In this chapter, we presented two hypothesis tests that employ the chi-square distribution. In Section 14.1, we discussed a chi-square goodness of fit test. Here we considered a situation in which we study how count data are distributed among various categories. In particular, we considered a multinomial experiment in which randomly selected items are classified into several groups, and we saw how to perform a goodness of fit test for the multinomial probabilities associated with these groups. We also explained how to perform a goodness of fit test to check the normality of the scores.

In Section 14.2, we presented a chi-square test for independence. Here we classify count data on two dimensions, and we summarize the cross-classification in the form of a contingency table. We use the cross-classified data to test whether the two classifications are statistically independent, which is really a way to see whether the classifications are related. We also learned that we can use graphical analysis to investigate the nature of the relationship between the classifications.

KEY TERMS

chi-square test for independence
contingency table (also called a two-way cross-classification table)
goodness of fit test for multinomial probabilities

goodness of fit test to check the normality of the scores
multinomial experiment
test for homogeneity

IMPORTANT FORMULAS AND TESTS

Goodness of fit test for multinomial probabilities

Test for homogeneity

Goodness of fit test for a normal distribution

Chi-square test for independence

SUPPLEMENTARY EXERCISES

connect Practise and learn online with *Connect*. Items for which there are online data sets are marked with ✎.

14.24 Leonard has just handed in his statistics midterm exam. It was a multiple-choice exam with 50 questions. He is curious—and a little worried—about the distribution of his responses. On a scrap piece of paper, he recorded the number of As, Bs, Cs, and Ds he selected. The results are as follows:

A	B	C	D
10	14	17	9

a. At $\alpha = .05$, carry out a test of homogeneity for these data.
b. Leonard believes that the answers to any multiple-choice test should be distributed evenly. Is this true in his case?

14.25 An occupant traffic study was carried out to aid in the remodelling of a large building on a college campus. The building has five entrances, and the choice of entrance was recorded for a random sample of 300 people entering the building. The results obtained are given in the following table:

Entrance				
I	II	III	IV	V
30	91	97	40	42

Test the null hypothesis that the five entrances are equally used by setting α equal to .05. Find a 95 percent confidence interval for the proportion of all people who use Entrance III.

14.26 In a 1993 article in *Accounting and Business Research*, Meier, Alam, and Pearson studied auditor lobbying on several proposed U.S. accounting standards that affect banks and savings and loan associations. As part of this study, the authors investigated auditors' positions regarding proposed changes in accounting standards that would increase client firms' reported earnings. It was hypothesized that auditors would favour such proposed changes because their clients' managers would receive higher compensation (salary, bonuses, and so on) when client earnings were reported to be higher. Table 14.12 summarizes auditor and client positions (in favour or opposed) regarding proposed changes in accounting standards that would increase client firms' reported earnings. Here the auditor and client positions are cross-classified versus the size of the client firm.

a. Test to determine whether auditor positions regarding earnings-increasing changes in accounting standards depend on the size of the client firm. Use $\alpha = .05$.
b. Test to determine whether client positions regarding earnings-increasing changes in accounting standards depend on the size of the client firm. Use $\alpha = .05$.
c. Carry out a graphical analysis to investigate a possible relationship between (1) auditor positions and the size of the client firm and (2) client positions and the size of the client firm.
d. Does the relationship between position and the size of the client firm seem to be similar for both auditors and clients? Explain.

TABLE **14.12** Auditor and Client Positions Regarding Earnings-Increasing Changes in Accounting Standards

(a) Auditor Positions

	Large Firms	Small Firms	Total
In Favour	13	130	143
Opposed	10	24	34
Total	23	154	177

(b) Client Positions

	Large Firms	Small Firms	Total
In Favour	12	120	132
Opposed	11	34	45
Total	23	154	177

Source: "Auditor lobbying for accounting standards: The case of banks and savings and loan associations," by Heidi Hylton Meier, Pervaiz Alam, and Michael A. Pearson, *Accounting and Business Research*, 23, No. 92 (1993), pp. 477–487.

14.27 Consider the situation in Exercise 14.26. Table 14.13 summarizes auditor positions regarding proposed changes in accounting standards that would decrease client firms' reported earnings. Determine whether the relationship between auditor position and the size of the client firm is the same for earnings-decreasing changes in accounting standards as it is for earnings-increasing changes in accounting standards. Justify your answer using both a statistical test and a graphical analysis.

TABLE **14.13** Auditor Positions Regarding Earnings-Decreasing Changes in Accounting Standards

	Large Firms	Small Firms	Total
In Favour	27	152	179
Opposed	29	154	183
Total	56	306	362

Source: "Auditor lobbying for accounting standards: The case of banks and savings and loan associations," by Heidi Hylton Meier, Pervaiz Alam, and Michael A. Pearson, *Accounting and Business Research*, 23, no. 92 (1993), pp. 477–487.

14.28 In the book *Business Research Methods* (5th ed.), Cooper and Emory discuss a market researcher for an automaker who is studying consumer preferences for styling features of larger sedans. Buyers, who were classified as first-time buyers or repeat buyers, were asked to express their preference for one of two types of styling—European styling or Japanese styling. Of 40 first-time buyers, 8 preferred European styling and 32 preferred Japanese styling. Of 60 repeat buyers, 40 preferred European styling and 20 preferred Japanese styling.

a. Set up a contingency table for these data.

b. Test the hypothesis that buyer status (repeat versus first-time) and styling preference are independent at the .05 level of significance. What do you conclude?

c. Carry out a graphical analysis to investigate the nature of any relationship between buyer status and styling preference. Describe the relationship.

14.29 The manager of a chain of three drug stores wants to investigate the level of coupon redemption at the stores. All three stores have the same sales volume so the manager will randomly sample 200 customers at each store with regard to coupon usage. The survey results are given below. Test the hypothesis that redemption level and location are independent with $\alpha = 0.01$.

Coupon Redemption Level	Midtown	Store Location North Side	South Side	Total
High	69	97	52	218
Medium	101	93	76	270
Low	30	10	72	112
Total	200	200	200	600

14.30 THE VIDEO GAME SATISFACTION RATING CASE

Consider the sample of 65 customer satisfaction ratings given in Table 14.14. Carry out a chi-square goodness of fit test of normality for the population of all customer satisfaction ratings. Recall that we previously calculated $\bar{X} = 42.95$ and $s = 2.6424$ for the 65 ratings.

TABLE **14.14** A Sample of 65 Customer Satisfaction Ratings

39	46	42	40	45	44	44	44	45
45	44	46	46	46	41	46	46	
38	40	40	41	43	38	48	39	
42	39	47	43	47	43	44	41	
42	40	44	39	43	36	41	44	
41	42	43	43	41	44	45	42	
38	45	45	46	40	44	44	47	
42	44	45	45	43	45	44	43	

14.31 An Internet company offers an online proficiency course in basic accounting. Completion of this online course satisfies the *Fundamentals of Accounting* course requirement in many MBA programs. In the first semester, 315 students have enrolled in the course. The marketing research manager divided the country into seven regions of approximately equal populations. The course enrolment values in each of the seven regions are given below. The manager wants to know if there is equal interest in the course across all regions.

Region	1	2	3	4	5	6	7
Enrolment	45	60	30	40	50	55	35

a. Calculate the expected enrolment (frequency) for all 7 regions (Hint: $p_1 = p_2 = p_3 = p_4 = p_5 = p_6 = p_7$).

b. Calculate the value of the chi-square statistic.

c. How many degrees of freedom are associated with the chi-square test? Use $\alpha = .05$ and determine the rejection point condition of the chi-square statistic.

d. At a significance level of .05, test

H_0: Probabilities are equal for all seven regions

e. At a significance level of .01, test

H_0: Probabilities are equal for all seven regions

f. Assume that $H_0: p_1 = p_2 = p_3 = p_4 = p_5 = p_6 = p_7$ is rejected. Write a one-sentence managerial conclusion.

g. Assume that $H_0: p_1 = p_2 = p_3 = p_4 = p_5 = p_6 = p_7$ is not rejected and write a one-sentence managerial conclusion.

14.32 At a local casino, a dice game is played in which the shooter bets on the number of sixes she or he will roll with three dice. The payout is proportional to the number of sixes actually rolled. A player has been rolling the dice for a few hours. The observed frequencies for the number of sixes rolled are as follows:

Number of Sixes Rolled	0	1	2	3
Frequency	45	40	14	1

The casino has become quite suspicious of this person, and they have hired you to analyze the data. Conduct the appropriate chi-square goodness of fit test to see whether this player is using fair dice. Run the test using $\alpha = .05$. What do you conclude?

14.33 A random sample of police records was obtained and the following table shows the number of crimes committed in a midsized Canadian city for each day of the week:

Day	Number of Crimes
Sunday	79
Monday	68
Tuesday	54
Wednesday	69
Thursday	81
Friday	97
Saturday	118

Use a chi-square goodness of fit test to determine whether the number of crimes committed in this city is uniformly distributed over a seven-day week. Test this hypothesis at $\alpha = .05$.

14.34 The leading or first digit of legitimate records, such as invoices or expense claims, tends to follow a distribution that is referred to as Benford's law. The distribution is given as follows:

Leading Digit	Probability
1	0.301
2	0.176
3	0.125
4	0.097
5	0.079
6	0.067
7	0.058
8	0.051
9	0.046

Suppose you suspect that your purchasing manager, who does not know about this law, is faking invoices and redirecting money to his own account. You investigate by taking a random sample of 81 invoices to an auditor. Here are the observed counts for the leading digits on these invoices:

Leading Digit	1	2	3	4	5	6	7	8	9
Observed Frequency	11	11	6	9	7	11	11	4	11

Is there evidence to suggest that these invoices have been faked? Conduct a chi-square goodness of fit test at $\alpha = .05$ to test whether these invoices follow Benford's law.

14.35 INTERNET EXERCISE

2012 marked the 100th anniversary of the Calgary Stampede. The Stampede runs for 10 days. Go to news.calgarystampede.com and enter "2012 daily attendance" in the search window. Using the actual Stampede days in the resulting list (not the "Sneak-a-Peek" day), record the daily attendance numbers. Use these data to assess whether the proportion of visitors is the same every day: i.e., $p(\text{Day1}) = p(\text{Day2}) = \cdots = p(\text{Day10})$.

Note: You will need to compute the total attendance number to obtain the expected value for each day.

a. What is the obtained chi-square value?

b. What are the degrees of freedom?

c. What is the critical chi-square value at $\alpha = .01$?

d. What conclusion can you draw from the results?

CHAPTER **15**
Decision Theory

LEARNING OBJECTIVES

After reading this chapter, you should be able to

LO1 Make decisions under uncertainty and under risk

LO2 Construct a decision tree

LO3 Assess the value of perfect information

LO4 Make decisions using utility theory

LO5 Use posterior analysis to assess the value of sample information

CHAPTER OUTLINE

15.1 Introduction to Decision Theory

15.2 Decision Making Using Posterior Probabilities

15.3 Introduction to Utility Theory

Every day, businesses and the people who run them face a myriad of decisions. For instance, a manufacturer might need to decide where to locate a new factory and might also need to decide how large the new facility should be. Or an investor might decide where to invest money from among several possible investment choices. In this chapter, we study some probabilistic methods that can help a decision maker to make intelligent decisions. In Section 15.1, we introduce decision theory, discuss the elements of a decision problem, and present strategies for making decisions when we face various levels of uncertainty. We also show how to construct a decision tree, which is a diagram that can help us analyze a decision problem, and we show how the concept of expected value can help us make decisions.

In Section 15.2 we show how to use sample information to help make decisions, and we demonstrate how to assess the worth of sample information to decide whether the sample information should be obtained. We conclude this chapter with Section 15.3, which introduces the use of utility theory to help with decision making.

15.1 INTRODUCTION TO DECISION THEORY

Suppose that a real estate developer is proposing the development of a condominium complex on an exclusive parcel of lakefront property. The developer wants to choose between three possible options: building a large complex, building a medium-sized complex, and building a small complex. The profitability of each option depends on the level of demand for condominium units after the complex has been built. For simplicity, the developer considers only two possible levels of demand: high or low—the developer must choose whether to build a large, medium, or small complex based on an assessment of whether demand for condominium units will be high or low.

The real estate developer's situation requires a decision. **Decision theory** is a general approach that helps decision makers make intelligent choices. A decision theory problem typically involves the following elements:

1 **States of nature** are a set of potential future conditions that affect the results of the decision. For instance, the level of demand (high or low) for condominium units will affect profits after the developer chooses to build a large, medium, or small complex. So we have two states of nature: high demand and low demand.

2 **Alternatives** for the real estate developer to choose from include the choice of whether to build a large, medium, or small condominium complex. So the developer has three alternatives: large, medium, and small.

3 A payoff exists for each alternative under each potential state of nature. The payoffs are often summarized in a **payoff table**. For instance, Table 15.1 gives a payoff table for the condominium complex situation. This table gives the profit[1] for each alternative under the different states of nature. For example, the payoff table tells us that, if the developer builds a large complex and if demand for units turns out to be high, a profit of $22 million will be realized. However, if the developer builds a large complex and if demand for units turns out to be low, a loss of $11 million will be suffered.

Once the states of nature have been identified, the alternatives have been listed, and the payoffs have been determined, we evaluate the alternatives by using a **decision criterion** that depends on the degree of uncertainty associated with the states of nature. The three possibilities are

LO1

1 **Certainty**—we know for certain which state of nature will actually occur.

2 **Uncertainty**—we have no information about the likelihood of any of the various states of nature.

3 **Risk**—the likelihood (probability) of each state of nature can be estimated.

Decision making under certainty In the unlikely event that we know for certain which state of nature will actually occur, we simply choose the alternative that gives the best payoff for that state of nature. For instance, in the condominium complex situation, if we know that demand for units will be high, then the payoff table (Table 15.1) tells us that the best alternative is to build a large complex and that this choice will yield a profit of $22 million. On the other hand, if we know that demand for units will be low, then the payoff table tells us that the best alternative is to build a small complex and that this choice will yield a profit of $8 million.

TABLE **15.1** A Payoff Table for the Condominium Complex Situation

	States of Nature	
Alternatives	Low Demand	High Demand
Small complex	$8 million	$8 million
Medium complex	$5 million	$15 million
Large complex	−$11 million	$22 million

[1]Here, profits are really present values representing current dollar values of expected future income minus costs.

Of course, we rarely (if ever) know for certain which state of nature will actually occur. However, analyzing the payoff table in this way often provides insight into the nature of the problem. For instance, examining the payoff table tells us that, if we know that demand for units will be low, then building either a small complex or a medium complex will be far superior to building a large complex (which would yield an $11 million loss).

Decision making under uncertainty Decision making under uncertainty means that we have no information about how likely the different states of nature are. Therefore, we have no idea how to assign probabilities to the different states of nature. In such a case, several approaches are possible; we will discuss two commonly used methods. The first is called the *maximin criterion*.

Maximin criterion: Find the worst possible payoff for each alternative and then choose the alternative that yields the maximum worst possible payoff (or the best of the worst situations).

For instance, to apply the maximin criterion to the condominium complex situation, we proceed as follows (see Table 15.1):

1   If a small complex is built, the worst possible payoff is $8 million.

2   If a medium complex is built, the worst possible payoff is $5 million.

3   If a large complex is built, the worst possible payoff is −$11 million.

Since the maximum of these worst possible payoffs is $8 million, the developer should choose to build a small complex.

The maximin criterion is a *pessimistic approach* because it considers the worst possible payoff for each alternative. When an alternative is chosen using the maximin criterion, the actual payoff obtained may be higher than the maximum worst possible payoff. However, using the maximin criterion assures a "guaranteed minimum" payoff.

A second approach is called the *maximax criterion.*

Maximax criterion: Find the best possible payoff for each alternative, and then choose the alternative that yields the maximum best possible payoff.

To apply the maximax criterion to the condominium complex situation, we proceed as follows (see Table 15.1):

1   If a small complex is built, the best possible payoff is $8 million.

2   If a medium complex is built, the best possible payoff is $15 million.

3   If a large complex is built, the best possible payoff is $22 million.

Since the maximum of these best possible payoffs is $22 million, the developer should choose to build a large complex.

The maximax criterion is an *optimistic approach* because we always choose the alternative that yields the highest possible payoff. This is a "go for broke" strategy, and the actual payoff obtained may be far less than the highest possible payoff. For example, in the condominium complex situation, if a large complex is built and the demand for units turns out to be low, an $11 million loss will be suffered instead of a $22 million profit.

Decision making under risk In the case of decision making under risk, we can estimate the probability of occurrence for each state of nature. This means that we have more information about the states of nature than in the case of uncertainty and less information than in the case of certainty. Here a commonly used approach is to use the **expected monetary value criterion**, which involves computing the expected monetary payoff for each alternative and choosing the alternative with the largest expected payoff.

The expected value criterion can be employed by using *prior probabilities*. As an example, suppose that in the condominium complex situation the developer assigns prior probabilities of .7 and .3 to high and low demands, respectively, as shown in the decision tree diagram in

FIGURE 15.1   A Decision Tree for the Condominium Complex Situation

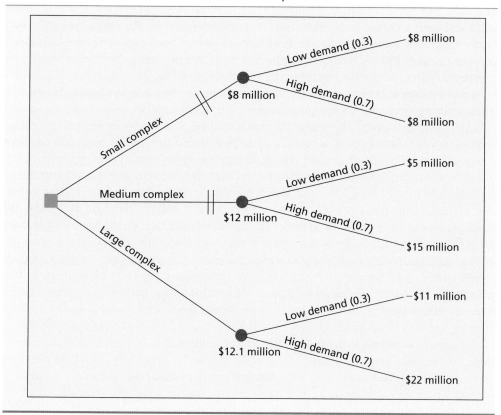

Figure 15.1. We find the expected monetary value for each alternative by multiplying the probability of occurrence for each state of nature by the payoff associated with the state of nature and by summing these products. Referring to the payoff table in Table 15.1, the expected monetary values are as follows:

> Small complex: Expected value = .3($8 million) + .7($8 million) = $8 million
> Medium complex: Expected value = .3($5 million) + .7($15 million) = $12 million
> Large complex: Expected value = .3(−$11 million) + .7($22 million) = $12.1 million

Choosing the alternative with the highest expected monetary value, the developer would choose to build a large complex.

Expected payoffs do not always equal actual payoffs   **ROADBLOCK**
The expected payoff is not necessarily equal to the actual payoff that will be realized. Rather, the expected payoff is the long-run average payoff that would be realized if many identical decisions were made. For instance, the expected monetary payoff of $12.1 million for a large complex is the average payoff that would be obtained if many large condominium complexes were built. So the expected monetary value criterion is best used when many similar decisions will be made.

Using a decision tree It is often convenient to depict the alternatives, states of nature, payoffs, and probabilities (in the case of risk) in the form of a **decision tree** (or **tree diagram**). The diagram is made up of nodes and branches. Square nodes denote decision points and circular nodes denote chance events. The branches emanating from a decision point represent alternatives, and the branches emanating from a circular node represent the possible states of nature. As we have seen, Figure 15.1 presents a decision tree for the condominium complex situation (in the case of risk).

LO2

Notice that the payoffs are shown at the rightmost end of each branch and that the probabilities associated with the various states of nature are given in parentheses corresponding to each branch emanating from a chance node. The expected monetary values for the alternatives are shown below the chance nodes. The double slashes placed through the small complex and medium complex branches indicate that these alternatives would not be chosen (because of their lower expected payoffs) and that the large complex alternative would be selected.

A decision tree is particularly useful when a problem involves a sequence of decisions. For instance, in the condominium complex situation, if demand turns out to be small, it might be possible to improve payoffs by selling the condominiums at lower prices. Figure 15.2 shows a decision tree in which, after a decision to build a small, medium, or large condominium complex is made, the developer can choose to either keep the same prices or charge lower prices for condominium units. To analyze the decision tree, we start with the last (rightmost) decision to be made. For each decision we choose the alternative that gives the highest payoff. For instance, if the developer builds a large complex and demand turns out to be low, the developer should lower prices (as indicated by the double slash through the alternative of same prices). If decisions are followed by chance events, we choose the alternative that gives the highest expected monetary value. For example, in Figure 15.2, we see that a medium complex should now be built because of its highest expected monetary value ($14.1 million). This is indicated by the double slashes drawn through the small and large complex alternatives. Looking at the entire decision tree in Figure 15.2, we see that the developer should build a medium complex and should sell condominium units at lower prices if demand turns out to be low.

Sometimes it is possible to determine which state of nature will occur in the future. For example, in the condominium complex situation, the level of demand for units might depend on whether a new resort casino is built in the area. While the developer may have prior probabilities concerning whether the casino will be built, it might be feasible to postpone a decision about the size of the condominium complex until a final decision about the resort casino has been made.

FIGURE 15.2   A Decision Tree with Sequential Decisions

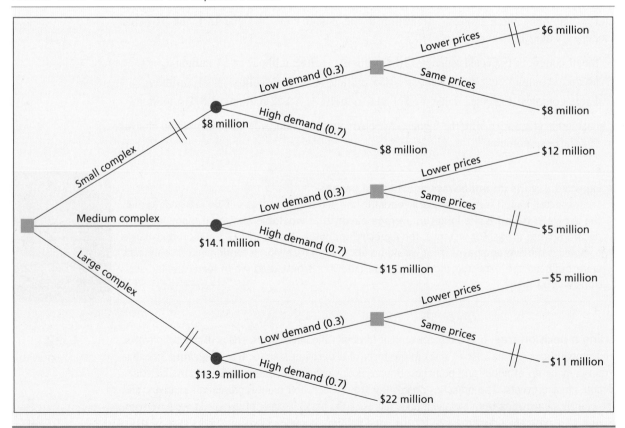

LO3

If we can find out exactly which state of nature will occur, we say we have obtained **perfect information**. There is usually a cost involved in obtaining this information, if it can be obtained at all. For instance, we might have to acquire an option on the lakefront property on which the condominium complex is to be built in order to postpone a decision about the size of the complex. Or information might be acquired by conducting some sort of research that must be paid for. A question that arises here is whether it is worth the cost to obtain information. We can answer this question by computing the **expected value of perfect information (EVPI)**. The EVPI is defined as follows:

$$EVPI = \text{Expected payoff under certainty} - \text{Expected payoff under risk}$$

ROADBLOCK

Perfection is theoretical
The concept of "perfect" here is a theoretical one because, in reality, there is no such thing as perfect information.

For instance, if we consider the condominium complex situation depicted in the decision tree in Figure 15.1, we find that the expected payoff under risk is $12.1 million (which is the expected payoff associated with building a large complex). To find the expected payoff under certainty, we find the highest payoff under each state of nature. Referring to Table 15.1, we see that if demand is low, the highest payoff is $8 million (when we build a small complex); we see that if demand is high, the highest payoff is $22 million (when we build a large complex). Since the prior probabilities of high and low demand are, respectively, .7 and .3, the expected payoff under certainty is .7($22 million) + .3($8 million) = $17.8 million. Therefore, the expected value of perfect information is $17.8 million − $12.1 million = $5.7 million. This is the maximum amount of money that the developer should be willing to pay to obtain perfect information. That is, the land option should be purchased if it costs $5.7 million or less. Then, if the casino is not built (and demand is low), a small condominium complex should be built; if the casino is built (and demand is high), a large condominium complex should be built. On the other hand, if the land option costs more than $5.7 million, the developer should choose the alternative having the highest expected payoff (which would mean building a large complex—see Figure 15.1).

Finally, another approach to dealing with risk involves assigning what we call *utilities* to monetary values. **Utility** reflects the decision maker's attitude toward risk: Does the decision maker avoid risk or is he or she a risk taker? Here the decision maker chooses the alternative that maximizes expected utility (see Section 15.3).

LO4

Exercises for Section **15.1**

CONCEPTS

15.1 Explain the differences between (a) decision making under certainty, (b) decision making under uncertainty, and (c) decision making under risk.

15.2 Explain how to use the (a) maximin criterion, (b) maximax criterion, and (c) expected monetary value criterion.

15.3 Explain how to find the expected value of perfect information.

METHODS AND APPLICATIONS

Exercises 15.4 through 15.9 refer to an example in the book *Production/Operations Management* by William J. Stevenson. The example involves a capacity-planning problem in which a company must choose to build a small, medium, or large production facility. The payoff obtained will depend on whether future demand is low, moderate, or high, and the payoffs are as given in the following table:

Alternatives	Possible Future Demand		
	Low	Moderate	High
Small facility	$10*	$10	$10
Medium facility	7	12	12
Large facility	−4	2	16

*Present value in $ millions.
Source: W. J. Stevenson, *Production/Operations Management*, 5th ed. (Burr Ridge, IL: Richard D. Irwin, 1996), p. 73.

15.4 Find the best alternative (and the resulting payoff) in the given payoff table if it is known with certainty that demand will be
a. Low   **b.** Moderate   **c.** High

15.5 Given the payoff table, find the alternative that would be chosen using the maximin criterion.

15.6 Given the payoff table, find the alternative that would be chosen using the maximax criterion.

15.7 Suppose that the company assigns prior probabilities of .3, .5, and .2 to low, moderate, and high demands, respectively.
   a. Find the expected monetary value for each alternative (small, medium, and large).
   b. What is the best alternative if we use the expected monetary value criterion?

15.8 Construct a decision tree for the information in the payoff table assuming that the prior probabilities of low, moderate, and high demands are, respectively, .3, .5, and .2.

15.9 For the information in the payoff table find
   a. The expected payoff under certainty.
   b. The expected value of perfect information, EVPI.

15.10 A firm wants to choose the location for a new factory. Profits obtained will depend on whether a new railroad spur is constructed to serve the town in which the new factory will be located. The following payoff table summarizes the relevant information:

Alternatives	New Railroad Spur Built	No New Railroad Spur
Location A	$1*	$14
Location B	2	10
Location C	4	6

*Profits in $ millions.

Determine the location that should be chosen if the firm uses:
   a. The maximin criterion.   **b.** The maximax criterion.

FIGURE 15.3   Decision Tree for Exercise 15.13

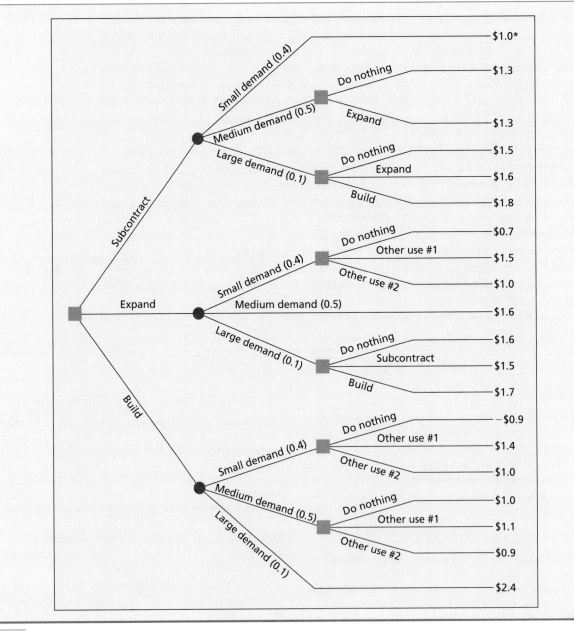

*Net present value in millions.

Source: Decision tree from W. J. Stevenson, *Production/Operations Management*, 6/e, p. 228, and problem from p. 73 © 1999 McGraw-Hill Companies, Inc.

15.11 Refer to the information given in Exercise 15.10. Using
the probabilities of .60 for a new railroad spur and .40
for no new railroad spur
   a. Compute the expected monetary value for each location.
   b. Find the location that should be selected using the
      expected monetary value criterion.
   c. Compute the EVPI, expected value of perfect
      information.

15.12 Construct a decision tree for the information given in
Exercises 15.10 and 15.11.

15.13 Figure 15.3 gives a decision tree presented in
the book *Production/Operations Management*
by William J. Stevenson. Use this tree diagram to
do the following:
   a. Find the expected monetary value for each of the
      alternatives (subcontract, expand, and build).
   b. Determine the alternative that should be selected
      to maximize the expected monetary value.

15.2 DECISION MAKING USING POSTERIOR PROBABILITIES

LO5

We have seen that the *expected monetary value criterion* tells us to choose the alternative having
the highest expected payoff. In Section 15.1, we computed expected payoffs by using *prior probabilities*. When we use the expected monetary value criterion to choose the best alternative based
on expected values computed using prior probabilities, we call this **prior decision analysis**.
Often, however, sample information can be obtained to help us make decisions. In such a case,
we compute expected values by using *posterior probabilities*, and we call the analysis **posterior
decision analysis**. In Example 15.1, we demonstrate how to carry out posterior analysis.

Example 15.1 The Oil Drilling Example

An Alberta oil company wants to decide whether to drill for oil on a particular site. The
company has assigned prior probabilities .7, .2, and .1 to the states of nature $S_1 \equiv$ No oil,
$S_2 \equiv$ Some oil, and $S_3 \equiv$ Much oil, respectively. Figure 15.4 gives a decision tree and payoff
table for a *prior analysis* of the oil drilling situation. Here, using the prior probabilities, the
expected monetary value associated with drilling is

$$.7(-\$700,000) + .2(\$500,000) + .1(\$2,000,000) = -\$190,000$$

while the expected monetary value associated with not drilling is

$$.7(0) + .2(0) + .1(0) = 0$$

Therefore, *prior analysis* tells us that the oil company should not drill.

FIGURE 15.4   A Decision Tree and Payoff Table for a Prior Analysis of the Oil Drilling Example

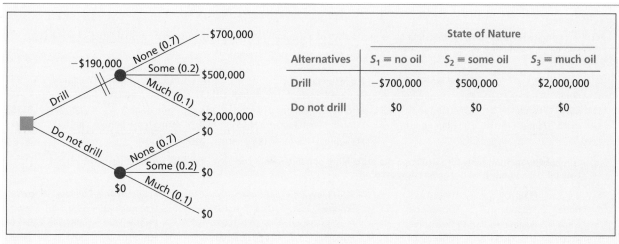

	State of Nature		
Alternatives	$S_1 \equiv$ no oil	$S_2 \equiv$ some oil	$S_3 \equiv$ much oil
Drill	−$700,000	$500,000	$2,000,000
Do not drill	$0	$0	$0

The oil company can obtain more information about the drilling site by performing a seismic experiment with three possible readings: low, medium, and high. The accuracy of the seismic experiment is expressed by the conditional probabilities in part (a) of Figure 15.5. For example, $P(\text{high}|\text{none}) = .04$, $P(\text{high}|\text{some}) = .02$, and $P(\text{high}|\text{much}) = .96$. Also, we can revise the prior probabilities $P(\text{none}) = .7$, $P(\text{some}) = .2$, and $P(\text{much}) = .1$ to posterior probabilities by using Bayes' theorem. For example, it can be calculated that

$$P(\text{high}) = P(\text{none} \cap \text{high}) + P(\text{some} \cap \text{high}) + P(\text{much} \cap \text{high})$$
$$= P(\text{none})P(\text{high}|\text{none}) + P(\text{some})P(\text{high}|\text{some}) + P(\text{much})P(\text{high}|\text{much})$$
$$= (.7)(.04) + (.2)(.02) + (.1)(.96) = .128$$

FIGURE 15.5   A Tree Diagram and Probability Revision Tables for Bayes' Theorem in the Oil Drilling Example

(a) A tree diagram illustrating the prior and conditional probabilities

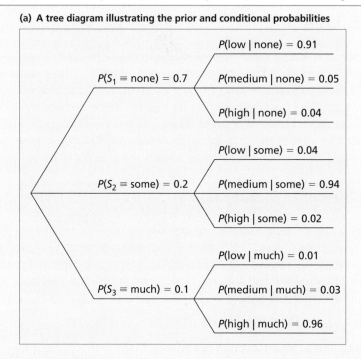

(b) A probability revision table for calculating the probability of a high reading and the posterior probabilities of no oil (S_1), some oil (S_2), and much oil (S_3) given a high reading

S_j	$P(S_j)$	$P(\text{high}\|S_j)$	$P(S_j \cap \text{high}) = P(S_j)P(\text{high}\|S_j)$	$P(S_j\|\text{high}) = P(S_j \cap \text{high})/P(\text{high})$
$S_1 \equiv$ none	$P(\text{none}) = .7$	$P(\text{high}\|\text{none}) = .04$	$P(\text{none} \cap \text{high}) = .7(.04) = .028$	$P(\text{none}\|\text{high}) = .028/.128 = .21875$
$S_2 \equiv$ some	$P(\text{some}) = .2$	$P(\text{high}\|\text{some}) = .02$	$P(\text{some} \cap \text{high}) = .2(.02) = .004$	$P(\text{some}\|\text{high}) = .004/.128 = .03125$
$S_3 \equiv$ much	$P(\text{much}) = .1$	$P(\text{high}\|\text{much}) = .96$	$P(\text{much} \cap \text{high}) = .1(.96) = .096$	$P(\text{much}\|\text{high}) = .096/.128 = .75$
Total	1		$P(\text{high}) = .028 + .004 + .096 = .128$	1

(c) A probability revision table for calculating the probability of a medium reading and the posterior probabilities of no oil (S_1), some oil (S_2), and much oil (S_3) given a medium reading

S_j	$P(S_j)$	$P(\text{medium}\|Sj)$	$P(S_j \cap \text{medium}) = P(S_j)P(\text{medium}\|S_j)$	$P(S_j\|\text{medium}) = P(S_j \cap \text{medium})/P(\text{medium})$
$S_1 \equiv$ none	$P(\text{none}) = .7$	$P(\text{medium}\|\text{none}) = .05$	$P(\text{none} \cap \text{medium}) = .7(.05) = .035$	$P(\text{none}\|\text{medium}) = .035/.226 = .15487$
$S_2 \equiv$ some	$P(\text{some}) = .2$	$P(\text{medium}\|\text{some}) = .94$	$P(\text{some} \cap \text{medium}) = .2(.94) = .188$	$P(\text{some}\|\text{medium}) = .188/.226 = .83186$
$S_3 \equiv$ much	$P(\text{much}) = .1$	$P(\text{medium}\|\text{much}) = .03$	$P(\text{much} \cap \text{medium}) = .1(.03) = .003$	$P(\text{much}\|\text{medium}) = .003/.226 = .01327$
Total	1		$P(\text{medium}) = .035 + .188 + .003 = .226$	1

(d) A probability revision table for calculating the probability of a low reading and the posterior probabilities of no oil (S_1), some oil (S_2) and much oil (S_3) given a low reading

S_j	$P(S_j)$	$P(\text{low}\|S_j)$	$P(S_j \cap \text{low}) = P(S_j)P(\text{low}\|S_j)$	$P(S_j\|\text{low}) = P(S_j \cap \text{low})/P(\text{low})$
$S_1 \equiv$ none	$P(\text{none}) = .7$	$P(\text{low}\|\text{none}) = .91$	$P(\text{none} \cap \text{low}) = .7(.91) = .637$	$P(\text{none}\|\text{low}) = .637/.646 = .98607$
$S_2 \equiv$ some	$P(\text{some}) = .2$	$P(\text{low}\|\text{some}) = .04$	$P(\text{some} \cap \text{low}) = .2(.04) = .008$	$P(\text{some}\|\text{low}) = .008/.646 = .01238$
$S_3 \equiv$ much	$P(\text{much}) = .1$	$P(\text{low}\|\text{much}) = .01$	$P(\text{much} \cap \text{low}) = .1(.01) = .001$	$P(\text{much}\|\text{low}) = .001/.646 = .00155$
Total	1		$P(\text{low}) = .637 + .008 + .001 = .646$	1

Then Bayes' theorem says that

$$P(\text{none}|\text{high}) = \frac{P(\text{none} \cap \text{high})}{P(\text{high})} = \frac{P(\text{none})P(\text{none}|\text{high})}{P(\text{high})} = \frac{.7(.04)}{.128} = .21875$$

Similarly, we can compute $P(\text{some}|\text{high})$ and $P(\text{much}|\text{high})$ as follows:

$$P(\text{some}|\text{high}) = \frac{P(\text{some} \cap \text{high})}{P(\text{high})} = \frac{P(\text{some})P(\text{high}|\text{some})}{P(\text{high})} = \frac{.2(.02)}{.128} = .03125$$

$$P(\text{much}|\text{high}) = \frac{P(\text{much} \cap \text{high})}{P(\text{high})} = \frac{P(\text{much})P(\text{high}|\text{much})}{P(\text{high})} = \frac{.1(.96)}{.128} = .75$$

These calculations are summarized in the *probability revision table* in Figure 15.5(b). This table also shows that

$$P(\text{high}) = P(\text{none} \cap \text{high}) + P(\text{some} \cap \text{high}) + P(\text{much} \cap \text{high})$$
$$= .028 + .004 + .096 = .128$$

Part (c) of Figure 15.5 gives a probability revision table for calculating the probability of a medium reading and the posterior probabilities of no oil, some oil, and much oil given a medium reading, while part (d) of Figure 15.5 gives a probability revision table for calculating the probability of a low reading and the posterior probabilities of no oil, some oil, and much oil given a low reading. We find that $P(\text{medium}) = .226$ and that $P(\text{low}) = .646$.

Figure 15.6 presents a decision tree for a *posterior analysis* of the oil drilling problem. The leftmost decision node represents the decision of whether to conduct the seismic experiment. The upper branch (no seismic survey) contains a second decision node representing the alternatives in our decision problem (that is, drill or do not drill). At the ends of the "drill" and "do not drill" branches, we have chance nodes that branch into the three states of nature: no oil (none), some oil (some), and much oil (much). The appropriate payoff is placed at the rightmost end of each branch, and because this uppermost branch corresponds to "no seismic survey," the probabilities in parentheses for the states of nature are the prior probabilities. The expected payoff associated with drilling (found to be $-\$190,000$) is shown at the chance node for the "drill" branch, and the expected payoff associated with not drilling (found to be 0) is shown at the chance node for the "do not drill" branch.

The lower branch of the decision tree (seismic survey) has an extra chance node that branches into the three possible outcomes of the seismic experiment: low, medium, and high. The probabilities of these outcomes are shown on their respective branches. From the low, medium, and high branches, the tree branches into alternatives (drill and do not drill) and from alternatives into states of nature (none, some, and much). However, the probabilities in parentheses written beside the none, some, and much branches are the posterior probabilities computed in the probability revision tables in Figure 15.5. This is because advancing to the end of a particular branch in the lower part of the decision tree is conditional; that is, it depends on obtaining a particular experimental result (low, medium, or high).

We can now use the decision tree to determine the alternative (drill or do not drill) that should be selected given that the seismic experiment has been performed and has resulted in a particular outcome. First, suppose that the seismic experiment results in a high reading. Looking at the branch of the decision tree corresponding to a high reading, the expected monetary values associated with the "drill" and "do not drill" alternatives are

Drill: $.21875(-\$700,000) + .03125(\$500,000) + .75(\$2,000,000) = \$1,362,500$

Do not drill: $.21875(0) + .03125(0) + .75(0) = \$0$

These expected monetary values are placed on the decision tree corresponding to the "drill" and "do not drill" alternatives. They tell us that, if the seismic experiment results in a high reading, then the company should drill and the expected payoff will be $1,362,500$. The double slash placed through the "do not drill" branch (at the very bottom of the decision tree) blocks off that branch and indicates that the company should drill if a high reading is obtained.

FIGURE **15.6**   A Decision Tree for a Posterior Analysis of the Oil Drilling Example

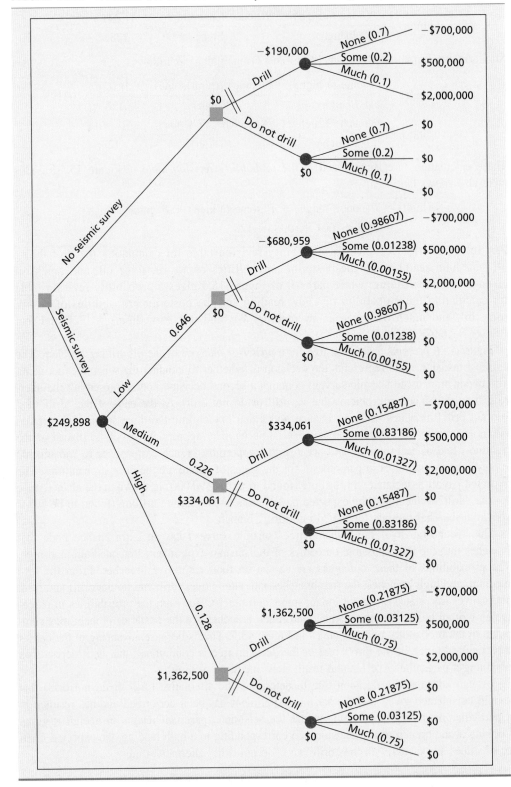

Next, suppose that the seismic experiment results in a medium reading. Looking at the branch corresponding to a medium reading, the expected monetary values are

Drill: .15487(−$700,000) + .83186($500,000) + .01327($2,000,000) = $334,061
Do not drill: .15487($0) + .83186($0) + .01327($0) = $0

Therefore, if the seismic experiment results in a medium reading, the oil company should drill and the expected payoff will be $334,061.

Finally, suppose that the seismic experiment results in a low reading. Looking at the branch corresponding to a low reading, the expected monetary values are

Drill: $.98607(-\$700,000) + .01238(\$500,000) + .00155(\$2,000,000) = -\$680,959$

Do not drill: $.98607(\$0) + .01238(\$0) + .00155(\$0) = \$0$

Therefore, if the seismic experiment results in a low reading, the oil company should not drill on the site.

We can summarize the results of our posterior analysis as follows:

Outcome of Seismic Experiment	Probability of Outcome	Decision	Expected Payoff
High	.128	Drill	$1,362,500
Medium	.226	Drill	$334,061
Low	.646	Do not drill	$0

If we carry out the seismic experiment, we now know what action should be taken for each possible outcome (low, medium, or high). However, there is a cost involved when we conduct the seismic experiment. If, for instance, it costs $100,000 to perform the seismic experiment, we need to investigate whether the experiment is worth the cost. This will depend on the expected worth of the information provided by the experiment. Naturally, we must decide whether the experiment is worth it *before* our posterior analysis is actually done. Therefore, when assessing the worth of the sample information, we are performing a **preposterior analysis**.

To assess the worth of the sample information, we compute the expected payoff of sampling. To calculate this result, we find the expected payoff and the probability of each sample outcome (that is, at each possible outcome of the seismic experiment). Looking at the decision tree in Figure 15.6, we find the following:

Experimental Outcome	Expected Payoff	Probability
Low	$0	.646
Medium	$334,061	.226
High	$1,362,500	.128

Therefore, the expected payoff of sampling (EPS), is

$$\text{EPS} = .646(\$0) + .226(\$334,061) + .128(\$1,362,500) = \$249,898$$

To find the worth of the sample information, we compare the expected payoff of sampling to the expected payoff of no sampling (EPNS). The EPNS is the expected payoff of the alternative that we would choose by using the expected monetary value criterion with the prior probabilities. Recalling that we summarized our prior analysis in the tree diagram in Figure 15.4, we found that (based on the prior probabilities) we should choose not to drill and that the expected payoff of this action is $0. Therefore, EPNS = $0.

We compare the EPS and the EPNS by computing the **expected value of sample information (EVSI)**, which is defined to be the expected payoff of sampling minus the expected payoff of no sampling. Therefore,

$$\text{EVSI} = \text{EPS} - \text{EPNS} = \$249,898 - \$0 = \$249,898$$

The EVSI is the expected gain from conducting the seismic experiment, and the oil company should pay no more than this amount to carry out the seismic experiment. If the experiment costs $100,000, then it is worth the expense to conduct the experiment. Moreover, the difference between the EVSI and the cost of sampling is called the **expected net gain of sampling (ENGS)**. Here

$$\text{ENGS} = \text{EVSI} - \$100,000 = \$249,898 - \$100,000 = \$149,898$$

As long as the ENGS is greater than $0, it is worthwhile to carry out the seismic experiment. That is, the oil company should carry out the seismic experiment before it decides whether to drill. Then, as discussed earlier, our posterior analysis says that if the experiment gives a medium or high reading, the oil company should drill and if the experiment gives a low reading, the oil company should not drill.

Exercises for Section **15.2**

CONCEPTS

15.14 Explain what is meant by each of the following and describe the purpose of each:
   a. Prior analysis.   **b.** Posterior analysis.
   c. Preposterior analysis.

15.15 Define and interpret each of the following:
   a. Expected payoff of sampling, EPS.
   b. Expected payoff of no sampling, EPNS.
   c. Expected value of sample information, EVSI.
   d. Expected net gain of sampling, ENGS.

METHODS AND APPLICATIONS ✎

Exercises 15.16 through 15.21 refer to the following situation.

In the book *Making Hard Decisions: An Introduction to Decision Analysis* (2nd ed.), Robert T. Clemen presents an example in which an investor wants to choose between investing money in (1) a high-risk stock, (2) a low-risk stock, or (3) a savings account. The payoffs received from the two stocks will depend on the behaviour of the stock market (whether the market goes up, stays the same, or goes down over the investment period). In addition, to obtain more information about the market behaviour that might be anticipated during the investment period, the investor can hire an economist as a consultant who will predict the future market behaviour. The results of the consultation will be one of the following three possibilities: (1) "Economist says up," (2) "Economist says flat" (the same), or (3) "Economist says down." The conditional probabilities that express the ability of the economist to accurately forecast market behaviour are given in the following table:

| Economist's Prediction | True Market State | | |
	Up	Flat	Down
"Economist says up"	.80	.15	.20
"Economist says flat"	.10	.70	.20
"Economist says down"	.10	.15	.60

For instance, using this table we see that P("Economist says up"|market up) = .80. Figure 15.7 gives an incomplete decision tree for the investor's situation. Notice that this decision tree gives all relevant payoffs and also gives the prior probabilities of up, flat, and down, which are, respectively, .5, .3, and .2.

Using the information provided here and in the decision tree of Figure 15.7, follow the instructions given for each exercise.

15.16 Identify and list each of the following for the investor's decision problem:
   a. The investor's alternative actions.
   b. The states of nature.
   c. The possible results of sampling (that is, of information gathering).

15.17 Write the payoff table for the investor's decision problem.

15.18 Carry out a prior analysis of the investor's decision problem. That is, determine the investment choice that should be made and find the expected monetary value of that choice assuming that the investor does not consult the economist about future stock market behaviour.

15.19 Set up probability revision tables to
   a. Find the probability that the "Economist says up" and find the posterior probabilities of market up, market flat, and market down given that the "Economist says up."
   b. Find the probability that the "Economist says flat," and find the posterior probabilities of market up, market flat, and market down given that the "Economist says flat."
   c. Find the probability that the "Economist says down," and find the posterior probabilities of market up, market flat, and market down given that the "Economist says down."
   d. Reproduce the decision tree in Figure 15.7 and insert the probabilities you found in parts (a), (b), and (c) in their appropriate locations.

15.20 Carry out a posterior analysis of the investor's decision problem. That is, determine the investment choice that should be made and find the expected monetary value of that choice assuming
   a. The economist says "market up."
   b. The economist says "market flat."
   c. The economist says "market down."

15.21 Carry out a preposterior analysis of the investor's decision problem by finding
   a. The expected monetary value associated with consulting the economist; that is, find the EPS.
   b. The expected monetary value associated with not consulting the economist; that is, find the EPNS.
   c. The expected value of sample information, EVSI.
   d. The maximum amount the investor should be willing to pay for the economist's consulting advice.

Exercises 15.22 through 15.28 refer to the following situation.

A firm designs and manufactures automatic electronic control devices that are installed at customers' plant sites. The control devices are shipped by truck to customers' sites and, while in transit, the devices sometimes get out of alignment. More specifically, a device has a prior probability of .10 of getting out of alignment during shipment. When a control device is delivered to the customer's plant, the customer can install the device. If the customer installs the device and if the device is in alignment, the manufacturer of the control device will realize a profit of $15,000. If the customer installs the device and if the device is out of alignment, the manufacturer must dismantle, realign, and reinstall the device for the

FIGURE **15.7**   An Incomplete Decision Tree for the Investor's Decision Problem of
Exercises 15.16 through 15.21

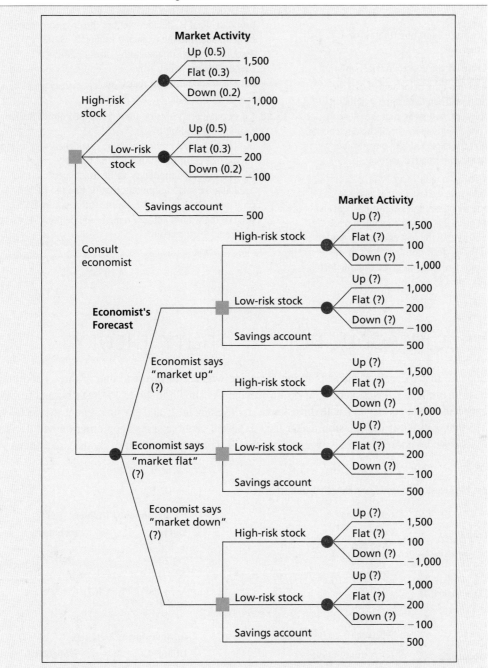

Source: From *Making Hard Decisions: An Introduction to Decision Analysis,* 2nd ed., by R. T. Clemen, © 1996. Reprinted with permission of Brooks/Cole, an imprint of the Wadsworth Group, a division of Thomson Learning. Fax 800-730-2215. P. 443

customer. This procedure costs $3,000, and therefore the manufacturer will realize a profit of $12,000. As an alternative to customer installation, the manufacturer can send two engineers to the customer's plant to check the alignment of the control device, to realign the device if necessary before installation, and to supervise the installation. Because it is less costly to realign the device before it is installed, sending the engineers costs $500. Therefore, if the engineers are sent to assist with the installation, the

manufacturer realizes a profit of $14,500 (this is true whether or not the engineers must realign the device at the site).

Before a control device is installed, a piece of test equipment can be used by the customer to check the device's alignment. The test equipment has two readings, "in" or "out" of alignment. Given that the control device is in alignment, there is a .8 probability that the test equipment will read "in." Given that the control device is out of alignment, there is a .9 probability that the test equipment will read "out."

15.22 Identify and list each of the following for the control device situation:

  a. The manufacturer's alternative courses of action.
  b. The states of nature.
  c. The possible results of sampling (that is, of information gathering).

15.23 Write the payoff table for the control device situation.

15.24 Construct a decision tree for a prior analysis of the control device situation. Then determine whether the engineers should be sent, assuming that the piece of test equipment is not employed to check the device's alignment. Also find the expected monetary value associated with the best alternative action.

15.25 Set up probability revision tables to

  a. Find the probability that the test equipment reads "in," and find the posterior probabilities of in alignment and out of alignment given that the test equipment reads "in."
  b. Find the probability that the test equipment reads "out," and find the posterior probabilities of in alignment and out of alignment given that the test equipment reads "out."

15.26 Construct a decision tree for a posterior and preposterior analysis of the control device situation.

15.27 Carry out a posterior analysis of the control device problem. That is, decide whether the engineers should be sent, and find the expected monetary value associated with either sending or not sending (depending on which is best) the engineers assuming

  a. The test equipment reads "in."
  b. The test equipment reads "out."

15.28 Carry out a preposterior analysis of the control device problem by finding

  a. The expected monetary value associated with using the test equipment; that is, find the EPS.
  b. The expected monetary value associated with not using the test equipment; that is, find the EPNS.
  c. The expected value of sample information, EVSI.
  d. The maximum amount that should be paid for using the test equipment.

15.3 INTRODUCTION TO UTILITY THEORY

Suppose that a decision maker is trying to decide whether to invest in one of three opportunities: Investment 1, Investment 2, or no investment. As shown in Table 15.2(a), (b), and (c), the expected profits associated with Investment 1, Investment 2, and no investment are $32,000, $28,000, and $0. If the decision maker uses expected profit as a decision criterion and decides to choose no more than one investment, the decision maker should choose Investment 1.

TABLE 15.2   Three Possible Investments and Their Expected Utilities

(a) Investment 1 Profits

Profit	Probability
$50,000	.7
$10,000	.1
−$20,000	.2

Expected profit = 50,000(.7) + 10,000(.1) + (−20,000)(.2) = 32,000

(b) Investment 2 Profits

Profit	Probability
$40,000	.6
$30,000	.2
−$10,000	.2

Expected profit = 40,000(.6) + 30,000(.2) + (−10,000)(.2) = 28,000

(c) No Investment Profit

Profit	Probability
$0	1

Expected profit = 0(1) = 0

(d) Utilities

Profit	Utility
$50,000	1
$40,000	.95
$30,000	.90
$10,000	.75
$0	.60
−$10,000	.45
−$20,000	0

(e) A Utility Curve

Profit (in units of $1,000)

(f) Investment 1 Utilities

Utility	Probability
1	.7
.75	.1
0	.2

Expected utility = 1(.7) + .75(.1) + 0(.2) = .775

(g) Investment 2 Utilities

Utility	Probability
.95	.6
.90	.2
.45	.2

Expected utility = .95(.6) + .90(.2) + .45(.2) = .84

(h) No Investment Utility

Utility	Probability
.60	1

Expected utility = .60(1) = .60

However, as discussed earlier, the expected profit for an investment is the long-run average profit that would be realized if many identical investments could be made. If the decision maker, perhaps because of limited capital, makes only a limited number of investments, she or he may not realize the expected profit. For example, a single undertaking of Investment 1 will result in either a profit of $50,000, a profit of $10,000, or a loss of $20,000. Some decision makers might prefer a single undertaking of Investment 2, because the potential loss is only $10,000. Other decision makers might be unwilling to risk $10,000 and would choose no investment.

There is a way to combine the various profits, probabilities, and the decision maker's individual attitude toward risk to make a decision that is best for the decision maker. The method is based on a theory of utility discussed by J. Von Neumann and O. Morgenstern in *Theory of Games and Economic Behavior* (Princeton University Press, Princeton, N. J., 1st ed., 1944, 2nd ed., 1947). This theory says that if a decision maker agrees with certain assumptions about rational behaviour, then the decision maker should replace the profits in the various investments by utilities and choose the investment that gives the highest expected utility.

Assumption of rational decision making   **ROADBLOCK**
In the true rational decision-making model, an assumption is that all possible solutions are available to the decision maker. Rarely is this the case.

To find the utility of a particular profit, we first arrange the profits from largest to smallest. The utility of the largest profit is 1 and the utility of the smallest profit is 0. The utility of any particular intermediate profit is the probability (abbreviated u) that the decision maker is indifferent between (1) getting the particular intermediate profit with certainty or (2) playing a lottery (or game) in which the probability is u of getting the highest profit and the probability is $1 - u$ of getting the smallest profit. Table 15.2(d) arranges the profits in Table 15.2(a), (b), and (c) in increasing order and gives a specific decision maker's utility for each profit. The utility of .95 for $40,000 means that the decision maker is indifferent between (1) getting $40,000 with certainty or (2) playing a lottery in which the probability is .95 of getting $50,000 and the probability is .05 of losing $20,000. The utilities for the other profits are interpreted similarly. Table 15.2(f), (g), and (h) show the investments with profits replaced by utilities, and because Investment 2 has the highest expected utility, the decision maker should choose Investment 2.

Table 15.2(e) shows a plot of the specific decision maker's utilities versus the profits. The curve connecting the plot points is the utility curve for the decision maker and is an example of a risk averter's curve. In general, a risk averter's curve portrays a rapid increase in utility for initial amounts of money followed by a gradual levelling off for larger amounts of money. This curve is appropriate for many individuals and businesses because the marginal value of each additional dollar is not as great once a large amount of money has been earned. A risk averter's curve is shown below, as are a risk seeker's curve and a risk neutral's curve. The risk seeker's curve represents an individual who is willing to take large risks to have the opportunity to make large profits. The risk neutral's curve represents an individual for whom each additional dollar has the same value. It can be shown that this individual should choose the investment having the highest expected profit.

A risk averter's curve: A risk seeker's curve: A risk neutral's curve:
Utility   Utility   Utility

Dollar amount   Dollar amount   Dollar amount

THEORY TO PRACTICE

The types of personalities described above (risk averter, risk seeker, and risk neutral) characterize people in certain situations. For example, an individual making personal investments (for retirement, for example) might be risk averse but the same person might be risk seeking when investing his or her company's money (for example, in a new product development program).

Exercises for Section **15.3**

CONCEPTS

15.29 What is a utility?

15.30 What is a risk averter? A risk seeker? A risk neutral?

METHODS AND APPLICATIONS

15.31 Suppose that a decision maker has the opportunity to invest in an oil well drilling operation that has a .3 chance of yielding a profit of $1,000,000, a .4 chance of yielding a profit of $400,000, and a .3 chance of yielding a profit of $-$100,000. Also, suppose that the decision maker's utilities for $400,000 and $0 are .9 and .7. Explain the meanings of these utilities.

15.32 Consider Exercise 15.31. Find the expected utility of the oil well drilling operation. Find the expected utility of not investing. What should the decision maker do if she or he wants to maximize expected utility?

CHAPTER SUMMARY

In Section 15.1, we presented an introduction to decision theory. We saw that a decision problem involves states of nature, alternatives, payoffs, and decision criteria, and we considered three degrees of uncertainty: certainty, uncertainty, and risk. In the case of *certainty,* we know which state of nature will actually occur. Here we simply choose the alternative that gives the best payoff. In the case of *uncertainty,* we have no information about the likelihood of the different states of nature. Here we discussed two commonly used decision criteria—the maximin criterion and the maximax criterion. In the case of *risk,* we are able to estimate the probability of occurrence for each state of nature. In this case, we learned how to use the expected monetary value criterion. We also

learned how to construct a decision tree in Section 15.1, and we saw how to use such a tree to analyze a decision problem.

In Section 15.2, we learned how to make decisions by using posterior probabilities. We explained how to perform a posterior analysis to determine the best alternative for each of several sampling results. Then we showed how to carry out a preposterior analysis, which allows us to assess the worth of sample information. In particular, we saw how to obtain the expected value of sample information. This quantity is the expected gain from sampling, which tells us the maximum amount we should be willing to pay for sample information. We concluded this chapter with Section 15.3, which introduced using utility theory to help make decisions.

KEY TERMS

alternatives
certainty
decision criterion
decision theory
decision tree (or tree diagram)
expected monetary value criterion
expected net gain of sampling (ENGS)
expected value of perfect information (EVPI)
expected value of sample information (EVSI)
maximax criterion

maximin criterion
payoff table
perfect information
posterior decision analysis
preposterior analysis
prior decision analysis
risk
states of nature
uncertainty
utility

IMPORTANT FORMULAS

Probability revision table

Maximin criterion

Maximax criterion

Expected monetary value criterion

Decision tree

Expected value of perfect information

Expected payoff of sampling

Expected payoff of no sampling

Expected value of sample information

Expected net gain of sampling

Expected utility

SUPPLEMENTARY EXERCISES

Connect Practise and learn online with *Connect.* Items for which there are online data sets are marked with ✎.

15.33 In the book *Making Hard Decisions: An Introduction to Decision Analysis,* Robert T. Clemen presents a decision tree for a research and development decision (note that payoffs are given in millions of dollars, which is denoted by M). Based on this decision tree (shown in Figure 15.8), answer the following:

a. Should development of the research project be continued or stopped? Justify your answer by using relevant calculations, and explain your reasoning.

b. If development is continued and if a patent is awarded, should the new technology be licensed, or should the company develop production and marketing to sell the product directly? Justify your answer by using relevant calculations and explain your reasoning.

15.34 In the book *Production/Operations Management,* William J. Stevenson presents a decision tree concerning a firm's decision about the size of a production facility. This decision tree is given in Figure 15.9 (payoffs are given in millions of dollars). Use the decision tree to determine which alternative (build small or build large) should be chosen to maximize the expected monetary payoff. What is the expected monetary payoff associated with the best alternative?

FIGURE **15.8** A Decision Tree for a Research and Development Decision for Exercise 15.33

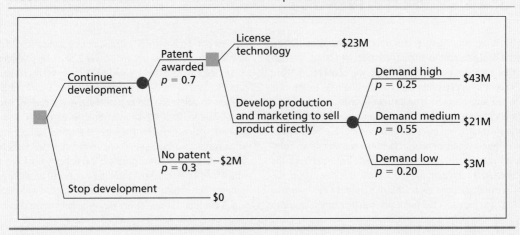

Source: A Decision tree from *Making Hard Decisions: An Introduction to Decision Analysis,* 2nd edition, by R. T. Clemen, © 1996. Reprinted with permission of Brooks/Cole, a division of Thomson Learning. Fax 800-730-2215. P. 77.

FIGURE **15.9** A Decision Tree for a Production Facility Decision for Exercises 15.34 and 15.35

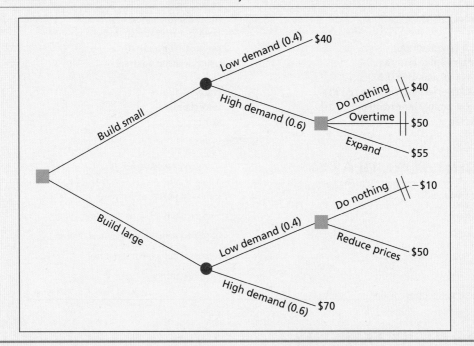

Source: Decision tree from W. J. Stevenson, *Production/Operations Management,* 6/e, p. 70, © 1999 McGraw-Hill Companies, Inc.

15.35 Consider the decision tree in Figure 15.9 and the situation described in Exercise 15.34. Suppose that a marketing research study can be done to obtain more information about whether demand will be high or low. The marketing research study will result in one of two outcomes: "favourable" (indicating that demand will be high) or "unfavourable" (indicating that demand will be low). The accuracy of marketing research studies like the one to be carried out can be expressed by the conditional probabilities in the following table:

	True Demand	
Study Outcome	**High**	**Low**
Favourable	.9	.2
Unfavourable	.1	.8

For instance, $P(\text{favourable}|\text{high}) = .9$ and $P(\text{unfavourable}|\text{low}) = .8$. Given the prior probabilities and payoffs in Figure 15.9, do the following:

a. Carry out a posterior analysis. Find the best alternative (build small or build large) for each possible study result (favourable or unfavourable), and find the associated expected payoffs.

b. Carry out a preposterior analysis. Determine the maximum amount that should be paid for the marketing research study.

15.36 THE OIL DRILLING EXAMPLE

Again consider the oil drilling example that was described in Example 15.1. Recall that the oil company wants to decide whether to drill and that the prior probabilities of no oil, some oil, and much oil are $P(\text{none}) = .7$, $P(\text{some}) = .2$, and $P(\text{much}) = .1$. Suppose that, instead of performing the seismic survey to obtain more information about the site, the oil company can perform a cheaper magnetic experiment with two possible results: a high reading and a low reading. The past performance of the magnetic experiment can be summarized as follows:

Magnetic Experiment Result	State of Nature		
	None	Some	Much
Low reading	.8	.4	.1
High reading	.2	.6	.9

Here, for example, $P(\text{low}|\text{none}) = .8$ and $P(\text{high}|\text{some}) = .6$. Recalling that the payoffs associated with no oil, some oil, and much oil are $-\$700{,}000$, $\$500{,}000$, and $\$2{,}000{,}000$, respectively, do the following:

a. Draw a decision tree for this decision problem.

b. Carry out a posterior analysis. Find the best alternative (drill or do not drill) for each possible result of the magnetic experiment (low or high), and find the associated expected payoffs.

c. Carry out a preposterior analysis. Determine the maximum amount that should be paid for the magnetic experiment.

15.37 In an exercise in the book *Production/Operations Management,* 5th ed. (1996), William Stevenson considers a theme park whose lease is about to expire. The theme park's management wants to decide whether to renew its lease for another 10 years or relocate near the site of a new motel complex. The town planning board is debating whether to approve the motel complex. A consultant estimates the payoffs of the theme park's alternatives under each state of nature are as shown in the following payoff table:

Theme Park Options	Motel Approved	Motel Rejected
Renew lease	$500,000	$4,000,000
Relocate	$5,000,000	$100,000

a. What alternative should the theme park choose if it uses the maximax criterion? What is the resulting payoff of this choice?

b. What alternative should the theme park choose if it uses the maximin criterion? What is the resulting payoff of this choice?

15.38 Again consider the situation described in Exercise 15.37, and suppose that management believes there is a .35 probability that the motel complex will be approved.

a. Draw a decision tree for the theme park's decision problem.

b. Which alternative should be chosen if the theme park uses the maximum expected monetary value criterion? What is the expected monetary payoff for this choice?

c. Suppose that management is offered the option of a temporary lease while the planning board decides whether to approve the motel complex. If the lease costs $100,000, should the theme park's management sign the lease? Justify your answer.

INTERNET EXERCISE

15.39 Decide first on two cities in Canada where you might like to live. Generate a list of all of the features you may want to consider that will have an impact on which city you choose (for example, cost of housing, employment rates, crime rates, etc.). Access Statistics Canada's website (statcan.gc.ca) and explore the variables and cities you are interested in. Compare your two cities and make a choice.

CHAPTER **16**
Time Series Forecasting

Demand for some products changes over time. For example, Canadians tend to be in the market for lawn mowers more in the summer than in the winter, whereas the opposite pattern exists for snow blowers. How suppliers meet these changing demands is the focus of this chapter, which deals with **time series analysis**, or collecting observations on a variable of interest in time order.

In this chapter, we discuss developing and using univariate time series models, which forecast future values of a time series *solely on the basis of past values.* Univariate time series models often forecast future values by extrapolating the trend and/or seasonal patterns exhibited by past values.

16.1 TIME SERIES COMPONENTS AND MODELS   LO1

To identify patterns in time series data, it is often convenient to think of such data as consisting of several components: trend, cycle, seasonal variations, and irregular fluctuations. **Trend** refers to the upward or downward movement that characterizes a time series over time, so it reflects the long-run growth or decline in the time series. Trend movements can represent a variety of factors. For example, long-run movements in the sales of a particular industry might be determined by changes in consumer tastes, increases in total population, and increases in per capita income. *Cycle* refers to recurring up-and-down **cyclical variations** around trend levels. These fluctuations can last from two to ten years or even longer, measured from peak to peak or trough to trough. One of the common cyclical fluctuations found in time series data is the business cycle, which is represented by fluctuations in the time series caused by recurrent periods of prosperity and recession.

Seasonal variations are periodic patterns in a time series that complete themselves within a calendar year or less and then are repeated on a regular basis. Seasonal variations often occur yearly. For example, soft drink sales and hotel room occupancies are annually higher in the summer months, while department store sales are annually higher during the winter holiday season. Seasonal variations can also last less than one year. For example, daily restaurant patronage might exhibit within-week seasonal variation, with daily patronage higher on Fridays and Saturdays. The **irregular component** is what is left over in a time series after trend, cycle, and seasonal variations have been accounted for.

Time series that exhibit trend, seasonal, and cyclical components are illustrated in Figure 16.1. In Figure 16.1(a), a time series of sales observations that has an essentially straight-line or linear trend is plotted. Figure 16.1(b) portrays a time series of sales observations that contains a seasonal pattern that repeats annually, with higher sales in the winter months. Figure 16.1(c) exhibits a time series of agricultural yields that is cyclical, repeating a cycle about once every ten years.

Time series models attempt to identify significant patterns in the components of a time series. Then, assuming that these patterns will continue into the future, time series models extrapolate these patterns to forecast future time series values. In Sections 16.2 and 16.3, we discuss forecasting by time series regression models, which assume that the time series components remain essentially constant over time. If a time series exhibits increasing (or decreasing) seasonal variation, then we use the multiplicative decomposition model discussed in Section 16.4. If the time series components are changing slowly over time, then it is appropriate to forecast using exponential smoothing, which is discussed in Section 16.5. If the time series components might be changing fairly quickly over time, it is appropriate to forecast by using the Box–Jenkins methodology (see Appendix I on *Connect*).

FIGURE 16.1   Time Series Exhibiting Trend, Seasonal, and Cyclical Components

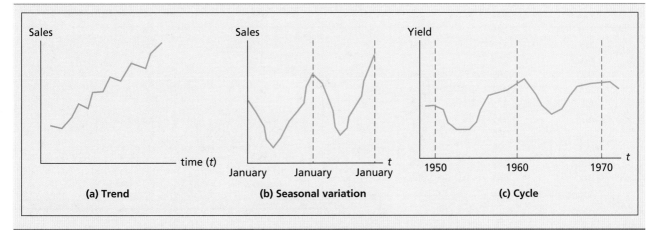

(a) Trend   (b) Seasonal variation   (c) Cycle

> **ROADBLOCK** **Using the past to predict the future**
> Although past values may be the best predictor of future values, as used in time series models, caution should always be taken when trying to predict the future as those values are outside the experimental region.

16.2 TIME SERIES REGRESSION: BASIC MODELS

Modelling trend components We begin this section with two examples.

Example 16.1 The Cod Catch Example

LO2

The Coast City Seafood Company owns a fleet of fishing trawlers and operates a fish-processing plant. To forecast its minimum and maximum possible revenues from cod sales and plan the operations of its fish-processing plant, the company wants to make both point forecasts and prediction interval forecasts of its monthly cod catch (measured in tonnes). The company has recorded monthly cod catch for the previous two years (years 1 and 2). The cod history is given in Table 16.1. A runs plot (or time series plot) shows that the cod catches appear to randomly fluctuate around a constant average level (see the plot in Figure 16.2).

Because the company subjectively believes that this data pattern will continue in the future, it seems reasonable to use the no-trend regression model

$$y_t = \beta_0 + \varepsilon_t$$

to forecast cod catch in future months. In the no-trend regression model, the least squares point estimate b_0 of β_0 is $\bar{y}$, the average of the n observed time series values. Because the average $\bar{y}$ of the $n = 24$ observed cod catches is 351.29, then $\hat{y}_t = b_0 = 351.29$ is the point prediction of the cod catch (y_t) in any future month. Furthermore, it can be shown that a $100(1 - \alpha)$ percent prediction interval for any future y_t value described by the no-trend model is $[\hat{y}_t \pm t_{\alpha/2}s\sqrt{1 + (1/n)}]$. Here s is the sample standard deviation of the n observed time series values, and $t_{\alpha/2}$ is based on $n - 1$ degrees of freedom. For example, the s is 33.82 for the $n = 24$ cod catches, and because $t_{.025}$ based on $n - 1 = 23$ degrees of freedom is 2.069, it follows that a 95 percent prediction interval for the cod catch in any future month is $[351.29 \pm 2.069(33.82)\sqrt{1 + (1/24)}]$, or [279.87, 422.71].

TABLE 16.1 Cod Catch (in Tonnes)

Month	Year 1	Year 2
Jan.	362	276
Feb.	381	334
Mar.	317	394
Apr.	297	334
May	399	384
Jun.	402	314
Jul.	375	344
Aug.	349	337
Sep.	386	345
Oct.	328	362
Nov.	389	314
Dec.	343	365

FIGURE 16.2 Plot of Cod Catch versus Time

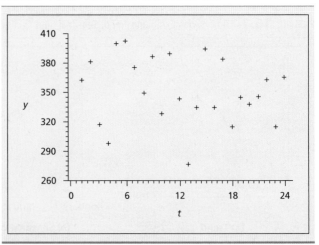

Example 16.2 The DVD Player Sales Example

For the previous two years, Smith's Department Stores has carried a new type of DVD player, the X-12. Sales of this product have generally increased over these two years. Smith's inventory policy attempts to ensure that stores will have enough DVD players to meet practically all demand for the product, while at the same time ensuring that Smith's does not needlessly tie up its money by ordering more DVD players than can be sold. To implement this inventory policy in future months, Smith's requires both point predictions and prediction intervals for total monthly demand.

The monthly demand data for the previous two years are given in Table 16.2. A runs plot of the demand data is shown in Figure 16.3. The demands appear to randomly fluctuate around an average level that increases over time in a linear fashion. Furthermore, Smith's believes that this trend will continue for at least the next year, so it is reasonable to use the linear trend regression model

$$y_t = \beta_0 + \beta_1 t + \varepsilon_t$$

to forecast sales in future months. Notice that this model is just a simple linear regression model in which the time period, t, plays the role of the independent variable. The least squares point estimates of β_0 and β_1 can be calculated to be $b_0 = 198.028986$ and $b_1 = 8.074348$. Therefore, for example, point forecasts of product demand in January and February of year 3 (time periods 25 and 26) are, respectively,

$$\hat{y}_{25} = 198.028986 + 8.074348(25) = 399.9$$

and

$$\hat{y}_{26} = 198.028986 + 8.074348(26) = 408.0$$

Note that the Excel output under Table 16.2 gives these point forecasts. In addition, it can be shown using either the formulas for simple linear regression or a computer software application that a 95 percent prediction interval for demand is [328.6, 471.2] in time period 25 and [336.0, 479.9] in time period 26. These prediction intervals can help Smith's implement its inventory policy. For instance, if Smith's stocks 472 DVD players in January of year 3, we can be reasonably sure that monthly demand will be met.

TABLE **16.2** DVD Player Sales Data

Month	Year 1	Year 2
Jan.	197	296
Feb.	211	276
Mar.	203	305
Apr.	247	308
May	239	356
Jun.	269	393
Jul.	308	363
Aug.	262	386
Sep.	258	443
Oct.	256	308
Nov.	261	358
Dec.	288	384

A	B	C	D
358	23		
384	24		
399.8877	25	USING TREND	
407.962	26		

FIGURE **16.3** Plot of DVD Player Sales versus Time

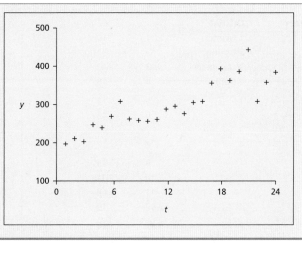

Example 16.1 illustrates that the intercept β_0 can be used to model a lack of trend over time and Example 16.2 illustrates that the expression $\beta_0 + \beta_1 t$ can model a linear trend over time. In addition, as will be illustrated in the exercises, the expression $\beta_0 + \beta_1 t + \beta_2 t^2$ can model a quadratic trend over time.

Modelling seasonal components We next consider how to forecast time series described by trend and seasonal components.

Example 16.3 The Bike Sales Example

Table 16.3 presents quarterly sales of the TRK-50 mountain bike for the previous four years. Figure 16.4 shows that the bike sales exhibit a linear trend and a strong seasonal pattern, with bike sales being higher in the spring and summer quarters than in the winter and fall quarters. If we let y_t denote the number of TRK-50 mountain bikes sold in time period t, then a regression model describing y_t is

$$y_t = \beta_0 + \beta_1 t + \beta_{Q2}Q_2 + \beta_{Q3}Q_3 + \beta_{Q4}Q_4 + \varepsilon_t$$

Here the expression $\beta_0 + \beta_1 t$ models the linear trend evident in Figure 16.4. Q_2, Q_3, and Q_4 are dummy variables defined for quarters 2, 3, and 4. Specifically, Q_2 equals 1 if quarterly bike sales were observed in quarter 2 (spring) and 0 otherwise, Q_3 equals 1 if quarterly bike sales were observed in quarter 3 (summer) and 0 otherwise, and Q_4 equals 1 if quarterly bike sales were observed in quarter 4 (fall) and 0 otherwise.

Note: We have not defined a dummy variable for quarter 1 (winter) as this point becomes a reference point.

It follows that the regression parameters β_{Q2}, β_{Q3}, and β_{Q4} compare quarters 2, 3, and 4 with quarter 1. For example, β_{Q4} is the difference, excluding trend, between the level of the time series (y_t) in quarter 4 (fall) and the level of the time series in quarter 1 (winter). A positive β_{Q4} implies that, excluding trend, bike sales in the fall can be expected to be higher than bike sales in the winter. A negative β_{Q4} implies that, excluding trend, bike sales in the fall can be expected to be lower than bike sales in the winter.

Figure 16.5 gives the Excel output of a regression analysis of the quarterly bike sales by using the dummy variable model. An example of the Excel input columns using dummy

TABLE **16.3** Quarterly Sales of the TRK-50 Mountain Bike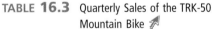

Year	Quarter	t	Sales, y_t
1	1 (winter)	1	10
	2 (spring)	2	31
	3 (summer)	3	43
	4 (fall)	4	16
2	1	5	11
	2	6	33
	3	7	45
	4	8	17
3	1	9	13
	2	10	34
	3	11	48
	4	12	19
4	1	13	15
	2	14	37
	3	15	51
	4	16	21

FIGURE **16.4** Plot of TRK-50 Bike Sales

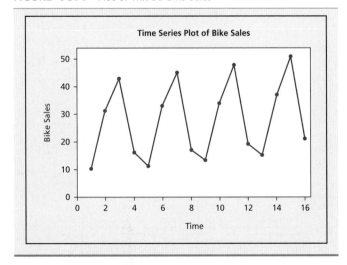

FIGURE 16.5 Excel Output of an Analysis of the Quarterly Bike Sales by Using Dummy Variable Regression

SUMMARY OUTPUT

Regression Statistics

Multiple R	0.999164927
R Square	0.998330551
Adjusted R Square	0.997723479
Standard Error	0.674199862
Observations	16

ANOVA

	df	SS	MS	F	Significance F
Regression	4	2990	747.5	1644.5	3.43916E-15
Residual	11	5	0.454545		
Total	15	2995			

	Coefficients	Standard Error	t Stat	P-value	Lower 95%	Upper 95%	Lower 95.0%	Upper 95.0%
Intercept	8.75	0.428063823	20.44088	4.23E-10	7.807837402	9.6921626	7.807837402	9.692162598
Time	0.5	0.037688918	13.2665	4.12E-08	0.417047209	0.58295279	0.417047209	0.582952791
Q2	21	0.478218759	43.91296	1.04E-13	19.94744708	22.0525529	19.94744708	22.05255292
Q3	33.5	0.48265365	69.40795	6.89E-16	32.43768594	34.5623141	32.43768594	34.56231406
Q4	4.5	0.489955935	9.184499	1.72E-06	3.421613713	5.57838629	3.421613713	5.578386287

coding is provided in the margin. The output tells us that the linear trend and the seasonal dummy variables are significant (every t statistic has a related p-value less than .01). Also notice that the least squares point estimates of β_{Q2}, β_{Q3}, and β_{Q4} are, respectively, $b_{Q2} = 21$, $b_{Q3} = 33.5$, and $b_{Q4} = 4.5$. It follows that, excluding trend, expected bike sales in quarter 2 (spring), quarter 3 (summer), and quarter 4 (fall) are estimated to be, respectively, 21, 33.5, and 4.5 bikes greater than expected bike sales in quarter 1 (winter). Furthermore, using all of the least squares point estimates in Figure 16.5, we can compute point forecasts of bike sales in quarters 1 through 4 of next year (periods 17 through 20) as follows:

$$\hat{y}_{17} = b_0 + b_1(17) + b_{Q2}(0) + b_{Q3}(0) + b_{Q4}(0) = 8.75 + .5(17) = 17.250$$
$$\hat{y}_{18} = b_0 + b_1(18) + b_{Q2}(1) + b_{Q3}(0) + b_{Q4}(0) = 8.75 + .5(18) + 21 = 38.750$$
$$\hat{y}_{19} = b_0 + b_1(19) + b_{Q2}(0) + b_{Q3}(1) + b_{Q4}(0) = 8.75 + .5(19) + 33.5 = 51.750$$
$$\hat{y}_{20} = b_0 + b_1(20) + b_{Q2}(0) + b_{Q3}(0) + b_{Q4}(1) = 8.75 + .5(20) + 4.5 = 23.250$$

Quarter	Time	Q2	Q3	Q4	Bike Sales
1	1	0	0	0	10
2	2	1	0	0	31
3	3	0	1	0	43
4	4	0	0	1	16
1	5	0	0	0	11
2	6	1	0	0	33
3	7	0	1	0	45
4	8	0	0	1	17
1	9	0	0	0	13
2	10	1	0	0	34
3	11	0	1	0	48
4	12	0	0	1	19
1	13	0	0	0	15
2	14	1	0	0	37
3	15	0	1	0	51
4	16	0	0	1	21

We next consider Table 16.4, which presents a time series of hotel room occupancies observed by Traveller's Rest, a corporation that operates four hotels. Analysts in the operating division of the corporation were asked to develop a model that could be used to obtain short-term forecasts (up to one year) of the number of occupied rooms in the hotels. These forecasts were needed by various personnel to assist in hiring additional help during the summer months, ordering materials that have long delivery lead times, budgeting local advertising expenditures, and so on. The available historical data consisted of the number of occupied rooms during each day for the previous 14 years. Because monthly forecasts were wanted, these data were reduced to monthly averages by dividing each monthly total by the number of days in the month. The monthly room averages for the previous 14 years are the time series values given in Table 16.4. A runs plot of these values in Figure 16.6 shows that the monthly room averages follow a strong trend and have a seasonal pattern with one major and several minor peaks during the year. Note that the major peak each year occurs during the summer travel months of June, July, and August.

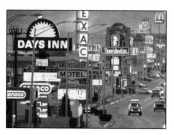

Although the quarterly bike sales and monthly hotel room averages both exhibit seasonal variation, they exhibit different kinds of seasonal variation. The quarterly bike sales plotted in Figure 16.4 exhibit constant seasonal variation, which is seasonal variation where the magnitude of the seasonal swing does not depend on the level of the time series. On the other hand, increasing seasonal variation is seasonal variation where the magnitude of the

TABLE **16.4**   Monthly Hotel Room Averages

t	y_t	t	y_t	t	y_t	t	y_t	t	y_t	t	y_t	t	y_t	t	y_t
1	501	22	587	43	785	64	657	85	645	106	759	127	1,067	148	827
2	488	23	497	44	830	65	680	86	602	107	643	128	1,038	149	788
3	504	24	558	45	645	66	759	87	601	108	728	129	812	150	937
4	578	25	555	46	643	67	878	88	709	109	691	130	790	151	1,076
5	545	26	523	47	551	68	881	89	706	110	649	131	692	152	1,125
6	632	27	532	48	606	69	705	90	817	111	656	132	782	153	840
7	728	28	623	49	585	70	684	91	930	112	735	133	758	154	864
8	725	29	598	50	553	71	577	92	983	113	748	134	709	155	717
9	585	30	683	51	576	72	656	93	745	114	837	135	715	156	813
10	542	31	774	52	665	73	645	94	735	115	995	136	788	157	811
11	480	32	780	53	656	74	593	95	620	116	1,040	137	794	158	732
12	530	33	609	54	720	75	617	96	698	117	809	138	893	159	745
13	518	34	604	55	826	76	686	97	665	118	793	139	1,046	160	844
14	489	35	531	56	838	77	679	98	626	119	692	140	1,075	161	833
15	528	36	592	57	652	78	773	99	649	120	763	141	812	162	935
16	599	37	578	58	661	79	906	100	740	121	723	142	822	163	1,110
17	572	38	543	59	584	80	934	101	729	122	655	143	714	164	1,124
18	659	39	565	60	644	81	713	102	824	123	658	144	802	165	868
19	739	40	648	61	623	82	710	103	937	124	761	145	748	166	860
20	758	41	615	62	553	83	600	104	994	125	768	146	731	167	762
21	602	42	697	63	599	84	676	105	781	126	885	147	748	168	877

FIGURE **16.6**   Plot of the Monthly Hotel Room Averages versus Time

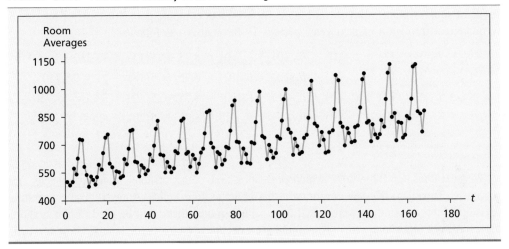

seasonal swing increases as the level of the time series increases. Figure 16.6 shows that the monthly hotel room averages exhibit increasing seasonal variation. As illustrated with the bike sales data, we can use dummy variables to model constant seasonal variation. The number of dummy variables that we use is, in general, the number of seasons minus 1. For example, if we model quarterly data, we use three dummy variables (as in the bike sales case). If we model monthly data, we use 11 dummy variables (this will be illustrated in Section 16.3). If a time series exhibits increasing seasonal variation, one approach is to first use a fractional power transformation to produce a transformed time series exhibiting constant seasonal variation. Then, as will be shown in Section 16.3, we use dummy variables to model the constant seasonal variation. A second approach to modelling increasing seasonal variation is to use a multiplicative model and a technique called *multiplicative decomposition*. This approach is discussed in Section 16.4.

Exercises for Section **16.2**

CONCEPTS

16.1 Discuss how to model no trend and a linear trend.

16.2 Discuss the difference between constant seasonal variation and increasing seasonal variation.

16.3 Discuss how to use dummy variables to model constant seasonal variation.

METHODS AND APPLICATIONS

16.4 CANADIAN TIRE SALES

Table 16.5 provides the consolidated quarterly results from Canadian Tire's *2010 Second Quarter Report to Shareholders*.

In this report, Canadian Tire states that "the second and fourth quarters of each year are typically when we experience stronger revenues and earnings in our retail businesses because of the seasonal nature" of their merchandise.

a. Plot the values and determine if you agree with Canadian Tire's statement from the data provided.

b. Demonstrate that a linear regression model would not be the best fit to the data.

TABLE 16.5 Net Earnings (in $ millions) for Canadian Tire ✎

Year	Quarter	Time	Net Earnings
2008	3	1	109.1
2008	4	2	101.5
2009	1	3	49.7
2009	2	4	103.7
2009	3	5	85.4
2009	4	6	96.2
2010	1	7	49.4
2010	2	8	119.9

Source: *Canadian Tire 2010 Second Quarter Report to Shareholders*; corp.canadiantire.ca/EN/Investors.

16.5 THE WATCH SALES EXAMPLE

The past 20 monthly sales figures for a new type of watch sold at Lambert's Discount Stores are given in Table 16.6.

a. Plot the watch sales values versus time and discuss why the plot indicates that the model

$$y_t = \beta_0 + \beta_1 t + \varepsilon_t$$

might appropriately describe these values.

b. The least squares point estimates of β_0 and β_1 can be calculated to be $b_0 = 290.089474$ and $b_1 = 8.667669$. Use b_0 and b_1 to show that a point forecast of watch sales in period 21 is $\hat{y}_{21} = 472.1$ (see the Excel output in Table 16.6). Use the formulas of simple linear regression analysis or a computer software application to show that a 95 percent prediction interval for watch sales in period 21 is [421.5, 522.7].

TABLE 16.6 Watch Sales Values ✎

Month	Sales	Month	Sales
1	298	11	356
2	302	12	371
3	301	13	399
4	351	14	392
5	336	15	425
6	361	16	411
7	407	17	455
8	351	18	457
9	357	19	465
10	346	20	481

A	B	C	D
465	19		
481	20		
472.1105	21	USING	TREND

16.6 THE AIR CONDITIONER SALES EXAMPLE

Quarterly sales of the Bargain 8000-BTU Air Conditioner at the Bargain Department Stores chain over the past three years are given in Table 16.7.

TABLE 16.7 Air Conditioner Sales ✎

Year	Quarter	Sales	SUMMARY OUTPUT
1	1	2,915	**Regression Statistics**
	2	8,032	Multiple R 0.999224341
	3	10,411	R Square 0.998449283
	4	2,427	Adjusted R Square 0.997563159
			Standard Error 177.9879109
2	1	4,381	Observations 12
	2	9,138	
	3	11,386	**ANOVA**
	4	3,382	
3	1	5,105	
	2	9,894	
	3	12,300	
	4	4,013	

ANOVA

	df	SS	MS	F	Significance F
Regression	4	142781674.8	35695419	1126.76	6.60013E-10
Residual	7	221757.875	31679.7		
Total	11	143003432.7			

	Coefficients	Standard Error	t Stat	P-value	Lower 95%	Upper 95%	Lower 95.0%	Upper 95.0%
Intercept	2957.572917	129.4115123	22.85402	7.78E-08	2651.563535	3263.582	2651.563535	3263.582298
Q2	4652.447917	146.1755631	31.82781	7.81E-09	4306.797882	4998.098	4306.797882	4998.097951
Q3	6761.5625	148.6936049	45.47312	6.5E-10	6409.958247	7113.167	6409.958247	7113.166753
Q4	-1565.3229217	152.7981553	-10.244438	1.82E-05	-1926.632882	-1204.013	-1926.632882	-1204.012951
Time	235.21875	15.73205735	14.95156	1.44E-06	198.0183723	272.4191	198.0183723	272.4191277

a. Plot sales versus time and discuss why the plot indicates that the model

$$y_t = \beta_0 + \beta_1 t + \beta_{Q2}Q_2 + \beta_{Q3}Q_3 + \beta_{Q4}Q_4 + \varepsilon_t$$

might appropriately describe the sales values. In this model, Q_2, Q_3, and Q_4 are appropriately defined dummy variables for quarters 2, 3, and 4.

To the right of Table 16.7 is the Excel output of a regression analysis of the air conditioner sales data using this model.

b. Define the dummy variables Q_2, Q_3, and Q_4. Then use the Excel output to find, report, and interpret the least squares point estimates of β_{Q2}, β_{Q3}, and β_{Q4}.

c. Using the regression equation, calculate the projected sales for the first quarter of year 4.

16.7 In Table 16.8 are the data for the production of eggs in Canada for the years 2007 to 2011 from Statistics Canada. Enter the data into Excel and then use a linear trend regression model in MegaStat to estimate the production of eggs for Canada for 2012 and 2013.

TABLE 16.8 Egg Production for Canada

Year	Quantity (Thousands of Dozens)
2007	607,772
2008	617,039
2009	621,085
2010	637,383
2011	643,810

16.3 TIME SERIES REGRESSION: MORE ADVANCED MODELS

Example 16.4 The Traveller's Rest Example

If we take the square roots, quartic roots, and natural logarithms of the monthly hotel room averages in Table 16.4 and plot the resulting three sets of transformed values versus time, we find that the quartic root transformation best equalizes the seasonal variation. Figure 16.7 presents a plot of the quartic roots of the monthly hotel room averages versus time. Letting y_t denote the hotel room average observed in time period t, it follows that a regression model describing the quartic root of y_t is

$$y_t^{.25} = \beta_0 + \beta_1 t + \beta_{M1}M_1 + \beta_{M2}M_2 + \cdots + \beta_{M11}M_{11} + \varepsilon_t$$

LO3

The expression $\beta_0 + \beta_1 t$ models the linear trend evident in Figure 16.7. Furthermore, M_1, M_2, ..., M_{11} are dummy variables defined for January (month 1) through November (month 11). For example, M_1 equals 1 if a monthly room average was observed in January, and 0 otherwise; M_2 equals 1 if a monthly room average was observed in February, and 0 otherwise. (Note that we have not defined a dummy variable for December [month 12]. It follows that the regression parameters β_{M1}, β_{M2}, ..., β_{M11} compare January through November with December.)

FIGURE 16.7 Plot of the Quartic Roots of the Monthly Hotel Room Averages versus Time

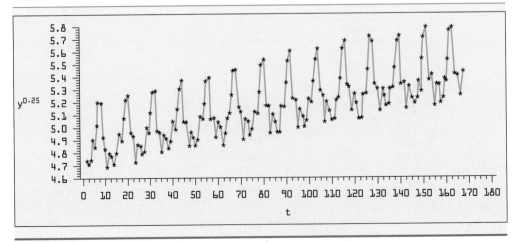

FIGURE 16.8 MegaStat Output of an Analysis of the Quartic Roots of the Room Averages Using Dummy Variable Regression (TFY2 $= y_t^{.25}$)

Regression output variables	coefficients	std. error	t (df = 155)	p-value	confidence interval 95% lower	95% upper
Intercept	4.807318	0.00846255	568.070	4.06E-259	4.7906	4.8240
t	0.003515	0.00004449	79.009	3.95E-127	0.0034	0.0036
M1	−0.052467	0.01055475	−4.971	1.75E-06	−0.0733	−0.0316
M2	−0.140790	0.01055278	−13.342	1.59E-27	−0.1616	−0.1199
M3	−0.107103	0.01055100	−10.151	7.02E-19	−0.1279	−0.0863
M4	0.049882	0.01054940	4.728	5.05E-06	0.0290	0.0707
M5	0.025417	0.01054800	2.410	0.0171	0.0046	0.0463
M6	0.190170	0.01054678	18.031	6.85E-40	0.1693	0.2110
M7	0.382455	0.01054575	36.266	1.28E-77	0.3616	0.4033
M8	0.413370	0.01054490	39.201	2.41E-82	0.3925	0.4342
M9	0.071417	0.01054424	6.773	2.47E-10	0.0506	0.0922
M10	0.050641	0.01054377	4.803	3.66E-06	0.0298	0.0715
M11	−0.141943	0.01054349	−13.463	7.47E-28	−0.1628	−0.1211

Durbin-Watson = 1.26

Predicted values for: TFY2

t	Predicted	95% Confidence Intervals lower	upper	95% Prediction Intervals lower	upper	Leverage
169	5.3489	5.3322	5.3656	5.2913	5.4065	0.092
170	5.2641	5.2474	5.2808	5.2065	5.3217	0.092
171	5.3013	5.2846	5.3180	5.2437	5.3589	0.092
172	5.4618	5.4451	5.4785	5.4042	5.5194	0.092
173	5.4409	5.4241	5.4576	5.3833	5.4984	0.092
174	5.6091	5.5924	5.6258	5.5515	5.6667	0.092
175	5.8049	5.7882	5.8216	5.7473	5.8625	0.092
176	5.8394	5.8226	5.8561	5.7818	5.8969	0.092
177	5.5009	5.4842	5.5176	5.4433	5.5585	0.092
178	5.4837	5.4669	5.5004	5.4261	5.5412	0.092
179	5.2946	5.2779	5.3113	5.2370	5.3522	0.092
180	5.4400	5.4233	5.4568	5.3825	5.4976	0.092

For example, β_{M1} is the difference, excluding trend, between the level of the time series ($y_t^{.25}$) in January and the level of the time series in December. A positive β_{M1} implies that, excluding trend, the value of the time series in January can be expected to be greater than the value in December. A negative β_{M1} implies that, excluding trend, the value of the time series in January can be expected to be smaller than the value in December.

Figure 16.8 gives relevant portions of the MegaStat output of a regression analysis of the hotel room data using the quartic root dummy variable model. The MegaStat output tells us that the linear trend and the seasonal dummy variables are significant (every t statistic has a related p-value less than .05). In addition, although not shown on the output, $R^2 = .988$. Now consider time period 169, which is January of next year and which therefore implies that $M_1 = 1$ and that all the other dummy variables equal 0. Using the least squares point estimates in Figure 16.8, we compute a point forecast of $y_{169}^{.25}$ to be

$$b_0 + b_1(169) + b_{M1}(1) = 4.807318 + .003515(169) + (−.052467)(1)$$
$$= 5.3489$$

Note that this point forecast is given in Figure 16.8 (see time period 169). It follows that a point forecast of y_{169} is

$$(5.3489)^4 = 818.57$$

Furthermore, the MegaStat output shows that a 95 percent prediction interval for $y_{169}^{.25}$ is [5.2913, 5.4065]. It follows that a 95 percent prediction interval for y_{169} is

$$[(5.2913)^4, (5.4065)^4] = [783.88, 854.41]$$

This interval says that Traveller's Rest can be 95 percent confident that the monthly hotel room average in period 169 will be no less than 783.88 rooms per day and no more than 854.41 rooms per day. Lastly, note that the MegaStat output also gives point forecasts of and 95 percent prediction intervals for the quartic roots of the hotel room averages in February through December of next year (time periods 170 through 180).

ROADBLOCK

Error terms are not independent in time series regression models
The validity of the regression methods just illustrated requires that the independence assumption be satisfied. However, when time series data are analyzed, this assumption is often violated. It is quite common for the time-ordered error terms to exhibit positive or negative autocorrelation. We can use residual plots to check for these kinds of autocorrelation.

One type of positive or negative autocorrelation is called *first-order autocorrelation*. It says that ε_t, the error term in time period t, is related to ε_{t-1}, the error term in time period $t - 1$, by the equation

$$\varepsilon_t = \phi \varepsilon_{t-1} + a_t$$

Here we assume that ϕ (phi) is the correlation coefficient that measures the relationship between error terms separated by one time period, and a_t is an error term (often called a *random shock*) that satisfies the usual regression assumptions. To check for positive or negative first-order autocorrelation, we can use the Durbin–Watson statistic, d, which was discussed in Section 11.10. For example, it can be verified that this statistic shows no evidence of positive or negative first-order autocorrelation in the error terms of the DVD player sales model or in the error terms of the bike sales model. However, note from the MegaStat output in Figure 16.8 that the Durbin–Watson statistic for the dummy variable regression model describing the quartic roots of the hotel room averages is $d = 1.26$.

Because the dummy variable regression model uses $k = 12$ independent variables, and because most statistical tables do not give the Durbin–Watson critical points corresponding to $k = 12$, we cannot test for autocorrelation using these tables. However, it can be shown that $d = 1.26$ is quite small and indicates positive autocorrelation in the error terms. One approach to dealing with first-order autocorrelation in the error terms is to predict future values of the error terms by using the model $\varepsilon_t = \phi \varepsilon_{t-1} + a_t$. Of course the error term ε_t could be related to more than just the previous error term ε_{t-1}. It could be related to any number of previous error terms. The autoregressive error term model of order q,

$$\varepsilon_t = \phi_1 \varepsilon_{t-1} + \phi_2 \varepsilon_{t-2} + \cdots + \hat{y}_q \varepsilon_{t-q} + a_t$$

relates ε_t, the error term in time period t, to the previous error terms, $\varepsilon_{t-1}, \varepsilon_{t-2}, \ldots, \varepsilon_{t-q}$. Here $\phi_1, \phi_2, \ldots, \phi_q$ are unknown parameters, and a_t is an error term (random shock) with mean 0 that satisfies the regression assumptions. The Box–Jenkins methodology can be used to systematically identify an autoregressive error term model that relates ε_t to an appropriate number of past error terms. More generally, the Box–Jenkins methodology can be employed to predict future time series values (y_t) by using a procedure that combines the autoregressive error term model of order q with the model

$$y_t = \beta_0 + \beta_1 y_{t-1} + \beta_2 y_{t-2} + \cdots + \beta_p y_{t-p} + \varepsilon_t$$

TABLE **16.9**   Historical Data, Including Price Differences, Concerning Demand for Fresh Detergent ✈

Sales Period	Price for Fresh Detergent, x_1 (Dollars)	Average Industry Price, x_2 (Dollars)	Price Difference, $x_4 = x_2 - x_1$ (Dollars)	Advertising Expenditure for Fresh Detergent, x_3 (Hundreds of Thousands of Dollars)	Demand for Fresh Detergent, y (Hundreds of Thousands of Bottles)
1	3.85	3.80	−0.05	5.50	7.38
2	3.75	4.00	0.25	6.75	8.51
3	3.70	4.30	0.60	7.25	9.52
4	3.70	3.70	0	5.50	7.50
5	3.60	3.85	0.25	7.00	9.33
6	3.60	3.80	0.20	6.50	8.28
7	3.60	3.75	0.15	6.75	8.75
8	3.80	3.85	0.05	5.25	7.87
9	3.80	3.65	−0.15	5.25	7.10
10	3.85	4.00	0.15	6.00	8.00
11	3.90	4.10	0.20	6.50	7.89
12	3.90	4.00	0.10	6.25	8.15
13	3.70	4.10	0.40	7.00	9.10
14	3.75	4.20	0.45	6.90	8.86
15	3.75	4.10	0.35	6.80	8.90
16	3.80	4.10	0.30	6.80	8.87
17	3.70	4.20	0.50	7.10	9.26
18	3.80	4.30	0.50	7.00	9.00
19	3.70	4.10	0.40	6.80	8.75
20	3.80	3.75	−0.05	6.50	7.95
21	3.80	3.75	−0.05	6.25	7.65
22	3.75	3.65	−0.10	6.00	7.27
23	3.70	3.90	0.20	6.50	8.00
24	3.55	3.65	0.10	7.00	8.50
25	3.60	4.10	0.50	6.80	8.75
26	3.65	4.25	0.60	6.80	9.21
27	3.70	3.65	−0.05	6.50	8.27
28	3.75	3.75	0	5.75	7.67
29	3.80	3.85	0.05	5.80	7.93
30	3.70	4.25	0.55	6.80	9.26

This latter model, which is called the autoregressive observation model of order p, expresses the observation y_t in terms of the previous observations, $y_{t-1}, y_{t-2}, \ldots, y_{t-p}$, and an error term ε_t. The Box–Jenkins methodology, which is discussed in Appendix I on *Connect*, identifies which previous observations and which previous error terms describe y_t.

Although techniques such as the Box–Jenkins methodology can be quite useful, studies show that the regression techniques discussed in Section 16.2 and in this section often provide accurate forecasts, even if we ignore the autocorrelation in the error terms. In fact, whenever we observe time series data, we should determine whether trend and/or seasonal effects exist. For example, the demand for Fresh detergent data in Table 16.9 are time series data observed over 30 consecutive four-week sales periods. Although we can predict demand for Fresh detergent on the basis of price difference and advertising expenditure, this demand could also be affected by a linear or quadratic trend over time and/or by seasonal effects [for example, more laundry detergent might be sold in summer sales periods when children are home from school; see Figure 16.9(a) and (b)]. If we try using trend equations and dummy variables to search for trend and seasonal effects, we find that these effects do not exist in the Fresh detergent demand data. However, in the supplementary exercises (see Exercise 16.38), we present a situation where we use trend equations and seasonal dummy variables, as well as causal variables such as price difference and advertising expenditure, to predict demand for a fishing lure.

FIGURE 16.9 Scatter Plots of the Fresh Detergent Demand Data

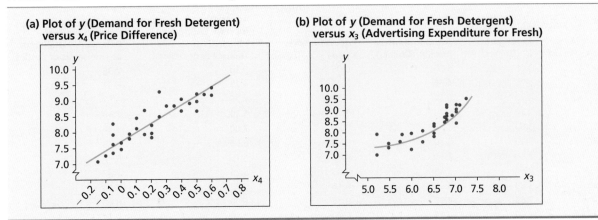

(a) Plot of y (Demand for Fresh Detergent) versus x_4 (Price Difference)

(b) Plot of y (Demand for Fresh Detergent) versus x_3 (Advertising Expenditure for Fresh)

Exercises for Section 16.3

CONCEPTS

16.8 What transformations can be used to transform a time series exhibiting increasing seasonal variation into a time series exhibiting constant seasonal variation?

16.9 What is the purpose of an autoregressive error term model?

METHODS AND APPLICATIONS

16.10 Table 16.10 gives the monthly international passenger totals over the last 11 years for an airline company. A plot of these passenger totals reveals an upward trend with increasing seasonal variation, and the natural logarithmic transformation is found to best equalize the seasonal variation [see Figure 16.10(a) and (b)]. Figure 16.10(c) gives the Excel output of a regression analysis of the monthly international passenger totals by using the model

$$\ln y_t = \beta_0 + \beta_1 t + \beta_{M1}M_1 + \beta_{M2}M_2 + \cdots + \beta_{M11}M_{11} + \varepsilon_t$$

Here $M_1, M_2, \ldots, M_{11}$ are appropriately defined dummy variables for January (month 1) through November (month 11). Using the results presented in the output, compose the regression equation.

16.11 Use the Durbin–Watson statistic given at the bottom of the Excel output in Figure 16.10(c) to test for positive autocorrelation.

TABLE 16.10 Monthly International Passenger Totals (Thousands of Passengers)

Year	Jan.	Feb.	Mar.	Apr.	May	Jun.	Jul.	Aug.	Sep.	Oct.	Nov.	Dec.
1	112	118	132	129	121	135	148	148	136	119	104	118
2	115	126	141	135	125	149	170	170	158	133	114	140
3	145	150	178	163	172	178	199	199	184	162	146	166
4	171	180	193	181	183	218	230	242	209	191	172	194
5	196	196	236	235	229	243	264	272	237	211	180	201
6	204	188	235	227	234	264	302	293	259	229	203	229
7	242	233	267	269	270	315	364	347	312	274	237	278
8	284	277	317	313	318	374	413	405	355	306	271	306
9	315	301	356	348	355	422	465	467	404	347	305	336
10	340	318	362	348	363	435	491	505	404	359	310	337
11	360	342	406	396	420	472	548	559	463	407	362	405

Source: *FAA Statistical Handbook of Civil Aviation* (several annual issues). These data were originally presented by Box and Jenkins (1976). We have updated the situation in this exercise to be more modern.

FIGURE 16.10 Analysis of the Monthly International Passenger Totals

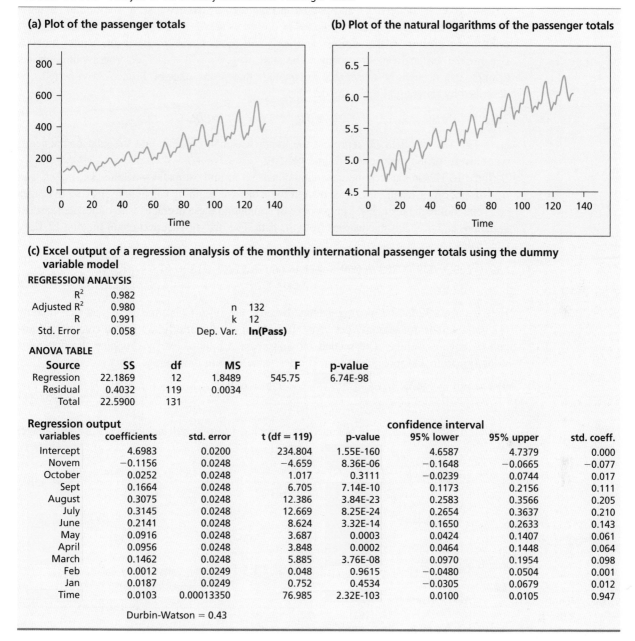

(a) Plot of the passenger totals

(b) Plot of the natural logarithms of the passenger totals

(c) Excel output of a regression analysis of the monthly international passenger totals using the dummy variable model

REGRESSION ANALYSIS

R^2	0.982		
Adjusted R^2	0.980	n	132
R	0.991	k	12
Std. Error	0.058	Dep. Var.	**ln(Pass)**

ANOVA TABLE

Source	SS	df	MS	F	p-value
Regression	22.1869	12	1.8489	545.75	6.74E-98
Residual	0.4032	119	0.0034		
Total	22.5900	131			

Regression output

confidence interval

variables	coefficients	std. error	t (df = 119)	p-value	95% lower	95% upper	std. coeff.
Intercept	4.6983	0.0200	234.804	1.55E-160	4.6587	4.7379	0.000
Novem	−0.1156	0.0248	−4.659	8.36E-06	−0.1648	−0.0665	−0.077
October	0.0252	0.0248	1.017	0.3111	−0.0239	0.0744	0.017
Sept	0.1664	0.0248	6.705	7.14E-10	0.1173	0.2156	0.111
August	0.3075	0.0248	12.386	3.84E-23	0.2583	0.3566	0.205
July	0.3145	0.0248	12.669	8.25E-24	0.2654	0.3637	0.210
June	0.2141	0.0248	8.624	3.32E-14	0.1650	0.2633	0.143
May	0.0916	0.0248	3.687	0.0003	0.0424	0.1407	0.061
April	0.0956	0.0248	3.848	0.0002	0.0464	0.1448	0.064
March	0.1462	0.0248	5.885	3.76E-08	0.0970	0.1954	0.098
Feb	0.0012	0.0249	0.048	0.9615	−0.0480	0.0504	0.001
Jan	0.0187	0.0249	0.752	0.4534	−0.0305	0.0679	0.012
Time	0.0103	0.00013350	76.985	2.32E-103	0.0100	0.0105	0.947

Durbin-Watson = 0.43

16.4 MULTIPLICATIVE DECOMPOSITION

When a time series exhibits increasing (or decreasing) seasonal variation, we can use the multiplicative decomposition method to decompose the time series into its trend, seasonal, cyclical, and irregular components. This is illustrated in the following example.

Example 16.5 The Tasty Cola Example

The Discount Cola Shop owns and operates ten soft drink stores and sells Tasty Cola, a soft drink introduced just three years ago and gaining in popularity. Discount Cola orders Tasty Cola from the regional distributor. To better implement its inventory policy, Discount Cola needs to forecast monthly Tasty Cola sales (in hundreds of cases).

Discount Cola has recorded monthly Tasty Cola sales for the previous three years. This time series is given in Table 16.11 and plotted in Figure 16.11. Notice that, in addition to having a linear trend, the Tasty Cola sales time series possesses seasonal variation, with sales of the soft drink being greatest in the summer and early fall months and lowest in the winter months. Because the seasonal variation seems to be increasing, we will see as we progress through this example that it might be reasonable to conclude that y_t, the sales of Tasty Cola in period t, is described by the multiplicative model

$$y_t = TR_t \times SN_t \times CL_t \times IR_t$$

Here TR_t, SN_t, CL_t, and IR_t represent the trend, seasonal, cyclical, and irregular components, respectively, of the time series in time period t.

Table 16.12 summarizes the calculations needed to find estimates—denoted tr_t, sn_t, cl_t, and ir_t—of TR_t, SN_t, CL_t, and IR_t. As shown in the table, we begin by calculating **moving averages** and centred moving averages. The purpose of computing these averages is to eliminate seasonal variations and irregular fluctuations from the data. The first moving average of the first 12 Tasty Cola sales values is

$$\frac{189 + 229 + 249 + 289 + 260 + 431 + 660 + 777 + 915 + 613 + 485 + 277}{12} = 447.833$$

Here we use a 12-period moving average because the Tasty Cola time series data are monthly (12 time periods or "seasons" per year). If the data were quarterly, we would compute a four-period moving average. The second moving average is obtained by dropping the first sales value (y_1) from and including the next sales value (y_{13}) in the average. So we obtain

$$\frac{229 + 249 + 289 + 260 + 431 + 660 + 777 + 915 + 613 + 485 + 277 + 244}{12} = 452.417$$

The third moving average is obtained by dropping y_2 from and including y_{14} in the average. We obtain

$$\frac{249 + 289 + 260 + 431 + 660 + 777 + 915 + 613 + 485 + 277 + 244 + 296}{12} = 458$$

TABLE **16.11** Monthly Sales of Tasty Cola (in Hundreds of Cases)

Year	Month	t	Sales, y_t	Year	Month	t	Sales, y_t
1	1 (Jan.)	1	189	2	7	19	831
	2 (Feb.)	2	229		8	20	960
	3 (Mar.)	3	249		9	21	1,152
	4 (Apr.)	4	289		10	22	759
	5 (May)	5	260		11	23	607
	6 (Jun.)	6	431		12	24	371
	7 (Jul.)	7	660	3	1	25	298
	8 (Aug.)	8	777		2	26	378
	9 (Sep.)	9	915		3	27	373
	10 (Oct.)	10	613		4	28	443
	11 (Nov.)	11	485		5	29	374
	12 (Dec.)	12	277		6	30	660
2	1	13	244		7	31	1,004
	2	14	296		8	32	1,153
	3	15	319		9	33	1,388
	4	16	370		10	34	904
	5	17	313		11	35	715
	6	18	556		12	36	441

FIGURE **16.11** Monthly Sales of Tasty Cola (in Hundreds of Cases)

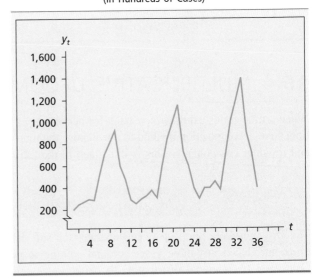

TABLE 16.12 Tasty Cola Sales and the Multiplicative Decomposition Method

t, Time Period	y_t, Tasty Cola Sales	First Step, 12-Period Moving Average	$tr_t \times cl_t$, Centred Moving Average	$sn_t \times ir_t$, $\dfrac{y_t}{tr_t \times cl_t}$	sn_t	d_t, $\dfrac{y_t}{sn_t}$	tr_t, $380.163 + 9.489t$	$tr_t \times sn_t$, Multiply tr_t by sn_t	$cl_t \times ir_t$, $\dfrac{y_t}{tr_t \times sn_t}$	cl_t, 3-Period Moving Average	ir_t, $\dfrac{y_t}{tr_t \times sn_t \times cl_t}$
1 (Jan.)	189				0.493	383.37	389.652	192.10	0.9839		
2	229				0.596	384.23	399.141	237.89	0.9626	0.9902	0.9721
3	249				0.595	418.49	408.630	243.13	1.0241	1.0010	1.0231
4	289				0.680	425	418.119	284.32	1.0165	1.0396	0.9778
5	260				0.564	460.99	427.608	241.17	1.0781	1.0315	1.0452
6	431	447.833			0.986	437.12	437.097	430.98	1.0000	1.0285	0.9723
7	660	452.417	450.125	1.466	1.467	449.9	446.586	655.14	1.0074	1.0046	1.0028
8	777	458	455.2085	1.707	1.693	458.95	456.075	772.13	1.0063	1.0004	1.0059
9	915	463.833	460.9165	1.985	1.990	459.79	465.564	926.47	0.9876	0.9937	0.9939
10	613	470.583	467.208	1.312	1.307	469.01	475.053	620.89	0.9873	0.9825	1.0049
11	485	475	472.7915	1.026	1.029	471.33	489.542	498.59	0.9727	0.9648	1.0082
12	277	485.417	480.2085	0.577	0.600	461.67	494.031	296.42	0.9345	0.9634	0.9700
13 (Jan.)	244	499.667	492.542	0.495	0.493	494.97	503.520	248.24	0.9829	0.9618	1.0219
14	296	514.917	507.292	0.583	0.596	496.64	513.009	305.75	0.9681	0.9924	0.9755
15	319	534.667	524.792	0.608	0.595	536.13	522.498	310.89	1.0261	1.0057	1.0203
16	370	546.833	540.75	0.684	0.680	544.12	531.987	361.75	1.0228	1.0246	0.9982
17	313	557	551.9165	0.567	0.564	554.97	541.476	305.39	1.0249	1.0237	1.0012
18	556	564.833	560.9165	0.991	0.986	563.89	550.965	543.25	1.0235	1.0197	1.0037
19	831	569.333	567.083	1.465	1.467	566.46	560.454	822.19	1.0107	1.0097	1.0010
20	960	576.167	572.75	1.676	1.693	567.04	569.943	964.91	0.9949	1.0016	0.9933
21	1,152	580.667	578.417	1.992	1.990	578.89	579.432	1,153.07	0.9991	0.9934	1.0057
22	759	586.75	583.7085	1.300	1.307	580.72	588.921	769.72	0.9861	0.9903	0.9958
23	607	591.833	589.2915	1.030	1.029	589.89	598.410	615.76	0.9858	0.9964	0.9894
24	371	600.5	596.1665	0.622	0.600	618.33	607.899	364.74	1.0172	0.9940	1.0233
25 (Jan.)	298	614.917	607.7085	0.490	0.493	604.46	617.388	304.37	0.9791	1.0027	0.9765
26	378	631	622.9585	0.607	0.596	634.23	626.877	373.62	1.0117	0.9920	1.0199
27	373	650.667	640.8335	0.582	0.595	626.89	636.366	378.64	0.9851	1.0018	0.9833
28	443	662.75	656.7085	0.675	0.680	651.47	645.855	439.18	1.0087	1.0030	1.0057
29	374	671.75	667.25	0.561	0.564	663.12	655.344	369.61	1.0119	1.0091	1.0028
30	660	677.583	674.6665	0.978	0.986	669.37	664.833	655.53	1.0068	1.0112	0.9956
31	1,004				1.467	684.39	674.322	989.23	1.0149	1.0059	1.0089
32	1,153				1.693	681.04	683.811	1,157.69	0.9959	1.0053	0.9906
33	1,388				1.990	697.49	693.300	1,379.67	1.0060	0.9954	1.0106
34	904				1.307	691.66	702.789	918.55	0.9842	0.9886	0.9955
35	715				1.029	694.85	712.278	732.93	0.9755	0.9927	0.9827
36	441				0.600	735	721.767	433.06	1.0183		

Successive moving averages are computed similarly until we include y_{36} in the last moving average. Note that we use the term "moving average" here because, as we calculate these averages, we move along by dropping the most remote observation (typically the earliest observation) in the previous average and including the next observation in the new average.

The first moving average corresponds to a time that is midway between periods 6 and 7, the second moving average corresponds to a time that is midway between periods 7 and 8, and so forth. To obtain averages corresponding to time periods in the original Tasty Cola time series, we calculate centred moving averages. The centred moving averages are 2-period moving averages of the previously computed 12-period moving averages. So the first centred moving average is

$$\frac{447.833 + 452.417}{2} = 450.125$$

The second centred moving average is

$$\frac{452.417 + 458}{2} = 455.2085$$

Successive centred moving averages are calculated similarly. The 12-period moving averages and centred moving averages for the Tasty Cola sales time series are given in Table 16.12.

If the original moving averages had been computed using an odd number of time series values, the centring procedure would not have been necessary. For example, if we had three seasons per year, we would compute three-period moving averages. Then the first moving average would correspond to period 2, the second moving average would correspond to period 3, and so on. However, most seasonal time series are quarterly, monthly, or weekly, so the centring procedure is necessary.

The centred moving average in time period t is considered to equal $tr_t \times cl_t$, the estimate of $TR_t \times CL_t$, because the averaging procedure is assumed to have removed seasonal variations (note that each moving average is computed using exactly one observation from each season) and (short-term) irregular fluctuations. The (longer-term) trend effects and cyclical effects—that is, $tr_t \times cl_t$—remain.

Because the model

$$y_t = TR_t \times SN_t \times CL_t \times IR_t$$

implies that

$$SN_t \times IR_t = \frac{y_t}{TR_t \times CL_t}$$

it follows that the estimate $sn_t \times ir_t$ of $SN_t \times IR_t$ is

$$sn_t \times ir_t = \frac{y_t}{tr_t \times cl_t}$$

Noting that the values of $sn_t \times ir_t$ are calculated in Table 16.12, we can find sn_t by grouping the values of $sn_t \times ir_t$ by months and calculating an average, $\overline{sn}_t$, for each month. These monthly averages are given for the Tasty Cola data in Table 16.13. The monthly averages are then normalized so that they sum to the number of time periods in a year. Denoting the number of time periods in a year by L (for instance, $L = 4$ for quarterly data and $L = 12$ for monthly data), we accomplish the normalization by multiplying each value of $\overline{sn}_t$ by the quantity

$$\frac{L}{\sum \overline{sn}_t} = \frac{12}{.4925 + .595 + \cdots + .5995}$$

$$= \frac{12}{11.9895} = 1.0008758$$

This normalization process results in the estimate $sn_t = 1.0008758(\overline{sn}_t)$, which is the estimate of SN_t. These calculations are summarized in Table 16.13.

Having calculated the values of sn_t and placed them in Table 16.12, we next define the deseasonalized observation in time period t to be

$$d_t = \frac{y_t}{sn_t}$$

Deseasonalized observations are computed from a **deseasonalized time series** analysis to better estimate the trend component TR_t. Dividing y_t by the estimated seasonal factor removes the seasonality from the data and allows us to better understand the nature of the trend. The deseasonalized observations are calculated in Table 16.12 and plotted in Figure 16.12 and because the deseasonalized observations have a straight-line appearance, it seems reasonable to assume a linear trend,

$$TR_t = \beta_0 + \beta_1 t$$

TABLE **16.13** Estimation of the Seasonal Factors 🖊

		sn_t × ir_t = y_t/ (tr_t × cl_t)		$\overline{sn_t}$	sn_t = 1.0008758($\overline{sn_t}$)
		Year 1	Year 2		
1	Jan.	0.495	0.490	0.4925	0.493
2	Feb.	0.583	0.607	0.595	0.596
3	Mar.	0.608	0.582	0.595	0.595
4	Apr.	0.684	0.675	0.6795	0.680
5	May	0.567	0.561	0.564	0.564
6	Jun.	0.991	0.978	0.9845	0.986
7	Jul.	1.466	1.465	1.4655	1.467
8	Aug.	1.707	1.676	1.6915	1.693
9	Sep.	1.985	1.992	1.9885	1.990
10	Oct.	1.312	1.300	1.306	1.307
11	Nov.	1.026	1.030	1.028	1.029
12	Dec.	0.577	0.622	0.5995	0.600

FIGURE **16.12** Plot of Tasty Cola Sales and Deseasonalized Sales

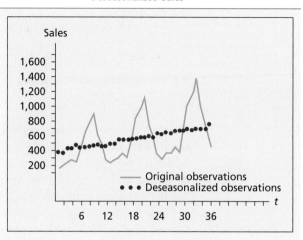

We estimate TR_t by fitting a straight line to the deseasonalized observations. That is, we compute the least squares point estimates of the parameters in the simple linear regression model relating the dependent variable, d_t, to the independent variable, t:

$$d_t = \beta_0 + \beta_1 t + \varepsilon_t$$

We obtain $b_0 = 380.163$ and $b_1 = 9.489$. It follows that the estimate of TR_t is

$$tr_t = b_0 + b_1 t = 380.163 + 9.489t$$

The values of tr_t are calculated in Table 16.12. Note that, for example, although $y_{22} = 759$ (the Tasty Cola sales in period 22 [October of year 2]) is larger than $tr_{22} = 588.921$ (the estimated trend in period 22), $d_{22} = 580.72$ is smaller than $tr_{22} = 588.921$. This implies that on a deseasonalized basis, Tasty Cola sales were slightly down in October of year 2. This might have been caused by a slightly colder October than usual.

So far we have found estimates sn_t and tr_t of SN_t and TR_t. Because the model

$$y_t = TR_t \times SN_t \times CL_t \times IR_t$$

implies that

$$CL_t \times IR_t = \frac{y_t}{TR_t \times SN_t}$$

it follows that the estimate of $CL_t \times IR_t$ is

$$cl_t \times ir_t = \frac{y_t}{tr_t \times sn_t}$$

Moreover, when considering either monthly or quarterly data, we can average out ir_t and so calculate the estimate, cl_t, of CL_t by computing a three-period moving average of the $cl_t \times ir_t$ values.

Finally, we calculate the estimate, ir_t, of IR_t by using the equation

$$ir_t = \frac{cl_t \times ir_t}{cl_t} = \frac{y_t}{tr_t \times sn_t \times cl_t}$$

The calculations of the values cl_t and ir_t for the Tasty Cola data are summarized in Table 16.12. Because there are only three years of data and because most of the values of cl_t are near 1, we cannot discern a well-defined cycle. Furthermore, examining the values of ir_t, we cannot detect a pattern in the estimates of the irregular factors.

Traditionally, the estimates tr_t, sn_t, cl_t, and ir_t obtained by using the multiplicative decomposition method are used to describe the time series. However, we can also use these estimates to forecast future values of the time series. If there is no pattern in the irregular component, we predict IR_t to equal 1. Therefore, the point forecast of y_t is

$$\hat{y}_t = tr_t \times sn_t \times cl_t$$

if a well-defined cycle exists and can be predicted. The point forecast is

$$\hat{y}_t = tr_t \times sn_t$$

if a well-defined cycle does not exist or if CL_t cannot be predicted, as in the Tasty Cola example. Because values of $tr_t \times sn_t$ have been calculated in column 9 of Table 16.12, these values are the point forecasts of the $n = 36$ historical Tasty Cola sales values. Furthermore, we present in Table 16.14 point forecasts of future Tasty Cola sales in the 12 months of year 4. Recalling that the estimated trend equation is $tr_t = 380.163 + 9.489t$ and that the estimated seasonal factor for August is 1.693 (see Table 16.13), it follows, for example, that the point forecast of Tasty Cola sales in period 44 (August of year 4) is

$$\hat{y}_{44} = tr_{44} \times sn_{44}$$
$$= (380.163 + 9.489(44))(1.693)$$
$$= 797.699(1.693)$$
$$= 1350.50$$

Although there is no theoretically correct prediction interval for y_t, a *fairly accurate approximate $100(1 - \alpha)$ percent prediction interval for y_t* is obtained by computing an interval that is centred at $\hat{y}_t$ and has a length equal to the length of the $100(1 - \alpha)$ percent prediction interval for the *deseasonalized observation d_t*. Here the interval for d_t is obtained by using the model

$$d_t = TR_t + \varepsilon_t$$
$$= \beta_0 + \beta_1 t + \varepsilon_t$$

For instance, if a 95 percent prediction interval for d_{44} is [769.959, 825.439], with length equal to $825.439 - 769.959 = 55.48$, it follows that an approximate 95 percent prediction interval for y_{44} is

$$\left[\hat{y}_{44} \pm \frac{55.48}{2} \right] = [1350.50 \pm 27.74]$$
$$= [1322.76, 1378.24]$$

In Table 16.14, we give the approximate 95 percent prediction intervals (calculated by the above method) for Tasty Cola sales in the 12 months of year 4.

TABLE **16.14**   Forecasts of Future Values of Tasty Cola Sales Calculated Using the Multiplicative Decomposition Method

t	sn_t	$tr_t = 380.163 + 9.489t$	Point Prediction, $\hat{y}_t = tr_t \times sn_t$	Approximate 95% Prediction Interval	y_t
37	0.493	731.273	360.52	[333.72, 387.32]	352
38	0.596	740.762	441.48	[414.56, 468.40]	445
39	0.595	750.252	446.40	[419.36, 473.44]	453
40	0.680	759.741	516.62	[489.45, 543.79]	541
41	0.564	769.231	433.85	[406.55, 461.15]	457
42	0.986	778.720	767.82	[740.38, 795.26]	762
43	1.467	788.209	1,156.30	[1,128.71, 1,183.89]	1,194
44	1.693	797.699	1,350.50	[1,322.76, 1,378.24]	1,361
45	1.990	807.188	1,606.30	[1,578.41, 1,634.19]	1,615
46	1.307	816.678	1,067.40	[1,039.35, 1,095.45]	1,059
47	1.029	826.167	850.12	[821.90, 878.34]	824
48	0.600	835.657	501.39	[473, 529.78]	495

FIGURE **16.13** A Plot of the Observed and Forecast Tasty Cola Sales Values

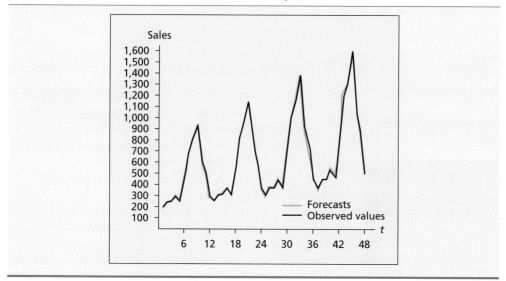

Next suppose we actually observe Tasty Cola sales in year 4 and these sales are as given in Table 16.14. In Figure 16.13, we plot the observed and forecast sales for all 48 sales periods. In practice, the comparison of the observed and forecast sales in years 1 through 3 would be used by the analyst to determine whether the forecasting equation adequately fits the historical data. An adequate fit (as indicated by Figure 16.13, for example) might prompt an analyst to use this equation to calculate forecasts for future time periods. One reason that the Tasty Cola forecasting equation

$$\hat{y}_t = tr_t \times sn_t$$
$$= (380.163 + 9.489t)sn_t$$

provides reasonable forecasts is that this equation multiplies tr_t by sn_t. Therefore, as the average level of the time series (determined by the trend) increases, the seasonal swing of the time series increases, which is consistent with the data plots in Figures 16.11 and 16.13. For example, note from Table 16.13 that the estimated seasonal factor for August is 1.693. The forecasting equation yields a prediction of Tasty Cola sales in August of year 1 equal to

$$\hat{y}_8 = [380.163 + 9.489(8)]1.693$$
$$= (456.075)(1.693)$$
$$= 772.13$$

This implies a seasonal swing of $772.13 - 456.075 = 316.055$ (hundreds of cases) above 456.075, the estimated trend level. The forecasting equation yields a prediction of Tasty Cola sales in August of year 2 equal to

$$\hat{y}_{20} = [380.163 + 9.489(20)]1.693$$
$$= (569.943)(1.693)$$
$$= 964.91$$

which implies an increased seasonal swing of $964.91 - 569.943 = 394.967$ (hundreds of cases) above 569.943, the estimated trend level. In general, then, the forecasting equation is appropriate for forecasting a time series with a seasonal swing that is proportional to the average level of the time series as determined by the trend—that is, a time series exhibiting increasing seasonal variation.

MegaStat estimates the seasonal factors and the trend line as described in this section. MegaStat does not estimate the cyclical and irregular components, however, because it is often reasonable to make forecasts by using estimates of the seasonal factors and trend line.

Exercises for Section **16.4**

CONCEPTS

16.12 Explain how the multiplicative decomposition model estimates seasonal factors.

16.13 Explain how the multiplicative decomposition method estimates the trend effect.

16.14 Discuss how the multiplicative decomposition method makes point forecasts of future time series values.

METHODS AND APPLICATIONS

Exercises 16.15 through 16.19 are based on the following situation: International Machinery produces a tractor and wants to use quarterly tractor sales data observed in the last four years to predict quarterly tractor sales next year. The MegaStat output in Figure 16.14 gives the tractor sales data and the estimates of the seasonal factors and trend line for the data.

16.15 Find and identify the four seasonal factors for quarters 1, 2, 3, and 4.

16.16 What type of trend is indicated by the plot of the deseasonalized data?

16.17 What is the equation of the estimated trend that has been calculated using the deseasonalized data?

16.18 Compute a point forecast of tractor sales (based on trend and seasonal factors) for each of the quarters next year.

16.19 Compute an approximate 95 percent prediction interval forecast of tractor sales for each of the quarters next year. Use the fact that the half-lengths of 95 percent prediction intervals for the deseasonalized sales values in the four quarters of next year are 14, 14.4, 14.6, and 15.

16.20 Use the deseasonalized method in MegaStat to analyze the quarterly bicycle sales data given in Table 16.3.
a. What are the quarterly seasonal factors?
b. If a straight line is fitted to the deseasonalized values, what is the estimate of the trend?

FIGURE 16.14   MegaStat Output of Tractor Sales Data for Exercises 16.15 through 16.19

t	Year	Quarter	Sales, y	Centred Moving Average	Ratio to Centred Moving Average	Seasonal Indexes	Sales, y, Deseasonalized
1	1	1	293			1.191	245.9
2	1	2	392			1.521	257.7
3	1	3	221	275.125	0.803	0.804	275.0
4	1	4	147	302.000	0.487	0.484	303.9
5	2	1	388	325.250	1.193	1.191	325.7
6	2	2	512	338.125	1.514	1.521	336.6
7	2	3	287	354.125	0.810	0.804	357.1
8	2	4	184	381.500	0.482	0.484	380.4
9	3	1	479	405.000	1.183	1.191	402.0
10	3	2	640	417.375	1.533	1.521	420.7
11	3	3	347	435.000	0.798	0.804	431.8
12	3	4	223	462.125	0.483	0.484	461.0
13	4	1	581	484.375	1.199	1.191	487.7
14	4	2	755	497.625	1.517	1.521	496.3
15	4	3	410			0.804	510.2
16	4	4	266			0.484	549.9

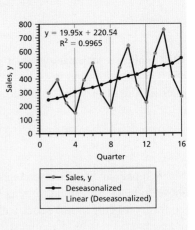

$y = 19.95x + 220.54$
$R^2 = 0.9965$

Sales, y
Deseasonalized
Linear (Deseasonalized)

Calculation of Seasonal Indexes

	1	2	3	4	
1			0.803	0.487	
2	1.193	1.514	0.810	0.482	
3	1.183	1.533	0.798	0.483	
4	1.199	1.517			
mean:	1.192	1.522	0.804	0.484	4.001
adjusted:	1.191	1.521	0.804	0.484	4.000

16.5 EXPONENTIAL SMOOTHING

In ongoing forecasting systems, forecasts of future time series values are made for succeeding periods. At the end of each period, the estimates of the time series parameters and the forecasting equation need to be updated to account for the most recent observation. This updating accounts for possible changes in the parameters that may occur over time. In addition, such changes may imply that unequal weights should be applied to the time series observations when the estimates of the parameters are updated.

Simple exponential smoothing We begin by assuming that a time series is appropriately described by the no-trend equation

$$y_t = \beta_0 + \varepsilon_t$$

When the parameter β_0 remains constant over time, we have seen that it is reasonable to forecast future values of y_t by using regression analysis (see Example 16.1). In such a case, the least squares point estimate of β_0 is

$$b_0 = \bar{y} = \text{Average of the observed time series values}$$

When we compute the point estimate b_0, we are *equally weighting* each of the previously observed time series values $y_1, y_2, \ldots, y_n$.

When the value of the parameter β_0 is slowly changing over time, the equal-weighting scheme may not be appropriate. Instead, it may be desirable to weight recent observations more heavily than remote observations. Simple **exponential smoothing** is a forecasting method that applies unequal weights to the time series observations. This unequal weighting is accomplished by using a **smoothing constant** that determines how much weight is attached to each observation. The most recent observation is given the most weight. More distantly past observations are given successively smaller weights. The procedure allows the forecaster to update the estimate of β_0 so that changes in the value of this parameter can be detected and incorporated into the forecasting equation. We illustrate simple exponential smoothing in Example 16.6.

Example 16.6 The Cod Catch Example

Consider the cod catch data in Example 16.1 (Table 16.1). The plot of these data in Figure 16.2 (repeated here) suggests that the no-trend model

$$y_t = \beta_0 + \varepsilon_t$$

may appropriately describe the cod catch series. The parameter β_0 could also be slowly changing over time.

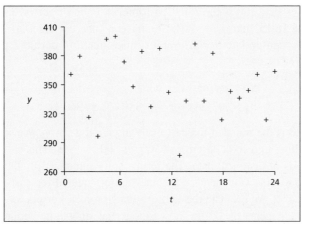

We begin the simple exponential smoothing procedure by calculating an initial estimate of the average level, β_0, of the series. This estimate is denoted S_0 and is computed by averaging the first six time series values. We obtain

$$S_0 = \frac{\sum_{t=1}^{6} y_t}{6} = \frac{362 + 381 + \cdots + 402}{6} = 359.67$$

Note that because simple exponential smoothing attempts to track changes over time in the average level β_0 by using newly observed values to update the estimates of β_0, we use only six of the $n = 24$ time series observations to calculate the initial estimate of β_0. If we do this, then 18 observations remain to tell us how β_0 may be changing over time. In general, it is reasonable to calculate initial estimates in exponential smoothing procedures by using half of the historical data. However, it can be shown that in simple exponential smoothing, using six observations is reasonable (it would not, however, be reasonable to use a very small number of observations, because doing so might make the initial estimate so different from the true value of β_0 that the exponential smoothing procedure would be adversely affected).

Next assume that at the end of time period $T - 1$ we have an estimate S_{T-1} of β_0. Then, assuming that in time period T we obtain a new observation y_T, we can update S_{T-1} to S_T, which is an estimate made in period T of β_0. We compute the updated estimate by using the smoothing equation

$$S_T = \alpha y_T + (1 - \alpha)S_{T-1}$$

Here α is a smoothing constant between 0 and 1. The updating equation says that S_T, the estimate made in time period T of β_0, equals a fraction, α (for example, .1), *of the newly* observed time series observation y_T plus a fraction, $1 - \alpha$ (for example, .9), of S_{T-1}, the estimate made in time period $T - 1$ of β_0. The more the average level of the process is changing, the more a newly observed time series value should influence our estimate, so the larger the smoothing constant α should be set. In the following, we use historical data to determine an appropriate value of α.

We begin with the initial estimate $S_0 = 359.67$ and update this initial estimate by applying the smoothing equation to the 24 observed cod catches. To do this, we arbitrarily set α equal to .02, and to judge the appropriateness of this choice of α we calculate one-period-ahead forecasts of the historical cod catches as we carry out the smoothing procedure. Because the initial estimate of β_0 *is* $S_0 = 359.67$, it follows that 360 is the rounded forecast made at time 0 for y_1, the value of the time series in period 1. Because we see from Table 16.15 that $y_1 = 362$, we have a forecast error of $362 - 360 = 2$. Using $y_1 = 362$, we can update S_0 to S_1, an estimate made in period 1 of the average level of the time series, by using the equation

$$
\begin{aligned}
S_1 &= \alpha y_1 + (1 - \alpha)S_0 \\
&= .02(362) + .98(359.67) = 359.72
\end{aligned}
$$

Because this implies that 360 is the rounded forecast made in period 1 for y_2 and because we see from Table 16.15 that $y_2 = 381$, we have a forecast error of $381 - 360 = 21$. Using $y_2 = 381$, we can update S_1 to S_2, an estimate made in period 2 of β_0, by using the equation

$$
\begin{aligned}
S_2 &= \alpha y_2 + (1 - \alpha)S_1 \\
&= .02(381) + .98(359.72) = 360.14
\end{aligned}
$$

This implies that 360 is the rounded forecast made in period 2 for y_3. We see from Table 16.15 that $y_3 = 317$, resulting in a forecast error of $317 - 360 = -43$. This procedure is continued through all 24 periods of historical data. The results are summarized in Table 16.15. Using the results in this table, we find that for $\alpha = .02$, the sum of squared forecast errors is 27,744. To find a "good" value of α, we evaluate the sum of squared forecast errors for values of α ranging from .02 to .30 in increments of .02 (in most exponential smoothing applications, the value of

TABLE **16.15** One-Period-Ahead Forecasting of the Historical Cod Catch Time Series Using Simple Exponential Smoothing with $\alpha = 0.02$ ✍

Year	Month	Actual Cod Catch, y_T	Smoothed Estimate, S_T ($S_0 = 359.67$)	Forecast Made Last Period	Forecast Error	Squared Forecast Error
1	Jan.	362	359.72	360	2	4
	Feb.	381	360.14	360	21	441
	Mar.	317	359.28	360	−43	1,849
	Apr.	297	358.03	359	−62	3,844
	May	399	358.85	358	41	1,681
	Jun.	402	359.71	359	43	1,849
	Jul.	375	360.02	360	15	225
	Aug.	349	359.80	360	−11	121
	Sep.	386	360.32	360	26	676
	Oct.	328	359.68	360	−32	1,024
	Nov.	389	360.26	360	29	841
	Dec.	343	359.92	360	−17	289
2	Jan.	276	358.24	360	−84	7,056
	Feb.	334	357.75	358	−24	576
	Mar.	394	358.48	358	36	1,296
	Apr.	334	357.99	358	−24	576
	May	384	358.51	358	26	676
	Jun.	314	357.62	359	−45	2,025
	Jul.	344	357.35	358	−14	196
	Aug.	337	356.94	357	−20	400
	Sep.	345	356.70	357	−12	144
	Oct.	362	356.81	357	5	25
	Nov.	314	355.95	357	−43	1,849
	Dec.	365	356.13	356	9	81

the smoothing constant used is between .01 and .30). When we do this, we find that $\alpha = .02$ minimizes the sum of squared forecast errors. Since this minimizing value of α is small, it appears to be best to apply small weights to new observations, which tells us that the level of the time series is not changing very much.

In general, simple exponential smoothing is carried out as shown in the following boxed feature.

Simple Exponential Smoothing

1 Suppose that the time series $y_1, \ldots, y_n$ is described by the equation

$$y_t = \beta_0 + \varepsilon_t$$

where the average level, β_0, of the process may be slowly changing over time. Then the estimate S_T of β_0 made in time period T is given by the smoothing equation

$$S_T = \alpha y_T + (1 - \alpha)S_{T-1}$$

where α is a smoothing constant between 0 and 1 and S_{T-1} is the estimate of β_0 made in time period $T - 1$.

2 A point forecast made in time period T for any future value of the time series is S_T.

3 If we observe y_{T+1} in time period $T + 1$, we can update S_T to S_{T+1} by using the equation

$$S_{T+1} = \alpha y_{T+1} + (1 - \alpha)S_T$$

and a point forecast made in time period $T + 1$ for any future value of the time series is S_{T+1}.

Example 16.7 The Cod Catch Example

In Example 16.6, we saw that $\alpha = .02$ is a "good" value of the smoothing constant when forecasting the 24 observed cod catches in Table 16.15, so we will use simple exponential smoothing with $\alpha = .02$ to forecast future monthly cod catches. From Table 16.15, we see that $S_{24} = 356.13$ is the estimate made in month 24 of the average level β_0 of the monthly cod catches. It follows that the point forecast made in month 24 of any future monthly cod catch is 356.13 tonnes of cod. Now, assuming that we observe a cod catch in January of year 3 of $y_{25} = 384$, we can update S_{24} to S_{25} by using the equation

$$S_{25} = \alpha y_{25} + (1 - \alpha)S_{24}$$
$$= .02(384) + .98(356.13)$$
$$= 356.69$$

This implies that the point forecast made in month 25 of any future monthly cod catch is 356.69 tonnes of cod.

By using the smoothing equation

$$S_T = \alpha y_T + (1 - \alpha)S_{T-1}$$

it can be shown that S_T, the estimate made in time period T of the average level β_0 of the time series, can be expressed as

$$S_T = \alpha y_T + \alpha(1 - \alpha)y_{T-1} + \alpha(1 - \alpha)^2 y_{T-2} + \cdots + \alpha(1 - \alpha)^{T-1}y_1 + (1 - \alpha)^T S_0$$

The coefficients measuring the contributions of the observations $y_T, y_{T-1}, y_{T-2}, \ldots, y_1$—that is, α, $\alpha(1 - \alpha)$, $\alpha(1 - \alpha)^2, \ldots, \alpha(1 - \alpha)^{T-1}$—decrease *exponentially* with time. For this reason, we refer to this procedure as *simple exponential smoothing*.

Because the coefficients measuring the contributions of $y_T, y_{T-1}, y_{T-2}, \ldots, y_1$ are decreasing exponentially, the most recent observation, y_T, makes the largest contribution to the current estimate of β_0. Older observations make smaller and smaller contributions to this estimate, so remote observations are damped out of the current estimate of β_0 as time advances. The rate at which remote observations are damped out depends on the smoothing constant α. For values of α near 1, remote observations are damped out quickly. For example, if $\alpha = .9$, we obtain coefficients .9, .09, .009, .0009, ... For values of α near 0, remote observations are damped out more slowly (if $\alpha = .1$, we obtain coefficients .1, .09, .081, .0729, . . .). The choice of a smoothing constant α is usually made by simulated forecasting of a historical data set, as illustrated in Example 16.6.

ROADBLOCK

Mathematical forecast values might not make sense
Computer software applications can be used to implement exponential smoothing. These applications generate different smoothing constant(s) by using different methods and also compute approximate prediction intervals in different ways. Optimally, the user should carefully investigate how the computer software implements exponential smoothing. At a minimum, the user should not trust the forecasts given by the software if these forecasts seem to be illogical.

Figure 16.15 gives the MegaStat output of using simple exponential smoothing to forecast in month 24 the cod catches in future months. The point forecast of the cod catch in any future month is 356. Looking at the data in Figure 16.15(b), these forecasts seem to be intuitively reasonable.

FIGURE 16.15   Example of Using Simple Exponential Smoothing to Forecast the Cod Catches

(a) The graphical forecasts

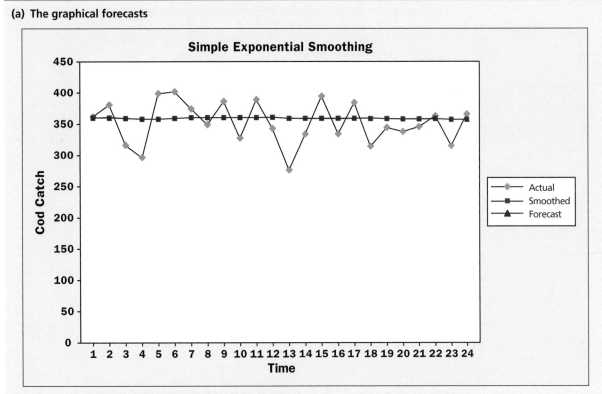

(b) The numerical forecasts of the cod catch in month 25 (and any other future month)

Simple Exponential Smoothing

		Alpha		
		0.02		
t	CodCatch	Smoothed	Forecast	% error
		359.7 *		
1	362	359.7	360	0.6
2	381	360.1	360	5.5
3	317	359.3	360	−13.6
4	297	358.0	359	−20.9
5	399	358.9	358	10.3
6	402	359.7	359	10.7
7	375	360.0	360	4.0
8	349	359.8	360	−3.2
9	386	360.3	360	6.7
10	328	359.7	360	−9.8
11	389	360.3	360	7.5
12	343	359.9	360	−5.0
13	276	358.2	360	−30.4
14	334	357.8	358	−7.2
15	394	358.5	358	9.1
16	334	358.0	358	−7.2
17	384	358.5	358	6.8
18	314	357.6	359	−14.3
19	344	357.3	358	−4.1
20	337	356.9	357	−5.9
21	345	356.7	357	−3.5
22	362	356.8	357	1.4
23	314	356.0	357	−13.7
24	365	356.1	356	2.5
			356	

1,156.0	Mean Squared Error
8.5%	Mean Absolute Percent Error
45.8%	Percent Positive Errors

* initial value - mean of first six data values

FIGURE **16.16** MegaStat Output of Using Double Exponential Smoothing to Forecast DVD Player Sales

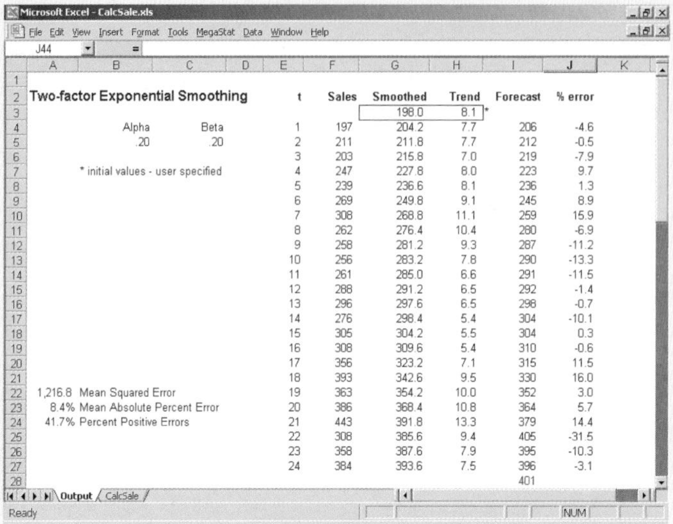
Microsoft Excel - CalcSale.xls

Two-factor Exponential Smoothing

Alpha .20 Beta .20

* initial values - user specified

1,216.8 Mean Squared Error
8.4% Mean Absolute Percent Error
41.7% Percent Positive Errors

t	Sales	Smoothed	Trend	Forecast	% error
		198.0	8.1 *		
1	197	204.2	7.7	206	-4.6
2	211	211.8	7.7	212	-0.5
3	203	215.8	7.0	219	-7.9
4	247	227.8	8.0	223	9.7
5	239	236.6	8.1	236	1.3
6	269	249.8	9.1	245	8.9
7	308	268.8	11.1	259	15.9
8	262	276.4	10.4	280	-6.9
9	258	281.2	9.3	287	-11.2
10	256	283.2	7.8	290	-13.3
11	261	285.0	6.6	291	-11.5
12	288	291.2	6.5	292	-1.4
13	296	297.6	6.5	298	-0.7
14	276	298.4	5.4	304	-10.1
15	305	304.2	5.5	304	0.3
16	308	309.6	5.4	310	-0.6
17	356	323.2	7.1	315	11.5
18	393	342.6	9.5	330	16.0
19	363	354.2	10.0	352	3.0
20	386	368.4	10.8	364	5.7
21	443	391.8	13.3	379	14.4
22	308	385.6	9.4	405	-31.5
23	358	387.6	7.9	395	-10.3
24	384	393.6	7.5	396	-3.1
				401	

Holt–Winters' models Various extensions of simple exponential smoothing can be used to forecast time series that are described by models different from the model

$$y_t = \beta_0 + \varepsilon_t$$

For example, Holt–Winters' double exponential smoothing can forecast time series that are described by the linear trend model

$$y_t = \beta_0 + \beta_1 t + \varepsilon_t$$

Here we assume that β_0 and β_1 (and thus the linear trend) may be changing slowly over time. To implement Holt–Winters' double exponential smoothing, we find initial estimates of β_0 and β_1 and then use updating equations to track changes in these estimates. The updating equation for the estimate of β_0 uses a smoothing constant that MegaStat calls *alpha* and the updating equation for the estimate of β_1 uses a smoothing constant that MegaStat calls *beta*. We show in Figure 16.16 the MegaStat output of using double exponential smoothing to forecast the sales of the X-12 DVD player.

Exercises for Section **16.5**

CONCEPTS

16.21 In general, when it is appropriate to use exponential smoothing?

16.22 What is the purpose of the smoothing constant in exponential smoothing?

16.23 What are the differences between the types of time series forecast by simple exponential smoothing and double exponential smoothing?

METHODS AND APPLICATIONS

16.24 THE COD CATCH EXAMPLE

Consider Table 16.15. Verify that S_3, an estimate made in period 3 of β_0, is 359.28. Also verify that the one-period-ahead forecast error for period 4 is -62, as shown in Table 16.15.

16.25 THE LUMBER PRODUCTION EXAMPLE

Figure 16.17 gives the MegaStat output of using simple exponential smoothing to forecast yearly lumber production. Use the output to find and report the point prediction of the total lumber production in a future year.

16.26 THE WATCH SALES EXAMPLE

Figure 16.18 gives the MegaStat output of using double exponential smoothing in month 20 to forecast watch sales in month 21. Here we have used MegaStat's default option that sets each of the smoothing constants alpha and beta equal to .02. Find and report the point prediction of watch sales in month 21.

FIGURE 16.17 MegaStat Output of Using Simple Exponential Smoothing to Forecast Lumber Production

Simple Exponential Smoothing

Alpha
0.02

t	Production	Smoothed	Forecast	% error	t	Production	Smoothed	Forecast	% error
		35,239.7 *			19	38,902	35,409.3	35,338	9.2
1	35,404	35,243.0	35,240	0.5	20	37,858	35,458.3	35,409	6.5
2	37,462	35,287.3	35,243	5.9	21	32,926	35,407.6	35,458	−7.7
3	32,901	35,239.6	35,287	−7.3	22	35,697	35,413.4	35,408	0.8
4	33,178	35,198.4	35,240	−6.2	23	34,548	35,396.1	35,413	−2.5
5	34,449	35,183.4	35,198	−2.2	24	32,087	35,329.9	35,396	−10.3
6	38,044	35,240.6	35,183	7.5	25	37,515	35,373.6	35,330	5.8
7	36,762	35,271.0	35,241	4.1	26	38,629	35,438.8	35,374	8.4
8	36,742	35,300.4	35,271	4.0	27	32,019	35,370.4	35,439	−10.7
9	33,385	35,262.1	35,300	−5.7	28	35,710	35,377.1	35,370	1.0
10	34,171	35,240.3	35,262	−3.2	29	36,693	35,403.5	35,377	3.6
11	36,124	35,258.0	35,240	2.4	30	37,153	35,438.5	35,403	4.7
12	38,658	35,326.0	35,258	8.8				35,438	
13	32,901	35,277.5	35,326	−7.4				4,188,430.4	Mean Squared Error
14	36,356	35,299.1	35,277	3.0				5.0%	Mean Absolute Percent Error
15	37,166	35,336.4	35,299	5.0					
16	35,733	35,344.3	35,336	1.1				63.3%	Percent Positive Errors
17	35,791	35,353.3	35,344	1.2					
18	34,592	35,338.0	35,353	−2.2	* initial value - mean of first six data values				

FIGURE 16.18 MegaStat Output of Using Double Exponential Smoothing to Forecast Watch Sales

Two-factor Exponential Smoothing

t	Sales	Alpha 0.02 Smoothed	Beta 0.02 Trend	Forecast	% error	t	Sales	Smoothed	Trend	Forecast	% error
		278.1	13.3 *			14	392	456.7	13.2	458	−16.8
1	298	291.1	13.3	291	2.3	15	425	469.1	13.2	470	−10.6
2	302	304.0	13.3	304	−0.7	16	411	480.6	13.1	482	−17.3
3	301	316.7	13.3	317	−5.3	17	455	493.2	13.1	494	−8.6
4	351	330.4	13.3	330	6.0	18	457	505.0	13.1	506	−10.7
5	336	343.8	13.3	344	−2.4	19	465	516.9	13.1	518	−11.4
6	361	357.1	13.3	357	1.1	20	481	529.0	13.1	530	−10.2
7	407	370.7	13.3	370	9.1					542	
8	351	383.3	13.3	384	−9.4					2,003.6	Mean Squared Error
9	357	396.2	13.3	397	−11.2						
10	346	408.7	13.3	410	−18.5					9.9%	Mean Absolute Percent Error
11	356	420.7	13.3	422	−18.5						
12	371	432.7	13.2	434	−17.0					20.0%	Percent Positive Errors
13	399	445.1	13.2	446	−11.8	* initial values - estimated by linear trend of first six values					

16.6 FORECAST ERROR COMPARISONS

A forecast error is the difference (or deviation) between the actual value (y_t) and the predicted value $\hat{y}_t$. Forecast errors can be used to compare forecast values generated by various prediction methods, in that the model with the smallest error value is the best predicting model. Table 16.16 gives the actual values of Tasty Cola sales in periods 37 through 48 and the multiplicative decomposition method point forecast values. Three criteria by which to compare forecasting methods are the mean absolute deviation (MAD), the mean squared deviation (MSD), and the percentage error (PE).

TABLE **16.16** Forecast Errors Given by the Multiplicative Decomposition Method for the Tasty Cola Data

t	y_t	$\hat{y}_t$	$y_t - \hat{y}_t$	$abs(y_t - \hat{y}_t)$	$(y_t - \hat{y}_t)^2$	$[(y_t - \hat{y}_t)/y_t]100$	$abs(PE)$
37	352	360.52	−8.52	8.52	72.5904	−2.42045455	2.420455
38	445	441.48	3.52	3.52	12.3904	0.791011236	0.791011
39	453	446.4	6.6	6.6	43.56	1.456953642	1.456954
40	541	516.62	24.38	24.38	594.3844	4.506469501	4.50647
41	457	433.85	23.15	23.15	535.9225	5.065645514	5.065646
42	762	767.82	−5.82	5.82	33.8724	−0.76377953	0.76378
43	1194	1156.3	37.7	37.7	1421.29	3.157453936	3.157454
44	1361	1350.5	10.5	10.5	110.25	0.77149155	0.771492
45	1615	1606.3	8.7	8.7	75.69	0.53869969	0.5387
46	1059	1067.4	−8.4	8.4	70.56	−0.79320113	0.793201
47	824	850.12	−26.12	26.12	682.2544	−3.16990291	3.169903
48	495	501.39	−6.39	6.39	40.8321	−1.29090909	1.290909

To calculate the MAD, we find the absolute value of each forecast error and then average the absolute values:

$$\text{MAD} = \frac{\sum abs(y_t - \hat{y}_t)}{t}$$

For example, if we find the absolute value of each of the 12 forecast errors given by the multiplicative decomposition method in Table 16.16, sum the 12 absolute values, and divide the sum by 12, we find that the MAD is 14.15.

To calculate the MSD, we find the squared value of each forecast error and then average the squared values:

$$\text{MSD} = \frac{\sum (y_t - \hat{y}_t)^2}{t}$$

LO4

For example, if we find the squared value of each of the 12 forecast errors given by the multiplicative decomposition method in Table 16.16, sum the 12 squared values, and divide the sum by 12, we find that the MSD is 307.80. Note, however, that the MSD is the average of the squared forecast errors. It follows that the MSD, unlike the MAD, penalizes a forecasting method much more for large forecast errors than for small forecast errors. Therefore, the forecasting method that gives the smallest MSD might not be the forecasting method that gives the smallest MAD.

The MAD and the MSD provide estimates of the forecasting errors, but the values might not be easily interpretable. In contrast, the PE provides a more interpretable value. To calculate the PE, subtract the forecasted value from the observed value, divide the result by the observed value, and multiply by 100:

$$\text{PE} = \frac{y_t - \hat{y}_t}{y_t} \times 100$$

A PE value is computed for each forecasted value. For example, in Table 16.16, the PE values are given in the second-last column.

Two further statistics can then be generated using the PE values: the mean percentage error (MPE) and the mean absolute percentage error (MAPE). To compute the MPE, sum the PE values and divide by the number of PE values (number of time estimates). For the Tasty Cola data, the MPE is .65. Because negative values will have a cancelling effect on positive values, many researchers prefer the MAPE, which is the average of the absolute PE values. These values are given in the last column of Table 16.16. For these data, the MAPE is 2.06 percent, suggesting that the forecasted values are "off" by about 2 percent on average.

Exercises for Section **16.6**

CONCEPTS

16.27 What is the MAD? What is the MSD? What is the MAPE? How are these quantities used?

16.28 Why does the MSD penalize a forecasting method much more for large forecast errors than for small forecast errors?

METHODS AND APPLICATIONS

Exercises 16.29 and 16.30 compare two forecasting methods—method A and method B. Suppose that method A gives the

point forecasts 57, 61, and 70 of three future time series values. Method B gives the point forecasts 59, 65, and 73 of these three future values. The three future values turn out to be 60, 64, and 67.

16.29 Calculate the MAD, the MSD, and the MAPE for method A. Calculate the MAD, the MSD and the MAPE for method B.

16.30 Which method—method A or method B—gives the smaller MAD? The smaller MSD? The smaller MAPE?

16.7 INDEX NUMBERS

We often want to compare a value of a time series to another value of the time series. For example, Statistics Canada reported in November 2012 that "Consumer prices rose 0.8% in the 12 months to November, following a 1.2% gain in October." To make such comparisons, we must describe the time series. We have seen (in Section 16.4) that time series decomposition can be used to describe a time series. Another way to describe time-related data is to use index numbers.

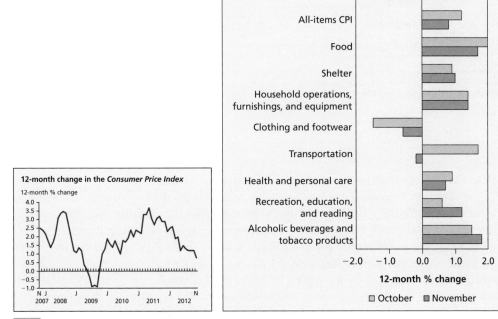

Source: Statistics Canada, *The Daily*, December 21, 2012, "Consumer Price Index, November 2012."

When we compare time series values to the same previous value, we say that the previous value is in the base time period and successive comparisons of time series values to the value in the base period form a sequence of index numbers. More formally, a simple **index number** (or simple index) is defined as follows:

A simple index is obtained by dividing the current value of a time series by the value of the time series in the base time period and multiplying this ratio by 100. That is, if y_t denotes the current value and y_0 denotes the value in the base time period, then the simple index number is

$$\frac{y_t}{y_0} \times 100$$

FIGURE **16.19**   Bank of Canada Inflation Calculator (To access this online, enter "Bank of Canada Inflation Calculator" in the search window)

Inflation Calculator

About the Calculator

The Inflation Calculator uses monthly consumer price index (CPI) data from 1914 to the present to show changes in the cost of a fixed "basket" of consumer purchases. These include food, shelter, furniture, clothing, transportation, and recreation. An increase in this cost is called inflation.

The calculator's results are based on the most recent month for which the CPI data are available. This will normally be about two months prior to the current month.

How to Use the Calculator

Enter any dollar amount, and the years you wish to compare, then click the **Calculate** button.

A "basket" of goods and services that cost:	$ 100.00 in 1999
...would cost:	$ 131.27 in 2013

Clear   Calculate

Per cent change:	31.27
Number of Years:	14
Average Annual Rate of Inflation (%) / Decline in the Value of Money:	1.96
CPI for first year:	(Oct. 1999) 93.7
CPI for second year:	(Oct. 2013) 123.0

June 2002 CPI = 100.0

Data Source: Statistics Canada, Consumer Price Indexes for Canada, Monthly, 1914–2006 (V41690973 series.)

LO5   The time series values used to construct an index are often quantities or prices. In Canada, the Consumer Price Index (CPI) was originally tabulated by the Department of Labour in the early 1990s. Today's monthly CPI is compiled by Statistics Canada and represents the retail price of 600 goods and services considered to be "a representative shopping basket" that encompasses an average household's costs, such as food, clothing, and housing. Each item in the basket is weighted based on the purchasing patterns of consumers, and the sum is computed. As explained by the Bank of Canada (bankofcanada.ca), purchasing food typically costs more than buying clothing, so an increase in food prices has a greater weight or impact on the consumer. The CPI is then used for cost-of-living adjustments and represents a measure of inflation.

In Canada in 2013, the CPI is computed against a base year of 2002 (and the base year is always set to $100; previously, the base year was 1992). The Bank of Canada has an online "Inflation Calculator" (see Figure 16.19), which uses CPI indexes from 1914. For example, a $100 bag of groceries and services in 1914 would be equivalent to $1,998.36 in 2012 with an average annual inflation rate of 3.10 percent (over 98 years). For a shorter time interval, $100 in 2006 would be equivalent to $111.63 in 2012 with the average inflation rate of 1.85 percent over the six years.

Because the CPI deals with prices and these values are quantities, the time series of index values can also be called a *quantity index*. In addition, because the CPI represents the total sum of expenditures, it is also referred to as an aggregate price index, computed as shown in the following boxed feature.

An aggregate price index is

$$\left(\frac{\sum p_t}{\sum p_0}\right) \times 100$$

where $\sum p_t$ is the sum of the prices in the current time period and $\sum p_0$ is the sum of the prices in the base year.

In addition, as mentioned above, Statistics Canada weights the items in the CPI calculations based on the relative importance of the items. For example, weights given by Statistics Canada for CPI items are listed in Table 16.17. In this table, the sum of the weights is 100. As can be seen in this table, shelter has a greater weight than food, which in turn has more than three times the weight of clothing and footwear. This weighting means that the CPI could also be referred to as a *weighted aggregate price index*.

TABLE **16.17** Relative Importance Weights for the Canadian CPI for August 2010 🖈

Item	Relative Importance
All-items	100.00
Food	17.0
Shelter	26.6
Household operations and furnishings	11.1
Clothing and footwear	5.4
Transportation	19.9
Health and personal care	4.7
Recreation, education, and reading	12.2
Alcoholic beverages and tobacco products	3.1

Source: Statistics Canada, *The Consumer Price Index, August 2010*, Catalogue No 62-001-X.

Two versions of this kind of index are commonly used. The first version is called a *Laspeyres index*, in which the quantities that are specified for the base year are also used for all succeeding time periods. In general, we have the following:

A Laspeyres index is

$$\frac{\sum p_t q_0}{\sum p_0 q_0} \times 100$$

where p_0 represents a base period price, q_0 represents a base period quantity, and p_t represents a current period price.

Because the Laspeyres index employs the base period quantities in all succeeding time periods, this index allows for ready comparison of prices for identical quantities of goods purchased. Such an index is useful as long as the base quantities provide a reasonable representation of consumption patterns in succeeding time periods. However, purchasing patterns can sometimes change drastically as consumer preferences change or as dramatic price changes occur. If consumption patterns in the current period are very different from the quantities specified in the base period, then a Laspeyres index can be misleading because it relates to quantities of goods that few people would purchase.

A second version of the weighted aggregate price index is called a *Paasche index*, in which we update the quantities so that they reflect consumption patterns in the current time period, as shown in the following boxed feature.

A Paasche index is

$$\frac{\sum p_t q_t}{\sum p_0 q_t} \times 100$$

where p_0 represents a base period price, p_t represents a current period price, and q_t represents a current period quantity.

Because the Paasche index uses quantities from the current period, it reflects current buying habits. However, the Paasche index requires quantity data for each year, which can be difficult to obtain. Furthermore, although each period is compared to the base period, it is difficult to compare the index at other points in time because different quantities are used in different periods. Changes in the index are therefore affected by changes in both prices and quantities.

THEORY TO PRACTICE

An index number is a practical numeric to reflect change in a continuously measured variable. When choosing the base year in which to make comparisons, certain criteria should be considered. Economically, the base year should reflect a quiet and stable time. If, for example, 2008 was used as a base year, then subsequent years may reflect massive growth because of the economic slump (some say *recession*) in 2008 with the international banking collapses and bailouts (luckily, Canadian banks were spared).

Choosing certain base years could be strategic, depending on the purpose of the index. For example, if an organization had a major change, such as layoffs or a merger, using the pre-change year versus the change year as the base year would result in a different story.

When interpreting an index, always ensure that both the comparison year and the base year are considered.

Exercises for Section **16.7**

CONCEPTS

16.31 Explain the difference between a simple index and an aggregate index.

16.32 Explain the difference between a Laspeyres index and a Paasche index.

METHODS AND APPLICATIONS ✒

16.33 Following are the statistics for new motor vehicle sales in Canada between 2005 and 2009 as reported by Statistics Canada:

Year	2005	2006	2007	2008	2009
Sales (1,000s)	1,630	1,666	1,690	1,674	1,485

Source: Statistics Canada, *New Motor Vehicle Sales, July 2010*, Catalogue No. 63-007-X

a. By using the year 2005 as the base year, construct a simple index for the new motor vehicle sales data.
b. Interpret the index in each of the years 2008 and 2009.
c. Plot the values and assess the overall pattern.

16.34 Below are the statistics for the production of building materials (sawn lumber) in Canada between 2007 and 2011, as reported by Statistics Canada.

Production of building materials: Standard Classification of Goods (*SCG*)				
Sawn lumber				
Thousand cubic metres				
2007	**2008**	**2009**	**2010**	**2011**
Total 72,042.6	57,250.1	45,248.5	53,311.1	53,609.5

Source: Statistics Canada, *Sawn Lumber Production and Shipments*, Table 303-0009 and Catalogue No. 35-003-X.

a. By using 2007 as the base year, calculate a simple index for sawn lumber production.
b. What is the overall trend in the production values?
c. What is a possible reason for the trend in the production of sawn lumber?

16.35 In the following table, we present the average prices of three precious metals—gold, silver, and platinum—for the years 1988 through 1996:

Year	Gold Price ($US/Fine Oz.)	Silver Price ($US/Fine Oz.)	Platinum Price ($US/Troy Oz.)
1988	438	6.53	523
1989	383	5.50	507
1990	385	4.82	467
1991	363	4.04	371
1992	345	3.94	360
1993	361	4.30	374
1994	385	5.29	411
1995	368	5.15	425
1996	390	5.30	410

Source: Through 1994, U.S. Bureau of Mines; thereafter, U.S. Geological Survey, *Minerals Yearbook and Mineral Commodities Summaries,* as presented in *Statistical Abstract of the United States,* 1997, p. 701.

a. By using the year 1988 as the base year, construct a simple index for each of gold, silver, and platinum.
b. Using the three indexes you constructed in part (a), describe price trends for gold, silver, and platinum from 1988 to 1996.
c. By using the year 1988 as the base year, construct an aggregate price index for these precious metals. Using the aggregate price index, describe trends for precious metals prices from 1988 to 1996.
d. By using the year 1990 as the base year, construct an aggregate price index for these precious metals.

16.36 In the following table, we present prices for three commonly used products—bread, fruits, and beverages—for the years 2000 through 2006.

Year	Bread ($ per Loaf)	Fruits ($ per kg)	Beverages ($ per L)
2000	$1.22	$1.71	$0.66
2001	$1.20	$1.64	$0.67
2002	$1.19	$1.74	$0.68
2003	$1.17	$2.04	$0.69
2004	$1.17	$1.85	$0.69
2005	$1.21	$1.55	$0.69
2006	$1.29	$2.25	$0.69

a. Consider a large family that consumes 1,850 loaves of bread, 150 kg of fruits, and 1,700 L of beverages every year. Construct the Laspeyres index for these food products using 2000 as the base year. Then describe how food prices have changed for this family over this period.
b. Consider a large family with the following food consumption pattern from 2000 to 2006. Construct the Paasche index for these food products using 2000 as the base year. How does the Paasche index compare to the Laspeyres index you constructed in part (a)?

Year	Bread (Loaves)	Fruits (kg)	Beverages (L)
2000	2,200	150	1,500
2001	2,100	150	1,600
2002	2,000	150	1,700
2003	1,950	150	1,800
2004	1,950	150	2,000
2005	1,900	150	2,100
2006	1,750	150	2,250

CHAPTER SUMMARY

In this chapter, we discussed using univariate time series models to forecast future time series values. We began by seeing that it can be useful to think of a time series as consisting of trend, seasonal, cyclical, and irregular components. If these components remain constant over time, then it is appropriate to describe and forecast the time series by using a time series regression model. We discussed using such models to describe no trend, a linear trend, a quadratic trend, and constant seasonal variation by utilizing dummy variables. We also considered various transformations of increasing seasonal variation into constant seasonal variation, and we saw that we can use the Durbin–Watson test to check for first-order autocorrelation.

As an alternative to using a transformation and dummy variables to model increasing seasonal variation, we can use the multiplicative decomposition method. We discussed this intuitive method and saw how to calculate approximate prediction intervals when using it. We then turned to a consideration of exponential smoothing, which is appropriate to use if the components of a time series might be changing slowly over time. Specifically, we discussed simple exponential smoothing and Holt–Winters' double exponential smoothing.

We next considered how to compare forecasting methods by using the mean absolute deviation (MAD), the mean squared deviation (MSD), and the percentage error (PE). We concluded this chapter by showing how to use index numbers to describe time-related data.

KEY TERMS

cyclical variations	moving averages
deseasonalized time series	seasonal variations
exponential smoothing	smoothing constant
index number	time series analysis
irregular component	trend

IMPORTANT FORMULAS AND TESTS

No trend	Mean absolute deviation (MAD)
Linear trend	Mean squared deviation (MSD)
Quadratic trend	Mean absolute percentage error (MAPE)
Modelling constant seasonal variation by using dummy variables	Simple index
Multiplicative decomposition method	Aggregate price index
Simple exponential smoothing	Laspeyres index
Double exponential smoothing	Paasche index

SUPPLEMENTARY EXERCISES

connect   Practise and learn online with *Connect*. Items for which there are online data sets are marked with 🏊.

16.37 The Workplace Safety and Insurance Board of Ontario (wsib.on.ca) compiles statistics about workplace accidents and deaths. Table 16.18 shows the percentage of deaths that took place on the job in Ontario from 1991 to 2008. The linear regression curve is shown in Figure 16.20.

  a. Enter the raw data into a computer application. Did the percentages of deaths on the job decrease significantly in this time period? What is the calculated F-value?

  b. Using the output generated in part (a), forecast the predicted values for the next five years. How would you assess the accuracy of these predicted numbers?

16.38 Alluring Tackle, a manufacturer of fishing equipment, makes the Bass Grabber, a type of fishing lure. The company would like to develop a prediction model that can be used to obtain point forecasts and prediction interval forecasts of the sales of the Bass Grabber. The sales (in tens of thousands of lures) of the Bass Grabber in sales period t, where each sales period is defined to last four

weeks, are denoted by the symbol y_t and are believed to be partially determined by one or more of the independent variables $x_1 =$ Price in period t of the Bass Grabber as offered by Alluring Tackle (in dollars), $x_2 =$ Average industry price in period t of competitors' similar lures (in dollars), and $x_3 =$ Advertising expenditure in period t of Alluring Tackle to promote the Bass Grabber (in tens of thousands of dollars).

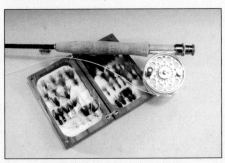

TABLE 16.18 Percentage of Fatalities Claimed That Represent Death on the Job 🖋

Year	Percentage of Deaths	Year	Percentage of Deaths
1991	40	2000	27
1992	32	2001	30
1993	27	2002	23
1994	25	2003	26
1995	26	2004	22
1996	31	2005	18
1997	25	2006	20
1998	29	2007	20
1999	26	2008	19

Source: Workplace Safety and Insurance Board of Ontario, *2008 Annual Report*; wsib.on.ca.

FIGURE 16.20 Percentage of Fatalities Claimed That Represent Death on the Job

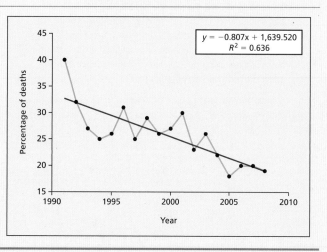

TABLE 16.19 Sales of the Bass Grabber (in Tens of Thousands of Lures) 🖋

Period, t	Sales, y_t	Price, x_1	Average Industry Price, x_2	Advertising Expenditure, x_3
1	4.797	3.85	3.80	5.50
2	6.297	3.75	4.00	6.75
3	8.010	3.70	4.30	7.25
4	7.800	3.70	3.70	5.50
5	9.690	3.60	3.85	7.00
6	10.871	3.60	3.80	6.50
7	12.425	3.60	3.75	6.75
8	10.310	3.80	3.85	5.25
9	8.307	3.80	3.65	5.25
10	8.960	3.85	4.00	6.00
11	7.969	3.90	4.10	6.50
12	6.276	3.90	4.00	6.25
13	4.580	3.70	4.10	7.00
14	5.759	3.75	4.20	6.90
15	6.586	3.75	4.10	6.80
16	8.199	3.80	4.10	6.80
17	9.630	3.70	4.20	7.10
18	9.810	3.80	4.30	7.00
19	11.913	3.70	4.10	6.80
20	12.879	3.80	3.75	6.50
21	12.065	3.80	3.75	6.25
22	10.530	3.75	3.65	6.00
23	9.845	3.70	3.90	6.50
24	9.524	3.55	3.65	7.00
25	7.354	3.60	4.10	6.80
26	4.697	3.65	4.25	6.80
27	6.052	3.70	3.65	6.50
28	6.416	3.75	3.75	5.75
29	8.253	3.80	3.85	5.80
30	10.057	3.70	4.25	6.80

The data in Table 16.19 have been observed over the past 30 sales periods, and a plot of these data indicates that sales of the Bass Grabber have been increasing in a linear fashion over time and have been seasonal, with sales of the lure being greatest in the spring and summer, when most recreational fishing takes place. Alluring Tackle believes that this pattern will continue in the future. So, remembering that each year consists of 13 four-week seasons, a possible regression model for predicting y_t would relate y_t to x_1, x_2, x_3, t, and the seasonal dummy variables $S_2, S_3, \ldots, S_{13}$.

Here, for example, S_2 equals 1 if sales period t is the second four-week season and 0 otherwise. As another example, S_{13} equals 1 if sales period t is the 13th four-week season and 0 otherwise. If we calculate the least squares point estimates of the parameters of the model, we obtain the following prediction equation (the t statistic for the importance of each independent variable is given in parentheses under the independent variable):

$$\hat{y}_t = .1776 + .4071x_1 - .7837x_2 + .9934x_3 + .0435t$$
$$\quad\ (.05) \quad\ (.42) \quad\quad (-1.51) \quad (4.89) \quad\ (6.49)$$
$$+ .7800S_2 + 2.373S_3 + 3.488S_4 + 3.805S_5$$
$$\quad\ (3.16) \quad\quad (9.28) \quad\quad (12.88) \quad\ (13.01)$$
$$+ 5.673S_6 + 6.738S_7 + 6.097S_8 + 4.301S_9$$
$$\quad\ (19.41) \quad\ (23.23) \quad\ (21.47) \quad\ (14.80)$$
$$+ 3.856S_{10} + 2.621S_{11} + .9969S_{12} - 1.467S_{13}$$
$$\quad\ (13.89) \quad\quad (9.24) \quad\quad (3.50) \quad\quad (-4.70)$$

a. For sales period 31, which is the fifth season of the year, x_1 will be 3.80, x_2 will be 3.90, and x_3 will be 6.80. Using these values, it can be shown that a point prediction of and a 95 percent prediction interval for sales of the Bass Grabber are, respectively, 10.578 and [9.683, 11.473]. Using the given prediction equation, verify that the point prediction is 10.578.

b. Some t statistics indicate that some of the independent variables might not be important. Using the regression techniques in Chapter 12, try to find a better model for predicting sales of the Bass Grabber.

16.39 Below are the total exports (in thousands of Canadian dollars) of mining exports to the United Kingdom from Canada between 2005 and 2009, as reported by Industry Canada from its Trade Data Online (TDO) feature (ic.gc.ca).

a. Describe the trend in exports over the time span plotted.

b. Using MegaStat, predict the 2010 export value.

Canadian Trade with the United Kindom:
Total Exports in Mining (Excluding Oil and Gas)

Year	Amount
2005	2,959,387
2006	3,950,007
2007	3,865,555
2008	6,120,554
2009	6,833,459

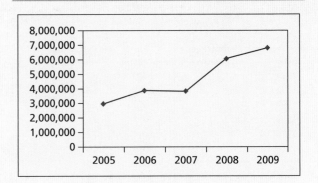

16.40 INTERNET EXERCISE

Below are the seasonally adjusted CPI values for Canada for the month of January from 1992 to 2008, as reported by Statistics Canada.

Year	Jan. CPI	Year	Jan. CPI
1989	72.7	1999	91.5
1990	76.7	2000	93.5
1991	82.0	2001	96.3
1992	83.3	2002	97.6
1993	85.0	2003	102.0
1994	86.1	2004	103.3
1995	86.6	2005	105.3
1996	88.0	2006	108.2
1997	89.9	2007	109.4
1998	90.9	2008	111.8

a. Plot the values and assess whether a linear trend is occurring.

b. Enter the data into a spreadsheet and do a regression analysis to calculate the predicted CPI value for January 2009, January 2010, January 2011, and January 2012.

c. Go to the Statistics Canada website (statcan.gc.ca) and determine the actual CPI values. How accurate were the predictions made by the regression analysis?

d. How do the prediction errors change with time?

GLOSSARY

A

alternative (research) hypothesis A statement that will be accepted only if there is convincing sample evidence that it is true. Sometimes it is a statement for which we need to attempt to find supportive evidence.

alternatives Several alternative actions for a decision maker to choose from.

analysis of variance (ANOVA) An analysis of means across experimental conditions.

analysis of variance (ANOVA) table A table that summarizes the sums of squares, mean squares, F statistic(s), and p value(s) for an ANOVA.

B

bar chart A graphical display of categorical data (data in categories) made up of vertical or horizontal bars.

Bayes' theorem A theorem (formula) that is used to compute posterior probabilities by revising prior probabilities.

Bayesian statistics An area of statistics that uses Bayes' theorem to update prior belief about a probability or population parameter to posterior belief.

binomial distribution The probability distribution that describes a binomial random variable.

binomial experiment An experiment that consists of n independent, identical trials, each of which results in either a success or a failure and is such that the probability of success on any trial is the same.

binomial random variable A random variable that is defined to be the total number of successes in n trials of a binomial experiment.

binomial tables Tables in which we can look up binomial probabilities.

C

capable process A process that is able to consistently produce output that meets (or conforms to) specifications (requirements).

census An examination of all of the units in a population.

central limit theorem Tells us that when the sample size n is sufficiently large, then the population of all possible sample means is approximately normally distributed no matter what probability distribution describes the sampled population.

central tendency Refers to the middle of a data set (a population or sample of measurements).

certainty When we know for certain which state of nature will actually occur.

Chebyshev's theorem A theorem that (for any population) allows us to find an interval that contains a specified percentage of the individual measurements in the population.

chi-square test for independence A test to determine whether two classifications are independent.

D

cluster sampling (multistage cluster sampling) A sampling design in which we sequentially cluster population units into subpopulations.

coefficient of determination The proportion of the total variation in the observed values of the dependent variable that is explained by the simple linear regression model.

coefficient of variation A quantity that measures the variation of a population or sample relative to its mean.

complement of an event If A is an event, the complement of A is the event that A will not occur.

completely randomized experimental design An experimental design in which independent, random samples of experimental units are assigned to IV conditions.

conditional probability The probability that one event will occur given that we know that another event occurs.

confidence coefficient The (before sampling) probability that a confidence interval for a population parameter will contain the population parameter.

confidence interval An interval of numbers computed so that we can be very confident (say, 95 percent confident) that a population parameter is contained in the interval.

confidence level The percentage of time that a confidence interval would contain a population parameter if all possible samples were used to calculate the interval.

contingency table (also called a *two-way cross-classification table*) A table that summarizes data that have been classified on two dimensions or scales.

continuous probability distributions (or probability curves) Curves that are defined so that the probability that a random variable will be in a specified interval of numbers is the area under the curve corresponding to the interval.

continuous random variable A random variable whose values correspond to one or more intervals of numbers on the real number line.

correlation coefficient (r) A measure of the strength of the linear relationship between x and y that does not depend on the units in which x and y are measured.

critical value The value of the test statistic is compared with a critical value in order to decide whether the null hypothesis can be rejected.

cross-sectional data Data that are observed at a single point in time.

cumulative normal table A table in which we can look up areas under the standard normal curve.

cyclical variations Recurring up-and-down movements of a time series around trend levels that last more than one calendar year (often two to ten years) from peak to peak or trough to trough.

D

decision criterion A rule used to make a decision.

decision theory An approach that helps decision makers to make intelligent choices.

decision tree (or tree diagram) A diagram consisting of nodes and branches that depicts the information for a decision problem.

degrees of freedom A parameter that describes the exact spread of the curve of a t distribution.

dependent events When the probability of one event is influenced by whether another event occurs, the events are said to be dependent.

dependent variable (denoted y) A variable that we wish to describe, predict, or control.

descriptive statistics The science of describing the important characteristics of a population or a sample.

deseasonalized time series A time series that has had the effect of seasonal variation removed.

discrete random variable A random variable whose values can be counted or listed.

distance value A measure of the distance between a particular value x_0 of the independent variable x and $\bar{x}$, the average of the previously observed values of x (the centre of the experimental region).

dummy variable A variable that takes on the value 0 or 1 and is used to describe the effects of the different levels of a qualitative independent variable in a regression model.

E

empirical rule For a normally distributed population, this rule tells us that 68.26 percent, 95.44 percent, and 99.73 percent of the population measurements are within one, two, and three standard deviations, respectively, of the population mean.

event A set of sample space outcomes.

expected monetary value criterion The expected monetary payoff for each alternative is computed and then the alternative yielding the largest expected payoff is chosen.

expected net gain of sampling (ENGS) The difference between the expected value of sample information and the cost of sampling. If this quantity is positive, sampling would be worthwhile.

expected value of a random variable The mean of the population of all possible observed values of a random variable. That is, the long-run average value obtained if values of a random variable are observed (theoretically) an infinite number of times.

expected value of perfect information (EVPI) The difference between the expected payoff under certainty and the expected payoff under risk.

expected value of sample information (EVSI) The difference between the expected payoff of sampling and the expected payoff of no sampling. This measures the expected gain from sampling.

experiment A process of observation that has an uncertain outcome.

experimental region The range of the previously observed values of the independent variable(s).

experimental units The entities (such as objects, people) to which the IV conditions are assigned.

exponential distribution A probability distribution that describes the time or space between successive occurrences of an event when the number of times the event occurs over an interval of time or space is described by a Poisson distribution.

exponential smoothing A forecasting method that weights recent observations more heavily than remote observations.

extreme outliers (in a box-and-whiskers display) Measurements located outside the outer fences.

F

F distribution A continuous probability curve having a shape that depends on two parameters—the numerator degrees of freedom, df_1, and the denominator degrees of freedom, df_2.

factor A variable that might influence the response variable; an independent variable (IV).

finite population A population that contains a finite number of units.

first quartile (denoted Q_1) A value below which approximately 25 percent of the measurements lie; the 25th percentile.

frame A list of all of the units in a population. This is needed in order to select a random sample.

frequency The count of the number of measurements in a class or the number of measurements with a particular value.

frequency distribution A numerical summary that divides the values of a variable into classes and gives the number of values in each class.

G

goodness of fit test for multinomial probabilities A test to determine whether multinomial probabilities are equal to a specific set of values.

goodness of fit test to check the normality of the scores A test to determine if a sample has been randomly selected from a normally distributed population.

greater than alternative An alternative hypothesis that is stated as a *greater than* ($>$) inequality.

grouped data Data presented in the form of a frequency distribution or a histogram.

H

histogram A graphical portrayal of a data set that shows the data set's distribution. It divides the data into classes and gives the frequency for each class. Histograms are particularly useful for summarizing large data sets.

hypergeometric distribution The probability distribution that describes a hypergeometric random variable.

hypergeometric random variable A random variable that is defined to be the number of successes obtained in a random sample selected without replacement from a finite population of N elements that contains r successes and $N - r$ failures.

I

independent events When the probability of one event is not influenced by whether another event occurs, the events are said to be independent.

independent samples experiment An experiment in which there is no relationship between the measurements in the different samples.

independent variable (denoted x) A predictor variable that can be used to describe, predict, or control a dependent variable (y).

index number A number that compares a value of a time series to another value of the time series.

infinite population A population that is defined so that there is no limit to the number of units that could potentially belong to the population.

influential observation An observation that causes the least squares point estimates (or other aspects of the regression analysis) to be substantially different from what they would be if the observation was removed from the data.

inner fences (in a box-and-whiskers display) Points located $1.5 \times IQR$ below Q_1 and $1.5 \times IQR$ above Q_3.

interaction When the mean responses of one factor depend on the level of the other factor.

interquartile range (denoted IQR) The difference between the third quartile and the first quartile (that is, $Q_3 - Q_1$).

interval level of measurement The first level in the quantitative level of measurement; at this level, the distances between data points are fixed but the ratios of a quantitative variable's values are not meaningful and there is not an inherently defined zero value.

irregular component What is left over in a time series after trend, cycle, and seasonal variations have been accounted for.

K

Kruskal–Wallis H test A nonparametric test for comparing the locations of three or more populations by using independent random samples.

L

least squares point estimates The point estimates of the slope and y intercept of the simple linear regression model that minimize the sum of squared residuals.

less than alternative An alternative hypothesis that is stated as a *less than* ($<$) inequality.

M

margin of error The quantity that is added to and subtracted from a point estimate of a population parameter to obtain a confidence interval for the parameter. It gives the maximum distance between the population parameter of interest and its point estimate when we assume the parameter is inside the confidence interval.

maximax criterion The best possible payoff for each alternative is identified and then the alternative that yields the maximum best possible payoff is chosen.

maximin criterion The worst possible payoff for each alternative is identified and then the alternative that yields the maximum worst possible payoff is chosen.

mean, or expected value, of a discrete random variable The mean of the population of all possible observed values of a random variable. That is, the long-run average value obtained if values of a random variable are observed (theoretically) an infinite number of times.

measurement The process of assigning a value of a variable to each of the units in a population or sample.

median (denoted M_d) A measure of central tendency that divides a population or sample into two roughly equal parts.

mild outliers (in a box-and-whiskers display) Measurements located between the inner and outer fences.

minimum-variance unbiased point estimate An unbiased point estimate of a population parameter having a variance that is smaller than the variance of any other unbiased point estimate of the parameter.

mode (denoted M_o) The measurement in a sample or a population that occurs most frequently.

mound-shaped Description of a relative frequency curve that is "piled up in the middle."

moving averages Averages of successive groups of time series observations.

multinomial experiment An experiment that concerns count data that are classified into more than two categories.

multiple regression model An equation that describes the relationship between a dependent variable and more than one independent variable.

mutually exclusive events Events that have no sample space outcomes in common, and, therefore, cannot occur simultaneously.

N

negative autocorrelation The situation in which positive errors tend to be followed over time by negative errors and negative errors tend to be followed over time by positive errors.

negatively skewed (to the left) Description of a relative frequency curve with a long tail to the left.

nominative (nominal) measurement level The "lowest" (most basic) level of measurement; a qualitative variable at this level is used for categorizing only and has no meaningful order.

nonparametric test A hypothesis test that requires no assumptions about the distribution(s) of the sampled population(s).

nonresponse A situation in which population units selected to participate in a survey do not respond to the survey instrument.

normal curve A bell-shaped, symmetrical relative frequency curve. We will present the exact equation that gives this curve in Chapter 5.

normal plot A residual plot that is used to check the normality assumption.

normal probability distribution The most important continuous probability distribution. Its probability curve is the *bell-shaped* normal curve.

not equal to alternative An alternative hypothesis that is stated as a *not equal to* ($\neq$) inequality.

null hypothesis The statement being tested in a hypothesis test. It is often a statement of "no difference" or "no effect" and it is not rejected unless there is convincing sample evidence that it is false.

O

one-sided alternative hypothesis An alternative hypothesis that is stated as either a *greater than* ($>$) or a *less than* ($<$) inequality.

one-way ANOVA A method used to estimate and compare the effects of the different levels of a single factor on a response variable.

ordinal level of measurement The measurements at this level might be nonnumerical or numerical; there is a meaningful ordering or ranking of the categories of a qualitative variable.

outer fences Points located $3 \times IQR$ below Q_1 and $3 \times IQR$ above Q_3.

outliers Unusually large or small observations that are well separated from the remaining observations.

P

p-value (probability value) The probability of making a Type I error, computed assuming that the null hypothesis H_0 is true, of observing a value of the test statistic that is at least as contradictory to H_0 and supportive of H_a as the value actually computed from the sample data. The p-value measures how much doubt is cast on the null hypothesis by the sample data. The smaller the p-value, the more we doubt the null hypothesis.

pth percentile For a set of measurements arranged in increasing order, a value such that p percent of the measurements fall at or below the value, and $(100 - p)$ percent of the measurements fall at or above the value.

paired difference experiment An experiment in which two different measurements are taken on the same units and inferences are made using the differences between the pairs of measurements.

Pareto chart A bar chart of the frequencies or percentages for various types of defects. These are used to identify opportunities for improvement.

payoff table A tabular summary of the payoffs in a decision problem.

percentile The value such that a specified percentage of the measurements in a population or sample fall at or below it.

perfect information Information that tells us exactly which state of nature will occur.

point estimate A one-number estimate for the value of a population parameter.

Poisson distribution The probability distribution that describes a Poisson random variable.

Poisson random variable A discrete random variable that can often be used to describe the number of occurrences of an event over a specified interval of time or space.

population A set of existing or potential units (such as people, objects, or events) that we want to study.

population mean (denoted m) The average of a population of measurements.

population parameter A descriptive measure of a population. It is calculated using the population measurements.

population proportion (denoted p) The proportion of population units that are contained in a category of interest.

population standard deviation (denoted σ) The square root of the population variance. It is a measure of the variation of the population measurements.

population variance (denoted σ^2) The average of the squared deviations of the individual population measurements from the population mean. It is a measure of the variation of the population measurements.

positive autocorrelation The situation in which positive errors tend to be followed over time by positive errors and negative errors tend to be followed over time by negative errors.

positively skewed (to the right) Description of a relative frequency curve with a long tail to the right.

posterior decision analysis Using a decision criterion based on posterior probabilities to choose the best alternative in a decision problem.

posterior probability A revised probability obtained by updating a prior probability after receiving new information.

power of a statistical test The probability of rejecting the null hypothesis when it is false (beta or β).

preposterior analysis The worth of sample information is assessed before a posterior decision analysis is performed.

prior decision analysis Using a decision criterion based on prior probabilities to choose the best alternative in a decision problem.

prior probability The initial probability that an event will occur.

probability distribution (of a discrete random variable) A table, graph, or formula that gives the probability associated with each of the random variable's values.

probability of an event A number that measures the chance, or likelihood, that an event will occur.

probability value (p-value) The probability, computed assuming that the null hypothesis H_0 is true, of observing a value of the test statistic that is at least as contradictory to H_0 and supportive of H_a as the value actually computed from the sample data. The p-value measures how much doubt is cast on the null hypothesis by the sample data. The smaller the p-value, the more we doubt the null hypothesis.

process A sequence of operations that takes inputs and turns them into outputs.

Q

qualitative or categorical variable A variable with values that indicate in which of several categories a population unit belongs.

quantitative variable A variable with values that are numbers representing quantities.

queueing theory A methodology that attempts to determine the number of servers that strikes an optimal balance between the time customers wait for service and the cost of providing service.

R

random number table Contains random digits and can be used to select a random sample.

random sample A sample selected so that on each selection from the population, every unit remaining in the population on that selection has the same chance of being chosen.

random variable A variable that assumes numerical values that are determined by the outcome of an experiment. That is, a variable that represents an uncertain numerical outcome.

randomized block design An experimental design that compares p IV levels by using b blocks (experimental units or sets of experimental units). Each block is used exactly once to measure the effect of each IV combination.

range The difference between the largest and smallest measurements in a population or sample. It is a simple measure of variation.

ratio level of measurement A quantitative variable with a meaningful zero and equal distances between points is the highest level of measurement.

relative frequency The frequency of a class divided by the total number of measurements.

relative frequency histogram A graphical portrayal of a data set that shows the data set's distribution. It divides the data into classes, gives the relative frequency for each class, and is particularly useful for summarizing large data sets.

replication When a treatment is applied to more than one experimental unit.

residual The difference between the observed value of the dependent variable and the corresponding predicted value of the dependent variable.

residual plot A plot of the residuals against some criterion. The plot is used to check the validity of one or more regression assumptions.

response bias A situation in which survey participants do not respond truthfully to the survey questions.

response variable The variable of interest in an experiment; the dependent variable (DV).

risk When the likelihood (probability) of each state of nature can be estimated.

runs plot A graph of individual process measurements versus time (sometimes called a *time series plot*).

S

sample A subset of the units in a population.

sample mean (denoted $\bar{x}$) The average of the measurements in a sample. It is the point estimate of the population mean.

sample proportion (denoted $\hat{p}$) The proportion of sample elements that are contained in a category of interest.

sample size (denoted n) The number of measurements in a sample.

sample space The set of all possible experimental outcomes (sample space outcomes).

sample space outcome A distinct outcome of an experiment (that is, an element in the sample space).

sample standard deviation (denoted s) The square root of the sample variance. It is the point estimate of the population standard deviation.

sample statistic A descriptive measure of a sample. It is calculated from the measurements in the sample.

sample variance (denoted s^2) A measure of the variation of the sample measurements. It is the point estimate of the population variance.

sampling distribution of a sample statistic The probability distribution of the population of all possible values of the sample statistic.

sampling distribution of the sample mean $\bar{x}$ The probability distribution of the population of all possible sample means obtained from samples of a particular size n.

sampling distribution of the sample proportion $\hat{p}$ The probability distribution of the population of all possible sample proportions obtained from samples of a particular size n.

sampling distribution of $\hat{p}_1 - \hat{p}_2$ The probability distribution that describes the population of all possible values of $\hat{p}_1 - \hat{p}_2$, where $\hat{p}_1$ is the sample proportion for a random sample taken from one population and $\hat{p}_2$ is the sample proportion for a random sample taken from a second population.

sampling distribution of s_1^2/s_2^2 The probability distribution that describes the population of all possible values of s_1^2/s_2^2, where s_1^2 is the sample variance of a random sample taken from one population and s_2^2 is the sample variance of a random sample taken from a second population.

sampling distribution of $\bar{x}_1 - \bar{x}_2$ The probability distribution that describes the population of all possible values of $\bar{x}_1 - \bar{x}_2$, where $\bar{x}_1$ is the sample mean of a random sample taken from one population and $\bar{x}_2$ is the sample mean of a random sample taken from a second population.

sampling with replacement A sampling procedure in which we place any unit that has been chosen back into the population to give the unit a chance to be chosen on succeeding selections (true random selection).

sampling without replacement A sampling procedure in which we do not place previously selected units back into the population and, therefore, do not give these units a chance to be chosen on succeeding selections.

scatter plot or scatter diagram A plot of the values of a dependent variable y versus the values of an independent variable x.

seasonal variations Periodic patterns in a time series that repeat themselves within a calendar year and are then repeated yearly.

sign test A hypothesis test about a population median that requires no assumptions about the sampled population.

simple linear (or straight-line) regression model An equation that describes the straight-line relationship between a dependent variable and an independent variable.

slope (of the simple linear regression model) The change in the mean value of the dependent variable that is associated with a one-unit increase in the value of the independent variable.

smoothing constant A number that determines how much weight is attached to each observation when using exponential smoothing.

Spearman's rank correlation coefficient A correlation coefficient computed using the ranks of the observed values of two variables, x and y.

standard deviation (of a random variable) The standard deviation of the population of all possible observed values of a random variable. It measures the spread of the population of all possible observed values of the random variable.

standard error The standard deviation of the sampling distribution of the sample mean, or the sample proportion

standard normal distribution (or curve) A normal distribution (or curve) having mean 0 and standard deviation 1.

states of nature A set of potential future conditions that will affect the results of a decision.

statistical control A state in which a process does not exhibit any unusual variations. This often means that the process displays a uniform amount of variation around a constant, or horizontal, level.

statistical inference The science of using a sample of measurements to make generalizations about the important aspects of a population.

stem-and-leaf display A graphical portrayal of a data set that shows the data set's distribution. It displays the data in the form of stems and leaves.

strata The subpopulations in a stratified sampling design.

stratified random sampling A sampling design in which we divide a population into nonoverlapping subpopulations and then select a random sample from each subpopulation (stratum).

subjective probability A probability assessment that is based on experience, intuitive judgment, or expertise.

systematic sample A sample taken by moving systematically through the population. For instance, we might randomly select one of the first 200 population units and then systematically sample every 200th population unit thereafter.

T

t **distribution** A commonly used continuous probability distribution that is described by a distribution curve similar to a normal curve. The *t* curve is symmetrical around zero and is more spread out than a standard normal curve.

t **point,** t_α The point on the horizontal axis under a *t* curve that gives a right-hand tail area equal to *a*.

t **table** A table of *t* point values listed according to the area in the tail of the *t* curve and according to values of the degrees of freedom.

test for homogeneity A test of the null hypothesis that all multinomial probabilities are equal.

test statistic A statistic computed from sample data in a hypothesis test. It is either compared with a critical value or used to compute a *p*-value.

third quartile (denoted Q_3**)** A value below which approximately 75 percent of the measurements lie; the 75th percentile.

time series analysis Collecting observations on a variable of interest in time order.

time series data Data that are observed in time sequence.

tolerance interval An interval of numbers that contains a specified percentage of the individual measurements in a population.

trend The long-run upward or downward movement that characterizes a time series over a period of time.

two-factor factorial experiment An experiment in which we randomly assign *m* experimental units to each combination of levels of two factors.

two-sided alternative hypothesis An alternative hypothesis that is stated as a *not equal to* ($\neq$) inequality.

two-way ANOVA A method used to study the effects of two factors on a response variable.

Type I error Rejecting a true null hypothesis (alpha or α).

Type II error Failing to reject a false null hypothesis (beta or β).

unbiased point estimate A sample statistic is an unbiased point estimate of a population parameter if the mean of the population of all possible values of the sample statistic equals the population parameter.

U

uncertainty When we have no information about the likelihoods of the various states of nature.

undercoverage A situation in sampling in which some groups of population units are under-represented.

uniform distribution A rectangular-shaped continuous probability distribution that says the probability is distributed evenly (or uniformly) over an interval of numbers.

utility A measure of monetary value based on an individual's attitude toward risk.

V

variable A characteristic of a population unit.

variance (of a random variable) The variance of the population of all possible observed values of a random variable. It measures the spread of the population of all possible observed values of the random variable.

W

weighted mean A mean where different measurements are given different weights based on their importance.

Wilcoxon rank sum test (also called the *Mann–Whitney test*) A nonparametric test for comparing the locations of two populations when an independent-samples experiment has been carried out.

Wilcoxon signed ranks test A nonparametric test for comparing the locations of two populations when a paired-differences experiment has been carried out.

Y

y **intercept (of the simple linear regression model)** The mean value of the dependent variable when the value of the independent variable is 0.

Z

z_α **point** The point on the horizontal axis under the standard normal curve that gives a right-hand tail area equal to α.

$-z_\alpha$ **point** The point on the horizontal axis under the standard normal curve that gives a left-hand tail area equal to α.

z **score (of a measurement)** The number of standard deviations that a measurement is from the mean. This quantity indicates the relative location of a measurement within its distribution.

z **value** Tells us the number of standard deviations that a value *x* is from the mean of a normal curve. If the *z* value is positive, then *x* is above the mean. If the *z* value is negative, then *x* is below the mean.

APPENDIX A

Statistical Tables

TABLE A.1   A Binomial Probability Table:
Binomial Probabilities (n between 2 and 6)

n = 2   **p**

x↓	0.05	0.10	0.15	0.20	0.25	0.30	0.35	0.40	0.45	0.50	
0	0.9025	0.8100	0.7225	0.6400	0.5625	0.4900	0.4225	0.3600	0.3025	0.2500	2
1	0.0950	0.1800	0.2550	0.3200	0.3750	0.4200	0.4550	0.4800	0.4950	0.5000	1
2	0.0025	0.0100	0.0225	0.0400	0.0625	0.0900	0.1225	0.1600	0.2025	0.2500	0
	0.95	0.90	0.85	0.80	0.75	0.70	0.65	0.60	0.55	0.50	x↑

n = 3   **p**

x↓	0.05	0.10	0.15	0.20	0.25	0.30	0.35	0.40	0.45	0.50	
0	0.8574	0.7290	0.6141	0.5120	0.4219	0.3430	0.2746	0.2160	0.1664	0.1250	3
1	0.1354	0.2430	0.3251	0.3840	0.4219	0.4410	0.4436	0.4320	0.4084	0.3750	2
2	0.0071	0.0270	0.0574	0.0960	0.1406	0.1890	0.2389	0.2880	0.3341	0.3750	1
3	0.0001	0.0010	0.0034	0.0080	0.0156	0.0270	0.0429	0.0640	0.0911	0.1250	0
	0.95	0.90	0.85	0.80	0.75	0.70	0.65	0.60	0.55	0.50	x↑

n = 4   **p**

x↓	0.05	0.10	0.15	0.20	0.25	0.30	0.35	0.40	0.45	0.50	
0	0.8145	0.6561	0.5220	0.4096	0.3164	0.2401	0.1785	0.1296	0.0915	0.0625	4
1	0.1715	0.2916	0.3685	0.4096	0.4219	0.4116	0.3845	0.3456	0.2995	0.2500	3
2	0.0135	0.0486	0.0975	0.1536	0.2109	0.2646	0.3105	0.3456	0.3675	0.3750	2
3	0.0005	0.0036	0.0115	0.0256	0.0469	0.0756	0.1115	0.1536	0.2005	0.2500	1
4	0.0000	0.0001	0.0005	0.0016	0.0039	0.0081	0.0150	0.0256	0.0410	0.0625	0
	0.95	0.90	0.85	0.80	0.75	0.70	0.65	0.60	0.55	0.50	x↑

n = 5   **p**

x↓	0.05	0.10	0.15	0.20	0.25	0.30	0.35	0.40	0.45	0.50	
0	0.7738	0.5905	0.4437	0.3277	0.2373	0.1681	0.1160	0.0778	0.0503	0.0313	5
1	0.2036	0.3281	0.3915	0.4096	0.3955	0.3602	0.3124	0.2592	0.2059	0.1563	4
2	0.0214	0.0729	0.1382	0.2048	0.2637	0.3087	0.3364	0.3456	0.3369	0.3125	3
3	0.0011	0.0081	0.0244	0.0512	0.0879	0.1323	0.1811	0.2304	0.2757	0.3125	2
4	0.0000	0.0005	0.0022	0.0064	0.0146	0.0284	0.0488	0.0768	0.1128	0.1563	1
5	0.0000	0.0000	0.0001	0.0003	0.0010	0.0024	0.0053	0.0102	0.0185	0.0313	0
	0.95	0.90	0.85	0.80	0.75	0.70	0.65	0.60	0.55	0.50	x↑

n = 6   **p**

x↓	0.05	0.10	0.15	0.20	0.25	0.30	0.35	0.40	0.45	0.50	
0	0.7351	0.5314	0.3771	0.2621	0.1780	0.1176	0.0754	0.0467	0.0277	0.0156	6
1	0.2321	0.3543	0.3993	0.3932	0.3560	0.3025	0.2437	0.1866	0.1359	0.0938	5
2	0.0305	0.0984	0.1762	0.2458	0.2966	0.3241	0.3280	0.3110	0.2780	0.2344	4
3	0.0021	0.0146	0.0415	0.0819	0.1318	0.1852	0.2355	0.2765	0.3032	0.3125	3
4	0.0001	0.0012	0.0055	0.0154	0.0330	0.0595	0.0951	0.1382	0.1861	0.2344	2
5	0.0000	0.0001	0.0004	0.0015	0.0044	0.0102	0.0205	0.0369	0.0609	0.0938	1
6	0.0000	0.0000	0.0000	0.0001	0.0002	0.0007	0.0018	0.0041	0.0083	0.0156	0
	0.95	0.90	0.85	0.80	0.75	0.70	0.65	0.60	0.55	0.50	x↑

(table continued)

TABLE A.1 *(continued)*   Binomial Probabilities (*n* between 7 and 10)

n = 7   **p**

x↓	0.05	0.10	0.15	0.20	0.25	0.30	0.35	0.40	0.45	0.50	
0	0.6983	0.4783	0.3206	0.2097	0.1335	0.0824	0.0490	0.0280	0.0152	0.0078	7
1	0.2573	0.3720	0.3960	0.3670	0.3115	0.2471	0.1848	0.1306	0.0872	0.0547	6
2	0.0406	0.1240	0.2097	0.2753	0.3115	0.3177	0.2985	0.2613	0.2140	0.1641	5
3	0.0036	0.0230	0.0617	0.1147	0.1730	0.2269	0.2679	0.2903	0.2918	0.2734	4
4	0.0002	0.0026	0.0109	0.0287	0.0577	0.0972	0.1442	0.1935	0.2388	0.2734	3
5	0.0000	0.0002	0.0012	0.0043	0.0115	0.0250	0.0466	0.0774	0.1172	0.1641	2
6	0.0000	0.0000	0.0001	0.0004	0.0013	0.0036	0.0084	0.0172	0.0320	0.0547	1
7	0.0000	0.0000	0.0000	0.0000	0.0001	0.0002	0.0006	0.0016	0.0037	0.0078	0
	0.95	0.90	0.85	0.80	0.75	0.70	0.65	0.60	0.55	0.50	x↑

n = 8   **p**

x↓	0.05	0.10	0.15	0.20	0.25	0.30	0.35	0.40	0.45	0.50	
0	0.6634	0.4305	0.2725	0.1678	0.1001	0.0576	0.0319	0.0168	0.0084	0.0039	8
1	0.2793	0.3826	0.3847	0.3355	0.2670	0.1977	0.1373	0.0896	0.0548	0.0313	7
2	0.0515	0.1488	0.2376	0.2936	0.3115	0.2965	0.2587	0.2090	0.1569	0.1094	6
3	0.0054	0.0331	0.0839	0.1468	0.2076	0.2541	0.2786	0.2787	0.2568	0.2188	5
4	0.0004	0.0046	0.0185	0.0459	0.0865	0.1361	0.1875	0.2322	0.2627	0.2734	4
5	0.0000	0.0004	0.0026	0.0092	0.0231	0.0467	0.0808	0.1239	0.1719	0.2188	3
6	0.0000	0.0000	0.0002	0.0011	0.0038	0.0100	0.0217	0.0413	0.0703	0.1094	2
7	0.0000	0.0000	0.0000	0.0001	0.0004	0.0012	0.0033	0.0079	0.0164	0.0313	1
8	0.0000	0.0000	0.0000	0.0000	0.0000	0.0001	0.0002	0.0007	0.0017	0.0039	0
	0.95	0.90	0.85	0.80	0.75	0.70	0.65	0.60	0.55	0.50	x↑

n = 9   **p**

x↓	0.05	0.10	0.15	0.20	0.25	0.30	0.35	0.40	0.45	0.50	
0	0.6302	0.3874	0.2316	0.1342	0.0751	0.0404	0.0207	0.0101	0.0046	0.0020	9
1	0.2985	0.3874	0.3679	0.3020	0.2253	0.1556	0.1004	0.0605	0.0339	0.0176	8
2	0.0629	0.1722	0.2597	0.3020	0.3003	0.2668	0.2162	0.1612	0.1110	0.0703	7
3	0.0077	0.0446	0.1069	0.1762	0.2336	0.2668	0.2716	0.2508	0.2119	0.1641	6
4	0.0006	0.0074	0.0283	0.0661	0.1168	0.1715	0.2194	0.2508	0.2600	0.2461	5
5	0.0000	0.0008	0.0050	0.0165	0.0389	0.0735	0.1181	0.1672	0.2128	0.2461	4
6	0.0000	0.0001	0.0006	0.0028	0.0087	0.0210	0.0424	0.0743	0.1160	0.1641	3
7	0.0000	0.0000	0.0000	0.0003	0.0012	0.0039	0.0098	0.0212	0.0407	0.0703	2
8	0.0000	0.0000	0.0000	0.0000	0.0001	0.0004	0.0013	0.0035	0.0083	0.0176	1
9	0.0000	0.0000	0.0000	0.0000	0.0000	0.0000	0.0001	0.0003	0.0008	0.0020	0
	0.95	0.90	0.85	0.80	0.75	0.70	0.65	0.60	0.55	0.50	x↑

n = 10   **p**

x↓	0.05	0.10	0.15	0.20	0.25	0.30	0.35	0.40	0.45	0.50	
0	0.5987	0.3487	0.1969	0.1074	0.0563	0.0282	0.0135	0.0060	0.0025	0.0010	10
1	0.3151	0.3874	0.3474	0.2684	0.1877	0.1211	0.0725	0.0403	0.0207	0.0098	9
2	0.0746	0.1937	0.2759	0.3020	0.2816	0.2335	0.1757	0.1209	0.0763	0.0439	8
3	0.0105	0.0574	0.1298	0.2013	0.2503	0.2668	0.2522	0.2150	0.1665	0.1172	7
4	0.0010	0.0112	0.0401	0.0881	0.1460	0.2001	0.2377	0.2508	0.2384	0.2051	6
5	0.0001	0.0015	0.0085	0.0264	0.0584	0.1029	0.1536	0.2007	0.2340	0.2461	5
6	0.0000	0.0001	0.0012	0.0055	0.0162	0.0368	0.0689	0.1115	0.1596	0.2051	4
7	0.0000	0.0000	0.0001	0.0008	0.0031	0.0090	0.0212	0.0425	0.0746	0.1172	3
8	0.0000	0.0000	0.0000	0.0001	0.0004	0.0014	0.0043	0.0106	0.0229	0.0439	2
9	0.0000	0.0000	0.0000	0.0000	0.0000	0.0001	0.0005	0.0016	0.0042	0.0098	1
10	0.0000	0.0000	0.0000	0.0000	0.0000	0.0000	0.0000	0.0001	0.0003	0.0010	0
	0.95	0.90	0.85	0.80	0.75	0.70	0.65	0.60	0.55	0.50	x↑

(table continued)

TABLE **A.1** *(continued)*   Binomial Probabilities (*n* equal to 12, 14, and 15)

n = 12   p

x↓	0.05	0.10	0.15	0.20	0.25	0.30	0.35	0.40	0.45	0.50	
0	0.5404	0.2824	0.1422	0.0687	0.0317	0.0138	0.0057	0.0022	0.0008	0.0002	12
1	0.3413	0.3766	0.3012	0.2062	0.1267	0.0712	0.0368	0.0174	0.0075	0.0029	11
2	0.0988	0.2301	0.2924	0.2835	0.2323	0.1678	0.1088	0.0639	0.0339	0.0161	10
3	0.0173	0.0852	0.1720	0.2362	0.2581	0.2397	0.1954	0.1419	0.0923	0.0537	9
4	0.0021	0.0213	0.0683	0.1329	0.1936	0.2311	0.2367	0.2128	0.1700	0.1208	8
5	0.0002	0.0038	0.0193	0.0532	0.1032	0.1585	0.2039	0.2270	0.2225	0.1934	7
6	0.0000	0.0005	0.0040	0.0155	0.0401	0.0792	0.1281	0.1766	0.2124	0.2256	6
7	0.0000	0.0000	0.0006	0.0033	0.0115	0.0291	0.0591	0.1009	0.1489	0.1934	5
8	0.0000	0.0000	0.0001	0.0005	0.0024	0.0078	0.0199	0.0420	0.0762	0.1208	4
9	0.0000	0.0000	0.0000	0.0001	0.0004	0.0015	0.0048	0.0125	0.0277	0.0537	3
10	0.0000	0.0000	0.0000	0.0000	0.0000	0.0002	0.0008	0.0025	0.0068	0.0161	2
11	0.0000	0.0000	0.0000	0.0000	0.0000	0.0000	0.0001	0.0003	0.0010	0.0029	1
12	0.0000	0.0000	0.0000	0.0000	0.0000	0.0000	0.0000	0.0000	0.0001	0.0002	0
	0.95	**0.90**	**0.85**	**0.80**	**0.75**	**0.70**	**0.65**	**0.60**	**0.55**	**0.50**	x↑

n = 14   p

x↓	0.05	0.10	0.15	0.20	0.25	0.30	0.35	0.40	0.45	0.50	
0	0.4877	0.2288	0.1028	0.0440	0.0178	0.0068	0.0024	0.0008	0.0002	0.0001	14
1	0.3593	0.3559	0.2539	0.1539	0.0832	0.0407	0.0181	0.0073	0.0027	0.0009	13
2	0.1229	0.2570	0.2912	0.2501	0.1802	0.1134	0.0634	0.0317	0.0141	0.0056	12
3	0.0259	0.1142	0.2056	0.2501	0.2402	0.1943	0.1366	0.0845	0.0462	0.0222	11
4	0.0037	0.0349	0.0998	0.1720	0.2202	0.2290	0.2022	0.1549	0.1040	0.0611	10
5	0.0004	0.0078	0.0352	0.0860	0.1468	0.1963	0.2178	0.2066	0.1701	0.1222	9
6	0.0000	0.0013	0.0093	0.0322	0.0734	0.1262	0.1759	0.2066	0.2088	0.1833	8
7	0.0000	0.0002	0.0019	0.0092	0.0280	0.0618	0.1082	0.1574	0.1952	0.2095	7
8	0.0000	0.0000	0.0003	0.0020	0.0082	0.0232	0.0510	0.0918	0.1398	0.1833	6
9	0.0000	0.0000	0.0000	0.0003	0.0018	0.0066	0.0183	0.0408	0.0762	0.1222	5
10	0.0000	0.0000	0.0000	0.0000	0.0003	0.0014	0.0049	0.0136	0.0312	0.0611	4
11	0.0000	0.0000	0.0000	0.0000	0.0000	0.0002	0.0010	0.0033	0.0093	0.0222	3
12	0.0000	0.0000	0.0000	0.0000	0.0000	0.0000	0.0001	0.0005	0.0019	0.0056	2
13	0.0000	0.0000	0.0000	0.0000	0.0000	0.0000	0.0000	0.0001	0.0002	0.0009	1
14	0.0000	0.0000	0.0000	0.0000	0.0000	0.0000	0.0000	0.0000	0.0000	0.0001	0
	0.95	**0.90**	**0.85**	**0.80**	**0.75**	**0.70**	**0.65**	**0.60**	**0.55**	**0.50**	x↑

n = 15   p

x↓	0.05	0.10	0.15	0.20	0.25	0.30	0.35	0.40	0.45	0.50	
0	0.4633	0.2059	0.0874	0.0352	0.0134	0.0047	0.0016	0.0005	0.0001	0.0000	15
1	0.3658	0.3432	0.2312	0.1319	0.0668	0.0305	0.0126	0.0047	0.0016	0.0005	14
2	0.1348	0.2669	0.2856	0.2309	0.1559	0.0916	0.0476	0.0219	0.0090	0.0032	13
3	0.0307	0.1285	0.2184	0.2501	0.2252	0.1700	0.1110	0.0634	0.0318	0.0139	12
4	0.0049	0.0428	0.1156	0.1876	0.2252	0.2186	0.1792	0.1268	0.0780	0.0417	11
5	0.0006	0.0105	0.0449	0.1032	0.1651	0.2061	0.2123	0.1859	0.1404	0.0916	10
6	0.0000	0.0019	0.0132	0.0430	0.0917	0.1472	0.1906	0.2066	0.1914	0.1527	9
7	0.0000	0.0003	0.0030	0.0138	0.0393	0.0811	0.1319	0.1771	0.2013	0.1964	8
8	0.0000	0.0000	0.0005	0.0035	0.0131	0.0348	0.0710	0.1181	0.1647	0.1964	7
9	0.0000	0.0000	0.0001	0.0007	0.0034	0.0116	0.0298	0.0612	0.1048	0.1527	6
10	0.0000	0.0000	0.0000	0.0001	0.0007	0.0030	0.0096	0.0245	0.0515	0.0916	5
11	0.0000	0.0000	0.0000	0.0000	0.0001	0.0006	0.0024	0.0074	0.0191	0.0417	4
12	0.0000	0.0000	0.0000	0.0000	0.0000	0.0001	0.0004	0.0016	0.0052	0.0139	3
13	0.0000	0.0000	0.0000	0.0000	0.0000	0.0000	0.0001	0.0003	0.0010	0.0032	2
14	0.0000	0.0000	0.0000	0.0000	0.0000	0.0000	0.0000	0.0000	0.0001	0.0005	1
15	0.0000	0.0000	0.0000	0.0000	0.0000	0.0000	0.0000	0.0000	0.0000	0.0000	0
	0.95	**0.90**	**0.85**	**0.80**	**0.75**	**0.70**	**0.65**	**0.60**	**0.55**	**0.50**	x↑

(table continued)

TABLE **A.1** *(continued)*   Binomial Probabilities (*n* equal to 16 and 18)

n = 16						*p*					
x↓	0.05	0.10	0.15	0.20	0.25	0.30	0.35	0.40	0.45	0.50	
0	0.4401	0.1853	0.0743	0.0281	0.0100	0.0033	0.0010	0.0003	0.0001	0.0000	16
1	0.3706	0.3294	0.2097	0.1126	0.0535	0.0228	0.0087	0.0030	0.0009	0.0002	15
2	0.1463	0.2745	0.2775	0.2111	0.1336	0.0732	0.0353	0.0150	0.0056	0.0018	14
3	0.0359	0.1423	0.2285	0.2463	0.2079	0.1465	0.0888	0.0468	0.0215	0.0085	13
4	0.0061	0.0514	0.1311	0.2001	0.2252	0.2040	0.1553	0.1014	0.0572	0.0278	12
5	0.0008	0.0137	0.0555	0.1201	0.1802	0.2099	0.2008	0.1623	0.1123	0.0667	11
6	0.0001	0.0028	0.0180	0.0550	0.1101	0.1649	0.1982	0.1983	0.1684	0.1222	10
7	0.0000	0.0004	0.0045	0.0197	0.0524	0.1010	0.1524	0.1889	0.1969	0.1746	9
8	0.0000	0.0001	0.0009	0.0055	0.0197	0.0487	0.0923	0.1417	0.1812	0.1964	8
9	0.0000	0.0000	0.0001	0.0012	0.0058	0.0185	0.0442	0.0840	0.1318	0.1746	7
10	0.0000	0.0000	0.0000	0.0002	0.0014	0.0056	0.0167	0.0392	0.0755	0.1222	6
11	0.0000	0.0000	0.0000	0.0000	0.0002	0.0013	0.0049	0.0142	0.0337	0.0667	5
12	0.0000	0.0000	0.0000	0.0000	0.0000	0.0002	0.0011	0.0040	0.0115	0.0278	4
13	0.0000	0.0000	0.0000	0.0000	0.0000	0.0000	0.0002	0.0008	0.0029	0.0085	3
14	0.0000	0.0000	0.0000	0.0000	0.0000	0.0000	0.0000	0.0001	0.0005	0.0018	2
15	0.0000	0.0000	0.0000	0.0000	0.0000	0.0000	0.0000	0.0000	0.0001	0.0002	1
	0.95	0.90	0.85	0.80	0.75	0.70	0.65	0.60	0.55	0.50	x↑

n = 18						*p*					
x↓	0.05	0.10	0.15	0.20	0.25	0.30	0.35	0.40	0.45	0.50	
0	0.3972	0.1501	0.0536	0.0180	0.0056	0.0016	0.0004	0.0001	0.0000	0.0000	18
1	0.3763	0.3002	0.1704	0.0811	0.0338	0.0126	0.0042	0.0012	0.0003	0.0001	17
2	0.1683	0.2835	0.2556	0.1723	0.0958	0.0458	0.0190	0.0069	0.0022	0.0006	16
3	0.0473	0.1680	0.2406	0.2297	0.1704	0.1046	0.0547	0.0246	0.0095	0.0031	15
4	0.0093	0.0700	0.1592	0.2153	0.2130	0.1681	0.1104	0.0614	0.0291	0.0117	14
5	0.0014	0.0218	0.0787	0.1507	0.1988	0.2017	0.1664	0.1146	0.0666	0.0327	13
6	0.0002	0.0052	0.0301	0.0816	0.1436	0.1873	0.1941	0.1655	0.1181	0.0708	12
7	0.0000	0.0010	0.0091	0.0350	0.0820	0.1376	0.1792	0.1892	0.1657	0.1214	11
8	0.0000	0.0002	0.0022	0.0120	0.0376	0.0811	0.1327	0.1734	0.1864	0.1669	10
9	0.0000	0.0000	0.0004	0.0033	0.0139	0.0386	0.0794	0.1284	0.1694	0.1855	9
10	0.0000	0.0000	0.0001	0.0008	0.0042	0.0149	0.0385	0.0771	0.1248	0.1669	8
11	0.0000	0.0000	0.0000	0.0001	0.0010	0.0046	0.0151	0.0374	0.0742	0.1214	7
12	0.0000	0.0000	0.0000	0.0000	0.0002	0.0012	0.0047	0.0145	0.0354	0.0708	6
13	0.0000	0.0000	0.0000	0.0000	0.0000	0.0002	0.0012	0.0045	0.0134	0.0327	5
14	0.0000	0.0000	0.0000	0.0000	0.0000	0.0000	0.0002	0.0011	0.0039	0.0117	4
15	0.0000	0.0000	0.0000	0.0000	0.0000	0.0000	0.0000	0.0002	0.0009	0.0031	3
16	0.0000	0.0000	0.0000	0.0000	0.0000	0.0000	0.0000	0.0000	0.0001	0.0006	2
17	0.0000	0.0000	0.0000	0.0000	0.0000	0.0000	0.0000	0.0000	0.0000	0.0001	1
	0.95	0.90	0.85	0.80	0.75	0.70	0.65	0.60	0.55	0.50	x↑

(table continued)

TABLE **A.1** *(concluded)*   Binomial Probabilities (*n* equal to 20)

n = 20						p						
x↓	0.05	0.10	0.15	0.20	0.25	0.30	0.35	0.40	0.45	0.50	
0	0.3585	0.1216	0.0388	0.0115	0.0032	0.0008	0.0002	0.0000	0.0000	0.0000	20
1	0.3774	0.2702	0.1368	0.0576	0.0211	0.0068	0.0020	0.0005	0.0001	0.0000	19
2	0.1887	0.2852	0.2293	0.1369	0.0669	0.0278	0.0100	0.0031	0.0008	0.0002	18
3	0.0596	0.1901	0.2428	0.2054	0.1339	0.0716	0.0323	0.0123	0.0040	0.0011	17
4	0.0133	0.0898	0.1821	0.2182	0.1897	0.1304	0.0738	0.0350	0.0139	0.0046	16
5	0.0022	0.0319	0.1028	0.1746	0.2023	0.1789	0.1272	0.0746	0.0365	0.0148	15
6	0.0003	0.0089	0.0454	0.1091	0.1686	0.1916	0.1712	0.1244	0.0746	0.0370	14
7	0.0000	0.0020	0.0160	0.0545	0.1124	0.1643	0.1844	0.1659	0.1221	0.0739	13
8	0.0000	0.0004	0.0046	0.0222	0.0609	0.1144	0.1614	0.1797	0.1623	0.1201	12
9	0.0000	0.0001	0.0011	0.0074	0.0271	0.0654	0.1158	0.1597	0.1771	0.1602	11
10	0.0000	0.0000	0.0002	0.0020	0.0099	0.0308	0.0686	0.1171	0.1593	0.1762	10
11	0.0000	0.0000	0.0000	0.0005	0.0030	0.0120	0.0336	0.0710	0.1185	0.1602	9
12	0.0000	0.0000	0.0000	0.0001	0.0008	0.0039	0.0136	0.0355	0.0727	0.1201	8
13	0.0000	0.0000	0.0000	0.0000	0.0002	0.0010	0.0045	0.0146	0.0366	0.0739	7
14	0.0000	0.0000	0.0000	0.0000	0.0000	0.0002	0.0012	0.0049	0.0150	0.0370	6
15	0.0000	0.0000	0.0000	0.0000	0.0000	0.0000	0.0003	0.0013	0.0049	0.0148	5
16	0.0000	0.0000	0.0000	0.0000	0.0000	0.0000	0.0000	0.0003	0.0013	0.0046	4
17	0.0000	0.0000	0.0000	0.0000	0.0000	0.0000	0.0000	0.0000	0.0002	0.0011	3
18	0.0000	0.0000	0.0000	0.0000	0.0000	0.0000	0.0000	0.0000	0.0000	0.0002	2
	0.95	0.90	0.85	0.80	0.75	0.70	0.65	0.60	0.55	0.50	x↑

Source: Computed by D. K. Hildebrand. Found in D. K. Hildebrand and L. Ott, *Statistical Thinking for Managers*, 3rd ed. (Boston, MA: PWS-KENT Publishing Company, 1991).

TABLE **A.2**   A Poisson Probability Table
Poisson Probabilities (μ between 0.1 and 2.0)

					μ					
x	0.1	0.2	0.3	0.4	0.5	0.6	0.7	0.8	0.9	1.0
0	0.9048	0.8187	0.7408	0.6703	0.6065	0.5488	0.4966	0.4493	0.4066	0.3679
1	0.0905	0.1637	0.2222	0.2681	0.3033	0.3293	0.3476	0.3595	0.3659	0.3679
2	0.0045	0.0164	0.0333	0.0536	0.0758	0.0988	0.1217	0.1438	0.1647	0.1839
3	0.0002	0.0011	0.0033	0.0072	0.0126	0.0198	0.0284	0.0383	0.0494	0.0613
4	0.0000	0.0001	0.0003	0.0007	0.0016	0.0030	0.0050	0.0077	0.0111	0.0153
5	0.0000	0.0000	0.0000	0.0001	0.0002	0.0004	0.0007	0.0012	0.0020	0.0031
6	0.0000	0.0000	0.0000	0.0000	0.0000	0.0000	0.0001	0.0002	0.0003	0.0005

					μ					
x	1.1	1.2	1.3	1.4	1.5	1.6	1.7	1.8	1.9	2.0
0	0.3329	0.3012	0.2725	0.2466	0.2231	0.2019	0.1827	0.1653	0.1496	0.1353
1	0.3662	0.3614	0.3543	0.3452	0.3347	0.3230	0.3106	0.2975	0.2842	0.2707
2	0.2014	0.2169	0.2303	0.2417	0.2510	0.2584	0.2640	0.2678	0.2700	0.2707
3	0.0738	0.0867	0.0998	0.1128	0.1255	0.1378	0.1496	0.1607	0.1710	0.1804
4	0.0203	0.0260	0.0324	0.0395	0.0471	0.0551	0.0636	0.0723	0.0812	0.0902
5	0.0045	0.0062	0.0084	0.0111	0.0141	0.0176	0.0216	0.0260	0.0309	0.0361
6	0.0008	0.0012	0.0018	0.0026	0.0035	0.0047	0.0061	0.0078	0.0098	0.0120
7	0.0001	0.0002	0.0003	0.0005	0.0008	0.0011	0.0015	0.0020	0.0027	0.0034
8	0.0000	0.0000	0.0001	0.0001	0.0001	0.0002	0.0003	0.0005	0.0006	0.0009

(table continued)

TABLE **A.2** *(continued)* Poisson Probabilities (μ between 2.1 and 5.0)

	μ									
x	2.1	2.2	2.3	2.4	2.5	2.6	2.7	2.8	2.9	3.0
0	0.1225	0.1108	0.1003	0.0907	0.0821	0.0743	0.0672	0.0608	0.0550	0.0498
1	0.2572	0.2438	0.2306	0.2177	0.2052	0.1931	0.1815	0.1703	0.1596	0.1494
2	0.2700	0.2681	0.2652	0.2613	0.2565	0.2510	0.2450	0.2384	0.2314	0.2240
3	0.1890	0.1966	0.2033	0.2090	0.2138	0.2176	0.2205	0.2225	0.2237	0.2240
4	0.0992	0.1082	0.1169	0.1254	0.1336	0.1414	0.1488	0.1557	0.1622	0.1680
5	0.0417	0.0476	0.0538	0.0602	0.0668	0.0735	0.0804	0.0872	0.0940	0.1008
6	0.0146	0.0174	0.0206	0.0241	0.0278	0.0319	0.0362	0.0407	0.0455	0.0504
7	0.0044	0.0055	0.0068	0.0083	0.0099	0.0118	0.0139	0.0163	0.0188	0.0216
8	0.0011	0.0015	0.0019	0.0025	0.0031	0.0038	0.0047	0.0057	0.0068	0.0081
9	0.0003	0.0004	0.0005	0.0007	0.0009	0.0011	0.0014	0.0018	0.0022	0.0027
10	0.0001	0.0001	0.0001	0.0002	0.0002	0.0003	0.0004	0.0005	0.0006	0.0008
11	0.0000	0.0000	0.0000	0.0000	0.0000	0.0001	0.0001	0.0001	0.0002	0.0002

	μ									
x	3.1	3.2	3.3	3.4	3.5	3.6	3.7	3.8	3.9	4.0
0	0.0450	0.0408	0.0369	0.0334	0.0302	0.0273	0.0247	0.0224	0.0202	0.0183
1	0.1397	0.1304	0.1217	0.1135	0.1057	0.0984	0.0915	0.0850	0.0789	0.0733
2	0.2165	0.2087	0.2008	0.1929	0.1850	0.1771	0.1692	0.1615	0.1539	0.1465
3	0.2237	0.2226	0.2209	0.2186	0.2158	0.2125	0.2087	0.2046	0.2001	0.1954
4	0.1733	0.1781	0.1823	0.1858	0.1888	0.1912	0.1931	0.1944	0.1951	0.1954
5	0.1075	0.1140	0.1203	0.1264	0.1322	0.1377	0.1429	0.1477	0.1522	0.1563
6	0.0555	0.0608	0.0662	0.0716	0.0771	0.0826	0.0881	0.0936	0.0989	0.1042
7	0.0246	0.0278	0.0312	0.0348	0.0385	0.0425	0.0466	0.0508	0.0551	0.0595
8	0.0095	0.0111	0.0129	0.0148	0.0169	0.0191	0.0215	0.0241	0.0269	0.0298
9	0.0033	0.0040	0.0047	0.0056	0.0066	0.0076	0.0089	0.0102	0.0116	0.0132
10	0.0010	0.0013	0.0016	0.0019	0.0023	0.0028	0.0033	0.0039	0.0045	0.0053
11	0.0003	0.0004	0.0005	0.0006	0.0007	0.0009	0.0011	0.0013	0.0016	0.0019
12	0.0001	0.0001	0.0001	0.0002	0.0002	0.0003	0.0003	0.0004	0.0005	0.0006
13	0.0000	0.0000	0.0000	0.0000	0.0001	0.0001	0.0001	0.0001	0.0002	0.0002

	μ									
x	4.1	4.2	4.3	4.4	4.5	4.6	4.7	4.8	4.9	5.0
0	0.0166	0.0150	0.0136	0.0123	0.0111	0.0101	0.0091	0.0082	0.0074	0.0067
1	0.0679	0.0630	0.0583	0.0540	0.0500	0.0462	0.0427	0.0395	0.0365	0.0337
2	0.1393	0.1323	0.1254	0.1188	0.1125	0.1063	0.1005	0.0948	0.0894	0.0842
3	0.1904	0.1852	0.1798	0.1743	0.1687	0.1631	0.1574	0.1517	0.1460	0.1404
4	0.1951	0.1944	0.1933	0.1917	0.1898	0.1875	0.1849	0.1820	0.1789	0.1755
5	0.1600	0.1633	0.1662	0.1687	0.1708	0.1725	0.1738	0.1747	0.1753	0.1755
6	0.1093	0.1143	0.1191	0.1237	0.1281	0.1323	0.1362	0.1398	0.1432	0.1462
7	0.0640	0.0686	0.0732	0.0778	0.0824	0.0869	0.0914	0.0959	0.1002	0.1044
8	0.0328	0.0360	0.0393	0.0428	0.0463	0.0500	0.0537	0.0575	0.0614	0.0653
9	0.0150	0.0168	0.0188	0.0209	0.0232	0.0255	0.0281	0.0307	0.0334	0.0363
10	0.0061	0.0071	0.0081	0.0092	0.0104	0.0118	0.0132	0.0147	0.0164	0.0181
11	0.0023	0.0027	0.0032	0.0037	0.0043	0.0049	0.0056	0.0064	0.0073	0.0082
12	0.0008	0.0009	0.0011	0.0013	0.0016	0.0019	0.0022	0.0026	0.0030	0.0034
13	0.0002	0.0003	0.0004	0.0005	0.0006	0.0007	0.0008	0.0009	0.0011	0.0013
14	0.0001	0.0001	0.0001	0.0001	0.0002	0.0002	0.0003	0.0003	0.0004	0.0005
15	0.0000	0.0000	0.0000	0.0000	0.0001	0.0001	0.0001	0.0001	0.0001	0.0002

(table continued)

TABLE **A.2** *(concluded)*   Poisson Probabilities (μ between 5.5 and 20.0)

					μ					
x	**5.5**	**6.0**	**6.5**	**7.0**	**7.5**	**8.0**	**8.5**	**9.0**	**9.5**	**10.0**
0	0.0041	0.0025	0.0015	0.0009	0.0006	0.0003	0.0002	0.0001	0.0001	0.0000
1	0.0225	0.0149	0.0098	0.0064	0.0041	0.0027	0.0017	0.0011	0.0007	0.0005
2	0.0618	0.0446	0.0318	0.0223	0.0156	0.0107	0.0074	0.0050	0.0034	0.0023
3	0.1133	0.0892	0.0688	0.0521	0.0389	0.0286	0.0208	0.0150	0.0107	0.0076
4	0.1558	0.1339	0.1118	0.0912	0.0729	0.0573	0.0443	0.0337	0.0254	0.0189
5	0.1714	0.1606	0.1454	0.1277	0.1094	0.0916	0.0752	0.0607	0.0483	0.0378
6	0.1571	0.1606	0.1575	0.1490	0.1367	0.1221	0.1066	0.0911	0.0764	0.0631
7	0.1234	0.1377	0.1462	0.1490	0.1465	0.1396	0.1294	0.1171	0.1037	0.0901
8	0.0849	0.1033	0.1188	0.1304	0.1373	0.1396	0.1375	0.1318	0.1232	0.1126
9	0.0519	0.0688	0.0858	0.1014	0.1144	0.1241	0.1299	0.1318	0.1300	0.1251
10	0.0285	0.0413	0.0558	0.0710	0.0858	0.0993	0.1104	0.1186	0.1235	0.1251
11	0.0143	0.0225	0.0330	0.0452	0.0585	0.0722	0.0853	0.0970	0.1067	0.1137
12	0.0065	0.0113	0.0179	0.0263	0.0366	0.0481	0.0604	0.0728	0.0844	0.0948
13	0.0028	0.0052	0.0089	0.0142	0.0211	0.0296	0.0395	0.0504	0.0617	0.0729
14	0.0011	0.0022	0.0041	0.0071	0.0113	0.0169	0.0240	0.0324	0.0419	0.0521
15	0.0004	0.0009	0.0018	0.0033	0.0057	0.0090	0.0136	0.0194	0.0265	0.0347
16	0.0001	0.0003	0.0007	0.0014	0.0026	0.0045	0.0072	0.0109	0.0157	0.0217
17	0.0000	0.0001	0.0003	0.0006	0.0012	0.0021	0.0036	0.0058	0.0088	0.0128
18	0.0000	0.0000	0.0001	0.0002	0.0005	0.0009	0.0017	0.0029	0.0046	0.0071
19	0.0000	0.0000	0.0000	0.0001	0.0002	0.0004	0.0008	0.0014	0.0023	0.0037
20	0.0000	0.0000	0.0000	0.0000	0.0001	0.0002	0.0003	0.0006	0.0011	0.0019
21	0.0000	0.0000	0.0000	0.0000	0.0000	0.0001	0.0001	0.0003	0.0005	0.0009
22	0.0000	0.0000	0.0000	0.0000	0.0000	0.0000	0.0001	0.0001	0.0002	0.0004
23	0.0000	0.0000	0.0000	0.0000	0.0000	0.0000	0.0000	0.0000	0.0001	0.0002

					μ					
x	**11.0**	**12.0**	**13.0**	**14.0**	**15.0**	**16.0**	**17.0**	**18.0**	**19.0**	**20.0**
0	0.0000	0.0000	0.0000	0.0000	0.0000	0.0000	0.0000	0.0000	0.0000	0.0000
1	0.0002	0.0001	0.0000	0.0000	0.0000	0.0000	0.0000	0.0000	0.0000	0.0000
2	0.0010	0.0004	0.0002	0.0001	0.0000	0.0000	0.0000	0.0000	0.0000	0.0000
3	0.0037	0.0018	0.0008	0.0004	0.0002	0.0001	0.0000	0.0000	0.0000	0.0000
4	0.0102	0.0053	0.0027	0.0013	0.0006	0.0003	0.0001	0.0001	0.0000	0.0000
5	0.0224	0.0127	0.0070	0.0037	0.0019	0.0010	0.0005	0.0002	0.0001	0.0001
6	0.0411	0.0255	0.0152	0.0087	0.0048	0.0026	0.0014	0.0007	0.0004	0.0002
7	0.0646	0.0437	0.0281	0.0174	0.0104	0.0060	0.0034	0.0019	0.0010	0.0005
8	0.0888	0.0655	0.0457	0.0304	0.0194	0.0120	0.0072	0.0042	0.0024	0.0013
9	0.1085	0.0874	0.0661	0.0473	0.0324	0.0213	0.0135	0.0083	0.0050	0.0029
10	0.1194	0.1048	0.0859	0.0663	0.0486	0.0341	0.0230	0.0150	0.0095	0.0058
11	0.1194	0.1144	0.1015	0.0844	0.0663	0.0496	0.0355	0.0245	0.0164	0.0106
12	0.1094	0.1144	0.1099	0.0984	0.0829	0.0661	0.0504	0.0368	0.0259	0.0176
13	0.0926	0.1056	0.1099	0.1060	0.0956	0.0814	0.0658	0.0509	0.0378	0.0271
14	0.0728	0.0905	0.1021	0.1060	0.1024	0.0930	0.0800	0.0655	0.0514	0.0387
15	0.0534	0.0724	0.0885	0.0989	0.1024	0.0992	0.0906	0.0786	0.0650	0.0516
16	0.0367	0.0543	0.0719	0.0866	0.0960	0.0992	0.0963	0.0884	0.0772	0.0646
17	0.0237	0.0383	0.0550	0.0713	0.0847	0.0934	0.0963	0.0936	0.0863	0.0760
18	0.0145	0.0255	0.0397	0.0554	0.0706	0.0830	0.0909	0.0936	0.0911	0.0844
19	0.0084	0.0161	0.0272	0.0409	0.0557	0.0699	0.0814	0.0887	0.0911	0.0888
20	0.0046	0.0097	0.0177	0.0286	0.0418	0.0559	0.0692	0.0798	0.0866	0.0888
21	0.0024	0.0055	0.0109	0.0191	0.0299	0.0426	0.0560	0.0684	0.0783	0.0846
22	0.0012	0.0030	0.0065	0.0121	0.0204	0.0310	0.0433	0.0560	0.0676	0.0769
23	0.0006	0.0016	0.0037	0.0074	0.0133	0.0216	0.0320	0.0438	0.0559	0.0669
24	0.0003	0.0008	0.0020	0.0043	0.0083	0.0144	0.0226	0.0328	0.0442	0.0557
25	0.0001	0.0004	0.0010	0.0024	0.0050	0.0092	0.0154	0.0237	0.0336	0.0446
26	0.0000	0.0002	0.0005	0.0013	0.0029	0.0057	0.0101	0.0164	0.0246	0.0343
27	0.0000	0.0001	0.0002	0.0007	0.0016	0.0034	0.0063	0.0109	0.0173	0.0254
28	0.0000	0.0000	0.0001	0.0003	0.0009	0.0019	0.0038	0.0070	0.0117	0.0181
29	0.0000	0.0000	0.0001	0.0002	0.0004	0.0011	0.0023	0.0044	0.0077	0.0125
30	0.0000	0.0000	0.0000	0.0001	0.0002	0.0006	0.0013	0.0026	0.0049	0.0083
31	0.0000	0.0000	0.0000	0.0000	0.0001	0.0003	0.0007	0.0015	0.0030	0.0054
32	0.0000	0.0000	0.0000	0.0000	0.0001	0.0001	0.0004	0.0009	0.0018	0.0034
33	0.0000	0.0000	0.0000	0.0000	0.0000	0.0001	0.0002	0.0005	0.0010	0.0020

Source: Computed by D. K. Hildebrand. Found in D. K. Hildebrand and L. Ott, *Statistical Thinking for Managers*, 3rd ed. (Boston, MA: PWS-KENT Publishing Company, 1991).

TABLE A.3 A Table of Areas under the Standard Normal Curve

z	.00	.01	.02	.03	.04	.05	.06	.07	.08	.09
0.0	0.0000	0.0040	0.0080	0.0120	0.0160	0.0199	0.0239	0.0279	0.0319	0.0359
0.1	0.0398	0.0438	0.0478	0.0517	0.0557	0.0596	0.0636	0.0675	0.0714	0.0753
0.2	0.0793	0.0832	0.0871	0.0910	0.0948	0.0987	0.1026	0.1064	0.1103	0.1141
0.3	0.1179	0.1217	0.1255	0.1293	0.1331	0.1368	0.1406	0.1443	0.1480	0.1517
0.4	0.1554	0.1591	0.1628	0.1664	0.1700	0.1736	0.1772	0.1808	0.1844	0.1879
0.5	0.1915	0.1950	0.1985	0.2019	0.2054	0.2088	0.2123	0.2157	0.2190	0.2224
0.6	0.2257	0.2291	0.2324	0.2357	0.2389	0.2422	0.2454	0.2486	0.2517	0.2549
0.7	0.2580	0.2611	0.2642	0.2673	0.2704	0.2734	0.2764	0.2794	0.2823	0.2852
0.8	0.2881	0.2910	0.2939	0.2967	0.2995	0.3023	0.3051	0.3078	0.3106	0.3133
0.9	0.3159	0.3186	0.3212	0.3238	0.3264	0.3289	0.3315	0.3340	0.3365	0.3389
1.0	0.3413	0.3438	0.3461	0.3485	0.3508	0.3531	0.3554	0.3577	0.3599	0.3621
1.1	0.3643	0.3665	0.3686	0.3708	0.3729	0.3749	0.3770	0.3790	0.3810	0.3830
1.2	0.3849	0.3869	0.3888	0.3907	0.3925	0.3944	0.3962	0.3980	0.3997	0.4015
1.3	0.4032	0.4049	0.4066	0.4082	0.4099	0.4115	0.4131	0.4147	0.4162	0.4177
1.4	0.4192	0.4207	0.4222	0.4236	0.4251	0.4265	0.4279	0.4292	0.4306	0.4319
1.5	0.4332	0.4345	0.4357	0.4370	0.4382	0.4394	0.4406	0.4418	0.4429	0.4441
1.6	0.4452	0.4463	0.4474	0.4484	0.4495	0.4505	0.4515	0.4525	0.4535	0.4545
1.7	0.4554	0.4564	0.4573	0.4582	0.4591	0.4599	0.4608	0.4616	0.4625	0.4633
1.8	0.4641	0.4649	0.4656	0.4664	0.4671	0.4678	0.4686	0.4693	0.4699	0.4706
1.9	0.4713	0.4719	0.4726	0.4732	0.4738	0.4744	0.4750	0.4756	0.4761	0.4767
2.0	0.4772	0.4778	0.4783	0.4788	0.4793	0.4798	0.4803	0.4808	0.4812	0.4817
2.1	0.4821	0.4826	0.4830	0.4834	0.4838	0.4842	0.4846	0.4850	0.4854	0.4857
2.2	0.4861	0.4864	0.4868	0.4871	0.4875	0.4878	0.4881	0.4884	0.4887	0.4890
2.3	0.4893	0.4896	0.4898	0.4901	0.4904	0.4906	0.4909	0.4911	0.4913	0.4916
2.4	0.4918	0.4920	0.4922	0.4925	0.4927	0.4929	0.4931	0.4932	0.4934	0.4936
2.5	0.4938	0.4940	0.4941	0.4943	0.4945	0.4946	0.4948	0.4949	0.4951	0.4952
2.6	0.4953	0.4955	0.4956	0.4957	0.4959	0.4960	0.4961	0.4962	0.4963	0.4964
2.7	0.4965	0.4966	0.4967	0.4968	0.4969	0.4970	0.4971	0.4972	0.4973	0.4974
2.8	0.4974	0.4975	0.4976	0.4977	0.4977	0.4978	0.4979	0.4979	0.4980	0.4981
2.9	0.4981	0.4982	0.4982	0.4983	0.4984	0.4984	0.4985	0.4985	0.4986	0.4986
3.0	0.4987	0.4987	0.4987	0.4988	0.4988	0.4989	0.4989	0.4989	0.4990	0.4990

Source: A. Hald, *Statistical Tables and Formulas* (New York: Wiley, 1952), abridged from Table 1. Reproduced by permission of the publisher.

TABLE **A.4**   A Table of Cumulative Areas under the Standard Normal Curve

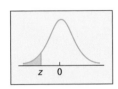

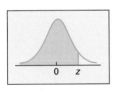

z	.00	.01	.02	.03	.04	.05	.06	.07	.08	.09
−3.4	0.0003	0.0003	0.0003	0.0003	0.0003	0.0003	0.0003	0.0003	0.0003	0.0002
−3.3	0.0005	0.0005	0.0005	0.0004	0.0004	0.0004	0.0004	0.0004	0.0004	0.0003
−3.2	0.0007	0.0007	0.0006	0.0006	0.0006	0.0006	0.0006	0.0006	0.0005	0.0005
−3.1	0.0010	0.0009	0.0009	0.0009	0.0008	0.0008	0.0008	0.0008	0.0007	0.0007
−3.0	0.0013	0.0013	0.0013	0.0012	0.0012	0.0011	0.0011	0.0011	0.0010	0.0010
−2.9	0.0019	0.0018	0.0018	0.0017	0.0016	0.0016	0.0015	0.0015	0.0014	0.0014
−2.8	0.0026	0.0025	0.0024	0.0023	0.0023	0.0022	0.0021	0.0021	0.0020	0.0019
−2.7	0.0035	0.0034	0.0033	0.0032	0.0031	0.0030	0.0029	0.0028	0.0027	0.0026
−2.6	0.0047	0.0045	0.0044	0.0043	0.0041	0.0040	0.0039	0.0038	0.0037	0.0036
−2.5	0.0062	0.0060	0.0059	0.0057	0.0055	0.0054	0.0052	0.0051	0.0049	0.0048
−2.4	0.0082	0.0080	0.0078	0.0075	0.0073	0.0071	0.0069	0.0068	0.0066	0.0064
−2.3	0.0107	0.0104	0.0102	0.0099	0.0096	0.0094	0.0091	0.0089	0.0087	0.0084
−2.2	0.0139	0.0136	0.0132	0.0129	0.0125	0.0122	0.0119	0.0116	0.0113	0.0110
−2.1	0.0179	0.0174	0.0170	0.0166	0.0162	0.0158	0.0154	0.0150	0.0146	0.0143
−2.0	0.0228	0.0222	0.0217	0.0212	0.0207	0.0202	0.0197	0.0192	0.0188	0.0183
−1.9	0.0287	0.0281	0.0274	0.0268	0.0262	0.0256	0.0250	0.0244	0.0239	0.0233
−1.8	0.0359	0.0351	0.0344	0.0336	0.0329	0.0322	0.0314	0.0307	0.0301	0.0294
−1.7	0.0446	0.0436	0.0427	0.0418	0.0409	0.0401	0.0392	0.0384	0.0375	0.0367
−1.6	0.0548	0.0537	0.0526	0.0516	0.0505	0.0495	0.0485	0.0475	0.0465	0.0455
−1.5	0.0668	0.0655	0.0643	0.0630	0.0618	0.0606	0.0594	0.0582	0.0571	0.0559
−1.4	0.0808	0.0793	0.0778	0.0764	0.0749	0.0735	0.0721	0.0708	0.0694	0.0681
−1.3	0.0968	0.0951	0.0934	0.0918	0.0901	0.0885	0.0869	0.0853	0.0838	0.0823
−1.2	0.1151	0.1131	0.1112	0.1093	0.1075	0.1056	0.1038	0.1020	0.1003	0.0985
−1.1	0.1357	0.1335	0.1314	0.1292	0.1271	0.1251	0.1230	0.1210	0.1190	0.1170
−1.0	0.1587	0.1562	0.1539	0.1515	0.1492	0.1469	0.1446	0.1423	0.1401	0.1379
−0.9	0.1841	0.1814	0.1788	0.1762	0.1736	0.1711	0.1685	0.1660	0.1635	0.1611
−0.8	0.2119	0.2090	0.2061	0.2033	0.2005	0.1977	0.1949	0.1922	0.1894	0.1867
−0.7	0.2420	0.2389	0.2358	0.2327	0.2296	0.2266	0.2236	0.2206	0.2177	0.2148
−0.6	0.2743	0.2709	0.2676	0.2643	0.2611	0.2578	0.2546	0.2514	0.2483	0.2451
−0.5	0.3085	0.3050	0.3015	0.2981	0.2946	0.2912	0.2877	0.2843	0.2810	0.2776
−0.4	0.3446	0.3409	0.3372	0.3336	0.3300	0.3264	0.3228	0.3192	0.3156	0.3121
−0.3	0.3821	0.3783	0.3745	0.3707	0.3669	0.3632	0.3594	0.3557	0.3520	0.3483
−0.2	0.4207	0.4168	0.4129	0.4090	0.4052	0.4013	0.3974	0.3936	0.3897	0.3859
−0.1	0.4602	0.4562	0.4522	0.4483	0.4443	0.4404	0.4364	0.4325	0.4286	0.4247
−0.0	0.5000	0.4960	0.4920	0.4880	0.4840	0.4801	0.4761	0.4721	0.4681	0.4641
0.0	0.5000	0.5040	0.5080	0.5120	0.5160	0.5199	0.5239	0.5279	0.5319	0.5359
0.1	0.5398	0.5438	0.5478	0.5517	0.5557	0.5596	0.5636	0.5675	0.5714	0.5753
0.2	0.5793	0.5832	0.5871	0.5910	0.5948	0.5987	0.6026	0.6064	0.6103	0.6141
0.3	0.6179	0.6217	0.6255	0.6293	0.6331	0.6368	0.6406	0.6443	0.6480	0.6517
0.4	0.6554	0.6591	0.6628	0.6664	0.6700	0.6736	0.6772	0.6808	0.6844	0.6879
0.5	0.6915	0.6950	0.6985	0.7019	0.7054	0.7088	0.7123	0.7157	0.7190	0.7224
0.6	0.7257	0.7291	0.7324	0.7357	0.7389	0.7422	0.7454	0.7486	0.7517	0.7549
0.7	0.7580	0.7611	0.7642	0.7673	0.7704	0.7734	0.7764	0.7794	0.7823	0.7852
0.8	0.7881	0.7910	0.7939	0.7967	0.7995	0.8023	0.8051	0.8078	0.8106	0.8133
0.9	0.8159	0.8186	0.8212	0.8238	0.8264	0.8289	0.8315	0.8340	0.8365	0.8389
1.0	0.8413	0.8438	0.8461	0.8485	0.8508	0.8531	0.8554	0.8577	0.8599	0.8621
1.1	0.8643	0.8665	0.8686	0.8708	0.8729	0.8749	0.8770	0.8790	0.8810	0.8830
1.2	0.8849	0.8869	0.8888	0.8907	0.8925	0.8944	0.8962	0.8980	0.8997	0.9015
1.3	0.9032	0.9049	0.9066	0.9082	0.9099	0.9115	0.9131	0.9147	0.9162	0.9177
1.4	0.9192	0.9207	0.9222	0.9236	0.9251	0.9265	0.9279	0.9292	0.9306	0.9319
1.5	0.9332	0.9345	0.9357	0.9370	0.9382	0.9394	0.9406	0.9418	0.9429	0.9441
1.6	0.9452	0.9463	0.9474	0.9484	0.9495	0.9505	0.9515	0.9525	0.9535	0.9545
1.7	0.9554	0.9564	0.9573	0.9582	0.9591	0.9599	0.9608	0.9616	0.9625	0.9633
1.8	0.9641	0.9649	0.9656	0.9664	0.9671	0.9678	0.9686	0.9693	0.9699	0.9706
1.9	0.9713	0.9719	0.9726	0.9732	0.9738	0.9744	0.9750	0.9756	0.9761	0.9767
2.0	0.9772	0.9778	0.9783	0.9788	0.9793	0.9798	0.9803	0.9808	0.9812	0.9817
2.1	0.9821	0.9826	0.9830	0.9834	0.9838	0.9842	0.9846	0.9850	0.9854	0.9857
2.2	0.9861	0.9864	0.9868	0.9871	0.9875	0.9878	0.9881	0.9884	0.9887	0.9890
2.3	0.9893	0.9896	0.9898	0.9901	0.9904	0.9906	0.9909	0.9911	0.9913	0.9916
2.4	0.9918	0.9920	0.9922	0.9925	0.9927	0.9929	0.9931	0.9932	0.9934	0.9936
2.5	0.9938	0.9940	0.9941	0.9943	0.9945	0.9946	0.9948	0.9949	0.9951	0.9952
2.6	0.9953	0.9955	0.9956	0.9957	0.9959	0.9960	0.9961	0.9962	0.9963	0.9964
2.7	0.9965	0.9966	0.9967	0.9968	0.9969	0.9970	0.9971	0.9972	0.9973	0.9974
2.8	0.9974	0.9975	0.9976	0.9977	0.9977	0.9978	0.9979	0.9979	0.9980	0.9981
2.9	0.9981	0.9982	0.9982	0.9983	0.9984	0.9984	0.9985	0.9985	0.9986	0.9986
3.0	0.9987	0.9987	0.9987	0.9988	0.9988	0.9989	0.9989	0.9989	0.9990	0.9990
3.1	0.9990	0.9991	0.9991	0.9991	0.9992	0.9992	0.9992	0.9992	0.9993	0.9993
3.2	0.9993	0.9993	0.9994	0.9994	0.9994	0.9994	0.9994	0.9995	0.9995	0.9995
3.3	0.9995	0.9995	0.9995	0.9996	0.9996	0.9996	0.9996	0.9996	0.9996	0.9997
3.4	0.9997	0.9997	0.9997	0.9997	0.9997	0.9997	0.9997	0.9997	0.9997	0.9998

TABLE **A.5**   A *t* Table: Values of t_α for $df = 1$ through 48

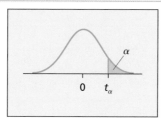

df	$t_{0.100}$	$t_{0.05}$	$t_{0.025}$	$t_{0.01}$	$t_{0.005}$	$t_{0.001}$	$t_{0.0005}$
1	3.078	6.314	12.706	31.821	63.657	318.309	636.619
2	1.886	2.920	4.303	6.965	9.925	22.327	31.599
3	1.638	2.353	3.182	4.541	5.841	10.215	12.924
4	1.533	2.132	2.776	3.747	4.604	7.173	8.610
5	1.476	2.015	2.571	3.365	4.032	5.893	6.869
6	1.440	1.943	2.447	3.143	3.707	5.208	5.959
7	1.415	1.895	2.365	2.998	3.499	4.785	5.408
8	1.397	1.860	2.306	2.896	3.355	4.501	5.041
9	1.383	1.833	2.262	2.821	3.250	4.297	4.781
10	1.372	1.812	2.228	2.764	3.169	4.144	4.587
11	1.363	1.796	2.201	2.718	3.106	4.025	4.437
12	1.356	1.782	2.179	2.681	3.055	3.930	4.318
13	1.350	1.771	2.160	2.650	3.012	3.852	4.221
14	1.345	1.761	2.145	2.624	2.977	3.787	4.140
15	1.341	1.753	2.131	2.602	2.947	3.733	4.073
16	1.337	1.746	2.120	2.583	2.921	3.686	4.015
17	1.333	1.740	2.110	2.567	2.898	3.646	3.965
18	1.330	1.734	2.101	2.552	2.878	3.610	3.922
19	1.328	1.729	2.093	2.539	2.861	3.579	3.883
20	1.325	1.725	2.086	2.528	2.845	3.552	3.850
21	1.323	1.721	2.080	2.518	2.831	3.527	3.819
22	1.321	1.717	2.074	2.508	2.819	3.505	3.792
23	1.319	1.714	2.069	2.500	2.807	3.485	3.768
24	1.318	1.711	2.064	2.492	2.797	3.467	3.745
25	1.316	1.708	2.060	2.485	2.787	3.450	3.725
26	1.315	1.706	2.056	2.479	2.779	3.435	3.707
27	1.314	1.703	2.052	2.473	2.771	3.421	3.690
28	1.313	1.701	2.048	2.467	2.763	3.408	3.674
29	1.311	1.699	2.045	2.462	2.756	3.396	3.659
30	1.310	1.697	2.042	2.457	2.750	3.385	3.646
31	1.309	1.696	2.040	2.453	2.744	3.375	3.633
32	1.309	1.694	2.037	2.449	2.738	3.365	3.622
33	1.308	1.692	2.035	2.445	2.733	3.356	3.611
34	1.307	1.691	2.032	2.441	2.728	3.348	3.601
35	1.306	1.690	2.030	2.438	2.724	3.340	3.591
36	1.306	1.688	2.028	2.434	2.719	3.333	3.582
37	1.305	1.687	2.026	2.431	2.715	3.326	3.574
38	1.304	1.686	2.024	2.429	2.712	3.319	3.566
39	1.304	1.685	2.023	2.426	2.708	3.313	3.558
40	1.303	1.684	2.021	2.423	2.704	3.307	3.551
41	1.303	1.683	2.020	2.421	2.701	3.301	3.544
42	1.302	1.682	2.018	2.418	2.698	3.296	3.538
43	1.302	1.681	2.017	2.416	2.695	3.291	3.532
44	1.301	1.680	2.015	2.414	2.692	3.286	3.526
45	1.301	1.679	2.014	2.412	2.690	3.281	3.520
46	1.300	1.679	2.013	2.410	2.687	3.277	3.515
47	1.300	1.678	2.012	2.408	2.685	3.273	3.510
48	1.299	1.677	2.011	2.407	2.682	3.269	3.505

(table continued)

TABLE A.5 *(concluded)*   A *t* Table: Values of t_α for *df* = 49 through 100, 120, and ∞

df	$t_{0.100}$	$t_{0.05}$	$t_{0.025}$	$t_{0.01}$	$t_{0.005}$	$t_{0.001}$	$t_{0.0005}$
49	1.299	1.677	2.010	2.405	2.680	3.265	3.500
50	1.299	1.676	2.009	2.403	2.678	3.261	3.496
51	1.298	1.675	2.008	2.402	2.676	3.258	3.492
52	1.298	1.675	2.007	2.400	2.674	3.255	3.488
53	1.298	1.674	2.006	2.399	2.672	3.251	3.484
54	1.297	1.674	2.005	2.397	2.670	3.248	3.480
55	1.297	1.673	2.004	2.396	2.668	3.245	3.476
56	1.297	1.673	2.003	2.395	2.667	3.242	3.473
57	1.297	1.672	2.002	2.394	2.665	3.239	3.470
58	1.296	1.672	2.002	2.392	2.663	3.237	3.466
59	1.296	1.671	2.001	2.391	2.662	3.234	3.463
60	1.296	1.671	2.000	2.390	2.660	3.232	3.460
61	1.296	1.670	2.000	2.389	2.659	3.229	3.457
62	1.295	1.670	1.999	2.388	2.657	3.227	3.454
63	1.295	1.669	1.998	2.387	2.656	3.225	3.452
64	1.295	1.669	1.998	2.386	2.655	3.223	3.449
65	1.295	1.669	1.997	2.385	2.654	3.220	3.447
66	1.295	1.668	1.997	2.384	2.652	3.218	3.444
67	1.294	1.668	1.996	2.383	2.651	3.216	3.442
68	1.294	1.668	1.995	2.382	2.650	3.214	3.439
69	1.294	1.667	1.995	2.382	2.649	3.213	3.437
70	1.294	1.667	1.994	2.381	2.648	3.211	3.435
71	1.294	1.667	1.994	2.380	2.647	3.209	3.433
72	1.293	1.666	1.993	2.379	2.646	3.207	3.431
73	1.293	1.666	1.993	2.379	2.645	3.206	3.429
74	1.293	1.666	1.993	2.378	2.644	3.204	3.427
75	1.293	1.665	1.992	2.377	2.643	3.202	3.425
76	1.293	1.665	1.992	2.376	2.642	3.201	3.423
77	1.293	1.665	1.991	2.376	2.641	3.199	3.421
78	1.292	1.665	1.991	2.375	2.640	3.198	3.420
79	1.292	1.664	1.990	2.374	2.640	3.197	3.418
80	1.292	1.664	1.990	2.374	2.639	3.195	3.416
81	1.292	1.664	1.990	2.373	2.638	3.194	3.415
82	1.292	1.664	1.989	2.373	2.637	3.193	3.413
83	1.292	1.663	1.989	2.372	2.636	3.191	3.412
84	1.292	1.663	1.989	2.372	2.636	3.190	3.410
85	1.292	1.663	1.988	2.371	2.635	3.189	3.409
86	1.291	1.663	1.988	2.370	2.634	3.188	3.407
87	1.291	1.663	1.988	2.370	2.634	3.187	3.406
88	1.291	1.662	1.987	2.369	2.633	3.185	3.405
89	1.291	1.662	1.987	2.369	2.632	3.184	3.403
90	1.291	1.662	1.987	2.368	2.632	3.183	3.402
91	1.291	1.662	1.986	2.368	2.631	3.182	3.401
92	1.291	1.662	1.986	2.368	2.630	3.181	3.399
93	1.291	1.661	1.986	2.367	2.630	3.180	3.398
94	1.291	1.661	1.986	2.367	2.629	3.179	3.397
95	1.291	1.661	1.985	2.366	2.629	3.178	3.396
96	1.290	1.661	1.985	2.366	2.628	3.177	3.395
97	1.290	1.661	1.985	2.365	2.627	3.176	3.394
98	1.290	1.661	1.984	2.365	2.627	3.175	3.393
99	1.290	1.660	1.984	2.365	2.626	3.175	3.392
100	1.290	1.660	1.984	2.364	2.626	3.174	3.390
120	1.289	1.658	1.980	2.358	2.617	3.160	3.373
∞	1.282	1.645	1.960	2.326	2.576	3.090	3.291

Source: Provided by J. B. Orris using Excel.

TABLE A.6 An *F* Table: Values of $F_{0.10}$

									Numerator Degrees of Freedom (df_1)										
df_2 \ df_1	1	2	3	4	5	6	7	8	9	10	12	15	20	24	30	40	60	120	∞
1	39.86	49.50	53.59	55.83	57.24	58.20	58.91	59.44	59.86	60.19	60.71	61.22	61.74	62.00	62.26	62.53	62.79	63.06	63.33
2	8.53	9.00	9.16	9.24	9.29	9.33	9.35	9.37	9.38	9.39	9.41	9.42	9.44	9.45	9.46	9.47	9.47	9.48	9.49
3	5.54	5.46	5.39	5.34	5.31	5.28	5.27	5.25	5.24	5.23	5.22	5.20	5.18	5.18	5.17	5.16	5.15	5.14	5.13
4	4.54	4.32	4.19	4.11	4.05	4.01	3.98	3.95	3.94	3.92	3.90	3.87	3.84	3.83	3.82	3.80	3.79	3.78	3.76
5	4.06	3.78	3.62	3.52	3.45	3.40	3.37	3.34	3.32	3.30	3.27	3.24	3.21	3.19	3.17	3.16	3.14	3.12	3.10
6	3.78	3.46	3.29	3.18	3.11	3.05	3.01	2.98	2.96	2.94	2.90	2.87	2.84	2.82	2.80	2.78	2.76	2.74	2.72
7	3.59	3.26	3.07	2.96	2.88	2.83	2.78	2.75	2.72	2.70	2.67	2.63	2.59	2.58	2.56	2.54	2.51	2.49	2.47
8	3.46	3.11	2.92	2.81	2.73	2.67	2.62	2.59	2.56	2.54	2.50	2.46	2.42	2.40	2.38	2.36	2.34	2.32	2.29
9	3.36	3.01	2.81	2.69	2.61	2.55	2.51	2.47	2.44	2.42	2.38	2.34	2.30	2.28	2.25	2.23	2.21	2.18	2.16
10	3.29	2.92	2.73	2.61	2.52	2.46	2.41	2.38	2.35	2.32	2.28	2.24	2.20	2.18	2.16	2.13	2.11	2.08	2.06
11	3.23	2.86	2.66	2.54	2.45	2.39	2.34	2.30	2.27	2.25	2.21	2.17	2.12	2.10	2.08	2.05	2.03	2.00	1.97
12	3.18	2.81	2.61	2.48	2.39	2.33	2.28	2.24	2.21	2.19	2.15	2.10	2.06	2.04	2.01	1.99	1.96	1.93	1.90
13	3.14	2.76	2.56	2.43	2.35	2.28	2.23	2.20	2.16	2.14	2.10	2.05	2.01	1.98	1.96	1.93	1.90	1.88	1.85
14	3.10	2.73	2.52	2.39	2.31	2.24	2.19	2.15	2.12	2.10	2.05	2.01	1.96	1.94	1.91	1.89	1.86	1.83	1.80
15	3.07	2.70	2.49	2.36	2.27	2.21	2.16	2.12	2.09	2.06	2.02	1.97	1.92	1.90	1.87	1.85	1.82	1.79	1.76
16	3.05	2.67	2.46	2.33	2.24	2.18	2.13	2.09	2.06	2.03	1.99	1.94	1.89	1.87	1.84	1.81	1.78	1.75	1.72
17	3.03	2.64	2.44	2.31	2.22	2.15	2.10	2.06	2.03	2.00	1.96	1.91	1.86	1.84	1.81	1.78	1.75	1.72	1.69
18	3.01	2.62	2.42	2.29	2.20	2.13	2.08	2.04	2.00	1.98	1.93	1.89	1.84	1.81	1.78	1.75	1.72	1.69	1.66
19	2.99	2.61	2.40	2.27	2.18	2.11	2.06	2.02	1.98	1.96	1.91	1.86	1.81	1.79	1.76	1.73	1.70	1.67	1.63
20	2.97	2.59	2.38	2.25	2.16	2.09	2.04	2.00	1.96	1.94	1.89	1.84	1.79	1.77	1.74	1.71	1.68	1.64	1.61
21	2.96	2.57	2.36	2.23	2.14	2.08	2.02	1.98	1.95	1.92	1.87	1.83	1.78	1.75	1.72	1.69	1.66	1.62	1.59
22	2.95	2.56	2.35	2.22	2.13	2.06	2.01	1.97	1.93	1.90	1.86	1.81	1.76	1.73	1.70	1.67	1.64	1.60	1.57
23	2.94	2.55	2.34	2.21	2.11	2.05	1.99	1.95	1.92	1.89	1.84	1.80	1.74	1.72	1.69	1.66	1.62	1.59	1.55
24	2.93	2.54	2.33	2.19	2.10	2.04	1.98	1.94	1.91	1.88	1.83	1.78	1.73	1.70	1.67	1.64	1.61	1.57	1.53
25	2.92	2.53	2.32	2.18	2.09	2.02	1.97	1.93	1.89	1.87	1.82	1.77	1.72	1.69	1.66	1.63	1.59	1.56	1.52
26	2.91	2.52	2.31	2.17	2.08	2.01	1.96	1.92	1.88	1.86	1.81	1.76	1.71	1.68	1.65	1.61	1.58	1.54	1.50
27	2.90	2.51	2.30	2.17	2.07	2.00	1.95	1.91	1.87	1.85	1.80	1.75	1.70	1.67	1.64	1.60	1.57	1.53	1.49
28	2.89	2.50	2.29	2.16	2.06	2.00	1.94	1.90	1.87	1.84	1.79	1.74	1.69	1.66	1.63	1.59	1.56	1.52	1.48
29	2.89	2.50	2.28	2.15	2.06	1.99	1.93	1.89	1.86	1.83	1.78	1.73	1.68	1.65	1.62	1.58	1.55	1.51	1.47
30	2.88	2.49	2.28	2.14	2.05	1.98	1.93	1.88	1.85	1.82	1.77	1.72	1.67	1.64	1.61	1.57	1.54	1.50	1.46
40	2.84	2.44	2.23	2.09	2.00	1.93	1.87	1.83	1.79	1.76	1.71	1.66	1.61	1.57	1.54	1.51	1.47	1.42	1.38
60	2.79	2.39	2.18	2.04	1.95	1.87	1.82	1.77	1.74	1.71	1.66	1.60	1.54	1.51	1.48	1.44	1.40	1.35	1.29
120	2.75	2.35	2.13	1.99	1.90	1.82	1.77	1.72	1.68	1.65	1.60	1.55	1.48	1.45	1.41	1.37	1.32	1.26	1.19
∞	2.71	2.30	2.08	1.94	1.85	1.77	1.72	1.67	1.63	1.60	1.55	1.49	1.42	1.38	1.34	1.30	1.24	1.17	1.00

Denominator Degrees of Freedom (df_2)

Source: M. Merrington and C. M. Thompson, "Tables of Percentage Points of the Inverted Beta (*F*)-Distribution," *Biometrika* 33 (1943), pp. 73–88. Reproduced by permission of the Biometrika Trustees.

TABLE A.7   An F Table: Values of $F_{0.05}$

df_2 \ df_1	1	2	3	4	5	6	7	8	9	10	12	15	20	24	30	40	60	120	∞
1	161.4	199.5	215.7	224.6	230.2	234.0	236.8	238.9	240.5	241.9	243.9	245.9	248.0	249.1	250.1	251.1	252.2	253.3	254.3
2	18.51	19.00	19.16	19.25	19.30	19.33	19.35	19.37	19.38	19.40	19.41	19.43	19.45	19.45	19.46	19.47	19.48	19.49	19.50
3	10.13	9.55	9.28	9.12	9.01	8.94	8.89	8.85	8.81	8.79	8.74	8.70	8.66	8.64	8.62	8.59	8.57	8.55	8.53
4	7.71	6.94	6.59	6.39	6.26	6.16	6.09	6.04	6.00	5.96	5.91	5.86	5.80	5.77	5.75	5.72	5.69	5.66	5.63
5	6.61	5.79	5.41	5.19	5.05	4.95	4.88	4.82	4.77	4.74	4.68	4.62	4.56	4.53	4.50	4.46	4.43	4.40	4.36
6	5.99	5.14	4.76	4.53	4.39	4.28	4.21	4.15	4.10	4.06	4.00	3.94	3.87	3.84	3.81	3.77	3.74	3.70	3.67
7	5.59	4.74	4.35	4.12	3.97	3.87	3.79	3.73	3.68	3.64	3.57	3.51	3.44	3.41	3.38	3.34	3.30	3.27	3.23
8	5.32	4.46	4.07	3.84	3.69	3.58	3.50	3.44	3.39	3.35	3.28	3.22	3.15	3.12	3.08	3.04	3.01	2.97	2.93
9	5.12	4.26	3.86	3.63	3.48	3.37	3.29	3.23	3.18	3.14	3.07	3.01	2.94	2.90	2.86	2.83	2.79	2.75	2.71
10	4.96	4.10	3.71	3.48	3.33	3.22	3.14	3.07	3.02	2.98	2.91	2.85	2.77	2.74	2.70	2.66	2.62	2.58	2.54
11	4.84	3.98	3.59	3.36	3.20	3.09	3.01	2.95	2.90	2.85	2.79	2.72	2.65	2.61	2.57	2.53	2.49	2.45	2.40
12	4.75	3.89	3.49	3.26	3.11	3.00	2.91	2.85	2.80	2.75	2.69	2.62	2.54	2.51	2.47	2.43	2.38	2.34	2.30
13	4.67	3.81	3.41	3.18	3.03	2.92	2.83	2.77	2.71	2.67	2.60	2.53	2.46	2.42	2.38	2.34	2.30	2.25	2.21
14	4.60	3.74	3.34	3.11	2.96	2.85	2.76	2.70	2.65	2.60	2.53	2.46	2.39	2.35	2.31	2.27	2.22	2.18	2.13
15	4.54	3.68	3.29	3.06	2.90	2.79	2.71	2.64	2.59	2.54	2.48	2.40	2.33	2.29	2.25	2.20	2.16	2.11	2.07
16	4.49	3.63	3.24	3.01	2.85	2.74	2.66	2.59	2.54	2.49	2.42	2.35	2.28	2.24	2.19	2.15	2.11	2.06	2.01
17	4.45	3.59	3.20	2.96	2.81	2.70	2.61	2.55	2.49	2.45	2.38	2.31	2.23	2.19	2.15	2.10	2.06	2.01	1.96
18	4.41	3.55	3.16	2.93	2.77	2.66	2.58	2.51	2.46	2.41	2.34	2.27	2.19	2.15	2.11	2.06	2.02	1.97	1.92
19	4.38	3.52	3.13	2.90	2.74	2.63	2.54	2.48	2.42	2.38	2.31	2.23	2.16	2.11	2.07	2.03	1.98	1.93	1.88
20	4.35	3.49	3.10	2.87	2.71	2.60	2.51	2.45	2.39	2.35	2.28	2.20	2.12	2.08	2.04	1.99	1.95	1.90	1.84
21	4.32	3.47	3.07	2.84	2.68	2.57	2.49	2.42	2.37	2.32	2.25	2.18	2.10	2.05	2.01	1.96	1.92	1.87	1.81
22	4.30	3.44	3.05	2.82	2.66	2.55	2.46	2.40	2.34	2.30	2.23	2.15	2.07	2.03	1.98	1.94	1.89	1.84	1.78
23	4.28	3.42	3.03	2.80	2.64	2.53	2.44	2.37	2.32	2.27	2.20	2.13	2.05	2.01	1.96	1.91	1.86	1.81	1.76
24	4.26	3.40	3.01	2.78	2.62	2.51	2.42	2.36	2.30	2.25	2.18	2.11	2.03	1.98	1.94	1.89	1.84	1.79	1.73
25	4.24	3.39	2.99	2.76	2.60	2.49	2.40	2.34	2.28	2.24	2.16	2.09	2.01	1.96	1.92	1.87	1.82	1.77	1.71
26	4.23	3.37	2.98	2.74	2.59	2.47	2.39	2.32	2.27	2.22	2.15	2.07	1.99	1.95	1.90	1.85	1.80	1.75	1.69
27	4.21	3.35	2.96	2.73	2.57	2.46	2.37	2.31	2.25	2.20	2.13	2.06	1.97	1.93	1.88	1.84	1.79	1.73	1.67
28	4.20	3.34	2.95	2.71	2.56	2.45	2.36	2.29	2.24	2.19	2.12	2.04	1.96	1.91	1.87	1.82	1.77	1.71	1.65
29	4.18	3.33	2.93	2.70	2.55	2.43	2.35	2.28	2.22	2.18	2.10	2.03	1.94	1.90	1.85	1.81	1.75	1.70	1.64
30	4.17	3.32	2.92	2.69	2.53	2.42	2.33	2.27	2.21	2.16	2.09	2.01	1.93	1.89	1.84	1.79	1.74	1.68	1.62
40	4.08	3.23	2.84	2.61	2.45	2.34	2.25	2.18	2.12	2.08	2.00	1.92	1.84	1.79	1.74	1.69	1.64	1.58	1.51
60	4.00	3.15	2.76	2.53	2.37	2.25	2.17	2.10	2.04	1.99	1.92	1.84	1.75	1.70	1.65	1.59	1.53	1.47	1.39
120	3.92	3.07	2.68	2.45	2.29	2.17	2.09	2.02	1.96	1.91	1.83	1.75	1.66	1.61	1.55	1.50	1.43	1.35	1.25
∞	3.84	3.00	2.60	2.37	2.21	2.10	2.01	1.94	1.88	1.83	1.75	1.67	1.57	1.52	1.46	1.39	1.32	1.22	1.00

Numerator Degrees of Freedom (df_1)

Denominator Degrees of Freedom (df_2)

Source: M. Merrington and C. M. Thompson, "Tables of Percentage Points of the Inverted Beta (F)-Distribution," *Biometrika* 33 (1943), pp. 73–88. Reproduced by permission of the Biometrika Trustees.

TABLE A.8   An F Table: Values of $F_{0.025}$

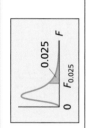

									Numerator Degrees of Freedom (df_1)										
df_2	1	2	3	4	5	6	7	8	9	10	12	15	20	24	30	40	60	120	∞
1	647.8	799.5	864.2	899.6	921.8	937.1	948.2	956.7	963.3	968.6	976.7	984.9	993.1	997.2	1,001	1,006	1,010	1,014	1,018
2	38.51	39.00	39.17	39.25	39.30	39.33	39.36	39.37	39.39	39.40	39.41	39.43	39.45	39.46	39.46	39.47	39.48	39.49	39.50
3	17.44	16.04	15.44	15.10	14.88	14.73	14.62	14.54	14.47	14.42	14.34	14.25	14.17	14.12	14.08	14.04	13.99	13.95	13.90
4	12.22	10.65	9.98	9.60	9.36	9.20	9.07	8.98	8.90	8.84	8.75	8.66	8.56	8.51	8.46	8.41	8.36	8.31	8.26
5	10.01	8.43	7.76	7.39	7.15	6.98	6.85	6.76	6.68	6.62	6.52	6.43	6.33	6.28	6.23	6.18	6.12	6.07	6.02
6	8.81	7.26	6.60	6.23	5.99	5.82	5.70	5.60	5.52	5.46	5.37	5.27	5.17	5.12	5.07	5.01	4.96	4.90	4.85
7	8.07	6.54	5.89	5.52	5.29	5.12	4.99	4.90	4.82	4.76	4.67	4.57	4.47	4.42	4.36	4.31	4.25	4.20	4.14
8	7.57	6.06	5.42	5.05	4.82	4.65	4.53	4.43	4.36	4.30	4.20	4.10	4.00	3.95	3.89	3.84	3.78	3.73	3.67
9	7.21	5.71	5.08	4.72	4.48	4.32	4.20	4.10	4.03	3.96	3.87	3.77	3.67	3.61	3.56	3.51	3.45	3.39	3.33
10	6.94	5.46	4.83	4.47	4.24	4.07	3.95	3.85	3.78	3.72	3.62	3.52	3.42	3.37	3.31	3.26	3.20	3.14	3.08
11	6.72	5.26	4.63	4.28	4.04	3.88	3.76	3.66	3.59	3.53	3.43	3.33	3.23	3.17	3.12	3.06	3.00	2.94	2.88
12	6.55	5.10	4.47	4.12	3.89	3.73	3.61	3.51	3.44	3.37	3.28	3.18	3.07	3.02	2.96	2.91	2.85	2.79	2.72
13	6.41	4.97	4.35	4.00	3.77	3.60	3.48	3.39	3.31	3.25	3.15	3.05	2.95	2.89	2.84	2.78	2.72	2.66	2.60
14	6.30	4.86	4.24	3.89	3.66	3.50	3.38	3.29	3.21	3.15	3.05	2.95	2.84	2.79	2.73	2.67	2.61	2.55	2.49
15	6.20	4.77	4.15	3.80	3.58	3.41	3.29	3.20	3.12	3.06	2.96	2.86	2.76	2.70	2.64	2.59	2.52	2.46	2.40
16	6.12	4.69	4.08	3.73	3.50	3.34	3.22	3.12	3.05	2.99	2.89	2.79	2.68	2.63	2.57	2.51	2.45	2.38	2.32
17	6.04	4.62	4.01	3.66	3.44	3.28	3.16	3.06	2.98	2.92	2.82	2.72	2.62	2.56	2.50	2.44	2.38	2.32	2.25
18	5.98	4.56	3.95	3.61	3.38	3.22	3.10	3.01	2.93	2.87	2.77	2.67	2.56	2.50	2.44	2.38	2.32	2.26	2.19
19	5.92	4.51	3.90	3.56	3.33	3.17	3.05	2.96	2.88	2.82	2.72	2.62	2.51	2.45	2.39	2.33	2.27	2.20	2.13
20	5.87	4.46	3.86	3.51	3.29	3.13	3.01	2.91	2.84	2.77	2.68	2.57	2.46	2.41	2.35	2.29	2.22	2.16	2.09
21	5.83	4.42	3.82	3.48	3.25	3.09	2.97	2.87	2.80	2.73	2.64	2.53	2.42	2.37	2.31	2.25	2.18	2.11	2.04
22	5.79	4.38	3.78	3.44	3.22	3.05	2.93	2.84	2.76	2.70	2.60	2.50	2.39	2.33	2.27	2.21	2.14	2.08	2.00
23	5.75	4.35	3.75	3.41	3.18	3.02	2.90	2.81	2.73	2.67	2.57	2.47	2.36	2.30	2.24	2.18	2.11	2.04	1.97
24	5.72	4.32	3.72	3.38	3.15	2.99	2.87	2.78	2.70	2.64	2.54	2.44	2.33	2.27	2.21	2.15	2.08	2.01	1.94
25	5.69	4.29	3.69	3.35	3.13	2.97	2.85	2.75	2.68	2.61	2.51	2.41	2.30	2.24	2.18	2.12	2.05	1.98	1.91
26	5.66	4.27	3.67	3.33	3.10	2.94	2.82	2.73	2.65	2.59	2.49	2.39	2.28	2.22	2.16	2.09	2.03	1.95	1.88
27	5.63	4.24	3.65	3.31	3.08	2.92	2.80	2.71	2.63	2.57	2.47	2.36	2.25	2.19	2.13	2.07	2.00	1.93	1.85
28	5.61	4.22	3.63	3.29	3.06	2.90	2.78	2.69	2.61	2.55	2.45	2.34	2.23	2.17	2.11	2.05	1.98	1.91	1.83
29	5.59	4.20	3.61	3.27	3.04	2.88	2.76	2.67	2.59	2.53	2.43	2.32	2.21	2.15	2.09	2.03	1.96	1.89	1.81
30	5.57	4.18	3.59	3.25	3.03	2.87	2.75	2.65	2.57	2.51	2.41	2.31	2.20	2.14	2.07	2.01	1.94	1.87	1.79
40	5.42	4.05	3.46	3.13	2.90	2.74	2.62	2.53	2.45	2.39	2.29	2.18	2.07	2.01	1.94	1.88	1.80	1.72	1.64
60	5.29	3.93	3.34	3.01	2.79	2.63	2.51	2.41	2.33	2.27	2.17	2.06	1.94	1.88	1.82	1.74	1.67	1.58	1.48
120	5.15	3.80	3.23	2.89	2.67	2.52	2.39	2.30	2.22	2.16	2.05	1.94	1.82	1.76	1.69	1.61	1.53	1.43	1.31
∞	5.02	3.69	3.12	2.79	2.57	2.41	2.29	2.19	2.11	2.05	1.94	1.83	1.71	1.64	1.57	1.48	1.39	1.27	1.00

Denominator Degrees of Freedom (df_2)

Source: M. Merrington and C. M. Thompson, "Tables of Percentage Points of the Inverted Beta (F)-Distribution," *Biometrika* 33 (1943), pp. 73–88. Reproduced by permission of the Biometrika Trustees.

TABLE A.9   An F Table: Values of $F_{0.01}$

df_2 \ df_1	1	2	3	4	5	6	7	8	9	10	12	15	20	24	30	40	60	120	∞
1	4,052	4,999.5	5,403	5,625	5,764	5,859	5,928	5,982	6,022	6,056	6,106	6,157	6,209	6,235	6,261	6,287	6,313	6,339	6,366
2	98.50	99.00	99.17	99.25	99.30	99.33	99.36	99.37	99.39	99.40	99.42	99.43	99.45	99.46	99.47	99.47	99.48	99.49	99.50
3	34.12	30.82	29.46	28.71	28.24	27.91	27.67	27.49	27.35	27.23	27.05	26.87	26.69	26.60	26.50	26.41	26.32	26.22	26.13
4	21.20	18.00	16.69	15.98	15.52	15.21	14.98	14.80	14.66	14.55	14.37	14.20	14.02	13.93	13.84	13.75	13.65	13.56	13.46
5	16.26	13.27	12.06	11.39	10.97	10.67	10.46	10.29	10.16	10.05	9.89	9.72	9.55	9.47	9.38	9.29	9.20	9.11	9.02
6	13.75	10.92	9.78	9.15	8.75	8.47	8.26	8.10	7.98	7.87	7.72	7.56	7.40	7.31	7.23	7.14	7.06	6.97	6.88
7	12.25	9.55	8.45	7.85	7.46	7.19	6.99	6.84	6.72	6.62	6.47	6.31	6.16	6.07	5.99	5.91	5.82	5.74	5.65
8	11.26	8.65	7.59	7.01	6.63	6.37	6.18	6.03	5.91	5.81	5.67	5.52	5.36	5.28	5.20	5.12	5.03	4.95	4.86
9	10.56	8.02	6.99	6.42	6.06	5.80	5.61	5.47	5.35	5.26	5.11	4.96	4.81	4.73	4.65	4.57	4.48	4.40	4.31
10	10.04	7.56	6.55	5.99	5.64	5.39	5.20	5.06	4.94	4.85	4.71	4.56	4.41	4.33	4.25	4.17	4.08	4.00	3.91
11	9.65	7.21	6.22	5.67	5.32	5.07	4.89	4.74	4.63	4.54	4.40	4.25	4.10	4.02	3.94	3.86	3.78	3.69	3.60
12	9.33	6.93	5.95	5.41	5.06	4.82	4.64	4.50	4.39	4.30	4.16	4.01	3.86	3.78	3.70	3.62	3.54	3.45	3.36
13	9.07	6.70	5.74	5.21	4.86	4.62	4.44	4.30	4.19	4.10	3.96	3.82	3.66	3.59	3.51	3.43	3.34	3.25	3.17
14	8.86	6.51	5.56	5.04	4.69	4.46	4.28	4.14	4.03	3.94	3.80	3.66	3.51	3.43	3.35	3.27	3.18	3.09	3.00
15	8.68	6.36	5.42	4.89	4.56	4.32	4.14	4.00	3.89	3.80	3.67	3.52	3.37	3.29	3.21	3.13	3.05	2.96	2.87
16	8.53	6.23	5.29	4.77	4.44	4.20	4.03	3.89	3.78	3.69	3.55	3.41	3.26	3.18	3.10	3.02	2.93	2.84	2.75
17	8.40	6.11	5.18	4.67	4.34	4.10	3.93	3.79	3.68	3.59	3.46	3.31	3.16	3.08	3.00	2.92	2.83	2.75	2.65
18	8.29	6.01	5.09	4.58	4.25	4.01	3.84	3.71	3.60	3.51	3.37	3.23	3.08	3.00	2.92	2.84	2.75	2.66	2.57
19	8.18	5.93	5.01	4.50	4.17	3.94	3.77	3.63	3.52	3.43	3.30	3.15	3.00	2.92	2.84	2.76	2.67	2.58	2.49
20	8.10	5.85	4.94	4.43	4.10	3.87	3.70	3.56	3.46	3.37	3.23	3.09	2.94	2.86	2.78	2.69	2.61	2.52	2.42
21	8.02	5.78	4.87	4.37	4.04	3.81	3.64	3.51	3.40	3.31	3.17	3.03	2.88	2.80	2.72	2.64	2.55	2.46	2.36
22	7.95	5.72	4.82	4.31	3.99	3.76	3.59	3.45	3.35	3.26	3.12	2.98	2.83	2.75	2.67	2.58	2.50	2.40	2.31
23	7.88	5.66	4.76	4.26	3.94	3.71	3.54	3.41	3.30	3.21	3.07	2.93	2.78	2.70	2.62	2.54	2.45	2.35	2.26
24	7.82	5.61	4.72	4.22	3.90	3.67	3.50	3.36	3.26	3.17	3.03	2.89	2.74	2.66	2.58	2.49	2.40	2.31	2.21
25	7.77	5.57	4.68	4.18	3.85	3.63	3.46	3.32	3.22	3.13	2.99	2.85	2.70	2.62	2.54	2.45	2.36	2.27	2.17
26	7.72	5.53	4.64	4.14	3.82	3.59	3.42	3.29	3.18	3.09	2.96	2.81	2.66	2.58	2.50	2.42	2.33	2.23	2.13
27	7.68	5.49	4.60	4.11	3.78	3.56	3.39	3.26	3.15	3.06	2.93	2.78	2.63	2.55	2.47	2.38	2.29	2.20	2.10
28	7.64	5.45	4.57	4.07	3.75	3.53	3.36	3.23	3.12	3.03	2.90	2.75	2.60	2.52	2.44	2.35	2.26	2.17	2.06
29	7.60	5.42	4.54	4.04	3.73	3.50	3.33	3.20	3.09	3.00	2.87	2.73	2.57	2.49	2.41	2.33	2.23	2.14	2.03
30	7.56	5.39	4.51	4.02	3.70	3.47	3.30	3.17	3.07	2.98	2.84	2.70	2.55	2.47	2.39	2.30	2.21	2.11	2.01
40	7.31	5.18	4.31	3.83	3.51	3.29	3.12	2.99	2.89	2.80	2.66	2.52	2.37	2.29	2.20	2.11	2.02	1.92	1.80
60	7.08	4.98	4.13	3.65	3.34	3.12	2.95	2.82	2.72	2.63	2.50	2.35	2.20	2.12	2.03	1.94	1.84	1.73	1.60
120	6.85	4.79	3.95	3.48	3.17	2.96	2.79	2.66	2.56	2.47	2.34	2.19	2.03	1.95	1.86	1.76	1.66	1.53	1.38
∞	6.63	4.61	3.78	3.32	3.02	2.80	2.64	2.51	2.41	2.32	2.18	2.04	1.88	1.79	1.70	1.59	1.47	1.32	1.00

Numerator Degrees of Freedom (df_1)

Denominator Degrees of Freedom (df_2)

Source: M. Merrington and C. M. Thompson, "Tables of Percentage Points of the Inverted Beta (F)-Distribution," *Biometrika* 33 (1943), pp. 73–88. Reproduced by permission of the Biometrika Trustees.

TABLE A.10 A Table of Percentage Points of the Studentized Range
(Note: r is the "first value" and v is the "second value" referred to in Chapter 10.)

Entry is $q_{0.10}$

r

v	2	3	4	5	6	7	8	9	10	11	12	13	14	15	16	17	18	19	20
1	8.93	13.4	16.4	18.5	20.2	21.5	22.6	23.6	24.5	25.2	25.9	26.5	27.1	27.6	28.1	28.5	29.0	29.3	29.7
2	4.13	5.73	6.77	7.54	8.14	8.63	9.05	9.41	9.72	10.0	10.3	10.5	10.7	10.9	11.1	11.2	11.4	11.5	11.7
3	3.33	4.47	5.20	5.74	6.16	6.51	6.81	7.06	7.29	7.49	7.67	7.83	7.98	8.12	8.25	8.37	8.48	8.58	8.68
4	3.01	3.98	4.59	5.03	5.39	5.68	5.93	6.14	6.33	6.49	6.65	6.78	6.91	7.02	7.13	7.23	7.33	7.41	7.50
5	2.85	3.72	4.26	4.66	4.98	5.24	5.46	5.65	5.82	5.97	6.10	6.22	6.34	6.44	6.54	6.63	6.71	6.79	6.86
6	2.75	3.56	4.07	4.44	4.73	4.97	5.17	5.34	5.50	5.64	5.76	5.87	5.98	6.07	6.16	6.25	6.32	6.40	6.47
7	2.68	3.45	3.93	4.28	4.55	4.78	4.97	5.14	5.28	5.41	5.53	5.64	5.74	5.83	5.91	5.99	6.06	6.13	6.19
8	2.63	3.37	3.83	4.17	4.43	4.65	4.83	4.99	5.13	5.25	5.36	5.46	5.56	5.64	5.72	5.80	5.87	5.93	6.00
9	2.59	3.32	3.76	4.08	4.34	4.54	4.72	4.87	4.99	5.13	5.23	5.33	5.42	5.51	5.58	5.66	5.72	5.79	5.85
10	2.56	3.27	3.70	4.02	4.26	4.47	4.64	4.78	4.91	5.01	5.13	5.23	5.32	5.40	5.47	5.54	5.61	5.67	5.73
11	2.54	3.23	3.66	3.96	4.20	4.40	4.57	4.71	4.84	4.95	5.05	5.15	5.23	5.31	5.38	5.45	5.51	5.57	5.63
12	2.52	3.20	3.62	3.92	4.16	4.35	4.51	4.65	4.78	4.89	4.99	5.08	5.16	5.24	5.31	5.37	5.44	5.49	5.55
13	2.50	3.18	3.59	3.88	4.12	4.30	4.46	4.60	4.72	4.83	4.93	5.02	5.10	5.18	5.25	5.31	5.37	5.43	5.48
14	2.49	3.16	3.56	3.85	4.08	4.27	4.42	4.56	4.68	4.79	4.88	4.97	5.05	5.12	5.19	5.25	5.32	5.37	5.43
15	2.48	3.14	3.54	3.83	4.05	4.23	4.39	4.52	4.64	4.75	4.84	4.93	5.01	5.08	5.15	5.21	5.27	5.32	5.38
16	2.47	3.12	3.52	3.80	4.03	4.21	4.36	4.49	4.61	4.71	4.81	4.89	4.97	5.04	5.11	5.17	5.23	5.28	5.33
17	2.46	3.11	3.50	3.78	4.00	4.18	4.33	4.46	4.58	4.68	4.77	4.86	4.93	5.01	5.07	5.13	5.19	5.24	5.30
18	2.45	3.10	3.49	3.77	3.98	4.16	4.31	4.44	4.55	4.65	4.75	4.83	4.90	4.98	5.04	5.10	5.16	5.21	5.26
19	2.45	3.09	3.47	3.75	3.97	4.14	4.29	4.42	4.53	4.63	4.72	4.80	4.88	4.95	5.01	5.07	5.13	5.18	5.23
20	2.44	3.08	3.46	3.74	3.95	4.12	4.27	4.40	4.51	4.61	4.70	4.78	4.85	4.92	4.99	5.05	5.10	5.16	5.20
24	2.42	3.05	3.42	3.69	3.90	4.07	4.21	4.34	4.44	4.54	4.63	4.70	4.78	4.85	4.91	4.97	5.02	5.07	5.12
30	2.40	3.02	3.39	3.65	3.85	4.02	4.16	4.28	4.38	4.47	4.56	4.64	4.71	4.77	4.83	4.89	4.94	4.99	5.03
40	2.38	2.99	3.35	3.60	3.80	3.96	4.10	4.21	4.32	4.41	4.49	4.56	4.63	4.69	4.75	4.81	4.86	4.90	4.95
60	2.36	2.96	3.31	3.56	3.75	3.91	4.04	4.16	4.25	4.34	4.42	4.49	4.56	4.62	4.67	4.73	4.78	4.82	4.86
120	2.34	2.93	3.28	3.52	3.71	3.86	3.99	4.10	4.19	4.28	4.35	4.42	4.48	4.54	4.60	4.65	4.69	4.74	4.78
∞	2.33	2.90	3.24	3.48	3.66	3.81	3.93	4.04	4.13	4.21	4.28	4.35	4.41	4.47	4.52	4.57	4.61	4.65	4.69

(table continued)

TABLE A.10 *(continued)*

Entry is $q_{0.05}$

v	\multicolumn{19}{c}{r}																		
	2	3	4	5	6	7	8	9	10	11	12	13	14	15	16	17	18	19	20
1	18.0	27.0	32.8	37.1	40.4	43.1	45.4	47.4	49.1	50.6	52.0	53.2	54.3	55.4	56.3	57.2	58.0	58.8	59.6
2	6.08	8.33	9.80	10.9	11.7	12.4	13.0	13.5	14.0	14.4	14.7	15.1	15.4	15.7	15.9	16.1	16.4	16.6	16.8
3	4.50	5.91	6.82	7.50	8.04	8.48	8.85	9.18	9.46	9.72	9.95	10.2	10.3	10.5	10.7	10.8	11.0	11.1	11.2
4	3.93	5.04	5.76	6.29	6.71	7.05	7.35	7.60	7.83	8.03	8.21	8.37	8.52	8.66	8.79	8.91	9.03	9.13	9.23
5	3.64	4.60	5.22	5.67	6.03	6.33	6.58	6.80	6.99	7.17	7.32	7.47	7.60	7.72	7.83	7.93	8.03	8.12	8.21
6	3.46	4.34	4.90	5.30	5.63	5.90	6.12	6.32	6.49	6.65	6.79	6.92	7.03	7.14	7.24	7.34	7.43	7.51	7.59
7	3.34	4.16	4.68	5.06	5.36	5.61	5.82	6.00	6.16	6.30	6.43	6.55	6.66	6.76	6.85	6.94	7.02	7.10	7.17
8	3.26	4.04	4.53	4.89	5.17	5.40	5.60	5.77	5.92	6.05	6.18	6.29	6.39	6.48	6.57	6.65	6.73	6.80	6.87
9	3.20	3.95	4.41	4.76	5.02	5.24	5.43	5.59	5.74	5.87	5.98	6.09	6.19	6.28	6.36	6.44	6.51	6.58	6.64
10	3.15	3.88	4.33	4.65	4.91	5.12	5.30	5.46	5.60	5.72	5.83	5.93	6.03	6.11	6.19	6.27	6.34	6.40	6.47
11	3.11	3.82	4.26	4.57	4.82	5.03	5.20	5.35	5.49	5.61	5.71	5.81	5.90	5.98	6.06	6.13	6.20	6.27	6.33
12	3.08	3.77	4.20	4.51	4.75	4.95	5.12	5.27	5.39	5.51	5.61	5.71	5.80	5.88	5.95	6.02	6.09	6.15	6.21
13	3.06	3.73	4.15	4.45	4.69	4.88	5.05	5.19	5.32	5.43	5.53	5.63	5.71	5.79	5.86	5.93	5.99	6.05	6.11
14	3.03	3.70	4.11	4.41	4.64	4.83	4.99	5.13	5.25	5.36	5.46	5.55	5.64	5.71	5.79	5.85	5.91	5.97	6.03
15	3.01	3.67	4.08	4.37	4.59	4.78	4.94	5.08	5.20	5.31	5.40	5.49	5.57	5.65	5.72	5.78	5.85	5.90	5.96
16	3.00	3.65	4.05	4.33	4.56	4.74	4.90	5.03	5.15	5.26	5.35	5.44	5.52	5.59	5.66	5.73	5.79	5.84	5.90
17	2.98	3.63	4.02	4.30	4.52	4.70	4.86	4.99	5.11	5.21	5.31	5.39	5.47	5.54	5.61	5.67	5.73	5.79	5.84
18	2.97	3.61	4.00	4.28	4.49	4.67	4.82	4.96	5.07	5.17	5.27	5.35	5.43	5.50	5.57	5.63	5.69	5.74	5.79
19	2.96	3.59	3.98	4.25	4.47	4.65	4.79	4.92	5.04	5.14	5.23	5.31	5.39	5.46	5.53	5.59	5.65	5.70	5.75
20	2.95	3.58	3.96	4.23	4.45	4.62	4.77	4.90	5.01	5.11	5.20	5.28	5.36	5.43	5.49	5.55	5.61	5.66	5.71
24	2.92	3.53	3.90	4.17	4.37	4.54	4.68	4.81	4.92	5.01	5.10	5.18	5.25	5.32	5.38	5.44	5.49	5.55	5.59
30	2.89	3.49	3.85	4.10	4.30	4.46	4.60	4.72	4.82	4.92	5.00	5.08	5.15	5.21	5.27	5.33	5.38	5.43	5.47
40	2.86	3.44	3.79	4.04	4.23	4.39	4.52	4.63	4.73	4.82	4.90	4.98	5.04	5.11	5.16	5.22	5.27	5.31	5.36
60	2.83	3.40	3.74	3.98	4.16	4.31	4.44	4.55	4.65	4.73	4.81	4.88	4.94	5.00	5.06	5.11	5.15	5.20	5.24
120	2.80	3.36	3.68	3.92	4.10	4.24	4.36	4.47	4.56	4.64	4.71	4.78	4.84	4.90	4.95	5.00	5.04	5.09	5.13
∞	2.77	3.31	3.63	3.86	4.03	4.17	4.29	4.39	4.47	4.55	4.62	4.68	4.74	4.80	4.85	4.89	4.93	4.97	5.01

(table continued)

TABLE **A.10** (concluded)

Entry is $q_{0.01}$

v	2	3	4	5	6	7	8	9	10	11	12	13	14	15	16	17	18	19	20
1	90.0	135	164	186	202	216	227	237	246	253	260	266	272	277	282	286	290	294	298
2	14.0	19.0	22.3	24.7	26.6	28.2	29.5	30.7	31.7	32.6	33.4	34.1	34.8	35.4	36.0	36.5	37.0	37.5	37.9
3	8.26	10.6	12.2	13.3	14.2	15.0	15.6	16.2	16.7	17.1	17.5	17.9	18.2	18.5	18.8	19.1	19.3	19.5	19.8
4	6.51	8.12	9.17	9.96	10.6	11.1	11.5	11.9	12.3	12.6	12.8	13.1	13.3	13.5	13.7	13.9	14.1	14.2	14.4
5	5.70	6.97	7.80	8.42	8.91	9.32	9.67	9.97	10.2	10.5	10.7	10.9	11.1	11.2	11.4	11.6	11.7	11.8	11.9
6	5.24	6.33	7.03	7.56	7.97	8.32	8.61	8.87	9.10	9.30	9.49	9.65	9.81	9.95	10.1	10.2	10.3	10.4	10.5
7	4.95	5.92	6.54	7.01	7.37	7.68	7.94	8.17	8.37	8.55	8.71	8.86	9.00	9.12	9.24	9.35	9.46	9.55	9.65
8	4.74	5.63	6.20	6.63	6.96	7.24	7.47	7.68	7.87	8.03	8.18	8.31	8.44	8.55	8.66	8.76	8.85	8.94	9.03
9	4.60	5.43	5.96	6.35	6.66	6.91	7.13	7.32	7.49	7.65	7.78	7.91	8.03	8.13	8.23	8.32	8.41	8.49	8.57
10	4.48	5.27	5.77	6.14	6.43	6.67	6.87	7.05	7.21	7.36	7.48	7.60	7.71	7.81	7.91	7.99	8.07	8.15	8.22
11	4.39	5.14	5.62	5.97	6.25	6.48	6.67	6.84	6.99	7.13	7.25	7.36	7.46	7.56	7.65	7.73	7.81	7.88	7.95
12	4.32	5.04	5.50	5.84	6.10	6.32	6.51	6.67	6.81	6.94	7.06	7.17	7.26	7.36	7.44	7.52	7.59	7.66	7.73
13	4.26	4.96	5.40	5.73	5.98	6.19	6.37	6.53	6.67	6.79	6.90	7.01	7.10	7.19	7.27	7.34	7.42	7.48	7.55
14	4.21	4.89	5.32	5.63	5.88	6.08	6.26	6.41	6.54	6.66	6.77	6.87	6.96	7.05	7.12	7.20	7.27	7.33	7.39
15	4.17	4.83	5.25	5.56	5.80	5.99	6.16	6.31	6.44	6.55	6.66	6.76	6.84	6.93	7.00	7.07	7.14	7.20	7.26
16	4.13	4.78	5.19	5.49	5.72	5.92	6.08	6.22	6.35	6.46	6.56	6.66	6.74	6.82	6.90	6.97	7.03	7.09	7.15
17	4.10	4.74	5.14	5.43	5.66	5.85	6.01	6.15	6.27	6.38	6.48	6.57	6.66	6.73	6.80	6.87	6.94	7.00	7.05
18	4.07	4.70	5.09	5.38	5.60	5.79	5.94	6.08	6.20	6.31	6.41	6.50	6.58	6.65	6.72	6.79	6.85	6.91	6.96
19	4.05	4.67	5.05	5.33	5.55	5.73	5.89	6.02	6.14	6.25	6.34	6.43	6.51	6.58	6.65	6.72	6.78	6.84	6.89
20	4.02	4.64	5.02	5.29	5.51	5.69	5.84	5.97	6.09	6.19	6.29	6.37	6.45	6.52	6.59	6.65	6.71	6.76	6.82
24	3.96	4.54	4.91	5.17	5.37	5.54	5.69	5.81	5.92	6.02	6.11	6.19	6.26	6.33	6.39	6.45	6.51	6.56	6.61
30	3.89	4.45	4.80	5.05	5.24	5.40	5.54	5.65	5.76	5.85	5.93	6.01	6.08	6.14	6.20	6.26	6.31	6.36	6.41
40	3.82	4.37	4.70	4.93	5.11	5.27	5.39	5.50	5.60	5.69	5.77	5.84	5.90	5.96	6.02	6.07	6.12	6.17	6.21
60	3.76	4.28	4.60	4.82	4.99	5.13	5.25	5.36	5.45	5.53	5.60	5.67	5.73	5.79	5.84	5.89	5.93	5.98	6.02
120	3.70	4.20	4.50	4.71	4.87	5.01	5.12	5.21	5.30	5.38	5.44	5.51	5.56	5.61	5.66	5.71	5.75	5.79	5.83
∞	3.64	4.12	4.40	4.60	4.76	4.88	4.99	5.08	5.16	5.23	5.29	5.35	5.40	5.45	5.49	5.54	5.57	5.61	5.65

r

Source: *The Analysis of Variance*, pp. 414–16, by Henry Scheffe, © 1959 by John Wiley & Sons, Inc. Reprinted by permission of John Wiley & Sons, Inc.

TABLE **A.11** A Table of Critical Values of r ($df = N - 2$ and N Is the Number of Pairs of Scores)

Degrees of Freedom (df)	5%	1%	Degrees of Freedom (df)	5%	1%
1	0.997	1.000	24	0.388	0.496
2	0.950	0.990	25	0.381	0.487
3	0.878	0.959	26	0.374	0.478
4	0.811	0.917	27	0.367	0.470
5	0.754	0.874	28	0.361	0.463
6	0.707	0.834	29	0.355	0.456
7	0.666	0.798	30	0.349	0.449
8	0.632	0.765	35	0.325	0.418
9	0.602	0.735	40	0.304	0.393
10	0.576	0.708	45	0.288	0.372
11	0.553	0.684	50	0.273	0.354
12	0.532	0.661	60	0.250	0.325
13	0.514	0.641	70	0.232	0.302
14	0.497	0.623	80	0.217	0.283
15	0.482	0.606	90	0.205	0.267
16	0.468	0.590	100	0.195	0.254
17	0.456	0.575	125	0.174	0.228
18	0.444	0.561	150	0.159	0.208
19	0.433	0.549	200	0.138	0.181
20	0.423	0.537	300	0.113	0.148
21	0.413	0.526	400	0.098	0.128
22	0.404	0.515	500	0.088	0.115
23	0.396	0.505	1000	0.062	0.081

Source: This table is adapted from Table VII of Fisher and Yates, *Statistical Tables for Biological, Agricultural and Medical Research*, published by Longman Group Ltd, London (previously published by Oliver and Boyd, Edinburgh), and by permission of Pearson Education Limited.

TABLE **A.12**   A Table of Critical Values for the Durbin–Watson d Statistic ($\alpha = 0.05$)

	k = 1		k = 2		k = 3		k = 4		k = 5	
n	$d_{L,0.05}$	$d_{U,0.05}$	$d_{L,0.05}$	$d_{U,0.05}$	$d_{L,0.05}$	$d_{U,0.05}$	$d_{L,0.05}$	$d_{U,0.05}$	$d_{L,0.05}$	$d_{U,0.05}$
15	1.08	1.36	0.95	1.54	0.82	1.75	0.69	1.97	0.56	2.21
16	1.10	1.37	0.98	1.54	0.86	1.73	0.74	1.93	0.62	2.15
17	1.13	1.38	1.02	1.54	0.90	1.71	0.78	1.90	0.67	2.10
18	1.16	1.39	1.05	1.53	0.93	1.69	0.82	1.87	0.71	2.06
19	1.18	1.40	1.08	1.53	0.97	1.68	0.86	1.85	0.75	2.02
20	1.20	1.41	1.10	1.54	1.00	1.68	0.90	1.83	0.79	1.99
21	1.22	1.42	1.13	1.54	1.03	1.67	0.93	1.81	0.83	1.96
22	1.24	1.43	1.15	1.54	1.05	1.66	0.96	1.80	0.86	1.94
23	1.26	1.44	1.17	1.54	1.08	1.66	0.99	1.79	0.90	1.92
24	1.27	1.45	1.19	1.55	1.10	1.66	1.01	1.78	0.93	1.90
25	1.29	1.45	1.21	1.55	1.12	1.66	1.04	1.77	0.95	1.89
26	1.30	1.46	1.22	1.55	1.14	1.65	1.06	1.76	0.98	1.88
27	1.32	1.47	1.24	1.56	1.16	1.65	1.08	1.76	1.01	1.86
28	1.33	1.48	1.26	1.56	1.18	1.65	1.10	1.75	1.03	1.85
29	1.34	1.48	1.27	1.56	1.20	1.65	1.12	1.74	1.05	1.84
30	1.35	1.49	1.28	1.57	1.21	1.65	1.14	1.74	1.07	1.83
31	1.36	1.50	1.30	1.57	1.23	1.65	1.16	1.74	1.09	1.83
32	1.37	1.50	1.31	1.57	1.24	1.65	1.18	1.73	1.11	1.82
33	1.38	1.51	1.32	1.58	1.26	1.65	1.19	1.73	1.13	1.81
34	1.39	1.51	1.33	1.58	1.27	1.65	1.21	1.73	1.15	1.81
35	1.40	1.52	1.34	1.58	1.28	1.65	1.22	1.73	1.16	1.80
36	1.41	1.52	1.35	1.59	1.29	1.65	1.24	1.73	1.18	1.80
37	1.42	1.53	1.36	1.59	1.31	1.66	1.25	1.72	1.19	1.80
38	1.43	1.54	1.37	1.59	1.32	1.66	1.26	1.72	1.21	1.79
39	1.43	1.54	1.38	1.60	1.33	1.66	1.27	1.72	1.22	1.79
40	1.44	1.54	1.39	1.60	1.34	1.66	1.29	1.72	1.23	1.79
45	1.48	1.57	1.43	1.62	1.38	1.67	1.34	1.72	1.29	1.78
50	1.50	1.59	1.46	1.63	1.42	1.67	1.38	1.72	1.34	1.77
55	1.53	1.60	1.49	1.64	1.45	1.68	1.41	1.72	1.38	1.77
60	1.55	1.62	1.51	1.65	1.48	1.69	1.44	1.73	1.41	1.77
65	1.57	1.63	1.54	1.66	1.50	1.70	1.47	1.73	1.44	1.77
70	1.58	1.64	1.55	1.67	1.52	1.70	1.49	1.74	1.46	1.77
75	1.60	1.65	1.57	1.68	1.54	1.71	1.51	1.74	1.49	1.77
80	1.61	1.66	1.59	1.69	1.56	1.72	1.53	1.74	1.51	1.77
85	1.62	1.67	1.60	1.70	1.57	1.72	1.55	1.75	1.52	1.77
90	1.63	1.68	1.61	1.70	1.59	1.73	1.57	1.75	1.54	1.78
95	1.64	1.69	1.62	1.71	1.60	1.73	1.58	1.75	1.56	1.78
100	1.65	1.69	1.63	1.72	1.61	1.74	1.59	1.76	1.57	1.78

TABLE **A.13**   A Table of Critical Values for the Durbin–Watson d Statistic ($\alpha = 0.025$)

	k = 1		k = 2		k = 3		k = 4		k = 5	
n	$d_{L,0.025}$	$d_{U,0.025}$	$d_{L,0.025}$	$d_{U,0.025}$	$d_{L,0.025}$	$d_{U,0.025}$	$d_{L,0.025}$	$d_{U,0.025}$	$d_{L,0.025}$	$d_{U,0.025}$
15	0.95	1.23	0.83	1.40	0.71	1.61	0.59	1.84	0.48	2.09
16	0.98	1.24	0.86	1.40	0.75	1.59	0.64	1.80	0.53	2.03
17	1.01	1.25	0.90	1.40	0.79	1.58	0.68	1.77	0.57	1.98
18	1.03	1.26	0.93	1.40	0.82	1.56	0.72	1.74	0.62	1.93
19	1.06	1.28	0.96	1.41	0.86	1.55	0.76	1.72	0.66	1.90
20	1.08	1.28	0.99	1.41	0.89	1.55	0.79	1.70	0.70	1.87
21	1.10	1.30	1.01	1.41	0.92	1.54	0.83	1.69	0.73	1.84
22	1.12	1.31	1.04	1.42	0.95	1.54	0.86	1.68	0.77	1.82
23	1.14	1.32	1.06	1.42	0.97	1.54	0.89	1.67	0.80	1.80
24	1.16	1.33	1.08	1.43	1.00	1.54	0.91	1.66	0.83	1.79
25	1.18	1.34	1.10	1.43	1.02	1.54	0.94	1.65	0.86	1.77
26	1.19	1.35	1.12	1.44	1.04	1.54	0.96	1.65	0.88	1.76
27	1.21	1.36	1.13	1.44	1.06	1.54	0.99	1.64	0.91	1.75
28	1.22	1.37	1.15	1.45	1.08	1.54	1.01	1.64	0.93	1.74
29	1.24	1.38	1.17	1.45	1.10	1.54	1.03	1.63	0.96	1.73
30	1.25	1.38	1.18	1.46	1.12	1.54	1.05	1.63	0.98	1.73
31	1.26	1.39	1.20	1.47	1.13	1.55	1.07	1.63	1.00	1.72
32	1.27	1.40	1.21	1.47	1.15	1.55	1.08	1.63	1.02	1.71
33	1.28	1.41	1.22	1.48	1.16	1.55	1.10	1.63	1.04	1.71
34	1.29	1.41	1.24	1.48	1.17	1.55	1.12	1.63	1.06	1.70
35	1.30	1.42	1.25	1.48	1.19	1.55	1.13	1.63	1.07	1.70
36	1.31	1.43	1.26	1.49	1.20	1.56	1.15	1.63	1.09	1.70
37	1.32	1.43	1.27	1.49	1.21	1.56	1.16	1.62	1.10	1.70
38	1.33	1.44	1.28	1.50	1.23	1.56	1.17	1.62	1.12	1.70
39	1.34	1.44	1.29	1.50	1.24	1.56	1.19	1.63	1.13	1.69
40	1.35	1.45	1.30	1.51	1.25	1.57	1.20	1.63	1.15	1.69
45	1.39	1.48	1.34	1.53	1.30	1.58	1.25	1.63	1.21	1.69
50	1.42	1.50	1.38	1.54	1.34	1.59	1.30	1.64	1.26	1.69
55	1.45	1.52	1.41	1.56	1.37	1.60	1.33	1.64	1.30	1.69
60	1.47	1.54	1.44	1.57	1.40	1.61	1.37	1.65	1.33	1.69
65	1.49	1.55	1.46	1.59	1.43	1.62	1.40	1.66	1.36	1.69
70	1.51	1.57	1.48	1.60	1.45	1.63	1.42	1.66	1.39	1.70
75	1.53	1.58	1.50	1.61	1.47	1.64	1.45	1.67	1.42	1.70
80	1.54	1.59	1.52	1.62	1.49	1.65	1.47	1.67	1.44	1.70
85	1.56	1.60	1.53	1.63	1.51	1.65	1.49	1.68	1.46	1.71
90	1.57	1.61	1.55	1.64	1.53	1.66	1.50	1.69	1.48	1.71
95	1.58	1.62	1.56	1.65	1.54	1.67	1.52	1.69	1.50	1.71
100	1.59	1.63	1.57	1.65	1.55	1.67	1.53	1.70	1.51	1.72

TABLE **A.14**   A Table of Critical Values for the Durbin–Watson d Statistic ($\alpha = 0.01$)

n	$k = 1$		$k = 2$		$k = 3$		$k = 4$		$k = 5$	
	$d_{L,0.01}$	$d_{U,0.01}$	$d_{L,0.01}$	$d_{U,0.01}$	$d_{L,0.01}$	$d_{U,0.01}$	$d_{L,0.01}$	$d_{U,0.01}$	$d_{L,0.01}$	$d_{U,0.01}$
15	0.81	1.07	0.70	1.25	0.59	1.46	0.49	1.70	0.39	1.96
16	0.84	1.09	0.74	1.25	0.63	1.44	0.53	1.66	0.44	1.90
17	0.87	1.10	0.77	1.25	0.67	1.43	0.57	1.63	0.48	1.85
18	0.90	1.12	0.80	1.26	0.71	1.42	0.61	1.60	0.52	1.80
19	0.93	1.13	0.83	1.26	0.74	1.41	0.65	1.58	0.56	1.77
20	0.95	1.15	0.86	1.27	0.77	1.41	0.68	1.57	0.60	1.74
21	0.97	1.16	0.89	1.27	0.80	1.41	0.72	1.55	0.63	1.71
22	1.00	1.17	0.91	1.28	0.83	1.40	0.75	1.54	0.66	1.69
23	1.02	1.19	0.94	1.29	0.86	1.40	0.77	1.53	0.70	1.67
24	1.04	1.20	0.96	1.30	0.88	1.41	0.80	1.53	0.72	1.66
25	1.05	1.21	0.98	1.30	0.90	1.41	0.83	1.52	0.75	1.65
26	1.07	1.22	1.00	1.31	0.93	1.41	0.85	1.52	0.78	1.64
27	1.09	1.23	1.02	1.32	0.95	1.41	0.88	1.51	0.81	1.63
28	1.10	1.24	1.04	1.32	0.97	1.41	0.90	1.51	0.83	1.62
29	1.12	1.25	1.05	1.33	0.99	1.42	0.92	1.51	0.85	1.61
30	1.13	1.26	1.07	1.34	1.01	1.42	0.94	1.51	0.88	1.61
31	1.15	1.27	1.08	1.34	1.02	1.42	0.96	1.51	0.90	1.60
32	1.16	1.28	1.10	1.35	1.04	1.43	0.98	1.51	0.92	1.60
33	1.17	1.29	1.11	1.36	1.05	1.43	1.00	1.51	0.94	1.59
34	1.18	1.30	1.13	1.36	1.07	1.43	1.01	1.51	0.95	1.59
35	1.19	1.31	1.14	1.37	1.08	1.44	1.03	1.51	0.97	1.59
36	1.21	1.32	1.15	1.38	1.10	1.44	1.04	1.51	0.99	1.59
37	1.22	1.32	1.16	1.38	1.11	1.45	1.06	1.51	1.00	1.59
38	1.23	1.33	1.18	1.39	1.12	1.45	1.07	1.52	1.02	1.58
39	1.24	1.34	1.19	1.39	1.14	1.45	1.09	1.52	1.03	1.58
40	1.25	1.34	1.20	1.40	1.15	1.46	1.10	1.52	1.05	1.58
45	1.29	1.38	1.24	1.42	1.20	1.48	1.16	1.53	1.11	1.58
50	1.32	1.40	1.28	1.45	1.24	1.49	1.20	1.54	1.16	1.59
55	1.36	1.43	1.32	1.47	1.28	1.51	1.25	1.55	1.21	1.59
60	1.38	1.45	1.35	1.48	1.32	1.52	1.28	1.56	1.25	1.60
65	1.41	1.47	1.38	1.50	1.35	1.53	1.31	1.57	1.28	1.61
70	1.43	1.49	1.40	1.52	1.37	1.55	1.34	1.58	1.31	1.61
75	1.45	1.50	1.42	1.53	1.39	1.56	1.37	1.59	1.34	1.62
80	1.47	1.52	1.44	1.54	1.42	1.57	1.39	1.60	1.36	1.62
85	1.48	1.53	1.46	1.55	1.43	1.58	1.41	1.60	1.39	1.63
90	1.50	1.54	1.47	1.56	1.45	1.59	1.43	1.61	1.41	1.64
95	1.51	1.55	1.49	1.57	1.47	1.60	1.45	1.62	1.42	1.64
100	1.52	1.56	1.50	1.58	1.48	1.60	1.46	1.63	1.44	1.65

Source: J. Durbin and G. S. Watson, "Testing for Serial Correlation in Least Squares Regression, II," *Biometrika* 30 (1951), pp. 159–78. Reproduced by permission of the Biometrika Trustees.

TABLE **A.15** A Wilcoxon Rank Sum Table: Values of T_L and T_U

(a) $\alpha = 0.025$ one-sided; $\alpha = 0.05$ two-sided

n_2 \ n_1	3		4		5		6		7		8		9		10	
	T_L	T_U	T_L	T_U	T_L	T_U	T_L	T_U	T_L	T_U	T_L	T_U	T_L	T_U	T_L	T_U
3	5	16	6	18	6	21	7	23	7	26	8	28	8	31	9	33
4	6	18	11	25	12	28	12	32	13	35	14	38	15	41	16	44
5	6	21	12	28	18	37	19	41	20	45	21	49	22	53	24	56
6	7	23	12	32	19	41	26	52	28	56	29	61	31	65	32	70
7	7	26	13	35	20	45	28	56	37	68	39	73	41	78	43	83
8	8	28	14	38	21	49	29	61	39	73	49	87	51	93	54	98
9	8	31	15	41	22	53	31	65	41	78	51	93	63	108	66	114
10	9	33	16	44	24	56	32	70	43	83	54	98	66	114	79	131

(b) $\alpha = 0.05$ one-sided; $\alpha = 0.10$ two-sided

n_2 \ n_1	3		4		5		6		7		8		9		10	
	T_L	T_U	T_L	T_U	T_L	T_U	T_L	T_U	T_L	T_U	T_L	T_U	T_L	T_U	T_L	T_U
3	6	15	7	17	7	20	8	22	9	24	9	27	10	29	11	31
4	7	17	12	24	13	27	14	30	15	33	16	36	17	39	18	42
5	7	20	13	27	19	36	20	40	22	43	24	46	25	50	26	54
6	8	22	14	30	20	40	28	50	30	54	32	58	33	63	35	67
7	9	24	15	33	22	43	30	54	39	66	41	71	43	76	46	80
8	9	27	16	36	24	46	32	58	41	71	52	84	54	90	57	95
9	10	29	17	39	25	50	33	63	43	76	54	90	66	105	69	111
10	11	31	18	42	26	54	35	67	46	80	57	95	69	111	83	127

Source: F. Wilcoxon and R. A. Wilcox, "Some Rapid Approximate Statistical Procedures" (New York: American Cyanamid Company, 1964), pp. 20–23. Reproduced with the permission of American Cyanamid Company.

TABLE A.16   A Wilcoxon Signed Ranks Table: Values of T_0

One-Sided	Two-Sided	$n = 5$	$n = 6$	$n = 7$	$n = 8$	$n = 9$	$n = 10$
$\alpha = 0.05$	$\alpha = 0.10$	1	2	4	6	8	11
$\alpha = 0.025$	$\alpha = 0.05$		1	2	4	6	8
$\alpha = 0.01$	$\alpha = 0.02$			0	2	3	5
$\alpha = 0.005$	$\alpha = 0.01$				0	2	3
		$n = 11$	$n = 12$	$n = 13$	$n = 14$	$n = 15$	$n = 16$
$\alpha = 0.05$	$\alpha = 0.10$	14	17	21	26	30	36
$\alpha = 0.025$	$\alpha = 0.05$	11	14	17	21	25	30
$\alpha = 0.01$	$\alpha = 0.02$	7	10	13	16	20	24
$\alpha = 0.005$	$\alpha = 0.01$	5	7	10	13	16	19
		$n = 17$	$n = 18$	$n = 19$	$n = 20$	$n = 21$	$n = 22$
$\alpha = 0.05$	$\alpha = 0.10$	41	47	54	60	68	75
$\alpha = 0.025$	$\alpha = 0.05$	35	40	46	52	59	66
$\alpha = 0.01$	$\alpha = 0.02$	28	33	38	43	49	56
$\alpha = 0.005$	$\alpha = 0.01$	23	28	32	37	43	49
		$n = 23$	$n = 24$	$n = 25$	$n = 26$	$n = 27$	$n = 28$
$\alpha = 0.05$	$\alpha = 0.10$	83	92	101	110	120	130
$\alpha = 0.025$	$\alpha = 0.05$	73	81	90	98	107	117
$\alpha = 0.01$	$\alpha = 0.02$	62	69	77	85	93	102
$\alpha = 0.005$	$\alpha = 0.01$	55	61	68	76	84	92
		$n = 29$	$n = 30$	$n = 31$	$n = 32$	$n = 33$	$n = 34$
$\alpha = 0.05$	$\alpha = 0.10$	141	152	163	175	188	201
$\alpha = 0.025$	$\alpha = 0.05$	127	137	148	159	171	183
$\alpha = 0.01$	$\alpha = 0.02$	111	120	130	141	151	162
$\alpha = 0.005$	$\alpha = 0.01$	100	109	118	128	138	149
		$n = 35$	$n = 36$	$n = 37$	$n = 38$	$n = 39$	
$\alpha = 0.05$	$\alpha = 0.10$	214	228	242	256	271	
$\alpha = 0.025$	$\alpha = 0.05$	195	208	222	235	250	
$\alpha = 0.01$	$\alpha = 0.02$	174	186	198	211	224	
$\alpha = 0.005$	$\alpha = 0.01$	160	171	183	195	208	
		$n = 40$	$n = 41$	$n = 42$	$n = 43$	$n = 44$	$n = 45$
$\alpha = 0.05$	$\alpha = 0.10$	287	303	319	336	353	371
$\alpha = 0.025$	$\alpha = 0.05$	264	279	295	311	327	344
$\alpha = 0.01$	$\alpha = 0.02$	238	252	267	281	297	313
$\alpha = 0.005$	$\alpha = 0.01$	221	234	248	262	277	292
		$n = 46$	$n = 47$	$n = 48$	$n = 49$	$n = 50$	
$\alpha = 0.05$	$\alpha = 0.10$	389	408	427	446	466	
$\alpha = 0.025$	$\alpha = 0.05$	361	379	397	415	434	
$\alpha = 0.01$	$\alpha = 0.02$	329	345	362	380	398	
$\alpha = 0.005$	$\alpha = 0.01$	307	323	339	356	373	

Source: F. Wilcoxon and R. A. Wilcox, "Some Rapid Approximate Statistical Procedures" (New York: American Cyanamid Company, 1964), p. 28. Reproduced with the permission of American Cyanamid Company.

TABLE **A.17**   A Table of Critical Values for Spearman's Rank Correlation Coefficient

n	$\alpha = 0.05$	$\alpha = 0.025$	$\alpha = 0.01$	$\alpha = 0.005$	n	$\alpha = 0.05$	$\alpha = 0.025$	$\alpha = 0.01$	$\alpha = 0.005$
5	0.900	—	—	—	18	0.399	0.476	0.564	0.625
6	0.829	0.886	0.943	—	19	0.388	0.462	0.549	0.608
7	0.714	0.786	0.893	—	20	0.377	0.450	0.534	0.591
8	0.643	0.738	0.833	0.881	21	0.368	0.438	0.521	0.576
9	0.600	0.683	0.783	0.833	22	0.359	0.428	0.508	0.562
10	0.564	0.648	0.745	0.794	23	0.351	0.418	0.496	0.549
11	0.523	0.623	0.736	0.818	24	0.343	0.409	0.485	0.537
12	0.497	0.591	0.703	0.780	25	0.336	0.400	0.475	0.526
13	0.475	0.566	0.673	0.745	26	0.329	0.392	0.465	0.515
14	0.457	0.545	0.646	0.716	27	0.323	0.385	0.456	0.505
15	0.441	0.525	0.623	0.689	28	0.317	0.377	0.448	0.496
16	0.425	0.507	0.601	0.666	29	0.311	0.370	0.440	0.487
17	0.412	0.490	0.582	0.645	30	0.305	0.364	0.432	0.478

Source: E. G. Olds, "Distribution of Sums of Squares of Rank Differences for Small Samples," *Annals of Mathematical Statistics,* 1938, 9. Reproduced with the permission of the editor, *Annals of Mathematical Statistics.*

TABLE **A.18**   A Chi-Square Table: Values of χ_α^2

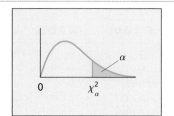

df	$\chi_{0.995}^2$	$\chi_{0.99}^2$	$\chi_{0.975}^2$	$\chi_{0.95}^2$	$\chi_{0.90}^2$
1	0.0000393	0.0001571	0.0009821	0.0039321	0.0157908
2	0.0100251	0.0201007	0.0506356	0.102587	0.210720
3	0.0717212	0.114832	0.215795	0.341846	0.584375
4	0.206990	0.297110	0.484419	0.710721	0.063623
5	0.411740	0.554300	0.831211	1.145476	1.61031
6	0.675727	0.872085	1.237347	1.63539	2.20413
7	0.989265	1.239043	1.68987	2.16735	2.83311
8	1.344419	1.646482	2.17973	2.73264	3.48954
9	1.734926	2.087912	2.70039	3.32511	4.16816
10	2.15585	2.55821	3.24697	3.94030	4.86518
11	2.60321	3.05347	3.81575	4.57481	5.57779
12	3.07382	3.57056	4.40379	5.22603	6.30380
13	3.56503	4.10691	5.00874	5.89186	7.04150
14	4.07468	4.66043	5.62872	6.57063	7.78953
15	4.60094	5.22935	6.26214	7.26094	8.54675
16	5.14224	5.81221	6.90766	7.96164	9.31223
17	5.69724	6.40776	7.56418	8.67176	10.0852
18	6.26481	7.01491	8.23075	9.39046	10.8649
19	6.84398	7.63273	8.90655	10.1170	11.6509
20	7.43386	8.26040	9.59083	10.8508	12.4426
21	8.03366	8.89720	10.28293	11.5913	13.2396
22	8.64272	9.54249	10.9823	12.3380	14.0415
23	9.26042	10.19567	11.6885	13.0905	14.8479
24	9.88623	10.8564	12.4011	13.8484	15.6587
25	10.5197	11.5240	13.1197	14.6114	16.4734
26	11.1603	12.1981	13.8439	15.3791	17.2919
27	11.8076	12.8786	14.5733	16.1513	18.1138
28	12.4613	13.5648	15.3079	16.9279	18.9392
29	13.1211	14.2565	16.0471	17.7083	19.7677
30	13.7867	14.9535	16.7908	18.4926	20.5992
40	20.7065	22.1643	24.4331	26.5093	29.0505
50	27.9907	29.7067	32.3574	34.7642	37.6886
60	35.5346	37.4848	40.4817	43.1879	46.4589
70	43.2752	45.4418	48.7576	51.7393	55.3290
80	51.1720	53.5400	57.1532	60.3915	64.2778
90	59.1963	61.7541	65.6466	69.1260	73.2912
100	67.3276	70.0648	74.2219	77.9295	82.3581

(table continued)

TABLE **A.18** *(concluded)* A Chi-Square Table: Values of χ_{α}^2

df	$\chi_{0.10}^2$	$\chi_{0.05}^2$	$\chi_{0.025}^2$	$\chi_{0.01}^2$	$\chi_{0.005}^2$
1	2.70554	3.84146	5.02389	6.63490	7.87944
2	4.60517	5.99147	7.37776	9.21034	10.5966
3	6.25139	7.81473	9.34840	11.3449	12.8381
4	7.77944	9.48773	11.1433	13.2767	14.8602
5	9.23635	11.0705	12.8325	15.0863	16.7496
6	10.6446	12.5916	14.4494	16.8119	18.5476
7	12.0170	14.0671	16.0128	18.4753	20.2777
8	13.3616	15.5073	17.5346	20.0902	21.9550
9	14.6837	16.9190	19.0228	21.6660	23.5893
10	15.9871	18.3070	20.4831	23.2093	25.1882
11	17.2750	19.6751	21.9200	24.7250	26.7569
12	18.5494	21.0261	23.3367	26.2170	28.2995
13	19.8119	22.3621	24.7356	27.6883	29.8194
14	21.0642	23.6848	26.1190	29.1413	31.3193
15	22.3072	24.9958	27.4884	30.5779	32.8013
16	23.5418	26.2962	28.8454	31.9999	34.2672
17	24.7690	27.5871	30.1910	33.4087	35.7185
18	25.9894	28.8693	31.5264	34.8053	37.1564
19	27.2036	30.1435	32.8523	36.1908	38.5822
20	28.4120	31.4104	34.1696	37.5662	39.9968
21	29.6151	32.6705	35.4789	38.9321	41.4010
22	30.8133	33.9244	36.7807	40.2894	42.7956
23	32.0069	35.1725	38.0757	41.6384	44.1813
24	33.1963	36.4151	39.3641	42.9798	45.5585
25	34.3816	37.6525	40.6465	44.3141	46.9278
26	35.5631	38.8852	41.9232	45.6417	48.2899
27	36.7412	40.1133	43.1944	46.9630	49.6449
28	37.9159	41.3372	44.4607	48.2782	50.9933
29	39.0875	42.5569	45.7222	49.5879	52.3356
30	40.2560	43.7729	46.9792	50.8922	53.6720
40	51.8050	55.7585	59.3417	63.6907	66.7659
50	63.1671	67.5048	71.4202	76.1539	79.4900
60	74.3970	79.0819	83.2976	88.3794	91.9517
70	85.5271	90.5312	95.0231	100.425	104.215
80	96.5782	101.879	106.629	112.329	116.321
90	107.565	113.145	118.136	124.116	128.299
100	118.498	124.342	129.561	135.807	140.169

Source: C. M. Thompson, "Tables of the Percentage Points of the χ^2 Distribution," *Biometrika* 32 (1941), pp. 188–89. Reproduced by permission of the Biometrika Trustees.

ANSWERS TO MOST ODD-NUMBERED EXERCISES

Chapter 1

1.1 A set of units

1.3
a. Quantitative
b. Quantitative
c. Qualitative
d. Quantitative
e. Qualitative

1.9 Most between .4 and 11.6 minutes
Less than 6 minutes = .6

1.11 A sequence of operations that turns inputs into outputs

1.13 Graph of individual process measurements versus time
Statistical control will have constant variation around a horizontal level.

1.15 a. The process does not seem to be in control.

1.17
a. Yes, the process is in control.
b. Most breaking strengths will be between 21.3 kg and 24.5 kg.

1.21 Ordinal, nominative, ordinal, nominative, ordinal, and nominative

1.23 Define construct, generate item pool, pilot test items

1.25
a. Rich source of information but costly in terms of time
b. Test large numbers of people but lower response rate
c. Test large numbers of people but negative reactions from people, require shorter questionnaires, etc.

1.31 1853/100 and round down to 18. Select a random number between 1 and 18. This is the first unit sampled. Take every 18th unit by successively counting down 18 from the 1st chosen unit.

1.35 Nominal, ordinal, ordinal, ordinal, nominal, nominal

1.37 Not in statistical control

Chapter 2

2.1
b. Two distinct high points
c. Long tail to the left
d. Long tail to the right

2.5
a. $2^6 = 64$ and $2^7 = 128$. Because $2^6 < n = 100$ and $2^7 > n = 100$, use $K = 7$ classes   Class length = 1.6
b. Somewhat positively skewed (tail to the right)

2.7 The 61 home runs hit by Maris would be considered an outlier, although an exceptional individual achievement.

2.9 About 9 free throws will be missed. This is the stem with the most data.

2.11
a. Equal or roughly equal
b. Mean < Median < Mode
c. Mean > Median > Mode
d. Equal

2.13
a. N = 10, Mean = 20, Median = 20, Mode = 20
b. N = 7, Mean = 503, Median = 501, Mode = 501

2.15
a. Yes, because $\bar{x} < 6$.
b. Median = 5.25. The mean is slightly larger than the median; distribution is somewhat skewed right.

2.17
a. Mean = 272.333; Median = 68 (Canada's value)
b. U.S. numbers skew the distribution.
c. Histogram is probably best plot for the data

2.19
a. Mean = 2,201.0000; Median = 1,478 (Mexico's value)
b. Mean > Median (because of U.S. values)
c. Histogram probably best for plotting

2.21
b. Only two values, so the mean is the median
c. Histogram probably best for plotting

2.25 The variance and standard deviation are calculated by using all of the data, while the range is calculated using only the largest and smallest values.

2.27 Capable process: A process that is able to consistently produce output that meets specification
Specification limits: A particular quality characteristic is supposed to be inside an acceptable range of values.

2.29 Range = 78,375, Variance = 705,139,612.50, Standard deviation = 26,554.47

2.31
a. $\bar{x} = \dfrac{157 + 132 + 109 + 145 + 125 + 139}{6} = 134.5$

$s^2 = \dfrac{(157 - 134.5)^2 + (132 - 134.5)^2 + \cdots + (139 - 134.5)^2}{6 - 1} = 276.7$

$s = \sqrt{276.7} = 16.63$

Also $\Sigma x_i^2 = 157^2 + 132^2 + 109^2 + 145^2 + 125^2 + 139^2 = 109,925$

$(\Sigma x_i)^2 = (157 + 132 + 109 + 145 + 125 + 139)^2 = (807)^2 = 651,249$

$s^2 = \dfrac{1}{n-1}\left[\Sigma x_i^2 - \dfrac{1}{n}(\Sigma x_i)^2\right] = \dfrac{1}{6-1}\left[109,925 - \dfrac{1}{6}(651,249)\right] = 276.7$

b. $[\bar{x} \pm s] = [134.5 \pm 16.63] = [117.87, 151.13]$
$[\bar{x} \pm 2s] = [134.5 \pm 2(16.63)] = [101.24, 167.76]$
$[\bar{x} \pm 3s] = [134.5 \pm 3(16.63)] = [84.61, 184.39]$
c. Yes, because $190 is not within the 99.73% interval.
d. $z_{157} = \dfrac{157 - 134.5}{16.63} = 1.353$

$z_{132} = -.150$
$z_{109} = -1.533$
$z_{145} = .631$
$z_{125} = -.571$
$z_{139} = .271$

2.33
a. It is somewhat reasonable.
b. $[\bar{x} \pm s] = [5.46 \pm 2.475] = [2.985, 7.935]$
$[\bar{x} \pm 2s] = [5.46 \pm 2(2.475)] = [.51, 10.41]$
$[\bar{x} \pm 3s] = [5.46 \pm 3(2.475)] = [-1.965, 12.885]$

c. Yes, because the upper limit of the 68.26% interval is less than 8 minutes.
d. 66% fall into $[\bar{x} \pm s]$, 96% fall into $[\bar{x} \pm 2s]$, 100% fall into $[\bar{x} \pm 3s]$. Yes, they are reasonably valid.

2.35
b. $[\bar{x} \pm s] = [36.56 \pm 4.475] = [32.085, 41.035]: 73\%$
$[\bar{x} \pm 2s] = [36.56 \pm 2(4.475)] = [27.61, 45.51]: 95.24\%$
$[\bar{x} \pm 3s] = [36.56 \pm 3(4.475)] = [23.135, 49.985]: 96.83\%$
c. They are inconsistent with the empirical rule, but consistent with Chebyshev's theorem.
d. The transaction times are positively skewed (to the right).

2.37
a. An estimated 99.73% tolerance interval is $[\bar{x} \pm 3s] = [3.0028 \pm 3(.01437)] = [2.96, 3.046]$
The process is not capable of meeting specifications of $3.00 \pm .03$.
b. Yes.
c. An estimated 99.73% tolerance interval is $[\bar{x} \pm 3s] = [3 \pm 3(.00786)] = [2.976, 3.024]$
The estimated 99.73% tolerance interval is now inside the specifications.

2.39
a. The distribution is skewed to the right.
b. The middle 50% is more spread out than the upper and lower 25%. A look at the shape of the distribution may show a double peak.
c. This may indicate a skewness to the right.
d. The middle 50% has very little variation.

2.41
a. Mean = 1.740, Median = 1.750, Mode = 1.900, Standard deviation = .246, Variance = .060, Range = .8
c. Mean = 7.690, Median = 8.000, Mode = 8.000, Standard deviation = 1.282, Variance = 1.643, Range = 3.8

2.51 Data are scattered around a straight line with negative slope.

2.53 a. Yes; the relationship appears to be linear (y increases as x increases).
b. Low sales
c. Not necessarily

2.55 The differences in the heights of the bars are more pronounced.

2.57 The administration's plot indicates a steep increase over the four years, while the union organizer's plot shows a gradual increase.

2.59 Classes are weighted by credit hours.

2.61 The actual measurements are unknown.

2.63 $$\mu = \frac{255.9(15.3) + 78.9(11.8) + 499.6(9.5) + 400.1(8.1) + 4{,}196.7(8.8)}{255.9 + 78.9 + 499.6 + 400.1 + 4{,}196.7}$$
$$= 9.1627$$

2.65 $$\mu = \frac{1(24.5) + 17(74.5) + 5(124.5) + 4(174.5) + 1(224.5) + 2(274.5)}{30} = \frac{3{,}385}{30} = 112.83\%$$

$$\sigma^2 = \frac{1(24.5 - 112.83)^2 + 17(74.5 - 112.83)^2 + 5(124.5 - 112.83)^2 + 4(174.5 - 112.83)^2 + 1(224.5 - 112.83)^2 + 2(274.5 - 112.83)^2}{20}$$

$$= \frac{113{,}416.667}{30} = 3{,}780.56$$

$$\sigma = \sqrt{3{,}780.56} = 61.49\%$$

2.67 c. Yes; perhaps those greater than 24 hours

2.69 a., b., c.

Money Market: $[\mu \pm \sigma] = [2.75 \pm .08] = [2.67 \text{ to } 2.83]$
$[\mu \pm 2\sigma] = [2.75 \pm 2(.08)] = [2.59 \text{ to } 2.91]$
$[\mu \pm 3\sigma] = [2.75 \pm 3(.08)] = [2.51 \text{ to } 2.99]$

Fixed Income: $[\mu \pm \sigma] = [.8 \pm 1] = [-.2 \text{ to } 1.8]$
$[\mu \pm 2\sigma] = [.8 \pm 2(1)] = [-1.2 \text{ to } 2.8]$
$[\mu \pm 3\sigma] = [.8 \pm 3(1)] = [-2.2 \text{ to } 3.8]$

Balanced: $[\mu \pm \sigma] = [6.4 \pm 1.48] = [4.92 \text{ to } 7.88]$
$[\mu \pm 2\sigma] = [6.4 \pm 2(1.48)] = [3.44 \text{ to } 9.36]$
$[\mu \pm 3\sigma] = [6.4 \pm 3(1.48)] = [1.96 \text{ to } 10.84]$

Canadian Equity: $[\mu \pm \sigma] = [19.6 \pm 2.75] = [16.85 \text{ to } 22.35]$
$[\mu \pm 2\sigma] = [19.6 \pm 2(2.75)] = [14.1 \text{ to } 25.1]$
$[\mu \pm 3\sigma] = [19.6 \pm 3(2.75)] = [11.35 \text{ to } 27.85]$

U.S. Equity: $[\mu \pm \sigma] = [12.4 \pm 3.1] = [9.3 \text{ to } 15.5]$
$[\mu \pm 2\sigma] = [12.4 \pm 2(3.1)] = [6.2 \text{ to } 18.6]$
$[\mu \pm 3\sigma] = [12.4 \pm 3(3.1)] = [3.1 \text{ to } 21.7]$

Global Equity: $[\mu \pm \sigma] = [22.3 \pm 5.1] = [17.2 \text{ to } 27.4]$
$[\mu \pm 2\sigma] = [22.3 \pm 2(5.1)] = [12.1 \text{ to } 32.5]$
$[\mu \pm 3\sigma] = [22.3 \pm 3(5.1)] = [7.0 \text{ to } 37.6]$

Sector Funds: $[\mu \pm \sigma] = [33.1 \pm 5.9] = [27.2 \text{ to } 39.0]$
$[\mu \pm 2\sigma] = [33.1 \pm 2(5.9)] = [21.3 \text{ to } 44.9]$
$[\mu \pm 3\sigma] = [33.1 \pm 3(5.9)] = [15.4 \text{ to } 50.8]$

2.71 a. $538 \pm 3(41) = 538 \pm 123 = [415, 661]$
b. Yes, it is beyond the interval.

2.73 The graph indicates that Chevy trucks far exceed Ford and Dodge in terms of resale value, but the y-axis scale is misleading.

Chapter 3

3.3 b. (1) AA
(2) AA, BB, CC
(3) AB, AC, BA, BC, CA, CB
(4) AA, AB, AC, BA, CA
(5) AA, AB, BA, BB
c. (1) 1/9
(2) 1/3
(3) 2/3
(4) 5/9
(5) 4/9

3.5 b. (1) $PPPN, PPNP, PNPP, NPPP$
(2) $PPNN, PNPN, PNNP, PNNN,$
$NPPN, NPNP, NPNN, NNPP,$
$NNPN, NNNP, NNNN$
(3) All outcomes except $NNNN$
(4) $PPPP, NNNN$
c. (1) 1/4, (2) 11/16, (3) 15/16, (4) 1/8

3.7 a. .095;
b. .89;
c. .30;
d. 94,500

3.9 87.4 (rounded to 88)

3.11 .50

3.13 $P(\text{Natural}) = .22; P(\text{Craps}) = .11$

3.17 a. (1) .25, (2) .40, (3) .10;
c. (1) .55, (2) .45, (3) .45

3.19 a. 5/8;
b. 21/40;
c. 19/40;
d. 3/8;
e. 31/40

3.21 a. .291;
b. .565;
c. .435;
d. .433

3.23 a. 30%;
b. 42%;
c. 27%;
d. 6.7%

3.27 a. .6;
b. .4;
c. Dependent.

3.29 .55

3.31 .1692

3.33 .31

3.35 b. .4;
c. .4

3.37 a. .874;
b. .996;
c. .004

3.39 a. .0295;
b. .9705;
c. Probably not

3.43 $P(A_1|B) = .098; P(A_2|B) = .610;$
$P(A_3|B) = .292$

3.45 a. .089;
b. No

3.47 $P(\text{Spec. 1}|\text{Incorrect}) = .247;$
$P(\text{Spec. 2}|\text{Incorrect}) = .616;$
$P(\text{Spec. 3}|\text{Incorrect}) = .137$

3.49 a. .75 (Yes, the data support his claim of 75% accuracy);
b. .84;
c. .21

3.51 $P(C \mid D) = .387; P(TS \mid D) = .200$

3.53 Both stocks rise: 1/9; both stocks decline: 1/9; exactly one declines: 4/9

3.55 Both decline: .04; exactly one rises: .56; exactly one is unchanged: .26; both rise: .32

3.57 Male = .28; Female = .31

3.59 .32

3.61 .721

3.63 .362

3.65 .502

3.67 Slight dependence: $P(\text{Violence increased}) = .721$ vs. $P(\text{Violence increased} \mid \text{Quality declined}) = .797$. They are close but not equal.

3.69 a. .2075;
b. .25;
c. .105;
d. .42;
e. Yes. The probabilities are not equal, so the events are not independent.

3.71 .3077

3.73 a. .186;
b. It doesn't help the case, as the probability is quite low.
c. .625;
d. It offers much more support than before.
e. .833; very strong case

Chapter 4

4.3 a. discrete;
b. discrete;
c. continuous;
d. discrete;
e. discrete;
f. continuous;
g. continuous

4.9 a. Mean = .8, SD = .4;
b. Mean = 1.15, SD = .9097;
c. Mean = 1.6, SD = 2.1071

4.11 a. Mean = .667, SD = .667;
b. Mean = 1.5, SD = .866;
c. Mean = 2, SD = 1

4.13 b. If numerous oil wells were dug, the average profit would be $500.

4.15 a.

x	$400	$-$49,600
$P(x)$	.995	.005

b. $150;
c. $1,250

4.17 −$4.20 (you would expect a loss of $4.20)

4.23 a. $P(x) = \dfrac{6!}{x!(6-x)!}(.3)^x(.7)^{6-x}$;
b. (1) .0102, (2) .2557, (3) .7443, (4) .8824

4.25 a. .7857;
b. .2143;
c. .9999;
d. .0238;
e. No, the probability of this result is small if the claim is true.

4.27 a. Mean = 1.8, SD = 1.1225, $[\mu_x \pm 2\sigma_x] = [-.445, 4.045]$, $P(x \le 4) = .9891$;
b. Mean = 13.5, SD = 1.1619, $[\mu_x \pm 2\sigma_x] = [11.18, 15.82]$, $P(x \ge 12) = .9444$;
c. Mean = .24, SD = .4874, $[\mu_x \pm 2\sigma_x] = [-.73, 1.21]$, $P(x \le 1) = .9761$

4.31 a. $P(x) = \dfrac{e^{-2}(2)^x}{x!}$ for $x = 0, 1, 2, 3, \ldots$
b.

x	0	1	2	3	4	5	6	7	8
$P(x)$	.1353	.2707	.2707	.1804	.0902	.0361	.0120	.0034	.0009

d. .2707;
e. .9473;
f. .8571;
g. $P(x \ge 1) = .8647, P(x > 2) = .3233$;
h. .8120;
i. .2706;
j. .5774

4.33 a. .0710;
b. .9015;
c. .0985

4.35 a. .0498;
b. Perhaps not; if the agency's claim is true, the probability of no patrol cars is quite small.
c. .000498

4.37 a. .0190;
b. Probably not; the probability of 4 or more defective batteries is small if the claim is true.

4.41 a. $P(x) = \dfrac{\binom{4}{x}\binom{6}{3-x}}{\binom{10}{3}}$;
b. Mean = 1.2, SD = .748

4.43 .7

4.45 a.

x	0	1	2
$P(x)$	$\frac{4}{9}$	$\frac{4}{9}$	$\frac{1}{9}$

b.

x	0	1	2
$P(x)$	.16	.48	.36

c.

x	0	1	2
$P(x)$	.12	.56	.32

4.47 a. Mean = .667, SD = .667;
b. Mean = 1.2, SD = .693;
c. Mean = 1.2, SD = .693

4.49 a. $12,000;
b. at least $6,000

4.51 a. Binomial, $n = 8, p = .8$;
b. .0104;
c. No; if the claim is true, the probability of 3 or fewer patients experiencing pain relief is very small.

4.53 Poisson distribution with $\mu = 3$
a. Poisson with $\mu = 3$, .0498;
b. .9962;
c. .0038;
d. Poisson with $\mu = 6$, .9574;
e. Poisson with $\mu = 9$, .1157

4.55 .9995

4.57 $P(x \le 17) = .3232$ (not much evidence against it)

4.59 Poisson distribution with $\mu = 10$;
$P(x \le 4) = .0293$ (claim is probably not true)

Chapter 5

5.7 1/125

5.9 a. Mean = 3, SD = 1.732;
b. .5773

5.11 a. $f(x) = \begin{cases} \dfrac{1}{140-120} = \dfrac{1}{20} & \text{for } 120 \le x \le 140 \\ 0 & \text{otherwise} \end{cases}$;
c. .5;
d. .25

5.13 a. $f(x) = \begin{cases} \dfrac{1}{6-3} = \dfrac{1}{3} & \text{for } 3 \le x \le 6 \\ 0 & \text{otherwise} \end{cases}$;
c. $P(x \ge 4) = .6667, P(x \ge 5) = .3333, P(x \ge 4.5) = .5$

5.15 a. $f(x) = \begin{cases} \dfrac{1}{25-3} = \dfrac{1}{22} & \text{for } 3 \le x \le 25 \\ 0 & \text{otherwise} \end{cases}$;
b. $P(x \ge 10) = .68, P(x \le 15) = .55, P(x < 3) = 0$

5.23 a. −1;
b. −3;
c. 0;
d. 2;
e. 4

5.25 a. 2.33;
b. 1.645;
c. 2.054 (rounded);
d. −2.33;
e. −1.645;
f. −1.28

5.27 a. .025;
b. .05;
c. .025;
d. .015;
e. .985;
f. .95;
g. .975;
h. .0228;
i. .9772

5.29 a. (1) .9830, (2) .0033, (3) .0456;
b. 947

5.31 a. .0001;
b. Claim is probably not true.

5.33 .0401

5.35 a. −13.968;
b. $Q_1: k = -1.402, Q_2: k = 26.202$

5.37 a. $[\mu \pm 2.33\sigma]$;
b. [46.745, 54.405]

5.39 a. Process A: .3085, Process B: .4013 (B is investigated more often);
b. Process A: .8413, Process B: .6915 (A is investigated more often);
c. B will be investigated more often.
d. $P(X > k) = .3085$ implies that $z = \dfrac{k-0}{10,000} = .5$. So $k = 5,000$. Investigate if cost variance exceeds $5,000.
$P(X > 5,000) = P\left(z > \dfrac{5,000 - 7,500}{10,000}\right)$
$= P(z > .25) = .5 + .0987 = .5987$

5.41 Mean = 700, SD = 100

5.45 b. (1) .0576, (2) .9874, (3) .0126, (4) .0024, (5) .0015

5.47 a. (1) Both np and $n(1-p)$ exceed 5. (2) Mean = 200, Standard deviation = 12.6491, (3) < .001;
b. No.

5.49 a. Mean = 12.5, Standard deviation = 3.446, Probability = 0;
   b. No.
5.51 a. 50,000;
   b. .0359;
   c. .0416;
   d. [172, 228]
5.55 a. $f(x) = \begin{cases} 2e^{-2x} & \text{for } x \geq 0 \\ 0 & \text{otherwise} \end{cases}$;
   c. .8647;
   d. .4712;
   e. .0183;
   f. Mean = .5, SD = .5;
   g. .9502
5.57 a. $f(x) = \begin{cases} \dfrac{7}{15}e^{-\frac{7x}{15}} & \text{for } x \geq 0 \\ 0 & \text{otherwise} \end{cases}$;
   c. (1) .2338, (2) .3729, (3) .2466, (4) .5966;
   d. Mean = 15/7, SD = 15/7;
   e. $[\mu_x \pm \sigma_x] = .8647$, $[\mu_x \pm 2\sigma_x] = .9502$
5.59 a. $\mu_x = 250$, $\lambda = \dfrac{1}{250}$;
   b. $f(x) = \begin{cases} \dfrac{1}{250}e^{-\frac{x}{250}} & \text{for } x \geq 0 \\ 0 & \text{otherwise} \end{cases}$;
   d. .0198;
   e. .3691;
   f. Probably not
5.61 .0062 or 62%
5.63 a. .9082;
   b. 75.325
5.65 a. .8944;
   b. .7967;
   c. .6911
5.67 298
5.69 .9306
5.71 .0107
5.73 a. .2231;
   b. .1353
5.75 a. .0256;
   b. Yes.
5.77 Minority Canadians: $748.01 to $757.99, non-minority Canadians: $844.59 to $857.41; Canadian-born individuals: $824.97 to $837.03; immigrants: $846.36 to $859.64

Chapter 6

6.3 a. Mean = 10, SD = .4;
   b. Mean = 500, SD = .05;
   c. Mean = 3, SD = .05;
   d. Mean = 100, SD = .025
6.5 b. Mean = 20, SD = .5;
   c. .0228;
   d. .1093
6.7 30, 40, 50, 50, 60, 70
6.9 2/3
6.11 b. Mean = 6, SD = .247;
   c. .0146;
   d. 1.43%; conclude that μ is less than 6
6.13 a. .2206;
   b. .0027;
   c. Yes, the probability of observing the sample is very small if the mean is actually 1.0.
6.19 a. Mean = .5, SD = .0316;
   b. Mean = .1, SD = .03;

c. Mean = .8, SD = .02;
   d. Mean = .98, SD = .004427
6.21 b. Mean = .9, SD = .03
6.23 a. .0089;
   b. Yes, the probability of observing this sample is very small if $p = .20$. The true p is probably less than .20.
6.25 a. .0122;
   b. Yes, the probability of observing this sample is very small if $p = .48$. The true p is probably more than .48.
6.29 a. .0294;
   b. Yes, the probability of this sample is small if $p = .70$. The true p is probably greater than .70.
6.31 a. .9954;
   b. .8414;
   c. .5222;
   d. No. No; the probabilities are too small.
6.33 a. .0228
6.35 a. SD = 11.63, Interval: [−26.76, 19.76]

Chapter 7

7.3 a. $H_0: \mu \leq 42$ versus $H_a: \mu > 42$;
   b. Type I: Decide the mean is > 42 (customers satisfied) when it is really ≤ 42; Type II: Decide the mean is ≤ 42 (customers not satisfied) when it is really > 42
7.5 a. $H_0: \mu = 3$ versus $H_a: \mu \neq 3$, where μ = Mean diameter;
   b. Type I: Decide $\mu \neq 3$ (assign team) when $\mu = 3$ (team is not needed); Type II: Decide $\mu = 3$ (do not assign team) when $\mu \neq 3$ (team may be needed)
7.7 a. $H_0: \mu \leq 15$ versus $H_a: \mu > 15$, where μ = Mean temperature of waste water;
   b. Type I: Decide $\mu > 15$ (shut down) when $\mu \leq 15$ (water is cool enough, no shutdown needed); Type II: Decide $\mu \leq 15$ (do not shut down) when $\mu > 15$ (water is too warm, shutdown needed);
   c. Set $\alpha = .05$ to make the probability of a Type II error smaller.
7.11 a. −2;
   b. $z = -2 > z_{\text{crit}} = -2.33$, fail to reject H_0;
   c. .0228;
   d. Since .0228 is less than .10 and .05 but not less than .01 and 001, reject H_0 at $\alpha = .10$ and .05 but not at $\alpha = .01$ or .001.
   e. Since p-value = .0228 is less than .05, there is strong evidence against H_0.
7.13 a. $H_0: \mu \leq 42$ versus $H_a: \mu > 42$;
   b. $z = 2.91 > z_{.01} = 2.33 > z_{.05} = 1.645 > z_{.10} = 1.28$, therefore reject H_0 at alphas of .10, .05, and .01;
   c. p-value = .0018, therefore reject H_0 at alphas of .10, .05, and .01, but not at an alpha of .001.
   d. Very strong evidence against H_0.
7.15 a. $H_0: \mu \leq 15$ versus $H_a: \mu > 15$;
   b. $z = 2.41 > z_{\text{crit}} = 1.645$, therefore reject H_0 at alpha = .05. p-value = $1 - .9920 = .0080$, therefore reject H_0 at alpha = .05.

7.17 $z = 3.09 > z_{\text{crit}} = 1.645$; therefore, reject H_0 at alpha = .05.
7.19 a. $H_0: \mu = 500$ versus $H_a: \mu \neq 500$;
   b. (1) For Mean = 501.56, $z = 3$, p-value = .0026, reject H_0. (2) for Mean = 498.75, $z = -2.4$, p-value = .0164, reject H_0. (3) For Mean = 500.63, $z = 1.2$, p-value = .2302, fail to reject H_0. (4) For Mean = 498.125, $z = -3.6$, p-value = .0003, therefore reject H_0.
7.23 a. $z = -2.18 > z_{\text{crit}} = -2.575$, therefore fail to reject H_0.
   b. .0292;
   c. Reject H_0 at alphas of 0.10 and 0.05, but not 0.01 or 0.001.
7.25 a. $H_0: p \leq .25$ versus $H_a: p > .25$;
   b. $z = 5.31 > z_{.001} = 3.09$, therefore reject H_0 at alphas of .10, .05, .01, and .001;
   c. p-value < .001, therefore reject H_0 at all given values of alpha;
   d. Probably: .365 is significantly higher than .25.
7.27 $H_0: p \leq .5$ versus $H_a: p > .5$; $z = -3.81 < z_{.001} = -3.09$, therefore reject H_0 at alphas of .10, .05, .01, and .001; p-value < .001, therefore reject H_0 at all given values of alpha.
7.29 a. $H_0: p = .95$ versus $H_a: p < .95$;
   b. $z = -14.68 < z_{.001} = -3.09$, therefore reject H_0 at alphas of .10, .05, .01, and .001;
   c. Probably, as .79 is substantially below .95.
7.33 a. $z = 10 > z_{\text{crit}} = 1.645$, therefore reject H_0;
   b. p-value = .0228, therefore reject H_0 at alphas of .10 and .05, but not .01 or .001.
7.35 a. H_0: There is no difference in the mean audit delay for the two types of companies versus H_a: The mean audit delay for public owner-controlled companies is less than that for manager-controlled companies;
   b. $z = -2.0967 < z_{\text{crit}} = -1.645$, therefore reject H_0;
   c. p-value = .0179, therefore reject H_0 at alphas of .10 and .05, but not .01 or .001.
7.37 a. $H_0: \mu_1 - \mu_2 \leq 0$ versus $H_a: \mu_1 - \mu_2 > 0$;
   b. $z = 1.41 < z_{\text{crit}} = 1.645$, therefore fail to reject H_0
7.39 a. $H_0: \mu_1 - \mu_2 = 0$ versus $H_a: \mu_1 - \mu_2 \neq 0$;
   b. $z = 5.06 > z_{\text{crit}} = 1.96$, therefore reject H_0;
   c. p-value < .001, therefore reject H_0 at all given values of alpha.
7.43 p-value = .0188, therefore reject H_0 at alphas of .10 and .05, but not .01 or .001.
7.45 a. $H_0: p_1 - p_2 = 0$ versus $H_a: p_1 - p_2 \neq 0$;
   b. $z = .50$, p-value = .617, therefore fail to reject H_0 and conclude that there is little or no evidence that p_1 and p_2 differ.

7.47 a. Using two-tailed hypothesis tests and an alpha of .05: Canada vs. United States: $z = 16.96 > z_{crit} = 1.96$, therefore reject H_0; Canada vs. Britain: $z = 26.79 > z_{crit} = 1.96$, therefore reject H_0; Canada vs. Australia: $z = .496 < z_{crit} = 1.96$, therefore fail to reject H_0;

b. Australia: $z = 6.82 > z_{crit} = 1.96$, therefore reject H_0; Britain: $z = 22.14 > z_{crit} = 1.96$, therefore reject H_0; Canada: $z = 4.16 > z_{crit} = 1.96$, therefore reject H_0; United States: $z = 14.43 > z_{crit} = 1.96$, therefore reject H_0. All of the countries are significantly more optimistic about the future than would seem to be warranted by their enthusiasm for their economies.

7.53 a.

μ	β
15.1	.9279
15.2	.8315
15.3	.6772
15.4	.4840
15.5	.2946
15.6	.1492
15.7	.0618
15.8	.0207
15.9	.0055
16.0	.0012

b. No. $\beta = .2946$ when $\mu = 15.5$. Should increase sample size.

7.55 245.86 (round up to 246)

7.61 $d = .5$. This effect size is actually a medium-sized effect, suggesting that, all things being equal, the effect would have been demonstrated to be statistically significant if you had had enough individuals in your division.

7.63 .365; small to medium effect (possibly important)

7.65 a. $H_0: p \geq .05$ versus $H_a: p < .05$;

b. $z_{.001} = -3.09 < z = -2.43 < z_{.01} = -2.33$, therefore reject H_0 at alphas of .10, .05, and .01 but not at an alpha of .001;

p-value $= .0075$, therefore reject H_0 at alphas of .10, .05, and .01 but not at an alpha of .001.

7.67 a. Since p-value $= .0139$, we reject H_0 for alphas of .10 and .05, but not for .01 or .001;

b. Strong evidence

7.69 a. $H_0: p \leq .60$, $H_a: p > .60$;

b. $z_{.001} = 3.09 > z = 2.58 > z_{.01} = 2.33$. Reject H_0 for alphas of .10, .05, and .01, but not .001.

7.71 Wife entitled to half of the assets: $z_{.0005} = 3.29 > z = 3.13 > z_{.005} = 2.576$, reject at .01 but not at .001.
Pension split evenly: $z = 3.35 > z_{.0005} = 3.29 > z_{.005} = 2.576$, reject at all alphas
Stock options split evenly: $z = 3.99 > z_{.0005} = 3.29 > z_{.005} = 2.576$, reject at all alphas
Managing the household: $z = 3.92 > z_{.0005} = 3.29 > z_{.005} = 2.576$, reject at all alphas

Corporate wife who travels: $z = 4.01 > z_{.0005} = 3.29 > z_{.005} = 2.576$, reject at all alphas
Lifestyle of corporate wife: $z = 4.11 > z_{.0005} = 3.29 > z_{.005} = 2.576$, reject at all alphas

Chapter 8

8.5 Two-tailed hypothesis test with 8 degrees of freedom: $t_{.0005} = -5.041 < t = -4.30 < t_{.005} = -3.355$, reject at .10, .05, .01, but not .001

8.7 Since $.01 < .02 < .05$, there is strong evidence against H_0.

8.9 a. $H_0: \mu = 42$, $H_A: \mu > 42$, $\alpha = .01$;
b. $t = 2.899 > t_{.01} = 2.39$, $g = .36$

8.11 a. $H_0: \mu = 750$ versus $H_a: \mu \neq 750$
b. $t = 6.94 > t_{.005} = 4.604$, $g = 3.10$.

8.13 $H_0: \mu = 50$ versus $H_a: \mu > 50$; $t = 2.5 > t_{.01} = 2.492$, $g = .50$.

8.19 Two-tailed hypothesis test with 12 degrees of freedom: $t_{.0005} = 4.318 > t = 3.39 > t_{.005} = 3.055$, reject at .10, .05, 01, but not at .001

8.21 a. $t = 6.64 > t_{.05} = 1.717$ (22 df), reject H_0, $g = 2.71$;
b. $t = 2.15 > t_{.05} = 1.717$, reject H_0, $g = 2.71$.

8.23 a. $g = 4.35$;
b. $t = 9.73 > t_{.0005} = 3.922$ (18 df);
c. the p-value given is much lower than any of the given alphas;
d. $H_0: \mu_M - \mu_A \leq 5$ versus $H_a: \mu_M - \mu_A > 5$, $t_{.001} = 3.610 > t = 2.89 > t_{.01} = 2.552$ (18 df), therefore reject H_0 at alphas of .10, .05, and .01 but not .001.

8.25 a. $H_0: \mu_f - \mu_v = 0$ versus $H_a: \mu_f - \mu_v \neq 0$;
b. $t_{.0005} = 4.437 > t = 3.7431 > t_{.005} = 3.106$ (11 df), therefore reject H_0 at alphas of .10, .05, and .01 but not .001, $g = 2.13$;
c. p-value $= .0032$, therefore reject H_0 at alphas of .10, .05, and .01 but not .001;
d. $H_0: \mu_f - \mu_v \leq .4$ versus $H_a: \mu_f - \mu_v > .4$, $t = 2.404 > t_{.05} = 1.796$ (11 df), therefore reject H_0.

8.31 a. $t = 5 > t_{.0005} = 3.551$ (48 df, "rounded down" to 40, in order to use table in text), therefore reject H_0 at each value of alpha,; $g = .71$;
b. $t = 2 > t_{.05} = 1.684$, therefore reject H_0 at alphas of .10 and .05, but not at alphas of .01 or .001.

8.33 a. $H_0: \mu_d \leq 0$ versus $H_a: \mu_d > 0$;
b. $t = 4.19 > t_{.05} = 1.8331$ (9 df), therefore reject H_0 at alpha of .05; $g = 1.33$

8.35 a. $H_0: \mu_d \geq 0$ versus $H_a: \mu_d < 0$;
b. $t_{.001} = -4.297 < t = -3.612 < t_{.01} = -2.821$ (9 df), $g = 1.14$, therefore reject H_0 at an alpha of .01, but not at an alpha of .001;
c. p-value $= .0028$, suggesting that we have very strong evidence that account age has been reduced.

8.39 a. 3.34;
b. 3.22;
c. 3.44;
d. 4.88

8.41 a. $F = 5 < F_{.025} = 5.60$, therefore fail to reject H_0 at alpha $= .05$ (two-tailed);
b. $F = 5 > F_{.05} = 4.15$, therefore reject H_0 at alpha $= .05$ (one-tailed).

8.43 $F = 9.55 > F_{.025} = 2.88$, therefore reject H_0 at alpha $= .05$. This suggests that the variances are unequal.

8.45 a. $H_0: \mu \geq 25$ versus $H_a: \mu < 25$;
b. $t_{.001} = -3.265 < t = -2.63 < t_{.01} = -2.405$, therefore reject H_0 at alpha $= .01$, but not at alpha $= .001$.

8.47 a. $t_{.001} = 3.467 > t = 2.5 > t_{.01} = 2.492$, therefore reject H_0 at alpha $= .01$, but not at alpha $= .001$;
b. $t = 1.11$, therefore fail to reject H_0 at any of the given values of alpha.

8.49 Since $p = .078$ is $< .1$ there is some evidence.

8.51 $t = 1.54$, therefore fail to reject H_0 at any of the given values of alpha.

8.53 a. $t = 8.251 > t_{.0005} = 4.015$ (16 df), therefore reject H_0 at alpha $= .001$;
b. $t = 2.627 > t_{.05} = 1.746$ (16 df), therefore reject H_0 at alpha $= .05$.

Chapter 9

9.7 a. 95%: [25.064, 26.086], 99%: [24.392, 26.758];
b. Yes, 95% confidence interval (CI) is entirely above 25;
c. No, 99% CI extends below 25;
d. Fairly confident, as the 95% CI is above 25 even though the 99% CI contains 25.

9.9 a. 95%: [42.308, 43.592], 99%: [42.107, 43.793];
b. Yes, 95% interval is entirely above 42.
c. Yes, 99% interval is entirely above 42.
d. Very confident, as the 99% CI is entirely above 42.

9.11 a. [76.132, 89.068];
b. [85.748, 100.252];
c. Audit delay for public owner-controlled companies appears to be shorter, as there is only a small amount of overlap of the intervals.

9.15 For 11 df $t_{.10} = 1.363$, $t_{.025}$, $= 2.201$, $t_{.001} = 4.025$
For 6 df $t_{.05} = 1.440$, $t_{.005} = 2.447$, $t_{.0005} = 5.208$

9.17 a. 95%: [4.311, 7.689], 99%: [3.442, 8.558];
b. Can be 95% confident the claim is true; cannot be 99% confident the claim is true

9.19 a. [6.832, 7.968];
b. Yes, 95% interval is entirely below 8.

9.21 a. [786.609, 835.391];
b. Yes, 95% interval is entirely above 750.

9.23 t-based 95% CI: [4.965, 5.955]. The interval is entirely below 6, so we are confident that the mean is less than 6.

9.29 a. 259;
b. 447

9.31 a. 47;
b. 328

9.33 54

9.35 a. $p = .5$;
b. $p = .3$;
c. $p = .8$

9.37 a. [.304, .496], [.286, .514], [.274, .526];
   b. [.066, .134], [.060, .140], [.055, .145];
   c. [.841, .959], [.830, .970], [.823, .977];
   d. [.464, .736], [.439, .761], [.422, .778]
9.39 a. [.473, .610];
   b. No, the interval includes .5.
9.41 a. [.311, .349];
   b. [68.58%, 71.42%];
   c. Margin of error is 1.42%, which is approximately equal to "1.5 percentage points" (1.5%).
9.43 a. [.611, .729];
   b. Yes, as the interval is entirely above .60.
9.45 a. [.264, .344];
   b. Yes, as the interval is entirely above .20.
9.47 a. [.0077, .0323];
   b. [.034, .074];
   c. Yes, as the intervals do not overlap at all.
9.49 1,428
9.53 [23.568, 36.432]. This suggests that the difference is greater than 20, as the interval is entirely above this point. The equal variance assumption is applied as the variances are very similar and the n sizes are equal.
9.55 a. [.509, .971]. This suggests that the difference is more than .5% as the interval is entirely above this point;
   b. [.50756, .97244]. Note that the unequal variance formula yields a wider interval.
9.57 [.4606, 1.7750]
9.59 [2.99, 7.01]. This suggests that we can be 95% certain that there is a difference (the interval does not contain zero).
9.63 [.0511, .1709]. This suggests that we can be 95% certain that there is a difference (the interval does not contain zero).
9.65 [.0107, .0573]. We can be 95% certain that the smallest difference between these values will be .0107.
9.67 a. [.263, .347];
   b. We can be 95% confident that the proportion is greater than .25, as the interval is entirely above this value.
   c. 905
9.69 a. [.686, .806]. This suggests that we cannot be 95% confident that the proportion is greater than .70, as the interval contains this value;
   b. [3.892, 5.868]. This suggests that we can be 95% confident that the proportion is greater than 3, as the interval is entirely above this value
9.71 a. [1.469%, 3.991%]. This suggests that we can be 99% certain that the true score is below 5%, as the interval is entirely below this value;
   b. [15.259%, 54.261%]. The interval is wide because s is large and n is small. To narrow the interval, increase the sample size or decrease your required level of confidence for the interval.
9.73 [523.92, 552.08]
9.75 [49.648, 51.918]. This suggests that we cannot be 95% confident that the mean is at least 50, as this value lies within the interval.

Chapter 10

10.1 Response variable = Variable of interest in an experiment; Dependent variable
   Factor = Independent variable in a designed experiment
   Treatments = Values of a factor (or combination of factors)
   Experimented units = Entities to which the treatments are assigned
10.3 Response: Time to stabilize emergency condition
   Factor: Display panels
   Treatments: Panels A, B, C
   Experimental units: Controllers
10.5 Constant variance, normality, independence
10.7 If the one-way ANOVA F test leads us to conclude that at least two of the treatment (group) means differ, then we want to investigate which of the means differ and estimate how large the differences are.
10.9 a. $F = 184.57$, p-value = .000: Reject H_0. Shelf location has different effects on sales.
   b. $(\bar{x}_B - \bar{x}_M) \pm q_{.05}\sqrt{\dfrac{MSE}{m}}$
   $= (55.8 - 77.2) \pm 3.67\sqrt{\dfrac{6.16}{6}}$
   $= -21.4 \pm 3.72$
   Bottom–middle: -21.4, $[-25.12, -17.68]$
   Bottom–top: 4.3, [.58, 8.02]
   Middle–top: 25.7, [21.98, 29.42]
   Middle shelf maximizes the differences.
10.11 a. $F = 43.36$, p-value = .000; Reject H_0: Bottle design does have an impact on sales.
   b. $\mu_B - \mu_A$: $\left[16.2 \pm (3.77)\sqrt{\dfrac{7.5667}{5}}\right]$
   $= [11.56, 20.84]$
   $\mu_C - \mu_A$: [3.56, 12.84]
   $\mu_C - \mu_B$: $[-12.64, -3.36]$
   c. (1) $[16.2 \pm (2.179)(1.73973178)]$
   $= [12.41, 19.99]$
   (2) [4.41, 11.99]
   (3) $[-11.79, -4.21]$
   d. μ_A: 16.60, [13.92, 19.28]
   μ_B: 32.8, [30.12, 35.48]
   μ_C: 24.8, [22.12, 27.48]
10.13 Tukey $q_{.05} = 4.05$, $MSE = 606.15$, $m = 5$
   Divot – Alpha: $(336.6 - 253.6) \pm 44.59 = [38.41, 127.59]$
   Divot – Century: $(336.6 - 241.8) \pm 44.59 = [50.21, 139.39]$
   Divot – Best: $(336.6 - 306.4) \pm 44.59 = [-14.39, 74.79]$
   Century – Alpha: $(241.8 - 253.6) \pm 44.59 = [-56.39, 32.79]$
   Century – Best: $(241.8 - 306.4) \pm 44.59 = [-109.19, -20.01]$
   Best – Alpha: $(306.4 - 253.6) \pm 44.59 = [8.21, 97.39]$
   Best and Divot appear to be the most durable
   $t_{.025} = 2.120$, $MSE = 606.16$, $n = 5$
   Divot: $336.6 \pm 23.34 = [313.26, 359.94]$
   Best: $306.4 \pm 23.34 = [283.06, 329.74]$
   Alpha: $253.6 \pm 23.34 = [230.26, 276.94]$
   Century: $241.8 \pm 23.34 = [218.46, 265.14]$

10.15 Use when there are differences between the experimental units that are concealing any true differences between the treatments.
10.17 a. $F = 36.23$, p-value = .000; Reject H_0: There is a difference in sales methods,
   b. $F = 12.87$, p-value = .007; Reject H_0: Salesmen do have an effect on sales.
   c. $(\bar{X}_1 - \bar{X}_2) \pm q_{.05}\dfrac{s}{\sqrt{b}}$
   $= (\bar{X}_1 - \bar{X}_2) \pm 4.90\left(\dfrac{.928}{\sqrt{3}}\right)$
   $= (\bar{X}_1 - \bar{X}_2) \pm 2.63$
   Method 1 – Method 2: $(30.33 - 30) \pm 2.63 = [-2.30, 2.96]$
   Method 1 – Method 3: $(30.33 - 25.33) \pm 2.63 = [2.37, 7.63]$
   Method 1 – Method 4: $(30.33 - 24) \pm 2.63 = [3.70, 8.96]$
   Method 2 – Method 3: $(30 - 25.33) \pm 2.63 = [2.04, 7.30]$
   Method 2 – Method 4: $(30 - 24) \pm 2.63 = [3.37, 8.63]$
   Method 3 – Method 4: $(25.33 - 24) \pm 2.63 = [-1.30, 3.96]$
   It appears that Methods 1 and 2 maximize mean weekly sales.
10.19 a. $F(2,6) = 441.75$, $p < .001$. Keyboard brands do have an impact on the mean number of words entered.
   b. $F(3,6) = 107.69$, $p < .001$. Specialist does have an impact on the mean number of words entered.
   c. Tukey $q_{.05} = 4.34$, $MSE = .444$, $s = .666$, $b = 4$
   AB: $(72.25 - 62.25) \pm 4.34(.666/2) = 10 \pm 1.45 = [8.55, 11.45]$
   AC: $(72.25 - 58.75) \pm 1.45 = [12.05, 14.95]$
   BC: $(62.25 - 58.75) \pm 1.45 = [2.05, 4.95]$
   Keyboard A maximizes the mean number of words entered per minute.
10.21 a. $F = 5.78$, p-value = .0115; Reject H_0: The soft drinks differ in terms of mean sales.
   b. Tukey $q_{.05} = 3.61$, $MSE = 691.319$, $s = 26.287$, $b = 10$
   Coke Classic – New Coke: $(102.8 - 64.8) \pm 3.61 (26.287/3.162) = 38 \pm 30.01 = [7.99, 68.01]$
   Coke Classic – Pepsi: $(102.8 - 73.0) \pm 30.01 = [-.21, 59.81]$
   New Coke – Pepsi: $(64.8 - 73.0) \pm 30.01 = [-38.21, 21.81]$
   From MegaStat output:
   Coke Classic – New Coke = 3.23, $p < .01$
   Coke Classic – Pepsi = 2.53, $p < .05$
   New Coke – Pepsi = .70, $p > .40$
   c. Yes; mean sales for New Coke are less than those for Pepsi, even though the Tukey test indicates this difference is not significant.
10.23 a. Plotted lines intersect.
   b. Plotted lines are parallel.
10.25 a. Panel B requires less time to stabilize the emergency condition.
   $F(\text{int}) = .66$, p-value = .681; cannot reject H_0, no interaction exists.
   b. $F = 26.49$, p-value = .000; reject H_0.

c. $F = 100.80$, p-value $= .000$; reject H_0.

d. Tukey $q_{.05} = 3.77$, $MSE = 4.13$

$$\sqrt{MSE\left(\frac{1}{4*2}\right)} = .7185$$

$u_A - u_B$: $3.2 \pm 3.77(.7185)$
$= 3.2 \pm 2.71 = [.49, 5.91]$

$u_A - u_C$: -4.1 ± 2.71
$= [-6.81, -1.39]$

$u_B - u_C$: -7.3 ± 2.71
$= [-10.01, -4.59]$

A vs. $B = 3.20$, $p < .01$
A vs. $C = 4.06$, $p < .01$
B vs. $C = 7.26$, $p < .001$

e. 1 vs. $2 = 6.25$, $p < .001$
1 vs. $3 = 12.79$, $p < .001$
1 vs. $4 = 3.27$, $p < .01$
2 vs. $3 = 6.54$, $p < .001$
2 vs. $4 = 9.52$, $p < .001$
3 vs. $4 = 16.06$, $p < .001$

f. Panel B. No, there is no interaction.

g. $\bar{y}_{B4} = 9.5$, $\bar{y}_{B4} \pm t_{.025}\sqrt{\dfrac{MSE}{m}}$

$= 9.5 \pm 2.179\sqrt{\dfrac{4.13}{2}} = 9.5 \pm 3.13$

$= [6.37, 12.63]$

10.27 a. Interaction is present: $F = 24.73$, p-value $= .001$.
Reject H_0; conclude interaction exists.

b. House design C/Supervisor 1

$18.8 \pm t_{.025}\sqrt{\dfrac{MSE}{m}}$

$= 18.8 \pm 2.447\sqrt{\dfrac{.390}{2}}$

$= 18.8 \pm 1.08 = [17.72, 19.88]$

10.29 $F = 40.79$, p-value $< .0001$; conclude treatment means differ. All pairwise differences are significant with p-values less than $.01$: X vs. $Y = 5.23$, X vs. $Z = 3.77$, Y vs. $Z = 8.99$ ($.01$ critical value $= 3.42$)

10.31 At $\alpha = .05$, loan officer effects differ and method effects differ (p-values $< .0001$). $t_{.025} = 2.447$ with 6 degrees of freedom.

$\mu_{l4} - \mu_{l1}$: $[-4 \pm 2.447(.2357)]$
$= [-4 \pm .577] = [-4.58, -3.42]$

$\mu_{l3} - \mu_{l1}$: $[-3 \pm .577]$
$= [-3.58, -2.42]$

$\mu_{l2} - \mu_{l1}$: $[-1.33 \pm .577]$
$= [-1.91, -.75]$

$\mu_{l4} - \mu_{l2}$: $[-2.67 \pm .577]$
$= [-3.25, -2.09]$

$\mu_{l3} - \mu_{l2}$: $[-1.67 \pm .577]$
$= [-2.25, -1.09]$

$\mu_{l4} - \mu_{l3}$: $[-1 \pm .577] = [-1.58, -.42]$

$\mu_{Dh} - \mu_{Bh}$: $[-3.75 \pm 2.447(.2041)]$
$= [-3.75 \pm .499] = [-4.25, -3.25]$

$\mu_{Fh} - \mu_{Bh}$: $[-2.75 \pm .499]$
$= [-3.25, -2.25]$

$\mu_{Dh} - \mu_{Fh}$: $[-1 \pm .499] = [-1.50, -.50]$

10.33 a. 6 cells
b. 10 employees per cell
c. Factor 1 $F(2,54) = 35.62$, $p < .001$;
Factor 2 $F(1,54) = 4.13$, $p < .05$;
Interaction $F(2,54) = 8.36$, $p < .001$
d. Greatest comfort with arm rests and smallest key size

10.35 At $\alpha = .05$, the treatment means differ, no interaction exists, fertilizer type effects differ and wheat type effects differ.

Chapter 11

11.1 Covariance is the strength of the linear relationship between x and y. If there is no covariance between x and y, then the linear relationship between these two variables looks like a circle or a zero.

11.3 $s_{xy} = 10.2281/23 = .4447$
$r = .4447 / (.7053)(.6515) = .9678$
Very strong positive relationship

11.5 ρ is the actual population (unknown) value of the correlation between two variables.

11.7 $t = .23(14.07)/.97 = 3.34$, $t_{critical}$ at alpha $= .001$ is 3.09, x and y are strongly related.

11.9 When there appears to be a linear relationship between y and x

11.11 β_1: The change in the mean value of the dependent variable that is associated with a one-unit increase in the value of the independent variable
β_0: The mean value of the dependent variable when the value of the independent variable is zero

11.13 The straight line appearance suggests that the simple linear regression model with a positive slope might be appropriate.

11.15 Looks reasonably linear.

11.17 b. Yes, the plot looks linear, positive slope

11.19 b. Yes, the relationship looks to be linear with a positive slope.

11.21 (1) Mean of error terms $= 0$
(2) Constant variance
(3) Normality
(4) Independence

11.23 The quality or "goodness" of the fit of the least squares line to the observed data

11.25 Evaluate $\hat{y} = b_0 + b_1 x$ for the given value of x.

11.27 $s^2 = \dfrac{SSE}{n-2} = \dfrac{191.7017}{11-2} = 21.3002$
$s = \sqrt{s^2} = \sqrt{21.30018} = 4.61521$

11.29 $s^2 = \dfrac{746.7624}{10} = 74.67624$,
$s = 8.64154$

11.31 $s^2 = \dfrac{SSE}{n-2} = \dfrac{222.8242}{10-2} = 27.8530$
$s = \sqrt{s^2} = \sqrt{27.8530} = 5.2776$

11.33 a. $b_0 = 11.4641$ $b_1 = 24.6022$
$b_0 - 0$ copiers, 11.46 minutes of service
b_1 - each additional copier adds 24.6022 minutes of service on average.
No. The interpretation of b_0 does not make practical sense since it indicates that 11.46 minutes of service would be required for a customer with no copiers.

b. $\hat{y} = 11.4641 + 24.6022(4) = 109.873$, or 109.9 minutes

11.35 a. $SS_{xy} = \sum x_i y_i - \dfrac{(\sum x_i)(\sum y_i)}{n}$
$= 365,027 - \dfrac{(548)(5,782)}{12}$
$= 100,982.33$

$SS_{xx} = \sum x_i^2 - \dfrac{(\sum x_i)^2}{n}$
$= 34,978 - \dfrac{(548)^2}{12}$
$= 9,952.667$

$b_1 = \dfrac{SS_{xy}}{SS_{xx}} = \dfrac{100,982.33}{9,952.667}$
$= 10.1463$

$b_0 = \bar{y} - b_1\bar{x}$
$= \left(\dfrac{5,782}{12}\right) - 10.1463\left(\dfrac{548}{12}\right)$
$= 18.4875$

b. b_1 is the estimated increase in mean labour cost (10.1463) for every 1-unit increase in the batch size.
b_0 is the estimated mean labour cost (18.4875) when batch size $= 0$; no.

c. $\hat{y} = 18.4880 + 10.1463x$
d. $\hat{y} = 18.4880 + 10.1463(60)$
$= 627.266$

11.37 a. Strong ($\alpha = .05$) evidence that the regression relationship is significant.
b. Very strong ($\alpha = .01$) evidence that the regression relationship is significant.

11.39 a. $b_0 = 11.4641$ $b_1 = 24.6022$
b. $SSE = 191.7017$
c. $s_{b_1} = .8045$ $t = 30.580$
$t = b_1/s_{b_1} = 24.602/.8045 = 30.580$
d. $t = 30.580$; $df = 9$; $t_{.025} = 2.262$. Reject H_0, strong evidence of a significant relationship between x and y.
e. $t = 30.580$; $t_{.005} = 3.250$. Reject H_0, very strong evidence of a significant relationship between x and y.
f. p-value $= .000$. Reject at all α, extremely strong evidence of a significant relationship between x and y.
g. $[24.6022 \pm 2.262(.8045)]$
$= [22.782, 26.422]$
h. $s_{b_0} = 3.4390$ $t = 3.334$
$t = b_0/s_{b_0} = 11.464/3.439 = 3.334$
i. p-value $= .0087$. Reject at all α except .001.

11.41 a. $b_0 = 18.488$, $b_1 = 10.1463$
b. $SSE = 746.7624$
c. $s_{b_1} = .0866$, $t = 117.1344$
d. $t = 117.13$, $df = 10$; $t_{.025} = 2.23$. Reject H_0, strong evidence of a significant relationship between x and y.
e. $t = 117.13$, $t_{.005} = 3.17$. Reject H_0, very strong evidence of a significant relationship between x and y.
f. p-value $= .000$; reject H_0 at each value of α.
g. $[10.1463 \pm 2.228(.0866)]$
$= [9.953, 10.339]$
h. $s_{b_0} = 4.677$, $t = 3.95$
$t = b_0/s_{b_0} = 18.488/4.677 = 3.95$
i. p-value $= .003$; fail to reject H_0 at $\alpha = .001$. Reject H_0 at all other values of α.

11.43 95% CI for $\beta_1 = -.87$ to $-.11$

11.45 A confidence interval is for the mean value of y.

A prediction interval is for an individual value of y.

11.47 a. 109.873, [106.721, 113.025]

b. 109.873, [98.967, 120.779]

c. We have $x = 4$, $\bar{x} = 3.90$, $SS_{xx} = 32.90$, $n = 11$

Distance value

$$= \frac{1}{11} + \frac{(4-3.90)^2}{32.90} = .090657961$$

So the confidence interval is

$$109.873 \pm (2.262)(4.615)\sqrt{.090657961}$$
$$= [106.729, 113.016]$$

This compares (within rounding) to the computer generated output. For the prediction interval with the same quantities we get

$$109.873 \pm (2.262)(4.615)\sqrt{1.090657961}$$
$$= [98.971, 120.775],$$ which also compares within rounding.

d. 113 minutes

11.49 a. 627.26, [621.05, 633.47]

b. 627.26, [607.03, 647.49]

c. $s\sqrt{Distance} = 2.7868$,

$s = 8.642$,

$$Distance = \left(\frac{2.79}{8.642}\right)^2 = .104000$$

99% confidence interval:

$[627.26 \pm 3.169(2.79)]$
$= [(618.42, 636.10)]$

99% prediction interval:

$[627.26 \pm 3.169(8.642)\sqrt{1.104227}]$
$= [598.48, 656.04]$

11.51 $\hat{y} = b_0 + b_1(11)$
$= 66.2121 + 4.4303(11)$
$= 114.945$

95% CI: [110.604, 119.287]

11.53 Proportion of the total variation in the n observed values of y that is explained by the simple linear regression model

11.55 Explained variation $= 13.459 - 2.806$
$= 10.653$
$r^2 = 10.653/13.459 = .792$
$r = +\sqrt{.792} = .890$
79.2% of the variation in demand can be explained by variation in price differential.

11.57 Explained variation $= 7,492.4 - 888.96$
$= 6,603.4$
$r^2 = 6,603.4/7,492.4 = .88$
$r = +\sqrt{.88} = .939$
88% of the variation in sales can be explained by variation in coupons issued.

11.59 A two-tailed t test on β_1

11.61 a. $F = 10.65268/(2.805902/28) =$
106.303

b. $F_{.05} = 4.20$, reject H_0 ($df_1 = 1$, $df_2 = 28$). Strong evidence of a significant relationship between x and y.

c. $F_{.01} = 7.64$, reject H_0 ($df_1 = 1$, $df_2 = 28$). Very strong evidence of a significant relationship between x and y.

d. p-value $=$ less than .001, reject H_0 at all levels of α. Extremely strong evidence of a significant relationship between x and y.

e. $t^2 = (10.310)^2 = 106.303$ (within rounding error)
$(t_{.025})^2 = 4.19 = F_{.05}$

11.63 a. $F = 6,603.445/(888.9553571/8)$
$= 59.4266$

b. $F_{.05} = 5.32$, $df_1 = 1$, $df_2 = 8$
Since $59.43 > 5.32$, reject H_0 at .05, strong evidence of a significant relationship between x and y.

c. $F_{.01} = 11.26$, $df_1 = 1$, $df_2 = 8$
Since $59.43 > 11.3$, reject H_0 at .01, very strong evidence of a significant relationship between x and y.

d. p-value $= .000$; reject H_0 at all levels of α, extremely strong evidence of a significant relationship between x and y.

e. $t^2 = (7.71)^2 = 59.44$ (approximately equals $F = 59.43$)
$(t_{.025})^2 = (2.306)^2 = 5.32 = F_{.05}$

11.67 Possible violations of the normality and constant-variance assumptions

11.69 a. $\dfrac{3(i)-1}{3n+1} = \dfrac{3(4)-1}{33+1} = .3235$
$.5000 - .3235 = .1765, \Rightarrow z = -.46$
$\dfrac{3(i)-1}{3n+1} = \dfrac{3(10)-1}{33+1} = .8529$
$.8529 - .5000 = .3529, \Rightarrow z = 1.05$

b. No

11.71 a. $\ln y_t = 2.07012 + .25688t$
$\ln y_{16} = 2.07012 + .25688(16)$
$= 6.1802$

b. $e^{6.1802} = 483.09$
$e^{5.9945} = 401.22$
$e^{6.3659} = 581.67$

c. $d = 1.87643$
$d_{L.05} = 1.08$. Since $d > 1.10$, we fail to reject.

d. Growth rate $= e^{.25688} = 1.293$
This means the growth rate is expected to be 29.3% per year.

11.73 a. Yes
$\hat{y} = 7(25.0069) = 175.048$

b. 95% CI[7(21.4335),7(28.5803)]
$= [150.0345, 200.0621]$
95% PI[7(13.3044),7(36.7094)]
$= [93.1308, 256.9658]$
Allow 200 minutes.

11.75 a. $b_1 = -6.44$

b. $p < .000$

c. $r = .99$, eta$^2 = .9836$, 98.36% of the variance in accidents overlaps with bridge width.

11.77 a. $r = .86$, strong relationship between debt and population

b. $R = .86$, same value

c. Smallest = Nigeria, largest = Pakistan

Chapter 12

12.7 a. The plots show a linear (or somewhat linear) relationship between Price and Demand, IndPrice and Demand, PriceDiff and Demand, and AdvExp and Demand.

b. The mean demand for the large-sized bottle of Fresh when the price of Fresh is $3.70, the average industry price of competitors' similar detergents is $3.90, and the advertising expenditure to promote Fresh is $6.50 ($650,000).

c. $\beta_0 =$ Meaningless in practical terms
$\beta_1 =$ Mean change in demand for each additional dollar in the price of

Fresh, holding all other predictor variables constant
$\beta_2 =$ Mean change in demand for each additional dollar in the average price of competitors' detergents, holding all other predictor variables constant
$\beta_3 =$ Mean change in demand for each additional $100,000 spent on advertising Fresh, holding all other predictor variables constant
$\varepsilon =$ All other factors that influence the demand for Fresh detergent

d. The plots for Demand vs. AdvExp and Demand vs. PriceDif appear to be more linear than the other two plots.

12.15 a. $SSE = 1.4318$, $s^2 = .0551$;

b. Total variation $= 13.4586$, Explained variation $= 12.0268$;

c. $R^2 = .894$, Adjusted $R^2 = .881$. Approximately 89% of the variance in demand is predicted by price, average price, and advertising, which drops to 88% when adjusted for the number of predictors;

d. 72.80;

e. Significant at alpha $= .05$, $F_{.05} = 2.98$;

f. Significant at alpha $= .01$, $F_{.01} = 4.64$;

g. p-value $= .000000000000888$

12.17 $b_0 = 44.66$, $b_1 = 5.74$, $b_2 = .34$; b_0 is attendance when job satisfaction $= 0$ and commute distance $= 0$ (meaningless, as the scenario would exist only if people lived at work); $b_1 = 5.74$ suggests that attendance increases by 5.74 days for each one-point increase in job satisfaction rating score, when commute distance stays constant; $b_2 = .34$ suggests that attendance increases by .34 days when commute distance increases by 1 km when job satisfaction ratings remain constant.

12.19 a. $b_0 = 1,946.8020$, $b_1 = .0386$, $b_2 = 1.0394$, $b_3 = -413.7578$; $b_0 =$ Labour hours when XRay $= 0$, BedDays $= 0$, and LengthStay $= 0$; $b_1 = .04$ suggests that labour hours increase .04 for each unit increase in XRay, when BedDays and LengthStay remain constant; $b_2 = 1.04$ suggests that labour hours increase by 1.04 for each unit of increase in BedDays when XRay and LengthStay remain constant; $b_3 = -413.76$ implies that labour hours *decrease* by 413.76 when LengthStay decreases by one unit and both XRay and BedDays remain constant;

b. $\hat{y} = 1,946.802 + .0386 (56,194)$
$+ 1.0394 (14,077.88) - 413.7578$
$(6.89) = 15,897.65$;

c. Actual hours were 1,311.06 hours greater than predicted.

12.23 a to f:
$y = \beta_0 + \beta_1 x_1 + \beta_2 x_2 + \beta_3 x_3 + \varepsilon$
$n - (k + 1) = 30 - (3 + 1) = 26$
Rejection points:
$t_{.025} = 2.056$ $t_{.005} = 2.779$
$H_0: \beta_0 = 0$ $t = \dfrac{7.5891}{2.4450} = 3.104$;
reject H_0 at $\alpha = .05$,
$\alpha = .01$

$H_0: \beta_1 = 0$ $t = \dfrac{-2.3577}{.6379} = -3.696$;
reject H_0 at $\alpha = .05$,
not $.01$

$H_0: \beta_2 = 0$ $t = \dfrac{1.6122}{.2954} = 5.459$;
reject H_0 at $\alpha = .05$,
$\alpha = .01$

$H_0: \beta_3 = 0$ $t = \dfrac{.5012}{.1259} = 3.981$;
reject H_0 at $\alpha = .05$,
$\alpha = .01$

p-value for testing
$H_0: \beta_1 = 0$ is $.001$;
reject H_0 at $\alpha = .01$
$H_0: \beta_2 = 0$ is less than
$.001$; reject H_0 at
$\alpha = .001$
$H_0: \beta_3 = 0$ is $.0005$; reject
H_0 at $\alpha = .001$
95% CI: $[b_j \pm 2.056 s_{b_j}]$
99% CI: $[b_j \pm 2.779 s_{b_j}]$

12.27 a. Point estimate is $\hat{y} = 91.27$; 95%
prediction interval is $[71.68, 110.87]$.
b. Point prediction is $\hat{y} = 58.89$; 95%
prediction interval is $[36.79, 80.99]$.
c. Larger distance value when $x_1 = 2$
and $x_2 = 8$

12.29 $y = 17,207.31$ is above the upper limit
of the interval $[14,906.2, 16,886.3]$; this
y-value is unusually high.

12.37 $\hat{y} = -2.3497 + 2.3611x_1 + 4.1831x_2$
$- .3489x_1x_2$
$x_1 = $ Radio/TV; $x_2 = $ Print
a. $x_2 = 1$, Slope $= 2.0122$; $x_2 = 2$,
Slope $= 1.6633$; $x_2 = 3$, Slope $=$
1.3144; $x_2 = 4$, Slope $= .9655$;
$x_2 = 5$, Slope $= .6166$
b. $x_1 = 1$, Slope $= 3.8342$; $x_1 = 2$,
Slope 3.4853; $x_1 = 3$, Slope $= 3.1364$,
$x_1 = 4$, 2.7875; $x_1 = 5$, Slope $= 2.4386$
c. The smallest print slope is bigger than
the largest radio/TV slope.

12.45 b. $\hat{y} = 8.61178$ (861,178 bottles).
95% prediction interval $= [8.27089,$
$8.95266]$—slightly bigger.

12.49 Model 3—Complete
Model 1—Reduced
$H_0: \beta_4 = \beta_5 = \beta_6 = \beta_7 = 0$
$F = \dfrac{\frac{1.4318 - .5347}{4}}{\frac{.5347}{22}} = 9.228$
$F_{.05} = 2.82$ based on 4 and 22 degrees of
freedom.
$F_{.01} = 4.31$ based on 4 and 22 degrees of
freedom.
Since $9.228 > 4.31$, reject H_0 at $\alpha = .05$
and $.01$; Because the null hypothesis was
that the equations have the same slope
and intercept, rejecting the H_0 means
that at least one of these claims is false.

12.51 $\hat{y} = 30,626 + 3.893(28,000) -$
$29,607(1.56) + 86.52(1,821.7) \cong 251,056$

12.55 a. Interaction term is not a significant
predictor ($p > .10$).
b. Introducing the interaction term
decreases the F-value but increases
the multiple R slightly.

12.57 a. β_5: $b_5 = .2137$, Confidence interval $=$
$[.0851, .3423]$, p–value $= .0022$,
significant at $.01$ but not $.001$, so we
have very strong evidence.
β_5: $b_6 = .3818$, Confidence interval $=$
$[.2551, .5085]$, p–value $< .001$,
significant at $.001$, so we have
extremely strong evidence.
b. $b_6 = .1681$, Confidence interval:
$[.0363, .2999]$, p–value $= .0147$,
strong evidence

Chapter 13

13.1 A test that does not require assumptions
about the shape of the probability
distribution of the sampled populations.
A small sample might not accurately
represent the shape of the population.

13.3 a. $S = 4$, p-value $= .375$; do not reject H_0.
b. $S = 5$, p-value $= .031$; reject H_0.

13.5 a. Significant at $p < .05$
b. Calculated median is 5.

13.7 a. $S_1 = 4$, $S_2 = 5$, $S = 5$
b. p-value $= 1.0$
Do not reject H_0 at any of the given
values of α. Conclude no difference
in preference for Coke and Pepsi.

13.9 Independent samples z or t test; normal
distribution

13.11 $T_1 = 120.5$ $T_2 = 89.5$
$T_1 \ngtr T_U = 131$ and $T_1 \nless T_L = 79$; do
not reject H_0 and conclude no difference
between plants.

13.13 Men and women do differ in their
opinions regarding the frequency in
which people become sick consuming
food prepared at outdoor fairs and
festivals.

13.15 Paired difference t test; when normally
distributed

13.17 Suggests a non-significant difference;
therefore no change.

13.19 Post-exposure attitudes are significantly
higher at p-value $< .05$.

13.21 One-way ANOVA

13.23 Reject H_0, there is a difference.

13.25 $H = 13.35$. Reject H_0. There is a
difference in sales based on shelf
location.
Reject H_0. When the analysis is repeated,
there is still a difference in sales based
on shelf location. Median sales for the
middle shelf have increased. Output:

Kruskal-Wallis Test

Median	n	Avg. Rank	
55.75	6	9.17	Bottom
78.10	5	15.00	Middle
51.50	6	3.83	Top
55.70	17		Total

13.346	H
2	d.f.
.0013	p-value

multiple comparison values for avg. ranks
7.18 (.05)   8.81 (.01)

13.27 At $\alpha = 5\%$ we would reject H_0. There is
evidence to suggest that the study times
are not all the same.

13.29 a. $r_S = 1 - \dfrac{6 \sum d_i^2}{n(n^2 - 1)}$
b. For each tie, calculate an average
rank and assign that value to the tied
cases.

13.31 $r_s = .986$. Reject H_0 if $r_s > r_\alpha$; since
$.986 > .523$ and $.623$ and $.736$ and $.818$,
reject H_0.

13.33 Reject H_0; the drugs are different.

13.35 Use the Wilcoxon signed-rank test for
paired differences. There is a significant
decrease in the ages of its customers'
accounts from 2012 to 2013.

13.37 Reject H_0; the loan rates do differ.
Output:

Wilcoxon - Mann/Whitney Test

n	sum of ranks	
8	75	Fixed-Rate (%)
5	16	Variable-Rate (%)
13	91	total

56.00 expected value
6.81 standard deviation
2.72 z, corrected for ties
.0066 p-value (two-tailed)

Chapter 14

14.1 (1) We perform an experiment in which
we carry out n identical trials and in
which there are k possible outcomes
on each trial.
(2) The probabilities of the k outcomes
are denoted $p_1, p_2, \ldots, p_k$, where
$p_1 + p_2 + \cdots + p_k = 1$. These
probabilities stay the same from trial
to trial.
(3) The trials in the experiment are
independent.
(4) The results of the experiment are
observed counts of the number of
trials that result in each of the k
possible outcomes. The counts are
denoted $f_1, f_2, \ldots, f_k$. That is, f_1 is the
number of trials resulting in the first
possible outcome, f_2 is the number of
trials resulting in the second possible
outcome, and so forth.

14.3 For normality: A test to determine if a
sample has been randomly selected from
a normally distributed population. For
multinomial probabilities: A test to
determine whether multinomial
probabilities are equal to a specific set
of values.

14.5 A variable that may change the nature of
the relationship when introduced

14.7   a. Each expected value is ≥ 5.

b. $\chi^2 = \sum\left(\dfrac{(391-360)^2}{360} + \dfrac{(202-260)^2}{260} + \dfrac{(275-210)^2}{210} + \dfrac{(53-90)^2}{90} + \dfrac{(79-80)^2}{80}\right) = 50.951$

$\chi^2_{.05} = 9.488$

because $50.951 > 9.488$, reject H_0; the city market shares differ from those of the province.

14.9   a. Each expected value is ≥ 5.

b. $\chi^2 = 880.52$

$\chi^2_{.05} = 12.592$

Since $880.52 > 12.592$, reject H_0; not consistent.

14.11 $\chi^2(1) = 6.89$, $p < .01$ (significantly different; better than the expected)

14.13   a. $\chi^2 = \sum\left(\dfrac{(131-200)^2}{200} + \dfrac{(273-200)^2}{200} + \dfrac{(119-200)^2}{200} + \dfrac{(301-200)^2}{200} + \dfrac{(176-200)^2}{200} + \dfrac{(200-200)^2}{200}\right) = 137.14$

$\chi^2_{.025} = 12.8325$

Reject H_0.

b. There is a difference between brand preferences.

14.15   a. $\bar{x} = 18.1077$, $s = 3.9612$

$\bar{x} - 2s = 18.1077 - 2(3.9612) = 10.185$

$\bar{x} - s = 18.1077 - 3.9612 = 14.147$

$\bar{x} + s = 18.1077 + 3.9612 = 22.069$

$\bar{x} + 2s = 18.1077 + 2(3.9612) = 26.030$

(1) $[-\infty, 10.185]$

(2) $[10.185, 14.147]$

(3) $[14.147, 18.108]$

(4) $[18.108, 22.069]$

(5) $[22.069, 26.030]$

(6) $[26.030, \infty]$

b. (1) For instance, $P(x < 10.185) = P\left(z < \dfrac{10.185 - 18.1077}{3.9612}\right) = P(z < -2) = .5 - .4772 = .0228$ and

$E_1 = .0228(65) = 1.482. \approx 1.5$

(2) $.1359$, $E_2 = 8.8335 \approx 9$

(3) $.3413$, $E_3 = 22.1845 \approx 22$

(4) $.3413$, $E_4 = 22.1845 \approx 22$

(5) $.1359$, $E_5 = 8.8335 \approx 9$

(6) $.0228$, $E_6 = 1.482 \approx 1.5$

c. We can use the chi-square test since the average of the E_i values is 10.833 (which is ≥ 5) and since the smallest E_i value is 1.482 (which is ≥ 1).

d. H_0: The probabilities that a randomly selected payment time will be in intervals 1, 2, 3, 4, 5, and 6 are $p_1 = .0228$, $p_2 = .1359$, $p_3 = .3413$, $p_4 = .3413$, $p_5 = .1359$, and $p_6 = .0228$ versus

H_a: The above null hypothesis is not true.

e. 1, 9, 30, 15, 8, 2

$\chi^2 = \dfrac{(1-1.5)^2}{1.5} + \dfrac{(9-9)^2}{9} + \dfrac{(30-22)^2}{22} + \dfrac{(15-22)^2}{22} + \dfrac{(8-9)^2}{9} + \dfrac{(2-1.5)^2}{1.5}$

$= 1.67 + 0 + 2.909 + 2.227 + .111 + .167$

$= 5.581$

f. Fail to reject H_0 since $5.581 < \chi^2_{.05} = 7.81473$ (with $6 - 1 - 2 = 3$ degrees of freedom). Conclude normality.

14.17   Studying the relationship between two variables

14.19   c. $\chi^2 = \dfrac{(16-8)^2}{8} + \dfrac{(24-32)^2}{32} + \dfrac{(4-12)^2}{12} + \dfrac{(56-48)^2}{48}$

$= 8 + 2 + 5.333 + 1.333 = 16.667$

H_0: Whether a person drinks wine and whether a person watches tennis are independent versus H_a: Dependent. Since $16.667 > \chi^2_{.05} = 3.84146$ (with $(2-1)(2-1) = 1$ degree of freedom), we reject H_0. Conclude dependent.

14.21   a. $\chi^2(1) = 611.55$, which is much greater than χ^2 critical of 3.84; reject H_0 and conclude that sex and unemployment are dependent.

b. Women are more likely to be employed part-time.

14.23   a. $\chi^2 = \dfrac{(37-53.5)^2}{53.5} + \dfrac{(48-53.5)^2}{53.5} + \dfrac{(56-53.5)^2}{53.5} + \dfrac{(73-53.5)^2}{53.5} + \dfrac{(213-196.5)^2}{196.5}$

$+ \dfrac{(202-196.5)^2}{196.5} + \dfrac{(194-196.5)^2}{196.5} + \dfrac{(177-196.5)^2}{196.5} = 16.385$

$\chi^2_{.05} = 7.815$ with 3 degrees of freedom

Since $16.385 > 7.815$, reject H_0: Independence

b. $(.148 - .292) \pm 1.96\sqrt{\dfrac{.148(.852)}{250} + \dfrac{.292(.708)}{250}} = -.144 \pm .0715 = [-.216, -.072]$

14.25 $\chi^2 = \dfrac{(30-60)^2}{60} + \dfrac{(91-60)^2}{60} + \dfrac{(97-60)^2}{60} + \dfrac{(40-60)^2}{60} + \dfrac{(42-60)^2}{60}$

$= 15 + 16.02 + 22.82 + 6.67 + 5.4$

$= 65.91$

Since $65.91 > \chi^2_{.05} = 9.48773$ (with $5 - 1 = 4$ degrees of freedom), we reject H_0: $p_1 = p_2 = p_3 = p_4 = p_5 = .2$; entrances not equally used.

95% CI: $\left[.323 \pm 1.96\sqrt{\dfrac{.323(.677)}{299}}\right] = [.27, .376]$

14.27 For instance, for the first (upper-left) cell, expected $= \left(\dfrac{179}{362}\right)\left(\dfrac{56}{362}\right)(362) = 27.69$.

Others are as follows:

27.69	151.31
28.31	154.69

$$\chi^2 = \frac{(27-27.69)^2}{27.69} + \frac{(152-151.31)^2}{151.31} + \frac{(29-28.31)^2}{28.31} + \frac{(154-154.69)^2}{154.69}$$
$$= .017 + .003 + .017 + .003 = .04$$

Since $.04 < \chi^2_{.05} = 3.84146$ (with $(2-1)(2-1) = 1$ degree of freedom), we do not reject H_0: Independence.

14.29 Chi-square $= 71.476$, p-value $= .000$. Reject H_0: Independence

14.31
a. 45
b. 15.56
c. 6, Reject H_0 if chi-square > 12.592, $df = 7 - 1 = 6$
d. Reject H_0.
e. Failed to reject H_0.
f. It appears that the enrolment for the Internet course in *Fundamentals of Accounting* differs among some of the seven regions.
g. It appears that the enrolment for the Internet course in *Fundamentals of Accounting* is equal among all of the seven regions.

14.33 We want to test H_0: Crimes are uniformly distributed throughout the week vs. H_a: Crimes are not uniformly distributed. There were a total of $n = 566$ crimes committed in this Canadian city.

$$\chi^2 = \left(\frac{(79-80.857)^2}{80.857} + \frac{(68-80.857)^2}{80.857}\right.$$
$$+ \frac{(54-80.857)^2}{80.857} + \frac{(69-80.857)^2}{80.857}$$
$$+ \frac{(81-80.857)^2}{80.857} + \frac{(97-80.857)^2}{80.857}$$
$$\left. + \frac{(118-80.857)^2}{80.857}\right) = 33.03$$

We did not combine any cells because the number of classes was 7 (exceeds 4) and the average of the expected cell frequencies is at least 5 and the smallest expected cell frequency is at least 1.
With $7 - 1 = 6$ df we see that $\chi^2_{0.05} = 12.5916$. At $\alpha = 5\%$ we would reject H_0 and conclude that it appears as though the crimes are not uniformly distributed throughout the days of the week.

Chapter 15

15.1 Certainty: We know for certain which state of nature will occur.
Uncertainty: No information about the likelihood of states of nature.
Risk: Probability of each state of nature can be estimated.

15.3 Reverse the order of the decision and the uncertainty node. The value of perfect information is the difference (gain) between the expected values.

15.5 Minimum payoffs: Large $= -\$4$ M, Medium $= \$7$M, Small $= \$10$M
Maximum payoff of the minimums: Small facility at $10M

15.7
a. Expected monetary value (small) $=$ $(10)(.3) + (10)(.5) + (10)(.2) = \$10$M
EMV(medium) $= (7)(.3) + (12)(.5) + (12)(.2) = \$10.5$M
EMV(large) $= (-4)(.3) + (2)(.5) + (16)(.2) = \$3$M
b. Best alternative: Medium facility

15.9
a. EVcertainty: $(10)(.3) + (12)(.5) + (16)(.2) = \$12.2$M
b. EVPI $=$ EVcertainty $-$ EMV $= 12.2 - 10.5 = \$1.7$M

15.11
a. Expected monetary value (Loc A) $=$ $(1)(.6) + (14)(.4) = \$6.2$M
EMV(Loc B) $= (2)(.6) + (10)(.4) = \$5.2$M
EMV(Loc C) $= (4)(.6) + (6)(.4) = \$4.8$M
b. Location A
c. EVcertainty: $(4)(.6) + (14)(.4) = \$8.0$M
EVPI $=$ EVcertainty $-$ EMV $= 8.0 - 6.2 = \$1.8$M

15.13
a. Expected monetary value (subcontract) $= (1)(.4) + (1.3)(.5) + (1.8)(.1) = \$1.23$M
EMV(expand) $= (1.5)(.4) + (1.6)(.5) + (1.7)(.1) = \$1.57$M
EMV(build) $= (1.4)(.4) + (1.1)(.5) + (2.4)(.1) = \$1.35$M
b. Expand

15.15
a. Expected value of the expected payoff
b. Expected payoff of alternative chosen using the expected monetary value criterion with the prior probabilities
c. Expected payoff of sampling minus the expected payoff of no sampling
d. Difference between the EVIS and the cost of sampling

15.17

	Up	Flat	Down
High Risk	1,500	100	−1,000
Low Risk	1,000	200	−100
Savings Acct.	500	500	500

15.19

Prior Probabilities: .50, .30, .20

Conditional Probabilities:

	Up	Flat	Down
"Economist says up"	.8	.15	.2
"Economist says flat"	.1	.70	.2
"Economist says down"	.1	.15	.6

Joint Probabilities:

	Up	Flat	Down	Total
"Economist says up"	.400	.045	.040	.485
"Economist says flat"	.050	.210	.040	.300
"Economist says down"	.050	.045	.120	.215

Revised Probabilities:

	Up	Flat	Down
"Economist says up"	.8247	.0928	.0825
"Economist says flat"	.1667	.7000	.1333
"Economist says down"	.2326	.2093	.5581

a. P("Economist says up") $= (.5)(.8) + (.15)(.3) + (.2)(.2) = .485$
Posterior probabilities: .8247, .0928, .0825
b. P("Economist says flat") $= (.5)(.1) + (.7)(.3) + (.2)(.2) = .300$
Posterior probabilities: .1667, .7000, .1333
c. P("Economist says flat") $= (.5)(.1) + (.15)(.3) + (.6)(.2) = .215$
Posterior probabilities: .2326, .2093, .5581

15.21
a. EPS $= (.485)(1163.92) + (.3)(500) + (.215)(500) = 821.96$
b. EPNS $= 580$
c. EVSI $= 821.96 - 580 = 241.96$
d. Maximum amount to pay economist for advice: 242.00

15.23 Payoff table:

	In	Out
Not send engineer	15,000	12,000
Send engineer	14,500	14,500

15.25

Prior Probabilities: .90, .10
Conditional Probabilities:

	In	Out
Reads "in"	.8	.1
Reads "out"	.2	.9

Joint Probabilities:

	In	Out	Total
Reads "in"	.720	.010	.730
Reads "out"	.180	.090	.270

Revised Probabilities:

	In	Out
Reads "in"	.9863	.0137
Reads "out"	.6667	.3333

a. P(reads "in") $= (.9)(.8) + (.1)(.1) = .730$
Posterior probabilities: .9863, .0137
b. P(reads "out") $= (.9)(.2) + (.1)(.9) = .270$
Posterior probabilities: .6667, .3333

15.27
a. Test equipment reads "in":
EMV(Not send) $= (15,000)(.9863) + (12,000)(.0137) = 14,958.90$
EMV(Send) $= 14,500$
Choose: Do not send engineer
b. Test equipment reads "out":
EMV(Not send) $= (15,000)(.6667) + (12,000)(.3333) = 14,000$
EMV(Send) $= 14,500$
Choose: Send engineer

15.29 Utility is a measure of monetary value based on an individual's attitude toward risk.

15.33
a. Research project should continue: $(.7)(23) + (.3)(-2) = \$15.5$.

b. Should be licensed; slightly better return:
    License: $23
    Develop: $(.25)(43) + (.55)(21) + (.2)(3) = \$22.9$

15.35

Prior Probabilities: .6, .4

Conditional Probabilities:

	High	Low
"Favourable"	.9	.2
"Unfavourable"	.1	.8

Joint Probabilities:

	High	Low	Total
"Favourable"	.54	.08	.62
"Unfavourable"	.06	.32	.38

Revised Probabilities:

	High	Low
"Favourable"	.871	.129
"Unfavourable"	.158	.842

a. Favourable:
    EMV(small) = $(40)(.129) + (55)(.871)$
    $= 53.065$
    EMV(large) = $(50)(.129) + (70)(.871)$
    $= 67.42$
    Choose: Build large
    Unfavourable:
    EMV(small) = $(40)(.842) + (55)(.158)$
    $= 42.37$
    EMV(large) = $(50)(.842) + (70)(.158)$
    $= 53.16$
    Choose: Build large
b. EPS = $(67.42)(.62) + (53.16)(.38)$
    $= 62$
    EPNS = $(50)(.4) + (70)(.6) = 62$
    EVSI = $62 - 62 = 0$
    Maximum amount to pay economist
    for advice: 0

15.37 a. Maximax: Relocate, highest of the highest payoffs of $5M
          b. Maximin: Renew lease, highest payoff of the minimum payoffs possible

Chapter 16

16.1 No long-run growth or decline in the time series over time
Straight-line long-run growth or decline over time

16.3 In general, the purpose of the dummy variables is to ensure that an appropriate seasonal parameter is included in the regression model in each time period. The number of dummy variables that we use is, in general, the number of seasons minus 1.

16.5 a. The data plot suggests that there is a long-run straight-line growth. Therefore, the linear trend model $y_t = \beta_0 + \beta_1 t + \varepsilon_t$ is reasonable.
          b. $\hat{y} = 290.089474 + 8.667669(21)$
              $= 472.1$
              95% prediction intervals are for y_{21}:
              [421.5, 522.7]

16.7 MegaStat output:
Predicted values for Y

		95% Confidence Intervals		95% Prediction Intervals		
t	Predicted	lower	upper	lower	upper	Leverage
2,012	653,143.8	643,011.6	663,276.0	639,144.1	667,143.5	1.100
2,013	662,385.8	649,424.6	675,347.0	646,220.3	678,551.3	1.800

16.9 It is quite common for time series data to violate the assumption of independence in the error terms. This type of model allows us to test for the type of autocorrelation present.

16.11 Durbin–Watson statistic, $d = .43$. Appendix table goes only to $k = 5$, but the Durbin–Watson statistic is very small. Positive correlation exists.

16.13 TR is estimated by fitting a straight line to deseasonalized observations.

16.15 The seasonal factors for quarters 1, 2, 3, and 4 are $sn_1 = 1.192$, $sn_2 = 1.521$, $sn_3 = .804$, and $sn_4 = .484$.

16.17 $tr_t = 220.54 + 19.95t$

16.19 95% prediction intervals:
Quarter 1 1997: $[666.6 \pm 14]$
$= [652.6, 680.6]$
Quarter 2 1997: $[881.6 \pm 14.4]$
$= [867.2, 896.0]$
Quarter 3 1997: $[482.1 \pm 14.6]$
$= [467.5, 496.7]$
Quarter 4 1997: $[299.9 \pm 15]$
$= [284.9, 314.9]$

16.21 When the equation $y_t = \beta_0 + \varepsilon_t$ describes the time series and when β_0 may be changing slowly over time

16.23 The variable "t" is included in the double smoothing model as a separate independent variable.

16.25 Forecast $= 35,438$

16.27 MAD = Mean absolute deviation
MSD = Mean squared deviation
MAPE = Mean absolute percentage error
These quantities are used to compare forecasting methods.

16.29 Method A: Forecast errors: 3, 3, −3.
MAD = 3; MSD = 9; MAPE = 4.72
Method B: Forecast errors: 1, −1, −6.
MAD = 2.67; MSD = 12.67;
MAPE = 4.06

16.31 A simple index is computed by using the values of one time series; an aggregate index is based on a "market basket" consisting of more than one time series.

16.33 a.

Year	Sales (1,000s)	Simple price index
2005	1,630 (Base)	100
2006	1,666	$(1,666/1,630)$ $\times 100 = 102.21$
2007	1,690	103.68
2008	1,674	102.70
2009	1,485	91.10

b. For 2008: $1,674/1,630 \times 100 = 102.70$; for 2009: 91.10; sales were up 11.6% in 2008 when compared to 2009.
c. Huge drop in sales in 2009 (year 5).

16.35
a.
Simple Index

Year	1988	1989	1990	1991	1992	1993	1994	1995	1996
Gold	100.00	87.44	87.90	82.88	78.77	82.42	87.90	84.02	89.04
Silver	100.00	84.23	73.81	61.87	60.34	65.85	81.01	78.87	81.16
Platin.	100.00	96.94	89.29	70.94	68.83	71.51	78.59	81.26	78.39

b. Prices of the precious metals are lower than those in the base year of 1988
c.
Aggregate Price Index

Year	1988	1989	1990	1991	1992	1993	1994	1995	1996
Index	100	92.56	88.56	76.28	73.27	76.41	82.82	82.49	83.23

Prices of the precious metals are lower than those in the base year of 1988
d.
Aggregate Price Index (Base = 1990)

Year	1988	1989	1990	1991	1992	1993	1994	1995	1996
Index	112.92	104.51	100.00	86.14	82.74	86.28	93.52	93.15	93.99

16.37 a. Yes; $F(1, 16) = 28.01$, $p < .001$.
          b. For 2009, predict 18.2; for 2010, predict 17.4; for 2011, predict 16.6; for 2012, predict 15.8; for 2013, predict 15.0; assess predicted values against actual values.

16.39 a. Increasing trend

REFERENCES

Ashton, Robert H., John J. Willingham, and Robert K. Elliott. "An Empirical Analysis of Audit Delay." *Journal of Accounting Research*, 25, 2 (Autumn 1987), pp. 275–92.

Bayus, Barry L. "The Consumer and Durable Replacement Buyer." *Journal of Marketing*, 55 (January 1991), pp. 42–51.

Beattie, Vivien, and Michael John Jones. "The Use and Abuse of Graphs in Annual Reports: Theoretical Framework and Empirical Study." *Accounting and Business Research*, 22, 88 (Autumn 1992), pp. 291–303.

Beckstead, Desmond, W. Mark Brown, Yusu Guo, and K. Bruce Newbold. *The Canadian Economy in Transition Cities and Growth: Earnings Levels Across Urban and Rural Areas: The Role of Human Capital*. Statistics Canada, 2010, Catalogue No. 11-622-M—No. 020.

Blauw, Jan Nico, and Willem E. During. "Total Quality Control in Dutch Industry." *Quality Progress* (February 1990), pp. 50–51.

Blodgett, Jeffrey G., Donald H. Granbois, and Rockney G. Walters. "The Effects of Perceived Justice on Complainants' Negative Word-of-Mouth Behavior and Repatronage Intentions." *Journal of Retailing, 69*, 4 (Winter 1993), pp. 399–428.

Boo, Huey Chern, Richard Ghiselli, and B. A. Almanza. "Consumers' Perceptions and Concerns about Safety and Healthfulness of Food Served at Fairs and Festivals." *Event Management*, 6, 2 (2000), pp. 85–92.

Bowerman, Bruce L., and Richard T. O'Connell. *Linear Statistical Models: An Applied Approach*. 2nd ed. Boston, MA: PWS-KENT Publishing Company, 1990, pp. 457, 460–64, 729–974.

Box, G. E. P., and G. M. Jenkins. *Time Series Analysis: Forecasting and Control*. 2nd ed. San Francisco, CA: Holden-Day, 1976.

Carslaw, Charles, and Steven E. Kaplan. "An Examination of Audit Delay. Further Evidence from New Zealand." *Accounting and Business Research, 22*, 85 (1991), pp. 21–32.

Church, B. K., and A. Schneider. "Auditor Objectivity: The Effect of Prior Involvement in Audit Program Design." *Accounting and Finance* (November 1993), pp. 61–78.

Cooper, Donald R., and C. William Emory. *Business Research Methods*. 5th ed. Homewood, IL: Richard D. Irwin, 1995, pp. 434–38, 450–51, 458–68.

Dawson, Scott. "Consumer Responses to Electronic Article Surveillance Alarms." *Journal of Retailing, 69, 3* (Fall 1993), pp. 353–62.

Deming, W. Edwards. *Out of the Crisis*. Cambridge, MA: Massachusetts Institute of Technology Center for Advanced Engineering Study, 1986, pp. 18–96, 312–14.

Diekhoff, G. *Statistics for the Social and Behavioral Sciences: Univariate, Bivariate, Multivariate*. Dubuque, IA: Wm. C. Brown, 1992.

Dillon, William R., Thomas J. Madden, and Neil H. Firtle. *Essentials of Marketing Research*. Homewood, IL: Richard D. Irwin Inc., 1993, pp. 382–84, 416–17, 419–20, 432–33, 445, 462–64, 524–27.

Farnum, Nicholas R. *Modern Statistical Quality Control and Improvement*. Belmont, CA: Duxbury Press, 1994, p. 55.

Fitzgerald, Neil. "Relations Overcast by Cloudy Conditions." *CA Magazine* (April 1993), pp. 28–35.

Gibbons, J. D. *Nonparametric Statistical Inference*. 2nd ed. New York: McGraw-Hill, 1985.

Gitlow, Howard, Shelly Gitlow, Alan Oppenheim, and Rosa Oppenheim. *Tools and Methods for the Improvement of Quality*. Homewood, IL: Richard D. Irwin, 1989, pp. 14–25, 533–53.

Gupta, Sachin, Pradeep Chintagunta, Anil Kaul, and Dick R. Wittink. "Do Household Scanner Data Provide Representative Inferences from Brand Choices? A Comparison with Store Data," *Journal of Marketing Research*, 33 (November 1996), p. 393 (Table 6).

Kumar, V., Roger A. Kerin, and Arun Pereira. "An Empirical Assessment of Merger and Acquisition Activity in Retailing." *Journal of Retailing*, 67, 3 (Fall 1991), pp. 321–38.

Magee, Robert P. *Advanced Managerial Accounting*. New York, NY: Harper & Row, 1986, p. 223.

Mahmood, Mo Adam, and Gary J. Mann. "Measuring the Organizational Impact of Information Technology Investment: An Exploratory Study." *Journal of Management Information Systems*, 10, 1 (Summer 1993), pp. 97–122.

Martocchio, Joseph J. "The Financial Cost of Absence Decisions." *Journal of Management*, 18, 1 (1992), pp. 133–52.

Meier, Heidi Hylton, Pervaiz Alam, and Michael A. Pearson. "Auditor Lobbying for Accounting Standards: The Case of Banks and Savings and Loan Associations." *Accounting and Business Research*, 23, 92 (1993), pp. 477–87.

The Miami University Report. 8, 26 (January 1989).

Moore, David S. *The Basic Practice of Statistics*. 2nd ed. New York: W. H. Freeman and Company, 2000.

Moore, David S., and George P. McCabe. *Introduction to the Practice of Statistics*. 2nd ed. New York: W. H. Freeman, 1993.

Morris, Michael H., Ramon A. Avila, and Jeffrey Allen. "Individualism and the Modern Corporation: Implications for Innovation and Entrepreneurship." *Journal of Management*, 19, 3 (1993), pp. 595–612.

Neter, J., M. Kutner, C. Nachtsheim, and W. Wasserman. *Applied Linear Statistical Models*. 4th ed. Homewood, IL: Irwin/McGraw-Hill, 1996.

Nunnally, Bennie H., Jr., and D. Anthony Plath. *Cases in Finance*. Burr Ridge, IL: Richard D. Irwin, 1995, pp. 12–1—12–7.

Oliveira, Michael. "How Do You Compare? New Report Reveals Stats about Social Media Usage in Canada," *The Canadian Press*, April 29, 2013.

Scheaffer, R. L., William Mendenhall, and Lyman Ott. *Elementary Survey Sampling*. 3rd ed. Boston, MA: Duxbury Press, 1986.

Scherkenbach, William. *The Deming Route to Quality and Productivity: Road Maps and Roadblocks*. Washington, DC: Ceepress Books, 1986.

Seigel, James C. "Managing with Statistical Models." *SAE Technical Paper 820520*. Warrendale, PA: Society for Automotive Engineers, Inc., 1982.

Silk, Alvin J., and Ernst R. Berndt. "Scale and Scope Effects on Advertising Agency Costs." *Marketing Science, 12*, 1 (Winter 1993), pp. 53–72.

Soldow, G. F., and V. Principe. "Response to Commercials as a Function of Program Content." *Journal of Advertising Research, 21* (1981), pp. 59–65.

Stevenson, William J. *Production/Operations Management*. 6th ed. Homewood, IL: Irwin/McGraw-Hill, 1999, p. 228.

Thompson, C. M. "Tables of the Percentage Points of the x^2 Distribution," *Biometrika 32* (1941), pp. 188–89. Reproduced by permission of the Biometrika Trustees.

Von Neumann, J., and O. Morgenstern. *Theory of Games and Economic Behavior*. 2nd ed. Princeton, N.J.: Princeton University Press, 1947.

Walton, Mary. *The Deming Management Method*. New York, NY: Dodd, Mead & Company, 1986.

Weinberger, Marc G., and Harlan E. Spotts. "Humor in U.S. versus U.K. TV Commercials: A Comparison." *Journal of Advertising, 18*, 2 (1989), pp. 39–44.

Wonnacott, Thomas H., and Ronald J. Wonnacott. *Introductory Statistics*. Hoboken, NJ: John Wiley & Sons, Inc., 1981.

Wright, Thomas A., and Douglas G. Bonett. "Role of Employee Coping and Performance in Voluntary Employee Withdrawal: A Research Refinement and Elaboration." *Journal of Management, 19*, 1 (1993), pp. 147–61.

PHOTO CREDITS

INDEX

A Table of Areas under the Standard Normal Curve

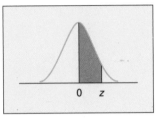

z	.00	.01	.02	.03	.04	.05	.06	.07	.08	.09
0.0	.0000	.0040	.0080	.0120	.0160	.0199	.0239	.0279	.0319	.0359
0.1	.0398	.0438	.0478	.0517	.0557	.0596	.0636	.0675	.0714	.0753
0.2	.0793	.0832	.0871	.0910	.0948	.0987	.1026	.1064	.1103	.1141
0.3	.1179	.1217	.1255	.1293	.1331	.1368	.1406	.1443	.1480	.1517
0.4	.1554	.1591	.1628	.1664	.1700	.1736	.1772	.1808	.1844	.1879
0.5	.1915	.1950	.1985	.2019	.2054	.2088	.2123	.2157	.2190	.2224
0.6	.2257	.2291	.2324	.2357	.2389	.2422	.2454	.2486	.2517	.2549
0.7	.2580	.2611	.2642	.2673	.2704	.2734	.2764	.2794	.2823	.2852
0.8	.2881	.2910	.2939	.2967	.2995	.3023	.3051	.3078	.3106	.3133
0.9	.3159	.3186	.3212	.3238	.3264	.3289	.3315	.3340	.3365	.3389
1.0	.3413	.3438	.3461	.3485	.3508	.3531	.3554	.3577	.3599	.3621
1.1	.3643	.3665	.3686	.3708	.3729	.3749	.3770	.3790	.3810	.3830
1.2	.3849	.3869	.3888	.3907	.3925	.3944	.3962	.3980	.3997	.4015
1.3	.4032	.4049	.4066	.4082	.4099	.4115	.4131	.4147	.4162	.4177
1.4	.4192	.4207	.4222	.4236	.4251	.4265	.4279	.4292	.4306	.4319
1.5	.4332	.4345	.4357	.4370	.4382	.4394	.4406	.4418	.4429	.4441
1.6	.4452	.4463	.4474	.4484	.4495	.4505	.4515	.4525	.4535	.4545
1.7	.4554	.4564	.4573	.4582	.4591	.4599	.4608	.4616	.4625	.4633
1.8	.4641	.4649	.4656	.4664	.4671	.4678	.4686	.4693	.4699	.4706
1.9	.4713	.4719	.4726	.4732	.4738	.4744	.4750	.4756	.4761	.4767
2.0	.4772	.4778	.4783	.4788	.4793	.4798	.4803	.4808	.4812	.4817
2.1	.4821	.4826	.4830	.4834	.4838	.4842	.4846	.4850	.4854	.4857
2.2	.4861	.4864	.4868	.4871	.4875	.4878	.4881	.4884	.4887	.4890
2.3	.4893	.4896	.4898	.4901	.4904	.4906	.4909	.4911	.4913	.4916
2.4	.4918	.4920	.4922	.4925	.4927	.4929	.4931	.4932	.4934	.4936
2.5	.4938	.4940	.4941	.4943	.4945	.4946	.4948	.4949	.4951	.4952
2.6	.4953	.4955	.4956	.4957	.4959	.4960	.4961	.4962	.4963	.4964
2.7	.4965	.4966	.4967	.4968	.4969	.4970	.4971	.4972	.4973	.4974
2.8	.4974	.4975	.4976	.4977	.4977	.4978	.4979	.4979	.4980	.4981
2.9	.4981	.4982	.4982	.4983	.4984	.4984	.4985	.4985	.4986	.4986
3.0	.4987	.4987	.4987	.4988	.4988	.4989	.4989	.4989	.4990	.4990